Intermediate Algebra

WITH APPLICATIONS

SEVENTH EDITION

Intermediate Algebra

WITH APPLICATIONS

Richard N. Aufmann
Palomar College, California

Vernon C. Barker
Palomar College, California

Joanne S. Lockwood
New Hampshire Community
Technical College, New Hampshire

Houghton Mifflin Company   **Boston   New York**

INTERMEDIATE ALGEBRA WITH APPLICATIONS, SEVENTH EDITION
by Richard N. Aufmann, Vernon C. Barker, Joanne S. Lockwood

Publisher: Richard Stratton
Senior Sponsoring Editor: Lynn Cox
Senior Marketing Manager: Katherine Greig
Marketing Associate: Naveen Hariprasad
Associate Editor: Noel Kamm
Editorial Assistant: Laura Ricci
Senior Project Editor: Kerry Falvey
Editorial Assistant: Joanna Carter
Art and Design Manager: Gary Crespo
Cover Design Manager: Anne S. Katzeff
Photo Editor: Marcy Kagan
Composition Buyer: Chuck Dutton

Cover photograph © Japack Company/CORBIS

PHOTOGRAPH CREDITS: xvi: Peter Bowater/Alamy; xxii: Courtesy of Edgar Fahs Smith. Image Collection/University of PALibrary, Philadelphia, PA 19104-6206; 1: © Gabe Palmer/CORBIS; 57: Dana White/PhotoEdit, Inc.; 73: Leonard de Selva/CORBIS; 86: Alan Oddie/PhotoEdit, Inc.; 87: AP/Wide World Photos; 107: Richard Cummins/CORBIS; 118: Stephen Chernin/Getty Images; 127: Bonnie Kamin/PhotoEdit, Inc.; 187: Eric Fowke/PhotoEdit, Inc.; 197: Bettmann/CORBIS; 222: © Michael Kevin Daly/CORBIS; 253: The Granger Collection; 260: Ken Redding/CORBIS; 269: Michael Newman/PhotoEdit, Inc.; 271: Michael Newman/PhotoEdit, Inc.; 286: Digital Vision/Getty Images; 298: Jeff Greenberg/PhotoEdit, Inc.; 299 (top): Getty Images; 299 (bottom): Bettmann/CORBIS; 372: Kathleen Nelson/Alamy; 392: AP/Wide World Photos; 393: Felicia Martinez/PhotoEdit, Inc.; 401: James Marshall/CORBIS; 407: Bill Aron/PhotoEdit, Inc.; 408 (top): Gunter Marx Photography/CORBIS; 408 (middle): Vicki Silbert/PhotoEdit, Inc.; 408 (bottom): FK PHOTO/CORBIS; 409: Lee Snider/Photo Images/CORBIS; 411: Michael S. Yamashita/CORBIS; 419: AP/Wide World Photos; 420: Cameraphoto Arte, Venice/Art Resource, NY; 434: Bonnie Kamin/PhotoEdit, Inc.; 437: Benjamin Sheam/Getty Images; 470: Bettmann/CORBIS; 473: Karl Weatherly/CORBIS; 495: AP/Wide World Photos; 519: Kevin Schafer/CORBIS; 531: Jonathan Nourak/PhotoEdit, Inc.; 575: AP/Wide World Photos; 586: Randy Wells/Getty Images; 603: Michael Newman/PhotoEdit, Inc.; 611: Peter Bowater/Alamy; 628: The Granger Collection; 655: Richard T. Nowtiz/CORBIS; 656: Courtesy of Edgar Fahs Smith. Image Collection/University of PA Library, Philadelphia, PA 19104-6206; 657: Bettmann/CORBIS; 660: Mark Harmel/Getty Images; 661: Myrleen Ferguson Cate/PhotoEdit, Inc.; 662: Roger Rossmeyer/CORBIS; 663: NOVASTOCK/PhotoEdit, Inc.; 664: Earth Imaging/Getty Images; 674: Laura Dwight/PhotoEdit, Inc.; 690: Stephen Ferry/Getty Images; 697: William James Warren/CORBIS; 703: Arthur Tilley/Getty Images; 704: The Granger Collection; 705: The Granger Collection; 712: Copyright © 2006 by Houghton Mifflin Company. Reproduced by permission from *The American Heritage Children's Dictionary*; 719: Tony Freeman/PhotoEdit, Inc.; 720: NASA Center: Johnson Space Center; 722: Photo by Jennifer Waddell. Courtesy of Houghton Mifflin Company; 723: Galen Rowell/CORBIS; 729: Bettmann/CORBIS; 758: Joseph Sohm; Visions of America/CORBIS.

Custom Publishing Editor: Dan Luciano
Custom Publishing Production Manager: Christina Battista
Project Coordinator: Sara Abbott

This book contains select works from existing Houghton Mifflin Company resources and was produced by Houghton Mifflin Custom Publishing for collegiate use. As such, those adopting and/or contributing to this work are responsible for editorial content, accuracy, continuity and completeness.

Printed in the United States of America.

ISBN-13: 978-0-618-97515-0
ISBN-10: 0-618-97515-2
1023629

1 2 3 4 5 6 7 8 9 – CM – 09 08 07

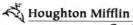 **Houghton Mifflin**
Custom Publishing

222 Berkeley Street • Boston, MA 02116

Address all correspondence and order information to the above address.

Contents

3   Linear Functions and Inequalities in Two Variables 127

4   Systems of Equations and Inequalities   222

5   Polynomials and Exponents   286

6   Rational Expressions   372

7   Rational Exponents and Radicals   437

12   Conic Sections   720

Preface

The seventh edition of *Intermediate Algebra with Applications* provides mathematically sound and comprehensive coverage of the topics considered essential in an intermediate algebra course. The text has been designed not only to meet the needs of the traditional college student, but also to serve the needs of returning students whose mathematical proficiency may have declined during years away from formal education.

In this new edition of *Intermediate Algebra with Applications,* we have continued to integrate some of the approaches suggested by AMATYC. Each chapter opens by illustrating and referencing a mathematical application within the chapter. At the end of each section there are "Applying Concepts" exercises that include writing, synthesis, critical thinking, and challenge problems. At the end of each chapter there is a "Focus on Problem Solving" section that introduces students to various problem-solving strategies. This is followed by "Projects and Group Activities," which can be used for cooperative learning activities.

NEW! Changes to the Content in this Edition

Chapter 3, Section 2, has been expanded to include not only evaluating functions but also graphing functions and the vertical line test. Section 3.3 now includes an explanation that the x-coordinate of an x-intercept is a zero of a function; students are asked to find zeros of linear functions. This earlier introduction of zeros lays the groundwork for finding zeros of other types of functions later in the text.

Users will notice several changes in Chapter 5. The first objective in Section 2, titled "Evaluate polynomial functions," includes graphs of polynomial functions. Here we revisit the vertical line test by noting that these graphs pass the vertical line test. In Section 5.4, we have added a new objective, "Divide a polynomial by a monomial." This instruction will provide students with the necessary background for Section 5.5, where they are asked to factor a monomial from a polynomial. In Objective 5.7.3, "Solving equations by factoring," we revisit the concept of zeros of a function by asking students to find zeros of quadratic functions.

Because the topics of graphing polynomial functions and the vertical line test, which were presented in Chapter 9 of the previous edition, are now presented earlier in the text, Chapter 9 of this edition now begins with graphing absolute value functions as an introduction to translations of graphs in Section 1. The earlier presentation and emphasis on functions will provide students with a stronger background for this chapter, the topic of which is "Functions and Relations."

The introductions to both exponential functions in Section 10.1 and logarithmic functions in Section 10.2 have been rewritten. Both topics are presented using applications. This development should lead to greater student understanding of and interest in these concepts.

NEW! Changes to Exercises in this Edition

Two new types of exercises have been added to this edition of the text: Interactive Exercises and Think About It Exercises.

The Interactive Exercises test students' understanding of the basic concepts presented in a lesson. Included when appropriate, these exercises generally appear at the beginning of an objective's exercise set and provide students with guided practice on some of the objective's underlying principles. Sometimes they test students' knowledge of the terms associated with a topic, but more often they are fill-in-the-blank exercises in which students are given part of a solution to a problem and are asked to complete the missing portions. These exercises act as stepping stones to the remaining exercises for the objective. We are confident that these Interactive Exercises will lead to greater student success in mastering the essential skills.

The Think About It Exercises are conceptual in nature. They generally appear near the end of an objective's exercise set and ask the students to think about the objective's concepts, make generalizations, and apply them to more abstract problems. Their focus is on mental mathematics, not calculation or computation, and they are meant to help students synthesize concepts. We are confident that their use will lead to a deeper conceptual understanding of the course content.

Throughout the text, data problems have been updated to reflect current data and trends. These application problems will demonstrate to students the variety of problems in real life that require mathematical analysis. Instructors will find that many of these problems may lead to interesting class discussions

NEW! Enhancements to the Instructional Media Package

HM Testing™ (powered by Diploma®) is a new computerized testing platform that provides instructors with a wide array of algorithmic test items, improved functionality, ease of use, and gradebook functions. HM Testing offers all the tools needed to create, author, deliver, and customize multiple types of tests—including authoring and editing algorithmic questions.

Eduspace®, Houghton Mifflin's Online Learning Tool (powered by Blackboard®), is a web-based learning system that provides instructors and students with powerful course management tools and text-specific content to support all of their online teaching and learning needs. Resources such as HM Assess, algorithmic automatically graded homework exercises, video explanations, an online multimedia eBook, live online tutoring with SMARTHINKING®, and additional study materials all come ready to use. Instructors can choose to use the content as is, modify it, or even add their own content.

HM Assess™ is a new diagnostic assessment tool that tests core concepts in mathematics and provides students with access to individual study paths for self-remediation. These paths are carefully designed to offer self-study options and to appeal to a variety of learning styles through review of the concepts, interactive lessons, similar examples, and additional practice exercises. Both course assessments and chapter assessments are available.

Students using Eduspace® with HM Assess™ can:

• Assess their core competencies and remediate themselves via individual study paths.
• Review and reinforce concepts with algorithmically generated exercises.
• View video tutorials.
• Access, complete, and submit homework online.

Acknowledgements

We would like to especially thank users of the previous edition for their helpful suggestions to improve the text. Also, we sincerely appreciate the suggestions and the time and effort of the following people who have reviewed this manuscript and/or its previous edition in preparation for the seventh edition.

Dorothy B. Allison, *Jones County Junior College, Ellisville, MS*
Peter Arvanites, *SUNY Rockland Community College, Suffern, NY*
Jeanne A. Baird, *Hillsborough Community College, Plant City, FL*
Joe Battaglia, *Pennsylvania State University, University Park, PA*
Pia Rodenzo Bauer, *Murray State College, Tishomingo, OK*
Beverly R. Broomell, *Suffolk County Community College, Selden, NY*
Jayne Carter, *Hazard Community College, Hazard, KY*
Oiyin Pauline Chow, *Harrisburg Area Community College, Gettysburg, PA*
John Christ, *East Los Angeles Community College, Monterey Park, CA*
Lacey P. Echols, *Butler University, Indianapolis, IN*
James A. Gauthier, *Louisiana State University, Alexandra, LA*
Sudhir Goel, *Valdosta State University, Valdosta, GA*
Melissa Joyce
Jane Keller, *Metropolitan Community College, Omaha, NE*
Sarah Laws, *Midway College, Midway, KY*
Susan B. Lloyd, *Wor-Wic Community College, Salisbury, MD*
Fred Safier, *City College of San Francisco, San Francisco, CA*
Radha Sankaran, *Passaic County Community College, Paterson, NJ*
Donald Solomon, *University of Wisconsin-Milwaukee, WI*
Kathy A. Stover, *College of Southern Idaho, Twin Falls, ID*
Joe Westfall, *Carl Albert State College, Poteau, OK*

STUDENT SUCCESS

Intermediate Algebra with Applications is designed to foster student success through an integrated text and media program.

AIM for Success

Welcome to *Intermediate Algebra with Applications*. As you begin this course, we know two important facts: (1) We want you to succeed. (2) You want to succeed. To do that requires an effort from each of us. For the next few pages, we are going to show you what is required of you to achieve that success and how you can use the features of this text to be successful.

Motivation

One of the most important keys to success is motivation. We can try to motivate you by offering interesting or important ways mathematics can benefit you. But, in the end, the motivation must come from you. On the first day of class, it is easy to be motivated. Eight weeks into the term, it is harder to keep that motivation.

To stay motivated, there must be outcomes from this course that are worth your time, money, and energy. List some reasons you are taking this course. Do not make a mental list—actually write them out.

Take Note

Motivation alone will not lead to success. For instance, suppose a person who cannot swim is placed in a boat, taken out to the middle of a lake, and then thrown overboard. That person has a lot of motivation but there is a high likelihood the person will drown without some help. Motivation gives us the desire to learn but is not the same as learning.

Although we hope that one of the reasons you listed was an interest in mathematics, we know that many of you are taking this course because it is required to graduate, it is a prerequisite for a course you must take, or because it is required for your major. Although you may not agree that this course is necessary, it is! If you are motivated to graduate or complete the requirements for your major, then use that motivation to succeed in this course. Do not become distracted from your goal to complete your education!

Commitment

To be successful, you must make a committment to succeed. This means devoting time to math so that you achieve a better understanding of the subject.

List some activities (sports, hobbies, talents such as dance, art, or music) that you enjoy and at which you would like to become better.

ACTIVITY	TIME SPENT	TIME WISHED SPENT

Thinking about these activities, put the number of hours that you spend each week practicing these activities next to the activity. Next to that number, indicate the number of hours per week you would like to spend on these activities.

Whether you listed surfing or sailing, aerobics or restoring cars, or any other activity you enjoy, note how many hours a week you spend doing it. To succeed in math, you must be willing to commit the same amount of ti Success requires some sacrifice.

page xxvi

AIM for Success

This preface helps students develop the study skills necessary to achieve success in college mathematics.

It also provides students with an explanation of how to effectively use the features of the text.

AIM for Success can be used as a lesson on the first day of class or as a student project. A lesson plan, with accompanying PowerPoint slides, is available for instructors on the Online Teaching Center.

Objective-Based Approach

All lessons, exercise sets, tests, and supplements are organized around a carefully constructed hierarchy of objectives. This organization serves as a framework for a complete learning system, allowing students to remediate their learning independently at any point in the process.

Each chapter's objectives are listed on the chapter opener page, which serves as a road-map to student learning.

A numbered objective describes the topic of each lesson.

CHAPTER

10 Exponential and Logarithmic Functions

OBJECTIVES

10.1 1 Evaluate exponential functions
      2 Graph exponential functions

10.2 1 Write equivalent exponential and logarithmic equations
      2 The properties of logarithms

10.3 1 Graph logarithmic functions

10.4 1 Solve exponential equations
      2 Solve logarithmic equations

10.5 1 Application problems

page 611

10.2 Introduction to Logarithms

OBJECTIVE 1 Write equivalent exponential and logarithmic equations

In Michael Crichton's novel *The Andromeda Strain*, we read, "A single cell of the bacterium *E. coli* would, under ideal circumstances, divide every twenty

page 622

All exercise sets correspond directly to objectives.

Answers to the Prep Tests, Chapter Review Exercises, Chapter Tests, and Cumulative Review Exercises refer students back to the original objectives for further study.

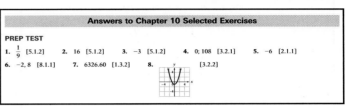

Prep Test

1. Simplify: 3^{-2}

2. Simplify: $\left(\dfrac{1}{2}\right)^{-4}$

3. Complete: $\dfrac{1}{8} = 2^?$

4. Evaluate $f(x) = x^4 + x^3$ for $x = -1$ and $x = 3$.

5. Solve: $3x + 7 = x - 5$

6. Solve: $16 = x^2 - 6x$

7. Evaluate $A(1 + i)^n$ for $A = 5000$, $i = 0.04$, and $n = 6$. Round to the nearest hundredth.

8. Graph: $f(x) = x^2 - 1$

Chapter 10 Summary

Key Words	Examples
A function of the form $f(x) = b^x$, where b is a positive real number not equal to 1, is an **exponential function**. The number b is the **base** of the exponential function. [10.1.1, p. 613]	$f(x) = 3^x$; 3 is the base of the function.
The function $f(x) = e^x$ is called the **natural exponential function**. [10.1.1, p. 614]	$f(x) = e^x$; e is an irrational number approximately equal to 2.71828183.
For $x > 0$, $b > 0$, $b \neq 1$, $y = \log_b x$ is equivalent to $x = b^y$. Read $\log_b x$ as "the **logarithm** of x, base b." [10.2.1, p. 623]	$\log_2 8 = 3$ is equivalent to $8 = 2^3$.
Common logarithms are logarithms to the base 10. [10.2.1, p. 626]	$\log_{10} 100 = 2$ is usually written as $\log 100 = 2$.

Cumulative Review Exercises

1. Solve: $4 - 2[x - 3(2 - 3x) - 4x] = 2x$

2. Solve $S = 2WH + 2WL + 2LH$ for L.

3. Solve: $|2x - 5| \leq 3$

4. Factor: $4x^{2n} + 7x^n + 3$

Assessment and Review

Prep Tests assess students' mastery of prerequisite skills for the upcoming chapter.

The Answers found at the back of the book refer them to the appropriate section objective for review.

The **end-of-chapter material** includes:

Chapter Summary

Chapter Review Exercises

Chapter Test

These resources help students prepare for tests.

Cumulative Review Exercises help students maintain skills learned in previous chapters.

Online Assessment and Remediation

Eduspace® (powered by Blackboard®), Houghton Mifflin's text-specific online learning system, now includes **HM Assess™**. This diagnostic assessment tool tests core concepts and provides students with access to *individual study paths* for self-remediation.

 Students using HM Assess can:

- Assess their core competencies and remediate themselves based on their individual learning style.
- Review and reinforce concepts with algorithmically generated exercises.
- View video tutorials.
- Take practice quizzes.

Online Practice Problems

Step-by-step guided solutions and fully worked similar examples in **Eduspace** provide further opportunities for students to actively develop their skills and understanding of the topics.

Live, Online Tutoring

SMARTHINKING® live, online tutoring provides guidance for students as they work through problems without ever giving them the answers.

Online Self Tests

Online Study Center **ACE Self Tests** on the student **Online Study Center** let students practice chapter tests to help them prepare for exams.

AUFMANN INTERACTIVE METHOD (AIM)

Intermediate Algebra with Applications uses an interactive style that engages students in trying new skills and reinforcing learning through structured exercises.

An Interactive Approach

page 658

page S31

- Each section of the text is divided into objectives, and every objective contains one or more sets of matched-pair examples. The first example in each set is worked out.

- The second example, called "Problem," is for the student to work. By solving this problem, the student actively practices concepts as they are presented in the text.

- *Complete worked-out* solutions to these Problems appear at the back of the book for students to check their work.

NEW! Interactive Exercises

Placed at the beginning of an objective's exercise set (when appropriate), these exercises provide guided practice and test students' understanding of the underlying concepts in a lesson. They also act as stepping-stones to the remaining exercises for the objective.

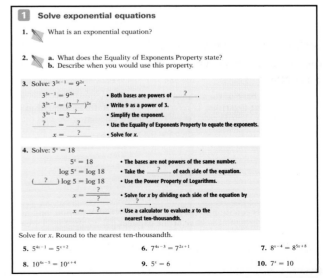

page 650

CONCEPTUAL UNDERSTANDING

Intermediate Algebra with Applications helps students understand the course concepts through the textbook exposition and feature set.

Features in the Exposition

Take Note

Crichton goes on to say, in the same paragraph, "In this way it can be shown that in a single day, one cell of *E. coli* could produce a super-colony equal in size and weight to the entire planet Earth." In the model we are using, where the bacteria divide once an hour (instead of three times an hour, as in *The Andromeda Strain*), it would take the colony 3 days to become the size of Earth.

This model would be true if uncontrolled biological growth were possible, but it is not. Other factors, such as food to sustain growth, would not be sufficient to support continued exponential growth.

To determine when there would be 32,000 bacteria in the culture, we would solve the exponential equation $32{,}000 = 1000(2^t)$ for t. Because $A = 1000(2^t)$ is a growth equation and 32,000 is between 8000 and 64,000, t must be between 3 h and 6 h. By trial and error, we find that $t = 5$ h.

$$A = 1000(2^t)$$
$$A = 1000(2^5) \qquad \bullet \text{ Replace } t \text{ by } 5.$$
$$A = 1000(32) = 32{,}000$$

Now suppose we want to find how long it would take for the colony to reach 1,000,000 bacteria. From the table, 1,000,000 is between 256,000 and 4,096,000, so this will happen sometime between 8 h and 12 h. If we try 10 h, halfway between 8 and 12, we have

$$A = 1000(2^t)$$
$$A = 1000(2^{10}) \qquad \bullet \text{ Replace } t \text{ by } 10.$$
$$A = 1000(1024) = 1{,}024{,}000$$

Because 1,000,000 is less than 1,024,000, the actual value of t is less than 10 h.

We could continue to use trial and error to find t, but it would be more efficient if we could just solve the equation $1{,}000{,}000 = 1000(2^t)$ for t. Using methods described earlier in the text, we have

$$1{,}000{,}000 = 1000(2^t)$$
$$1000 = 2^t \qquad \bullet \text{ Divide each side of the equation by 1000.}$$

To solve this equation, it would be helpful to have a function that would give the power of 2 that produces 1000. Around the mid-16th century, mathematicians created such a function, which we now call a *logarithmic function*. We write the solution of $1000 = 2^t$ as $t = \log_2 1000$. This is read "t equals the logarithm base 2 of 1000," and it means "t equals the power of 2 that produces 1000."

When logarithms were first introduced, tables were used to find the numerical value of t. Today, a calculator is used. Using a calculator, we can approximate the value of t as 9.97. Thus $9.97 \approx \log_2 1000$ and $1000 \approx 2^{9.97}$.

The ideas presented above are related to the concept of inverse function discussed in the last chapter. Because the exponential function given by $y = b^x$ is a 1–1 function, it has an inverse function. To find that function, we follow the same procedure we used to find the inverse of other functions.

$$y = b^x$$
$$x = b^y \qquad \bullet \text{ Interchange } x \text{ and } y.$$

The equation $x = b^y$ says that y equals the power of b that produces x. That is, y is the logarithm base b of x. The inverse of the exponential function $y = b^x$ is a logarithmic function.

Here is a general definition of logarithm.

Take Note

Recall that for the equation $2^t = 1000$, we said that "t equals the power of 2 that produces 1000" means that "t is the logarithm base 2 of 1000." We are doing the same with $x = b^y$.

Definition of Logarithm

If $x > 0$ and b is a positive constant not equal to 1, then $y = \log_b x$ is equivalent to $b^y = x$.

page 623

- Margin notes titled Take Note amplify the concept under discussion or alert students to points requiring special attention.

- Key concepts are presented in orange boxes in order to highlight them and provide for easy reference.

Logarithms base 10 are called **common logarithms.** We usually omit the base, 10, when writing the common logarithm of a number. Therefore, $\log_{10} x$ is written $\log x$. To find the common logarithm of most numbers, a calculator is necessary. A calculator was used to find the value of log 384, shown below.

$$\log 384 \approx 2.584331224$$

When e (the base of the natural exponential function) is used as a base of a logarithm, the logarithm is referred to as the **natural logarithm** and is abbreviated $\ln x$. This is read "el en x." Using a calculator, we find that

$$\ln 23 \approx 3.135494216$$

page 626

- Key terms, in bold, emphasize important vocabulary.

Compare this equation to the exponential growth equation, and note that for exponential growth, the base of the exponential expression is greater than 1, whereas for exponential decay, the base is between 0 and 1.

A method by which an archeologist can measure the age of a bone is called **carbon dating.** Carbon dating is based on a radioactive isotope of carbon called carbon-14, which has a half-life of approximately 5570 years. The ex-

page 655

- Important points are now highlighted, to help students recognize what is most important and to study more effectively.

CONCEPTUAL UNDERSTANDING

Intermediate Algebra with Applications helps students understand the course concepts through the textbook exposition and feature set.

Features in the Exercise Sets

10.1 Concept Review

Determine whether the following statements are always true, sometimes true, or never true.

1. The domain of an exponential function $f(x) = b^x$, $b > 0$, $b \neq 1$, is the set of positive numbers.

2. An exponential function $f(x) = b^x$, $b > 0$, $b \neq 1$, is a 1–1 function.

3. The graph of the exponential function $f(x) = b^x$, $b > 0$, $b \neq 1$, passes through the point $(0, 0)$.

4. For the function $f(x) = b^x$, $b > 0$, $b \neq 1$, the base b is a positive integer.

5. An exponential function $f(x) = b^x$, $b > 0$, $b \neq 1$, has two x-intercepts.

page 618

• **Concept Review** exercises appear at the beginning of each exercise set and are designed to test a student's understanding of the topic.

---

51. $b > 1$ and m and n are positive numbers such that $m > n$. Is $\log_b m$ less than, equal to, or greater than $\log_b n$?

52. $0 < b < 1$ and $m > 1$. Is $\log_b m$ less than, equal to, or greater than zero?

page 634

• **NEW! Think About It Exercises** are conceptual in nature. They ask the students to think about the objective's concepts, make generalizations, and apply them to more abstract problems. The focus is on mental mathematics, and they are designed to help students synthesize concepts.

10.4 Exercises

1 Solve exponential equations

1. What is an exponential equation?

2. **a.** What does the Equality of Exponents Property state?
   b. Describe when you would use this property.

page 650

• **Writing Exercises** require students to verbalize concepts, which is a crucial step in learning them.

10.3 Applying Concepts

31. Employment The proficiency of a typist decreases (without practice) over time. An equation that approximates this decrease is given by $S = 60 - 7 \ln(t + 1)$, where S is the typing speed in words per minute and t is the number of months without typing.
   a. Graph the equation.

   b. The point whose approximate coordinates are $(4, 49)$ is on the graph. Write a sentence that describes the meaning of this ordered pair.

32. Astronomy Astronomers use the *distance modulus* of a star as a method of determining the star's distance from Earth. The formula is $M = 5 \log s - 5$, where M is the distance modulus and s is the star's distance from Earth in parsecs. (One parsec $\approx 2.1 \times 10^{13}$ miles.)
   a. Graph the equation.

   b. The point whose approximate coordinates are $(25.1, 2)$ is on the graph. Write a sentence that describes the meaning of this ordered pair.

page 644

• **Applying Concepts** are more challenging problems involving multiple concepts that require interpretation, analysis, and critical thinking. They are designed to help students to apply and internalize concepts.

PROBLEM SOLVING

Intermediate Algebra with Applications emphasizes applications, problem solving, and critical thinking.

---

16. Demography The number of centenarians (people aged 100 or older) in the United States has been increasing dramatically. Based on data from the U.S. Census Bureau, and using $x = 0$ to correspond to the year 2000, the equation $y = 66.77(1.0532^x)$ approximates the projected U.S. centenarian population through 2050, where y is in thousands.

  a. According to the model, what is the predicted population of centenarians in 2015? Round to the nearest thousand.
  b. In what year does the model predict that the U.S. centenarian population will first exceed 250,000?

Chemistry For Exercises 17 and 18, use the equation $pH = -\log(H^+)$, where H^+ is the hydrogen ion concentration of a solution. Round to the nearest hundredth.

17. Find the pH of milk, for which the hydrogen ion concentration is 3.97×10^{-7}.

18. Find the pH of a baking soda solution, for which the hydrogen ion concentration is 3.98×10^{-9}.

page 661

Integrated Real-Life Applications

Wherever appropriate, the last objective of a section presents applications that require students to use problem-solving strategies, along with the skills covered in that section, to solve practical problems. This carefully integrated applied approach generates student awareness of the value of algebra as a real-life tool. Applications are taken from many disciplines and are emphasized through sourced data.

EXAMPLE 1 The number of words per minute a student can type will increase with practice and can be approximated by the equation $N = 100[1 - (0.9)^t]$, where N is the number of words typed per minute after t days of practice. In how many days will the student be able to type 60 words per minute?

Strategy To find the number of days, replace N by 60 and solve for t.

Solution
$$N = 100[1 - (0.9)^t]$$
$$60 = 100[1 - (0.9)^t]$$
$$0.6 = 1 - (0.9)^t \quad \bullet \text{ Divide each side of the equation by 100.}$$
$$-0.4 = -(0.9)^t \quad \bullet \text{ Subtract 1 from each side of the equation.}$$
$$0.4 = (0.9)^t$$
$$\log 0.4 = \log(0.9)^t$$
$$\log 0.4 = t \log 0.9$$
$$t = \frac{\log 0.4}{\log 0.9} \approx 8.6967184$$

After approximately 9 days the student will type 60 words per minute.

The graph at the left is the graph of $N = 100[1 - (0.9)^t]$. Note that t is approximately 8.7 when $N = 60$.

(graph: N on vertical axis labeled "Words per minute" with values 20, 40, 60, 80; t on horizontal axis labeled "Number of days" with values 0, 10, 20; point (8.7, 60))

PROBLEM 1 An investment of $3000 is placed into an account that earns 12% annual interest compounded monthly. In approximately how many years will the investment be worth twice the original amount? Round to the nearest whole number.

Solution See page S31.

The first applications of logarithms (and the main reason why they were developed) were to reduce computational drudgery. Today, with the widespread use of calculators and computers, the computational uses of logarithms have diminished. However, a number of other applications of logarithms have emerged.

A chemist measures the acidity or alkalinity of a solution by the formula $pH = -\log(H^+)$, where H^+ is the concentration of hydrogen ions in the solution. A neutral solution such as distilled water has a pH of 7, acids have a pH less than 7, and alkaline solutions (also ___) greater than 7.

Point of Interest

Søren Sørensen

The pH scale was created by the Danish biochemist Søren Sørensen in 1909 to measure the acidity of water used in the brewing of beer. pH is an abbreviation for pondus hydrogenii, which translates as "potential hydrogen."

Find the pH of vinegar for which H ___ nearest tenth.

Use the pH equation.
$H^+ = 1.26 \times 10^{-3}$.

The pH of vinegar is approximately ___

Problem-Solving Strategies

A carefully developed approach to problem solving emphasizes the importance of strategy when solving problems.

- Students are encouraged to develop their own strategies as part of their solutions to problems.

- Model strategies are always presented as guides for students to follow as they attempt the parallel Problems that accompany each numbered Example.

SECTION 10.5

Problem 1

Strategy ▶ To find the time, solve the compound interest formula for n. Use $P = 6000$, $A = 3000$, and $i = \frac{12\%}{12} = \frac{0.12}{12} = 0.01$.

Solution
$$P = A(1 + i)^n$$
$$6000 = 3000(1 + 0.01)^n$$
$$6000 = 3000(1.01)^n$$
$$2 = (1.01)^n$$
$$\log 2 = \log(1.01)^n$$
$$\log 2 = n \log 1.01$$
$$\frac{\log 2}{\log 1.01} = n$$
$$70 \approx n$$

70 months $\div$ 12 $\approx$ 5.8 years

In approximately 6 years, the investment will be worth $6000.

pages 656 and S31

Focus on Problem Solving

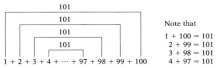

Find a Pattern   Polya's four recommended problem-solving steps are stated below.

1. Understand the problem.
2. Devise a plan.
3. Carry out the plan.
4. Review your solution

Point of Interest

Carl Friedrich Gauss (1777–1855) has been called the "Prince of Mathematicians" by some historians. He applied his genius to many areas of mathematics and science. A unit of magnetism, the gauss, is named in his honor. Some electronic appliances (televisions, for instance) contain a degausser that controls magnetic fields.

One of the several ways of devising a plan is first to try to find a pattern. Karl Friedrich Gauss supposedly used this method to solve a problem that was given to his math class when he was in elementary school. As the story goes, his teacher wanted to grade some papers while the class worked on a math problem. The problem the teacher gave to the class was to find the sum

$$1 + 2 + 3 + 4 + \cdots + 100$$

Gauss quickly solved the problem by seeing a pattern. Here is what he saw.

$$\begin{array}{c}101 \\ 101 \\ 101 \\ 101 \\ 1 + 2 + 3 + 4 + \cdots + 97 + 98 + 99 + 100\end{array}$$

Note that
$$1 + 100 = 101$$
$$2 + 99 = 101$$
$$3 + 98 = 101$$
$$4 + 97 = 101$$

Gauss noted that there were 50 sums of 101. Therefore, the sum of the first 100 natural numbers is

$$1 + 2 + 3 + 4 + \cdots + 97 + 98 + 99 + 100 = 50(101) = 5050$$

Try to solve the following problems by finding a pattern.

1. Find the sum $2 + 4 + 6 + \cdots + 96 + 98 + 100$.
2. Find the sum $1 + 3 + 5 + \cdots + 97 + 99 + 101$.
3. Find another method of finding the sum $1 + 3 + 5 + \cdots + 97 + 99 + 101$ given in the previous exercise.
4. Find the sum $\frac{1}{1 \cdot 2} + \frac{1}{2 \cdot 3} + \frac{1}{3 \cdot 4} + \cdots + \frac{1}{49 \cdot 50}$.

   Hint: $\frac{1}{1 \cdot 2} = \frac{1}{2}, \frac{1}{1 \cdot 2} + \frac{1}{2 \cdot 3} = \frac{2}{3}, \frac{1}{1 \cdot 2} + \frac{1}{2 \cdot 3} + \frac{1}{3 \cdot 4} = \frac{3}{4}$
5. The following problem shows that checking a few cases does not always result in a conjecture that is true for *all* cases. Select any two points on a circle and draw a *chord*, the line connecting the points (see the drawing in the left margin). The chord divides the circle into two regions. Now select three different points and draw chords connecting each of the three points with every other point. The chords divide the circle into four regions. Now select four points and connect each of the points with every other point. Make a conjecture about the relationship between the number

2 points, 2 regions   3 points, 4 regions

4 points, 8 regions   5 points, ? regions

page 210

Focus on Problem Solving

Students are introduced to various successful problem-solving strategies within the end-of-chapter material. Strategies include:

- drawing a diagram,
- applying solutions to other problems,
- working backwards,
- inductive reasoning,
- and trial and error.

NEW! Think About It Exercises

These exercises focus on concepts, not on calculation or computation, and will help develop students' critical thinking skills.

29. Which function(s) will have the same graph as the graph of the function $f(x) = \log_3 3x$?
    a. $g(x) = 3 \log_3 x$ **b.** $h(x) = 1 + \log_3 x$
    c. $F(x) = \log_3 x^3$ **d.** $G(x) = \dfrac{\log 3x}{\log 3}$

30. Which function(s) will have the same graph as the graph of the function $f(x) = -\log_b x$?
    a. $g(x) = \log_b(-x)$ **b.** $h(x) = \dfrac{1}{\log_b x}$
    c. $F(x) = \log_b \dfrac{1}{x}$ **d.** $G(x) = \dfrac{\log b}{\log x}$

page 643

Additional Resources—Get More from Your Textbook!

Instructor Resources

Instructor's Annotated Edition (IAE) The Instructor's Annotated Edition is ideal for seasoned instructors, teaching assistants, or adjuncts. Reduced student pages leave room in the margin of the IAE for extensive instructor support materials at point-of-use.

Online Teaching Center This web site offers instructors prep tests and chapter tests, instructor's solutions, quick quizzes, AIM for Success Practice Sheets, topic sequences, and more.

HM Testing™ (Powered by Diploma®) "Testing the way you want it" HM Testing offers all the tools needed to create, author/edit algorithmic questions, customize, and deliver multiple types of tests.

Student Resources

Student Solutions Manual Contains complete solutions to all odd-numbered exercises, and all of the solutions to the end-of-chapter material.

Math Study Skills Workbook, Third Edition, by Paul Nolting Helps students identify their strengths, weaknesses, and personal learning styles in math. Nolting offers study tips, proven test-taking strategies, a homework system, and recommendations for reducing anxiety and improving grades.

Online Study Center This free web site gives students access to ACE practice tests, glossary flashcards, chapter summaries, and other study resources.

Instructional DVDs Hosted by Dana Mosely, these text-specific DVDs cover all sections of the text and provide explanations of key concepts, examples, exercises, and applications in a lecture-based format. DVDs are now closed-captioned for the hearing-impaired.

Eduspace® (powered by Blackboard®) Eduspace is a web-based learning system that provides instructors with powerful course management tools and students with text-specific content to support all of their online teaching and learning needs. In addition to new, enhanced algorithms, Eduspace now includes:

HM Assess™ Houghton Mifflin's new diagnostic tool tests core concepts and provides students with individual study paths for self-remediation. Instructors can use HM Assess to quickly gauge which students are in jeopardy and identify which concepts to spend extra time reviewing.

Visit **www.eduspace.com** for more information.

SMARTHINKING® Live, Online Tutoring SMARTHINKING provides an easy-to-use and effective online, text-specific tutoring service. A dynamic **Whiteboard** and a **Graphing Calculator** function enable students and e-structors to collaborate easily.

Online Course Content for Blackboard®, WebCT®, and eCollege® Deliver program- or text-specific Houghton Mifflin content online using your institution's local course management system. Houghton Mifflin offers homework, tutorials, videos, and other resources formatted for Blackboard, WebCT, eCollege, and other course management systems. Add to an existing online course or create a new one by selecting from a wide range of powerful learning and instructional materials.

For more information, visit **college.hmco.com/pic/aufmannIAWA7e**
or contact your Houghton Mifflin sales representative.

Welcome to *Intermediate Algebra with Applications*. As you begin this course, we know two important facts: (1) We want you to succeed. (2) You want to succeed. To do that requires an effort from each of us. For the next few pages, we are going to show you what is required of you to achieve that success and how you can use the features of this text to be successful.

Motivation

One of the most important keys to success is motivation. We can try to motivate you by offering interesting or important ways mathematics can benefit you. But, in the end, the motivation must come from you. On the first day of class, it is easy to be motivated. Eight weeks into the term, it is harder to keep that motivation.

To stay motivated, there must be outcomes from this course that are worth your time, money, and energy. List some reasons you are taking this course. Do not make a mental list—actually write them out.

> ## Take Note
>
> Motivation alone will not lead to success. For instance, suppose a person who cannot swim is placed in a boat, taken out to the middle of a lake, and then thrown overboard. That person has a lot of motivation but there is a high likelihood the person will drown without some help. Motivation gives us the desire to learn but is not the same as learning.

Although we hope that one of the reasons you listed was an interest in mathematics, we know that many of you are taking this course because it is required to graduate, it is a prerequisite for a course you must take, or it is required for your major. Although you may not agree that this course is necessary, it is! If you are motivated to graduate or complete the requirements for your major, then use that motivation to succeed in this course. Do not become distracted from your goal to complete your education!

Commitment

To be successful, you must make a commitment to succeed. This means devoting time to math so that you achieve a better understanding of the subject.

List some activities (sports, hobbies, talents such as dance, art, or music) that you enjoy and at which you would like to become better.

ACTIVITY	*TIME SPENT*	*TIME WISHED SPENT*

Thinking about these activities, put the number of hours that you spend each week practicing these activities next to the activity. Next to that number, indicate the number of hours per week you would like to spend on these activities.

Whether you listed surfing or sailing, aerobics or restoring cars, or any other activity you enjoy, note how many hours a week you spend doing it. To succeed in math, you must be willing to commit the same amount of time. Success requires some sacrifice.

The "I Can't Do Math" Syndrome

There may be things you cannot do, such as lift a two-ton boulder. You can, however, do math. It is much easier than lifting the two-ton boulder. When you first learned the activities you listed above, you probably could not do them well. With practice, you got better. With practice, you will be better at math. Stay focused, motivated, and committed to success.

It is difficult for us to emphasize how important it is to overcome the "I Can't Do Math Syndrome." If you listen to interviews of very successful athletes after a particularly bad performance, you will note that they focus on the positive aspect of what they did, not the negative. Sports psychologists encourage athletes to always be positive—to have a "Can Do" attitude. Develop this attitude toward math.

Strategies for Success

Textbook Reconnaissance   Right now, do a 15-minute "textbook reconnaissance" of this book. Here's how:

First, read the table of contents. Do it in three minutes or less. Next, look through the entire book, page by page. Move quickly. Scan titles, look at pictures, notice diagrams.

A textbook reconnaissance shows you where a course is going. It gives you the big picture. That's useful because brains work best when going from the general to the specific. Getting the big picture before you start makes details easier to recall and understand later on.

Your textbook reconnaissance will work even better if, as you scan, you look for ideas or topics that are interesting to you. List three facts, topics, or problems that you found interesting during your textbook reconnaissance.

_____

_____

_____

The idea behind this technique is simple: It's easier to work at learning material if you know it's going to be useful to you.

Not all the topics in this book will be "interesting" to you. But that is true of any subject. Surfers find that on some days the waves are better than others, musicians find some music more appealing than other music, computer gamers find some computer games more interesting than others, and car enthusiasts find some cars more exciting than others. Some car enthusiasts would rather have a completely restored 1957 Chevrolet than a new Ferrari.

Know the Course Requirements   To do your best in this course, you must know exactly what your instructor requires. Course requirements may be stated in a *syllabus*, which is a printed outline of the main topics of the course, or they may be presented orally. When they are listed in a syllabus or on other printed pages, keep them in a safe place. When they are presented orally, make sure to take complete notes. In either case, it is important that you understand them completely and follow them exactly. Be sure you know the answer to the following questions.

1. What is your instructor's name?
2. Where is your instructor's office?
3. At what times does your instructor hold office hours?
4. Besides the textbook, what other materials does your instructor require?
5. What is your instructor's attendance policy?
6. If you must be absent from a class meeting, what should you do before returning to class? What should you do when you return to class?
7. What is the instructor's policy regarding collection or grading of homework assignments?

8. What options are available if you are having difficulty with an assignment? Is there a math tutoring center?
9. Is there a math lab at your school? Where is it located? What hours is it open?
10. What is the instructor's policy if you miss a quiz?
11. What is the instructor's policy if you miss an exam?
12. Where can you get help when studying for an exam?

Remember: Your instructor wants to see you succeed. If you need help, ask! Do not fall behind. If you are running a race and fall behind by 100 yards, you may be able to catch up but it will require more effort than had you not fallen behind.

Take Note

Besides time management, there must be realistic ideas of how much time is available. There are very few people who can *successfully* work full-time and go to school full-time. If you work 40 hours a week, take 15 units, spend the recommended study time given at the right, and sleep 8 hours a day, you will use over 80% of the available hours in a week. That leaves less than 20% of the hours in a week for family, friends, eating, recreation, and other activities.

Time Management   We know that there are demands on your time. Family, work, friends, and entertainment all compete for your time. We do not want to see you receive poor job evaluations because you are studying math. However, it is also true that we do not want to see you receive poor math test scores because you devoted too much time to work. When several competing and important tasks require your time and energy, the only way to manage the stress of being successful at both is to manage your time efficiently.

Instructors often advise students to spend twice the amount of time outside of class studying as they spend in the classroom. Time management is important if you are to accomplish this goal and succeed in school. The following activity is intended to help you structure your time more efficiently.

List the name of each course you are taking this term, the number of class hours each course meets, and the number of hours you should spend studying each subject outside of class. Then fill in a weekly schedule like the one below. Begin by writing in the hours spent in your classes, the hours spent at work (if you have a job), and any other commitments that are not flexible with respect to the time that you do them. Then begin to write down commitments that are more flexible, including hours spent studying. Remember to reserve time for activities such as meals and exercise. You should also schedule free time.

	Monday	Tuesday	Wednesday	Thursday	Friday	Saturday	Sunday
7–8 a.m.							
8–9 a.m.							
9–10 a.m.							
10–11 a.m.							
11–12 p.m.							
12–1 p.m.							
1–2 p.m.							
2–3 p.m.							
3–4 p.m.							
4–5 p.m.							
5–6 p.m.							
6–7 p.m.							
7–8 p.m.							
8–9 p.m.							
9–10 p.m.							
10–11 p.m.							
11–12 a.m.							

We know that many of you must work. If that is the case, realize that working 10 hours a week at a part-time job is equivalent to taking a three-unit class. If you must work, consider letting your education progress at a slower rate to allow you to be successful at both work and school. There is no rule that says you must finish school in a certain time frame.

Schedule Study Time As we encouraged you to do by filling out the time management form above, schedule a certain time to study. You should think of this time the way you would the time for work or class—that is, reasons for missing study time should be as compelling as reasons for missing work or class. "I just didn't feel like it" is not a good reason to miss your scheduled study time.

Although this may seem like an obvious exercise, list a few reasons you might want to study.

_____

_____

_____

Of course we have no way of knowing the reasons you listed, but from our experience one reason given quite frequently is "To pass the course." There is nothing wrong with that reason. If that is the most important reason for you to study, then use it to stay focused.

One method of keeping to a study schedule is to form a ***study group***. Look for people who are committed to learning, who pay attention in class, and who are punctual. Ask them to join your group. Choose people with similar educational goals but different methods of learning. You can gain insight from seeing the material from a new perspective. Limit groups to four or five people; larger groups are unwieldy.

There are many ways to conduct a study group. Begin with the following suggestions and see what works best for your group.

1. Test each other by asking questions. Each group member might bring two or three sample test questions to each meeting.
2. Practice teaching each other. Many of us who are teachers learned a lot about our subject when we had to explain it to someone else.
3. Compare class notes. You might ask other students about material in your notes that is difficult for you to understand.
4. Brainstorm test questions.
5. Set an agenda for each meeting. Set approximate time limits for each agenda item and determine a quitting time.

And finally, probably the most important aspect of studying is that it should be done in relatively small chunks. If you can only study three hours a week for this course (probably not enough for most people), do it in blocks of one hour on three separate days, preferably after class. Three hours of studying on a Sunday is not as productive as three hours of paced study.

Text Features That Promote Success

There are 12 chapters in this text. Each chapter is divided into sections, and each section is subdivided into learning objectives. Each learning objective is labeled with a number from 1 to 4.

Preparing for a Chapter   Before you begin a new chapter, you should take some time to review previously learned skills. There are two ways to do this. The first is to complete the ***Cumulative Review***, which occurs after every chapter (except Chapter 1). For instance, turn to page 369. The questions in this review are taken from the previous chapters. The answers for all these exercises can be found on pages A23 and A24. Turn to those pages now and locate the answers for the Chapter 5 Cumulative Review. After the answer to the first exercise, which is 4, you will see the objective reference [1.2.4]. This means that this question was taken from Chapter 1, Section 2, Objective 4. If you missed this question, you should return to that objective and restudy the material.

A second way of preparing for a new chapter is to complete the ***Prep Test***. This test focuses on the particular skills that will be required for the new chapter. Turn to page 287 to see a Prep Test. The answers for the Prep Test are the first set of answers in the answer section for a chapter. Turn to page A18 to see the answers for the Chapter 5 Prep Test. Note that an objective reference is given for each question. If you answer a question incorrectly, restudy the objective from which the question was taken.

Before the class meeting in which your professor begins a new section, you should read each objective statement for that section. Next, browse through the objective material, being sure to note each word in bold type. These words indicate important concepts that you must know in order to learn the material. Do not worry about trying to understand all the material. Your professor is there to assist you with that endeavor. The purpose of browsing through the material is so that your brain will be prepared to accept and organize the new information when it is presented to you.

Turn to page 2. Write down the title of the first objective in Section 1.1. Under the title of the objective, write down the words in the objective that are in bold print. It is not necessary for you to understand the meaning of these words. You are in this class to learn their meaning.

_____   _____   _____   _____

_____   _____   _____   _____

_____   _____   _____   _____

_____   _____   _____   _____

_____   _____   _____   _____

Math is Not a Spectator Sport   To learn mathematics you must be an active participant. Listening and watching your professor do mathematics is not enough. Mathematics requires that you interact with the lesson you are studying. If you filled in the blanks above, you were being interactive. There are other ways this textbook has been designed to help you be an active learner.

Instructional Examples Blue lines indicate an instructional example that usually has explanatory remarks to the left of the solution. These examples are used for two purposes. The first is to provide additional examples of important concepts. Secondly, these examples examine important techniques or principles that are often used in the solution of other types of problems.

$6x - 8 = 3x + 7$
$3x - 8 = 7$ (subtract 3x from both sides)
$3x = 15$ (add 8 to both sides)
$x = 5$ (divide both sides by 3)

Solve: $6x - 8 = 3x + 7$

$$6x - 8 = 3x + 7$$

Subtract $3x$ from each side of the equation. Then simplify.

$$6x - 3x - 8 = 3x - 3x + 7$$
$$3x - 8 = 7$$

Add 8 to each side of the equation. Then simplify.

$$3x - 8 + 8 = 7 + 8$$
$$3x = 15$$

Divide each side of the equation by 3.

$$\frac{3x}{3} = \frac{15}{3}$$

Then simplify.

$$x = 5$$

You should check the solution.

The solution is 5.

page 61

When you complete the example, get a clean sheet of paper. Write down the problem and then try to complete the solution without referring to your notes or the book. When you can do that, move on to the next part of the objective.

Leaf through the book now and write down the page numbers of two other occurrences of an instructional example.

Example/Problem Pairs One of the key instructional features of this text is Example/Problem pairs. Note that each Example is completely worked out and the "Problem" following the example is not. Study the worked-out example carefully by working through each step. Then work the Problem. If you get stuck, refer to the page number following the Problem which directs you to the page on which the Problem is solved—a complete worked-out solution is provided. Try to use the given solution to get a hint for the step you are stuck on. Then try to complete your solution.

EXAMPLE 1 Solve: $-\frac{2}{7}x = \frac{4}{21}$

Solution

$$-\frac{2}{7}x = \frac{4}{21}$$

$$\left(-\frac{7}{2}\right)\left(-\frac{2}{7}x\right) = \left(-\frac{7}{2}\right)\left(\frac{4}{21}\right)$$

• Multiply both sides of the equation by the reciprocal of $-\frac{2}{7}$. Then simplify.

$$x = -\frac{2}{3}$$

The solution is $-\frac{2}{3}$.

Problem 1:

$-3x = 18$
$\frac{-3x}{-3} = \frac{18}{-3}$
$x = -6$

The solution is -6.

PROBLEM 1 Solve: $-3x = -18$

Solution See page S2.

page 61

When you have completed your solution, check your work against the solution we provided. (Turn to page S2 to see the solution of Problem 1.) Be aware that frequently there is more than one way to solve a problem. Your answer, however, should be the same as the given answer. If you have any question as to whether your method will "always work," check with your instructor or with someone in the math center.

Browse through the textbook and write down the page numbers where two other Example/Problem pairs occur.

Remember: Be an active participant in your learning process. When you are sitting in class watching and listening to an explanation, you may think that you understand. However, until you actually try to do it, you will have no confirmation of the new knowledge or skill. Most of us have had the experience of sitting in class thinking we knew how to do something only to get home and realize that we didn't.

Word Problems   Word problems are difficult because we must read the problem, determine the quantity we must find, think of a method to do that, and then actually solve the problem. In short, we must formulate a *strategy* to solve the problem and then devise a *solution*.

Note in the Example/Problem pair below that both a strategy and a solution are provided for the word problem. The strategy is a written description of how we will solve the problem. In the corresponding Problem, you are asked to formulate a strategy. Do not skip this step, and be sure to write it out.

> **Take Note**
>
> There is a strong connection between reading and being a successful student in math or in any other subject. If you have difficulty reading, consider taking a reading course. Reading is much like other skills. There are certain things you can learn that will make you a better reader.

Problem 5:

Strategy:

Next year's salary: s

Next year's salary is the sum of this year's salary and the raise.

Solution:

s = 34,500 + 0.08(34,500)
  = 34,500 + 2760
  = 37,260

Next year's salary is $37,260.

EXAMPLE 5   The charges for a long-distance telephone call are $2.14 for the first three minutes and $.47 for each additional minute or fraction of a minute. If the charges for a long-distance call were $17.65, how many minutes did the phone call last?

Strategy   To find the length of the phone call in minutes, write and solve an equation using n to represent the total number of minutes of the call. Then $n - 3$ is the number of additional minutes after the first three minutes of the phone call. The fixed charge for the three minutes plus the charge for the additional minutes is the total cost of the phone call.

Solution
$$2.14 + 0.47(n - 3) = 17.65$$
$$2.14 + 0.47n - 1.41 = 17.65$$
$$0.47n + 0.73 = 17.65$$
$$0.47n = 16.92$$
$$n = 36$$

The phone call lasted 36 min.

PROBLEM 5   You are making a salary of $34,500 and receive an 8% raise for next year. Find your next year's salary.

Solution   See page S3.

page 64

Rule Boxes   Pay special attention to rules placed in boxes. These rules give you the reasons certain types of problems are solved the way they are. When you see a rule, try to rewrite the rule in your own words.

> **Take Note**
>
> If a rule has more than one part, be sure to make a notation to that effect.

Multiplying each side of an equation by the same number (<u>NOT</u> O) will not change the solution.

> ### The Multiplication Property of Equations
>
> If a, b, and c are algebraic expressions, and $c \neq 0$, then the equation $a = b$ has the same solutions as the equation $ac = bc$.

page 60

Find and write down two page numbers on which there are rule boxes.

Chapter Exercises   When you have completed studying an objective, do the exercises in the exercise set that correspond with that objective. The exercises are labeled with the same number as the objective. Math is a subject that needs to be learned in small sections and practiced continually in order to be mastered. Doing all of the exercises in each exercise set will help you master the problem-solving techniques necessary for success. As you work through the exercises for an objective, check your answers to the odd-numbered exercises with those in the back of the book.

Preparing for a Test   There are important features of this text that can be used to prepare for a test.

- Chapter Summary
- Chapter Review Exercises
- Chapter Test

After completing a chapter, read the Chapter Summary. (See page 464 for the Chapter 5 Summary.) This summary highlights the important topics covered in the chapter. The page number following each topic refers you to the page in the text on which you can find more information about the concept.

Following the Chapter Summary are Chapter Review Exercises (see page 366) and a Chapter Test (see page 368). Doing the review exercises is an important way of testing your understanding of the chapter. The answer to each review exercise is given at the back of the book, along with its objective reference. After checking your answers, restudy any objective from which a question you missed was taken. It may be helpful to retry some of the exercises for that objective to reinforce your problem-solving techniques.

The Chapter Test should be used to prepare for an exam. We suggest that you try the Chapter Test a few days before your actual exam. Take the test in a quiet place and try to complete the test in the same amount of time you will be allowed for your exam. When taking the Chapter Test, practice the strategies of successful test takers: (1) scan the entire test to get a feel for the questions; (2) read the directions carefully; (3) work the problems that are easiest for you first; and perhaps most importantly, (4) try to stay calm.

When you have completed the Chapter Test, check your answers. If you missed a question, review the material in that objective and rework some of the exercises from that objective. This will strengthen your ability to perform the skills in that objective.

Your career goal goes here. →   Is it difficult to be successful? YES! Successful music groups, artists, professional athletes, chefs, and _____ have to work very hard to achieve their goals. They focus on their goals and ignore distractions. The things we ask you to do to achieve success take time and commitment. We are confident that if you follow our suggestions, you will succeed.

Intermediate Algebra

WITH APPLICATIONS

1 Review of Real Numbers

Online Study Center

DVD **SSM**

Need help? For online student resources, such as section quizzes, visit the Online Study Center at college.hmco.com/info/aufmanndevmathhb.

No matter what you do in life, at some point you will be asked to solve a problem that will at first seem very difficult. When this happens, it's usually helpful to take a moment to ask yourself some questions: What do I need to do? How am I going to do it? Just as an architect develops a blueprint to decide how to build a house, you can develop a plan to solve your problem and find the answer. The basic steps involved in problem solving are outlined in the **Focus on Problem Solving on pages 48–49** and are used throughout the text. Problem solving is a necessary skill for future success, which will only improve with study and practice.

Prep Test

For Exercises 1 to 8, add, subtract, multiply, or divide.

1. $\dfrac{5}{12} + \dfrac{7}{30}$ **2.** $\dfrac{8}{15} - \dfrac{7}{20}$

3. $\dfrac{5}{6} \cdot \dfrac{4}{15}$ **4.** $\dfrac{4}{15} \div \dfrac{2}{5}$

5. $8 + 29.34 + 7.065$ **6.** $92 - 18.37$

7. $2.19(3.4)$ **8.** $32.436 \div 0.6$

9. Which of the following numbers are greater than -8?
   a. -6 **b.** -10 **c.** 0 **d.** 8

10. Match each fraction with its decimal equivalent.

   a. $\dfrac{1}{2}$ **A.** 0.75

   b. $\dfrac{7}{10}$ **B.** 0.89

   c. $\dfrac{3}{4}$ **C.** 0.5

   d. $\dfrac{89}{100}$ **D.** 0.7

1.1   Introduction to Real Numbers

OBJECTIVE 1   Inequality and absolute value

Point of Interest

The Big Dipper, known to the Greeks as Ursa Major, *the great bear, is a constellation that can be seen from northern latitudes. The stars of the Big Dipper are Alkaid, Mizar, Alioth, Megrez, Phecda, Merak, and Dubhe. The star at the bend of the handle, Mizar, is actually two stars, Mizar and Alcor. An imaginary line from Merak through Dubhe passes through Polaris, the north star.*

It seems to be a human characteristic to put similar items into the same place. For instance, an astronomer places stars in *constellations* and a geologist divides the history of the earth into *eras*.

Mathematicians likewise place objects with similar properties in *sets*. A **set** is a collection of objects. The objects are called **elements** of the set. Sets are denoted by placing braces around the elements in the set.

The numbers that we use to count things, such as the number of books in a library or the number of CDs sold by a record store, have similar characteristics. These numbers are called the *natural numbers*.

   Natural numbers = {1, 2, 3, 4, 5, 6, 7, 8, 9, 10, 11, ...}

Each natural number other than 1 is either a *prime* number or a *composite* number. A **prime number** is a number greater than 1 that is divisible (evenly) only by itself and 1. For example, 2, 3, 5, 7, 11, and 13 are the first six

Point of Interest

The concept of zero developed very gradually over many centuries. It has been variously denoted by a blank space, by a dot, and finally as 0. Negative numbers, although evident in Chinese manuscripts dating from 200 B.C., were not fully integrated into mathematics until late in the 14th century.

prime numbers. A natural number other than 1 that is not a prime number is a **composite number.** The numbers 4, 6, 8, and 9 are the first four composite numbers.

The natural numbers do not have a symbol to denote the concept of none—for instance, the number of trees taller than 1000 feet. The *whole numbers* include zero and the natural numbers.

$$\textbf{Whole numbers} = \{0, 1, 2, 3, 4, 5, 6, 7, 8, \ldots\}$$

The whole numbers alone do not provide all the numbers that are useful in applications. For instance, a meteorologist needs numbers below zero and above zero.

$$\textbf{Integers} = \{\ldots, -5, -4, -3, -2, -1, 0, 1, 2, 3, 4, 5, \ldots\}$$

The integers $\ldots, -5, -4, -3, -2, -1$ are **negative integers.** The integers $1, 2, 3, 4, 5, \ldots$ are **positive integers.** Note that the natural numbers and the positive integers are the same set of numbers. The integer zero is neither a positive nor a negative integer.

Still other numbers are necessary to solve the variety of application problems that exist. For instance, a landscape architect may need to purchase irrigation pipe that has a diameter of $\frac{5}{8}$ in. Numbers that can be written in the form of a fraction, $\frac{p}{q}$, where p and q are integers and $q \neq 0$, are called *rational numbers*.

$$\textbf{Rational numbers} = \left\{\frac{p}{q}, \text{ where } p \text{ and } q \text{ are integers and } q \neq 0\right\}$$

Examples of rational numbers are $\frac{2}{3}$, $-\frac{9}{2}$, and $\frac{5}{1}$. Note that $\frac{5}{1} = 5$, so all integers are rational numbers. The number $\frac{4}{\pi}$ is not a rational number because π is not an integer.

A rational number written as a fraction can be written in decimal notation by dividing the numerator by the denominator.

Write $\frac{3}{8}$ as a decimal.	Write $\frac{2}{15}$ as a decimal.
Divide 3 by 8.	Divide 2 by 15.

$$
\begin{array}{r}
0.375 \\
8\overline{)3.000} \\
-2\ 4 \\
\hline
60 \\
-56 \\
\hline
40 \\
-40 \\
\hline
0
\end{array}
$$
← This is a terminating decimal.

← The remainder is zero.

$$
\begin{array}{r}
0.133 \\
15\overline{)2.000} \\
-1\ 5 \\
\hline
50 \\
-45 \\
\hline
50 \\
-45 \\
\hline
5
\end{array}
$$
← This is a repeating decimal.

← The remainder is never zero.

$\frac{3}{8} = 0.375$

$\frac{2}{15} = 0.1\overline{3}$ ← The bar over 3 indicates that this digit repeats.

Some numbers cannot be written as terminating or repeating decimals. Such numbers include $0.01001000100001\dots$, $\sqrt{7} \approx 2.6457513$, and $\pi \approx 3.1415927$. These numbers have decimal representations that neither terminate nor repeat. They are called **irrational numbers.** The rational numbers and the irrational numbers taken together are the *real numbers.*

Real numbers = {rational numbers and irrational numbers}

The relationship among the various sets of numbers is shown in the following figure.

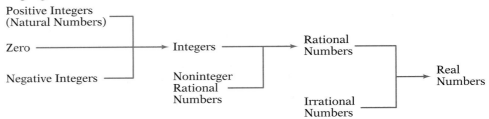

The **graph of a real number** is made by placing a heavy dot on a number line directly above the number. The graphs of some real numbers are shown below.

Consider these sentences:

A restaurant's chef prepared a dinner and served *it* to the customers.
A maple tree was planted, and *it* grew two feet in one year.

In the first sentence, "it" means dinner; in the second sentence, "it" means tree. In language, this word can stand for many different objects. Similarly, in mathematics, a letter of the alphabet can be used to stand for some number. A letter used in this way is a **variable.**

It is convenient to use a variable to represent, or stand for, any one of the elements of a set. For instance, the statement "x is an element of the set $\{0, 2, 4, 6\}$" means that x can be replaced by 0, 2, 4, or 6. The set $\{0, 2, 4, 6\}$ is called the **domain** of the variable.

The symbol for "is an element of" is $\in$; the symbol for "is not an element of" is $\notin$. For example,

$$2 \in \{1, 2, 4, 6\} \qquad 6 \in \{0, 2, 4, 6\} \qquad 7 \notin \{0, 2, 4\ 6\}$$

Variables are used in the next definition.

Definition of Inequality Symbols

If a and b are two real numbers and a is to the left of b on the number line, then a **is less than** b. This is written $a < b$.

If a and b are two real numbers and a is to the right of b on the number line, then a **is greater than** b. This is written $a > b$.

Here are some examples.

$$5 < 9 \qquad -4 > -10 \qquad \pi < \sqrt{17} \qquad 0 > -\frac{2}{3}$$

The inequality symbols $\leq$ (is less than or equal to) and $\geq$ (is greater than or equal to) are also important. Note the following examples.

$4 \leq 5$ is a true statement because $4 < 5$.

$5 \leq 5$ is a true statement because $5 = 5$.

The numbers 5 and -5 are the same distance from zero on the number line but on opposite sides of zero. The numbers 5 and -5 are called **additive inverses,** or **opposites,** of each other.

The additive inverse (or opposite) of 5 is -5. The additive inverse of -5 is 5. The symbol for additive inverse is $-$.

$-(4)$ means the opposite of *positive* 4. $-(4) = -4$

$-(-6)$ means the opposite of *negative* 6. $-(-6) = 6$

The **absolute value** of a number is a measure of its distance from zero on the number line. The symbol for absolute value is $|\ |$.

Note from the figure above that the distance from 0 to 5 is 5. Thus $|5| = 5$. The figure also shows that the distance from 0 to -5 is 5. Thus $|-5| = 5$.

Absolute Value

The absolute value of a positive number is the number itself. The absolute value of a negative number is the opposite of the negative number. The absolute value of zero is zero.

Evaluate: $-|-12|$

From the definition of absolute value, $|-12| = 12$. $-|-12| = -12$
The absolute value sign does not affect the negative sign in front of the absolute value sign.

EXAMPLE 1   Let $y \in \{-7, 0, 6\}$. For which values of y is the inequality $y < 4$ a true statement?

Solution $y < 4$

$-7 < 4$ True   • **Replace y by each of the elements of the set, and determine whether the inequality is true.**

$0 < 4$ True

$6 < 4$ False

The inequality is true for -7 and 0.

PROBLEM 1   Let $z \in \{-10, -5, 6\}$. For which values of z is the inequality $z > -5$ a true statement?

Solution   See page S1.

EXAMPLE 2 Let $a \in \{-12, 0, 4\}$. Determine $-a$, the opposite of a, for each element of the set.

Solution $-a$

$-(-12) = 12$ • **Replace a by each element of the set, and determine the value of the expression.**

$-(0) = 0$ • **0 is neither positive nor negative.**

$-(4) = -4$

PROBLEM 2 Let $z \in \{-11, 0, 8\}$. Evaluate $|z|$ for each element of the set.

Solution See page S1.

OBJECTIVE 2 ## Set operations and interval notation

The **roster method** of writing a set encloses the list of the elements of the set in braces. The set of whole numbers, written as $\{0, 1, 2, 3, 4, \ldots\}$, and the set of natural numbers, written as $\{1, 2, 3, 4, \ldots\}$, are **infinite sets.** The pattern of numbers continues without end. It is impossible to list all the elements of an infinite set.

The set of even natural numbers less than 10 is written $\{2, 4, 6, 8\}$. This is an example of a **finite set;** all the elements of the set can be listed.

The **empty set,** or **null set,** is the set that contains no elements. The symbol $\varnothing$ or $\{\ \}$ is used to represent the empty set.

EXAMPLE 3 Use the roster method to write the set of natural numbers less than 10.

Solution $\{1, 2, 3, 4, 5, 6, 7, 8, 9\}$

PROBLEM 3 Use the roster method to write the set of positive odd integers less than 12.

Solution See page S1.

A second method of representing a set is **set-builder notation.** Set-builder notation can be used to describe almost any set, but it is especially useful when writing infinite sets. In set-builder notation, the set of integers greater than -3 is written

$$\{x \,|\, x > -3, x \in \text{integers}\}$$

and is read "the set of all x such that x is greater than -3 and x is an element of the integers." This is an infinite set. It is impossible to list all the elements of the set, but the set can be described by using set-builder notation.

The set of real numbers less than 5 is written

$$\{x \,|\, x < 5, x \in \text{real numbers}\}$$

and is read "the set of all x such that x is less than 5 and x is an element of the real numbers."

EXAMPLE 4 Use set-builder notation to write the set of integers greater than −8.

Solution $\{x \mid x > -8, x \in \text{integers}\}$

PROBLEM 4 Use set-builder notation to write the set of real numbers less than 7.

Solution See page S1.

Just as operations such as addition and multiplication are performed on real numbers, operations are performed on sets. Two operations performed on sets are *union* and *intersection*.

Point of Interest

The symbols ∈, ∪, and ∩ were first used by Giuseppe Peano, in Arithmetices Principia, Nova Exposita (The Principle of Mathematics, a New Method of Exposition), published in 1889. The purpose of this book was to deduce the principles of mathematics from pure logic.

The **union** of two sets, written $A \cup B$, is the set of all elements that belong to either A **or** B. In set-builder notation, this is written

$$A \cup B = \{x \mid x \in A \quad \text{or} \quad x \in B\}$$

Given $A = \{2, 3, 4\}$ and $B = \{0, 1, 2, 3\}$, the union of A and B contains all the elements that belong to either A or B. The elements that belong to both sets are listed only once.

$$A \cup B = \{0, 1, 2, 3, 4\}$$

The **intersection** of two sets, written $A \cap B$, is the set of all elements that are common to both A **and** B. In set-builder notation, this is written

$$A \cap B = \{x \mid x \in A \quad \text{and} \quad x \in B\}$$

Given $A = \{2, 3, 4\}$ and $B = \{0, 1, 2, 3\}$, the intersection of A and B contains all the elements that are common to both A and B.

$$A \cap B = \{2, 3\}$$

EXAMPLE 5 Find $C \cup D$ given $C = \{1, 5, 9, 13, 17\}$ and $D = \{3, 5, 7, 9, 11\}$.

Solution $C \cup D = \{1, 3, 5, 7, 9, 11, 13, 17\}$

PROBLEM 5 Find $A \cup C$ given $A = \{-2, -1, 0, 1, 2\}$ and $C = \{-5, -1, 0, 1, 5\}$.

Solution See page S1.

EXAMPLE 6 Find $A \cap B$ given $A = \{x \mid x \in \text{natural numbers}\}$ and $B = \{x \mid x \in \text{negative integers}\}$.

Solution There are no natural numbers that are also negative integers. $A \cap B = \varnothing$

PROBLEM 6 Find $E \cap F$ given $E = \{x \mid x \in \text{odd integers}\}$ and $F = \{x \mid x \in \text{even integers}\}$.

Solution See page S1.

Set-builder notation and the inequality symbols $>$, $<$, $\geq$, and $\leq$ are used to describe infinite sets of real numbers. These sets can be graphed on the real number line.

The graph of $\{x \mid x > -2, x \in$ real numbers$\}$ is shown below. The set is the real numbers greater than -2. The parenthesis on the graph indicates that -2 is not included in the set.

The graph of $\{x \mid x \geq -2, x \in$ real numbers$\}$ is shown below. The set is the real numbers greater than or equal to -2. The bracket at -2 indicates that -2 is included in the set.

For the remainder of this section, all variables will represent real numbers. Using this convention, the above set is written $\{x \mid x \geq -2\}$.

> **Take Note**
>
> If we asked for the graph of $\{x \mid x \leq 3, x \in$ integers$\}$, the graph would appear as
>
>
>
> The domain of a variable affects its graph.

EXAMPLE 7   Graph: $\{x \mid x \leq 3\}$

Solution

• The set is the real numbers less than or equal to 3. Draw a right bracket at 3, and darken the number line to the left of 3.

PROBLEM 7   Graph: $\{x \mid x > -3\}$

Solution   See page S1.

The union of two sets is the set of all elements belonging to either one or the other of the two sets. The set $\{x \mid x \leq -1\} \cup \{x \mid x > 3\}$ is the set of real numbers that are either less than or equal to -1 or greater than 3.

The set is written $\{x \mid x \leq -1 \text{ or } x > 3\}$.

The set $\{x \mid x > 2\} \cup \{x \mid x > 4\}$ is the set of real numbers that are either greater than 2 or greater than 4.

The set is written $\{x \mid x > 2\}$.

The intersection of two sets is the set that contains the elements common to both sets. The set $\{x \mid x > -2\} \cap \{x \mid x < 5\}$ is the set of real numbers that are greater than -2 and less than 5.

The set can be written $\{x \mid x > -2 \text{ and } x < 5\}$. However, it is more commonly written $\{x \mid -2 < x < 5\}$. This set is read "the set of all x such that x is greater than -2 and less than 5."

The set $\{x \mid x < 4\} \cap \{x \mid x < 5\}$ is the set of real numbers that are less than 4 and less than 5.

The set is written $\{x \mid x < 4\}$.

EXAMPLE 8 Graph: $\{x \mid x < 0\} \cap \{x \mid x > -3\}$

Solution The set is $\{x \mid -3 < x < 0\}$.

PROBLEM 8 Graph: $\{x \mid x \geq 1\} \cup \{x \mid x \leq -3\}$

Solution See page S1.

Some sets can also be expressed using **interval notation.** For example, the interval notation $(-3, 2]$ indicates the interval of all real numbers greater than -3 and less than or equal to 2. As on the graph of a set, the left parenthesis indicates that -3 is not included in the set. The right bracket indicates that 2 is included in the set.

An interval is said to be **closed** if it includes both endpoints; it is **open** if it does not include either endpoint. An interval is **half-open** if one endpoint is included and the other is not. In each example given below, -3 and 2 are the **endpoints** of the interval. In each case, the set notation, the interval notation, and the graph of the set are shown.

$\{x \mid -3 < x < 2\}$ $(-3, 2)$ Open interval

$\{x \mid -3 \leq x \leq 2\}$ $[-3, 2]$ Closed interval

$\{x \mid -3 \leq x < 2\}$ $[-3, 2)$ Half-open interval

$\{x \mid -3 < x \leq 2\}$ $(-3, 2]$ Half-open interval

To indicate an interval that extends forever in one or both directions using interval notation, we use the **infinity symbol** ∞ or the **negative infinity symbol** $-\infty$. The infinity symbol is not a number; it is simply used as a notation to indicate that the interval is unlimited. In interval notation, a parenthesis is always used to the right of an infinity symbol or to the left of a negative infinity symbol, as shown in the following examples.

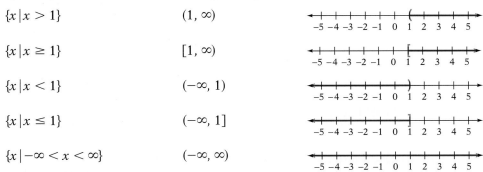

$\{x \mid x > 1\}$ $(1, \infty)$

$\{x \mid x \geq 1\}$ $[1, \infty)$

$\{x \mid x < 1\}$ $(-\infty, 1)$

$\{x \mid x \leq 1\}$ $(-\infty, 1]$

$\{x \mid -\infty < x < \infty\}$ $(-\infty, \infty)$

EXAMPLE 9 Write $\{x \mid 0 < x \leq 5\}$ using interval notation.

Solution $(0, 5]$ • **The set is the real numbers greater than 0 and less than or equal to 5.**

PROBLEM 9 Write $\{x \mid -8 \leq x < -1\}$ using interval notation.

Solution See page S1.

EXAMPLE 10 Write $(-\infty, 9]$ using set-builder notation.

     Solution $\{x \,|\, x \le 9\}$ • **The set is the real numbers less than or equal to 9.**

PROBLEM 10 Write $(-12, \infty)$ using set-builder notation.

     Solution   See page S1.

EXAMPLE 11 Graph: $(-\infty, 3) \cap [-1, \infty)$

     Solution   • **$(-\infty, 3) \cap [-1, \infty)$ is the set of real numbers greater than or equal to -1 and less than 3.**

PROBLEM 11 Graph: $(-\infty, -2) \cup (-1, \infty)$

     Solution   See page S1.

1.1 Concept Review

Determine whether the following statements are always true, sometimes true, or never true.

1. The absolute value of a number is positive.

2. Given $|x| = 3$, then x is a positive number.

3. Given x is an integer, then $-x$ is a negative integer.

4. If a, b, c, and d are real numbers, then $a < b$ and $c < d$ ensures that $a + c < b + d$.

5. If a and b are real numbers, then $a < b < 0$ ensures that $a^2 < b^2$.

6. If a, b, and c are nonzero real numbers and $a < b < c$, then $\frac{1}{a} < \frac{1}{b} < \frac{1}{c}$.

7. If x is less than zero, then the absolute value of x is $-x$.

1.1 Exercises

1 Inequality and absolute value

Determine which of the numbers are **a.** natural numbers, **b.** whole numbers, **c.** integers, **d.** positive integers, **e.** negative integers. List all that apply.

1. $-14, 9, 0, 53, 7.8, -626$

2. $31, -45, -2, 9.7, 8600, \frac{1}{2}$

Determine which of the numbers are **a.** integers, **b.** rational numbers, **c.** irrational numbers, **d.** real numbers. List all that apply.

3. $-\dfrac{15}{2}$, 0, −3, π, $2.\overline{33}$, 4.232232223..., $\dfrac{\sqrt{5}}{4}$, $\sqrt{7}$

4. −17, 0.3412, $\dfrac{3}{\pi}$, −1.010010001..., $\dfrac{27}{91}$, $6.1\overline{2}$

5. What is a terminating decimal? Provide an example.

6. What is a repeating decimal? Provide an example.

7. What is the additive inverse of a number?

8. What is the absolute value of a number?

9. A number such as 0.63633633363333. . . , whose decimal notation neither ends nor repeats, is an example of an ___?___ number.

10. The additive inverse of a negative number is a ___?___ number.

11. $y \in \{1, 3, 5, 7, 9\}$ is read "y ___?___ the set $\{1, 3, 5, 7, 9\}$."

12. Write the phrase "the opposite of the absolute value of n" in symbols.

Find the additive inverse of each of the following.

13. 27

14. −3

15. $\dfrac{3}{4}$

16. $\sqrt{17}$

17. 0

18. $-\pi$

19. $-\sqrt{33}$

20. −1.23

21. −91

22. $-\dfrac{2}{3}$

Solve.

23. Let $x \in \{-3, 0, 7\}$. For which values of x is $x < 5$ true?

24. Let $z \in \{-4, -1, 4\}$. For which values of z is $z > -2$ true?

25. Let $y \in \{-6, -4, 7\}$. For which values of y is $y > -4$ true?

26. Let $x \in \{-6, -3, 3\}$. For which values of x is $x < -3$ true?

27. Let $w \in \{-2, -1, 0, 1\}$. For which values of w is $w \leq -1$ true?

28. Let $p \in \{-10, -5, 0, 5\}$. For which values of p is $p \geq 0$ true?

29. Let $b \in \{-9, 0, 9\}$. Evaluate $-b$ for each element of the set.

30. Let $a \in \{-3, -2, 0\}$. Evaluate $-a$ for each element of the set.

31. Let $c \in \{-4, 0, 4\}$. Evaluate $|c|$ for each element of the set.

32. Let $q \in \{-3, 0, 7\}$. Evaluate $|q|$ for each element of the set.

33. Let $m \in \{-6, -2, 0, 1, 4\}$. Evaluate $-|m|$ for each element of the set.

34. Let $x \in \{-5, -3, 0, 2, 5\}$. Evaluate $-|x|$ for each element of the set.

35. Are there any real numbers x for which $-x > 0$? If so, describe them.

36. Are there any real numbers y for which $-|y| > 0$? If so, describe them.

2   Set operations and interval notation

37. Explain the difference between the union of two sets and the intersection of two sets.

38. Explain the difference between $\{x \,|\, x < 5\}$ and $\{x \,|\, x \leq 5\}$.

39. Two ways to write the set of natural numbers less than 5 are $\{1, 2, 3, 4\}$ and $\{n \,|\, n < 5, n \in \text{natural numbers}\}$. The first way uses the ___?___ method, and the second way uses ___?___ notation.

40. The symbol for "union" is ___?___. The symbol for "intersection" is ___?___.

41. The symbol ∞ is called the ___?___ symbol.

42. Replace each question mark with "includes" or "does not include" to make the following statement true. The set $[-4, 7)$ ___?___ the number -4 and ___?___ the number 7.

Use the roster method to write the set.

43. the integers between -3 and 5

44. the integers between -4 and 0

45. the even natural numbers less than 14

46. the odd natural numbers less than 14

47. the positive-integer multiples of 3 that are less than or equal to 30

48. the negative-integer multiples of 4 that are greater than or equal to -20

49. the negative-integer multiples of 5 that are greater than or equal to -35

50. the positive-integer multiples of 6 that are less than or equal to 36

Use set-builder notation to write the set.

51. the integers greater than 4

52. the integers less than -2

53. the real numbers greater than or equal to -2

54. the real numbers less than or equal to 2

55. the real numbers between 0 and 1

56. the real numbers between -2 and 5

57. the real numbers between 1 and 4, inclusive

58. the real numbers between 0 and 2, inclusive

Find $A \cup B$.

59. $A = \{1, 4, 9\}, B = \{2, 4, 6\}$

60. $A = \{-1, 0, 1\}, B = \{0, 1, 2\}$

61. $A = \{2, 3, 5, 8\}, B = \{9, 10\}$

62. $A = \{1, 3, 5, 7\}, B = \{2, 4, 6, 8\}$

63. $A = \{-4, -2, 0, 2, 4\}, B = \{0, 4, 8\}$

64. $A = \{-3, -2, -1\}, B = \{-2, -1, 0, 1\}$

65. $A = \{1, 2, 3, 4, 5\}, B = \{3, 4, 5\}$

66. $A = \{2, 4\}, B = \{0, 1, 2, 3, 4, 5\}$

Find $A \cap B$.

67. $A = \{6, 12, 18\}, B = \{3, 6, 9\}$

68. $A = \{-4, 0, 4\}, B = \{-2, 0, 2\}$

69. $A = \{1, 5, 10, 20\}, B = \{5, 10, 15, 20\}$

70. $A = \{1, 3, 5, 7, 9\}, B = \{1, 9\}$

71. $A = \{1, 2, 4, 8\}, B = \{3, 5, 6, 7\}$

72. $A = \{-3, -2, -1, 0\}, B = \{1, 2, 3, 4\}$

73. $A = \{2, 4, 6, 8, 10\}, B = \{4, 6\}$

74. $A = \{-9, -5, 0, 7\}, B = \{-7, -5, 0, 5, 7\}$

Graph.

75. $\{x \mid -1 < x < 5\}$

76. $\{x \mid 1 < x < 3\}$

77. $\{x \mid 0 \leq x \leq 3\}$

78. $\{x \mid -1 \leq x \leq 1\}$

79. $\{x \mid x < 2\}$

80. $\{x \mid x < -1\}$

81. $\{x \mid x \geq 1\}$

82. $\{x \mid x \leq -2\}$

83. $\{x \mid x > 1\} \cup \{x \mid x < -1\}$

84. $\{x \mid x \leq 2\} \cup \{x \mid x > 4\}$

85. $\{x \mid x \leq 2\} \cap \{x \mid x \geq 0\}$

86. $\{x \mid x > -1\} \cap \{x \mid x \leq 4\}$

87. $\{x \mid x > 1\} \cap \{x \mid x \geq -2\}$

88. $\{x \mid x < 4\} \cap \{x \mid x \leq 0\}$

89. $\{x\,|\,x > 2\} \cup \{x\,|\,x > 1\}$ **90.** $\{x\,|\,x < -2\} \cup \{x\,|\,x < -4\}$

Write each interval in set-builder notation.

91. $(0, 8)$ **92.** $(-2, 4)$ **93.** $[-5, 7]$ **94.** $[3, 4]$ **95.** $[-3, 6)$

96. $(4, 5]$ **97.** $(-\infty, 4]$ **98.** $(-\infty, -2)$ **99.** $(5, \infty)$ **100.** $[-2, \infty)$

Write each set of real numbers in interval notation.

101. $\{x\,|\,-2 < x < 4\}$ **102.** $\{x\,|\,0 < x < 3\}$ **103.** $\{x\,|\,-1 \le x \le 5\}$ **104.** $\{x\,|\,0 \le x \le 3\}$

105. $\{x\,|\,x < 1\}$ **106.** $\{x\,|\,x \le 6\}$ **107.** $\{x\,|\,-2 \le x < 6\}$ **108.** $\{x\,|\,x \ge 3\}$

109. $\{x\,|\,x \in \text{real numbers}\}$ **110.** $\{x\,|\,x > -1\}$

Graph.

111. $(-2, 5)$ **112.** $(0, 3)$ **113.** $[-1, 2]$

114. $[-3, 2]$ **115.** $(-\infty, 3]$ **116.** $(-\infty, -1)$

117. $[3, \infty)$ **118.** $[-2, \infty)$ **119.** $(-\infty, 2] \cup [4, \infty)$

120. $(-3, 4] \cup [-1, 5)$ **121.** $[-1, 2] \cap [0, 4]$ **122.** $[-5, 4) \cap (-2, \infty)$

123. $(2, \infty) \cup (-2, 4]$ **124.** $(-\infty, 2] \cup (4, \infty)$

125. Which set is the empty set?
   a. $\{x\,|\,x \in \text{integers}\} \cap \{x\,|\,x \in \text{rational numbers}\}$
   b. $\{-4, -2, 0, 2, 4\} \cup \{-3, -1, 1, 3\}$
   c. $[5, \infty) \cap (0, 5)$

126. Which set is *not* equivalent to the interval $[-1, 6)$?
   a. $\{x\,|\,-1 \le x < 6\}$
   b. $\{x\,|\,x \ge -1\} \cup \{x\,|\,x < 6\}$
   c. $\{x\,|\,x < 6\} \cap \{x\,|\,x \ge -1\}$

1.1 Applying Concepts

Let $R = \{x\,|\,x \in \text{real numbers}\}$, $A = \{x\,|\,-1 \le x \le 1\}$, $B = \{x\,|\,0 \le x \le 1\}$, $C = \{x\,|\,-1 \le x \le 0\}$, and $\varnothing = $ empty set. Indicate whether each of the following expressions is equivalent to R, A, B, C, or $\varnothing$.

127. $A \cup B$ **128.** $A \cup A$ **129.** $B \cap B$ **130.** $A \cup C$ **131.** $A \cap R$

132. $C \cap R$ **133.** $B \cup R$ **134.** $A \cup R$ **135.** $R \cup R$ **136.** $R \cap \varnothing$

137. The set $B \cap C$ cannot be expressed using R, A, B, C, or $\varnothing$. What real number is represented by $B \cap C$?

138. A student wrote $-3 > x > 5$ as the inequality that represents the real numbers less than -3 or greater than 5. Explain why this is incorrect.

Graph the set.

139. $\left\{x \mid x > \dfrac{3}{2}\right\} \cup \left\{x \mid x < -\dfrac{1}{2}\right\}$ **140.** $\{x \mid x \leq -2.5\} \cup \{x \mid x > 1.5\}$

141. $\left\{x \mid x > -\dfrac{5}{2}\right\} \cap \left\{x \mid x \leq \dfrac{7}{3}\right\}$ **142.** $\{x \mid x > -0.5\} \cap \{x \mid x \geq 3.5\}$

Graph the solution set.

143. $|x| < 2$ **144.** $|x| < 5$

145. $|x| > 3$ **146.** $|x| > 4$

Use set-builder notation to write $A \cup B$.

147. $A = \{1, 3, 5, 7, \ldots\}$
$B = \{2, 4, 6, 8, \ldots\}$

148. $A = \{\ldots, -6, -4, -2\}$
$B = \{\ldots, -5, -3, -1\}$

Use set-builder notation to write $A \cap B$.

149. $A = \{15, 17, 19, 21, \ldots\}$
$B = \{11, 13, 15, 17, \ldots\}$

150. $A = \{-12, -10, -8, -6, \ldots\}$
$B = \{-4, -2, 0, 2, \ldots\}$

151. Given that a, b, c, and d are positive real numbers, which of the following will ensure that $\dfrac{a - b}{c - d} \leq 0$?

a. $a \geq b$ and $c > d$ **b.** $a \leq b$ and $c > d$ **c.** $a \geq b$ and $c < d$ **d.** $a \leq b$ and $c < d$

1.2 Operations on Rational Numbers

OBJECTIVE 1 **Operations on integers**

An understanding of the operations on all numbers is necessary to succeed in algebra. Let's review those properties, beginning with the rules for addition.

Point of Interest

Rules for operating with positive and negative numbers have existed for a long time. Although there are older records of these rules (from the 3rd century), one of the most thorough appears in The Correct Astronomical System of Brahma, *written by the Indian mathematician Brahmagupta around* A.D. *600.*

Sign Rules for Addition

Numbers that have the same sign
To add numbers with the same sign, add the absolute values of the numbers. Then attach the sign of the addends.

Numbers that have different signs
To add numbers with different signs, find the absolute value of each number. Subtract the smaller of these absolute values from the larger. Then attach the sign of the number with the larger absolute value.

Add.   **A.** $-65 + (-48)$ **B.** $27 + (-53)$

A. The signs are the same. Add the absolute values of the numbers. Then attach the sign of the addends.

$-65 + (-48) = -113$

B. The signs are different.

$27 + (-53)$

Find the absolute value of each number.

$|27| = 27$ $|-53| = 53$

Subtract the smaller absolute value from the larger.

$53 - 27 = 26$

Because $|-53| > |27|$, attach the sign of -53.

$27 + (-53) = -26$

Subtraction is defined as addition of the additive inverse.

Subtraction of Real Numbers

If a and b are real numbers, then $a - b = a + (-b)$.

Subtract.   **A.** $48 - (-22)$ **B.** $-31 - 18$

A. Write the subtraction as the addition of the opposite number.

$48 - (-22) = 48 + 22$

Add the numbers.

$= 70$

B. Write the subtraction as the addition of the opposite number.

$-31 - 18 = -31 + (-18)$

Then add.

$= -49$

Sign Rules for Multiplication

Numbers that have the same sign
The product of two numbers with the same sign is positive.

Numbers that have different signs
The product of two numbers with different signs is negative.

Multiply.   **A.** $-4(-9)$ **B.** $84(-4)$

A. The product of two numbers with the same $-4(-9) = 36$
sign is positive.

B. The product of two numbers with different $84(-4) = -336$
signs is negative.

The **multiplicative inverse** of a nonzero number a is $\frac{1}{a}$. This number is also called the **reciprocal** of a. For instance, the reciprocal of 2 is $\frac{1}{2}$, and the reciprocal of $-\frac{3}{4}$ is $-\frac{4}{3}$. Division of real numbers is defined in terms of multiplication by the multiplicative inverse.

Division of Real Numbers

If a and b are real numbers, and $b \neq 0$, then $a \div b = a \cdot \dfrac{1}{b}$.

Because division is defined in terms of multiplication, the sign rules for dividing are the same as the sign rules for multiplying.

Divide.   **A.** $\dfrac{-54}{9}$ **B.** $(-21) \div (-7)$

A. The quotient of two numbers with different $\dfrac{-54}{9} = -6$
signs is negative.

B. The quotient of two numbers with the same $(-21) \div (-7) = 3$
sign is positive.

Note that $\frac{-12}{3} = -4$, $\frac{12}{-3} = -4$, and $-\frac{12}{3} = -4$. These results suggest the following rule.

If a and b are real numbers, and $b \neq 0$, then $\dfrac{-a}{b} = \dfrac{a}{-b} = -\dfrac{a}{b}$.

Properties of Zero and One in Division

Any number divided by one is the number.

$$\frac{a}{1} = a$$

Zero divided by any number other than zero is zero.

$$\frac{0}{a} = 0,\ a \neq 0$$

continued

Division by zero is not defined.

To understand that division by zero is not permitted, suppose $\frac{4}{0} = n$, where n is some number. Because each division problem has a related multiplication problem, $\frac{4}{0} = n$ means $n \cdot 0 = 4$. But $n \cdot 0 = 4$ is impossible because any number times 0 is 0. Therefore, division by 0 is not defined.

Any number other than zero divided by itself is 1.

$$\frac{a}{a} = 1, a \neq 0$$

EXAMPLE 1   Subtract: $-3 - (-5) - 9$

Solution $-3 - (-5) - 9 = -3 + 5 + (-9)$ • **Write subtraction as the addition of the opposite.**

$= 2 + (-9)$ • **Do the additions from left to right.**

$= -7$

PROBLEM 1   Subtract: $6 - (-8) - 10$

Solution   See page S1.

EXAMPLE 2   Simplify.   **A.** $-6|-5|(-15)$ **B.** $-\dfrac{42}{-3}$

Solution   **A.** $-6|-5|(-15) = -6(5)(-15)$ • $|-5| = 5$

$= -30(-15)$ • **Do multiplication from left to right.**

$= 450$

B. $-\dfrac{42}{-3} = -\left(\dfrac{42}{-3}\right) = -(-14) = 14$

PROBLEM 2   Simplify.   **A.** $2|-7|(-8)$ **B.** $-\dfrac{-36}{-3}$

Solution   See page S1.

OBJECTIVE **2**   ## Operations on rational numbers

Recall that a rational number is one that can be written in the form $\frac{p}{q}$, where p and q are integers and $q \neq 0$. Examples of rational numbers are $-\frac{5}{9}$ and $\frac{12}{5}$. The number $\frac{9}{\sqrt{7}}$ is not a rational number because $\sqrt{7}$ is not an integer. All integers are rational numbers. Terminating and repeating decimals are also rational numbers.

The sign rules are the same for rational numbers as for integers.

Add: $-15.23 + (-18.1)$

To add two decimals with the same sign, add the absolute values of the decimals. Then attach the sign of the addends.

$-15.23 + (-18.1) = -33.33$

Subtract: $-18.42 - (-9.354)$

To subtract decimals, write the subtraction as the addition of the opposite, and then add.

$$-18.42 - (-9.354) = -18.42 + 9.354$$
$$= -9.066$$

Multiply: $(-0.23)(0.04)$

The signs of the factors are different, so the product is negative.

$(-0.23)(0.04) = -0.0092$

Divide: $(-2.835) \div (-1.35)$

The signs of the dividend and divisor are negative, so the quotient is positive.

$(-2.835) \div (-1.35) = 2.1$

Addition of Fractions

The sum of two fractions with the same denominator is the sum of the numerators over the common denominator.

$$\frac{a}{c} + \frac{b}{c} = \frac{a + b}{c}$$

To add or subtract rational numbers written as fractions, first rewrite the fractions as equivalent fractions with a common denominator. A common denominator is the product of the denominators of the fractions. The **lowest common denominator (LCD)** is the **least common multiple (LCM)** of the denominators.

Add: $\dfrac{5}{6} + \left(-\dfrac{7}{8}\right)$

The common denominator is 24. Write each fraction in terms of the common denominator.

$$\dfrac{5}{6} + \left(-\dfrac{7}{8}\right) = \dfrac{5}{6}\cdot\dfrac{4}{4} + \left(\dfrac{-7}{8}\cdot\dfrac{3}{3}\right)$$

Add the numerators, and place the sum over the common denominator.

$$= \dfrac{20}{24} + \left(\dfrac{-21}{24}\right)$$
$$= \dfrac{20 + (-21)}{24}$$
$$= \dfrac{-1}{24} = -\dfrac{1}{24}$$

Multiplication of Fractions

The product of two fractions is the product of the numerators over the product of the denominators.

$$\dfrac{a}{b} \cdot \dfrac{c}{d} = \dfrac{ac}{bd}$$

Multiply: $-\dfrac{5}{12} \cdot \dfrac{8}{15}$

The signs are different, so the product is negative. Multiply the numerators, and multiply the denominators.

Write the answer in simplest form.

$$-\dfrac{5}{12} \cdot \dfrac{8}{15} = -\dfrac{5 \cdot 8}{12 \cdot 15}$$
$$= -\dfrac{40}{180}$$
$$= -\dfrac{20 \cdot 2}{20 \cdot 9}$$
$$= -\dfrac{2}{9}$$

In the last problem, the fraction was written in simplest form by dividing the numerator and denominator by 20, which is the largest integer that divides both 40 and 180. The number 20 is called the **greatest common factor (GCF)** of 40 and 180. To write a fraction in simplest form, divide the numerator and denominator by the GCF. If you have difficulty finding the GCF, try finding the prime factorization of the numerator and denominator, and then divide by the common prime factors. For instance,

$$-\dfrac{5}{12} \cdot \dfrac{8}{15} = -\dfrac{\cancel{5} \cdot (\cancel{2} \cdot \cancel{2} \cdot 2)}{(\cancel{2} \cdot \cancel{2} \cdot 3) \cdot (3 \cdot \cancel{5})} = -\dfrac{2}{9}$$

> ## Division of Fractions
>
> To divide two fractions, multiply the first fraction by the reciprocal of the divisor.
>
> $$\frac{a}{b} \div \frac{c}{d} = \frac{a}{b} \cdot \frac{d}{c}$$

Divide: $\dfrac{3}{8} \div \dfrac{9}{16}$

Multiply the first fraction by the reciprocal of the divisor.

Write the answer in simplest form.

$$\dfrac{3}{8} \div \dfrac{9}{16} = \dfrac{3}{8} \cdot \dfrac{16}{9}$$
$$= \dfrac{2}{3}$$

EXAMPLE 3   Multiply: $\left(-\dfrac{5}{12}\right)\left(\dfrac{4}{25}\right)$

Solution $\left(-\dfrac{5}{12}\right)\left(\dfrac{4}{25}\right) = -\dfrac{5 \cdot 4}{12 \cdot 25} = -\dfrac{1}{15}$

PROBLEM 3   Divide: $-\dfrac{5}{8} \div \left(-\dfrac{15}{16}\right)$

Solution   See page S1.

EXAMPLE 4   Simplify.

A. $\dfrac{3}{8} + \dfrac{5}{12} - \dfrac{9}{16}$ **B.** $6.329 - 12.49$ **C.** $14 - |3 - 18|$

Solution   **A.** $\dfrac{3}{8} + \dfrac{5}{12} - \dfrac{9}{16} = \dfrac{18}{48} + \dfrac{20}{48} + \left(-\dfrac{27}{48}\right)$

$$= \dfrac{18 + 20 + (-27)}{48} = \dfrac{11}{48}$$

B. $6.329 - 12.49 = 6.329 + (-12.49) = -6.161$

C. $14 - |3 - 18|$

$= 14 - |-15|$ • **Perform the indicated operation inside the absolute value symbols.**

$= 14 - 15$ • **Rewrite $|-15|$ as 15.**

$= -1$

PROBLEM 4   Simplify.

A. $-\dfrac{5}{12} \div \dfrac{10}{27}$ **B.** $-8.729 + 12.094$ **C.** $-8 - |5 - 12|$

Solution   See page S1.

EXAMPLE 5   Divide $0.0527 \div (-0.27)$. Round to the nearest hundredth.

Solution $0.0527 \div (-0.27) \approx -0.20$ • **The symbol $\approx$ is used to indicate that the quotient is an approximate value after being rounded off.**

> **PROBLEM 5**   Multiply $-4.027(0.49)$. Round to the nearest hundredth.
>
> ■ **Solution**   See page S1.

OBJECTIVE **3**   ## Exponential expressions

Repeated multiplication of the same factor can be written using an exponent.

$$2 \cdot 2 \cdot 2 \cdot 2 \cdot 2 \cdot 2 = 2^6 \longleftarrow \text{Exponent}$$
$$ \uparrow\!\!\!\text{—— Base}$$

$$b \cdot b \cdot b \cdot b \cdot b = b^5 \longleftarrow \text{Exponent}$$
$$ \uparrow\!\!\!\text{—— Base}$$

The **exponent** indicates how many times the factor, called the **base,** occurs in the multiplication. The multiplication $2 \cdot 2 \cdot 2 \cdot 2 \cdot 2 \cdot 2$ is in **factored form.** The exponential expression 2^6 is in **exponential form.**

2^1 is read "the first power of two" or just "two." $\longrightarrow$ Usually the exponent 1 is not written.

2^2 is read "the second power of two" or "two squared."

2^3 is read "the third power of two" or "two cubed."

2^4 is read "the fourth power of two."

2^5 is read "the fifth power of two."

b^5 is read "the fifth power of b."

> *n*th Power of *a*
>
> If a is a real number and n is a positive integer, then the nth power of a is the product of n factors of a.
>
> $$a^n = \underbrace{a \cdot a \cdot a \cdot \cdots \cdot a}_{a \text{ as a factor } n \text{ times}}$$

Take Note

Examine the results of $(-3)^4$ and -3^4 very carefully. As another example, $(-2)^6 = 64$ but $-2^6 = -64$.

$$5^3 = 5 \cdot 5 \cdot 5 = 125$$
$$(-3)^4 = (-3)(-3)(-3)(-3) = 81$$
$$-3^4 = -(3)^4 = -(3 \cdot 3 \cdot 3 \cdot 3) = -81$$

Note the difference between $(-3)^4$ and -3^4. The placement of the parentheses is very important.

EXAMPLE 6   Evaluate $(-6)^4$ and -6^4.

Solution $(-6)^4 = (-6)(-6)(-6)(-6) = 1296$
$-6^4 = -(6 \cdot 6 \cdot 6 \cdot 6)$
$ = -1296$

• **The negative of a number is taken to a power only when the negative sign is *inside* the parentheses.**

PROBLEM 6   Evaluate $(-4)^2$ and -4^2.

■ **Solution**   See page S1.

EXAMPLE 7   Evaluate $\left(-\dfrac{2}{3}\right)^2 \cdot 3^3$.

Solution $\left(-\dfrac{2}{3}\right)^2 \cdot 3^3 = \left(-\dfrac{2}{3}\right)\left(-\dfrac{2}{3}\right) \cdot (3)(3)(3) = 12$

PROBLEM 7   Evaluate $-\left(\dfrac{2}{5}\right)^3 \cdot 5^2$.

Solution   See page S1.

OBJECTIVE **4**   **The Order of Operations Agreement**

To prevent there being more than one value for the same numerical expression, an **Order of Operations Agreement** is followed.

> **The Order of Operations Agreement**
>
> Step 1 Perform operations inside grouping symbols. Grouping symbols include parentheses ( ), brackets [ ], the absolute value symbol | |, and the fraction bar.
>
> Step 2 Simplify exponential expressions.
>
> Step 3 Do multiplication and division as they occur from left to right.
>
> Step 4 Do addition and subtraction as they occur from left to right.

Simplify: $8 - \dfrac{12 - 2}{4 + 1} \div 2^2$

$$8 - \frac{12 - 2}{4 + 1} \div 2^2$$

Perform operations above and below the fraction bar.

$$= 8 - \frac{10}{5} \div 2^2$$

Simplify exponential expressions.

$$= 8 - \frac{10}{5} \div 4$$

Do multiplication and division as they occur from left to right. Note that a fraction bar can be read "÷."

$$= 8 - 2 \div 4$$

$$= 8 - \frac{1}{2}$$

Do addition and subtraction as they occur from left to right.

$$= \frac{15}{2}$$

One or more of the steps shown in the last example may not be needed to simplify an expression. In that case, proceed to the next step in the Order of Operations Agreement.

When an expression has grouping symbols inside grouping symbols, perform the operations inside the inner grouping symbols first.

Simplify: $4.3 - [(25 - 9) \div 2]^2$

Perform operations inside grouping symbols.

$$4.3 - [(25 - 9) \div 2]^2$$
$$= 4.3 - [16 \div 2]^2$$
$$= 4.3 - [8]^2$$

Simplify exponential expressions.

$$= 4.3 - 64$$

Perform addition and subtraction as they occur from left to right.

$$= -59.7$$

EXAMPLE 8   Simplify: $(-1.2)^3 - 8.4 \div 2.1$

Solution $(-1.2)^3 - 8.4 \div 2.1$
$$= -1.728 - 8.4 \div 2.1$$ • **Simplify exponential expressions.**
$$= -1.728 - 4$$ • **Do multiplication and division.**
$$= -5.728$$ • **Do addition and subtraction.**

PROBLEM 8   Simplify: $(3.81 - 1.41)^2 \div 0.036 - 1.89$

Solution   See page S1.

EXAMPLE 9   Simplify: $\left(\dfrac{1}{2}\right)^3 - \left[\left(\dfrac{2}{3} + \dfrac{1}{4}\right) \div \dfrac{5}{6}\right]$

Solution $\left(\dfrac{1}{2}\right)^3 - \left[\left(\dfrac{2}{3} + \dfrac{1}{4}\right) \div \dfrac{5}{6}\right]$

$$= \left(\dfrac{1}{2}\right)^3 - \left[\dfrac{11}{12} \div \dfrac{5}{6}\right]$$ • **Perform operations inside the inner grouping symbols.**

$$= \left(\dfrac{1}{2}\right)^3 - \dfrac{11}{10}$$ • **Perform operations inside the grouping symbols.**

$$= \dfrac{1}{8} - \dfrac{11}{10}$$ • **Simplify exponential expressions.**

$$= -\dfrac{39}{40}$$ • **Do addition and subtraction.**

PROBLEM 9   Simplify: $\dfrac{1}{3} + \dfrac{5}{8} \div \dfrac{15}{16} - \dfrac{7}{12}$

Solution   See page S1.

A **complex fraction** is a fraction whose numerator or denominator (or both) contains one or more fractions. Examples of complex fractions are shown below.

$$\dfrac{\dfrac{2}{3}}{\dfrac{1}{3}} \qquad \dfrac{\dfrac{2}{5} + 1}{\dfrac{7}{8}} \longleftarrow \text{Main fraction bar}$$

To simplify a complex fraction, perform operations above and below the main fraction bar as the first step in the Order of Operations Agreement.

Simplify: $\dfrac{\dfrac{3}{4} - \dfrac{1}{2}}{\dfrac{2}{3} + \dfrac{1}{4}}$

Perform operations above and below the main fraction bar.

$$\dfrac{\dfrac{3}{4} - \dfrac{1}{2}}{\dfrac{2}{3} + \dfrac{1}{4}} = \dfrac{\dfrac{3}{4} - \dfrac{2}{4}}{\dfrac{8}{12} + \dfrac{3}{12}}$$

Multiply the numerator of the complex fraction by the reciprocal of the denominator of the complex fraction.

$$= \dfrac{\dfrac{1}{4}}{\dfrac{11}{12}} = \dfrac{1}{4} \cdot \dfrac{12}{11}$$

Note that $\dfrac{\dfrac{1}{4}}{\dfrac{11}{12}} = \dfrac{1}{4} \div \dfrac{11}{12} = \dfrac{1}{4} \cdot \dfrac{12}{11}$.

$$= \dfrac{1 \cdot 12}{4 \cdot 11}$$

$$= \dfrac{3}{11}$$

EXAMPLE 10 Simplify: $9 \cdot \dfrac{\dfrac{5}{6} - 2}{\dfrac{3}{8}} \div \dfrac{7}{6}$

Solution $9 \cdot \dfrac{\dfrac{5}{6} - 2}{\dfrac{3}{8}} \div \dfrac{7}{6}$

$$= 9 \cdot \dfrac{-\dfrac{7}{6}}{\dfrac{3}{8}} \div \dfrac{7}{6}$$ • **Do operations above the main fraction bar.**

$$= 9 \cdot \left(-\dfrac{7}{6} \cdot \dfrac{8}{3}\right) \div \dfrac{7}{6}$$ • **Multiply the numerator of the complex fraction by the reciprocal of the denominator of the complex fraction.**

$$= 9 \cdot \left(-\dfrac{28}{9}\right) \div \dfrac{7}{6}$$

$$= -28 \div \dfrac{7}{6}$$ • **Do multiplication and division as they occur from left to right.**

$$= -28 \cdot \dfrac{6}{7}$$

$$= -24$$

PROBLEM 10   Simplify: $\dfrac{11}{12} - \dfrac{\dfrac{5}{4}}{2 - \dfrac{7}{2}} \cdot \dfrac{3}{4}$

Solution   See page S2.

1.2 Concept Review

Determine whether the following statements are always true, sometimes true, or never true.

1. The sum of two numbers of opposite signs is negative.

2. The product of two numbers with the same sign is positive.

3. The sum of two fractions is the sum of the numerators over the sum of the denominators.

4. To divide two fractions, multiply the first fraction by the reciprocal of the divisor.

5. The sum of a number and its additive inverse is zero.

6. The rule for multiplying two fractions is to multiply the numerators and place the product over the LCD of the denominators.

7. The Order of Operations Agreement says to simplify exponential expressions before performing operations inside grouping symbols.

8. The Order of Operations Agreement says to do multiplication before division.

9. If $-3x = 0$, then $x = 0$.

1.2 Exercises

1 Operations on integers

1. Explain how to add **a.** two integers with the same sign and **b.** two integers with different signs.

2. Explain the meaning of the words *minus* and *negative*.

3. Explain how to rewrite $8 - (-12)$ as addition of the opposite.

4. Explain how to multiply **a.** two integers with the same sign and **b.** two integers with different signs.

5. Simplify: $|-8 - (-3)|$

$|-8 - (-3)| = |-8 +$ _____?_____ $|$ • Write subtraction as addition of the opposite.

$= |$ _____?_____ $|$ • Add.

$=$ _____?_____   • Find the absolute value of the number in the absolute value symbols.

6. Write the division expression $63 \div (-9)$ as a fraction $\dfrac{?}{?}$. The quotient is

_____?_____.

Simplify.

7. $-18 + (-12)$ **8.** $-18 - 7$ **9.** $5 - 22$ **10.** $16 \cdot (-60)$

11. $3 \cdot 4(-8)$ **12.** $18 \cdot 0(-7)$ **13.** $18 \div (-3)$ **14.** $25 \div (-5)$

15. $-60 \div (-12)$ **16.** $(-9)(-2)(-3)(10)$ **17.** $-20(35)(-16)$ **18.** $54(19)(-82)$

19. $-271(-365)$ **20.** $|(-16)(10)|$ **21.** $|12(-8)|$ **22.** $|7 - 18|$

23. $|15 - (-8)|$ **24.** $|-16 - (-20)|$ **25.** $|-56 \div 8|$ **26.** $|81 \div (-9)|$

27. $|-153 \div (-9)|$ **28.** $|-4| - |-2|$ **29.** $-|-8| + |-4|$ **30.** $-|-16| - |24|$

31. $-30 + (-16) - 14 - 2$ **32.** $3 - (-2) + (-8) - 11$ **33.** $-2 + (-19) - 16 + 12$

34. $-6 + (-9) - 18 + 32$ **35.** $13 - |6 - 12|$ **36.** $-9 - |-7 - (-15)|$

37. $738 - 46 + (-105)$ **38.** $-871 - (-387) - 132$ **39.** $-442 \div (-17)$

40. $621 \div (-23)$ **41.** $-4897 \div 59$ **42.** $-17(-5)$

Complete Exercises 43 and 44 without using a calculator.

43. State whether the sum, difference, or product is positive or negative.
   a. the sum $567 + (-812)$
   b. the difference $-259 - (-327)$
   c. the product of four positive numbers and three negative numbers
   d. the product of three positive numbers and four negative numbers

44. State whether each quotient is positive, negative, zero, or undefined.
   a. $\dfrac{0}{-91}$ **b.** $-416 \div 52$ **c.** $-\dfrac{693}{-99}$ **d.** $-87 \div 0$

2   Operations on rational numbers

45. Describe **a.** the least common multiple of two numbers and **b.** the greatest common factor of two numbers.

46. ✎ Explain how to divide two rational numbers.

47. The least common multiple of the denominators of the fractions $\frac{5}{8}$, $-\frac{1}{28}$, and $\frac{2}{7}$ is ___?___. Write each fraction using the LCM as the denominator: $\frac{5}{8} = \frac{?}{56}$, $-\frac{1}{28} = -\frac{?}{56}$, and $\frac{2}{7} = \frac{?}{56}$.

48. The reciprocal of $-\frac{8}{27}$ is ___?___. To find the quotient $\frac{2}{3} \div \left(-\frac{8}{27}\right)$, find the product $\frac{2}{3} \cdot ($ ___?___ $)$. The quotient $\frac{2}{3} \div \left(-\frac{8}{27}\right)$ is ___?___.

49. The sum of 0.773 and -81.5 will have ___?___ decimal places.

50. The product of 0.773 and -81.5 will have ___?___ decimal places.

Simplify.

51. $\frac{7}{12} + \frac{5}{16}$

52. $\frac{3}{8} - \frac{5}{12}$

53. $-\frac{5}{9} - \frac{14}{15}$

54. $\frac{1}{2} + \frac{1}{7} - \frac{5}{8}$

55. $-\frac{1}{3} + \frac{5}{9} - \frac{7}{12}$

56. $\frac{1}{3} + \frac{19}{24} - \frac{7}{8}$

57. $\frac{2}{3} - \frac{5}{12} + \frac{5}{24}$

58. $-\frac{7}{10} + \frac{4}{5} + \frac{5}{6}$

59. $\frac{5}{8} - \frac{7}{12} + \frac{1}{2}$

60. $-\frac{1}{3} \cdot \frac{5}{8}$

61. $\left(\frac{6}{35}\right)\left(-\frac{5}{16}\right)$

62. $\frac{2}{3}\left(-\frac{9}{20}\right) \cdot \frac{5}{12}$

63. $-\frac{8}{15} \div \frac{4}{5}$

64. $-\frac{2}{3} \div \left(-\frac{6}{7}\right)$

65. $-\frac{11}{24} \div \frac{7}{12}$

66. $\frac{7}{9} \div \left(-\frac{14}{27}\right)$

67. $\left(-\frac{5}{12}\right)\left(\frac{4}{35}\right)\left(\frac{7}{8}\right)$

68. $\frac{6}{35}\left(-\frac{7}{40}\right)\left(-\frac{8}{21}\right)$

69. $-14.27 + 1.296$

70. $-0.4355 + 172.5$

71. $1.832 - 7.84$

72. $(3.52)(4.7)$

73. $(0.03)(10.5)(6.1)$

74. $(1.2)(3.1)(-6.4)$

75. $5.418 \div (-0.9)$

76. $-0.2645 \div (-0.023)$

77. $-0.4355 \div 0.065$

78. $-6.58 - 3.97 + 0.875$

Simplify. Round to the nearest hundredth.

79. $38.241 \div [-(-6.027)] - 7.453$

80. $-9.0508 - (-3.177) + 24.77$

81. $-287.3069 \div 0.1415$

82. $6472.3018 \div (-3.59)$

Complete Exercises 83 and 84 without actually finding the sums, differences, products, or quotients.

83. State whether each sum, difference, product, or quotient is positive or negative.

   a. $\left(-\dfrac{13}{22}\right)\left(-\dfrac{4}{5}\right)\left(-\dfrac{10}{11}\right)$ **b.** $-78.803 + 23.6$

   c. $-0.125 \div -1.25$ **d.** $\dfrac{1}{7} - \dfrac{1}{3}$

84. State whether each sum, difference, product, or quotient is positive or negative.

   a. $\dfrac{5}{6} + \dfrac{9}{10}$ **b.** $\dfrac{1}{4} \cdot \left(-\dfrac{1}{3}\right)$

   c. $0.14 - 0.137$ **d.** $-3.5 \div 3.4$

3   Exponential expressions

85. In the expression $(-6)^3$, -6 is called the ____?____ and 3 is called the ____?____. To evaluate $(-6)^3$, find the product ($\underline{\quad?\quad}$)($\underline{\quad?\quad}$)($\underline{\quad?\quad}$) = ____?____.

86. The exponential expression 7^2 is read "the ____?____ power of ____?____" or "seven ____?____." To evaluate 7^2, find the product ($\underline{\quad?\quad}$)($\underline{\quad?\quad}$) = ____?____.

Simplify.

87. 5^3 **88.** 3^4 **89.** -2^3 **90.** -4^3

91. $(-5)^3$ **92.** $(-8)^2$ **93.** $2^2 \cdot 3^4$ **94.** $4^2 \cdot 3^3$

95. $-2^2 \cdot 3^2$ **96.** $-3^2 \cdot 5^3$ **97.** $(-2)^3(-3)^2$ **98.** $(-4)^3(-2)^3$

99. $4 \cdot 2^3 \cdot 3^3$ **100.** $-4(-3)^2(4^2)$ **101.** $2^2 \cdot (-10)(-2)^2$ **102.** $-3(-2)^2(-5)$

103. $(-3)^3 \cdot 15 \cdot \left(-\dfrac{1}{3}\right)^4$ **104.** $-\dfrac{1}{4} \cdot 2^2 \cdot 5^5$ **105.** $\left(\dfrac{2}{3}\right)^3 \cdot (-3)^4 \cdot 4^5$ **106.** $4^4(-3)^5\left(-\dfrac{3}{2}\right)^2$

Complete Exercises 107 and 108 without actually finding the products.

107. Does the expression $(-9)^7$ simplify to a positive or a negative number?

108. Does the expression $-(3^4)(-2^5)\left(-\dfrac{1}{2}\right)$ simplify to a positive or a negative number?

4   The Order of Operations Agreement

109.   Why do we need an Order of Operations Agreement?

110.   Describe each step in the Order of Operations Agreement?

111. Simplify: $5^2 - (10 \div 2)^3 \div 5$

$$5^2 - (10 \div 2)^3 \div 5 = 5^2 - (\underline{\quad ? \quad})^3 \div 5$$
$$= \underline{\quad ? \quad} - \underline{\quad ? \quad} \div 5$$
$$= 25 - \underline{\quad ? \quad}$$
$$= \underline{\quad ? \quad}$$

- **Perform operations inside grouping symbols.**
- **Simplify exponential expressions.**
- **Do multiplication and division.**
- **Do addition and subtraction.**

112. Simplify: $\dfrac{\dfrac{2}{3}}{\dfrac{1}{2} - \dfrac{1}{3}}$

$$\frac{\dfrac{2}{3}}{\dfrac{1}{2} - \dfrac{1}{3}} = \frac{\dfrac{2}{3}}{\dfrac{?}{6} - \dfrac{?}{6}}$$

- **Write each fraction below the main fraction bar using the common denominator 6.**

$$= \frac{\dfrac{2}{3}}{\dfrac{?}{6}}$$

- **Subtract the fractions below the main fraction bar.**

$$= \frac{2}{3} \cdot \frac{6}{1}$$

- **Multiply the numerator of the complex fraction by the _____?_____ of the denominator.**

$$= \underline{\quad ? \quad}$$

- **Write the answer in simplest form.**

Simplify.

113. $5 - 3(8 \div 4)^2$

114. $4^2 - (5 - 2)^2 \cdot 3$

115. $16 - \dfrac{2^2 - 5}{3^2 + 2}$

116. $\dfrac{4(5 - 2)}{4^2 - 2^2} \div 4$

117. $\dfrac{3 + \dfrac{2}{3}}{\dfrac{11}{16}}$

118. $\dfrac{\dfrac{11}{14}}{4 - \dfrac{6}{7}}$

119. $5[(2 - 4) \cdot 3 - 2]$

120. $2[(16 \div 8) - (-2)] + 4$

121. $16 - 4\left(\dfrac{8 - 2}{3 - 6}\right) \div \dfrac{1}{2}$

122. $25 \div 5\left(\dfrac{16 + 8}{-2^2 + 8}\right) - 5$

123. $6[3 - (-4 + 2) \div 2]$

124. $12 - 4[2 - (-3 + 5) - 8]$

125. $\dfrac{1}{2} - \left(\dfrac{2}{3} \div \dfrac{5}{9}\right) + \dfrac{5}{6}$

126. $\left(-\dfrac{3}{5}\right)^2 - \dfrac{3}{5} \cdot \dfrac{5}{9} + \dfrac{7}{10}$

127. $\dfrac{1}{2} - \dfrac{\frac{17}{25}}{4 - \frac{3}{5}} + \dfrac{1}{5}$

128. $\dfrac{3}{4} + \dfrac{3 - \frac{7}{9}}{\frac{5}{6}} \cdot \dfrac{2}{3}$

129. $\dfrac{2}{3} - \left[\dfrac{3}{8} + \dfrac{5}{6}\right] \div \dfrac{3}{5}$

130. $\dfrac{3}{4} \div \left[\dfrac{5}{8} - \dfrac{5}{12}\right] + 2$

131. $0.4(1.2 - 2.3)^2 + 5.8$

132. $5.4 - (0.3)^2 \div 0.09$

133. $1.75 \div 0.25 - (1.25)^2$

134. $(3.5 - 4.2)^2 - 3.50 \div 2.5$

135. $25.76 \div (6.54 \div 3.27)^2$

136. $(3.09 - 4.77)^2 - 4.07 \cdot 3.66$

137. Which expression is equivalent to $8^2 - 2^2(5 - 3)^3$?
  a. $6^2(2)^3$ **b.** $64 - 4(8)$ **c.** $60(2)^3$ **d.** $64 - 8^3$

138. Which expression is equivalent to $32 + 32 \div 4 - 2^3$?
  a. $64 \div 4 - 8$ **b.** $32 + 32 \div (-4)$ **c.** $32 + 8 - 8$ **d.** $32 + 32 \div 8$

1.2   Applying Concepts

139. A number that is its own additive inverse is _____ .

140. Which two numbers are their own multiplicative inverse?

141. Do all real numbers have a multiplicative inverse? If not, which do not have a multiplicative inverse?

142. What is the tens digit of 11^{22}?

143. What is the ones digit of 7^{18}?

144. What are the last two digits of 5^{33}?

145. What are the last three digits of 5^{234}?

146. Does $(2^3)^4 = 2^{(3^4)}$? If not, which expression is larger?

147. What is the Order of Operations Agreement for a^{b^c}? (*Note:* Even calculators that normally follow the Order of Operations Agreement may not do so for this expression.)

1.3 Variable Expressions

OBJECTIVE **1**   ## The Properties of the Real Numbers

The Properties of the Real Numbers describe the way operations on numbers can be performed. Following is a list of some of the Properties of the Real Numbers and an example of each property.

The Commutative Property of Addition

$$a + b = b + a$$

$3 + 2 = 2 + 3$
$5 = 5$

The Commutative Property of Multiplication

$$a \cdot b = b \cdot a$$

$(3)(-2) = (-2)(3)$
$-6 = -6$

The Associative Property of Addition

$$(a + b) + c = a + (b + c)$$

$(3 + 4) + 5 = 3 + (4 + 5)$
$7 + 5 = 3 + 9$
$12 = 12$

The Associative Property of Multiplication

$$(a \cdot b) \cdot c = a \cdot (b \cdot c)$$

$(3 \cdot 4) \cdot 5 = 3 \cdot (4 \cdot 5)$
$12 \cdot 5 = 3 \cdot 20$
$60 = 60$

The Addition Property of Zero

$$a + 0 = 0 + a = a$$

$3 + 0 = 0 + 3 = 3$

The Multiplication Property of Zero

$$a \cdot 0 = 0 \cdot a = 0$$

$8 \cdot 0 = 0 \cdot 8 = 0$

The Multiplication Property of One

$$a \cdot 1 = 1 \cdot a = a$$

$5 \cdot 1 = 1 \cdot 5 = 5$

> ### The Inverse Property of Addition
>
> $$a + (-a) = (-a) + a = 0$$ $$4 + (-4) = (-4) + 4 = 0$$

$-a$ is called the **additive inverse** of a. Also, a is the additive inverse of $-a$. The sum of a number and its additive inverse is 0.

> ### The Inverse Property of Multiplication
>
> $$a \cdot \frac{1}{a} = \frac{1}{a} \cdot a = 1, \quad a \neq 0$$ $$(4)\left(\frac{1}{4}\right) = \left(\frac{1}{4}\right)(4) = 1$$

$\frac{1}{a}$ is called the **multiplicative inverse** of a. It is also called the **reciprocal** of a. The product of a number and its multiplicative inverse is 1.

> ### The Distributive Property
>
> $$a(b + c) = ab + ac$$
>
> $$3(4 + 5) = 3 \cdot 4 + 3 \cdot 5$$
> $$3 \cdot 9 = 12 + 15$$
> $$27 = 27$$

EXAMPLE 1 Complete the statement by using the Inverse Property of Addition.

$$3x + ? = 0$$

Solution $3x + (-3x) = 0$

PROBLEM 1 Complete the statement by using the Commutative Property of Multiplication.

$$(x)\left(\frac{1}{4}\right) = (?)(x)$$

Solution   See page S2.

EXAMPLE 2 Identify the property that justifies the statement.
$$3(x + 4) = 3x + 12$$

Solution   The Distributive Property

PROBLEM 2 Identify the property that justifies the statement.
$$(a + 3b) + c = a + (3b + c)$$

Solution   See page S2.

OBJECTIVE 2   Evaluate variable expressions

An expression that contains one or more variables is called a **variable expression**.

A variable expression is shown at the right. The expression has four addends that are called **terms** of the expression. The variable expression has three variable terms and one constant term.

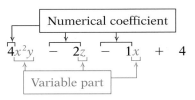

Each variable term is composed of a **numerical coefficient** and a **variable part.** When the numerical coefficient is 1 or −1, the 1 is usually not written.

$$4x^2y \quad - \quad 2z \quad - \quad 1x \quad + \quad 4$$

Replacing the variable in a variable expression by a numerical value and then simplifying the resulting expression is called **evaluating the variable expression.**

Evaluate $3 - 2|3x - 2y^2|$ when $x = -1$ and $y = 2$.

Replace each variable with its value.

$$3 - 2|3x - 2y^2|$$
$$3 - 2|3(-1) - 2(2)^2|$$

Use the Order of Operations Agreement to simplify the resulting numerical expression.

$$= 3 - 2|3(-1) - 2(4)|$$
$$= 3 - 2|-3 - 8|$$
$$= 3 - 2|-11|$$
$$= 3 - 2(11)$$
$$= 3 - 22$$
$$= -19$$

EXAMPLE 3 Evaluate $a^2 - (ab - c)$ when $a = -2$, $b = 3$, and $c = -4$.

Solution $a^2 - (ab - c)$
$(-2)^2 - [(-2)(3) - (-4)]$ • Replace each variable in the expression with its value.

$= (-2)^2 - [-6 - (-4)]$ • Use the Order of Operations Agreement
$= (-2)^2 - [-2]$ to simplify the resulting numerical
$= 4 - [-2]$ expression.
$= 6$

PROBLEM 3 Evaluate $(b - c)^2 \div ab$ when $a = -3$, $b = 2$, and $c = -4$.

Solution See page S2.

EXAMPLE 4 The radius of the base of a cylinder is 3 in. and the height is 6 in. Find the volume of the cylinder. Round to the nearest hundredth.

Solution $V = \pi r^2 h$ • Use the formula for the volume of a cylinder.
$V = \pi(3)^2 6$ • Substitute 3 for r and 6 for h.
$V = 54\pi$ • The exact volume of the cylinder is 54π in³. An approximate measure can be found by using the π key on a calculator.

$V \approx 169.65$

The approximate volume of the cylinder is 169.65 in³.

6 in.
3 in.

Take Note

For your reference, geometric formulas are provided at the back of this textbook.

PROBLEM 4   Find the surface area of a right circular cone with a radius of 5 cm and a slant height of 12 cm. Give both the exact area and an approximation to the nearest hundredth.

12 cm

5 cm

Solution   See page S2.

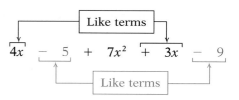

A graphing calculator can be used to evaluate variable expressions. When the value of each variable is stored in the calculator's memory and a variable expression is then entered on the calculator, the calculator evaluates that variable expression for the values of the variables stored in its memory. See the Appendix for a description of keystroking procedures.

OBJECTIVE 3   ## Simplify variable expressions

Like terms of a variable expression are terms with the same variable part.

Constant terms are like terms.

Like terms

$$4x \quad - \quad 5 \quad + \quad 7x^2 \quad + \quad 3x \quad - \quad 9$$

Like terms

To **combine like terms,** use the Distributive Property $ba + ca = (b + c)a$ to add the coefficients.

$$3x + 2x = (3 + 2)x = 5x$$

EXAMPLE 5   Simplify: $2(x + y) + 3(y - 3x)$

Solution
$$2(x + y) + 3(y - 3x)$$
$$= 2x + 2y + 3y - 9x$$
  • Use the Distributive Property to remove parentheses.
$$= (2x - 9x) + (2y + 3y)$$
  • Use the Commutative and Associative Properties of Addition to rearrange and group like terms.
$$= -7x + 5y$$
  • Combine like terms.

PROBLEM 5   Simplify: $(2x + xy - y) - (5x - 7xy + y)$

Solution   See page S2.

EXAMPLE 6   Simplify: $4y - 2[x - 3(x + y) - 5y]$

Solution
$$4y - 2[x - 3(x + y) - 5y]$$
$$= 4y - 2[x - 3x - 3y - 5y]$$
  • Use the Distributive Property to remove parentheses.
$$= 4y - 2[-2x - 8y]$$
  • Combine like terms.
$$= 4y + 4x + 16y$$
  • Use the Distributive Property to remove brackets.
$$= 4x + 20y$$
  • Combine like terms.

> **PROBLEM 6**   Simplify: $2x - 3[y - 3(x - 2y + 4)]$
>
> **Solution**   See page S2.

1.3 Concept Review

Determine whether the following statements are always true, sometimes true, or never true.

1. The reciprocal of a whole number is a whole number.

2. The Distributive Property is used to combine like terms.

3. Like terms are terms with the same variables.

4. The sum of a number and its multiplicative inverse is -1.

5. The product of a number and its multiplicative inverse is 1.

6. A real number has a multiplicative inverse.

1.3 Exercises

1   The Properties of the Real Numbers

1. The fact that two terms can be multiplied in either order is called the ___?___ Property of Multiplication.

2. The fact that three or more addends can be added by grouping them in any order is called the ___?___ Property of Addition.

3. The Multiplication Property of Zero tells us that the product of a number and zero is ___?___.

4. The Addition Property of Zero tells us that the sum of a number and ___?___ is the number.

Use the given Property of the Real Numbers to complete the statement.

5. Commutative Property of Multiplication
   $3 \cdot 4 = 4 \cdot ?$

6. The Commutative Property of Addition
   $7 + 15 = ? + 7$

7. The Associative Property of Addition
$(3 + 4) + 5 = ? + (4 + 5)$

8. The Associative Property of Multiplication
$(3 \cdot 4) \cdot 5 = 3 \cdot (? \cdot 5)$

9. A Division Property of Zero
$\dfrac{5}{?}$ is undefined.

10. The Addition Property of Zero
$4 + ? = 4$

11. The Distributive Property
$3(x + 2) = 3x + ?$

12. The Distributive Property
$5(y + 4) = ? \cdot y + 20$

13. A Division Property of Zero
$\dfrac{?}{-6} = 0$

14. The Inverse Property of Addition
$(x + y) + ? = 0$

15. The Inverse Property of Multiplication
$\dfrac{1}{mn}(mn) = ?$

16. The Multiplication Property of One
$? \cdot 1 = x$

17. The Associative Property of Multiplication
$2(3x) = ? \cdot x$

18. The Commutative Property of Addition
$ab + bc = bc + ?$

Identify the property that justifies the statement.

19. $\dfrac{0}{-5} = 0$

20. $-8 + 8 = 0$

21. $(-12)\left(-\dfrac{1}{12}\right) = 1$

22. $(3 \cdot 4) \cdot 2 = 2 \cdot (3 \cdot 4)$

23. $y + 0 = y$

24. $2x + (5y + 8) = (2x + 5y) + 8$

25. $\dfrac{-9}{0}$ is undefined.

26. $(x + y)z = xz + yz$

27. $6(x + y) = 6x + 6y$

28. $0 + 2 = 2$

29. $(ab)c = a(bc)$

30. $(x + y) + z = (y + x) + z$

31. The sum of a number n and its additive inverse is multiplied by the reciprocal of the number n. What is the result?

32. The product of a number n and its reciprocal is multiplied by the number n. What is the result?

2 Evaluate variable expressions

33. Explain the meaning of the phrase "evaluate a variable expression."

34. What is the difference between the meaning of "the value of the variable" and the meaning of "the value of the variable expression"?

35. Evaluate $n^2|m - n|$ when $n = -5$ and $m = -3$.

$n^2|m - n| = (-5)^2|-3 - (-5)|$ • Replace n with ___?___ and m with ___?___.

$ = (-5)^2|\underline{\quad?\quad}|$ • Perform operations inside the grouping symbols.

$ = (-5)^2(\underline{\quad?\quad})$ • Evaluate the absolute value.

$ = (\underline{\quad?\quad})(2)$ • Simplify the exponential expression.

$ = \underline{\quad?\quad}$ • Multiply.

36. The volume of a cone with height h and base of radius r is $V = \underline{\quad?\quad}$. If $r = 2$ in. and $h = 3$ in., then the exact volume of the cone is $V = \dfrac{1}{3}\pi(\underline{\quad?\quad})^2(\underline{\quad?\quad}) = (\underline{\quad?\quad})\pi$ in. Use the $\boxed{\pi}$ key on a calculator to approximate the volume to the nearest hundredth: $V \approx \underline{\quad?\quad}$ in³.

Evaluate the variable expression when $a = 2$, $b = 3$, $c = -1$, and $d = -4$.

37. $ab + dc$

38. $2ab - 3dc$

39. $4cd \div ac$

40. $b^2 - (d - c)^2$

41. $(b - 2a)^2 + c$

42. $(b - d)^2 \div (b - d)$

43. $(bc + a)^2 \div (d - b)$

44. $\dfrac{1}{3}b^3 - \dfrac{1}{4}d^3$

45. $\dfrac{1}{4}a^4 - \dfrac{1}{6}bc$

46. $2b^2 \div \dfrac{ad}{2}$

47. $\dfrac{3ac}{-4} - c^2$

48. $\dfrac{2d - 2a}{2bc}$

49. $\dfrac{3b - 5c}{3a - c}$

50. $\dfrac{2d - a}{b - 2c}$

51. $\dfrac{a - d}{b + c}$

52. $|a^2 + d|$

53. $-a|a + 2d|$

54. $d|b - 2d|$

55. $\dfrac{2a - 4d}{3b - c}$

56. $\dfrac{3d - b}{b - 2c}$

57. $-3d \div \left|\dfrac{ab - 4c}{2b + c}\right|$

58. $-2bc + \left|\dfrac{bc + d}{ab - c}\right|$

59. $2(d - b) \div (3a - c)$

60. $(d - 4a)^2 \div ac^3$

61. $-d^2 - c^3a$

62. $a^2c - d^3$

63. $-d^3 + 4ac$

64. b^a

65. 4^{a^2}

66. a^b

Geometry Find the volume of each figure. For calculations involving π, give both the exact value and an approximation to the nearest hundredth.

67.

6 in.
14 in.   10 in.

68.

14 ft
12 ft

69.

5 ft
3 ft
3 ft

70.
7.5 m
7.5 m   7.5 m

71.
3 cm

72.
8 cm
8 cm

Geometry Find the surface area of each figure. For calculations involving π, give both the exact value and an approximation to the nearest hundredth.

73.
3 m
5 m
4 m

74.
14 ft
14 ft   14 ft

75.
5 m
4 m
4 m

76.
2 cm

77.
2 in.
6 in.

78.
9 ft
3 ft

Complete Exercises 79 and 80 without a calculator.

79. If $\dfrac{abc}{b-a}$ is evaluated when $a = -38$, $b = -52$, and c is a positive integer, will the result be a positive or a negative number?

80. The formula for the volume of a right circular cylinder with height h and base of radius r is $V = \pi r^2 h$. Suppose a cylinder has a radius of 2 cm and a height of 3 cm.
a. Can the exact volume of the cylinder be V cm³, where V is a whole number?
b. Can the exact volume of the cylinder be V cm², where V is an irrational number?

3   Simplify variable expressions

81. Explain how the Distributive Property is used to combine like terms.

82. The four terms of the variable expression $5x - 6y + 4x - 8$ are ___?___, ___?___, ___?___, and ___?___. The terms $5x$ and $4x$ are called ___?___ terms. The coefficient of the y term is ___?___. The constant term is ___?___.

83. Simplify: $-5(y - 5x) + 9y$

$-5(y - 5x) + 9y = ($ _____?_____ $)y + ($ _____?_____ $)x + 9y$ • Use the Distributive Property to remove parentheses.

$= (-5y + 9y) + 25x$ • Use the _____?_____ and _____?_____ Properties of Addition to rearrange and group like terms.

$=$ _____?_____ $+ 25x$ • Combine like terms.

Simplify.

84. $5x + 7x$

85. $3x + 10x$

86. $-8ab - 5ab$

87. $-2x + 5x - 7x$

88. $3x - 5x + 9x$

89. $-2a + 7b + 9a$

90. $5b - 8a - 12b$

91. $12\left(\dfrac{1}{12}x\right)$

92. $\dfrac{1}{3}(3y)$

93. $-3(x - 2)$

94. $-5(x - 9)$

95. $(x + 2)5$

96. $-(x + y)$

97. $-(-x - y)$

98. $3(a - 5)$

99. $3(x - 2y) - 5$

100. $4x - 3(2y - 5)$

101. $-2a - 3(3a - 7)$

102. $3x - 2(5x - 7)$

103. $2x - 3(x - 2y)$

104. $3[a - 5(5 - 3a)]$

105. $5[-2 - 6(a - 5)]$

106. $3[x - 2(x + 2y)]$

107. $5[y - 3(y - 2x)]$

108. $-2(x - 3y) + 2(3y - 5x)$

109. $4(-a - 2b) - 2(3a - 5b)$

110. $5(3a - 2b) - 3(-6a + 5b)$

111. $-7(2a - b) + 2(-3b + a)$

112. $3x - 2[y - 2(x + 3[2x + 3y])]$

113. $2x - 4[x - 4(y - 2[5y + 3])]$

114. $4 - 2(7x - 2y) - 3(-2x + 3y)$

115. $3x + 8(x - 4) - 3(2x - y)$

116. $\dfrac{1}{3}[8x - 2(x - 12) + 3]$

117. $\dfrac{1}{4}[14x - 3(x - 8) - 7x]$

118. State whether the given number will be positive, negative, or zero after the variable expression $31a - 102b + 73 - 88a + 256b - 73$ is simplified.

a. the coefficient of a **b.** the coefficient of b **c.** the constant term

119. State whether the given expression is equivalent to $3[5 - 2(y - 6)]$.

a. $3[3(y - 6)]$ **b.** $15 - 6(y - 6)$

1.3 Applying Concepts

In each of the following, it is possible that at least one of the Properties of Real Numbers has been applied incorrectly. If the statement is incorrect, state the incorrect application of the Properties of Real Numbers and correct the answer. If the statement is correct, state the Property of Real Numbers that is being used.

120. $-4(5x - y) = -20x + 4y$

121. $4(3y + 1) = 12y + 4$

122. $6 - 6x = 0x = 0$

123. $2 + 3x = (2 + 3)x = 5x$

124. $3a - 4b = 4b - 3a$

125. $2(3y) = (2 \cdot 3)(2y) = 12y$

126. $x^4 \cdot \dfrac{1}{x^4} = 1, x \neq 0$

127. $-x^2 + y^2 = y^2 - x^2$

Name the property that justifies each lettered step used in simplifying the expression.

128. $3(x + y) + 2x$
    a. $(3x + 3y) + 2x$

    b. $(3y + 3x) + 2x$

    c. $3y + (3x + 2x)$

    d. $3y + (3 + 2)x$
       $3y + 5x$

129. $3a + 4(b + a)$
    a. $3a + (4b + 4a)$

    b. $3a + (4a + 4b)$

    c. $(3a + 4a) + 4b$

    d. $(3 + 4)a + 4b$
       $7a + 4b$

130. $y + (3 + y)$
    a. $y + (y + 3)$

    b. $(y + y) + 3$

    c. $(1y + 1y) + 3$

    d. $(1 + 1)y + 3$
       $2y + 3$

131. $5(3a + 1)$
    a. $5(3a) + 5(1)$

    b. $(5 \cdot 3)a + 5(1)$
       $15a + 5(1)$

    c. $15a + 5$

Verbal Expressions and Variable Expressions

OBJECTIVE **1**   **Translate a verbal expression into a variable expression**

One of the major skills required in applied mathematics is translating a verbal expression into a mathematical expression. Doing so requires recognizing the verbal phrases that translate into mathematical operations. Following is a partial list of the verbal phrases used to indicate the different mathematical operations.

Point of Interest

Mathematical symbolism, as shown on this page, has advanced through various stages: rhetorical, syncoptical, and modern. In the rhetorical stage, all mathematical description was through words. In the syncoptical stage, there was a combination of words and symbols. For instance, x plano 4 in y meant 4xy. The modern stage, which is used today, began in the 17th century. Modern symbolism is also changing. For example, there are advocates of a system of symbolism that would place all operations last. Using this notation, 4 plus 7 would be written 4 7 + and 6 divided by 4 would be written 6 4 ÷.

Addition	more than	8 more than w	$w + 8$
	added to	x added to 9	$9 + x$
	the sum of	the sum of z and 9	$z + 9$
	the total of	the total of r and s	$r + s$
	increased by	x increased by 7	$x + 7$
Subtraction	less than	12 less than b	$b - 12$
	the difference between	the difference between x and 1	$x - 1$
	minus	z minus 7	$z - 7$
	decreased by	17 decreased by a	$17 - a$
Multiplication	times	negative 2 times c	$-2c$
	the product of	the product of x and y	xy
	multiplied by	3 multiplied by n	$3n$
	of	three-fourths of m	$\dfrac{3}{4}m$
	twice	twice d	$2d$
Division	divided by	v divided by 15	$\dfrac{v}{15}$
	the quotient of	the quotient of y and 3	$\dfrac{y}{3}$
	ratio	the ratio of x to 7	$\dfrac{x}{7}$
Power	the square of or the second power of	the square of x	x^2
	the cube of or the third power of	the cube of r	r^3
	the fifth power of	the fifth power of a	a^5

Translating a phrase that contains the word *sum, difference, product,* or *quotient* can sometimes cause a problem. In the examples at the right, note where the operation symbol is placed.

the *sum* of x and y	$x + y$
the *difference* between x and y	$x - y$
the *product* of x and y	$x \cdot y$
the *quotient* of x and y	$\dfrac{x}{y}$

The sum of two numbers is 37. If x represents the smaller number, translate "twice the larger number" into a variable expression.

Write an expression for the larger number by subtracting the smaller number, x, from 37.	larger number: $37 - x$
Identify the words that indicate the mathematical operations.	<u>twice</u> the <u>larger number</u>
Use the identified words to write a variable expression.	$2(37 - x)$

Translate "five less than twice the difference between a number and seven" into a variable expression. Then simplify.

Assign a variable to the unknown number.	the unknown number: x
Identify the words that indicate the mathematical operations.	5 less than twice the difference between x and 7
Use the identified words to write the variable expression.	$2(x - 7) - 5$
Simplify the expression.	$= 2x - 14 - 5 = 2x - 19$

EXAMPLE 1   Translate and simplify "the total of five times a number and twice the difference between the number and three."

Solution   the unknown number: n • Assign a variable to one of the unknown quantities.

five times the number: $5n$ • Use the assigned variable to write the difference between the   an expression for any other number and three: $n - 3$ unknown quantity.
twice the difference between the number and three:
$2(n - 3)$
$5n + 2(n - 3)$ • Use the assigned variable to write the variable expression.

$= 5n + 2n - 6$ • Simplify the variable expression.
$= 7n - 6$

PROBLEM 1   Translate and simplify "a number decreased by the difference between eight and twice the number."

Solution   See page S2.

EXAMPLE 2   Translate and simplify "fifteen minus one-half the sum of a number and ten."

Solution   the unknown number: n • Assign a variable to one of the unknown quantities.

the sum of the number and   • Use the assigned variable to ten: $n + 10$ write an expression for any one-half the sum of the   other unknown quantity.

number and ten: $\frac{1}{2}(n + 10)$

$15 - \frac{1}{2}(n + 10)$ • Use the assigned variable to write the variable expression.

$= 15 - \frac{1}{2}n - 5$ • Simplify the variable expression.

$= -\frac{1}{2}n + 10$

PROBLEM 2   Translate and simplify "the sum of three-eighths of a number and five-twelfths of the number."

■   **Solution**   See page S2.

OBJECTIVE **2**   ## Application problems

Many of the applications of mathematics require that you identify the un-known quantity, assign a variable to that quantity, and then attempt to express other unknowns in terms of that quantity.

Ten gallons of paint were poured into two containers of different sizes. Express the amount of paint poured into the smaller container in terms of the amount poured into the larger container.

Assign a variable to the amount of paint poured into the larger container.

the number of gallons of paint poured into the larger container: g

Express the amount of paint poured into the smaller container in terms of g (g gallons of paint were poured into the larger container).

the number of gallons of paint poured into the smaller container: $10 - g$

EXAMPLE 3   A cyclist is riding at a rate that is twice the speed of a runner. Express the speed of the cyclist in terms of the speed of the runner.

Solution   the speed of the runner: r
the speed of the cyclist is twice r: $2r$

PROBLEM 3   A mixture of candy contains 3 lb more of milk chocolate than of caramel. Express the amount of milk chocolate in the mixture in terms of the amount of caramel in the mixture.

■   **Solution**   See page S2.

EXAMPLE 4   The length of a rectangle is 2 ft more than 3 times the width. Express the length of the rectangle in terms of the width.

Solution   the width of the rectangle: W
the length is 2 more than 3 times W: $3W + 2$

PROBLEM 4   The depth of the deep end of a swimming pool is 2 ft more than twice the depth of the shallow end. Express the depth of the deep end in terms of the depth of the shallow end.

■   **Solution**   See page S2.

1.4   Concept Review

Determine whether the following statements are always true, sometimes true, or never true.

1. The sum of two numbers is 12. If x represents the larger number, then the smaller number is represented by $x - 12$.

2. A rope L feet long is cut into two pieces. If x is the length of one piece of the rope, the length of the other piece is $x - L$.

3. The expression $2(x + 4)$ can be described by the statement "the sum of twice x and 4."

4. Four times the difference between x and 3 is given by $4x - 3$.

5. The square of $-x$ is $-x^2$.

6. The expressions $\frac{2x}{3}$ and $\frac{2}{3}x$ represent the same number.

1.4   Exercises

1   Translate a verbal expression into a variable expression

For each phrase in Exercises 1 to 3, identify the words that indicate mathematical operations.

1. ten more than the product of eight and a number

2. thirteen subtracted from the quotient of negative five and the cube of a number

3. the difference between ten times a number and sixteen times the number

4. The sum of two numbers is 24. To express both numbers in terms of the same variable, let x be one number. Then the other number is ____?____.

Translate into a variable expression. Then simplify.

5. a number minus the sum of the number and two

6. a number decreased by the difference between five and the number

7. the sum of one-third of a number and four-fifths of the number

8. the difference between three-eighths of a number and one-sixth of the number

9. five times the product of eight and a number

10. a number increased by two-thirds of the number

11. the difference between the product of seventeen and a number and twice the number

12. one-half of the total of six times a number and twenty-two

13. the difference between the square of a number and the total of twelve and the square of the number

14. eleven more than the square of a number added to the difference between the number and seventeen

15. the sum of five times a number and twelve added to the product of fifteen and the number

16. four less than twice the sum of a number and eleven

17. The sum of two numbers is 15. Using x to represent the smaller of the two numbers, translate "the sum of twice the smaller number and two more than the larger number" into a variable expression. Then simplify.

18. The sum of two numbers is 20. Using x to represent the smaller of the two numbers, translate "the difference between five times the larger number and three less than the smaller number" into a variable expression.

19. The sum of two numbers is 34. Using x to represent the larger of the two numbers, translate "the difference between two more than the smaller number and twice the larger number" into a variable expression. Then simplify.

20. The sum of two numbers is 33. Using x to represent the larger of the two numbers, translate "the difference between six more than twice the smaller number and three more than the larger number" into a variable expression. Then simplify.

21. Which phrase(s) translate(s) into the expression $8n^3 - 5$?
   a. the difference between five and the product of eight and the cube of a number
   b. five subtracted from the cube of eight and a number
   c. five less than the product of eight and the cube of a number

22. Which phrase(s) translate(s) into the expression $(5n + 2) + 15$?
   a. fifteen more than the sum of five times a number and two
   b. the total of two more than the product of five and a number plus fifteen
   c. fifteen added to two more than the product of five and a number

2 Application problems

23. The length of a rectangle is eight more than the width. To express the length and the width in terms of the same variable, let W be the ___?___. Then the length is ___?___.

24. The width of a rectangle is one-third the length. To express the length and the width in terms of the same variable, let L be the ___?___. Then the width is ___?___.

25. Demographics The population of New York City is four times the population of Houston, Texas. Express the population of New York City in terms of the population of Houston, Texas. (*Source: Information Please Almanac*)

26. 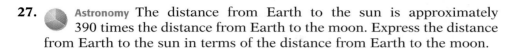 **Health** Heart disease is responsible for seven times as many deaths each year as are accidents. Express the number of deaths caused each year by heart disease in terms of the number of deaths each year caused by accidents. (*Source: Wall Street Journal Almanac*)

27. **Astronomy** The distance from Earth to the sun is approximately 390 times the distance from Earth to the moon. Express the distance from Earth to the sun in terms of the distance from Earth to the moon.

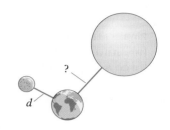

28. **Construction** The longest rail tunnel (from Hanshu to Hokkaido, Japan) is 23.36 mi longer than the longest road tunnel (from Goschenen to Airo, Switzerland). Express the length of the longest rail tunnel in terms of the length of the longest road tunnel.

29. **Investments** A financial advisor has invested $10,000 in two accounts. If one account contains x dollars, express the amount in the second account in terms of x.

30. **Recreation** A fishing line 3 ft long is cut into two pieces, one shorter than the other. Express the length of the shorter piece in terms of the length of the longer piece.

31. **Travel** The total flying time for a round trip between New York and San Diego is 13 h. Because of the jet stream, the time going is not equal to the time returning. Express the flying time between New York and San Diego in terms of the flying time between San Diego and New York.

32. **Carpentry** A 12-foot board is cut into two pieces of different lengths. Express the length of the longer piece in terms of the length of the shorter piece.

33. **Geometry** The measure of angle A of a triangle is twice the measure of angle B. The measure of angle C is twice the measure of angle A. Write expressions for angle A and angle C in terms of angle B.

34. **Geometry** The length of a rectangle is three more than twice the width. Express the length of the rectangle in terms of the width.

1.4 Applying Concepts

For each of the following, write a phrase that would translate into the given expression.

35. $2x + 3$ **36.** $5y - 4$ **37.** $2(x + 3)$ **38.** $5(y - 4)$

Some English phrases require more than one variable in order to be translated into a variable expression.

39. **Physics** Translate "the product of one-half the acceleration due to gravity (g) and the time (t) squared" into a variable expression. (This expression gives the distance a dropped object will fall during a certain time interval.)

40. Physics Translate "the product of mass (m) and acceleration (a)" into a variable expression. (This expression is used to calculate the force exerted on an accelerating object.)

41. Physics Translate "the product of the area (A) and the square of the velocity (v)" into a variable expression. (This expression is used to compute the force a wind exerts on a sail.)

42. Physics Translate "the square root of the quotient of the spring constant (k) and the mass (m)" into a variable expression. (This is part of the expression that is used to compute the frequency of oscillation of a mass on the end of a spring.)

Focus on Problem Solving

Polya's Four-Step Process

WEB

Your success in mathematics and your success in the workplace are heavily dependent on your ability to solve problems. One of the foremost mathematicians to study problem solving was George Polya (1887–1985). The basic structure that Polya advocated for problem solving has four steps, as outlined below. (There are many sites on the Internet dealing with problem solving. One such site is **www.askdrmath.com.** You can also conduct a search for "problem solving.")

1. Understand the Problem

You must have a clear understanding of the problem. To help you focus on understanding the problem, here are some questions to think about.

- Can you restate the problem in your own words?
- Can you determine what is known about these types of problems?
- Is there missing information that you need in order to solve the problem?
- Is there information given that is not needed?
- What is the goal?

2. Devise a Plan

Successful problem solvers use a variety of techniques when they attempt to solve a problem. Here are some frequently used strategies.

- Make a list of the known information.
- Make a list of information that is needed to solve the problem.
- Make a table or draw a diagram.
- Work backwards.
- Try to solve a similar but simpler problem.
- Research the problem to determine whether there are known techniques for solving problems of its kind.
- Try to determine whether some pattern exists.

Point of Interest

George Polya was born in Hungary and moved to the United States in 1940. He lived in Providence, Rhode Island, where he taught at Brown University until 1942, when he moved to California. There he taught at Stanford University until his retirement. While at Stanford, he published 10 books and a number of articles for mathematics journals. Of the books Polya published, How to Solve It *(1945) is one of his best known. In this book, Polya outlines a strategy for solving problems. This strategy, although frequently applied to mathematics, can be used to solve problems from virtually any discipline.*

• Write an equation.

3. Carry Out the Plan

Once you have devised a plan, you must carry it out.

• Work carefully.

• Keep an accurate and neat record of all your attempts.

• Realize that some of your initial plans will not work and that you may have to return to Step 2 and devise another plan or modify your existing plan.

4. Review Your Solution

Once you have found a solution, check the solution against the known facts.

• Ensure that the solution is consistent with the facts of the problem.

• Interpret the solution in the context of the problem.

• Ask yourself whether there are generalizations of the solution that could apply to other problems.

• Determine the strengths and weaknesses of your solution. For instance, is your solution only an approximation to the actual solution?

• Consider the possibility of alternative solutions.

1.5 in.

6 in.

1 in.

We will use Polya's four-step process to solve the following problem.

A large soft drink costs $1.25 at a college cafeteria. The dimensions of the cup are shown at the left. Suppose you don't put any ice in the cup. Determine the cost per ounce for the soft drink.

1. *Understand the problem.* We must determine the cost per ounce for the soda. To do this, we need the dimensions of the cup (which are given), the cost of the drink (given), and a formula for the volume of the cup (unknown). Also, because the dimensions are given in inches, the volume will be in cubic inches; we need a conversion factor that will convert cubic inches to fluid ounces.

2. *Devise a plan.* Consult a resource book that gives the volume of the figure, which is called a **frustrum.** The formula for the volume is

$$V = \frac{\pi h}{3}(r^2 + rR + R^2)$$

where h is the height, r is the radius of the base, and R is the radius of the top. Also from a reference book, 1 in^3 ≈ 0.55 fl oz. The general plan is to calculate the volume, convert the answer to fluid ounces, and then divide the cost by the number of fluid ounces.

3. *Carry out the plan.* Using the information from the drawing, evaluate the formula for the volume.

$$V = \frac{6\pi}{3}[1^2 + 1(1.5) + 1.5^2] = 9.5\pi \approx 29.8451 \text{ in}^3$$

$V \approx 29.8451(0.55) \approx 16.4148$ fl oz   • **Convert to fluid ounces.**

Cost per ounce $\approx \dfrac{1.25}{16.4148} \approx 0.07615$ • **Divide the cost by the volume.**

The cost of the soft drink is approximately 7.62 cents per ounce.

4. *Review your solution.* The cost of a 12-ounce can of soda from a vending machine is generally about 75¢. Therefore, the cost of canned soda is 75¢ ÷ 12 = 6.25¢ per ounce. This is consistent with our solution. This does not mean our solution is correct, but it does indicate that it is at least reasonable. Why might soda from a cafeteria be more expensive per ounce than soda from a vending machine?

Is there an alternative way to obtain the solution? There are probably many, but one possibility is to get a measuring cup, pour the soft drink into it, and read the number of ounces. Name an advantage and a disadvantage of this method.

Use the four-step solution process for the following problems.

1. A cup dispenser next to a water cooler holds cups that have the shape of a right circular cone. The height of the cone is 4 in. and the radius of the circular top is 1.5 in. How many ounces of water can the cup hold?

2. Soft drink manufacturers do research into the preferences of consumers with regard to the look and feel and size of a soft drink can. Suppose that a manufacturer has determined that people want to have their hand reach around approximately 75% of the can. If this preference is to be achieved, how tall should the can be if it contains 12 oz of fluid? Assume the can is a right circular cylinder.

Projects & Group Activities

Water Displacement   When an object is placed in water, the object displaces an amount of water that is equal to the volume of the object.

A sphere with a diameter of 4 in. is placed in a rectangular tank of water that is 6 in. long and 5 in. wide. How much does the water level rise? Round to the nearest hundredth.

$$V = \frac{4}{3}\pi r^3$$ • Use the formula for the volume of a sphere.

$$V = \frac{4}{3}\pi(2^3) = \frac{32}{3}\pi$$ • $r = \frac{1}{2}d = \frac{1}{2}(4) = 2$

Let x represent the amount of the rise in water level. The volume of the sphere will equal the volume displaced by the water. As shown at the left, this volume is the rectangular solid with width 5 in., length 6 in., and height x in.

$$V = LWH$$ • Use the formula for the volume of a rectangular solid.

$$\frac{32}{3}\pi = (6)(5)x$$ • Substitute $\frac{32}{3}\pi$ for V, 5 for W, and 6 for L.

$$\frac{32}{90}\pi = x$$

• **The exact height that the water will rise is $\frac{32}{90}\pi$ in.**

$$1.12 \approx x$$

• **Use a calculator to find an approximation.**

The water will rise approximately 1.12 in.

Figure 1   **Figure 2**   **Figure 3**

1. A cylinder with a 2-centimeter radius and a height of 10 cm is submerged in a tank of water that is 20 cm wide and 30 cm long (see Figure 1). How much does the water level rise? Round to the nearest hundredth.

2. A sphere with a radius of 6 in. is placed in a rectangular tank of water that is 16 in. wide and 20 in. long (see Figure 2). The sphere displaces water until two-thirds of the sphere is submerged. How much does the water level rise? Round to the nearest hundredth.

3. A chemist wants to know the density of a statue that weighs 15 lb. The statue is placed in a rectangular tank of water that is 12 in. long and 12 in. wide (see Figure 3). The water level rises 0.42 in. Find the density of the statue. Round to the nearest hundredth. (*Hint:* density = weight ÷ volume)

Chapter 1 Summary

Key Words   *Examples*

The **integers** are ..., −4, −3, −2, −1, 0, 1, 2, 3, ... [1.1.1, p. 3][1]

The **negative integers** are the integers ..., −4, −3, −2, −1. The **positive integers** are the integers 1, 2, 3, 4, ... The positive integers are also called the **natural numbers**. [1.1.1, p. 3]

---

[1]The numbers in brackets are a reference to the objective where the Key Word or Essential Rule or Procedure is first introduced. For example, the reference [1.1.1] stands for Chapter 1, Section 1, Objective 1. This notation will be used in all Chapter Summaries throughout the text.

The positive integers and zero are called the **whole numbers**. [1.1.1, p. 3]	0, 1, 2, 3, 4, …
A **rational number** is a number of the form $\frac{p}{q}$, where p and q are integers and q is not equal to zero. [1.1.1, p. 3]	$\frac{5}{6}, \frac{-3}{4}$, and $\frac{6}{1}$ are rational numbers.
An **irrational number** is a number whose decimal representation never terminates or repeats. [1.1.1, p. 4]	$\sqrt{3}, \pi$, and 0.21211211121111… are irrational numbers.
The rational numbers and the irrational numbers taken together are called the **real numbers**. [1.1.1, p. 4]	$-3, \sqrt{5}, \pi, \frac{-6}{7}$, and 0.232332333… are real numbers.
The **additive inverse**, or **opposite**, of a number is the same distance from zero on the number line, but on the opposite side. [1.1.1, p. 5]	The additive inverse of -3 is 3.
The **absolute value** of a number is the measure of its distance from zero on the number line. [1.1.1, p. 5]	$\lvert 4 \rvert = 4 \qquad \lvert -3 \rvert = 3 \qquad -\lvert -6 \rvert = -6$
A **set** is a collection of objects. The objects in the set are called the **elements** of the set. The **roster method** of writing a set encloses a list of the elements of the set in braces. [1.1.1, 1.1.2, pp. 2, 6]	The set $A = \{4, 5, 6, 7\}$ contains the elements 4, 5, 6, and 7.
The **empty set**, or **null set**, is the set that contains no elements. [1.1.2, p. 6]	The empty set is written as $\varnothing$ or { }.
A **finite set** is a set in which the elements can be counted. [1.1.2, p. 6]	$A = \{1, 2, 3, 4\}$
An **infinite set** is a set in which it is impossible to list all the elements. [1.1.2, p. 6]	$A = \{1, 2, 3, 4, …\}$
The **union** of two sets, written $A \cup B$, is the set that contains all the elements of A and all the elements of B. The elements that are in both set A and set B are listed only once. [1.1.2, p. 7]	If $A = \{2, 3, 4\}$ and $B = \{4, 5, 6\}$, then $A \cup B = \{2, 3, 4, 5, 6\}$.
The **intersection** of two sets, written $A \cap B$, is the set that contains the elements that are common to both A and B. [1.1.2, p. 7]	If $A = \{2, 3, 4\}$ and $B = \{4, 5, 6\}$, then $A \cap B = \{4\}$.
Interval notation is an alternative method of representing a set. An interval is **closed** if it includes both **endpoints**. An interval is **open** if it does not include either endpoint. An interval is **half-open** if one endpoint is included and the other endpoint is not included. A bracket is used to indicate an endpoint is included, and a parenthesis is used to indicate an endpoint is excluded. [1.1.2, p. 9]	Closed interval ⟵—[————]—⟶ Open interval ⟵—(————)—⟶ Half-open interval ⟵—[————)—⟶

The expression a^n is in **exponential form**, where a is the **base** and n is the **exponent**. [1.2.3, p. 22]

5^3 is in exponential form.

A **complex fraction** is a fraction whose numerator or denominator (or both) contains one or more fractions. [1.2.4, p. 24]

$\dfrac{\frac{3}{5} - 2}{\frac{4}{5}}$ is a complex fraction.

The **multiplicative inverse** of a number is the reciprocal of the number. [1.3.1, p. 33]

The multiplicative inverse of $\frac{3}{5}$ is $\frac{5}{3}$.

A **variable expression** is an expression that contains one or more variables. The **terms** of a variable expression are the addends of the expression. [1.3.2, pp. 33–34]

$3xy + x^2 - 4$ is a variable expression. $3xy$, x^2, and -4 are the terms of the expression.

A **variable term** is composed of a **numerical coefficient** and a **variable part**. [1.3.2, p. 34]

The numerical coefficient of $3xy$ is 3, and the variable part is xy.

Essential Rules and Procedures

To add two numbers with the same sign, add the absolute values of the two numbers and attach the sign of the numbers. [1.2.1, p. 16]

$-5 + (-6) = -11$
$4 + 2 = 6$

To add two numbers with different signs, find the difference between the absolute values of the two numbers and attach the sign of the number with the larger absolute value. [1.2.1, p. 16]

$-4 + 8 = 4$
$6 + (-11) = -5$

To subtract b from a, add the opposite of b to a. [1.2.1, p. 16]

$-4 - (-5) = -4 + 5 = 1$
$5 - 12 = 5 + (-12) = -7$

The product of two numbers with the same sign is positive.
The product of two numbers with different signs is negative. [1.2.1, p. 16]

$(4)(5) = 20 \qquad (-3)(-7) = 21$
$(-4)(2) = -8 \qquad (5)(-4) = -20$

The quotient of two numbers with the same sign is positive.
The quotient of two numbers with different signs is negative. [1.2.1, p. 17]

$8 \div 2 = 4 \qquad (-20) \div (-5) = 4$
$(-10) \div 5 = -2 \qquad 15 \div (-3) = -5$

Order of Operations Agreement [1.2.4, p. 23]
Step 1 Perform operations inside grouping symbols.
Step 2 Simplify exponential expressions.
Step 3 Do multiplication and division as they occur from left to right.
Step 4 Do addition and subtraction as they occur from left to right.

$(5 - 2) + 9^2 \div 3$
$= 3 + 9^2 \div 3$
$= 3 + 81 \div 3$
$= 3 + 27$

$= 30$

Properties of the Real Numbers for Addition [1.3.1, pp. 32–33]
Commutative: $a + b = b + a$
Associative: $(a + b) + c = a + (b + c)$
Property of Zero: $a + 0 = 0 + a = 0$
Inverse Property: $a + (-a) = (-a) + a = 0$

$3 + 2 = 2 + 3$
$(4 + 5) + 9 = 4 + (5 + 9)$
$0 + 4 = 4$
$8 + (-8) = 0$

Properties of the Real Numbers for Multiplication [1.3.1, pp. 32–33]
Commutative: $a \cdot b = b \cdot a$
Associative: $(a \cdot b) \cdot c = a \cdot (b \cdot c)$
Property of zero: $a \cdot 0 = 0 \cdot a = 0$
Property of One: $a \cdot 1 = 1 \cdot a = a$
Inverse Property: $a \cdot \dfrac{1}{a} = \dfrac{1}{a} \cdot a = 1$

$3 \cdot 5 = 5 \cdot 3$
$(2 \cdot 3) \cdot 5 = 2 \cdot (3 \cdot 5)$
$7 \cdot 0 = 0$
$6 \cdot 1 = 6$
$3\left(\dfrac{1}{3}\right) = 1$

The Distributive Property $a(b + c) = ab + ac$ [1.3.1, p. 33]

$3(x + 5) = 3x + 3(5) = 3x + 15$

Chapter 1 Review Exercises

1. Find the additive inverse of $-\dfrac{3}{4}$.

2. Let $x \in \{-4, -2, 0, 2\}$. For what values of x is $x > -1$ true?

3. Let $p \in \{-4, 0, 7\}$. Evaluate $-|p|$ for each element of the set.

4. Use the roster method to write the set of integers between -3 and 4.

5. Use set-builder notation to write the set of real numbers less than -3.

6. Write $[-2, 3]$ in set-builder notation.

7. Find $A \cup B$ given $A = \{1, 3, 5, 7\}$ and $B = \{2, 4, 6, 8\}$.

8. Find $A \cap B$ given $A = \{0, 1, 2, 3\}$ and $B = \{2, 3, 4, 5\}$.

9. Graph: $[-3, \infty)$

10. Graph: $\{x \,|\, x < 1\}$

11. Graph: $\{x \,|\, x \le -3\} \cup \{x \,|\, x > 0\}$

12. Graph: $(-2, 4]$

13. Subtract: $-10 - (-3) - 8$

14. Divide: $-204 \div (-17)$

15. Simplify: $18 - |-12 + 8|$

16. Simplify: $-2 \cdot (4^2) \cdot (-3)^2$

17. Simplify: $-\dfrac{3}{8} + \dfrac{3}{5} - \dfrac{1}{6}$

18. Multiply: $\dfrac{3}{5}\left(-\dfrac{10}{21}\right)\left(-\dfrac{7}{15}\right)$

19. Divide: $-\dfrac{3}{8} \div \dfrac{3}{5}$

20. Simplify: $-4.07 + 2.3 - 1.07$

21. Divide: $-3.286 \div (-1.06)$

22. Simplify: $20 \div \dfrac{3^2 - 2^2}{3^2 + 2^2}$

23. Evaluate $2a^2 - \dfrac{3b}{a}$ when $a = -3$ and $b = 2$.

24. Evaluate $(a - 2b^2) \div (ab)$ when $a = 4$ and $b = -3$.

25. Use the Distributive Property to complete the statement.
$6x - 21y = ?(2x - 7y)$

26. Use the Commutative Property of Addition to complete the statement.
$3(x + y) = 3(? + x)$

27. Use the Commutative Property of Multiplication to complete the statement.
$(ab)14 = 14?$

28. Use the Associative Property of Addition to complete the statement.
$3 + (4 + y) = (3 + ?) + y$

29. Identify the property that justifies the statement.
$(-4) + 4 = 0$

30. Identify the property that justifies the statement.
$2(3x) = (2 \cdot 3)x$

31. Simplify: $-2(x - 3) + 4(2 - x)$

32. Simplify: $4y - 3[x - 2(3 - 2x) - 4y]$

33. Translate and simplify "four times the sum of a number and four."

34. Translate and simplify "eight more than twice the difference between a number and two."

35. **Integer Problem** The sum of two numbers is 40. Using x to represent the smaller of the two numbers, translate "the sum of twice the smaller number and five more than the larger number" into a variable expression. Then simplify.

36. **Integer Problem** The sum of two numbers is 9. Using x to represent the larger of the two numbers, translate "the difference between three more than twice the smaller number and one more than the larger number" into a variable expression. Then simplify.

37. **Geometry** The length of a rectangle is 3 ft less than three times the width. Express the length of the rectangle in terms of the width.

38. **Integer Problem** A second integer is 5 more than four times the first integer. Express the second integer in terms of the first integer.

Chapter 1 Test

1. Find the additive inverse of -12.

2. Let $x \in \{-5, 3, 7\}$. For which values of x is $-1 > x$ true?

3. Simplify: $2 - (-12) + 3 - 5$

4. Multiply: $(-2)(-3)(-5)$

5. Divide: $-180 \div 12$

6. Simplify: $|-3 - (-5)|$

7. Simplify: $-5^2 \cdot 4$

8. Simplify: $(-2)^3(-3)^2$

9. Simplify: $\dfrac{2}{3} - \dfrac{5}{12} + \dfrac{4}{9}$

10. Multiply: $\left(-\dfrac{2}{3}\right)\left(\dfrac{9}{15}\right)\left(\dfrac{10}{27}\right)$

11. Simplify: $4.27 - 6.98 + 1.3$

12. Divide: $-15.092 \div 3.08$

13. Simplify: $12 - 4\left(\dfrac{5^2 - 1}{3}\right) \div 16$

14. Simplify: $8 - 4(2 - 3)^2 \div 2$

15. Evaluate $(a - b)^2 \div (2b + 1)$ when $a = 2$ and $b = -3$.

16. Evaluate $\dfrac{b^2 - c^2}{a - 2c}$ when $a = 2$, $b = 3$, and $c = -1$.

17. Use the Commutative Property of Addition to complete the statement.
$(3 + 4) + 2 = (? + 3) + 2$

18. Identify the property that justifies the statement.
$-2(x + y) = -2x - 2y$

19. Simplify: $3x - 2(x - y) - 3(y - 4x)$

20. Simplify: $2x - 4[2 - 3(x + 4y) - 2]$

21. Translate and simplify "thirteen decreased by the product of three less than a number and nine."

22. Translate and simplify "one-third of the total of twelve times a number and twenty-seven."

23. Find $A \cup B$ given $A = \{1, 3, 5, 7\}$ and $B = \{2, 3, 4, 5\}$.

24. Find $A \cup B$ given $A = \{-2, -1, 0, 1, 2, 3\}$ and $B = \{-1, 0, 1\}$.

25. Find $A \cap B$ given $A = \{1, 3, 5, 7\}$ and $B = \{5, 7, 9, 11\}$.

26. Find $A \cap B$ given $A = \{-3, -2, -1, 0, 1, 2, 3\}$ and $B = \{-1, 0, 1\}$.

27. Graph: $(-\infty, -1]$

28. Graph: $(3, \infty)$

29. Graph: $\{x \,|\, x \le 3\} \cup \{x \,|\, x < -2\}$

30. Graph: $\{x \,|\, x < 3\} \cap \{x \,|\, x > -2\}$

CHAPTER

First-Degree Equations and Inequalities

 DVD SSM **Online Study Center**

Need help? For online student resources, such as section quizzes, visit the Online Study Center at college.hmco.com/info/aufmanndevmathhb.

Many salespeople, whether paid by the hour or offered an annual salary, can make more money by earning commissions on every sale. Commissions are calculated as a percent of total sales made, and are an incentive for salespeople to sell as much as they possibly can. Keeping track of how much extra money is earned through commissions is necessary for salespeople to budget their monthly earnings. In **Exercise 108 on page 108,** we use first-degree equations to calculate the amount of sales needed to reach specific income goals.

Prep Test

For Exercises 1 to 5, add, subtract, multiply, or divide.

1. $8 - 12$

2. $-9 + 3$

3. $\dfrac{-18}{-6}$

4. $-\dfrac{3}{4}\left(-\dfrac{4}{3}\right)$

5. $-\dfrac{5}{8}\left(\dfrac{4}{5}\right)$

For Exercises 6 to 9, simplify.

6. $3x - 5 + 7x$

7. $6(x - 2) + 3$

8. $n + (n + 2) + (n + 4)$

9. $0.08x + 0.05(400 - x)$

10. Twenty ounces of a snack mixture contains nuts and pretzels. Let n represent the number of ounces of nuts in the mixture. Express the number of ounces of pretzels in the mixture in terms of n.

2.1   Equations in One Variable

OBJECTIVE **1**

Solve equations using the Addition and Multiplication Properties of Equations

An **equation** expresses the equality of two mathematical expressions. The expressions can be either numerical or variable expressions.

$$\left.\begin{array}{l} 2 + 8 = 10 \\ x + 8 = 11 \\ x^2 + 2y = 7 \end{array}\right\} \text{Equations}$$

The equation at the right is a **conditional equation.** The equation is *true* if the variable is replaced by 3. The equation is *false* if the variable is replaced by 4.

$x + 2 = 5$ Conditional equation

$3 + 2 = 5$ A true equation

$4 + 2 = 5$ A false equation

The replacement values of the variable that will make an equation true are called the **roots,** or **solutions,** of the equation.

The solution of the equation $x + 2 = 5$ is 3.

The equation at the right is an **identity.** Any replacement for x will result in a true equation.

$x + 2 = x + 2$ Identity

The equation at the right has *no solution* because there is no number that equals itself plus 1. Any replacement value for x will result in a false equation.

$x = x + 1$ No solution

Each of the equations at the right is a **first-degree equation in one variable.** All variables have an exponent of 1.

$$x + 2 = 12$$
$$3y - 2 = 5y$$
$$3(a + 2) = 14a$$

First-degree equations

Solving an equation means finding a solution of the equation. The simplest equation to solve is an equation of the form **variable = constant,** because the constant is the solution.

If $x = 3$, then 3 is the solution of the equation because $3 = 3$ is a true equation.

In solving an equation, the goal is to rewrite the given equation in the form *variable = constant*. The Addition Property of Equations can be used to rewrite an equation in this form.

> ### The Addition Property of Equations
>
> If a, b, and c are algebraic expressions, then the equation $a = b$ has the same solutions as the equation $a + c = b + c$.

The Addition Property of Equations states that the same quantity can be added to each side of an equation without changing the solution of the equation. This property is used to remove a term from one side of the equation by adding the opposite of that term to each side of the equation.

Solve: $x - 3 = 7$

Add the opposite of the constant term -3 to each side of the equation and simplify. After simplifying, the equation is in the form *variable = constant*.

$$x - 3 = 7$$
$$x - 3 + 3 = 7 + 3$$
$$x + 0 = 10$$
$$x = 10$$

To check the solution, replace the variable with 10. Simplify the left side of the equation. Because $7 = 7$ is a true equation, 10 is a solution.

Check:
$$\frac{x - 3 = 7}{10 - 3 \mid 7}$$
$$7 = 7$$

The solution is 10.

Because subtraction is defined in terms of addition, the Addition Property of Equations enables us to subtract the same number from each side of the equation without changing the solution of the equation.

Solve: $x + \dfrac{7}{12} = \dfrac{1}{2}$

Add the opposite of the constant term $\dfrac{7}{12}$ to each side of the equation. This is equivalent to subtracting $\dfrac{7}{12}$ from each side of the equation.

$$x + \frac{7}{12} = \frac{1}{2}$$
$$x + \frac{7}{12} - \frac{7}{12} = \frac{1}{2} - \frac{7}{12}$$
$$x + 0 = \frac{6}{12} - \frac{7}{12}$$
$$x = -\frac{1}{12}$$

The solution is $-\dfrac{1}{12}$.

Take Note

The model of an equation as a balance scale applies.

Adding a weight to one side of the equation requires adding the same weight to the other side of the equation so that the pans remain in balance.

Take Note

Remember to check the solution.

$$\frac{x + \dfrac{7}{12} = \dfrac{1}{2}}{}$$
$$\frac{-\dfrac{1}{12} + \dfrac{7}{12} \mid \dfrac{1}{2}}{}$$
$$\frac{\dfrac{6}{12} \mid \dfrac{1}{2}}{}$$
$$\frac{1}{2} = \frac{1}{2}$$

The Multiplication Property of Equations can also be used to rewrite an equation in the form *variable = constant*.

> ## The Multiplication Property of Equations
>
> If a, b, and c are algebraic expressions, and $c \neq 0$, then the equation $a = b$ has the same solutions as the equation $ac = bc$.

The Multiplication Property of Equations states that we can multiply each side of an equation by the same nonzero number without changing the solution of the equation. This property is used to remove a coefficient from a variable term in an equation by multiplying each side of the equation by the reciprocal of the coefficient.

Take Note

You should always check your work by substituting your answer into the original equation and simplifying the resulting numerical expressions. If the left and right sides are equal, your answer is the solution of the equation.

Solve: $-\frac{3}{4}x = 12$

Multiply each side of the equation by $-\frac{4}{3}$, the reciprocal of $-\frac{3}{4}$. After simplifying, the equation is in the form *variable = constant*.

$$-\frac{3}{4}x = 12$$

$$\left(-\frac{4}{3}\right)\left(-\frac{3}{4}\right)x = \left(-\frac{4}{3}\right)12$$

$$1x = -16$$

$$x = -16$$

Check: $\qquad -\frac{3}{4}x = 12$

$$-\frac{3}{4}(-16) \;\bigg|\; 12$$

$$12 = 12$$

The solution is -16.

Because division is defined in terms of multiplication, the Multiplication Property of Equations enables us to divide each side of an equation by the same nonzero number without changing the solution of the equation.

Solve: $-5x = 9$

Multiplying each side of the equation by the reciprocal of -5 is equivalent to dividing each side of the equation by -5.

$$-5x = 9$$

$$\frac{-5x}{-5} = \frac{9}{-5}$$

$$1x = -\frac{9}{5}$$

$$x = -\frac{9}{5}$$

You should check the solution.   The solution is $-\frac{9}{5}$.

When using the Multiplication Property of Equations, it is usually easier to multiply each side of the equation by the reciprocal of the coefficient when the coefficient is a fraction. Divide each side of the equation by the coefficient when the coefficient is an integer or a decimal.

EXAMPLE 1   Solve: $-\dfrac{2}{7}x = \dfrac{4}{21}$

Solution
$$-\dfrac{2}{7}x = \dfrac{4}{21}$$

$$\left(-\dfrac{7}{2}\right)\left(-\dfrac{2}{7}x\right) = \left(-\dfrac{7}{2}\right)\left(\dfrac{4}{21}\right)$$ • **Multiply both sides of the equation by the reciprocal of $-\dfrac{2}{7}$. Then simplify.**

$$x = -\dfrac{2}{3}$$

The solution is $-\dfrac{2}{3}$.

PROBLEM 1   Solve: $-3x = -18$

Solution   See page S2.

In solving an equation, it is often necessary to apply both the Addition and the Multiplication Properties of Equations.

Solve: $6x - 8 = 3x + 7$

$$6x - 8 = 3x + 7$$

Subtract $3x$ from each side of the equation. Then simplify.

$$6x - 3x - 8 = 3x - 3x + 7$$
$$3x - 8 = 7$$

Add 8 to each side of the equation. Then simplify.

$$3x - 8 + 8 = 7 + 8$$
$$3x = 15$$

Divide each side of the equation by 3.

$$\dfrac{3x}{3} = \dfrac{15}{3}$$

Then simplify.

$$x = 5$$

You should check the solution.   The solution is 5.

EXAMPLE 2   Solve: $3x - 5 = x + 2 - 7x$

Solution
$$3x - 5 = x + 2 - 7x$$
$$3x - 5 = -6x + 2$$ • **Simplify the right side of the equation by combining like terms.**

$$3x + 6x - 5 = -6x + 6x + 2$$ • **Add $6x$ to each side of the equation.**
$$9x - 5 = 2$$

$$9x - 5 + 5 = 2 + 5$$ • **Add 5 to each side of the equation.**
$$9x = 7$$

$$\dfrac{9x}{9} = \dfrac{7}{9}$$ • **Divide each side of the equation by the coefficient 9.**

$$x = \frac{7}{9}$$

The solution is $\frac{7}{9}$.

PROBLEM 2   Solve: $6x - 5 - 3x = 14 - 5x$

■   **Solution**   See page S2.

OBJECTIVE **2**   ## Solve equations using the Distributive Property

When an equation contains parentheses, one of the steps in solving the equation requires the use of the Distributive Property.

■   Solve: $3(x - 2) + 3 = 2(6 - x)$

	$3(x - 2) + 3 = 2(6 - x)$
Use the Distributive Property to remove parentheses. Simplify.	$3x - 6 + 3 = 12 - 2x$
	$3x - 3 = 12 - 2x$
Add $2x$ to each side of the equation.	$5x - 3 = 12$
Add 3 to each side of the equation.	$5x = 15$
Divide each side of the equation by the coefficient 5.	$x = 3$
You should check the solution.	The solution is 3.

EXAMPLE 3   Solve: $5(2x - 7) + 2 = 3(4 - x) - 12$

Solution
$$5(2x - 7) + 2 = 3(4 - x) - 12$$
$$10x - 35 + 2 = 12 - 3x - 12$$ • Use the Distributive Property.
$$10x - 33 = -3x$$ • Simplify.
$$-33 = -13x$$ • Subtract 10x from each side of the equation.

$$\frac{33}{13} = x$$ • Divide each side of the equation by −13.

The solution is $\frac{33}{13}$.

PROBLEM 3   Solve: $6(5 - x) - 12 = 2x - 3(4 + x)$

■   **Solution**   See page S3.

To solve an equation that contains fractions, first **clear denominators** by multiplying each side of the equation by the least common multiple (LCM) of the denominators.

Solve: $\dfrac{x}{2} - \dfrac{7}{9} = \dfrac{x}{6} + \dfrac{2}{3}$

$$\dfrac{x}{2} - \dfrac{7}{9} = \dfrac{x}{6} + \dfrac{2}{3}$$

Multiply each side of the equation by 18, the LCM of 2, 9, 6, and 3.

$$18\left(\dfrac{x}{2} - \dfrac{7}{9}\right) = 18\left(\dfrac{x}{6} + \dfrac{2}{3}\right)$$

Use the Distributive Property to remove parentheses.

$$\dfrac{18x}{2} - \dfrac{18 \cdot 7}{9} = \dfrac{18x}{6} + \dfrac{18 \cdot 2}{3}$$
$$9x - 14 = 3x + 12$$

Subtract $3x$ from each side of the equation.

$$6x - 14 = 12$$

Add 14 to each side of the equation.

$$6x = 26$$

Divide each side of the equation by the coefficient 6.

$$x = \dfrac{13}{3}$$

You should check the solution.

The solution is $\dfrac{13}{3}$.

EXAMPLE 4   Solve: $\dfrac{3x - 2}{12} - \dfrac{x}{9} = \dfrac{x}{2}$

Solution

$$\dfrac{3x - 2}{12} - \dfrac{x}{9} = \dfrac{x}{2}$$

• The LCM of 12, 9, and 2 is 36.

$$36\left(\dfrac{3x - 2}{12} - \dfrac{x}{9}\right) = 36\left(\dfrac{x}{2}\right)$$

• Multiply each side of the equation by the LCM.

$$\dfrac{36(3x - 2)}{12} - \dfrac{36x}{9} = \dfrac{36x}{2}$$

• Use the Distributive Property.

$$3(3x - 2) - 4x = 18x$$
$$9x - 6 - 4x = 18x$$
$$5x - 6 = 18x$$
$$-6 = 13x$$
$$-\dfrac{6}{13} = x$$

• Simplify.

The solution is $-\dfrac{6}{13}$.

PROBLEM 4   Solve: $\dfrac{2x - 7}{3} - \dfrac{5x + 4}{5} = \dfrac{-x - 4}{30}$

Solution   See page S3.

OBJECTIVE 3   Application problems

Solving application problems is primarily a skill in translating sentences into equations and then solving the equations. An equation states that two mathematical expressions are equal. Therefore, to translate a sentence into an equation requires recognizing the words or phrases that mean *equals*. These phrases include "is," "is equal to," "amounts to," and "represents."

Once the sentence is translated into an equation, solve the equation by rewriting the equation in the form *variable = constant*.

An electrician works 34 h and uses $642 worth of materials repairing the wiring in a home. The electrician receives an hourly wage of $32. Find the total cost of repairing the wiring.

Strategy
To find the total cost of repairing the wiring, write and solve an equation using C to represent the total cost. The total cost is the sum of the cost of labor and the cost of materials.

Solution
$C = (34)(32) + 642$
$C = 1088 + 642$
$C = 1730$

The total cost of repairing the wiring is $1730.

EXAMPLE 5   The charges for a long-distance telephone call are $2.14 for the first three minutes and $.47 for each additional minute or fraction of a minute. If the charges for a long-distance call were $17.65, how many minutes did the phone call last?

Strategy   To find the length of the phone call in minutes, write and solve an equation using n to represent the total number of minutes of the call. Then $n - 3$ is the number of additional minutes after the first three minutes of the phone call. The fixed charge for the three minutes plus the charge for the additional minutes is the total cost of the phone call.

Solution
$$2.14 + 0.47(n - 3) = 17.65$$
$$2.14 + 0.47n - 1.41 = 17.65$$
$$0.47n + 0.73 = 17.65$$
$$0.47n = 16.92$$
$$n = 36$$

The phone call lasted 36 min.

PROBLEM 5   You are making a salary of $34,500 and receive an 8% raise for next year. Find your next year's salary.

Solution   See page S3.

2.1   Concept Review

Determine whether the following statements are always true, sometimes true, or never true.

1. $6x + 5$ is an equation.

2. A first-degree equation has no solution.

3. An equation expresses the equality between two variable expressions.

4. The equation $x - 3 = x - 3$ has no solution.

5. The equation $x = x - 4$ is an identity.

6. Zero is a solution of $5x = 2x$.

7. Suppose a, b, and c are real numbers and $a = b$. Then $a + c = b + c$.

8. Suppose a, b, and c are real numbers and $a = b$. Then $\dfrac{a}{c} = \dfrac{b}{c}$.

2.1   Exercises

1   Solve equations using the Addition and Multiplication Properties of Equations

1. How does an equation differ from an expression?

2. What is the solution of an equation?

3. What is the Addition Property of Equations and how is it used?

4. What is the Multiplication Property of Equations and how is it used?

5. Is 1 a solution of $7 - 3m = 4$?

6. Is 5 a solution of $4y - 5 = 3y$?

7. Is -2 a solution of $6x - 1 = 7x + 1$?

8. Is 3 a solution of $x^2 = 4x - 5$?

9. To solve the equation $a - 42 = 13$, use the Addition Property of Equations to add ___?___ to each side of the equation. The solution is ___?___.

10. To solve the equation $12 + x = 5$, ___?___ 12 from each side of the equation. The solution is ___?___.

11. To solve the equation $-\dfrac{2}{5}n = 8$, use the Multiplication Property of Equations to multiply each side of the equation by ___?___. The solution is ___?___.

12. To solve the equation $9 = 18b$, ___?___ each side of the equation by 18. The solution is ___?___.

Solve and check.

13. $x - 2 = 7$

14. $x - 8 = 4$

15. $a + 3 = -7$

16. $-12 = x - 3$

17. $3x = 12$

18. $8x = 4$

19. $\dfrac{2}{7} + x = \dfrac{17}{21}$

20. $x + \dfrac{2}{3} = \dfrac{5}{6}$

21. $\dfrac{5}{8} - y = \dfrac{3}{4}$

22. $\dfrac{2}{3}y = 5$

23. $\dfrac{3}{5}y = 12$

24. $\dfrac{3t}{8} = -15$

25. $\dfrac{3a}{7} = -21$

26. $-\dfrac{5}{8}x = \dfrac{4}{5}$

27. $-\dfrac{5}{12}y = \dfrac{7}{16}$

28. $-\dfrac{3}{4}x = -\dfrac{4}{7}$

29. $b - 14.72 = -18.45$

30. $b + 3.87 = -2.19$

31. $3x + 5x = 12$

32. $2x - 7x = 15$

33. $2x - 4 = 12$

34. $3x - 12 = 5x$

35. $4x + 2 = 4x$

36. $3m - 7 = 3m$

37. $2x + 2 = 3x + 5$

38. $7x - 9 = 3 - 4x$

39. $2 - 3t = 3t - 4$

40. $7 - 5t = 2t - 9$

41. $2a - 3a = 7 - 5a$

42. $3a - 5a = 8a + 4$

43. $\dfrac{5}{8}b - 3 = 12$

44. $\dfrac{1}{3} - 2b = 3$

45. $b + \dfrac{1}{5}b = 2$

46. $3x - 2x + 7 = 12 - 4x$

47. $2x - 9x + 3 = 6 - 5x$

48. $7 + 8y - 12 = 3y - 8 + 5y$

49. $2y - 4 + 8y = 7y - 8 + 3y$

50. $2x - 5 + 7x = 11 - 3x + 4x$

51. $9 + 4x - 12 = -3x + 5x + 8$

52. $3.24a + 7.14 = 5.34a$

53. $5.3y + 0.35 = 5.02y$

54. r is a positive number less than 1. Is the solution of the equation $\dfrac{10}{9} + x = r$ positive or negative?

55. a is a negative number less than -5. Is the solution of the equation $a = -5b$ less than or greater than 1?

2   Solve equations using the Distributive Property

56. Use the Distributive Property to remove the parentheses from the equation $9x - 3(5 - x) = 3(8x + 7)$: $9x -$ _____?_____ $+$ _____?_____ $=$ _____?_____ $+$ _____?_____ .

57. To clear denominators from the equation $\dfrac{x}{7} + \dfrac{1}{14} = \dfrac{1}{6}$, multiply each side of the equation by _____?_____, the least common multiple of the denominators 7, 14, and 6.

Solve and check.

58. $2x + 2(x + 1) = 10$

59. $2x + 3(x - 5) = 15$

60. $2(a - 3) = 2(4 - 2a)$

61. $5(2 - b) = -3(b - 3)$

62. $3 - 2(y - 3) = 4y - 7$

63. $3(y - 5) - 5y = 2y + 9$

64. $4(x - 2) + 2 = 4x - 2(2 - x)$

65. $2x - 3(x - 4) = 2(3 - 2x) + 2$

66. $2(2d + 1) - 3d = 5(3d - 2) + 4d$

67. $-4(7y - 1) + 5y = -2(3y + 4) - 3y$

68. $4[3 + 5(3 - x) + 2x] = 6 - 2x$

69. $2[4 + 2(5 - x) - 2x] = 4x - 7$

70. $2[b - (4b - 5)] = 3b + 4$

71. $-3[x + 4(x + 1)] = x + 4$

72. $4[a - (3a - 5)] = a - 7$

73. $5 - 6[2t - 2(t + 3)] = 8 - t$

74. $-3(x - 2) = 2[x - 4(x - 2) + x]$

75. $3[x - (2 - x) - 2x] = 3(4 - x)$

76. $\dfrac{2}{9}t - \dfrac{5}{6} = \dfrac{1}{12}t$

77. $\dfrac{3}{4}t - \dfrac{7}{12} = \dfrac{1}{6}$

78. $\dfrac{2}{3}x - \dfrac{5}{6}x - 3 = \dfrac{1}{2}x - 5$

79. $\dfrac{1}{2}x - \dfrac{3}{4}x + \dfrac{5}{8} = \dfrac{3}{2}x - \dfrac{5}{2}$

80. $\dfrac{3x - 2}{4} - 3x = 12$

81. $\dfrac{2a - 9}{5} + 3 = 2a$

82. $\dfrac{x - 2}{4} - \dfrac{x + 5}{6} = \dfrac{5x - 2}{9}$

83. $\dfrac{2x - 1}{4} + \dfrac{3x + 4}{8} = \dfrac{1 - 4x}{12}$

84. $\dfrac{2}{3}(15 - 6a) = \dfrac{5}{6}(12a + 18)$

85. $\dfrac{1}{5}(20x + 30) = \dfrac{1}{3}(6x + 36)$

86. $\dfrac{1}{3}(x - 7) + 5 = 6x + 4$

87. $2(y - 4) + 8 = \dfrac{1}{2}(6y + 20)$

88. $\dfrac{7}{8}x - \dfrac{1}{4} = \dfrac{3}{4}x - \dfrac{1}{2}$

89. $\dfrac{1}{2}x - \dfrac{3}{5} = \dfrac{2}{5}x + \dfrac{1}{2}$

90. $-4.2(p + 3.4) = 11.13$

91. $-1.6(b - 2.35) = -11.28$

92. $0, 11x + 0.04(700 - x) = 0.06(700)$

93. $x + 0.06(60) = 0.20(x + 20)$

94. How many times will you uses the Distributive Property to remove grouping symbols as you solve the equation $-3[5 - 4(x - 2)] = 5(x - 5)$?

95. Which of the following equations is equivalent to the equation in Exercise 94?

a. $-15 + 12(x - 2) = 5x - 25$ **b.** $-3[x - 2] = 5(x - 5)$
c. $-3[5 - 4x - 8] = 5x - 25$

3   Application problems

96. When a sentence is translated into an equation, the word "is" translates into the _____?_____ sign.

97. Ten friends go to a restaurant. Some people in the group order the all-you-can-eat buffet, while the rest of the group order the soup-and-sandwich combo. If 2 people order the buffet, then the number of people who order the soup-and-sandwich combo is ___?___. If 7 people order the buffet, then the number of people who order the soup-and-sandwich combo is ___?___. If n people order the buffet, then an expression that represents the number of people who order the soup-and-sandwich combo is ___?___.

98. Temperature The Fahrenheit temperature is 59°. This is 32° more than $\frac{9}{5}$ of the Celsius temperature. Find the Celsius temperature.

99. Consumerism A local feed store sells a 100-pound bag of feed for $10.90. If a customer buys more than one bag, each additional bag costs $10.50. A customer bought $84.40 worth of feed. How many 100-pound bags of feed did this customer purchase?

100. Consumerism A Chinese restaurant charges $11.95 for the adult buffet and $7.25 for the children's buffet. One family's bill came to $79.35. If there were three adults in the family, how many children were there?

101. Labor The repair bill on your car is $316.55. The charge for parts was $148.55. A mechanic worked on your car for 4 h. What was the charge per hour for labor?

102. Paychecks An elementary school teacher has 26.8% of his gross biweekly paycheck deducted to cover union dues, insurance, and taxes. The biweekly pay is $1620.00. Find the teacher's take-home pay.

103. Wages A machine shop employee earned $642 last week. She worked 40 h on the line at her standard rate and 9 h at a time-and-a-half rate. Find her regular hourly rate.

104. Consumerism The Showcase Cinema of Lawrence charges $7.75 for an adult ticket and $4.75 for a child's ticket for all shows after 6:00 P.M. If a family of six pays $34.50 to get into an evening show, how many adult tickets and how many children's tickets did the family purchase?

105. Consumerism A group of 12 fraternity brothers decided to go to a Boston Red Sox game at Fenway Park. They were unable to get seats together. Some of them sat in the $27.00 outfield grandstand seats. The others sat in the $45.00 right field box seats. How many of each type of ticket were purchased if the total price of the tickets was $414.00?

106. Consumerism The admission charge for a family at a city zoo is $7.50 for the first person and $4.25 for each additional member of the family. How many people are in a family that is charged $28.75 for admission?

107. Consumerism A family of seven bought tickets for the afternoon show of a play. Not all the members of the family could sit together. Some were in the mezzanine ($50.00) and some were in the balcony ($35.00). The total cost of the tickets was $275.00. Find the number of mezzanine tickets that were purchased.

2.1 Applying Concepts

Solve.

108. $8 \div \dfrac{1}{x} = -3$ **109.** $\dfrac{1}{\dfrac{1}{y}} = -9$ **110.** $\dfrac{6}{\dfrac{7}{a}} = -18$ **111.** $\dfrac{10}{\dfrac{3}{x}} - 5 = 4x$

Solve. If the equation has no solution, write "no solution."

112. $3[4(y + 2) - (y + 5)] = 3(3y + 1)$ **113.** $2[3(x + 4) - 2(x + 1)] = 5x + 3(1 - x)$

114. $\dfrac{4(x - 5) - (x + 1)}{3} = x - 7$ **115.** $\dfrac{4[(x - 3) + 2(1 - x)]}{5} = x + 1$

116. $2584 \div x = 54\dfrac{46}{x}$ **117.** $3(2x + 2) - 4(x - 3) = 2(x + 9)$

2.2 Coin, Stamp, and Integer Problems

OBJECTIVE **1**   Coin and stamp problems

In solving problems dealing with coins and stamps of different values, it is necessary to represent the value of the coins or stamps in the same unit of money. The unit of money is frequently cents. For example,

The value of five 8¢ stamps is $5 \cdot 8$, or 40, cents.
The value of four 20¢ stamps is $4 \cdot 20$, or 80, cents.
The value of n 10¢ stamps is $n \cdot 10$, or $10n$, cents.

Solve: A collection of stamps consists of 5¢, 13¢, and 18¢ stamps. The number of 13¢ stamps is two more than three times the number of 5¢ stamps. The number of 18¢ stamps is five less than the number of 13¢ stamps. The total value of all the stamps is $1.68. Find the number of 18¢ stamps.

> **STRATEGY**   for solving a stamp problem
>
> ▶ For each denomination of stamp, write a numerical or variable expression for the number of stamps, the value of the stamp, and the total value of the stamps in cents. The results can be recorded in a table.

The number of 5¢ stamps: x
The number of 13¢ stamps: $3x + 2$
The number of 18¢ stamps: $(3x + 2) - 5 = 3x - 3$

	Number of stamps	·	Value of stamp in cents	=	Total value in cents
5¢ stamp	x	·	5	=	$5x$
13¢ stamp	$3x + 2$	·	13	=	$13(3x + 2)$
18¢ stamp	$3x - 3$	·	18	=	$18(3x - 3)$

▶ Determine the relationship among the total values of the stamps. Use the fact that the sum of the total values of each denomination of stamp is equal to the total value of all the stamps.

The sum of the total values of each denomination of stamp is equal to the total value of all the stamps (168 cents).

$$5x + 13(3x + 2) + 18(3x - 3) = 168$$
$$5x + 39x + 26 + 54x - 54 = 168$$
$$98x - 28 = 168$$
$$98x = 196$$
$$x = 2$$

The number of 18¢ stamps is $3x - 3$. Replace x by 2 and evaluate.

$$3x - 3 = 3(2) - 3 = 3$$

There are three 18¢ stamps in the collection.

Some of the problems in Section 4 of the chapter "Review of Real Numbers" involved using one variable to describe two numbers whose sum was known. For example, given that the sum of two numbers is 12, we let one of the two numbers be x. Then the other number is $12 - x$. Note that the sum of these two numbers, $x + 12 - x$, equals 12.

In Example 1 below, we are told that there are only nickels and dimes in a coin bank and that there is a total of twenty-two coins. This means that the sum of the number of nickels and the number of dimes is 22. Let the number of nickels be x. Then the number of dimes is $22 - x$. (If you let the number of dimes be x and the number of nickels be $22 - x$, the solution to the problem will be the same.)

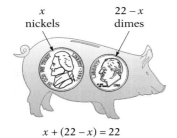

x nickels $22 - x$ dimes

$x + (22 - x) = 22$

EXAMPLE 1   A coin bank contains $1.80 in nickels and dimes. In all, there are twenty-two coins in the bank. Find the number of nickels and the number of dimes in the bank.

Strategy   ▶ Number of nickels: x
Number of dimes: $22 - x$

	Number	Value	Total value
Nickel	x	5	$5x$
Dime	$22 - x$	10	$10(22 - x)$

▶ The sum of the total values of each denomination of coin equals the total value of all the coins (180 cents).

Solution

$5x + 10(22 - x) = 180$
$5x + 220 - 10x = 180$
$-5x + 220 = 180$
$-5x = -40$
$x = 8$ • **There are 8 nickels in the bank.**
$22 - x = 22 - 8 = 14$ • **Substitute the value of x into the variable expression for the number of dimes.**

The bank contains 8 nickels and 14 dimes.

PROBLEM 1   A collection of stamps contains 3¢, 10¢, and 15¢ stamps. The number of 10¢ stamps is two more than twice the number of 3¢ stamps. There are three times as many 15¢ stamps as there are 3¢ stamps. The total value of the stamps is $1.56. Find the number of 15¢ stamps.

Solution   See page S3.

OBJECTIVE **2**   **Integer problems**

Recall that an **even integer** is an integer that is divisible by 2. An **odd integer** is an integer that is not divisible by 2.

Consecutive integers are integers that follow one another in order. Examples of consecutive integers are shown at the right.

8, 9, 10
$-3, -2, -1$
$n, n + 1, n + 2$, where n is an integer

Examples of **consecutive even integers** are shown at the right.

16, 18, 20
$-6, -4, -2$
$n, n + 2, n + 4$, where n is an even integer

Examples of **consecutive odd integers** are shown at the right.

11, 13, 15
$-23, -21, -19$
$n, n + 2, n + 4$, where n is an odd integer

Solve: The sum of three consecutive even integers is seventy-eight. Find the integers.

STRATEGY   **for solving an integer problem**

▶ Let a variable represent one of the integers. Express each of the other integers in terms of that variable. Remember that for consecutive integer problems, consecutive integers will differ by 1. Consecutive even or consecutive odd integers will differ by 2.

Represent three consecutive even integers.

First even integer: n
Second even integer: $n + 2$
Third even integer: $n + 4$

▶ Determine the relationship among the integers.

The sum of the three even integers is 78.

$$n + (n + 2) + (n + 4) = 78$$
$$3n + 6 = 78$$
$$3n = 72$$
$$n = 24$$

$$n + 2 = 24 + 2 = 26$$
$$n + 4 = 24 + 4 = 28$$

The three consecutive even integers are 24, 26, and 28.

EXAMPLE 2 Five times the first of three consecutive even integers is five more than the product of four and the third integer. Find the integers.

Strategy ▶ First even integer: n
Second even integer: $n + 2$
Third even integer: $n + 4$

▶ Five times the first integer equals five more than the product of four and the third integer.

Solution $5n = 4(n + 4) + 5$
$5n = 4n + 16 + 5$
$5n = 4n + 21$
$n = 21$

Because 21 is not an even integer, there is no solution.

PROBLEM 2 The sum of three numbers is eighty-one. The second number is twice the first number, and the third number is three less than four times the first number. Find the numbers.

Solution See page S3.

2.2 Concept Review

Determine whether the following statements are always true, sometimes true, or never true.

1. In solving coin problems, we find the total value of all the coins of one type by multiplying the value of one coin by the number of coins.

2. The expressions n and $n + 2$ represent two consecutive odd integers.

3. The expression $2n + 1$, where n is an integer, represents an odd integer.

4. If the sum of two numbers is n and one of the numbers is x, the other number is $x - n$.

5. Three consecutive odd integers are given by $n + 1$, $n + 3$, and $n + 5$.

2.2 Exercises

1 Coin and stamp problems

1. A bank contains 35 coins in nickels and quarters. Let n represent the number of nickels. Complete the following table.

Coin	Number of coins	·	Value of coin in cents	=	Total value in cents
Nickel	n	·	?	=	?
Quarter	?	·	?	=	?

2. The total value of the 35 coins in Exercise 1 is $4.25. The total value of the coins in cents is ____?____. Use this information and the information in the table in Exercise 1 to write an equation that can be solved to find the number of nickels in the bank: ____?____ + ____?____ = ____?____.

3. **a.** How many nickels are in d dollars?
 b. How many dimes are in d dollars?
 c. How many quarters are in d dollars?

4. **a.** How many cents are n 39¢ stamps and m 21¢ stamps worth?
 b. How many dollars are n 39¢ and m 21¢ stamps worth?

5. A collection of 56 coins has a value of $4.00. The collection contains only nickels and dimes. Find the number of dimes in the collection.

6. A collection of 22 coins has a value of $4.45. The collection contains dimes and quarters. Find the number of quarters in the collection.

7. A cashier has $730 in twenty-dollar bills and five-dollar bills. In all, the cashier has 68 bills. How many twenty-dollar bills does the cashier have?

8. In conducting its daily business, a department store uses twice as many five-dollar bills as ten-dollar bills. $2500 was obtained in five- and ten-dollar bills for the day's business. How many five-dollar bills were obtained?

9. A stamp collector has some 15¢ stamps and some 20¢ stamps. The number of 15¢ stamps is eight less than three times the number of 20¢ stamps. The total value is $4. Find the number of each type of stamp in the collection.

Frank Lloyd Wright 1867-1959 Fallingwater Mill Run PA
Architecture USA 20c

10. An office has some 20¢ stamps and some 28¢ stamps. Altogether the office has 140 stamps for a total value of $31.20. How many of each type of stamp does the office have?

11. A coin bank contains 25 coins in nickels, dimes, and quarters. There are four times as many dimes as quarters. The value of the coins is $2.05. How many dimes are in the bank?

12. A coin collection contains nickels, dimes, and quarters. There are twice as many dimes as quarters and seven more nickels than dimes. The total value of all the coins is $3.10. How many quarters are in the collection?

13. A stamp collection consists of 3¢, 8¢, and 13¢ stamps. The number of 8¢ stamps is three less than twice the number of 3¢ stamps. The number of 13¢ stamps is twice the number of 8¢ stamps. The total value of all the stamps is $2.53. Find the number of 3¢ stamps in the collection.

14. An account executive bought 300 stamps for $73.80. The purchase included 15¢ stamps, 20¢ stamps, and 40¢ stamps. The number of 20¢ stamps is four times the number of 15¢ stamps. How many 40¢ stamps were purchased?

15. A stamp collector has 8¢, 11¢, and 18¢ stamps. The collector has twice as many 8¢ stamps as 18¢ stamps. There are three more 11¢ than 18¢ stamps. The total value of the stamps in the collection is $3.48. Find the number of 18¢ stamps in the collection.

16. A stamp collection consists of 3¢, 12¢, and 15¢ stamps. The number of 3¢ stamps is five times the number of 12¢ stamps. The number of 15¢ stamps is four less than the number of 12¢ stamps. The total value of the stamps in the collection is $3.18. Find the number of 15¢ stamps in the collection.

2 Integer problems

17. Integers that follow one another in order are called ___?___ integers.

18. Two consecutive integers differ by ___?___. Two consecutive even integers differ by ___?___. Two consecutive odd integers differ by ___?___.

19. Explain how to represent three consecutive integers using only one variable.

20. Explain why both consecutive even integers and consecutive odd integers can be represented algebraically as $n, n + 2, n + 4, \ldots$.

21. The sum of two integers is ten. Three times the larger integer is three less than eight times the smaller integer. Find the integers.

22. The sum of two integers is thirty. Eight times the smaller integer is six more than five times the larger integer. Find the integers.

23. One integer is eight less than another integer. The sum of the two integers is fifty. Find the integers.

24. One integer is four more than another integer. The sum of the integers is twenty-six. Find the integers.

25. The sum of three integers is one hundred twenty-three. The second number is two more than twice the first number. The third number is five less than the product of three and the first number. Find the three numbers.

26. The sum of three numbers is forty-two. The second number is twice the first number, and the third number is three less than the second number. Find the three numbers.

27. The sum of three consecutive integers is negative fifty-seven. Find the integers.

28. The sum of three consecutive integers is one hundred twenty-nine. Find the integers.

29. Five times the smallest of three consecutive odd integers is ten more than twice the largest. Find the integers.

30. Find three consecutive even integers such that twice the sum of the first and third integers is twenty-one more than the second integer.

31. Find three consecutive odd integers such that three times the middle integer is seven more than the sum of the first and third integers.

32. Find three consecutive even integers such that four times the sum of the first and third integers is twenty less than six times the middle integer.

33. Which of the following could *not* be used to represent three consecutive odd integers?
a. $n + 1, n + 3, n + 5$ **b.** $n - 2, n, n + 2$
c. $n + 2, n + 4, n + 6$ **d.** $n, n + 3, n + 5$

34. True or false?
  a. The sum of three consecutive odd integers is odd.
  b. The sum of four consecutive integers is odd.
  c. The sum of four consecutive odd integers is odd.
  d. The sum of three consecutive even integers is even.

2.2   Applying Concepts

35. Coin Problem A coin bank contains only nickels and dimes. The number of dimes in the bank is two less than twice the number of nickels. There are 52 coins in the bank. How much money is in the bank?

36. Integer Problem Four times the first of three consecutive odd integers is five less than the product of three and the third integer. Find the integers.

37. Stamp Problem A collection of stamps consists of 3¢ stamps, 5¢ stamps, and 7¢ stamps. There are six more 3¢ stamps than 5¢ stamps and two more 7¢ stamps than 3¢ stamps. The total value of the stamps is $1.94. How many 3¢ stamps are in the collection?

38. Integer Problem The sum of four consecutive even integers is 100. What is the sum of the smallest and the largest of the four integers?

39. Integer Problem The sum of four consecutive odd integers is −64. What is the sum of the smallest and the largest of the four integers?

40. Integer Problem Find three consecutive odd integers such that the product of the second and third minus the product of the first and second is 42.

41. Integer Problem The sum of the digits of a three-digit number is 6. The tens digit is one less than the units digit, and the number is 12 more than 100 times the hundreds digit. Find the number.

2.3   Value Mixture and Motion Problems

OBJECTIVE 1   Value mixture problems

A **value mixture problem** involves combining two ingredients that have different prices into a single blend. For example, a coffee manufacturer may blend two types of coffee into a single blend.

A solution of a value mixture problem is based on the equation $AC = V$, where A is the amount of the ingredient, C is the cost per unit of the ingredient, and V is the value of the ingredient.

The value of 12 lb of coffee costing $5.25 per pound is

$$V = AC$$
$$V = 12(\$5.25)$$
$$V = \$63$$

Solve: How many pounds of peanuts that cost $2.25 per pound must be mixed with 40 lb of cashews that cost $6.00 per pound to make a mixture that costs $3.50 per pound?

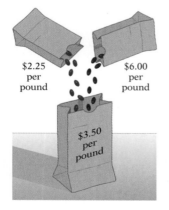

$2.25 per pound $6.00 per pound

$3.50 per pound

> **STRATEGY   for solving a value mixture problem**
>
> ▶ For each ingredient in the mixture, write a numerical or variable expression for the amount of the ingredient used, the unit cost of the ingredient, and the value of the amount used. For the mixture, write a numerical or variable expression for the amount, the unit cost of the mixture, and the value of the amount. The results can be recorded in a table.

Amount of peanuts: x

	Amount, A	·	Unit cost, C	=	Value, V
Peanuts	x	·	2.25	=	$2.25x$
Cashews	40	·	6.00	=	$6.00(40)$
Mixture	$x + 40$	·	3.50	=	$3.50(x + 40)$

▶ Determine how the values of the individual ingredients are related. Use the fact that the sum of the values of these ingredients is equal to the value of the mixture.

The sum of the values of the peanuts and the cashews is equal to the value of the mixture.

$$2.25x + 6.00(40) = 3.50(x + 40)$$
$$2.25x + 240 = 3.50x + 140$$
$$-1.25x + 240 = 140$$
$$-1.25x = -100$$
$$x = 80$$

The mixture must contain 80 lb of peanuts.

EXAMPLE 1   How many ounces of a gold alloy that costs $320 an ounce must be mixed with 100 oz of an alloy that costs $100 an ounce to make a mixture that costs $160 an ounce?

Strategy   ▶ Ounces of the $320 gold alloy: x

	Amount	Cost	Value
$320 alloy	x	320	$320x$
$100 alloy	100	100	$100(100)$
Mixture	$x + 100$	160	$160(x + 100)$

▶ The sum of the values before mixing equals the value after mixing.

Solution $$320x + 100(100) = 160(x + 100)$$
$$320x + 10,000 = 160x + 16,000$$
$$160x + 10,000 = 16,000$$
$$160x = 6000$$
$$x = 37.5$$

The mixture must contain 37.5 oz of the $320 gold alloy.

PROBLEM 1   A butcher combined hamburger that costs $4.00 per pound with hamburger that costs $2.80 per pound. How many pounds of each were used to make a 75-pound mixture that costs $3.20 per pound?

Solution   See page S3.

OBJECTIVE **2**   ## Uniform motion problems

Any object that travels at a constant speed in a straight line is said to be in *uniform motion*. **Uniform motion** means that the speed and direction of an object do not change. For instance, a train traveling at a constant speed of 50 mph on a straight track is in uniform motion.

The solution of a uniform motion problem is based on the equation $d = rt$, where d is the distance traveled, r is the rate of travel, and t is the time spent traveling. For instance, suppose a train travels for 2 h at an average speed of 45 mph. Because the time (2 h) and the rate (45 mph) are known, we can find the distance traveled by solving the equation $d = rt$ for d.

$$d = rt$$
$$d = 45(2) \qquad \bullet\, r = 45, t = 2$$
$$d = 90$$

The train travels a distance of 90 mi.

■   A chef leaves a restaurant and drives to his home, which is 16 mi away. If it takes him 20 min to get home, what is the chef's average rate of speed?

Because the answer must be in miles per *hour* and the given time is *minutes*, convert 20 min to $\frac{1}{3}$ h.

<table>
<tr><td>

Take Note

$20 \text{ min} = \dfrac{20}{60}\text{h}$

$= \dfrac{1}{3}\text{h}$

</td></tr>
</table>

To find the rate of speed, solve the equation $d = rt$ for r using $d = 16$ and $t = \frac{1}{3}$.

$$d = rt$$
$$16 = r\left(\frac{1}{3}\right)$$
$$16 = \frac{1}{3}r$$
$$(3)16 = (3)\frac{1}{3}r$$
$$48 = r$$

The average rate of speed is 48 mph.

Take Note

The abbreviation ft/s means feet per second.

If two objects are moving in opposite directions, then the rate at which the distance between them is increasing is the sum of the speeds of the two objects. For instance, in the diagram at the right, two joggers start from the same point and run in opposite directions. The distance between them is changing at a rate of 21 ft/s.

Similarly, if two objects are moving toward each other, the distance between them is decreasing at a rate that is equal to the sum of the speeds. The rate at which the two cyclists at the right are approaching one another is 35 mph.

9 ft/s   12 ft/s

9 ft/s + 12 ft/s = 21 ft/s

15 mph   20 mph

35 mph

■ Two cars start from the same point and move in opposite directions. The car moving west is traveling 50 mph, and the car moving east is traveling 65 mph. In how many hours will the cars be 230 mi apart?

The cars are moving in opposite directions, so the rate at which the distance between them is changing is the sum of the rates of the cars. Thus $r = 115$.

$$50 \text{ mph} + 65 \text{ mph} = 115 \text{ mph}$$

The distance is 230 mi. To find the time, solve $d = rt$ for t.

$$d = rt$$
$$230 = 115t$$
$$\frac{230}{115} = \frac{115t}{115}$$
$$2 = t$$

The time is 2 h.

Point of Interest

The jet stream that generally flows from west to east across the United States affects the time it takes a plane to fly from Los Angeles to New York. For instance, on a typical day, the flying time from New York City to Los Angeles is about 40 min longer than the trip from Los Angeles to New York City.

The typical cruising speed of a Boeing 777 jet is 525 mph. However, wind affects the speed of the plane. For example, when a plane is flying from California to New York, the wind is usually in the direction of the plane's flight, thereby increasing the effective speed of the plane. If the speed of the wind is 50 mph, then the effective speed of the plane is the sum of the plane's speed and the wind's speed: 525 mph + 50 mph = 575 mph.

If the plane is traveling from New York to California, the wind is generally in the opposite direction of the plane's flight, so it decreases the speed of the plane. If the speed of the wind is 50 mph, then the effective speed of the plane is the difference between the plane's speed and the wind's speed: 525 mph − 50 mph = 475 mph.

There are other situations in which these concepts may be applied.

EXAMPLE 2   A Mississippi River sightseeing tour takes tourists from the tour dock on a 30-mile trip down the river to a Civil War historical site, where they spend 1 h walking around the grounds. The tour then returns to the tour dock. If the speed of the boat is set to travel at 16 mph in calm water and the rate of the current is 4 mph, find the total time of the trip.

Strategy   To determine the total time:

▶ Find the time spent traveling down the river by solving $d = rt$ for t. The distance is 30 mi. Therefore, $d = 30$.

Because the boat is traveling with the current, the rate of the boat is the sum of the boat's speed in calm water and the speed of the current: 16 mph + 4 mph = 20 mph. Thus $r = 20$ mph.

▶ Find the time spent returning to the tour station by solving $d = rt$ for t. The distance is 30 mi. Therefore, $d = 30$. Because the boat is traveling against the current, the rate of the boat is the difference between the boat's speed in calm water and the speed of the current: 16 mph − 4 mph = 12 mph. Thus $r = 12$ mph.

▶ Add the time spent traveling down the river, the time spent at the historical site (1 h), and the time returning.

Solution

$d = rt$
$30 = 20t$ • $d = 30, r = 16 + 4 = 20$
$\dfrac{30}{20} = \dfrac{20t}{20}$
$1.5 = t$

The time spent traveling down the river is 1.5 h.

$d = rt$
$30 = 12t$ • $d = 30, r = 16 - 4 = 12$
$\dfrac{30}{12} = \dfrac{12t}{12}$
$2.5 = t$

The time spent returning to the tour station is 2.5 h.

Total time = 1.5 + 1 + 2.5 = 5

The total time of the trip is 5 h.

PROBLEM 2   A plane that can normally travel at 175 mph in calm air is flying into a headwind of 35 mph. How long will it take the plane to fly 350 mi?

Solution   See pages S3–S4.

For more difficult uniform motion problems, it may be helpful to record known information in a table. This is illustrated in the following example.

Solve: An executive has an appointment 785 mi from the office. The executive takes a helicopter from the office to the airport and a plane from the airport to the business appointment. The helicopter averages 70 mph, and the plane averages 500 mph. The total time spent traveling is 2 h. Find the distance from the executive's office to the airport.

STRATEGY   **for solving a uniform motion problem**

▶ For each object, write a numerical or variable expression for the distance, rate, and time. The results can be recorded in a table.

The total time of travel is 2 h.

Unknown time in the helicopter: t
Time in the plane: $2 - t$

	Rate, r	·	Time, t	=	Distance, d
Helicopter	70	·	t	=	$70t$
Plane	500	·	$2 - t$	=	$500(2 - t)$

▶ Determine how the distances traveled by the individual objects are related. For example, the total distance traveled by both objects may be known, or it may be known that the two objects traveled the same distance.

The total distance traveled is 785 mi.

$$70t + 500(2 - t) = 785$$
$$70t + 1000 - 500t = 785$$
$$-430t + 1000 = 785$$
$$-430t = -215$$
$$t = 0.5$$

|← 70t →|← 500(2 − t) →|
Office   Airport   Appointment
|←———— 785 mi ————→|

The time spent traveling from the office to the airport in the helicopter is 0.5 h. To find the distance between these two points, substitute 70 for r and 0.5 for t into the equation $rt = d$.

$$rt = d$$
$$70(0.5) = d$$
$$35 = d$$

The distance from the office to the airport is 35 mi.

EXAMPLE 3   A long-distance runner started a course running at an average speed of 6 mph. One and one-half hours later, a cyclist traveled the same course at an average speed of 12 mph. How long after the runner started did the cyclist overtake the runner?

Strategy   ▶ Unknown time for the cyclist: t
Time for the runner: $t + 1.5$

	Rate	Time	Distance
Runner	6	$t + 1.5$	$6(t + 1.5)$
Cyclist	12	t	$12t$

▶ The runner and the cyclist traveled the same distance.

Solution $6(t + 1.5) = 12t$
$$6t + 9 = 12t$$
$$9 = 6t$$
$$\frac{3}{2} = t$$ • **The cyclist traveled for 1.5 h.**

$t + 1.5 = 1.5 + 1.5$ • **Substitute the value of *t* into the variable expression for the runner's time.**

$$= 3$$

The cyclist overtook the runner 3 h after the runner started.

PROBLEM 3   Two small planes start from the same point and fly in opposite directions. The first plane is flying 30 mph faster than the second plane. In 4 h the planes are 1160 mi apart. Find the rate of each plane.

Solution   See page S4.

2.3   Concept Review

Determine whether the following statements are always true, sometimes true, or never true.

1. A gold alloy costing $300 per ounce was mixed with a gold alloy costing $200 per ounce. The cost of the mixture was $250 per ounce.

2. Two planes are flying in opposite directions. One plane is flying at a rate of x mph, and the other plane is flying at a rate of y mph. The distance between the planes is increasing at a rate of $(x + y)$ mph.

3. A runner starts a course running at a rate of x mph. One-half hour later, a cyclist travels the same course at a rate of y mph and overtakes the runner. If t is the total time for the runner, $t + \frac{1}{2}$ is the total time for the cyclist.

4. A car travels for 2 h at a rate of 40 mph, and another travels for 2 h at a rate of 60 mph. The average speed is 50 mph.

5. A car travels 120 mi at a rate of 40 mph. On the return trip, the car travels at a rate of 60 mph. The average speed is 50 mph.

2.3   Exercises

1   Value mixture problems

1. a. The total value of a 20-pound bag of bird seed that costs $.42 per pound is ___?___.
   b. The cost per ounce of a 24-ounce box of chocolates that has a total value of $16.80 is ___?___.

2. A dried fruit mixture is made from dried cranberries that cost $7.20 per pound and dried apricots that cost $4.50 per pound. Fifteen pounds of the mixture costs $5.40 per pound. Let x be the amount of dried cranberries in the mixture.
   a. Complete the following table.

	Amount, A	·	Unit cost, C	=	Value, V
Dried cranberries	x	·	?	=	?
Dried apricots	?	·	?	=	?
Mixture	?	·	?	=	?

   b. Use the expressions in the last column of the table in part a to write an equation that can be solved to find the number of pounds of dried cranberries in the mixture: _____?_____ + _____?_____ = _____?_____ .

3. A restaurant chef mixes 20 lb of snow peas costing $1.99 a pound with 14 lb of petite onions costing $1.19 a pound to make a vegetable medley for the evening meal. Find the cost per pound of the mixture.

4. A coffee merchant combines coffee costing $5.50 per pound with coffee costing $3.00 per pound. How many pounds of each should be used to make 40 lb of a blend costing $4.00 per pound?

5. Adult tickets for a play cost $5.00 and children's tickets cost $2.00. For one performance, 460 tickets were sold. Receipts for the performance were $1880. Find the number of adult tickets sold.

6. The tickets for a local production of Gilbert and Sullivan's *H.M.S. Pinafore* cost $6.00 for adults and $3.00 for children and seniors. The total receipts for 505 tickets were $1977. Find the number of adult tickets sold.

7. Fifty liters of pure maple syrup that costs $9.50 per liter are mixed with imitation maple syrup that costs $4.00 per liter. How much imitation maple syrup is needed to make a mixture that costs $5.00 per liter?

8. To make a flour mix, a miller combined soybeans that cost $8.50 per bushel with wheat that cost $4.50 per bushel. How many bushels of each were used to make a mixture of 800 bushels that cost $5.50 per bushel?

9. A hiking instructor is preparing a trail mix for a group of young hikers. She mixes nuts that cost $3.99 a pound with pretzels that cost $1.29 a pound to make a 20-pound mixture that costs $2.37 a pound. Find the number of pounds of nuts used.

10. A silversmith combined pure silver that costs $5.20 an ounce with 50 oz of a silver alloy that costs $2.80 an ounce. How many ounces of the pure silver were used to make an alloy of silver that costs $4.40 an ounce?

11. A tea mixture was made from 30 lb of tea that costs $6.00 per pound and 70 lb of tea that costs $3.20 per pound. Find the cost per pound of the tea mixture.

12. Find the cost per ounce of salad dressing mixture made from 64 oz of olive oil that costs $8.29 and 20 oz of vinegar that costs $1.99. Round to the nearest cent.

13. A fruitstand owner combined cranberry juice that costs $4.20 per gallon with 50 gal of apple juice that costs $2.10 per gallon. How much cranberry juice was used to make cranapple juice that costs $3.00 per gallon?

14. Walnuts that cost $4.05 per kilogram were mixed with cashews that cost $7.25 per kilogram. How many kilograms of each were used to make a 50-kilogram mixture that costs $6.25 per kilogram? Round to the nearest tenth.

15. A coffee merchant mixes a dark roast coffee that cost $10 per pound with a light roast coffee that cost $7 per pound. Which of the following could be true about the cost, C, per pound of the mixture? There may be more than one correct answer.
a. $C = \$17$ **b.** $C = \$10$ **c.** $C < \$7$ **d.** $C > \$7$ **e.** $C > \$10$
f. $C < \$10$

16. A snack mix is made from peanuts that cost $3 per pound and caramel popcorn that cost $2.20 per pound. The mixture costs $2.50 per pound. Does the mixture contain more peanuts or more popcorn?

2 Uniform motion problems

17. a. Marvin and Nancy start biking at the same time. Marvin bikes at 12 mph and Nancy bikes at 15 mph. After t hours, Marvin has biked ___?___ miles and Nancy has biked ___?___ miles.
b. A plane flies at a rate of 380 mph in calm air. The wind is blowing at 20 mph. Flying with the wind, the plane flies ___?___ mph. Flying against the wind, the plane flies ___?___ mph.

18. Sam and Jose leave a movie theatre and go in opposite directions. Sam bikes and Jose walks. Sam bikes four times faster than Jose walks. After a quarter of an hour, Sam and Jose are 3.75 mi apart. Let r represent Jose's rate.
a. Complete the following table.

	Rate, r	$\cdot$	Time, t	$=$	Distance, d
Sam	___?___	$\cdot$	___?___	$=$	___?___
Jose	r	$\cdot$	___?___	$=$	___?___

b. Use the expressions in the last column of the table in part a to write an equation that can be solved to find Jose's rate: ___?___ + ___?___ = ___?___.

19. 🗫 Mike and Mindy live 3 mi apart. They leave their houses at the same time and walk toward each other until they meet. Mindy walks faster than Mike.

    a. Is the distance walked by Mike less than, equal to, or greater than the distance walked by Mindy?

    b. Is the time spent walking by Mike less than, equal to, or greater than the time spent walking by Mindy?

    c. What is the total distance traveled by Mike and Mindy?

20. 🗫 Eric and James ride their bikes from Eric's house to school. James begins biking 10 min before Eric begins. Eric bikes faster than James and catches up with him just as they reach school.

    a. Is the distance biked by James less than, equal to, or greater than the distance biked by Eric?

    b. Is the time spent biking by James less than, equal to, or greater than the time spent biking by Eric?

21. It takes a student 30 min to drive from school to work, a distance of 20 mi. At what average rate of speed does the student drive?

22. A cyclist rides at a rate of 16 mph for 45 min. How far does the cyclist travel in that time?

23. The typical cruising speed for a Boeing 747-400 airplane is 30 mph faster than that for a Boeing 737-800. If a Boeing 747-400 can make a trip of 1680 mi in 3 h, how long would it take a Boeing 737-800 to make the same trip? Round to the nearest tenth.

24. Some hotels in Las Vegas use moving sidewalks to transport guests between various places. Suppose a hotel guest decides to get on a moving sidewalk that is 195 ft long. If the guest walks at a rate of 5 ft/s and the moving sidewalk moves at a rate of 7 ft/s, how many seconds will it take the guest to walk from one end of the moving sidewalk to the other end?

25. Two cyclists start at 1:00 P.M. from opposite ends of a 54-mile race course. The average rate of speed of the first cyclist is 17 mph, and the average rate of speed of the second cyclist is 19 mph. At what time will the two cyclists meet?

26. At 9:00 A.M., Katrina starts down an exercise path and walks at a rate of 4 mph. At 9:30 A.M., Carla leaves from the same place and begins chasing Katrina, catching her at 10:00 A.M. Find Carla's jogging rate.

27. A bicyclist traveling at 18 mph overtakes an in-line skater who is traveling at 10 mph and had a 0.5-hour head start. How far from the starting point does the bicyclist overtake the in-line skater?

28. A helicopter traveling 120 mph overtakes a speeding car traveling 90 mph. The car had a 0.5-hour head start. How far from the starting point did the helicopter overtake the car?

29. Two planes are 1380 mi apart and traveling toward each other. One plane is traveling 80 mph faster than the other plane. The planes meet in 1.5 h. Find the speed of each plane.

r

$r + 80$

30. Two jet skiers leave the same dock at the same time and travel in opposite directions. One skier is traveling 14 mph slower than the other skier. In half an hour the skiers are 48 mi apart. Find the rate of the slower skier.

31. Two planes start from the same point and fly in opposite directions. The first plane is flying 50 mph slower than the second plane. In 2.5 h, the planes are 1400 mi apart. Find the rate of each plane.

32. A commuter plane provides transportation from an international airport to surrounding cities. One commuter plane averaged 210 mph flying to a city and 140 mph returning to the international airport. The total flying time was 4 h. Find the distance between the two airports.

33. A ferry leaves a harbor and travels to a resort island at an average speed of 18 mph. On the return trip, the ferry travels at an average speed of 12 mph because of fog. The total time for the trip is 6 h. How far is the island from the harbor?

34. Two hikers start from the same point and hike in opposite directions around a lake whose shoreline is 13 mi long. One hiker walks 0.5 mph faster than the other hiker. How fast did each hiker walk if they meet in 2 h?

35. A student rode a bicycle to the repair shop and then walked home. The student averaged 14 mph riding to the shop and 3.5 mph walking home. The round trip took 1 h. How far is it between the student's home and the bicycle shop?

14 mph

3.5 mph

36. An express train leaves Grand Central Station 1 h after a freight train leaves the same station. The express train is traveling 15 mph faster than the freight train. Find the rate at which each train is traveling if the express train overtakes the freight train in 3 h.

37. At noon a train leaves Washington, D.C., headed for Pittsburgh, Pennsylvania, a distance of 260 mi. The train travels at a speed of 60 mph. At 1 P.M. a second train leaves Pittsburgh headed for Washington, D.C., traveling at 40 mph. How long after the train leaves Pittsburgh will the two trains pass each other?

38. A plane leaves an airport at 3 P.M. At 4 P.M. another plane leaves the same airport traveling in the same direction at a speed 150 mph faster than that of the first plane. Four hours after the first plane takes off, the second plane is 250 mi ahead of the first plane. How far did the second plane travel?

2.3   Applying Concepts

Uniform motion problems

39. In 1999, astronomers confirmed the existence of three planets orbiting a star other than the sun. The planets are approximately the size of Jupiter and orbit the star Upsilon Andromeda, which is approximately 260 trillion miles from Earth. How many years after leaving Earth would it take a spacecraft traveling 18 million miles per hour to reach this star? Round to the nearest hundred. (18 million miles per hour is about 1000 times faster than current spacecraft can travel.)

40. If a parade 2 mi long is proceeding at 3 mph, how long will it take a runner, jogging at 6 mph, to travel from the end of the parade to the start of the parade?

41. Two cars are headed directly toward each other at rates of 40 mph and 60 mph. How many miles apart are they 2 min before impact?

42. Solve the following problem, which appears in a math text written around A.D. 1200. "Two birds start flying from the tops of two towers 50 ft apart at the same time and at the same rate. One tower is 30 ft high, and the other tower is 40 ft high. The birds reach a grass seed on the ground at exactly the same time. How far is the grass seed from the 40-foot tower?"

43. A car travels at an average speed of 30 mph for 1 mi. Is it possible for it to increase its speed during the next mile so that its average speed for the 2 mi is 60 mph?

44. In December of 1986, pilots Dick Rutan and Jeana Yeager flew the *Voyager* in the first nonstop, nonrefueled flight around the world. They flew east from Edwards Air Force Base in California on December 14, traveled 24,986.727 mi around the world, and returned to Edwards 216 h 3 min 44 s after their departure.
   a. On what date did Rutan and Yeager land at Edwards Air Force Base after their flight?
   b. What was their average speed in miles per hour? Round to the nearest whole number
   c. Find the circumference of Earth in a reference almanac, and then calculate the approximate distance above Earth that the flight was flown. Round to the nearest whole number.

45. A student jogs 1 mi at a rate of 8 mph and jogs back at a rate of 6 mph. Does it seem reasonable that the average rate is 7 mph? Why or why not? Support your answer.

2.4 Applications: Problems Involving Percent

OBJECTIVE **1**   ## Investment problems

The annual simple interest that an investment earns is given by the equation *Pr = I*, where *P* is the principal, or the amount invested, *r* is the simple interest rate, and *I* is the simple interest. The solution of an investment problem is based on this equation.

The annual interest rate on a $3000 investment is 9%. The annual simple interest earned on the investment is

$$I = Pr$$
$$I = \$3000(0.09)$$
$$I = \$270$$

Solve: You have a total of $8000 invested in two simple interest accounts. On one account, a money market fund, the annual simple interest rate is 11.5%. On the second account, a bond fund, the annual simple interest rate is 9.75%. The total annual interest earned by the two accounts is $823.75. How much do you have invested in each account?

STRATEGY **for solving a problem involving money deposited in two simple interest accounts**

▶ For each amount invested, use the equation *Pr = I*. Write a numerical or variable expression for the principal, the interest rate, and the interest earned. The results can be recorded in a table.

The total amount invested is $8000.

Amount invested at 11.5%: x
Amount invested at 9.75%: $8000 - x$

	Principal, P	·	Interest rate, r	=	Interest earned, I
Amount at 11.5%	x	·	0.115	=	$0.115x$
Amount at 9.75%	$8000 - x$	·	0.0975	=	$0.0975(8000 - x)$

▶ Determine how the amounts of interest earned on the individual investments are related. For example, the total interest earned by both accounts may be known, or it may be known that the interest earned on one account is equal to the interest earned on the other account.

The total annual interest earned is $823.75.

$$0.115x + 0.0975(8000 - x) = 823.75$$
$$0.115x + 780 - 0.0975x = 823.75$$
$$0.0175x + 780 = 823.75$$
$$0.0175x = 43.75$$
$$x = 2500$$

The amount invested at 9.75% is $8000 - x$.
Replace x with 2500 and evaluate.

$$8000 - x = 8000 - 2500 = 5500$$

The amount invested at 11.5% is $2500.
The amount invested at 9.75% is $5500.

EXAMPLE 1 An investment of $4000 is made at an annual simple interest rate of 4.9%. How much additional money must be invested at an annual simple interest rate of 7.4% so that the total interest earned is 6.4% of the total investment?

Strategy ▶ Additional amount to be invested at 7.4%: x

	Principal	Rate	Interest
Amount at 4.9%	4000	0.049	0.049(4000)
Amount at 7.4%	x	0.074	0.074x
Amount at 6.4%	4000 + x	0.064	0.064(4000 + x)

▶ The sum of the amounts of interest earned by the two investments equals the interest earned by the total investment.

Solution
$$0.049(4000) + 0.074x = 0.064(4000 + x)$$
$$196 + 0.074x = 256 + 0.064x$$
$$196 + 0.01x = 256$$
$$0.01x = 60$$
$$x = 6000$$

$6000 must be invested at an annual simple interest rate of 7.4%.

PROBLEM 1 An investment of $3500 is made at an annual simple interest rate of 5.2%. How much additional money must be invested at an annual simple interest rate of 7.5% so that the total interest earned is $575?

Solution See page S4.

OBJECTIVE 2 Percent mixture problems

Take Note

As stated at the right, in a 10% hydrogen peroxide solution, 10% of the total solution is hydrogen peroxide. Here we are referring to weight: The solution is 10% hydrogen peroxide by weight. For example, if the solution weighs 100 g, then the hydrogen peroxide in the solution weighs 10 g and the water weighs 90% of 100 g, or 90 g.

The amount of a substance in a solution or alloy can be given as a percent of the total solution or alloy. For example, in a 10% hydrogen peroxide solution, 10% of the total solution is hydrogen peroxide. The remaining 90% is water.

The solution of a percent mixture problem is based on the equation $Ar = Q$, where A is the amount of solution or alloy, r is the percent of concentration, and Q is the quantity of a substance in the solution or alloy.

The number of grams of silver in 50 g of a 40% silver alloy is

$$Q = Ar$$
$$Q = 50(0.40)$$
$$Q = 20$$

Solve: A chemist mixes an 11% acid solution with a 4% acid solution. How many milliliters of each solution should the chemist use to make a 700-milliliter solution that is 6% acid?

STRATEGY for solving a percent mixture problem

▶ For each solution, use the equation $Ar = Q$. Write a numerical or variable expression for the amount of solution, the percent of concentration, and the quantity of the substance in the solution. The results can be recorded in a table.

The total amount of solution is 700 ml.

Amount of 11% solution: x
Amount of 4% solution: $700 - x$

	Amount of solution, A	·	Percent of concentration, r	=	Quantity of substance, Q
11% solution	x	·	0.11	=	$0.11x$
4% solution	$700 - x$	·	0.04	=	$0.04(700 - x)$
6% solution	700	·	0.06	=	$0.06(700)$

▶ Determine how the quantities of the substance in the individual solutions are related. Use the fact that the sum of the quantities of the substances being mixed is equal to the quantity of the substance after mixing.

The sum of the amounts of acid in the 11% solution and the 4% solution is equal to the amount of acid in the 6% solution.

$$0.11x + 0.04(700 - x) = 0.06(700)$$
$$0.11x + 28 - 0.04x = 42$$
$$0.07x + 28 = 42$$
$$0.07x = 14$$
$$x = 200$$

The amount of 4% solution is $700 - x$. Replace x by 200 and evaluate.

$$700 - x = 700 - 200 = 500$$

The chemist should use 200 ml of the 11% solution and 500 ml of the 4% solution.

EXAMPLE 2   How many grams of pure acid must be added to 60 g of an 8% acid solution to make a 20% acid solution?

Strategy   ▶ Grams of pure acid: x

60 g of 8% acid   + x g of 100% acid   = $(60 + x)$ g of 20% acid

	Amount	Percent	Quantity
Pure acid (100%)	x	1.00	x
8%	60	0.08	0.08(60)
20%	$x + 60$	0.20	$0.20(x + 60)$

▶ The sum of the quantities before mixing equals the quantity after mixing.

Solution
$$x + 0.08(60) = 0.20(x + 60)$$
$$x + 4.8 = 0.20x + 12$$
$$0.8x + 4.8 = 12$$
$$0.8x = 7.2$$
$$x = 9$$

To make the 20% acid solution, 9 g of pure acid must be used.

PROBLEM 2 A butcher has some hamburger that is 22% fat and some that is 12% fat. How many pounds of each should be mixed to make 80 lb of hamburger that is 18% fat?

Solution See page S4.

2.4 Concept Review

Determine whether the following statements are always true, sometimes true, or never true.

1. $10,000 is invested in two accounts. If x is invested in one account, then $x - 10,000$ is invested in the other account.

2. The equation $Q = Ar$, where A is the amount of solution or alloy, r is the percent concentration, and Q is the quantity of a substance in the solution or alloy, is used in solving percent mixture problems.

3. If one solution has a 5% concentration and another solution has a 20% concentration, the mixture will have a 25% concentration.

4. An investment of $8000 is divided equally between two accounts with one account paying 6% and the other account paying 8%. The interest received is equivalent to 7% of the total investment.

2.4 Exercises

1 Investment problems

1. Explain the meaning of each variable in the equation $I = Pr$. Give an example of how this equation is used.

2. You invest an amount of money at an annual simple interest rate of 6.25%. You invest a second amount, $500 less than the first, at an annual simple interest rate of 6%. Let x represent the amount invested at 6.25%. Complete the following table.

	Principal, P	$\cdot$	Interest rate, r	$=$	Interest earned, I
Amount at 6.25%	x	$\cdot$	_?_	$=$	_?_
Amount at 6%	_?_	$\cdot$	_?_	$=$	_?_

3. The total annual interest earned on the investments in Exercise 2 is $115. Use this information and the information in the table in Exercise 2 to write an equation that can be solved to find the amount of money invested at 6.25%: _?_ + _?_ = _?_ .

4. Suppose $5000 is invested in two simple interest accounts. On one account the annual simple interest rate is 6%, and on the other the annual simple interest rate is 7%. The total annual interest earned on the two accounts is $330. In the context of this situation, explain each term of the equation

$$0.06x + 0.07(5000 - x) = 330$$

5. Joseph Abruzzio decides to divide a gift of $5000 into two different accounts. He deposits $2000 in an IRA account that earns an annual simple interest rate of 5.5%. The remaining money is placed in an account that earns an annual simple interest rate of 7.25%. How much interest will Joseph earn in one year from the two accounts?

6. Kristi invests $1500 at a 7.25% annual simple interest rate, and her sister Kari invests $2000 at a 6.75% annual simple interest rate. Which of the two will earn the greater amount of interest after one year? How much greater?

7. Deon Brown purchases a municipal bond for $2000. The bond earns an annual simple interest rate of 6.4%. How much must Deon invest in an account that earns 8% annual simple interest so that both investments will earn the same amount of interest in one year?

8. A $5000 investment at an annual simple interest rate of 5.2% earned as much interest after one year as another investment in an account that earned 6.5% annual simple interest. How much was invested at 6.5%?

9. Two investments earn a total annual income of $2825. One investment is in a 6.75% annual simple interest certificate of deposit. The other is in a 7.25% tax-free annual simple interest account. The total amount invested is $40,000. Find the amount invested in the certificate of deposit.

10. Two investments earn an annual income of $765. One investment earns an annual simple interest rate of 8.5%, and the other investment earns an annual simple interest rate of 10.2%. The total amount invested is $8000. How much is invested in each account?

11. An investment club invested $5000 at an annual simple interest rate of 8.4%. How much additional money must be invested at an annual simple interest rate of 10.5% so that the total interest earned will be 9% of the total investment?

12. Two investments earn an annual income of $465. One investment is a 5.5% tax-free annual simple interest account, and the other is a 4.5% annual simple interest certificate of deposit. The total amount invested is $9600. How much is invested in each account?

13. Two investments earn an annual income of $575. One investment earns an annual simple interest rate of 8.5%, and the other investment earns an annual simple interest rate of 6.4%. The total amount invested is $8000. How much is invested in each account?

14. An investment club invested $6000 at an annual simple interest rate of 4.0%. How much additional money must be invested at an annual simple interest rate of 6.5% so that the total annual interest earned will be 5% of the total investment?

15. Dee Pinckney made an investment of $6000 at an annual simple interest rate of 5.5%. How much additional money must she invest at an annual simple interest rate of 10% in order for the total annual interest earned to be 7% of the investment?

16. An account executive deposited $42,000 into two simple interest accounts. On the tax-free account the annual simple interest rate is 3.5%, and on the money market fund the annual simple interest rate is 4.5%. How much should be invested in each account so that both accounts earn the same annual interest?

17. An investment club invested $13,600 into two simple interest accounts. On one account, the annual simple interest rate is 4.2%. On the other, the annual simple interest rate is 6%. How much should be invested in each account so that both accounts earn the same annual interest?

18. Orlando Salavarrio, a financial planner, recommended that 25% of a client's investment be placed in a 4% annual simple interest tax-free account, that 40% be placed in 6% certificates of deposit, and that the remainder be placed in a 9% high-risk investment. The total interest earned from the investments would be $6550. Find the total amount to be invested.

19. The amount of annual interest earned on the x dollars that Will invested in one simple interest account was $0.055x$, and the amount of annual interest earned on the money that Will invested in another simple interest account was $0.072(6000 - x)$.
   a. What were the interest rates on the two accounts?
   b. What was the total amount of money Will had invested in the two accounts?

20. Refer to the investments described in Exercise 19. Which of the following could be true about the total amount T of interest earned by Will's two accounts? There may be more than one correct answer.
   a. $T < 330$ **b.** $T < 432$ **c.** $T > 432$ **d.** $T > 330$

2   Percent mixture problems

21. The label on a 32-ounce bottle of lemonade says that it contains 10% real lemon juice. The amount of real lemon juice in the bottle is 32(___?___) = ___?___ oz.

22. A 25% acid solution is made by adding an amount of 75% acid solution to 50 ml of a 15% acid solution. Let x be the amount of 75% acid solution that is in the mixture.
   a. Complete the following table.

	Amount, A	·	Percent of concentration, r	=	Quantity, Q
15% acid solution	?	·	?	=	?
75% acid solution	x	·	?	=	?
Mixture	?	·	?	=	?

   b. Use the expressions in the last column of the table in part a to write an equation that can be solved to find the amount of 75% acid solution that is in the mixture: ___?___ + ___?___ = ___?___ .

23. A 32-ounce bottle of Orange Ade contains 8 oz of orange juice. At the same percent concentration, how much orange juice is contained in a 40-ounce bottle of Orange Ade?

24. A chemist has 4 L of a solution that contains 0.36 L of acetic acid. The chemist needs to prepare 6 L of a solution with the same percent concentration of acetic acid. How much acidic acid must the 6 L of the solution contain?

25. A 750-milliliter solution is 4% hydrogen peroxide. How much more hydrogen peroxide is in a 850-milliliter solution that is 5% hydrogen peroxide?

26. One 8-ounce bar of a silver alloy is 30% silver. The percent concentration of silver in a second bar, which weighs 12 oz, is 35%. Find the total amount of silver in the two bars.

27. A jeweler mixed 15 g of a 60% silver alloy with 45 g of a 20% silver alloy. What is the percent concentration of silver in the resulting alloy?

28. A goldsmith mixed 10 g of a 50% gold alloy with 40 g of a 15% gold alloy. What is the percent concentration of the resulting alloy?

29. A silversmith mixed 25 g of a 70% silver alloy with 50 g of a 15% silver alloy. What is the percent concentration of the resulting alloy?

30. A chemist mixed 100 ml of an 8% saline solution with 60 ml of a 5% saline solution. Find the percent concentration of the resulting mixture.

31. How many pounds of a 12% aluminum alloy must be mixed with 400 lb of a 30% aluminum alloy to make a 20% aluminum alloy?

32. How many pounds of a 20% copper alloy must be mixed with 600 lb of a 30% copper alloy to make a 27.5% copper alloy?

33. A hospital staff member mixed a 65% disinfectant solution with a 15% disinfectant solution. How many liters of each were used to make 50 L of a 40% disinfectant solution?

34. A butcher has some hamburger that is 20% fat and some hamburger that is 12% fat. How many pounds of each should be mixed to make 80 lb of hamburger that is 17% fat?

35. How many quarts of water must be added to 5 qt of an 80% antifreeze solution to make a 50% antifreeze solution?

36. Rubbing alcohol is typically diluted with water to 70% strength. If you need 3.5 oz of 45% rubbing alcohol, how many ounces of 70% rubbing alcohol and how much water should you combine?

37. How many ounces of pure water must be added to 60 oz of a 7.5% salt solution to make a 5% salt solution?

38. How much water must be evaporated from 10 gal of a 12% sugar solution in order to obtain a 15% sugar solution?

39. Many fruit drinks are actually only 5% real fruit juice. If you let 2 oz of water evaporate from 12 oz of a drink that is 5% fruit juice, what is the percent concentration of the result?

40. A student mixed 50 ml of a 3% hydrogen peroxide solution with 30 ml of a 12% hydrogen peroxide solution. Find the percent concentration of the resulting mixture. Round to the nearest tenth of a percent.

41. Eighty pounds of a 54% copper alloy is mixed with 200 lb of a 22% copper alloy. Find the percent concentration of the resulting mixture. Round to the nearest tenth of a percent.

42. A druggist mixed 100 cc (cubic centimeters) of a 15% alcohol solution with 50 cc of pure alcohol. Find the percent concentration of the resulting mixture. Round to the nearest tenth of a percent.

43. n ounces of a 30% salt solution is mixed with m ounces of a 50% salt solution. Which relationship between n and m will produce a mixture with a salt concentration of 40%?
   a. $m = 2n$ **b.** $m = n$ **c.** $m = 0.4n$

44. n ounces of a 20% acid solution is mixed with m ounces of a 60% salt solution. Which of the following are possible salt concentrations of the mixture? There may be more than one answer.

a. 40%   **b.** 80%   **c.** 15%   **d.** 25%   **e.** 55%

2.4 Applying Concepts

45. **Investment Problem** A financial manager invested 25% of a client's money in bonds paying 9% annual simple interest, 30% in an 8% annual simple interest account, and the remainder in 9.5% corporate bonds. Find the amount invested in each if the total annual interest earned is $1785.

46. **Percent Mixture Problem** A silversmith mixed 90 g of a 40% silver alloy with 120 g of a 60% silver alloy. Find the percent concentration of the resulting alloy. Round to the nearest tenth of a percent.

47. **Value Mixture Problem** Find the cost per pound of a tea mixture made from 50 lb of tea that costs $5.50 per pound and 75 lb of tea that costs $4.40 per pound.

48. **Percent Mixture Problem** How many kilograms of water must be evaporated from 75 kg of a 15% salt solution to produce a 20% salt solution?

49. **Percent Mixture Problem** A chemist added 20 g of pure acid to a beaker containing an unknown number of grams of pure water. The resulting solution was 25% acid. How many grams of water were in the beaker before the acid was added?

50. **Percent Mixture Problem** A radiator contains 6 L of a 25% antifreeze solution. How much should be drained and replaced with pure antifreeze to produce a 50% antifreeze solution?

51. **Consumer Price Index** The consumer price index (CPI), or the "cost-of-living index," measures the change in the price of consumer goods and services. The graph at the right shows the percent increase in the CPI for the years 1998 through 2005.

a. During which year shown was the percent increase in the CPI the greatest?

b. During which year was the cost of consumer goods and services highest?

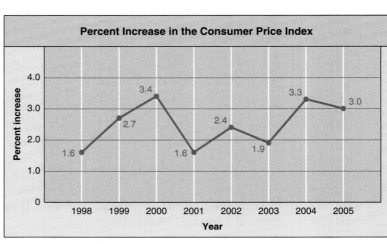

Source: Bureau of Labor Statistics

52. Write a report on series trade discounts. Explain how to convert a series discount to a single-discount equivalent.

2.5   Inequalities in One Variable

OBJECTIVE 1   Solve inequalities in one variable

The **solution set of an inequality** is a set of numbers, each element of which, when substituted for the variable, results in a true inequality.

The inequality at the right is true if the variable is replaced by 3, for example, or by -1.98, or by $\frac{2}{3}$.

$$x - 1 < 4$$
$$3 - 1 < 4$$
$$-1.98 - 1 < 4$$
$$\frac{2}{3} - 1 < 4$$

There are many values of the variable x that will make the inequality $x - 1 < 4$ true. The solution set of the inequality is any number less than 5. The solution set can be written in set-builder notation as $\{x \mid x < 5\}$.

The graph of the solution set of $x - 1 < 4$ is shown at the right.

In solving an inequality, use the Addition and Multiplication Properties of Inequalities to rewrite the inequality in the form *variable < constant* or *variable > constant*.

The Addition Property of Inequalities

If $a > b$ and c is a real number, then the inequalities $a > b$ and $a + c > b + c$ have the same solution set.

If $a < b$ and c is a real number, then the inequalities $a < b$ and $a + c < b + c$ have the same solution set.

The Addition Property of Inequalities states that the same number can be added to each side of an inequality without changing the solution set of the inequality. This property is also true for an inequality that contains the symbol $\leq$ or $\geq$.

The Addition Property of Inequalities is used to remove a term from one side of an inequality by adding the additive inverse of that term to each side of the inequality. Because subtraction is defined in terms of addition, the same number can be subtracted from each side of an inequality without changing the solution set of the inequality.

Solve: $3x - 4 < 2x - 1$

	$3x - 4 < 2x - 1$
Subtract $2x$ from each side of the inequality.	$x - 4 < -1$
Add 4 to each side of the inequality.	$x < 3$
Write the solution set. The solution set can be written in either set-builder notation or interval notation.	$\{x \mid x < 3\}$ $(-\infty, 3)$

The Multiplication Property of Inequalities is used to remove a coefficient from one side of an inequality so that the inequality can be written in the form *variable < constant* or *variable > constant*.

The Multiplication Property of Inequalities

Rule 1

If $a > b$ and $c > 0$, then the inequalities $a > b$ and $ac > bc$ have the same solution set.

If $a < b$ and $c > 0$, then the inequalities $a < b$ and $ac < bc$ have the same solution set.

Rule 2

If $a > b$ and $c < 0$, then the inequalities $a > b$ and $ac < bc$ have the same solution set.

If $a < b$ and $c < 0$, then the inequalities $a < b$ and $ac > bc$ have the same solution set.

Take Note

$c > 0$ means c is a positive number. Note that the inequality symbols are not changed.

$c < 0$ means c is a negative number. Note that the inequality symbols are reversed.

Rule 1 states that when each side of an inequality is multiplied by a positive number, the inequality symbol remains the same. However, Rule 2 states that when each side of an inequality is multiplied by a negative number, the inequality symbol must be reversed.

Here are some examples of this property.

	Rule 1			Rule 2	
$3 > 2$	$2 < 5$		$3 > 2$	$2 < 5$	
$3(4) > 2(4)$	$2(4) < 5(4)$		$3(-4) < 2(-4)$	$2(-4) > 5(-4)$	
$12 > 8$	$8 < 20$		$-12 < -8$	$-8 > -20$	

Because division is defined in terms of multiplication, when each side of an inequality is divided by a positive number, the inequality symbol remains the same. When each side of an inequality is divided by a negative number, the inequality symbol must be reversed.

The Multiplication Property of Inequalities is also true for the symbol $\leq$ or $\geq$.

Take Note

Each side of the inequality is divided *by* a negative number; the inequality symbol must be reversed.

■ Solve $-3x > 9$. Write the solution set in interval notation.

Divide each side of the inequality by the coefficient -3, and reverse the inequality symbol. Simplify.

Write the solution set.

$$-3x > 9$$
$$\frac{-3x}{-3} < \frac{9}{-3}$$
$$x < -3$$
$$(-\infty, -3)$$

EXAMPLE 1   Solve: $x + 3 > 4x + 6$
Write the solution set in set-builder notation.

Solution
$$x + 3 > 4x + 6$$
$$-3x + 3 > 6$$
$$-3x > 3$$
$$x < -1$$
$$\{x \mid x < -1\}$$

- Subtract 4x from each side of the inequality.
- Subtract 3 from each side of the inequality.
- Divide each side of the inequality by −3, and reverse the inequality symbol.
- Write the solution set.

PROBLEM 1   Solve: $2x - 1 < 6x + 7$
Write the solution set in set-builder notation.

■ **Solution**   See page S4.

When an inequality contains parentheses, the first step in solving the inequality is to use the Distributive Property to remove the parentheses.

EXAMPLE 2   Solve: $5(x - 2) \geq 9x - 3(2x - 4)$
Write the solution set in set-builder notation.

Solution

$5(x - 2) \geq 9x - 3(2x - 4)$

$5x - 10 \geq 9x - 6x + 12$ • **Use the Distributive Property to remove parentheses.**

$5x - 10 \geq 3x + 12$ • **Simplify.**

$2x - 10 \geq 12$ • **Subtract 3x from each side of the inequality.**

$2x \geq 22$ • **Add 10 to each side of the inequality.**

$x \geq 11$ • **Divide each side of the inequality by 2.**

$\{x \mid x \geq 11\}$

PROBLEM 2   Solve: $5x - 2 \leq 4 - 3(x - 2)$
Write the solution set in interval notation.

■ **Solution**   See page S4.

OBJECTIVE 2   ## Solve compound inequalities

A **compound inequality** is formed by joining two inequalities with a connective word such as "and" or "or." The inequalities shown below are compound inequalities.

$$2x < 4 \quad \text{and} \quad 3x - 2 > -8$$
$$2x + 3 > 5 \quad \text{or} \quad x + 2 < 5$$

The solution set of a compound inequality with the connective word *and* is the set of all elements common to the solution sets of both inequalities. Therefore, it is the *intersection* of the solution sets of the two inequalities.

Solve: $2x < 6$ and $3x + 2 > -4$
Write the solution set in interval notation.

Solve each inequality.

$$2x < 6 \quad \text{and} \quad 3x + 2 > -4$$
$$x < 3 \qquad\qquad 3x > -6$$
$$x > -2$$

$$\{x \mid x < 3\} \qquad \{x \mid x > -2\}$$

Find the intersection of the solution sets.

$$\{x \mid x < 3\} \cap \{x \mid x > -2\} = (-2, 3)$$

Take Note

This inequality is equivalent to the compound inequality
$-3 < 2x + 1$ and $2x + 1 < 5$.

Solve: $-3 < 2x + 1 < 5$
Write the solution set in set-builder notation.

$$-3 < 2x + 1 < 5$$

$$-3 < 2x + 1 \quad \text{and} \quad 2x + 1 < 5$$
$$-4 < 2x \qquad\qquad\qquad 2x < 4$$
$$-2 < x \qquad\qquad\qquad\quad x < 2$$

Find the intersection of the solution sets.

$$\{x \mid x > -2\} \qquad\qquad \{x \mid x < 2\}$$
$$\{x \mid x > -2\} \cap \{x \mid x < 2\} = \{x \mid -2 < x < 2\}$$

There is an alternative method for solving the inequality in the last example.

$$-3 < 2x + 1 < 5$$

Subtract 1 from each of the three parts of the inequality.
$$-3 - 1 < 2x + 1 - 1 < 5 - 1$$
$$-4 < 2x < 4$$

Divide each of the three parts of the inequality by the coefficient 2.
$$\frac{-4}{2} < \frac{2x}{2} < \frac{4}{2}$$
$$-2 < x < 2$$

$$\{x \mid -2 < x < 2\}$$

The solution set of a compound inequality with the connective word *or* is the *union* of the solution sets of the two inequalities.

Solve: $2x + 3 > 7$ or $4x - 1 < 3$
Write the solution set in set-builder notation.

Solve each inequality.
$$2x + 3 > 7 \quad \text{or} \quad 4x - 1 < 3$$
$$2x > 4 \qquad\qquad\quad 4x < 4$$
$$x > 2 \qquad\qquad\quad\; x < 1$$

$$\{x \mid x > 2\} \qquad\qquad \{x \mid x < 1\}$$

Find the union of the solution sets.
$$\{x \mid x > 2\} \cup \{x \mid x < 1\} = \{x \mid x > 2 \text{ or } x < 1\}$$

EXAMPLE 3 Solve: $1 < 3x - 5 < 4$
Write the solution set in interval notation.

Solution
$$1 < 3x - 5 < 4$$
$$1 + 5 < 3x - 5 + 5 < 4 + 5$$
• Add 5 to each of the three parts of the inequality.

$$6 < 3x < 9$$
• Simplify.

$$\frac{6}{3} < \frac{3x}{3} < \frac{9}{3}$$
• Divide each of the three parts of the inequality by 3.

$$2 < x < 3$$

$$(2, 3)$$
• Write the solution set.

PROBLEM 3 Solve: $-2 \le 5x + 3 \le 13$
Write the solution set in interval notation.

Solution See page S4.

EXAMPLE 4 Solve: $11 - 2x > -3$ and $7 - 3x < 4$
Write the solution set in set-builder notation.

Solution

$$
\begin{array}{ll}
11 - 2x > -3 & \text{and} \quad 7 - 3x < 4 \\
\quad -2x > -14 & \qquad -3x < -3 \\
\qquad x < 7 & \qquad\quad x > 1
\end{array}
$$
• Solve each inequality.

$\{x \mid x < 7\}$ $\qquad\qquad \{x \mid x > 1\}$

$\{x \mid x < 7\} \cap \{x \mid x > 1\} = \{x \mid 1 < x < 7\}$ • Find the intersection of the solution sets.

PROBLEM 4 Solve: $5 - 4x > 1$ and $6 - 5x < 11$
Write the solution set in interval notation.

Solution See page S4.

EXAMPLE 5 Solve: $3 - 4x > 7$ or $4x + 5 < 9$
Write the solution set in set-builder notation.

Solution

$$
\begin{array}{ll}
3 - 4x > 7 & \text{or} \quad 4x + 5 < 9 \\
\quad -4x > 4 & \qquad 4x < 4 \\
\qquad x < -1 & \qquad x < 1
\end{array}
$$
• Solve each inequality.

$\{x \mid x < -1\}$ $\qquad \{x \mid x < 1\}$

$\{x \mid x < -1\} \cup \{x \mid x < 1\} = \{x \mid x < 1\}$ • Find the union of the solution sets.

PROBLEM 5 Solve: $2 - 3x > 11$ or $5 + 2x > 7$
Write the solution set in set-builder notation.

Solution See page S5.

OBJECTIVE 3 **Application problems**

EXAMPLE 6 Company A rents cars for $6 a day and 14¢ for every mile driven. Company B rents cars for $12 a day and 8¢ for every mile driven. You want to rent a car for 5 days. How many miles can you drive a Company A car during the 5 days if it is to cost less than a Company B car?

Strategy To find the number of miles, write and solve an inequality using N to represent the number of miles.

Solution Cost of Company A car < cost of Company B car
$$
\begin{array}{l}
6(5) + 0.14N < 12(5) + 0.08N \\
30 + 0.14N < 60 + 0.08N \\
30 + 0.06N < 60 \\
0.06N < 30 \\
N < 500
\end{array}
$$

It is less expensive to rent from Company A if the car is driven less than 500 mi.

PROBLEM 6 The base of a triangle is 12 in., and the height is $(x + 2)$ in. Express as an integer the maximum height of the triangle when the area is less than 50 in².

Solution See page S5.

EXAMPLE 7   Find three consecutive odd integers whose sum is between 27 and 51.

Strategy   To find the three consecutive odd integers, write and solve a compound inequality using x to represent the first odd integer.

Solution $\dfrac{\text{Lower limit}}{\text{of the sum}} < \text{sum} < \dfrac{\text{upper limit}}{\text{of the sum}}$

$$27 < x + (x + 2) + (x + 4) < 51$$
$$27 < 3x + 6 < 51$$
$$27 - 6 < 3x + 6 - 6 < 51 - 6$$
$$21 < 3x < 45$$
$$\frac{21}{3} < \frac{3x}{3} < \frac{45}{3}$$
$$7 < x < 15$$

The three integers are 9, 11, and 13; or 11, 13, and 15; or 13, 15, and 17.

PROBLEM 7   An average score of 80 to 89 in a history course receives a B grade. A student has grades of 72, 94, 83, and 70 on four exams. Find the range of scores on the fifth exam that will give the student a B for the course.

Solution   See page S5.

2.5   Concept Review

Determine whether the following statements are always true, sometimes true, or never true.

1. If $a > b$, then $-a < -b$.

2. If $a < b$ and $a \neq 0$, $b \neq 0$, then $\frac{1}{a} < \frac{1}{b}$.

3. When dividing both sides of an inequality by an integer, we must reverse the inequality symbol.

4. When subtracting the same real number from both sides of an inequality, we must reverse the inequality symbol.

5. Suppose $a < 1$. Then $a^2 < a$.

6. Suppose $a < b < 0$ and $c < d < 0$. Then $ac > bd$.

2.5 Exercises

1 Solve inequalities in one variable

1. State the Addition Property of Inequalities and give numerical examples of its use.

2. State the Multiplication Property of Inequalities and give numerical examples of its use.

3. Which numbers are solutions of the inequality $x + 7 \leq -3$?
   a. -17 **b.** 8 **c.** -10 **d.** 0

4. Which numbers are solutions of the inequality $2x - 1 > 5$?
   a. 6 **b.** -4 **c.** 3 **d.** 5

Complete Exercises 5 to 8 by replacing the question mark with "remains the same" or "is reversed."

5. The inequality $x + 5 > 10$ can be solved by subtracting 5 from each side of the equation. The inequality symbol ___?___.

6. The inequality $\frac{1}{5}x > 10$ can be solved by multiplying each side of the equation by the reciprocal of $\frac{1}{5}$. The inequality symbol ___?___.

7. The inequality $-5x > 10$ can be solved by dividing each side of the equation by -5. The inequality symbol ___?___.

8. The inequality $x - 5 > -10$ can be solved by adding 5 to each side of the equation. The inequality symbol ___?___.

Solve. Write the solution set in set-builder notation.

9. $x - 3 < 2$ 10. $x + 4 \geq 2$ 11. $4x \leq 8$

12. $6x > 12$ 13. $-2x > 8$ 14. $-3x \leq -9$

15. $3x - 1 > 2x + 2$ 16. $5x + 2 \geq 4x - 1$ 17. $2x - 1 > 7$

18. $4x + 3 \leq -1$ 19. $6x + 3 > 4x - 1$ 20. $7x + 4 < 2x - 6$

21. $8x + 1 \geq 2x + 13$ 22. $5x - 4 < 2x + 5$ 23. $7 - 2x \geq 1$

24. $3 - 5x \leq 18$ 25. $4x - 2 < x - 11$ 26. $6x + 5 \geq x - 10$

Solve. Write the solution set in interval notation.

27. $x + 7 \geq 4x - 8$ **28.** $3x + 1 \leq 7x - 15$

29. $6 - 2(x - 4) \leq 2x + 10$ **30.** $4(2x - 1) > 3x - 2(3x - 5)$

31. $2(1 - 3x) - 4 > 10 + 3(1 - x)$ **32.** $2 - 5(x + 1) \geq 3(x - 1) - 8$

33. $\dfrac{3}{5}x - 2 < \dfrac{3}{10} - x$ **34.** $\dfrac{5}{6}x - \dfrac{1}{6} \leq x - 4$

35. $\dfrac{1}{3}x - \dfrac{3}{2} \geq \dfrac{7}{6} - \dfrac{2}{3}x$ **36.** $\dfrac{7}{12}x - \dfrac{3}{2} < \dfrac{2}{3}x + \dfrac{5}{6}$

37. $\dfrac{1}{2}x - \dfrac{3}{4} > \dfrac{7}{4}x - 2$ **38.** $\dfrac{2 - x}{4} - \dfrac{3}{8} \geq \dfrac{2}{5}x$

39. $2 - 2(7 - 2x) < 3(3 - x)$ **40.** $3 + 2(x + 5) \geq x + 5(x + 1) + 1$

State whether the solution set of an inequality in the given form contains only negative numbers, only positive numbers, or both positive and negative numbers.

41. $x + n > a$, where n and a are both positive and $n < a$

42. $nx > a$, where both n and a are negative

43. $nx > a$, where n is negative and a is positive

44. $x - n > -a$, where n and a are both positive and $n < a$

2   Solve compound inequalities

45.   **a.** Which set operation is used when a compound inequality is combined with *or*?
       b. Which set operation is used when a compound inequality is combined with *and*?

46.   Explain why writing $-3 > x > 4$ does not make sense.

47. To solve the compound inequality $4x \leq 4$ or $x + 2 > 8$, divide each side of the first inequality by ___?___, and subtract ___?___ from each side of the second inequality: $x \leq$ ___?___ or $x >$ ___?___.

48. The solution set in Exercise 47 can be written in interval notation as $(-\infty,$ ___?___$] \cup (6,$ ___?___$)$.

State whether the inequality describes the empty set, all real numbers, two intervals of real numbers, or one interval of real numbers.

49. $x > -3$ and $x > 2$

50. $x > -3$ or $x < 2$

51. $x < -3$ and $x > 2$

52. $x < -3$ or $x > 2$

Solve. Write the solution set in interval notation.

53. $3x < 6$ and $x + 2 > 1$ **54.** $x - 3 \le 1$ and $2x \ge -4$

55. $x + 2 \ge 5$ or $3x \le 3$ **56.** $2x < 6$ or $x - 4 > 1$

57. $-2x > -8$ and $-3x < 6$ **58.** $\frac{1}{2}x > -2$ and $5x < 10$

59. $\frac{1}{3}x < -1$ or $2x > 0$ **60.** $\frac{2}{3}x > 4$ or $2x < -8$

61. $x + 4 \ge 5$ and $2x \ge 6$ **62.** $3x < -9$ and $x - 2 < 2$

63. $-5x > 10$ and $x + 1 > 6$ **64.** $7x < 14$ and $1 - x < 4$

65. $2x - 3 > 1$ and $3x - 1 < 2$ **66.** $4x + 1 < 5$ and $4x + 7 > -1$

67. $3x + 7 < 10$ or $2x - 1 > 5$ **68.** $6x - 2 < -14$ or $5x + 1 > 11$

Solve. Write the solution set in set-builder notation.

69. $-5 < 3x + 4 < 16$ **70.** $5 < 4x - 3 < 21$

71. $0 < 2x - 6 < 4$ **72.** $-2 < 3x + 7 < 1$

73. $4x - 1 > 11$ or $4x - 1 \le -11$ **74.** $3x - 5 > 10$ or $3x - 5 < -10$

75. $2x + 3 \ge 5$ and $3x - 1 > 11$ **76.** $6x - 2 < 5$ or $7x - 5 < 16$

77. $9x - 2 < 7$ and $3x - 5 > 10$ **78.** $8x + 2 \le -14$ and $4x - 2 > 10$

79. $3x - 11 < 4$ or $4x + 9 \ge 1$ **80.** $5x + 12 \ge 2$ or $7x - 1 \le 13$

81. $3 - 2x > 7$ and $5x + 2 > -18$ **82.** $1 - 3x < 16$ and $1 - 3x > -16$

83. $5 - 4x > 21$ or $7x - 2 > 19$

84. $6x + 5 < -1$ or $1 - 2x < 7$

85. $3 - 7x \le 31$ and $5 - 4x > 1$

86. $9 - x \ge 7$ and $9 - 2x < 3$

87. $\frac{2}{3}x - 4 > 5$ or $x + \frac{1}{2} < 3$

88. $\frac{5}{8}x + 2 < -3$ or $2 - \frac{3}{5}x < -7$

89. $-\frac{3}{8} \le 1 - \frac{1}{4}x \le \frac{7}{2}$

90. $-2 \le \frac{2}{3}x - 1 \le 3$

3   Application problems

For Exercises 91 and 92, translate each sentence into an inequality.

91. The minimum value of a number n is 40.

92. A number n is between 150 and 300.

93. **Integer Problem** Five times the difference between a number and two is greater than the quotient of two times the number and three. Find the smallest integer that will satisfy the inequality.

94. **Integer Problem** Two times the difference between a number and eight is less than or equal to five times the sum of the number and four. Find the smallest number that will satisfy the inequality.

95. **Geometry** The length of a rectangle is 2 ft more than four times the width. Express as an integer the maximum width of the rectangle when the perimeter is less than 34 ft.

96. **Geometry** The length of a rectangle is 5 cm less than twice the width. Express as an integer the maximum width of the rectangle when the perimeter is less than 60 cm.

97. **Integer Problem** Find four consecutive integers whose sum is between 62 and 78.

98. **Integer Problem** Find three consecutive even integers whose sum is between 30 and 52.

99. **Geometry** One side of a triangle is 1 in. longer than the second side. The third side is 2 in. longer than the second side. Find, to the nearest whole number, the length of the second side of the triangle if the perimeter is more than 15 in. and less than 25 in.

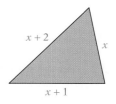

100. **Geometry** The length of a rectangle is 4 ft more than twice the width. Find, to the nearest whole number, the width of the rectangle if the perimeter is more than 28 ft and less than 40 ft.

101. Consumerism A cellular phone company offers its customers a rate of $49 for up to 200 min per month of cellular phone time, or a rate of $25 per month plus $.40 for each minute of cellular phone time. For how many minutes per month can a customer who chooses the second option use a cellular phone before the charges exceed those of the first option?

102. Consumerism In 2005, the computer service America Online offered its customers the option of paying $23.90 per month for unlimited use. Another option was a rate of $14.95 per month with 10 free hours plus $2.95 per hour thereafter. How many hours per month can you use this second option if it is to cost you less than the first option? Round to the nearest whole number.

103. Consumerism AirTouch advertises text messaging for $6.95 per month for up to 400 messages, and $.10 per message thereafter. A competitor advertises text messaging for $3.95 per month for up to 400 messages and $.15 per message thereafter. For what number of messages per month is the AirTouch plan less expensive?

104. Consumerism Suppose PayRite Rental Cars rents compact cars for $32 per day with unlimited mileage, and Otto Rentals offers compact cars for $19.99 per day but charges $.19 for each mile beyond 100 mi driven per day. You want to rent a car for one week. How many miles can you drive during the week if Otto Rental is to be less expensive than PayRite?

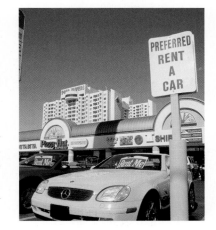

105. Consumerism During a weekday, to call a city 40 mi away from a certain pay phone costs $.70 for the first 3 min and $.15 for each additional minute. If you use a calling card, there is a $.35 fee, and then the rates are $.196 for the first minute and $.126 for each additional minute. How many minutes must a call last if it is to be cheaper to pay with coins rather than a calling card?

106. Consumerism Heritage National Bank offers two different checking accounts. The first charges $3 per month and $.50 per check after the first 10 checks. The second account charges $8 per month with unlimited check writing. How many checks can be written per month if the first account is to be less expensive than the second account?

107. Consumerism Glendale Federal Bank offers a checking account to small businesses. The charge is $8 per month plus $.12 per check after the first 100 checks. A competitor is offering an account for $5 per month plus $.15 per check after the first 100 checks. If a business chooses the Glendale Federal Bank account, how many checks does the business write monthly if it is assumed that this account will cost less than the competitor's account?

108. Commissions George Stoia earns $1000 per month plus 5% commission on the amount of sales. George's goal is to earn a minimum of $3200 per month. What amount of sales will enable George to earn $3200 or more per month?

109. Automobiles A new car will average at least 22 mpg for city driving and at most 27.5 mpg for highway driving. Find the range of miles that the car can travel on a full tank (19.5 gal) of gasoline.

110. Education An average score of 90 or above in an English course receives an A grade. A student has grades of 85, 88, 90, and 98 on four tests. Find the range of scores on the fifth test that will give the student an A grade.

2.5   Applying Concepts

Use the roster method to list the set of positive integers that are solutions of the inequality.

111. $8x - 7 < 2x + 9$

112. $2x + 9 \geq 5x - 4$

113. $5 + 3(2 + x) > 8 + 4(x - 1)$

114. $6 + 4(2 - x) > 7 + 3(x + 5)$

115. $-3x < 15$ and $x + 2 < 7$

116. $3x - 2 > 1$ and $2x - 3 < 5$

117. $-4 \leq 3x + 8 < 16$

118. $5 < 7x - 3 \leq 24$

119. Temperature The relationship between Celsius temperature and Fahrenheit temperature is given by the formula $F = \frac{9}{5}C + 32$. If the temperature is between 77°F and 86°F, what is the temperature range in degrees Celsius?

120. Integer Problem The average of two negative integers is less than or equal to −15. The smaller integer is 7 less than the larger integer. Find the greatest possible value for the smaller integer.

121. Consumerism The charges for a long-distance telephone call are $1.56 for the first three minutes and $.52 for each additional minute or fraction of a minute. What is the largest whole number of minutes a call can last if it is to cost you less than $5.40?

2.6 Absolute Value Equations and Inequalities

OBJECTIVE 1   **Absolute value equations**

The **absolute value** of a number is its distance from zero on the number line. Distance is always a positive number or zero. Therefore, the absolute value of a number is always a positive number or zero.

The distance from 0 to 3 or from 0 to -3 is 3 units.

$$|3| = 3 \qquad |-3| = 3$$

An equation containing an absolute value symbol is called an **absolute value equation**.

$$\left. \begin{array}{l} |x| = 3 \\ |x + 2| = 8 \\ |3x - 4| = 5x - 9 \end{array} \right\} \begin{array}{l} \text{Absolute} \\ \text{value} \\ \text{equations} \end{array}$$

> **Absolute Value Equations**
>
> If $a \geq 0$ and $|x| = a$, then $x = a$ or $x = -a$.

Given $|x| = 3$, then $x = 3$ or $x = -3$.

Solve: $|x + 2| = 8$

Remove the absolute value sign, and rewrite as two equations.

$$|x + 2| = 8$$
$$x + 2 = 8 \qquad x + 2 = -8$$

Solve each equation.

$$x = 6 \qquad x = -10$$

Check:
$$\begin{array}{c|c} |x + 2| = 8 & |x + 2| = 8 \\ |6 + 2| \;\; 8 & |-10 + 2| \;\; 8 \\ |8| & |-8| \\ 8 = 8 & 8 = 8 \end{array}$$

Write the solution.   The solutions are 6 and -10.

EXAMPLE 1   Solve.   **A.** $|x| = 15$ **B.** $|2 - x| = 12$
   C. $|2x| = -4$ **D.** $3 - |2x - 4| = -5$

Solution   **A.** $|x| = 15$
   $x = 15 \qquad x = -15$ • Remove the absolute value sign, and rewrite as two equations.

The solutions are 15 and -15.

Take Note

Remember to check the solutions. For Part B:

$\|2 - x\| = 12$	
$\|2 - (-10)\|$	12
$\|2 + 10\|$	12
$\|12\|$	12
12 = 12	

$\|2 - x\| = 12$	
$\|2 - 14\|$	12
$\|-12\|$	12
12 = 12	

Take Note

$3 - \|2x - 4\| = -5$	
$3 - \|2(6) - 4\|$	-5
$3 - \|12 - 4\|$	-5
$3 - \|8\|$	-5
$3 - 8$	-5
$-5 = -5$	

$3 - \|2x - 4\| = -5$	
$3 - \|2(-2) - 4\|$	-5
$3 - \|-4 - 4\|$	-5
$3 - \|-8\|$	-5
$3 - 8$	-5
$-5 = -5$	

B. $\|2 - x\| = 12$

$2 - x = 12 \qquad 2 - x = -12$ • **Remove the absolute value sign, and rewrite as two equations.**

$-x = 10 \qquad\qquad -x = -14$ • **Solve each equation.**
$x = -10 \qquad\qquad x = 14$

The solutions are -10 and 14.

C. $\|2x\| = -4$ • **The absolute value of a number must be nonnegative.**

There is no solution to the equation.

D. $3 - \|2x - 4\| = -5$

$-\|2x - 4\| = -8$ • **Solve for the absolute value.**
$\|2x - 4\| = 8$ • **Multiply each side of the equation by -1.**

$2x - 4 = 8 \qquad 2x - 4 = -8$ • **Remove the absolute value sign, and rewrite as two equations.**

$2x = 12 \qquad\qquad 2x = -4$ • **Solve each equation.**
$x = 6 \qquad\qquad x = -2$

The solutions are 6 and -2.

PROBLEM 1 Solve.   **A.** $\|x\| = 25$ **B.** $\|2x - 3\| = 5$
                            C. $\|x - 3\| = -2$ **D.** $5 - \|3x + 5\| = 3$

Solution See page S5.

OBJECTIVE 2   Absolute value inequalities

Recall that absolute value represents the distance between two points. For example, the solutions of the absolute value equation $\|x - 1\| = 3$ are the numbers whose distance from 1 is 3. Therefore, the solutions are -2 and 4.

The solutions of the **absolute value inequality** $\|x - 1\| < 3$ are the numbers whose distance from 1 is *less than* 3. Therefore, the solutions are the numbers greater than -2 and less than 4. The solution set is $\{x \mid -2 < x < 4\}$. *Note:* In this text, solutions to absolute value inequalities will always be written in set-builder notation.

Distance less than 3   Distance less than 3

Absolute Value Inequalities of the Form $\|ax + b\| < c$

To solve an absolute value inequality of the form $\|ax + b\| < c$, solve the equivalent compound inequality $-c < ax + b < c$.

The compound inequality $-c < ax + b < c$ is equivalent to the intersection of the two inequalities $-c < ax + b$ and $ax + b < c$. The intersection of these two inequalities is shown on the following number line.

From this number line, we see that the solution of $|ax + b| < c$ is all the numbers for which $ax + b$ is greater than $-c$ and less than c.

EXAMPLE 2   Solve: $|4x - 3| < 5$

Solution $|4x - 3| < 5$

• The distance from zero is less than 5 units. $4x - 3$ is between -5 and 5.

$$-5 < 4x - 3 < 5$$

• Solve the equivalent compound inequality.

$$-5 + 3 < 4x - 3 + 3 < 5 + 3$$
$$-2 < 4x < 8$$

• Add 3 to each of the three parts of the inequality.

$$\frac{-2}{4} < \frac{4x}{4} < \frac{8}{4}$$

• Divide each of three parts of the inequality by 4.

$$-\frac{1}{2} < x < 2$$

$$\left\{ x \,\middle|\, -\frac{1}{2} < x < 2 \right\}$$

• Write the solution set.

PROBLEM 2   Solve: $|3x + 2| < 8$

Solution   See page S5.

EXAMPLE 3   Solve: $|x - 3| < 0$

Solution $|x - 3| < 0$ • The absolute value of a number must be nonnegative.
                 $\varnothing$ • The solution set is the empty set.

PROBLEM 3   Solve: $|3x - 7| < 0$

Solution   See page S5.

The solutions of the absolute value inequality $|x + 1| > 2$ are the numbers whose distance from -1 is *greater than* 2. Therefore, the solutions are the numbers less than -3 or greater than 1. The solution set is $\{x \,|\, x < -3 \text{ or } x > 1\}$.

Distance   Distance
greater than 2   greater than 2

Absolute Value Inequalities of the Form $|ax + b| > c$

To solve an absolute value inequality of the form $|ax + b| > c$, solve the equivalent compound inequality $ax + b < -c$ or $ax + b > c$.

The solution of the compound inequality $ax + b < -c$ or $ax + b > c$ is shown on the following number line.

$$
\begin{array}{ccc}
 & & \\
-c & 0 & c
\end{array}
$$

From this number line we see that the solution of $|ax + b| > c$ is the union of the numbers less than $-c$ and greater than c.

Take Note

Carefully observe the difference between the solution method for $|ax + b| > c$ shown here and that for $|ax + b| < c$ shown in Example 2.

EXAMPLE 4   Solve: $|2x - 1| > 7$

Solution $|2x - 1| > 7$

$$
\begin{array}{ccc}
 & -7 & 7 \\
\end{array}
$$
$$
-10\ {-8}\ {-6}\ {-4}\ {-2}\ \ 0\ \ 2\ \ 4\ \ 6\ \ 8\ \ 10
$$

• The distance from zero is greater than 7. $2x - 1$ is less than -7 or greater than 7.

$$
\begin{array}{ccc}
2x - 1 < -7 & \text{or} & 2x - 1 > 7 \\
2x < -6 & & 2x > 8 \\
x < -3 & & x > 4
\end{array}
$$

• Solve the equivalent compound inequality.

$$
\begin{array}{cc}
\{x \,|\, x < -3\} & \{x \,|\, x > 4\}
\end{array}
$$

$$
\{x \,|\, x < -3\} \cup \{x \,|\, x > 4\}
$$
$$
= \{x \,|\, x < -3 \text{ or } x > 4\}
$$

• Find the union of the solution sets.

PROBLEM 4   Solve: $|5x + 3| > 8$

Solution   See page S5.

OBJECTIVE 3   Application problems

Piston

The **tolerance** of a component, or part, is the acceptable amount by which the component may vary from a given measurement. For example, the diameter of a piston may vary from the given measurement of 9 cm by 0.001 cm. This is written as 9 cm ± 0.001 cm, which is read "9 centimeters plus or minus 0.001 centimeter." The maximum diameter, or **upper limit,** of the piston is 9 cm + 0.001 cm = 9.001 cm. The minimum diameter, or **lower limit,** of the piston is 9 cm − 0.001 cm = 8.999 cm.

The lower and upper limits of the diameter could also be found by solving the absolute value inequality $|d - 9| \leq 0.001$, where d is the diameter of the piston.

$$
|d - 9| \leq 0.001
$$

$$
-0.001 \leq d - 9 \leq 0.001
$$
$$
-0.001 + 9 \leq d - 9 + 9 \leq 0.001 + 9
$$
$$
8.999 \leq d \leq 9.001
$$

The lower and upper limits of the diameter are 8.999 cm and 9.001 cm.

EXAMPLE 5   A doctor has prescribed 2 cc of medication for a patient. The tolerance is 0.03 cc. Find the lower and upper limits of the amount of medication to be given.

Strategy   Let p represent the prescribed amount of medication, T the tolerance, and m the given amount of medication. Solve the absolute value inequality $|m - p| \le T$ for m.

Solution $|m - p| \le T$
$|m - 2| \le 0.03$ • Substitute the values of p and T into the inequality.

$-0.03 \le m - 2 \le 0.03$ • Solve the equivalent compound inequality.
$1.97 \le m \le 2.03$

The lower and upper limits of the amount of medication to be given to the patient are 1.97 cc and 2.03 cc.

PROBLEM 5   A machinist must make a bushing that has a tolerance of 0.003 in. The diameter of the bushing is 2.55 in. Find the lower and upper limits of the diameter of the bushing.

■ **Solution**   See page S5.

2.6   Concept Review

Determine whether the following statements are always true, sometimes true, or never true.

1. If $a > 0$ and $|x| = a$, then $x = a$ or $x = -a$.

2. The absolute value inequality $|x| < a$, $a > 0$, is equivalent to the compound inequality $x > a$ or $x < -a$.

3. If $|x + 3| = 12$, then $|x + 3| = 12$ or $|x + 3| = -12$.

4. An absolute value equation has two solutions.

5. If $|x + b| < c$, then $x + b < -c$ or $x + b > c$.

2.6   Exercises

1   Absolute value equations

1. Is 2 a solution of $|x - 8| = 6$?

2. Is -2 a solution of $|2x - 5| = 9$?

3. Is -1 a solution of $|3x - 4| = 7$?

4. Is 1 a solution of $|6x - 1| = -5$?

5. If $|x| = 8$, then $x = \underline{\quad ? \quad}$ or $x = \underline{\quad ? \quad}$.

6. If $|x + 5| = 8$, then $x + 5 = \underline{\quad ? \quad}$ or $x + 5 = \underline{\quad ? \quad}$. Subtract 5 from each side of each equation to find that the two solutions of the equation $|x + 5| = 8$ are $\underline{\quad ? \quad}$ and $\underline{\quad ? \quad}$.

Solve.

7. $|x| = 7$

8. $|a| = 2$

9. $|-t| = 3$

10. $|-a| = 7$

11. $|-t| = -3$

12. $|-y| = -2$

13. $|x + 2| = 3$

14. $|x + 5| = 2$

15. $|y - 5| = 3$

16. $|y - 8| = 4$

17. $|a - 2| = 0$

18. $|a + 7| = 0$

19. $|x - 2| = -4$

20. $|x + 8| = -2$

21. $|2x - 5| = 4$

22. $|4 - 3x| = 4$

23. $|2 - 5x| = 2$

24. $|2x - 3| = 0$

25. $|5x + 5| = 0$

26. $|3x - 2| = -4$

27. $|2x + 5| = -2$

28. $|x - 2| - 2 = 3$

29. $|x - 9| - 3 = 2$

30. $|3a + 2| - 4 = 4$

31. $|8 - y| - 3 = 1$

32. $|2x - 3| + 3 = 3$

33. $|4x - 7| - 5 = -5$

34. $|2x - 3| + 4 = -4$

35. $|3x - 2| + 1 = -1$

36. $|6x - 5| - 2 = 4$

37. $|4b + 3| - 2 = 7$

38. $|3t + 2| + 3 = 4$

39. $|5x - 2| + 5 = 7$

40. $3 - |x - 4| = 5$

41. $2 - |x - 5| = 4$

42. $|2x - 8| + 12 = 2$

43. $|3x - 4| + 8 = 3$

44. $2 + |3x - 4| = 5$

45. $5 + |2x + 1| = 8$

46. $5 - |2x + 1| = 5$

47. $3 - |5x + 3| = 3$

48. $8 - |1 - 3x| = -1$

For Exercises 49 to 52, a and b are positive numbers such that $a < b$. State whether an absolute value equation in the given form has no solution, two negative solutions, two positive solutions, or one positive and one negative solution.

49. $|x - b| = a$

50. $|x - b| = -a$

51. $|x + b| = a$

52. $|x + a| = b$

2 Absolute value inequalities

53. If $|x| > 9$, then x ___?___ -9 or x ___?___ 9.

54. If $|x| < 5$, then ___?___ $< x <$ ___?___.

Solve.

55. $|x| > 3$

56. $|x| < 5$

57. $|x + 1| > 2$

58. $|x - 2| > 1$

59. $|x - 5| \leq 1$

60. $|x - 4| \leq 3$

61. $|2 - x| \geq 3$

62. $|3 - x| \geq 2$

63. $|2x + 1| < 5$ **64.** $|3x - 2| < 4$ **65.** $|5x + 2| > 12$ **66.** $|7x - 1| > 13$

67. $|4x - 3| \leq -2$ **68.** $|5x + 1| \leq -4$ **69.** $|2x + 7| > -5$ **70.** $|3x - 1| > -4$

71. $|4 - 3x| \geq 5$ **72.** $|7 - 2x| > 9$ **73.** $|5 - 4x| \leq 13$ **74.** $|3 - 7x| < 17$

75. $|6 - 3x| \leq 0$ **76.** $|10 - 5x| \geq 0$ **77.** $|2 - 9x| > 20$ **78.** $|5x - 1| < 16$

For Exercises 79 and 80, a and b are positive numbers such that $a < b$. State whether an absolute value inequality in the given form has no solution, all negative solutions, all positive solutions, or both positive and negative solutions.

79. $|x + b| < a$ **80.** $|x + a| < b$

3   Application problems

81. The desired dosage of a particular medicine is 50 mg, but it is acceptable for the dosage to vary by 0.5 mg from the desired dosage. The number 0.5 is called the ___?___ for the desired dosage of 50 mg. The value $50 + 0.5 = $ ___?___ mg is called the ___?___ limit for the dosage and the value $50 - 0.5 = $ ___?___ mg is called the ___?___ limit for the dosage.

82. The tolerance for the dosage described in Exercise 81 can be represented by an absolute value inequality by letting D be the actual dosage and stating that the distance between D and 50 must be less than or equal to 0.5: $|D - $ ___?___ $| \leq$ ___?___.

83. Mechanics The diameter of a bushing is 1.75 in. The bushing has a tolerance of 0.008 in. Find the lower and upper limits of the diameter of the bushing.

84. Mechanics A machinist must make a bushing that has a tolerance of 0.004 in. The diameter of the bushing is 3.48 in. Find the lower and upper limits of the diameter of the bushing.

85. Medicine A doctor has prescribed 2.5 cc of medication for a patient. The tolerance is 0.2 cc. Find the lower and upper limits of the amount of medication to be given.

86. Automobiles The diameter of a piston for an automobile is $3\frac{5}{16}$ in. with a tolerance of $\frac{1}{64}$ in. Find the lower and upper limits of the diameter of the piston.

87. Computers A power strip is utilized on a computer to prevent the loss of programming by electrical surges. The power strip is designed to allow 110 volts plus or minus 16.5 volts. Find the lower and upper limits of voltage to the computer.

88. Appliances An electric motor is designed to run on 220 volts plus or minus 25 volts. Find the lower and upper limits of voltage on which the motor will run.

89. Automobiles A piston rod for an automobile is $10\frac{3}{8}$ in. with a tolerance of $\frac{1}{32}$ in. Find the lower and upper limits of the length of the piston rod.

90. A dosage of medicine may safely range from 2.8 ml to 3.2 ml. What is the desired dosage of the medicine? What is the tolerance?

91. The tolerance for the diameter, in inches, of a piston is described by the absolute value inequality $|d - 5| \leq 0.01$. What is the desired diameter of the piston? By how much can the actual diameter of the piston vary from the desired diameter?

Electronics The tolerance of the resistors used in electronics is given as a percent of the resistance, which is measured in ohms. For example, if a 20,000-ohm resistor has a tolerance of 4%, then the tolerance is

$$0.04(20,000) = 800 \text{ ohms}$$

The lower and upper limits of the resistor can be found by solving the absolute value inequality $|M - 20,000| \leq 800$, where M represents the amount of ohms.

92. Find the lower and upper limits of a 29,000-ohm resistor with a 2% tolerance.

93. Find the lower and upper limits of a 15,000-ohm resistor with a 10% tolerance.

94. Find the lower and upper limits of a 25,000-ohm resistor with a 5% tolerance.

95. Find the lower and upper limits of a 56-ohm resistor with a 5% tolerance.

2.6   Applying Concepts

Solve.

96. $\left|\dfrac{2x - 5}{3}\right| = 7$

97. $\left|\dfrac{3x - 2}{4}\right| + 5 = 6$

98. $\left|\dfrac{4x - 2}{3}\right| > 6$

99. $\left|\dfrac{2x - 1}{5}\right| \leq 3$

For what values of the variable is the equation true? Write the solution set in set-builder notation.

100. $|x + 3| = x + 3$ **101.** $|y + 6| = y + 6$ **102.** $|a - 4| = 4 - a$ **103.** $|b - 7| = 7 - b$

104. For real numbers x and y, which of the following is always true?
     a. $|x + y| = |x| + |y|$ **b.** $|x + y| \leq |x| + |y|$ **c.** $|x + y| \geq |x| + |y|$

105. Write an absolute value inequality to represent all real numbers within 5 units of 2.

106. Write an absolute value inequality to represent all real numbers within k units of j. (Assume $k > 0$.)

107. Replace the question mark with $\leq$, $\geq$, or $=$.
     a. $|x + y| \, ? \, |x| + |y|$ **b.** $|x - y| \, ? \, |x| - |y|$ **c.** $||x| - |y|| \, ? \, |x| + |y|$
     d. $\left| \dfrac{x}{y} \right| \, ? \, \dfrac{|x|}{|y|}, y \neq 0$ **e.** $|xy| \, ? \, |x||y|$

Focus on Problem Solving

Understand the Problem   The first of the four steps that Polya advocated to solve problems is to *understand the problem.* This aspect of problem solving is frequently not given enough attention. There are various exercises that you can try to achieve a good understanding of a problem. Some of these are stated in the Focus on Problem Solving in the chapter entitled "Review of Real Numbers." They are also listed here:

- Try to restate the problem in your own words.
- Determine what is known about this type of problem.
- Determine what information is given.
- Determine what information is unknown.
- Determine whether any of the information given is unnecessary.
- Determine the goal.

To illustrate this aspect of problem solving, consider the following famous ancient riddle.

> As I was going to St. Ives,
> I met a man with seven wives;
> Each wife had seven sacks,
> Each sack had seven cats,
> Each cat had seven kits:
> Kits, cats, sacks, and wives,
> How many were going to St. Ives?

To answer the question in the poem, we will ask and answer some of the questions listed on page 117.

1. What is the goal?

    The goal is to determine how many were going to St. Ives. (We know this from reading the last line of the poem.)

2. What information is necessary and what information is unnecessary?

    The first line indicates that the poet was going to St. Ives. The next five lines describe a man the poet *met* on the way. This information is irrelevant.

The answer to the question, then, is 1. Only the poet was going to St. Ives.

Point of Interest

Try this brain teaser: You have two U.S. coins that add up to $.55. One is not a nickel. What are the two coins?

There are many other examples of the importance, in problem solving, of recognizing *irrelevant information*. One that frequently makes the college circuit is posed in the form of a test. The first line of a 100-question test states, "Read the entire test before you begin." The last line of the test reads, "Choose any *one* question to answer." Many people ignore the information given in the first line and just begin the test, only to find out much later that they did a lot more work than necessary.

To illustrate another aspect of Polya's first step in the problem-solving process, consider the problem of finding the area of the oval-shaped region (called an *ellipse*) shown in the diagram at the left. This problem can be solved by doing some research to determine *what information is known about this type of problem*. Mathematicians have found a formula for the area of an ellipse. That formula is $A = \pi a b$, where a and b are as shown in the diagram. Therefore, $A = \pi(6)(4) = 24\pi \approx 75.40$ square units. Without the formula, this problem is difficult to solve. With the formula, it is fairly easy.

For each of the following problems, examine the problem in terms of the first step in Polya's problem-solving method. *Do not solve the problem.*

1. Johanna spent one-third of her allowance on a book. She then spent $5.00 for a sandwich and iced tea. The cost of the iced tea was one-fifth the cost of the sandwich. Find the cost of the iced tea.

2. A flight from Los Angeles to Boston took 6 h. What was the average speed of the plane?

3. A major league baseball is approximately 5 in. in diameter and is covered with cowhide. Approximately how much cowhide is used to cover 10 baseballs?

4. How many donuts are in seven baker's dozen?

5. The smallest prime number is 2. Twice the difference between the eighth and the seventh prime numbers is two more than the smallest prime number. How large is the smallest prime number?

Projects & Group Activities

Venn Diagrams   Diagrams can be very useful when we are working with sets. The set diagrams shown below are called **Venn diagrams.**

In the Venn diagram at the right, the rectangle represents the set U, and the circles A and B represent subsets of set U. The common area of the two circles represents the intersection of A and B.

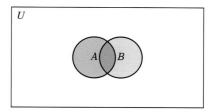

This Venn diagram represents the set $U = \{1, 2, 3, 4, 5, 6, 7, 8\}$. The sets $A = \{2, 3, 4, 5\}$ and $B = \{4, 5, 6, 7\}$ are subsets of U. Note that 1 and 8 are in set U but not in A or B. The numbers 4 and 5 are in both set A and set B.

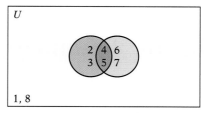

Sixty-five students at a small college enrolled in the following courses.

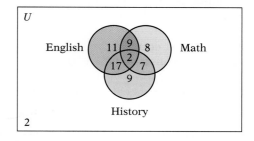

- 39 enrolled in English.
- 26 enrolled in mathematics.
- 35 enrolled in history.
- 19 enrolled in English and history.
- 11 enrolled in English and mathematics.
- 9 enrolled in mathematics and history.
- 2 enrolled in all three courses.

The Venn diagram is shown above. The diagram was drawn by placing the 2 students in the intersection of all three courses. Because 9 students took history and mathematics and 2 students are already in the intersection of history and mathematics, 7 more students are placed in the intersection of history and mathematics. Continue in this manner until all information is used.

Complete the following.

1. Use the Venn diagram above that shows course enrollments.
   a. How many students enrolled only in English and mathematics?
   b. How many students enrolled in English but did not enroll in mathematics or history?
   c. How many students did not enroll in any of the three courses?

2. Sketch the Venn diagram for $U = \{1, 2, 3, 4, 5, 6, 7, 8\}$, $A = \{2, 3, 4, 5, 6\}$, $B = \{4, 5, 6, 7, 8\}$, and $C = \{4, 5\}$.

3. A busload of 50 scouts stopped at a fast-food restaurant and ordered hamburgers. The scouts could have pickles, and/or tomatoes, and/or lettuce on their hamburgers.

> 31 ordered pickles.
> 36 ordered tomatoes.
> 31 ordered lettuce.
> 21 ordered pickles and tomatoes.
> 24 ordered tomatoes and lettuce.
> 22 ordered pickles and lettuce.
> 17 ordered all three.

a. How many scouts ordered a hamburger with pickles only?
b. How many scouts ordered a hamburger with lettuce and tomatoes without the pickles?
c. How many scouts ordered a hamburger without pickles, tomatoes, or lettuce?

Chapter 2 Summary

Key Words	*Examples*
An **equation** expresses the equality of two mathematical expressions. [2.1.1, p. 58]	$3 + 2 = 5 \qquad 2x - 5 = 4$
The simplest equation to solve is an equation of the form **variable = constant**. [2.1.1, p. 59]	$x = 5 \qquad -2 = x$
A **solution**, or **root, of an equation** is a replacement value for the variables that will make the equation true. [2.1.1, p. 58]	The root of $x + 5 = 2$ is -3.
Solving an equation means finding a solution of the equation. The goal is to rewrite the equation in the form **variable = constant**, because the constant is the solution. [2.1.1, p. 59]	The equation $x = 12$ is in the form *variable = constant*. The constant 12 is the solution of the equation.
An equation of the form $ax + b = c, a \neq 0$, is called a **first-degree equation**. [2.1.1, p. 59]	$3x - 2 = 5$
The **solution set of an inequality** is a set of numbers, each element of which, when substituted in the inequality, results in a true inequality. [2.5.1, p. 97]	Any number greater than 4 is a solution of the inequality $x > 4$.
A **compound inequality** is formed by joining two inequalities with a connective word such as "and" or "or." [2.5.2, p. 99]	$3x > 6 \quad$ and $\quad 2x + 5 < 7$ $2x + 2 < 3 \quad$ or $\quad x + 2 > 4$
An **absolute value equation** is an equation that contains an absolute value symbol. [2.6.1, p. 109]	$\lvert x - 2 \rvert = 3$
An **absolute value inequality** is an inequality that contains an absolute value symbol. [2.6.2, p. 110]	$\lvert x - 4 \rvert < 5 \qquad \lvert 2x - 3 \rvert > 6$

Essential Rules and Procedures

The Addition Property of Equations
If $a = b$, then $a + c = b + c$. [2.1.1, p. 59]

$$x + 5 = -3$$
$$x + 5 - 5 = -3 - 5$$
$$x = -8$$

The Multiplication Property of Equations
If $a = b$ and $c \neq 0$, then $ac = bc$. [2.1.1, p. 60]

$$\frac{2}{3}x = 4$$
$$\left(\frac{3}{2}\right)\left(\frac{2}{3}x\right) = \left(\frac{3}{2}\right)4$$
$$x = 6$$

Coin and Stamp Equation
$$\frac{\text{Number}}{\text{of items}} \cdot \frac{\text{Value of}}{\text{each item}} = \frac{\text{Total value}}{\text{of items}}$$ [2.2.1, p. 70]

A collection of stamps consists of 17¢ and 27¢ stamps. In all there are 15 stamps with a value of \$3.55. How many 17¢ stamps are in the collection?

$$17n + 27(15 - n) = 355$$

Consecutive Integers
$n, n + 1, n + 2, \ldots$ [2.2.2, p. 71]

The sum of three consecutive integers is 57.

$$n + (n + 1) + (n + 2) = 57$$

Consecutive Even or Odd Integers
$n, n + 2, n + 4, \ldots$ [2.2.2, p. 71]

The sum of three consecutive even integers is 132.

$$n + (n + 2) + (n + 4) = 132$$

Value Mixture Equation
$V = AC$ [2.3.1, p. 76]

A merchant combines coffee that costs \$6 per pound with coffee that costs \$3.20 per pound. How many pounds of each should be used to make 60 lb of a blend that costs \$4.50 per pound?

$$6x + 3.20(60 - x) = 4.50(60)$$

Uniform Motion Equation
$d = rt$ [2.3.2, p. 78]

Two planes are 1640 mi apart and traveling toward each other. One plane is traveling 60 mph faster than the other plane. The planes meet in 2 h. Find the speed of each plane.

$$2r + 2(r + 60) = 1640$$

Annual Simple Interest Equation
$I = Pr$ [2.4.1, p. 88]

An investment of \$4000 is made at an annual simple interest rate of 5%. How much additional money must be invested at an annual simple interest rate of 6.5% so that the total interest earned is \$720?

$$0.05(4000) + 0.065x = 720$$

Percent Mixture Problems
$Q = Ar$ [2.4.2, p. 89]

A silversmith mixed 120 oz of an 80% silver alloy with 240 oz of a 30% silver alloy. Find the percent concentration of the resulting silver alloy.

$$0.80(120) + 0.30(240) = x(360)$$

The Addition Property of Inequalities
If $a > b$, then $a + c > b + c$.
The property is also true for $a < b$. [2.5.1, p. 97]

$$x + 3 > -2$$
$$x + 3 - 3 > -2 - 3$$
$$x > -5$$

The Multiplication Property of Inequalities [2.5.1, p. 98]
Rule 1 If $a > b$ and $c > 0$, then $ac > bc$.
   If $a < b$ and $c > 0$, then $ac < bc$.

$$3x > 2$$
$$\left(\frac{1}{3}\right)(3x) > \left(\frac{1}{3}\right)2$$
$$x > \frac{2}{3}$$

Rule 2 If $a > b$ and $c < 0$, then $ac < bc$.
   If $a < b$ and $c < 0$, then $ac > bc$.

$$-2x < 5$$
$$\frac{-2x}{-2} > \frac{5}{-2}$$
$$x > -\frac{5}{2}$$

Chapter 2 Review Exercises

1. Solve: $x + 4 = -5$

2. Solve: $\frac{2}{3} = x + \frac{3}{4}$

3. Solve: $-3x = -21$

4. Solve: $\frac{2}{3}x = \frac{4}{9}$

5. Solve: $3y - 5 = 3 - 2y$

6. Solve: $3x - 3 + 2x = 7x - 15$

7. Solve: $2(x - 3) = 5(4 - 3x)$

8. Solve: $2x - (3 - 2x) = 4 - 3(4 - 2x)$

9. Solve: $\frac{1}{2}x - \frac{5}{8} = \frac{3}{4}x + \frac{3}{2}$

10. Solve: $\frac{2x - 3}{3} + 2 = \frac{2 - 3x}{5}$

11. Solve: $3x - 7 > -2$
Write the solution set in interval notation.

12. Solve: $2x - 9 < 8x + 15$
Write the solution set in interval notation.

13. Solve: $\dfrac{2}{3}x - \dfrac{5}{8} \geq \dfrac{5}{4}x + 3$
Write the solution set in set-builder notation.

14. Solve: $2 - 3(x - 4) \leq 4x - 2(1 - 3x)$
Write the solution set in set-builder notation.

15. Solve: $-5 < 4x - 1 < 7$
Write the solution set in interval notation.

16. Solve: $5x - 2 > 8$ or $3x + 2 < -4$
Write the solution set in interval notation.

17. Solve: $3x < 4$ and $x + 2 > -1$
Write the solution set in set-builder notation.

18. Solve: $3x - 2 > -4$ or $7x - 5 < 3x + 3$
Write the solution set in set-builder notation.

19. Solve: $|2x - 3| = 8$

20. Solve: $|5x + 8| = 0$

21. Solve: $6 + |3x - 3| = 2$

22. Solve: $|2x - 5| \leq 3$

23. Solve: $|4x - 5| \geq 3$

24. Solve: $|5x - 4| < -2$

25. **Mechanics** The diameter of a bushing is 2.75 in. The bushing has a tolerance of 0.003 in. Find the lower and upper limits of the diameter of the bushing.

26. **Medicine** A doctor has prescribed 2 cc of medication for a patient. The tolerance is 0.25 cc. Find the lower and upper limits of the amount of medication to be given.

27. **Integer Problem** The sum of two integers is twenty. Five times the smaller integer is two more than twice the larger integer. Find the integers.

28. **Integer Problem** Find three consecutive integers such that five times the middle integer is twice the sum of the other two integers.

29. **Coins** A coin collection contains 30 coins in nickels, dimes, and quarters. There are three more dimes than nickels. The value of the coins is $3.55. Find the number of quarters in the collection.

30. **Metallurgy** A silversmith combines 40 oz of pure silver that costs $8.00 per ounce with 200 oz of a silver alloy that costs $3.50 per ounce. Find the cost per ounce of the mixture.

31. **Food Mixtures** A grocer mixed apple juice that costs $3.20 per gallon with 40 gal of cranberry juice that costs $5.50 per gallon. How much apple juice was used to make cranapple juice that costs $4.20 per gallon?

32. Uniform Motion Two planes are 1680 mi apart and traveling toward each other. One plane is traveling 80 mph faster than the other plane. The planes meet in 1.75 h. Find the speed of each plane.

33. Investments Two investments earn an annual income of $635. One investment is earning 10.5% annual simple interest, and the other investment is earning 6.4% annual simple interest. The total investment is $8000. Find the amount invested in each account.

34. Metallurgy An alloy containing 30% tin is mixed with an alloy containing 70% tin. How many pounds of each were used to make 500 lb of an alloy containing 40% tin?

35. Compensation A sales executive earns $800 per month plus a 4% commission on the amount of sales. The executive's goal is to earn at least $3000 per month. What amount of sales will enable the executive to earn $3000 or more per month?

36. Test Scores An average score of 80 to 90 in a psychology class receives a B grade. A student has grades of 92, 66, 72, and 88 on four tests. Find the range of scores on the fifth test that will give the student a B for the course.

Chapter 2 Test

1. Solve: $x - 2 = -4$

2. Solve: $x + \dfrac{3}{4} = \dfrac{5}{8}$

3. Solve: $-\dfrac{3}{4}y = -\dfrac{5}{8}$

4. Solve: $3x - 5 = 7$

5. Solve: $\dfrac{3}{4}y - 2 = 6$

6. Solve: $2x - 3 - 5x = 8 + 2x - 10$

7. Solve: $2[x - (2 - 3x) - 4] = x - 5$

8. Solve: $\dfrac{2}{3}x - \dfrac{5}{6}x = 4$

9. Solve: $\dfrac{2x + 1}{3} - \dfrac{3x + 4}{6} = \dfrac{5x - 9}{9}$

10. Solve: $2x - 5 \geq 5x + 4$
Write the solution set in interval notation.

11. Solve: $4 - 3(x + 2) < 2(2x + 3) - 1$
Write the solution set in interval notation.

12. Solve: $3x - 2 > 4$ or $4 - 5x < 14$
Write the solution set in set-builder notation.

13. Solve: $4 - 3x \geq 7$ and $2x + 3 \geq 7$
Write the solution set in set-builder notation.

14. Solve: $|3 - 5x| = 12$

15. Solve: $2 - |2x - 5| = -7$

16. Solve: $|3x - 1| \leq 2$

17. Solve: $|2x - 1| > 3$

18. Solve: $4 + |2x - 3| = 1$

19. Rental Cars Agency A rents cars for $12 per day and 10¢ for every mile driven. Agency B rents cars for $24 per day with unlimited mileage. How many miles per day can you drive an Agency A car if it is to cost you less than an Agency B car?

20. Medicine A doctor prescribed 3 cc of medication for a patient. The tolerance is 0.1 cc. Find the lower and upper limits of the amount of medication to be given.

21. Stamps A stamp collection contains 11¢, 15¢, and 21¢ stamps. There are twice as many 11¢ stamps as 15¢ stamps. There are 30 stamps in all with a value of $4.22. How many 21¢ stamps are in the collection?

22. Food Mixtures A butcher combines 100 lb of hamburger that costs $2.60 per pound with 60 lb of hamburger that costs $4.20 per pound. Find the cost of the hamburger mixture.

23. Uniform Motion A jogger runs a distance at a speed of 8 mph and returns the same distance running at a speed of 6 mph. Find the total distance that the jogger runs if the total time running is 1 h and 45 min.

24. Investments An investment of $12,000 is deposited in two simple interest accounts. On one account, the annual simple interest rate is 7.8%. On the other, the annual simple interest rate is 9%. The total interest earned for one year is $1020. How much was invested in each account?

25. Mixture Problem How many ounces of pure water must be added to 60 oz of an 8% salt solution to make a 3% salt solution?

Cumulative Review Exercises

1. Simplify: $-2^2 \cdot 3^3$

2. Simplify: $4 - (2 - 5)^2 \div 3 + 2$

3. Simplify: $4 \div \dfrac{\frac{3}{8} - 1}{5} \cdot 2$

4. Evaluate $2a^2 - (b - c)^2$ when $a = 2$, $b = 3$, and $c = -1$.

5. Identify the property that justifies the statement.

$(2x + 3y) + 2 = (3y + 2x) + 2$

6. Find $A \cap B$ given $A = \{3, 5, 7, 9\}$ and $B = \{3, 6, 9\}$.

7. Simplify: $3x - 2[x - 3(2 - 3x) + 5]$

8. Simplify: $5[y - 2(3 - 2y) + 6]$

9. Solve: $4 - 3x = -2$

10. Solve: $-\dfrac{5}{6}b = -\dfrac{5}{12}$

11. Solve: $2x + 5 = 5x + 2$

12. Solve: $\dfrac{5}{12}x - 3 = 7$

13. Solve: $2[3 - 2(3 - 2x)] = 2(3 + x)$

14. Solve: $3[2x - 3(4 - x)] = 2(1 - 2x)$

15. Solve: $\dfrac{3x - 1}{4} - \dfrac{4x - 1}{12} = \dfrac{3 + 5x}{8}$

16. Solve: $3x - 2 \geq 6x + 7$
Write the solution set in set-builder notation.

17. Solve: $5 - 2x \geq 6$ and $3x + 2 \geq 5$
Write the solution set in set-builder notation.

18. Solve: $4x - 1 > 5$ or $2 - 3x < 8$
Write the solution set in set-builder notation.

19. Solve: $|3 - 2x| = 5$

20. Solve: $3 - |2x - 3| = -8$

21. Solve: $|3x - 5| \leq 4$

22. Solve: $|4x - 3| > 5$

23. Graph: $\{x \mid x \geq -2\}$

24. Graph: $\{x \mid x \geq 1\} \cup \{x \mid x < -2\}$

25. Translate and simplify "the sum of three times a number and six added to the product of three and the number."

26. Integer Problem Three times the sum of the first and third of three consecutive odd integers is fifteen more than the second integer. Find the first integer.

27. Stamps A stamp collection consists of 19¢ and 23¢ stamps. The number of 19¢ stamps is five less than twice the number of 23¢ stamps. The total value of the stamps is $3.93. Find the number of 19¢ stamps.

28. Recreation Tickets for a school play sold for $2.25 for each adult and $.75 for each child. The total receipts for 75 tickets were $128.25. Find the number of adult tickets sold.

29. Uniform Motion Two planes are 1400 mi apart and traveling toward each other. One plane is traveling 120 mph faster than the other plane. The planes meet in 2.5 h. Find the speed of the faster plane.

30. Mixture Problem How many liters of a 12% acid solution must be mixed with 4 L of a 5% acid solution to make an 8% acid solution?

31. Investments An investment advisor invested $10,000 in two accounts. One investment earned 9.8% annual simple interest, and the other investment earned 12.8% annual simple interest. The amount of interest earned in one year was $1085. How much was invested in the 9.8% account?

CHAPTER

3

Linear Functions and Inequalities in Two Variables

DVD **SSM** *Online Study Center*

Need help? For online student resources, such as section quizzes, visit the Online Study Center at college.hmco.com/info/aufmanndevmathhb.

Do you have a cellular phone? If you do, you probably know about the many payment options cellular phone companies offer. Many customers pay a monthly fee plus a small charge for each minute used. The amount charged per minute varies depending on each customer's payment plan. In **Exercise 57 on page 196** you will be asked to write a linear function that models the monthly cost of a cell phone in terms of the number of minutes you use. Being able to use a linear function to model a relationship between two variables is an important skill when it comes to budgeting your phone time—and your money!

Prep Test

1. Simplify: $-4(x - 3)$

2. Simplify: $\sqrt{(-6)^2 + (-8)^2}$

3. Simplify: $\dfrac{3 - (-5)}{2 - 6}$

4. Evaluate: $-2x + 5$ for $x = -3$.

5. Evaluate $\dfrac{2r}{r - 1}$ for $r = 5$.

6. Evaluate $2p^3 - 3p + 4$ for $p = -1$.

7. Evaluate $\dfrac{x_1 + x_2}{2}$ for $x_1 = 7$ and $x_2 = -5$.

8. Given $3x - 4y = 12$, find the value of x when $y = 0$.

3.1 The Rectangular Coordinate System

OBJECTIVE 1   ### Points on a rectangular coordinate system

Point of Interest

*A rectangular coordinate system is also called a **Cartesian** coordinate system in honor of Descartes.*

Before the 15th century, geometry and algebra were considered separate branches of mathematics. That changed when René Descartes, a French mathematician who lived from 1596 to 1650, founded **analytic geometry.** In this geometry, a *coordinate system* is used to study relationships between variables.

A **rectangular coordinate system** is formed by two number lines, one horizontal and one vertical, that intersect at the zero point of each line. The point of intersection is called the **origin.** The two lines are called **coordinate axes,** or simply **axes.**

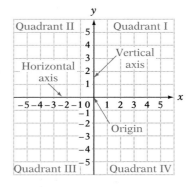

The axes determine a **plane,** which can be thought of as a large, flat sheet of paper. The two axes divide the plane into four regions called **quadrants.** The quadrants are numbered counterclockwise from I to IV.

Each point in the plane can be identified by a pair of numbers called an **ordered pair.** The first number of the pair measures a horizontal distance and is called the **abscissa.** The second number of the pair measures a vertical distance and is called the **ordinate.** The **coordinates** of the point are the numbers in the ordered pair associated with the point. The abscissa is also called the **first coordinate,** or **x-coordinate,** of the ordered pair, and the ordinate is also called the **second coordinate,** or **y-coordinate,** of the ordered pair.

Point of Interest

Gottfried Leibnitz introduced the words abscissa *and* ordinate. *Abscissa is from Latin meaning "to cut off." Originally, Leibnitz used* abscissa linea, *"cut off a line." The root of* ordinate *is a Latin word used to suggest the sense of order.*

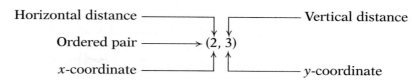

When drawing a rectangular coordinate system, we often label the horizontal axis x and the vertical axis y. In this case, the coordinate system is called an ***xy*-coordinate system.** To graph or plot a point in the *xy*-coordinate system, place a dot at the location given by the ordered pair. The **graph of an ordered pair** is the dot drawn at the coordinates of the point in the *xy*-coordinate system. The points whose coordinates are $(3, 4)$ and $(-2.5, -3)$ are graphed in the figure at the right.

The points whose coordinates are $(3, -1)$ and $(-1, 3)$ are graphed at the right. Note that the graphs are in different locations. The *order* of the coordinates of an ordered pair is important.

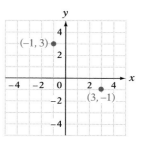

Take Note

The *ordered pair* is an important concept. Remember that there are two numbers (the *pair*) and that the *order* in which they are given is important.

The *xy*-coordinate system is used to graph equations in *two variables*. Examples of equations in two variables are shown at the right.

$$y = 3x + 7$$
$$y = x^2 - 4x + 3$$
$$x^2 + y^2 = 25$$
$$x = \frac{y}{y^2 + 4}$$

A **solution of an equation in two variables** is an ordered pair (x, y) whose coordinates make the equation a true statement.

■   Is the ordered pair $(-3, 7)$ a solution of the equation $y = -2x + 1$?

Replace x by -3 and replace y by 7. Then simplify.

$$
\begin{array}{c|c}
\multicolumn{2}{c}{y = -2x + 1} \\
\hline
7 & -2(-3) + 1 \\
7 & 6 + 1 \\
\end{array}
$$
$$7 = 7$$

Compare the results. If the resulting equation is a true statement, the ordered pair is a solution of the equation. If it is not a true statement, the ordered pair is not a solution of the equation.

Yes the ordered pair $(-3, 7)$ is a solution of the equation.

Besides the ordered pair $(-3, 7)$, there are many other ordered-pair solutions of the equation $y = -2x + 1$. For example, $(-5, 11)$, $(0, 1)$, $\left(-\frac{3}{2}, 4\right)$ and $(4, -7)$ are also solutions of the equation.

In general, an equation in two variables has an infinite number of solutions. By choosing any value of x and substituting that value into the equation, we can calculate a corresponding value of y. The resulting ordered-pair solution (x, y) of the equation can be graphed in a rectangular coordinate system.

Graph the solutions (x, y) of $y = x^2 - 1$ when x equals -2, -1, 0, 1, and 2.

Substitute each value of x into the equation and solve for y. Then graph the resulting ordered pairs. It is convenient to record the ordered-pair solutions in a table similar to the one shown below.

x	$y = x^2 - 1$	y	(x, y)
-2	$y = (-2)^2 - 1$	3	$(-2, 3)$
-1	$y = (-1)^2 - 1$	0	$(-1, 0)$
0	$y = 0^2 - 1$	-1	$(0, -1)$
1	$y = 1^2 - 1$	0	$(1, 0)$
2	$y = 2^2 - 1$	3	$(2, 3)$

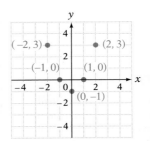

EXAMPLE 1   Determine the ordered-pair solution of $y = \dfrac{x}{x - 2}$ that corresponds to $x = 4$.

Solution $y = \dfrac{x}{x - 2}$

$y = \dfrac{4}{4 - 2}$ • **Replace x by 4 and solve for y.**

$y = 2$

The ordered-pair solution is $(4, 2)$.

PROBLEM 1   Determine the ordered-pair solution of $y = \dfrac{3x}{x + 1}$ that corresponds to $x = -2$.

Solution   See page S6.

EXAMPLE 2   Graph the ordered-pair solutions of $y = x^2 - x$ when $x = -1$, 0, 1, and 2.

Solution

x	y
-1	2
0	0
1	0
2	2

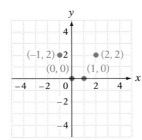

PROBLEM 2   Graph the ordered-pair solutions of $y = |x + 1|$ when $x = -3$, -2, -1, 0, and 1.

Solution   See page S6.

OBJECTIVE **2**   # Find the length and midpoint of a line segment

The distance between two points in an xy-coordinate system can be calculated by using the Pythagorean Theorem.

Take Note

A **right triangle** contains one 90° angle. The side opposite the 90° angle is called the **hypotenuse**. The other two sides are called **legs**.

Pythagorean Theorem

If a and b are the lengths of the legs of a right triangle and c is the length of the hypotenuse, then $a^2 + b^2 = c^2$.

Point of Interest

Although Pythagoras (c. 550 B.C.) is given credit for this theorem, a clay tablet called Plimpton 322 shows that the Babylonians knew the theorem 1000 years before Pythagoras!

Consider the two points and the right triangle shown at the right. The vertical distance between $P_1(x_1, y_1)$ and $P_2(x_2, y_2)$ is $|y_2 - y_1|$. The horizontal distance between the points $P_1(x_1, y_1)$ and $P_2(x_2, y_2)$ is $|x_2 - x_1|$.

The quantity d^2 is calculated by applying the Pythagorean Theorem to the right triangle.

$$d^2 = |x_2 - x_1|^2 + |y_2 - y_1|^2$$

Because the square of a number is always nonnegative, the absolute value signs are not necessary.

$$d^2 = (x_2 - x_1)^2 + (y_2 - y_1)^2$$

The distance d is the square root of d^2.

$$d = \sqrt{(x_2 - x_1)^2 + (y_2 - y_1)^2}$$

The Distance Formula

If $P_1(x_1, y_1)$ and $P_2(x_2, y_2)$ are two points in the plane, then the distance d between the two points is given by

$$d = \sqrt{(x_2 - x_1)^2 + (y_2 - y_1)^2}$$

EXAMPLE 3   Find the exact distance between the points whose coordinates are $(-3, 2)$ and $(4, -1)$.

Solution $d = \sqrt{(x_2 - x_1)^2 + (y_2 - y_1)^2}$ • **Use the distance formula.**

$\quad\quad\quad = \sqrt{[4 - (-3)]^2 + (-1 - 2)^2}$ • $(x_1, y_1) = (-3, 2)$ **and** $(x_2, y_2) = (4, -1)$.

$\quad\quad\quad = \sqrt{7^2 + (-3)^2} = \sqrt{49 + 9}$

$\quad\quad\quad = \sqrt{58}$

The distance between the points is $\sqrt{58}$.

PROBLEM 3   Find the exact distance between the points whose coordinates are $(5, -2)$ and $(-4, 3)$.

■   **Solution**   See page S6.

The **midpoint of a line segment** is equidistant from its endpoints. The coordinates of the midpoint of the line segment P_1P_2 are (x_m, y_m). The intersection of the horizontal line segment through P_1 and the vertical line segment through P_2 is Q, with coordinates (x_2, y_1).

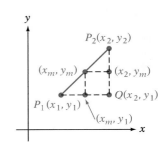

The x-coordinate x_m of the midpoint of the line segment P_1P_2 is the same as the x-coordinate of the midpoint of the line segment P_1Q. It is the average of the x-coordinates of the points P_1 and P_2.

$$x_m = \frac{x_1 + x_2}{2}$$

Similarly, the y-coordinate y_m of the midpoint of the line segment P_1P_2 is the same as the y-coordinate of the midpoint of the line segment P_2Q. It is the average of the y-coordinates of the points P_1 and P_2.

$$y_m = \frac{y_1 + y_2}{2}$$

The Midpoint Formula

If $P_1(x_1, y_1)$ and $P_2(x_2, y_2)$ are the endpoints of a line segment, then the coordinates of the midpoint (x_m, y_m) of the line segment are given by

$$x_m = \frac{x_1 + x_2}{2} \quad \text{and} \quad y_m = \frac{y_1 + y_2}{2}$$

EXAMPLE 4   Find the coordinates of the midpoint of the line segment with endpoints $(-5, 4)$ and $(-3, 7)$.

Solution $x_m = \dfrac{x_1 + x_2}{2}$ $y_m = \dfrac{y_1 + y_2}{2}$ • **Use the midpoint formula.**

$\qquad\qquad = \dfrac{-5 + (-3)}{2} \qquad\quad = \dfrac{4 + 7}{2}$ • $(x_1, y_1) = (-5, 4)$ and $(x_2, y_2) = (-3, 7)$.

$\qquad\qquad = -4 \qquad\qquad\qquad = \dfrac{11}{2}$

The midpoint is $\left(-4, \dfrac{11}{2}\right)$.

PROBLEM 4   Find the coordinates of the midpoint of the line segment with endpoints $(-3, -5)$ and $(-2, 3)$.

■   **Solution**   See page S6.

OBJECTIVE **3** **Graph a scatter diagram**

Discovering a relationship between two variables is an important task in the study of mathematics. These relationships occur in many forms and in a wide variety of applications. Here are some examples.

- A botanist wants to know the relationship between the number of bushels of wheat yielded per acre and the amount of watering per acre.
- An environmental scientist wants to know the relationship between the incidence of skin cancer and the amount of ozone in the atmosphere.
- A business analyst wants to know the relationship between the price of a product and the number of products that are sold at that price.

A researcher may investigate the relationship between two variables by means of *regression analysis,* which is a branch of statistics. The study of the relationship between two variables may begin with a **scatter diagram,** which is a graph of the ordered pairs of the known data.

The following table shows data collected by a university registrar comparing the grade-point averages (GPAs) of graduating high school seniors and their scores on a national test.

GPA, x	3.25	3.00	3.00	3.50	3.50	2.75	2.50	2.50	2.00	2.00	1.50
Score, y	1200	1200	1000	1500	1100	1000	1000	900	800	900	700

The scatter diagram for these data is shown at the right. Each ordered pair represents the GPA and the test score for a student. For example, the ordered pair (2.75, 1000) indicates that one student with a GPA of 2.75 had a test score of 1000.

EXAMPLE 5 The scatter diagram on the following page shows the number of computer majors, in thousands, in the United States and Canada in the fall of each year from 1999 to 2003. (*Source*: Computing Research Association Taulbee Survey)

A. How many students were computer majors in the fall of 2000?

B. In the fall of which year was the number of computer majors less than 19,000?

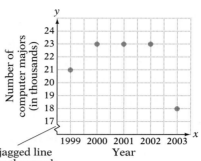

This jagged line means the graph does not begin at zero.

Strategy   **A.** Read the graph. Find 2000 on the horizontal axis. Follow that mark up vertically to determine the number of computer majors in the fall of that year.

B. Find the horizontal line that represents 19,000. Determine the year for which the number of students is below that line.

Solution   **A.** In the fall of 2000, 23,000 students were computer majors.

B. The number of computer majors was less than 19,000 in 2003.

PROBLEM 5   The table below shows the estimated number of adults, in millions, age 65 and older who will have some form of vision loss. Graph the scatter diagram for these data.

Year, x	2000	2010	2020	2030
Adults age 65 and older with vision loss (in millions), y	7.3	8.3	11.2	15.0

Source: Lighthouse National Survey on Vision Loss

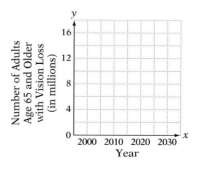

Solution   See page S6.

OBJECTIVE **4**   ## Average rate of change

The table at the left shows the population of California each decade from 1850 to 2000. (*Source:* U.S. Bureau of the Census). These data are graphed in the scatter diagram below.

Population of California

Year	Population (in millions)
1850	0.1
1860	0.4
1870	0.6
1880	0.9
1890	1.2
1900	1.5
1910	2.4
1920	3.4
1930	5.7
1940	6.9
1950	10.6
1960	15.7
1970	20.0
1980	23.7
1990	29.8
2000	33.9

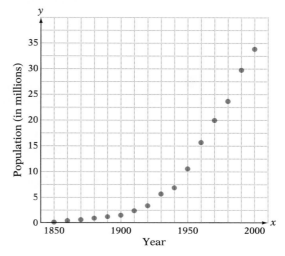

One way to describe how the population of California has changed over time is to calculate the change in population for a given time period. For example, we can find the change in population from 1990 to 2000.

Population in 2000 − population in 1990 = 33.9 million − 29.8 million
= 4.1 million

The amount of change in the population, 4.1 million, does not describe how rapid the growth in population was. To describe the rate of growth, or the *rate of change*, we must consider the number of years over which that growth took place. To determine how rapidly the population grew from 1990 to 2000, divide the change in population by the number of years during which that growth took place.

$$\frac{\text{Change in population}}{\text{Change in years}} = \frac{\text{population in 2000} - \text{population in 1990}}{2000 - 1990}$$

$$= \frac{33.9 - 29.8}{2000 - 1990}$$

$$= \frac{4.1}{10} = 0.41$$

The average rate of change was 0.41 million, or 410,000, people per year. This means that *on average*, from 1990 to 2000, the population of California increased 410,000 people per year.

Consider the two points on the graph that correspond to these years.

(1990, 29.8)   and   (2000, 33.9)

Note that the average rate of change is calculated by dividing the difference between the *y* values of the two points by the difference between the *x* values of the two points.

Average Rate of Change

The average rate of change of y with respect to x is $\dfrac{\text{change in } y}{\text{change in } x}$.

To calculate the average rate of change, think

$$\frac{y \text{ value of second point} - y \text{ value of first point}}{x \text{ value of second point} - x \text{ value of first point}}$$

 Find the average annual rate of change in the population of California from 1980 to 1990.

In 1980, the population was 23.7 million: (1980, 23.7)
In 1990, the population was 29.8 million: (1990, 29.8)

$$
\begin{aligned}
\text{Average rate of change} &= \frac{\text{change in } y}{\text{change in } x} \\[4pt]
&= \frac{\text{population in 1990} - \text{population in 1980}}{1990 - 1980} \\[4pt]
&= \frac{29.8 - 23.7}{1990 - 1980} \\[4pt]
&= \frac{6.1}{10} = 0.61
\end{aligned}
$$

The average rate of change in the population was 0.61 million, or 610,000, people per year.

Take Note

The rate of change in the population of California is not constant. It varies for different time periods.

From 1990 to 2000, the average rate of change was 410,000 people per year, whereas from 1980 to 1990, the average rate of change was 610,000 people per year. Therefore, the average rate of growth from 1980 to 1990 was greater than the average rate of growth from 1990 to 2000.

EXAMPLE 6 Find the average annual rate of change in California's population from 1850 to 1950.

Solution In 1850, the population was 0.1 million: (1850, 0.1)
In 1950, the population was 10.6 million: (1950, 10.6)

$$
\begin{aligned}
\text{Average rate of change} &= \frac{\text{change in } y}{\text{change in } x} \\[4pt]
&= \frac{\text{population in 1950} - \text{population in 1850}}{1950 - 1850} \\[4pt]
&= \frac{10.6 - 0.1}{1950 - 1850} \\[4pt]
&= \frac{10.5}{100} = 0.105
\end{aligned}
$$

The average rate of change in the population was 105,000 people per year.

Note that if the ordinates and abscissas are subtracted in the reverse order, the result is the same.

$$\text{Average rate of change} = \frac{\text{population in 1850} - \text{population in 1950}}{1850 - 1950}$$

$$= \frac{0.1 - 10.6}{1850 - 1950} = \frac{-10.5}{-100} = 0.105$$

PROBLEM 6   Find the average annual rate of change in California's population from 1900 to 2000.

Solution   See page S6.

The table below shows the median salaries in 1990, 1995, 2000, and 2005 for Boston Red Sox players and New York Yankees players. (*Source*: USAToday.com) Use these data for Example 7 and Problem 7.

Year	1990	1995	2000	2005
Median salary, Boston Red Sox	282,500	282,500	2,000,000	2,875,000
Median salary, New York Yankees	437,500	531,000	1,350,000	5,833,334

EXAMPLE 7   Find the average annual rate of change in the median salary of Boston Red Sox players between 1990 and 2005. Round to the nearest thousand dollars.

Solution   In 1990, the median salary was 282,500: (1990, 282,500)

In 2005, the median salary was 2,875,000: (2005, 2,875,000)

$$\text{The average rate of change} = \frac{\text{change in } y}{\text{change in } x}$$

$$= \frac{\text{median salary in 2005} - \text{median salary in 1990}}{2005 - 1990}$$

$$= \frac{2,875,000 - 282,500}{2005 - 1990}$$

$$= \frac{2,592,500}{15} \approx 173,000$$

The average rate of change was $173,000 per year.

PROBLEM 7   **A.** Find the average annual rate of change in the median salary of New York Yankees players between 1990 and 2005. Round to the nearest thousand dollars.

B. Was this greater than or less than the average annual rate of change in the median salary of Boston Red Sox players between 1990 and 2005?

Solution   See page S6.

3.1   Concept Review

Determine whether the following statements are always true, sometimes true, or never true.

1. An equation in two variables has an infinite number of solutions.

2. A rectangular coordinate system has two real number axes.

3. In the graph of an ordered pair, the first number is the *y*-coordinate and the second number is the *x*-coordinate.

4. The solution of an equation with two variables is an ordered pair.

5. The point $(-2, -4)$ is in the fourth quadrant.

6. In quadrant III, the *y*-coordinate of the point is negative.

3.1   Exercises

1   Points on a rectangular coordinate system

Complete Exercises 1 and 2 by replacing each question mark with the word *left, right, up,* or *down.*

1. To graph the point $(6, -2)$, start at the origin and move 6 units ___?___ and 2 units ___?___.

2. To graph the point $(-3, 5)$, start at the origin and move 3 units ___?___ and 5 units ___?___.

3. Graph the ordered pairs $(0, -1)$, $(2, 0)$, $(3, 2)$, and $(-1, 4)$.

4. Graph the ordered pairs $(-1, -3)$, $(0, -4)$, $(0, 4)$, and $(3, -2)$.

5. Find the coordinates of each point.

6. Find the coordinates of each point.

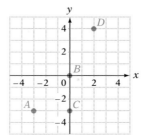

7. Draw a line through all points with an abscissa of 2.

8. Draw a line through all points with an abscissa of -3.

9. Draw a line through all points with an ordinate of -3.

10. Draw a line through all points with an ordinate of 4.

11. Graph the ordered-pair solutions of $y = x^2$ when $x = -2, -1, 0, 1,$ and 2.

12. Graph the ordered-pair solutions of $y = -x^2 + 1$ when $x = -2, -1, 0, 1,$ and 2.

13. Graph the ordered-pair solutions of $y = |x + 1|$ when $x = -5, -3, 0, 3,$ and 5.

14. Graph the ordered-pair solutions of $y = -2|x|$ when $x = -3, -1, 0, 1,$ and 3.

15. Graph the ordered-pair solutions of $y = -x^2 + 2$ when $x = -2, -1, 0, 1,$ and 2.

16. Graph the ordered-pair solutions of $y = -x^2 + 4$ when $x = -3, -1, 0, 1,$ and 3.

17. Graph the ordered-pair solutions of $y = x^3 - 2$ when $x = -1, 0, 1,$ and 2.

18. Graph the ordered-pair solutions of $y = -x^3 + 1$ when $x = -1, 0, 1,$ and $\frac{3}{2}$.

19. Let a and b be positive numbers such that $a < b$. In which quadrant is each point located?

   a. (a, b) **b.** $(-a, b)$ **c.** $(b - a, -b)$ **d.** $(a - b, -b - a)$

20. Let a and b be positive numbers. State whether the two given points lie on the x-axis, the y-axis, a horizontal line other than the x-axis, or a vertical line other than the y-axis.

   a. $(-a, -b)$ and $(a, -b)$ **b.** $(0, a)$ and $(0, -b)$

2   Find the length and midpoint of a line segment

21. For points $P_1(3, -3)$ and $P_2(-1, 4)$, identify each of the following values:
$x_1 = $ _____?_____ , $x_2 = $ _____?_____ , $y_1 = $ _____?_____ , and $y_2 = $ _____?_____ .

22. Find the length of the line segment between the points P_1 and P_2 given in Exercise 21.

$d = \sqrt{(x_2 - x_1)^2 + (y_2 - y_1)^2}$ • Use the ____?____ Formula.

$\quad = \sqrt{(\underline{\ ?\ } - \underline{\ ?\ })^2 + (\underline{\ ?\ } - \underline{\ ?\ })^2}$ • Substitute coordinates.

$\quad = \sqrt{(\underline{\ ?\ })^2 + (\underline{\ ?\ })^2}$ • Perform operations inside parentheses.

$\quad = \sqrt{\underline{\ ?\ } + \underline{\ ?\ }}$ • Simplify exponential expressions.

$\quad = \sqrt{\underline{\ ?\ }}$ • Add.

The length of the line segment between $P_1(3, -3)$ and $P_2(-1, 4)$ is ____?____ .

Find the length and midpoint of the line segment between the given points.

23. $P_1(3, 5)$ and $P_2(4, 1)$ **24.** $P_1(-2, 3)$ and $P_2(5, -1)$ **25.** $P_1(0, 3)$ and $P_2(-2, 4)$

26. $P_1(6, -1)$ and $P_2(-3, -2)$ **27.** $P_1(-3, -5)$ and $P_2(2, -4)$ **28.** $P_1(-7, -5)$ and $P_2(-2, -1)$

29. $P_1(5, -2)$ and $P_2(-1, 5)$ **30.** $P_1(3, -5)$ and $P_2(6, 0)$ **31.** $P_1(5, -5)$ and $P_2(2, -5)$

32. $a, b, c,$ and d are positive numbers such that $a > c$ and $b < d$. In what quadrant is the midpoint of the line segment joining $P_1(a, b)$ and $P_2(-c, -d)$?

33. $a, b, c,$ and d are positive numbers such that $a < c$ and $b < d$. In what quadrant is the midpoint of the line segment joining $P_1(-a, -b)$ and $P_2(c, d)$?

3   Graph a scatter diagram

Solve.

34.   **Chemistry**   The amount of a substance that can be dissolved in a fixed amount of water usually increases as the temperature of the water increases. Cerium selenate, however, does not behave in this manner. The graph at the right shows the number of grams of cerium selenate that will dissolve in 100 mg of water for various temperatures, in degrees Celsius.
a. Determine the temperature at which 25 g of cerium selenate will dissolve.
b. Determine the number of grams of cerium selenate that will dissolve when the temperature is 80°C.

35. 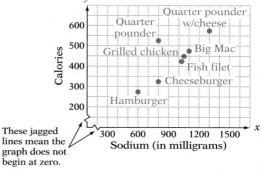 **Nutrition**   Sodium content in foods is a measure of the salt content in the food. The scatter diagram at the right shows the approximate amount of sodium and the number of calories in various sandwiches offered at a McDonald's restaurant. (*Source:* Gourmet Connection website/Convence Labs)

a. How many calories are in a hamburger?

b. How many milligrams of sodium are in a Big Mac?

36. **Automotive Technology**   When water freezes, it expands. This expansion is a potential problem for cars, because the freezing water can cause the engine block of a car to crack. Ethylene glycol is mixed with water to produce an antifreeze that helps prevent the water in the car from freezing. The scatter diagram at the right shows the changes in the freezing point of a solution of water and ethylene glycol that occur as the percent of ethylene glycol is increased.

a. At what temperature will a 45% mixture of ethylene glycol and water freeze?

b. What percent of ethylene glycol is required to protect the car to temperatures as low as −30°F?

37. 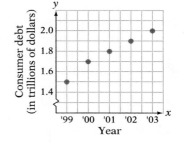 **Consumer Debt**   The scatter diagram at the right shows how much consumers owed in the years 1999 through 2003. (*Source:* Federal Reserve)

a. What was the consumer debt in 2001?

b. In which year was consumer debt first greater than $1.9 trillion?

c. Looking at the trend of the data, would you expect consumer debt in 2004 to be greater than or less than consumer debt in 2003?

38. Look at the table of data in Exercise 40. The lowest x-value is ___?___ and the highest x-value is ___?___. The lowest y-value is ___?___ and the highest y-value is ___?___. In a scatter diagram of the data, the x-axis must show values from at least ___?___ to ___?___, and the y-axis must show values from at least ___?___ to ___?___.

39. Look at the table of data in Exercise 41. The lowest x-value is ___?___ and the highest x-value is ___?___. The lowest y-value is ___?___ and the highest y-value is ___?___. In a scatter diagram of the data, the x-axis must show values from at least ___?___ to ___?___, and the y-axis must show values from at least ___?___ to ___?___.

40. 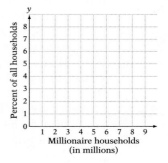 **Wealth**   The table shows the number of U.S. households with a net worth of $1 million or more every three years from 1992 to 2004. Also shown is the millionaire households as a percent of all households in the United States. (*Source:* Edward Wolff, professor of economics, New York University; Federal Reserve) Graph the scatter diagram for these data.

Millionaire households (in millions), x	3.1	3.4	4.1	5.0	8.2
Percent of all households, y		3.2	3.4	4.0	4.7	7.0

41. 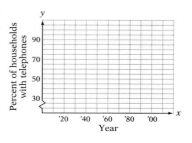 **Telecommunications** As shown in the table below, the percent of households with telephones has increased over the years. (*Source: U.S. Census Bureau/Federal Communications Commission*) Draw a scatter diagram for these data.

Year, x	'20	'30	'40	'50	'60	'70	'80	'90	'00
Percent, y	35	41	37	62	78	90	93	95	97

4   Average rate of change

42. **Temperature** On November 5 in midstate New Hampshire, the temperature at 6 A.M. was 34°F. At 2 P.M. on the same day, the temperature was 58°F. Find the average rate of change in temperature per hour.

43. **Demography** The table at the right shows the population of Texas each decade from 1850 to 2000. (*Source:* U.S. Bureau of the Census)
  a. Find the average annual rate of change in the population of Texas from 1900 to 2000.
  b. Was the average annual rate of change in the population from 1900 to 1950 greater than or less than the average annual rate of change in the population from 1950 to 2000?
  c. Was the average annual rate of change in the population of Texas from 1980 to 1990 greater than or less than the average annual rate of change in the population of California from 1980 to 1990? (See page 136 for the average annual rate of change in the population of California from 1980 to 1990.)

For Exercises 44 and 45, use the table in Exercise 43.

44. During which decade was the average annual rate of change in the population the least?

45. During which decade was the average annual rate of change in the population approximately 300,000 people?

46. **Cremation** In the United States in 1990, there were 2.15 million deaths and 367,975 cremations. In 1999, there were 2.35 million deaths and 595,617 cremations. (*Source:* Cremation Association of North America)
  a. In the 1990s, what was the average annual rate of change in the number of deaths in the United States? Round to the nearest thousand.
  b. In the 1990s, what was the average annual rate of change in the number of cremations in the United States? Round to the nearest thousand.
  c. In the 1990s, which increased at a greater rate, the number of deaths or the number of cremations?

47. **Traffic Fatalities** The number of pedestrians killed by motor vehicles in 1990 was 6482; in 2000 it was 4727. (*Source:* National Highway Transportation Safety Administration)

Population of Texas	
Year	Population (in millions)
1850	0.2
1860	0.6
1870	0.8
1880	1.6
1890	2.2
1900	3.0
1910	3.9
1920	4.7
1930	5.8
1940	6.4
1950	7.7
1960	9.6
1970	11.2
1980	14.2
1990	17.0
2000	20.9

a. Find the average annual rate of change in the number of pedestrian fatalities from 1990 to 2000. (*Note:* A negative average rate of change denotes a decrease.)

b. Why can the answer to part a be considered encouraging?

48. **Energy Prices** The table at the right shows the average price per gallon of gasoline in the United States each year from 1990 to 2004. (*Source*: Energy Information Administration)

a. Find the average rate of change per year in the price of a gallon of gasoline from 1990 to 2000.

b. Which was greater, the average rate of change per year from 1990 to 1995 or the average rate of change per year from 1995 to 2000? How much greater?

49. **Trademarks** The table below shows the number of applications for trademark registration in the United States in 1990, 1995, 2000, and 2005. (*Source: International Trademark Association*) One reason for the large number of applications is the increase in popularity of the Internet and the desire to register domain names and websites.

a. Find the average annual rate of change in the number of applications from 1990 to 2000.

b. How much greater was the average annual rate of change in the number of applications from 1995 to 2000 than from 1990 to 1995?

Year	Price per Gallon
1990	$1.16
1991	$1.14
1992	$1.13
1993	$1.11
1994	$1.11
1995	$1.15
1996	$1.23
1997	$1.23
1998	$1.06
1999	$1.17
2000	$1.51
2001	$1.46
2002	$1.36
2003	$1.59
2004	$1.88

Year	1990	1995	2000	2005
Applications (in thousands)	120	175	375	324

3.1 Applying Concepts

50. Graph the ordered pairs $\left(x, \frac{1}{x}\right)$, where $x \in \left\{-2, -1, -\frac{1}{2}, -\frac{1}{3}, \frac{1}{3}, \frac{1}{2}, 1, 2\right\}$.

51. Graph the ordered pairs (x, x^2), where $x \in \{-2, -1, 0, 1, 2\}$.

52. Draw a line passing through every point whose ordinate is the additive inverse of its abscissa.

53. Draw a line passing through every point whose abscissa equals its ordinate.

54. Describe the graph of all the ordered pairs (x, y) that are 5 units from the origin.

55. Consider two distinct fixed points in the plane. Describe the graph of all the points (x, y) that are equidistant from these fixed points.

3.2 Introduction to Functions

OBJECTIVE 1   Evaluate a function

Describing relationships between two quantities is an important aspect of mathematics. One way to describe a relationship between two quantities is in a graph. The graph in Figure 3.1, based on data from IDC, Inc., shows the projected number of users, worldwide, of WiFi subscribers.

Figure 3.1

The data in the graph can be written as ordered pairs: (2002, 1), (2003, 3), (2004, 5), (2005, 10), (2006, 17), and (2007, 25). The ordered pair (2004, 5) means that there were 5 million WiFi subscribers, worldwide, in 2004.

A table is another way of describing a relationship between two quantities. The table at the right shows a grading scale for an exam. This grading scale also can be described with ordered pairs. Some of the possible ordered pairs are (95, A), (72, C), (84, B), (92, A), (61, D), and (88, B).

Exam Score	Grade
90–100	A
80–89	B
70–79	C
60–69	D
0–59	F

A third way to describe a relationship between two quantities is an equation. In the early days of jet travel, the U.S. Air Force wanted to examine the physical effects of high altitudes on pilots in the event that the pilot had to eject from a plane. One of the experiments, on August 16, 1960, involved Joseph Kittinger. He ascended in Excelsior III, a helium-filled balloon, to a height of 102,800 ft above Earth. When he reached this altitude, he jumped from the gondola and began free-falling. The relationship between the distance, in feet, he fell in t seconds after leaving the gondola can be approximated by the equation $s = 16t^2$.

Point of Interest

About 28 s after Kittinger left the gondola, he was at an altitude of 90,000 ft and was traveling about 614 mph. This remains the fastest speed a human has ever attained without the aid of a propulsion system. As he continued to descend, air resistance slowed his speed. At 50,000 ft, his speed was about 250 mph. During the first 30 s, the equation $s = 16t^2$ was a good approximation of the distance he fell because air resistance was negligible. At lower altitudes, a different equation that considers air resistance would be more appropriate.

The numbers in the table were generated from the equation $s = 16t^2$. These numbers can be written as ordered pairs, where the first coordinate of the ordered pair is the time Kittinger was falling and the second coordinate is the distance fallen during that time. The ordered pairs are (5, 400), (10, 1600), (15, 3600), (20, 6400), and (25, 10,000). These are only some of the possible ordered pairs. Because there is a known equation relating the two quantities, we can find the distance for a given value of t. Some other possible ordered pairs are (11, 1936) and (16.4, 4303.36).

$16t^2 = s$	
5	400
10	1600
15	3600
20	6400
25	10,000

The three relationships given above have something in common: *ordered pairs*. The relationships can be described as the ordered pairs

(year, number of WiFi subscribers)
(exam score, letter grade)
(time, distance)

In mathematics, a set of ordered pairs is called a *relation*.

Definition of Relation

A **relation** is any set of ordered pairs.

The **domain** of a relation is the set of first coordinates of the ordered pairs of a relation. The **range** of a relation is the set of second coordinates of the ordered pairs of the relation.

For the year and number of WiFi subscribers relation,

$$\text{Domain} = \{2002, 2003, 2004, 2005, 2006, 2007\}$$
$$\text{Range} = \{1, 3, 5, 10, 17, 25\}$$

For the relation between an exam score and letter grade,

$$\text{Domain} = \{0, 1, 2, 3, 4, \ldots, 97, 98, 99, 100\}$$
$$\text{Range} = \{A, B, C, D, F\}$$

The domain and range for the falling pilot are a little more difficult because there are an infinite number of choices for time, t, the first coordinate of the ordered pair. As mentioned in the first Take Note of this section, the equation $s = 16t^2$ approximates the distance the pilot falls during the first 30 s. We can describe the domain (all of the times between 0 and 30) using set-builder notation or interval notation.

$$\text{Domain} = \{t \mid 0 \leq t \leq 30\} \qquad \text{or} \qquad \text{Domain} = [0, 30]$$

For each one of the choices of t, there is a corresponding distance s, the second coordinate of the ordered pair. Therefore, the range is an infinite set. The range is from 0 feet (just starting the descent) to the distance he fell in 30 s. Substituting 30 into $s = 16t^2$ gives $s = 14,400$. Thus

$$\text{Range} = \{s \mid 0 \leq s \leq 14,400\} \qquad \text{or} \qquad \text{Range} = [0, 14,400]$$

Although relations are important in mathematics, the concept of *function* is especially useful in applications.

Definition of a Function

A **function** is a relation in which no two ordered pairs have the same first coordinate.

To see the difference between a relation and a function, consider the situation of a meteorologist who is taking temperature and percent humidity readings at a weather station at the same time each day. Here are data from nine consecutive days.

Temperature (°F)	72	75	67	71	70	73	68	75	68
Percent humidity	47	50	39	41	36	50	37	44	48

The set of ordered pairs is

{(72, 47), (75, 50), (67, 39), (71, 41), (70, 36),
(73, 50), (68, 37), (75, 44), (68, 48)}.

The temperature and humidity relation is <u>not</u> a function because the ordered pairs (75, 50) and (75, 44) have the same first coordinate. The ordered pairs (68, 37) and (68, 48) also have the same first coordinate.

For the exam score and letter grade relation discussed earlier, if there were two ordered pairs with the same first coordinate and different second coordinates, it would mean that two students with the same exam score (first coordinate) would receive different letter grades (second coordinate)—for example, (83, B) and (83, F). But this does not happen with a grading scale. Thus there are no two ordered pairs with the same first coordinate. The exam score and grade relation is a function.

> ### Take Note
> Recall that when listing elements of a set, we list duplicate elements only once.

EXAMPLE 1 What are the domain and range of the following relation? Is the relation a function?

{(2, 4), (3, 6), (4, 8), (5, 10), (4, 6), (6, 10)}

Solution Domain = {3, 4, 5, 6}   • **The domain of the relation is the set of first coordinates of the ordered pairs.**

Range = {4, 6, 8, 10}   • **The range of the relation is the set of second coordinates of the ordered pairs.**

Because there are two ordered pairs with the same first coordinate and different second coordinates, (4, 8) and (4, 6), the relation is not a function.

PROBLEM 1 What are the domain and range of the following relation? Is the relation a function?

{(−2, 6), (−1, 3), (0, 0), (1, −3), (2, −6), (3, −9)}

Solution See page S7.

For each element of the domain of a relation, there is a corresponding element in the range of the relation. A possible diagram of the relation in Example 1 is

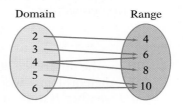

{(2, 4), (3, 6), (4, 8), (5, 10), (4, 6), (6, 10)}

Note from the diagram that there are two arrows from 4 in the domain to different elements, 6 and 8, in the range. This means that there are two ordered pairs, (4, 6) and (4, 6), with the same first coordinate and different second coordinates, and the relation is not a function.

■ What are the ordered pairs of the relation in the diagram below? Is the relation a function?

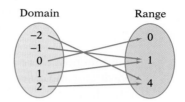

The relation is $\{(-2, 4), (-1, 1), (0, 0), (1, 1), (2, 4)\}$. There are no ordered pairs with the same first coordinate. The relation is a function.

Although a function can be described in terms of ordered pairs, in a table, or by a graph, a major focus of this text will be functions represented by equations in two variables.

For instance, the equation $s = 16t^2$ given earlier describes the relationship between the time, t, Joseph Kittinger fell and the distance, s, he fell. The ordered pairs can be written as (t, s), where $s = 16t^2$. By substituting $16t^2$ for s, we can also write the ordered pairs as $(t, 16t^2)$. Because the distance he falls *depends* on how long he has been falling, s is called the **dependent variable** and t is called the **independent variable.** For the equation $s = 16t^2$, we say that "distance is a function of time."

Take Note

Sometimes the independent variable is called the input of a function and the dependent variable is called the output.

A function can be thought of as a rule that pairs one number with another number. For instance, the **square function** pairs a real number with its square. This function can be represented by the equation $y = x^2$. This equation states that, given any element x in the domain, the value of y in the range is the square of x. In this case, the independent variable is x and the dependent variable is y. When $x = 6$, $y = 36$ and one ordered pair of the function is $(6, 36)$. When $x = -7$, $y = 49$. The ordered pair $(-7, 49)$ belongs to the function.

Other ordered pairs of the function are $(-2, 4)$, $\left(\dfrac{3}{4}, \dfrac{9}{16}\right)$, and $(-1.1, 1.21)$.

In many cases, you may think of a function as a machine that turns one number into another number. For instance, you can think of the square function machine at the right taking an **input** (an element from the domain) and creating an **output** (an element of the range) that is the square of the input.

$$-4 \quad 0 \quad 3$$

Square $\longrightarrow$ 16 0 9

$$f(x) = x^2$$

Not all equations in two variables define a function. For instance,

$$y^2 = x^2 + 9$$

is not an equation that defines a function. As shown on the next page, the ordered pairs $(4, 5)$ and $(4, -5)$ are solutions of the equation.

$y^2 = x^2 + 9$	
5^2	$4^2 + 9$
25	$16 + 9$
$25 = 25$	

- Let $(x, y) = (4, 5)$.
  Replace x by 4 and y by 5.
- $(4, 5)$ checks.

$y^2 = x^2 + 9$	
$(-5)^2$	$4^2 + 9$
25	$16 + 9$
$25 = 25$	

- Let $(x, y) = (4, -5)$.
  Replace x by 4 and y by 5.
- $(4, -5)$ checks.

Consequently, there are two ordered pairs, $(4, 5)$ and $(4, -5)$, with the same first coordinate and *different* second coordinates; the equation does not define a function. The phrase "*y* is a function of *x*," or a similar phrase with different variables, is used to describe those equations in two variables that define functions.

Function notation is frequently used for those equations that define functions. Just as x is commonly used as a variable for a number, the letter f is commonly used to name a function. For instance, using the square function, we can write $f(x) = x^2$. The symbol $f(x)$ is read "the *value* of f at x" or "f of x." The symbol $f(x)$ is the **value of the function** and represents the value of the dependent variable for a given value of the independent variable.

This is the value of the function.
It is the value of the dependent variable.

$$f(x) = x^2$$

The name of the function is f.   This is an algebraic expression that defines the relationship between the dependent variable and the independent variable.

The process of finding the value of $f(x)$ for a given value of x is called **evaluating the function.** For instance, to evaluate $f(x) = x^2$ when x is 4, replace x by 4 and simplify.

$$f(x) = x^2$$
$$f(4) = 4^2$$ • Replace x by 4. Then simplify.
$$= 16$$

The *value* of the function is 16 when $x = 4$. An ordered pair of the function is $(4, 16)$.

The letters used to represent a function are somewhat arbitrary. All of the following equations represent the same function. Note that more than one letter can be used.

$$f(x) = x^2 \qquad g(t) = t^2 \qquad P(v) = v^2 \qquad SQ(x) = x^2$$

These represent the square function.

We write $y = f(x)$ to emphasize the relationship between the independent variable, x, and the dependent variable, y. **Remember:** y and $f(x)$ are different symbols for the same number. Also, the name of the function is f; the value of the function at x is $f(x)$. For instance, the equation $s = 16t^2$ discussed at the beginning of this section could be written as $s(t) = 16t^2$. The name of the function is s. The value of the function when $t = 5$ is found by replacing t by 5.

$$s(t) = 16t^2$$
$$s(5) = 16(5)^2$$ • Replace t by 5.
$$= 16(25) = 400$$

The value of the function when $t = 5$ s is 400 ft.

Take Note

To evaluate a function, you can substitute open parentheses for the variable in each term. For instance,
$R(v) = v^3 + 3v^2 - 5v - 6$
$R(v) = (\ )^3 + 3(\ )^2 - 5(\ ) - 6$
To evaluate the function, fill each of the parentheses with the same number and then simplify.

■ Find the value of $R(v) = v^3 + 3v^2 - 5v - 6$ when $v = -2$.

$$R(v) = v^3 + 3v^2 - 5v - 6$$
$$R(-2) = (-2)^3 + 3(-2)^2 - 5(-2) - 6 \qquad \bullet\ \textbf{Replace } v \textbf{ by } -2.$$
$$= -8 + 12 + 10 - 6$$
$$= 8$$

The value of $R(v)$ when $v = -2$ is 8.

There are several ways to use a calculator to evaluate a function. The screens at the right, which illustrate the evaluation of $R(-2)$ given above, show one way. See the Appendix Keystroke Guide for other methods of evaluating a function.

EXAMPLE 2 Let $q(r) = 2r^3 + 5r^2 - 6$.

A. Find $q(-3)$.

B. Find the value of q when $r = 2$.

Solution

A. $q(r) = 2r^3 + 5r^2 - 6$

$q(-3) = 2(-3)^3 + 5(-3)^2 - 6$ • **Replace** r **by** -3.
$\qquad = 2(-27) + 5(9) - 6 = -54 + 45 - 6$ **Then simplify.**

$q(-3) = -15$

B. To find the value of q when $r = 2$ means to evaluate the function when $r = 2$.

$q(r) = 2r^3 + 5r^2 - 6$

$q(2) = 2(2)^3 + 5(2)^2 - 6$ • **Replace** r **by** 2.
$\qquad = 2(8) + 5(4) - 6 = 16 + 20 - 6$ **Then simplify.**
$\qquad = 30$

The value of the function when $r = 4$ is 30.

PROBLEM 2 Let $f(z) = z + |z|$.

A. Find $f(-4)$.

B. Find the value of f when $z = 3$.

Solution See page S7.

It is also possible to evaluate a function at another variable or at a variable expression.

Evaluate $p(x) = 2x^2 + 7x - 9$ when $x = a$.

$p(x) = 2x^2 + 7x - 9$

$p(a) = 2a^2 + 7a - 9$ • **Replace *x* by *a*.**

Evaluate $N(v) = 2v + 3$ when $v = 3 + k$.

$N(v) = 2v + 3$

$N(3 + k) = 2(3 + k) + 3$ • **Replace *v* by 3 + *k*.**

$= 6 + 2k + 3$ • **Simplify.**

$= 2k + 9$

EXAMPLE 3 Let $f(x) = 3 - 2x$. Find $f(3h - 2)$.

Solution

$$f(x) = 3 - 2x$$
$$f(3h - 2) = 3 - 2(3h - 2)$$ • **Replace *x* by 3*h* − 2.**
$$= 3 - 6h + 4$$ • **Simplify.**
$$= -6h + 7$$

PROBLEM 3 Let $r(s) = 3s - 6$. Find $r(2a + 3)$.

Solution See page S7.

The range of a function contains all the elements that result from evaluating the function for each element of the domain. If the domain contains an infinite number of elements, as in the case of the falling pilot, it may be difficult to find the range. However, if the domain has only a finite number of elements, then the range can be found by evaluating the function for each element of the given domain.

EXAMPLE 4 Find the range of $f(x) = x^2 + 2x - 1$ if the domain is $\{-3, -2, -1, 0, 1\}$.

Solution Evaluate the function for each element of the domain. The range includes the values of $f(-3)$, $f(-2)$, $f(-1)$, $f(0)$, and $f(1)$.

$$f(x) = x^2 + 2x - 1$$
$$f(-3) = (-3)^2 + 2(-3) - 1 = 2$$
$$f(-2) = (-2)^2 + 2(-2) - 1 = -1$$
$$f(-1) = (-1)^2 + 2(-1) - 1 = -2$$
$$f(0) = (0)^2 + 2(0) - 1 = -1$$
$$f(1) = (1)^2 + 2(1) - 1 = 2$$

The range is $\{-2, -1, 2\}$.

Take Note

The order of the elements in a set does not matter. We could have listed the range as $\{-1, 2, -2\}$, but it is customary to list the numbers from least to greatest.

PROBLEM 4 Find the range of $f(x) = x^3 + x$ if the domain is $\{-3, -2, -1, 0, 1, 2\}$.

■ Solution See page S7.

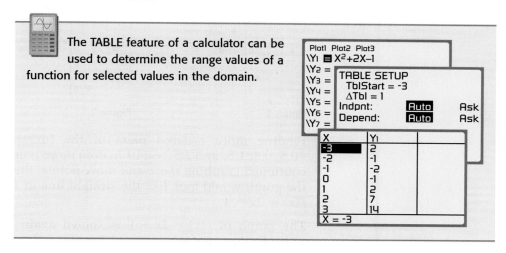

The TABLE feature of a calculator can be used to determine the range values of a function for selected values in the domain.

Given an element in the range of a function, we can find a corresponding element of the domain.

Take Note

You can check the answer in Example 5 by evaluating $f(x) = 3x + 1$ when $x = 2$.
$f(x) = 3x + 1$
$f(2) = 3(2) + 1$
$f(2) = 7$

EXAMPLE 5 Given $f(x) = 3x + 1$, find a number c in the domain of f such that $f(c) = 7$. Write the corresponding ordered pair of the function.

Solution
$f(x) = 3x + 1$
$f(c) = 3c + 1$ • **Replace x by c.**
$7 = 3c + 1$ • **$f(c) = 7$**
$6 = 3c$ • **Solve for c.**
$2 = c$

The value of c is 2. The corresponding ordered pair is (2, 7).

PROBLEM 5 Given $f(x) = 2x - 5$, find a number c in the domain of f such that $f(c) = -3$. Write the corresponding ordered pair of the function.

■ Solution See page S7.

OBJECTIVE **2** **Graph of a function**

Take Note

Recall that $f(x)$ and y are different symbols for the same quantity.

The **graph of a function** is the graph of the ordered pairs that belong to the function. Consider $f(x) = 2x - 1$. Evaluating this function when $x = -2$, -1, 0, 1, 2, and 3 produces some of the ordered pairs of the function. It is convenient to record the results in a table similar to the one shown above.

x	$y = f(x) = 2x - 1$	(x, y)
-2	$y = f(-2) = 2(-2) - 1 = -5$	$(-2, -5)$
-1	$y = f(-1) = 2(-1) - 1 = -3$	$(-1, -3)$
0	$y = f(0) = 2(0) - 1 = -1$	$(0, -1)$
1	$y = f(1) = 2(1) - 1 = 1$	$(1, 1)$
2	$y = f(2) = 2(2) - 1 = 3$	$(2, 3)$
3	$y = f(2) = 2(3) - 1 = 5$	$(2, 5)$

The graph of the ordered pairs is shown in Figure 1.

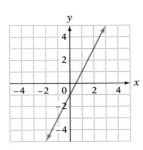

Figure 1   **Figure 2**   **Figure 3**

Finding more ordered pairs of the function, such as when $x = -1.5$, -0.5, 0.5, 1.5, and 2.5, results in even more points to graph. See Figure 2. If we continued graphing more and more points, there would be so many dots that the graph would look like the straight line in Figure 3, which is the graph of $f(x) = 2x - 1$.

The graph of $f(x) = 2x - 1$ is shown again at the right. Evaluating f when $x = -1.5$ and $x = 3$, we have

$$f(x) = 2x - 1 \qquad\qquad f(x) = 2x - 1$$
$$f(-1.5) = 2(-1.5) - 1 \qquad f(3) = 2(3) - 1$$
$$f(-1.5) = -4 \qquad\qquad f(3) = 5$$

Thus $(-1.5, -4)$ and $(3, 5)$ are the coordinates of points on the graph. Note also that the point with co-ordinates $(2, 1)$ is not on the graph and that $f(2) \neq 1$.
Every point on the graph of a function is an ordered pair of the function, and every ordered pair that belongs to the function corresponds to a point on the graph.

EXAMPLE 6   Graph $h(x) = x^2 - 3$ by evaluating the function when $x = -3$, $-2, -1, 0, 1, 2$, and 3. Plot the resulting ordered pairs. Then connect the points to form the graph.

Solution   Evaluate the function for the given values of x. This will produce some ordered pairs of the function. The results can be recorded in a table.

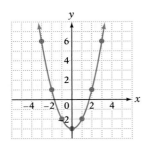

x	$y = h(x) = x^2 - 3$	(x, y)
-3	$h(-3) = (-3)^2 - 3 = 6$	$(-3, 6)$
-2	$h(-2) = (-2)^2 - 3 = 1$	$(-2, 1)$
-1	$h(-1) = (-1)^2 - 3 = -2$	$(-1, -2)$
0	$h(0) = (0)^2 - 3 = -3$	$(0, -3)$
1	$h(1) = (1)^2 - 3 = -2$	$(1, -2)$
2	$h(2) = (2)^2 - 3 = 1$	$(2, 1)$
3	$h(3) = (3)^2 - 3 = 6$	$(3, 6)$

Connect the points to form the graph.

PROBLEM 6   Graph $f(x) = -x^2 - 4x + 2$ by evaluating the function when $x = -5, -4, -3, -2, -1, 0,$ and 1. Plot the resulting ordered pairs. Then connect the points to form the graph.

Solution   See page S7.

The graph of an absolute value function will be used to illustrate various concepts throughout this text. We can graph $f(x) = |x|$ by evaluating the function for various values of x, plotting the resulting ordered pairs, and then connecting the points to produce the graph.

x	$y = f(x) = |x|$	(x, y)
-3	$f(-3) = |-3| = 3$	$(-3, 3)$
-2	$f(-2) = |-2| = 2$	$(-2, 2)$
-1	$f(-1) = |-1| = 1$	$(-1, 1)$
0	$f(0) = |0| = 0$	$(0, 0)$
1	$f(1) = |1| = 1$	$(1, 1)$
2	$f(2) = |2| = 2$	$(2, 2)$
3	$f(3) = |3| = 3$	$(3, 3)$

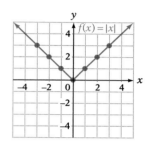

The V-shape of this graph is characteristic of the graph of an absolute value function.

EXAMPLE 7   Graph $f(x) = -|x| + 2$ by evaluating the function when $x = -3, -2, -1, 0, 1, 2,$ and 3. Plot the resulting ordered pairs. Then connect the points to form the graph.

Solution   Evaluate the function for the given values of x. Then connect the points to form a V-shape graph.

x	$y = f(x) = -|x| + 2$	(x, y)
-3	$f(-3) = -|-3| + 2 = -1$	$(-3, -1)$
-2	$f(-2) = -|-2| + 2 = 0$	$(-2, 0)$
-1	$f(-1) = -|-1| + 2 = 1$	$(-1, 1)$
0	$f(0) = -|0| + 2 = 2$	$(0, 2)$
1	$f(1) = -|1| + 2 = 1$	$(1, 1)$
2	$f(2) = -|2| + 2 = 0$	$(2, 0)$
3	$f(3) = -|3| + 2 = -1$	$(3, -1)$

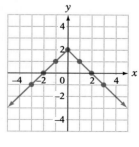

PROBLEM 7   Graph $f(x) = |x - 2|$ by evaluating the function when $x = -1, 0, 1, 2, 3, 4,$ and 5. Plot the resulting ordered pairs. Then connect the points to form the graph.

Solution   See page S7.

OBJECTIVE 3   **Vertical line test**

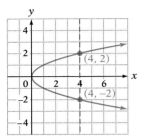

Figure 3.3

A graph is a visual description of a relation. For the relation shown in Figure 3.3, the two ordered pairs (4, 2) and (4, −2) belong to the graph, and those points lie on a vertical line. Because there are two ordered pairs with the same first coordinate, the set of ordered pairs of the graph is not a function. With this observation in mind, we can make use of a quick method to determine whether a graph is the graph of a function.

Vertical Line Test for the Graph of a Function

If every vertical line intersects a graph at most once, then the graph is the graph of a function.

This graphical interpretation of a function is often described by saying that each value in the domain of the function is paired with *exactly one* value in the range of the function.

Take Note

For the second graph on the right, note that there are values of x for which there is only one value of y. For instance, when $x = -5$, $y = 4$. For the relation to be a function, however, <u>every</u> value of x in the domain of the function must have exactly one value of y. If there is even one value of x that has two or more values of y, the condition for a function is not met. This is what the vertical line test states: If there is any place on the graph where a vertical line intersects the graph more than once, the graph is not the graph of a function.

For each x, there is *exactly one* value of y. For instance, when $x = -3$, $y = -6$. This is the graph of a function.

Some values of x can be paired with more than one value of y. For instance, 2 can be paired with −2, 1, and 3. This is not the graph of a function.

EXAMPLE 8   Use the vertical line test to determine whether the graph is the graph of a function.

A.

B.

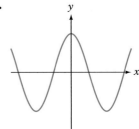

Solution

A. As shown at the right, there are vertical lines that intersect the graph at more than one point. Therefore, the graph is not the graph of a function.

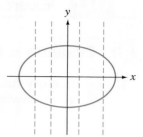

B. For the graph at the right, every vertical line intersects the graph at most once. Therefore, the graph is the graph of a function.

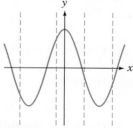

PROBLEM 8   For each of the graphs below, determine whether the graph defines a function.

A.

B.

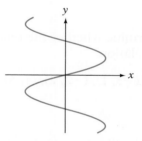

Solution   See page S7.

3.2   Concept Review

Determine whether the following statements are always true, sometimes true, or never true.

1. A set of ordered pairs is called a function.

2. A function is a relation.

3. The domain of a function is the set of real numbers.

4. Zero is excluded from the domain of a function.

5. $f(a)$ represents a value in the range of a function when a is a value in the domain of the function.

6. Two ordered pairs of a function can have the same first coordinate.

3.2 Exercises

1 Evaluate a function

1. Is every function a relation? Is every relation a function? Explain your answer.

2. What is the domain of a function? What is the range of a function?

3. Complete the following sentence using *exactly one* or *more than one*. For a function, each element of the domain is paired with ___?___ element of the range.

4. Complete the following sentences using *can* or *cannot*. If (5, 2) belongs to a function, then (5, 9) ___?___ belong to the function. If (5, 2) belongs to a relation, then (5, 9) ___?___ belong to the relation.

Determine whether the relation is a function. Give the domain and range of the relation.

5. {(−3, 1), (−2, 2), (1, 5), (4, −7)}

6. {(−5, 4), (−2, 3), (0, 1), (3, 2) (7, 11)}

7. {(1, 5), (2, 5), (3, 5), (4, 5), (5, 5)}

8. {(1, 0), (10, 1), (100, 2), (1000, 3), (10000, 4)}

9. $\left\{\left(-2, -\frac{1}{2}\right), (-1, -1), (1, 1), \left(2, \frac{1}{2}\right), \left(3, \frac{1}{3}\right)\right\}$

10. {(0, 0), (1, 1), (4, 2), (9, 3), (1, −1), (4, −2), (9, −3)}

11. {(2, 3), (4, 5), (6, 7), (8, 9), (6, 8)}

12. {(−1, 2), (−2, 4), (2, 4), (−2, 5), (4, 9)}

13. Does the diagram below represent a function? Explain your answer.

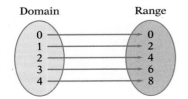

14. Does the diagram below represent a function? Explain your answer.

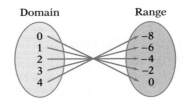

15. Does the diagram below represent a function? Explain your answer.

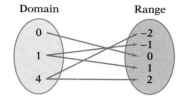

16. Does the diagram below represent a function? Explain your answer.

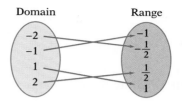

17. Does the diagram below represent a function? Explain your answer.

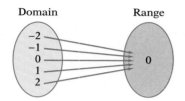

18. Does the diagram below represent a function? Explain your answer.

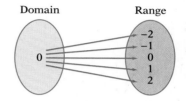

Solve.

19. Shipping The table at the right shows the cost to send an overnight package using United Parcel Service.
 a. Does the table define a function?
 b. Given $x = 3.54$ lb, find y.

Weight, in pounds (x)	Cost (y)
$0 < x \leq 1$	$22.75
$1 < x \leq 2$	$24.74
$2 < x \leq 3$	$27.00
$3 < x \leq 4$	$29.25
$4 < x \leq 5$	$31.50

20. Shipping The table at the right shows the cost to send an "Express Mail" package using U.S. Postal Service.
 a. Does the table define a function?
 b. Given $x = 0.5$ lb, find y.

Weight, in pounds (x)	Cost (y)
$0 < x \leq 0.5$	$13.65
$0.5 < x \leq 2$	$17.85
$2 < x \leq 3$	$21.05
$3 < x \leq 4$	$24.20
$4 < x \leq 5$	$27.30

21. What does it mean to evaluate a function? Explain how to evaluate $f(x) = 3x$ when $x = 2$.

22. What is the value of a function?

23. True or False: If f is a function, then it is possible that $f(0) = -2$ and $f(3) = -2$.

24. True or False: If f is a function, then it is possible that $f(4) = 3$ and $f(4) = 2$.

25. Given $f(x) = 5x - 7$, find $f(3)$ by completing the following.

$$f(x) = 5x - 7$$
$$f(\underline{\ ?\ }) = 5(\underline{\ ?\ }) - 7 \qquad \bullet \text{ Insert 3 in the parentheses.}$$
$$f(3) = \underline{\ ?\ } \qquad \bullet \text{ Simplify.}$$

26. Given $f(x) = x^2 - 3x + 1$, find $f(-2)$ by completing the following.

$$f(x) = x^2 - 3x + 1$$
$$f(\underline{\quad ? \quad}) = (\underline{\quad ? \quad})^2 - 3(\underline{\quad ? \quad}) + 1 \quad \bullet \text{ Insert } -2 \text{ in the parentheses.}$$
$$f(-2) = \underline{\quad ? \quad} \qquad\qquad \bullet \text{ Simplify.}$$

In Exercises 27 to 50, evaluate the function.

27. $f(x) = 4x + 5$
  a. $f(2)$ **b.** $f(-2)$ **c.** $f(0)$

28. $g(x) = -2x - 7$
  a. $g(-3)$ **b.** $g(1)$ **c.** $g(0)$

29. $v(s) = 6 - 3s$
  a. $v(3)$ **b.** $v(-2)$ **c.** $v\left(-\dfrac{2}{3}\right)$

30. $p(z) = 4 - 6z$
  a. $p\left(\dfrac{2}{3}\right)$ **b.** $p(4)$ **c.** $p\left(-\dfrac{5}{6}\right)$

31. $f(x) = -\dfrac{3}{2}x - 2$
  a. $f(4)$ **b.** $f(-2)$ **c.** $f\left(\dfrac{4}{3}\right)$

32. $f(x) = \dfrac{3}{4}x + 1$
  a. $f(8)$ **b.** $f(-4)$ **c.** $f\left(-\dfrac{8}{3}\right)$

33. $p(c) = \dfrac{1}{2}c - \dfrac{3}{4}$
  a. $p\left(\dfrac{7}{2}\right)$ **b.** $p\left(-\dfrac{1}{2}\right)$ **c.** $p\left(\dfrac{1}{2}\right)$

34. $H(x) = \dfrac{2}{3} - \dfrac{5}{6}x$
  a. $H\left(-\dfrac{2}{5}\right)$ **b.** $H(2)$ **c.** $H(0)$

35. $f(x) = 4x - 1$
  a. $f(a + 3)$ **b.** $f(2a)$

36. $f(x) = 3x - 2$
  a. $f(2 - h)$ **b.** $f(-4h)$

37. $f(x) = 2x^2 - 1$
  a. $f(3)$ **b.** $f(-2)$ **c.** $f(0)$

38. $f(x) = 2x^2 + 3$
  a. $f(0)$ **b.** $f(-3)$ **c.** $f(2)$

39. $h(t) = 3t^2 - 4t - 5$
  a. $h(-2)$ **b.** $h(-1)$ **c.** $h(w)$

40. $p(x) = 3 - 4t - 2t^2$
  a. $p(4)$ **b.** $p(-4)$ **c.** $f(0)$

41. $g(x) = x^2 + 2x - 1$
  a. $g(1)$ **b.** $g(-3)$ **c.** $g(a)$

42. $g(x) = 2x^2 - 4x + 1$
  a. $g(-2)$ **b.** $g(4)$ **c.** $g(z)$

43. $p(t) = 4t^2 - 8t + 3$
  a. $p(-2)$ **b.** $p\left(\dfrac{1}{2}\right)$ **c.** $p(-a)$

44. $r(s) = 3 - 6x - 3s^2$
  a. $r(-2)$ **b.** $r\left(-\dfrac{2}{3}\right)$ **c.** $r(-x)$

45. $f(x) = |x - 3|$
  a. $f(-1)$ **b.** $f(5)$ **c.** $f(3)$

46. $h(x) = |2x + 4|$
  a. $h(-2)$ **b.** $h(3)$ **c.** $h(-3)$

47. $C(r) = 3|x| - 2$
  a. $C(-3)$ **b.** $C(4)$ **c.** $C(0)$

48. $y(x) = 3 - |2x|$
  a. $y\left(\dfrac{1}{2}\right)$ **b.** $y\left(-\dfrac{3}{2}\right)$ **c.** $y\left(\dfrac{1}{4}\right)$

49. $K(p) = 5 - 3|x + 2|$
   a. $K(-2)$ **b.** $K(-7)$ **c.** $K(3)$

50. $R(s) = 2|1 - x| - 3$
   a. $R(-7)$ **b.** $R(4)$ **c.** $R(-1)$

51. Find the value of $s(t) = -16t^2 + 48t$ when $t = 3$.

52. Find the value of $T(s) = s^2 - 4s + 1$ when $s = \dfrac{3}{4}$.

53. Find the value of $P(x) = 3x^3 - 4x^2 + 6x - 7$ when $x = 2$.

54. Find the value of $R(s) = s^3 - 2s^2 - 5s + 2$ when $s = -3$.

55. Find the value of $R(p) = \dfrac{3p}{2p - 3}$ when $p = -3$.

56. Find the value of $f(x) = \dfrac{x + 1}{3x - 1}$ when $x = 3$.

Find the range of the function defined by each equation.

57. $f(x) = 3x - 5$; domain $= \{-3, -2, -1, 0, 1, 2\}$

58. $g(x) = 1 - 2x$; domain $= \{-4, -2, 0, 2, 4, 6\}$

59. $r(t) = \dfrac{t}{2}$; domain $= \{-3, -2, -1, 0, 1, 2\}$

60. $v(s) = \dfrac{3}{4}x - 1$; domain $= \{-8, -4, 0, 4, 8\}$

61. $f(x) = x^2 + 3$; domain $= \{-3, -2, -1, 0, 1, 2\}$

62. $r(t) = t^2 - t - 6$; domain $= \{-2, -1, 0, 1, 2, 3\}$

63. $c(n) = n^3 - n - 2$; domain $= \{-3, -2, -1, 0, 1, 2\}$

64. $q(z) = x^3 + 2x^2 - x - 2$; domain $= \{-3, -2, -1, 0, 1, 2\}$

65. Given $f(x) = 2x - 3$, find a number c in the domain of f such that $f(c) = 5$. Write the corresponding ordered pair of the function.

66. Given $f(x) = 3x + 1$, find a number c in the domain of f such that $f(c) = -8$. Write the corresponding ordered pair of the function.

67. Given $f(x) = 1 - 2x$, find a number c in the domain of f such that $f(c) = -7$. Write the corresponding ordered pair of the function.

68. Given $f(x) = -20 - 5x$, find a number c in the domain of f such that $f(c) = -10$. Write the corresponding ordered pair of the function.

69. Given $f(x) = \dfrac{2}{3}x - 2$, find a number c in the domain of f such that $f(c) = 0$. Write the corresponding ordered pair of the function.

70. Given $f(x) = 3x + 3$, find a number c in the domain of f such that $f(c) = 0$. Write the corresponding ordered pair of the function.

2 Graph of a function

71. 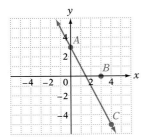 Which, if any, of the plotted points, *A*, *B*, or *C*, belong to the function?

72. Which, if any, of the plotted points, *A*, *B*, or *C*, belong to the function?

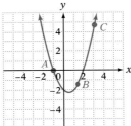

73. Does the ordered pair (4, −1) belong to the function graphed below?

74. Does the ordered pair (−3, 4) belong to the function graphed below?

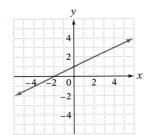

75. If $f(x) = 3x - 4$, does the ordered pair (−1, −7) belong to the function?

76. If $f(x) = x^2 - 4x$, does the ordered pair (2, 4) belong to the function?

Graph each function by evaluating the function at the given values of *x*. Plot the resulting ordered pairs. Then connect the points to form the graph.

77. $f(x) = x - 3$,
$x = -1, 0, 1, 2, 3, 4, 5$

78. $f(x) = -x + 2$,
$x = -2, -1, 0, 1, 2, 3, 4$

79. $g(x) = -2x + 2$,
$x = -2, -1, 0, 1, 2, 3$

80. $g(x) = 2x - 2$,
$x = -2, -1, 0, 1, 2, 3, 4$

81. $h(x) = \frac{1}{2}x - 1$,
$x = -6, -4, -2, 0, 2, 4, 6$

82. $h(x) = \frac{2}{3}x + 1$,
$x = -6, -3, 0, 3, 6$

83. $f(x) = x^2 - 4$,
    $x = -3, -2, -1, 0, 1, 2, 3$

84. $g(x) = -x^2 + 5$,
    $x = -3, -2, -1, 0, 1, 2, 3$

85. $h(x) = x^2 - 4x$,
    $x = -1, 0, 1, 2, 3, 4, 5$

86. $h(x) = x^2 + 2x$,
    $x = -4, -3, -2, -1, 0, 1, 2$

87. $g(x) = x^2 + 2x - 3$,
    $x = -4, -3, -2, -1, 0, 1, 2$

88. $f(x) = -x^2 + 4x + 2$,
    $x = -1, 0, 1, 2, 3, 4, 5$

89. $f(x) = |x| - 3$,
    $x = -6, -4, -2, 0, 2, 4, 6$

90. $f(x) = -|x| + 4$,
    $x = -6, -4, -2, 0, 2, 4, 6$

91. $h(x) = -2|x| + 5$,
    $x = -3, -2, -1, 0, 1, 2, 3$

92. $h(x) = |2x| - 5$,
    $x = -5, -3, -1, 0, 1, 3, 5$

93. $f(x) = |x - 2| - 3$,
    $x = -6, -4, 0, 2, 4, 5, 6$

94. $g(x) = -|x + 2| + 4$,
    $x = -6, -4, -2, 0, 2, 4, 6$

3   Vertical line test

Use the vertical line test to determine whether the graph is the graph of a function.

95.

96.

97.

98.

99.

100.

101.

102.

103.

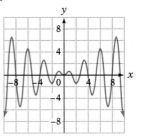

104. Does the graph of the equation pass the vertical line test?

   a. $f(x) = \sqrt{x}$

   b. $g(x) = -\sqrt{x}$

   c. $h(x) = \sqrt{x} + \sqrt{x}$

   d. $F(x) = \sqrt{x} - 2\sqrt{x}$

105. Does the graph of the equation pass the vertical line test?

   a. $f(x) = |x|$

   b. $g(x) = -|x|$

   c. $h(x) = |x| + |x|$

   d. $F(x) = |x| - 2|x|$

3.2 Applying Concepts

106. Given $f(x) = |x|$, find c in the domain of f such that $f(c) = 3$.

107. Given $f(x) = |x - 2|$, find c in the domain of f such that $f(c) = 4$.

108. Given $f(x) = |x| + 4$, is it possible to find a number c such that $f(c) = 2$? Is 2 in the range of f?

109. Given $f(x) = 4x + 7$, write $f(-2 + h) - f(-2)$ in simplest form.

110. Given $P(x) = 3 - 2x$, write $P(3 + h) - P(3)$ in simplest form.

111. Let $F = \{(-3, -6), (-2, -4), (-1, -2), (0, 0), (1, 2), (2, 4), (3, 6)\}$ and $G = \{(-3, 9), (-2, 4), (-1, 1), (0, 0), (1, 1), (2, 4), (3, 9)\}$.

   a. Is F a function?

   b. Is G a function?

c. Write the set of ordered pairs F' that consists of all the ordered pairs of F but with the coordinates reversed. For example, the first two ordered pairs of F' are $(-6, -3)$ and $(-4, -2)$. Is F' a function?

d. Write the set of ordered pairs G' that consists of all the ordered pairs of G but with the coordinates reversed. Is G' a function?

e. Using the results of part **c** and part **d**, if the ordered pairs of a function are reversed, is the resulting set of ordered pairs always a function?

112. Credit Card Debt The graph below shows the amount of interest a person with credit card debt of $1000 will pay and the time it will take to repay the debt if that person makes only the minimum monthly payment (and makes no additional charges).

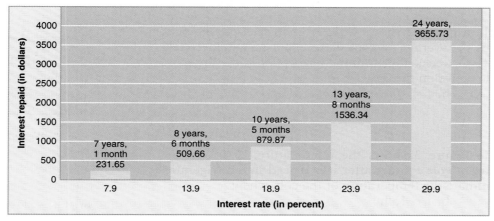

a. How much interest will this person repay if the credit card interest rate is 18.9% (a fairly typical rate)?

b. How many years and months will it take to repay the debt if the interest rate is 23.9%?

113. Automotive Technology The distance, s (in feet), that a car will skid on a certain road surface after the brakes are applied is a function of the car's velocity, v (in miles per hour). The function can be approximated by $s = f(v) = 0.017v^2$. How far will a car skid after its brakes are applied if it is traveling 60 mph?

114. Energy The power a windmill can generate is a function of the velocity of the wind. The function can be approximated by $P = f(v) = 0.015v^3$, where P is the power in watts and v is the velocity of the wind in meters per second. How much power will be produced by a windmill when the velocity of the wind is 15 m/s?

115. Find the set of ordered pairs (x, y) determined by the equation $y = x^3$, where $x \in \{-2, -1, 0, 1, 2\}$. Does the set of ordered pairs define a function? Why or why not?

116. Find the set of ordered pairs (x, y) determined by the equation $|y| = x$, where $x \in \{0, 1, 2, 3\}$. Does the set of ordered pairs define a function? Why or why not?

Each of the following graphs defines a function. Evaluate the function by estimating the ordinate (which is the value of the function) for the given value of t.

117. Physics The graph in Figure 1 shows the speed, v (in feet per second), at which a parachutist is falling during the first 20 s after jumping out of a plane. Estimate the speed at which the parachutist is falling when:
a. $t = 5$ s   **b.** $t = 15$ s

Figure 1

118. Psychology The graph in Figure 2 shows what an industrial psychologist has determined to be the average percent score, P, for an employee taking a performance test t weeks after training begins. Estimate the score an employee would receive on this test when:
a. $t = 4$ weeks   **b.** $t = 10$ weeks

Figure 2

119. Physics The graph in Figure 3 shows the temperature, T (in degrees Fahrenheit), of a can of cola t hours after it is placed in a refrigerator. Use the graph to estimate the temperature of the cola when:
a. $t = 10$ h   **b.** $t = 15$ h

Figure 3

120. Health Science The graph in Figure 4 shows the decrease in the heart rate, r (in beats per minute), of a runner t minutes after the completion of a race. Use the graph to estimate the heart rate of a runner when:
a. $t = 5$ min   **b.** $t = 20$ min

121. Write a report on the longitude-latitude coordinate system used to locate a position on Earth. Include in your report the definition of *nautical mile* and the coordinates of the city in which your school is located.

Figure 4

122. Investigate the relationship between two variables by collecting data, graphing the scatter diagram for these data, and discussing the results. For example, for each person in your classes who commutes to class by car, find out how many miles he or she commutes and the total number of miles on the odometer of the car he or she drives to class. Discuss whether you think there is a relationship between the two variables.

3.3   Linear Functions

OBJECTIVE   **1**   ### Graph a linear function

Recall that the ordered pairs of a function can be written as $(x, f(x))$ or (x, y). The **graph of a function** is a graph of the ordered pairs (x, y) that belong to the function. Certain functions have characteristic graphs. A function that can be written in the form $f(x) = mx + b$ (or $y = mx + b$) is called a **linear function** because its graph is a straight line.

Examples of linear functions are shown at the right. Note that the exponent on each variable is 1.

$$f(x) = 2x + 5 \qquad (m = 2, b = 5)$$
$$P(t) = 3t - 2 \qquad (m = 3, b = -2)$$
$$y = -2x \qquad (m = -2, b = 0)$$
$$y = -\frac{2}{3}x + 1 \qquad \left(m = -\frac{2}{3}, b = 1\right)$$
$$g(z) = z - 2 \qquad (m = 1, b = -2)$$

The equation $y = x^2 + 4x + 3$ is not a linear function because it includes a term with a variable squared. The equation $f(x) = \dfrac{3}{x - 2}$ is not a linear function because a variable occurs in the denominator. Another example of an equation that is not a linear function is $y = \sqrt{x} + 4$; this equation contains a variable within a radical and so is not a linear function.

Consider $f(x) = 2x + 1$. Evaluating the linear function when $x = -3, -2, -1, 0, 1,$ and 2 produces some of the ordered pairs of the function. It is convenient to record the results in a table similar to the one at the right. The graph of the ordered pairs is shown in Figure 1 below.

x	$f(x) = 2x + 1$	y	(x, y)
-3	$2(-3) + 1$	-5	$(-3, -5)$
-2	$2(-2) + 1$	-3	$(-2, -3)$
-1	$2(-1) + 1$	-1	$(-1, -1)$
0	$2(0) + 1$	1	$(0, 1)$
1	$2(1) + 1$	3	$(1, 3)$
2	$2(2) + 1$	5	$(2, 5)$

Evaluating the function when x is not an integer produces more ordered pairs to graph, such as $\left(-\frac{5}{2}, -4\right)$ and $\left(\frac{3}{2}, 4\right)$, as shown in Figure 2 below. Evaluating the function for still other values of x would result in more and more ordered pairs to graph. The result would be so many dots that the graph would look like the straight line shown in Figure 3, which is the graph of $f(x) = 2x + 1$.

Figure 1

Figure 2

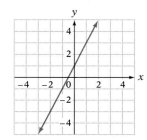

Figure 3

No matter what value of x is chosen, $2x + 1$ is a real number. This means the domain of $f(x) = 2x + 1$ is all real numbers. Therefore, we can use any real number when evaluating the function. Normally, however, values such as π and $\sqrt{5}$ are not used because it is difficult to graph the resulting ordered pairs.

Whether an equation is written as $f(x) = mx + b$ or $y = mx + b$, the equation represents a linear function, and the graph of the equation is a straight line.

Because the graph of a linear function is a straight line, and a straight line is determined by two points, the graph of a linear function can be drawn by finding only two of the ordered pairs of the functions. However, it is recommended that you find at least *three* ordered pairs to ensure accuracy.

Take Note

When the coefficient of x is a fraction, choose values of x that are multiples of the denominator of the fraction. This will result in coordinates that are integers.

EXAMPLE 1 Graph: $f(x) = -\dfrac{3}{2}x - 3$

Solution

x	$y = f(x)$
0	−3
−2	0
−4	3

• Find at least three ordered pairs. When the coefficient of x is a fraction, choose values of x that will simplify the evaluations. The ordered pairs can be displayed in a table.

• Graph the ordered pairs and draw a line through the points.

PROBLEM 1 Graph: $y = \dfrac{3}{5}x - 4$

Solution See page S7.

Graphing utilities create graphs by plotting points and then connecting the points to form a curve. Using a graphing utility, enter the equation $y = -\dfrac{3}{2}x - 3$ and verify the graph drawn in Example 1. (Refer to the Appendix on page 768 for suggestions on what domain and range to use.) Trace along the graph and verify that (0, −3), (−2, 0), and (−4, 3) are the coordinates of points on the graph. Now enter the equation $y = \dfrac{3}{5}x - 4$ given in Problem 1. Verify that the ordered pairs you found for this function are the coordinates of points on the graph.

OBJECTIVE 2 **Graph an equation of the form $Ax + By = C$**

A **literal equation** is an equation with more than one variable. Examples of literal equations are $P = 2L + 2W$, $V = LWH$, $d = rt$, and $3x + 2y = 6$.

Linear equations of the form $y = mx + b$ are literal equations. In some cases, a linear equation has the form $Ax + By = C$. In such a case, it may be convenient to solve the equation for y to get the equation in the form $y = mx + b$. To solve for y, we use the same rules and procedures that we use to solve equations with numerical values.

Write $4x - 3y = 6$ in the form $y = mx + b$.

$$4x - 3y = 6$$

Subtract $4x$ from each side of the equation.

$$4x - 4x - 3y = 6 - 4x$$

Simplify.

$$-3y = 6 - 4x$$

Divide both sides of the equation by -3.

$$\frac{-3y}{-3} = \frac{6 - 4x}{-3}$$

Simplify.

$$y = \frac{6 - 4x}{-3}$$

Divide each term in the numerator by the denominator.

$$y = \frac{6}{-3} - \frac{4x}{-3}$$

Simplify.

$$y = -2 + \frac{4}{3}x$$

Write the equation in the form $y = mx + b$.

$$y = \frac{4}{3}x - 2$$

We will show two methods of graphing an equation of the form $Ax + By = C$. In the first method, we solve the equation for y and then follow the same procedure used for graphing an equation of the form $y = mx + b$.

EXAMPLE 2   Graph: $3x + 2y = 6$

Solution

$$3x + 2y = 6$$
$$2y = -3x + 6$$
$$y = -\frac{3}{2}x + 3$$

• Solve the equation for y.

x	y
0	3
2	0
4	-3

• Find at least three solutions.

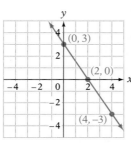

• Graph the ordered pairs in a rectangular coordinate system. Draw a straight line through the points.

PROBLEM 2   Graph: $-3x + 2y = 4$

Solution   See page S8.

Use a graphing utility to graph the equation $3x + 2y = 6$. First solve the equation for y and then enter the equation $y = -\frac{3}{2}x + 3$. Next trace along the graph and verify that $(0, 3)$, $(2, 0)$, and $(4, -3)$ are the coordinates of points on the graph. Follow the same procedure for Problem 2.

An equation in which one of the variables is missing has a graph that is either a horizontal or a vertical line.

The equation $y = -2$ can be written

$$0 \cdot x + y = -2$$

Because $0 \cdot x = 0$ for any value of x, y is -2 for every value of x.

Some of the possible ordered-pair solutions of $y = -2$ are given in the following table. The graph is shown at the right.

x	y
-2	-2
0	-2
3	-2

The equation $y = -2$ represents a function. Some of the ordered pairs of this function are $(-2, -2)$, $(0, -2)$, and $(3, -2)$. In functional notation we would write $f(x) = -2$. This function is an example of a constant function. No matter what value of x is selected, $f(x) = -2$.

Definition of the Constant Function

A function given by $f(x) = b$, where b is a constant, is a **constant function.** The graph of a constant function is a horizontal line passing through $(0, b)$.

Graph: $y + 4 = 0$

Solve for y.

$$y + 4 = 0$$
$$y = -4$$

The graph of $y = -4$ is a horizontal line passing through $(0, -4)$.

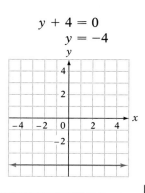

For each value in the domain of a constant function, the value of the function is the same (that is, it is constant). For instance, if $f(x) = 4$, then $f(2) = 4$, $f(3) = 4$, $f(\sqrt{3}) = 4$, $f(\pi) = 4$, and so on. The value of $f(x)$ is 4 for all values of x.

Evaluate $P(t) = -7$ when $t = 6$.

The value of the constant function is the same for all values of the variable.

$$P(t) = -7$$
$$P(6) = -7$$

For the equation $y = -2$, the coefficient of x is zero. For the equation $x = 2$, the coefficient of y is zero. For instance, the equation $x = 2$ can be written

$$x + 0 \cdot y = 2$$

No matter what value of y is chosen, $0 \cdot y = 0$ and therefore x is always 2.

Some of the possible ordered-pair solutions are given in the following table. The graph is shown at the right.

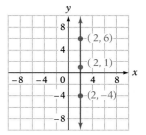

x	y
2	6
2	1
2	-4

Graph of $x = a$

The graph of $x = a$ is a vertical line passing through the point $(a, 0)$.

Recall that a function is a set of ordered pairs in which no two ordered pairs have the same first coordinate and different second coordinates. Because $(2, 6)$, $(2, 1)$, and $(2, -4)$ are ordered-pair solutions of the equation $x = 2$, this equation does not represent a function, and the graph is not the graph of a function.

EXAMPLE 3   Graph: $x = -4$

Solution

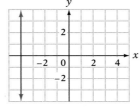

• The graph of an equation of the form $x = a$ is a vertical line passing through the point whose coordinates are $(a, 0)$.

PROBLEM 3   Graph: $y - 3 = 0$

Solution   See page S8.

A second method of graphing straight lines uses the *intercepts* of the graph.

The graph of the equation $x - 2y = 4$ is shown at the right. The graph crosses the *x*-axis at the point $(4, 0)$. This point is called the **x-intercept.** The graph also crosses the *y*-axis at the point $(0, -2)$. This point is called the **y-intercept.**

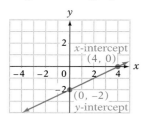

Take Note

The *x*-intercept occurs when $y = 0$. The *y*-intercept occurs when $x = 0$.

Find the *x*- and *y*-intercepts of the graph of the equation $3x + 4y = -12$.

To find the *x*-intercept, let $y = 0$.
(Any point on the *x*-axis has *x*-coordinate 0.)

$$3x + 4y = -12$$
$$3x + 4(0) = -12$$
$$3x = -12$$
$$x = -4$$

The *x*-intercept is $(-4, 0)$.

To find the *y*-intercept, let $x = 0$.
(Any point on the *y*-axis has *x*-coordinate 0.)

$$3x + 4y = -12$$
$$3(0) + 4y = -12$$
$$4y = -12$$
$$y = -3$$

The *y*-intercept is $(0, -3)$.

A linear equation can be graphed by finding the *x*- and *y*-intercepts and then drawing a line through the two points.

EXAMPLE 4   Graph $4x - y = 4$ by using the *x*- and *y*-intercepts.

Solution   *x*-intercept: $4x - y = 4$
$$4x - 0 = 4$$
$$4x = 4$$
$$x = 1$$

• To find the *x*-intercept, let $y = 0$.

The *x*-intercept is $(1, 0)$.

y-intercept: $4x - y = 4$
$$4(0) - y = 4$$
$$-y = 4$$
$$y = -4$$

• To find the *y*-intercept, let $x = 0$.

The *y*-intercept is $(0, -4)$.

• Graph the points $(1, 0)$ and $(0, -4)$. Draw a line through the two points.

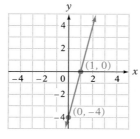

PROBLEM 4 Graph $3x - y = 2$ by using the x- and y-intercepts.

Solution See page S8.

Find the y-intercept of the graph of the equation $y = \frac{2}{3}x + 7$.

$$y = \frac{2}{3}x + 7$$

To find the y-intercept, let $x = 0$.

$$y = \frac{2}{3}(0) + 7$$
$$y = 7$$

The y-intercept is $(0, 7)$.

Note that the y-coordinate of the y-intercept $(0, 7)$ has the same value as the constant term of $y = \frac{2}{3}x + 7$. As shown below, this is always true.

To find the y-intercept, let $x = 0$.
$$y = mx + b$$
$$y = m(0) + b$$
$$y = b$$

Thus the y-intercept is $(0, b)$.

y-Intercept of a Straight Line

For any equation of the form $y = mx + b$, the y-intercept is $(0, b)$.

Find the x- and y-intercepts of $y = \frac{2}{3}x + 2$.

$$y = \frac{2}{3}x + 2$$

To find the x-intercept, let $y = 0$ and solve for x.

$$0 = \frac{2}{3}x + 2$$
$$-2 = \frac{2}{3}x$$

The x-intercept is $(-3, 0)$.

$$-3 = x$$

The y-intercept is $(0, b)$.

$$y = \frac{2}{3}x + 2$$

The y-intercept is $(2, 0)$.

$$b = 2$$

From the example above, for an equation written in the form $y = mx + b$, the x-intercept is found by letting $y = 0$ and then solving for x. If the equation were written in function notation as $f(x) = \dfrac{2}{3}x - 2$, then to find x-intercept, let $f(x) = 0$ and solve for x. A value of x for which $f(x) = 0$ is called a **zero** of the function.

Find the zero of $f(x) = 2x + 4$.

$f(x) = 2x + 4$

$0 = 2x + 4$ • To find a zero of a function, let **f(x) = 0.**

$-4 = 2x$ • Solve for **x.**

$-2 = x$

The zero of $f(x) = 2x + 4$ is -2.

The graph of $f(x) = 2x + 4$ is shown at the right. Note that the x-intercept for the graph is the point $(-2, 0)$. The x-coordinate of the x-intercept is -2, the zero of the function.

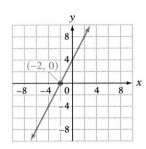

EXAMPLE 5   Find the zero of the function defined by $f(x) = -2x - 3$.

Solution $f(x) = -2x - 3$

$0 = -2x - 3$ • To find a zero of a function, let **f(x) = 0.**

$2x = -3$ • Solve for **x.**

$x = -\dfrac{3}{2}$

The zero is $-\dfrac{3}{2}$.

PROBLEM 5   Find the zero of the function defined by $f(x) = \dfrac{2}{3}x + 4$.

Solution   See page S8.

OBJECTIVE 3   ## Application problems

There are a variety of applications of linear functions.

On the basis of data from *The Joy of Cooking*, the daily caloric allowance for a woman can be approximated by the equation $C = -7.5A + 2187.5$, where C is the caloric intake and A is the age of the woman.

A. Graph this equation for $25 \le A \le 75$.

B. The point whose coordinates are $(45, 1850)$ is on the graph. Write a sentence that describes the meaning of this ordered pair.

A.

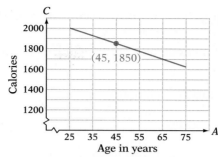

B. The ordered pair (45, 1850) means that the caloric allowance for a 45-year-old woman is 1850 calories per day.

EXAMPLE 6   An electronics technician charges $45 plus $1 per minute to repair defective wiring in a home or apartment. The equation that describes the total cost, C (in dollars), to have defective wiring repaired is given by the equation $C = t + 45$, where t is the number of minutes the technician works. Graph this equation for $0 \le t \le 60$. The point whose coordinates are (15, 60) is on the graph. Write a sentence that describes the meaning of this ordered pair.

Solution

The ordered pair (15, 60) means that it costs $60 for the technician to work 15 min.

PROBLEM 6   The height, h (in inches), of a person and the length, L (in inches), of that person's stride while walking are related. The equation $h = \frac{3}{4}L + 50$ approximates the relationship. Graph this equation for $15 \le L \le 40$. The point whose coordinates are (32, 74) is on the graph. Write a sentence that describes the meaning of this ordered pair.

Solution   See page S8.

3.3 Concept Review

Determine whether the following statements are always true, sometimes true, or never true.

1. The graph of $y = \frac{1}{x} + 2$ is the graph of a linear function.

2. The graph of $y - 3 = 0$ is a vertical line.

3. The graph of a straight line crosses the x-axis when $y = 0$.

4. The graph of a linear equation is a straight line.

5. The point at which a line crosses the y-axis is the x-intercept.

6. $xy + 2 = 0$ is an example of a linear equation.

3.3 Exercises

1 Graph a linear function

1. Explain how to graph a linear function by plotting points.

2. Give one example of a linear function and one example of a non-linear function.

3. Find three points on the graph of $y = 2x - 5$ by finding the y values that correspond to x values of -1, 0, and 1.
   a. When $x = -1$, $y =$ ___?___. A point on the graph is (___?___, ___?___).
   b. When $x = 0$, $y =$ ___?___. A point on the graph is (___?___, ___?___).
   c. When $x = 1$, $y =$ ___?___. A point on the graph is (___?___, ___?___).

4. To find points on the graph of $y = -\frac{1}{4}x + 1$, it is helpful to choose x values that are divisible by ___?___.

Graph.

5. $y = 3x - 4$

6. $y = -2x + 3$

7. $y = -\frac{2}{3}x$

8. $y = \dfrac{3}{2}x$

9. $y = \dfrac{2}{3}x - 4$

10. $y = \dfrac{3}{4}x + 2$

11. $y = -\dfrac{1}{3}x + 2$

12. $y = -\dfrac{3}{2}x - 3$

13. $y = \dfrac{3}{5}x - 1$

2 **Graph an equation of the form *Ax + By = C***

Graph.

14. $2x - y = 3$

15. $2x + y = -3$

16. $2x + 5y = 10$

17. $x - 4y = 8$

18. $y = -2$

19. $y = 1$

20. $x = -3$

21. $x = 4$

22. $x - 3y = 0$

23. $2x - 3y = 12$

24. $3x - y = -2$

25. $3x - 2y = 8$

26. a. The x-intercept of a graph of a linear equation is the point where the graph crosses the ___?___ . Its ___?___-coordinate is 0.
   b. The y-intercept of a graph of a linear equation is the point where the graph crosses the ___?___ . Its ___?___-coordinate is 0.

Find the x- and y-intercepts and graph.

27. $x - 2y = -4$

28. $3x + y = 3$

29. $2x - 3y = 9$

30. $4x - 2y = 5$ **31.** $2x - y = 4$ **32.** $2x + y = 3$

33. $3x + 2y = 5$ **34.** $4x - 3y = 8$ **35.** $3x + 2y = 4$

36. $2x - 3y = 4$ **37.** $3x - 5y = 9$ **38.** $4x - 3y = 6$

39. Suppose A and C are negative and B is positive. Is the y-intercept of the graph of $Ax + By = C$ above or below the x-axis?

40. Suppose A, B, and C are negative. Is the x-intercept of the graph of $Ax + By = C$ to the left or to the right of the y-axis?

41. The x-intercept of the graph of $f(x) = -\dfrac{4}{3}x - 4$ is $(-3, 0)$. What is the zero of f?

42. The x-intercept of the graph of $g(x) = -\dfrac{2}{5}x + 4$ is $(10, 0)$. What is the zero of f?

From the graph, determine the zero of the function.

43.

44.

45.

46.
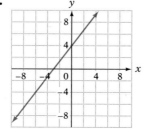

Find the zero of each linear function.

47. $f(x) = 2x - 6$ **48.** $g(x) = 3x + 6$ **49.** $g(x) = -2x + 5$ **50.** $f(x) = -3x - 9$

51. $y(x) = \dfrac{3}{4}x - 6$ **52.** $s(t) = -\dfrac{2}{5}t + 4$ **53.** $f(t) = \dfrac{t}{2} - 3$ **54.** $f(x) = \dfrac{3x}{2} + 3$

55. $g(x) = 3x + 8$ **56.** $h(z) = \dfrac{2}{3}z - 3$ **57.** $f(x) = -\dfrac{3}{4}x + 2$ **58.** $g(x) = \dfrac{5}{2}x + 4$

> For Exercises 59 and 60, use this information. The value, V, of an investment of \$1500 at an annual simple interest rate of 7% is given by the equation $V = 105t + 1500$, where t is the amount of time, in years, that the money is invested.

59. a. Find the value of V for $t = 0$: $V = 105(\_\_?\_\_) + 1500 = \_\_?\_\_$. This means that a point on the graph of the equation $V = 105t + 1500$ is $(0, \_\_?\_\_)$.
   b. Find the value of V for $t = 8$: $V = 105(\_\_?\_\_) + 1500 = \_\_?\_\_$. This means that a point on the graph of the equation $V = 105t + 1500$ is $(\_\_?\_\_, \_\_?\_\_)$.
   c. The graph of $V = 105t + 1500$ for $0 \le t \le 8$ is a straight line joining $(0, \_\_?\_\_)$ and $(8, \_\_?\_\_)$.

60. The point $(3, 1815)$ is on the graph of $V = 105t + 1500$.
   a. To confirm that this ordered pair is on the graph of $V = 105t + 1500$, substitute 3 for $\_\_?\_\_$ and find the corresponding value of $\_\_?\_\_$: $V = 105(\_\_?\_\_) + 1500 = \_\_?\_\_ + 1500 = \_\_?\_\_$.
   b. The meaning of the ordered pair $(3, 1815)$ in the context of this situation is that after $\_\_?\_\_$ years, the investment is worth $\_\_?\_\_$ dollars.

3   **Application problems**

Solve.

61. Amusement Parks The Kingda Ka roller coaster at Six Flags Great Adventure in Jackson, N.J., has a maximum speed of 188 ft/s. The equation that describes the total number of feet traveled by the roller coaster in t seconds at this speed is given by $D = 188t$. Use the coordinate axes at the right to graph this equation for $0 \le t \le 10$. The point $(5, 940)$ is on this graph. Write a sentence that describes the meaning of this ordered pair.

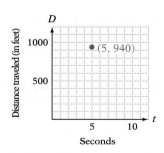

62. Sports A tennis pro is paid \$40 an hour for a private lesson by members of a condominium group. The equation that describes the total earnings, E (in dollars), received by the pro is $E = 40t$, where t is the total number of hours worked. Use the coordinate axes at the right to graph this equation for $0 \le t \le 30$. The point $(25, 1000)$ is on the graph. Write a sentence that describes the meaning of this ordered pair.

63. **Real Estate** A realtor receives $400 per month plus 6% commission on sales. The equation that describes the total monthly income, I (in dollars), of the realtor is $I = 0.06s + 400$, where s is the amount of sales. Use the coordinate axes at the right to graph this equation for $0 \leq s \leq 150{,}000$. The point $(60{,}000, 4000)$ is on the graph. Write a sentence that describes the meaning of this ordered pair.

64. **Human Resources** An electronics company pays line workers $9 per hour plus $.05 for each transistor produced. The equation that describes the hourly wage, W (in dollars), is $W = 0.05n + 9$, where n is the number of transistors produced during any given hour. Use the coordinate axes at the right to graph this equation for $0 \leq n \leq 20$. The point $(16, 9.80)$ is on the graph. Write a sentence that describes the meaning of this ordered pair.

65. **Food Science** A caterer charges a flat rate of $500 plus $.95 for each hot appetizer. The equation that describes the cost, C (in dollars), of catering a dinner party is $C = 0.95n + 500$, where n is the number of hot appetizers. Use the coordinate axes at the right to graph this equation for $0 \leq n \leq 300$. The point $(120, 614)$ is on the graph. Write a sentence that describes the meaning of this ordered pair.

66. **Environmental Science** A tree service charges $60 plus $35 for each tree removed. The equation that describes the cost, C (in dollars), is $C = 35n + 60$, where n is the number of trees removed. Use the coordinate axes at the right to graph this equation for $0 \leq n \leq 100$. The point $(50, 1810)$ is on the graph. Write a sentence that describes the meaning of this ordered pair.

3.3 Applying Concepts

67. **Business** The sale price of an item is a function, s, of the original price, p, where $s(p) = 0.80p$. If an item's original price is $200, what is the sale price of the item?

68. **Business** The markup of an item is a function, m, of its cost, c, where $m(c) = 0.25c$. If the cost of an item is $150, what is the markup of the item?

Use a graphing utility to draw the graph of each of the following equations.

69. $f(x) = 1.2x + 2.3$

70. $f(x) = 2.4x + 0.5$

71. $f(x) = \dfrac{2x}{3} - \dfrac{5}{3}$

72. $y = -\dfrac{3x}{4} - \dfrac{5}{2}$

73. $3x - y = 4$

74. $2x + y = 3$

75. Explain the relationship between the zero of a linear function and the x-intercept of the graph of that function.

76. There is a relationship between the number of times a cricket chirps and the air temperature. The function $f(C) = 7C - 30$, where C is the temperature in degrees Celsius, can be used to approximate the number of times per minute that a cricket chirps. Discuss the domain and range of this function, and explain the significance of its x-intercept.

77. Explain what the graph of an equation represents.

78. Explain why you cannot graph the equation $4x + 3y = 0$ by using just its intercepts.

3.4 Slope of a Straight Line

OBJECTIVE 1   Find the slope of a line given two points

The graphs of $y = 3x + 2$ and $y = \dfrac{2}{3}x + 2$ are shown at the left. Each graph crosses the y-axis at the point $(0, 2)$, but the graphs have different slants. The **slope** of a line is a measure of the slant of the line. The symbol for slope is m.

The slope of a line containing two points is the ratio of the change in the y values between the two points to the change in the x values. The line containing the points whose coordinates are $(-1, -3)$ and $(5, 2)$ is shown below.

The change in the y values is the difference between the y-coordinates of the two points.

$$\text{Change in } y = 2 - (-3) = 5$$

The change in the x values is the difference between the x-coordinates of the two points.

$$\text{Change in } x = 5 - (-1) = 6$$

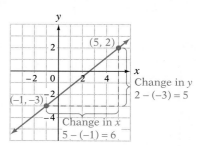

The slope of the line between the two points is the ratio of the change in y to the change in x.

$$\text{Slope} = m = \frac{\text{change in } y}{\text{change in } x} = \frac{5}{6} \qquad m = \frac{2 - (-3)}{5 - (-1)} = \frac{5}{6}$$

In general, if $P_1(x_1, y_1)$ and $P_2(x_2, y_2)$ are two points on a line, then

$$\text{Change in } y = y_2 - y_1 \qquad \text{Change in } x = x_2 - x_1$$

Using these ideas, we can state a formula for slope.

Slope Formula

The slope of the line containing the two points $P_1(x_1, y_1)$ and $P_2(x_2, y_2)$ is given by

$$m = \frac{y_2 - y_1}{x_2 - x_1}, \quad x_1 \neq x_2$$

Frequently, the Greek letter Δ (delta) is used to designate the change in a variable. Using this notation, we can write the equations for the change in y and the change in x as follows:

$$\text{Change in } y = y_2 - y_1 = \Delta y \qquad \text{Change in } x = x_2 - x_1 = \Delta x$$

With this notation, the slope formula is written $m = \frac{\Delta y}{\Delta x}$.

In Section 1, Objective 4, of this chapter, we calculated the average rate of change in the population of California for different intervals of time. In each case, the average rate of change was different. Note that the graph of the population data did not lie on a straight line.

The graph of an equation of the form $y = mx + b$ is a straight line, and the average rate of change is constant. We can calculate the average rate of change between any two points on the line, and the rate of change will always be the same. For a linear equation, the rate of change is referred to as slope.

Find the slope of the line containing the points whose coordinates are $(-2, 0)$ and $(4, 5)$.

Let $P_1 = (-2, 0)$ and $P_2 = (4, 5)$. (It does not matter which point is named P_1 and which P_2; the slope will be the same.)

$$m = \frac{y_2 - y_1}{x_2 - x_1} = \frac{5 - 0}{4 - (-2)} = \frac{5}{6}$$

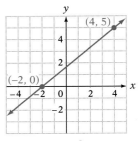

Positive slope

A line that slants upward to the right always has a **positive slope.**

Find the slope of the line containing the points whose coordinates are $(-3, 4)$ and $(4, 2)$.

Let $P_1 = (-3, 4)$ and $P_2 = (4, 2)$.

$$m = \frac{y_2 - y_1}{x_2 - x_1} = \frac{2 - 4}{4 - (-3)} = \frac{-2}{7} = -\frac{2}{7}$$

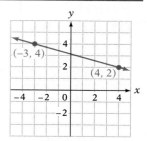

Negative slope

A line that slants downward to the right always has a **negative slope.**

Find the slope of the line containing the points whose coordinates are $(-2, 2)$ and $(4, 2)$.

Let $P_1 = (-2, 2)$ and $P_2 = (4, 2)$.

$$m = \frac{y_2 - y_1}{x_2 - x_1} = \frac{2 - 2}{4 - (-2)} = \frac{0}{6} = 0$$

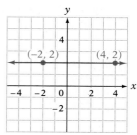

Zero slope

The horizontal line has **zero slope.**

Find the slope of the line containing the points whose coordinates are $(1, -2)$ and $(1, 3)$.

Let $P_1 = (1, -2)$ and $P_2 = (1, 3)$.

$$m = \frac{y_2 - y_1}{x_2 - x_1} = \frac{3 - (-2)}{1 - 1} = \frac{5}{0} \quad \text{Not a real number}$$

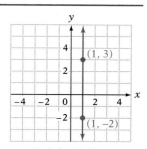

Undefined slope

The slope of a vertical line is **undefined.**

EXAMPLE 1   Find the slope of the line containing the points whose coordinates are $(2, -5)$ and $(-4, 2)$.

Solution $m = \dfrac{y_2 - y_1}{x_2 - x_1} = \dfrac{2 - (-5)}{-4 - 2} = \dfrac{7}{-6} = -\dfrac{7}{6}$ • Let $P_1 = (2, -5)$ and $P_2 = (-4, 2)$.

The slope is $-\dfrac{7}{6}$.

Point of Interest

One of the motivations for the discovery of calculus was to solve a more complicated version of the distance-rate problem at the right.

You may be familiar with twirling a ball on the end of a string. If you release the string, the ball flies off in a path as shown below.

The question that mathematicians tried to answer was essentially "What is the slope (relative to the horizontal) of the line represented by the arrow?"

Answering questions similar to this led to the development of one aspect of calculus.

PROBLEM 1   Find the slope of the line containing the points whose coordinates are $(4, -3)$ and $(2, 7)$.

Solution   See page S8.

There are many applications of slope. Here are two examples.

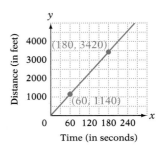

The first record for the one-mile run was recorded in 1865 in England. Richard Webster ran the mile in 4 min 36.5 s. His average speed was approximately 19 feet per second.

The graph at the right shows the distance Webster ran during that run. From the graph, note that after 60 s (1 min) he had traveled 1140 ft and that after 180 s (3 min) he had traveled 3420 ft.

Let the point $(60, 1140)$ be (x_1, y_1) and the point $(180, 3420)$ be (x_2, y_2). The slope of the line between these two points is

$$m = \frac{y_2 - y_1}{x_2 - x_1} = \frac{3420 - 1140}{180 - 60} = \frac{2280}{120} = 19$$

Note that the slope of the line is the same as Webster's average speed, 19 feet per second.

Average speed is related to slope.

The following example is related to agriculture.

The number of farm workers in the United States declined from 10 million in 1950 to 3 million in 2000. (*Source:* U.S. Department of Agriculture)

Let the point $(1950, 10)$ be (x_1, y_1) and the point $(2000, 3)$ be (x_2, y_2). The slope of the line between these two points is

$$m = \frac{y_2 - y_1}{x_2 - y_1}$$

$$= \frac{3 - 10}{2000 - 1950} = \frac{-7}{50} = -0.14$$

Note that if we interpret negative slope as decreasing population, then the slope of the line represents the annual rate at which the number of farm workers was decreasing, 0.14 million or 140,000 workers per year.

In general, any quantity that is expressed by using the word *per* is represented mathematically as slope. In the first example, the slope was 19 feet per second. In the second example, the slope was -0.14 per year.

EXAMPLE 2 The graph shows the
relationship between the cost
of an item and the sales tax.
Find the slope of the line
between the two points shown
on the graph. Write a sentence
that states the meaning of the
slope.

Solution $m = \dfrac{5.25 - 3.50}{75 - 50} = \dfrac{1.75}{25} = 0.07$

A slope of 0.07 means that the sales tax is $.07 per dollar.

PROBLEM 2 The graph shows the decrease
in the value of a printing press
for a period of six years. Find
the slope of the line between
the two points shown on the
graph. Write a sentence that
states the meaning of the
slope.

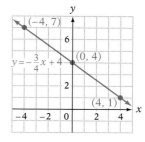

Solution   See page S8.

OBJECTIVE 2 Graph a line given a point and the slope

The graph of the equation $y = -\dfrac{3}{4}x + 4$ is shown
at the right. The points $(-4, 7)$ and $(4, 1)$ are on the
graph. The slope of the line is

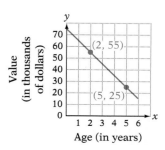

$$m = \frac{7 - 1}{-4 - 4} = \frac{6}{-8} = -\frac{3}{4}$$

Note that the slope of the line has the same value
as the coefficient of x. The y-intercept is $(0, 4)$.

Slope-Intercept Form of a Straight Line

The equation $y = mx + b$ is called the **slope-intercept form** of a
straight line. The slope of the line is m, the coefficient is x. The
y-intercept is $(0, b)$.

When the equation of a straight line is in the form $y = mx + b$, the graph can
be drawn by using the slope and the y-intercept. First locate the y-intercept.
Use the slope to find a second point on the line. Then draw a line through the
two points.

Graph $y = \frac{5}{3}x - 4$ by using the slope and the y-intercept.

The slope is the coefficient of x.

$$m = \frac{5}{3} = \frac{\text{change in } y}{\text{change in } x}$$

The y-intercept is $(0, -4)$.

Beginning at the y-intercept $(0, -4)$, move right 3 units (change in x) and then up 5 units (change in y).

The point whose coordinates $(3, 1)$ is a second point on the graph. Draw a line through the points $(0, -4)$ and $(3, 1)$.

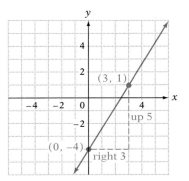

Graph $x + 2y = 4$ by using the slope and the y-intercept.

Solve the equation for y.

$$x + 2y = 4$$
$$2y = -x + 4$$
$$y = -\frac{1}{2}x + 2$$

The slope is $m = -\frac{1}{2} = \frac{-1}{2}$ and the y-intercept is $(0, 2)$.

Beginning at the y-intercept $(0, 2)$, move right 2 units (change in x) and then down 1 unit (change in y).

The point whose coordinates are $(2, 1)$ is a second point on the graph. Draw a line through the points $(0, 2)$ and $(2, 1)$.

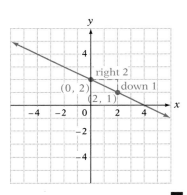

EXAMPLE 3   Graph: $y = -\frac{3}{2}x + 4$ by using the slope and the y-intercept.

Solution y-intercept $= (0, 4)$ • **Locate the y-intercept.**

$$m = -\frac{3}{2} = \frac{-3}{2}$$ • $m = \dfrac{\textbf{change in } y}{\textbf{change in } x}$

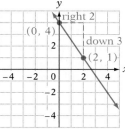

• **Beginning at the y-intercept, (0, 4), move right 2 units and then down 3 units. (2, 1) is a second point on the graph.**
• **Draw a line through the points (0, 4) and (2, 1).**

> **PROBLEM 3**   Graph: $2x + 3y = 6$ by using the slope and the y-intercept.
>
> ■ **Solution**   See page S8.

The graph of a line can be drawn when any point on the line and the slope of the line are given.

Graph the line that passes through the point $(-4, -4)$ and has slope 2.

When the slope is an integer, write it as a fraction with denominator 1.

$$m = 2 = \frac{2}{1} = \frac{\text{change in } y}{\text{change in } x}$$

Take Note

This example differs from the others in that a point other than the y-intercept is used. In this case, start at the given point.

Locate $(-4, -4)$ in the coordinate plane. Beginning at that point, move right 1 unit (change in x) and then up 2 units (change in y).

The point whose coordinates are $(-3, -2)$ is a second point on the graph. Draw a line through the points $(-4, -4)$ and $(-3, -2)$.

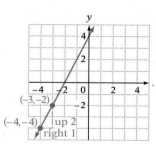

EXAMPLE 4   Graph the line that passes through the point $(-2, 3)$ and has slope $= -\frac{4}{3}$.

Solution

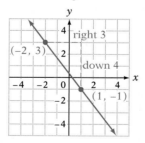

- $(x_1, y_1) = (-2, 3)$;

$$m = -\frac{4}{3} = \frac{-4}{3} = \frac{\text{change in } y}{\text{change in } x}$$

- Beginning at the point $(-2, 3)$, move right 3 units and then down 4 units. $(1, -1)$ is a second point on the line.
- Draw a line through the points $(-2, 3)$ and $(1, -1)$.

PROBLEM 4   Graph the line that passes through the point $(-3, -2)$ and has slope 3.

■ **Solution**   See page S8.

3.4   Concept Review

Determine whether the following statements are always true, sometimes true, or never true.

1. The slope of a line that slants downward to the left is positive.

2. The y-intercept of a line is the point at which the line crosses the y-axis.

3. The slope of a vertical line is zero.

4. A line whose slope is undefined is parallel to the y-axis.

3.4 Exercises

1 Find the slope of a line given two points

1. To find the slope m of the line containing $P_1(2, -4)$ and $P_2(3, -5)$, use the slope formula $m = \dfrac{y_2 - y_1}{x_2 - x_1}$. Identify each x and y value to substitute into the slope formula.

$y_2 = $ ___?___ , $y_1 = $ ___?___ , $x_2 = $ ___?___ , $x_1 = $ ___?___ .

2. The slope of the line containing $P_1(1, -6)$ and $P_2(5, -10)$ is $\dfrac{-10 - (?)}{5 - (?)} =$ ___?___ .

This line slants ___?___ (upward or downward) to the right.

Find the slope of the line containing the points P_1 and P_2.

3. $P_1(1, 3), P_2(3, 1)$

4. $P_1(2, 3), P_2(5, 1)$

5. $P_1(-1, 4), P_2(2, 5)$

6. $P_1(3, -2), P_2(1, 4)$

7. $P_1(-1, 3), P_2(-4, 5)$

8. $P_1(-1, -2), P_2(-3, 2)$

9. $P_1(0, 3), P_2(4, 0)$

10. $P_1(-2, 0), P_2(0, 3)$

11. $P_1(2, 4), P_2(2, -2)$

12. $P_1(4, 1), P_2(4, -3)$

13. $P_1(2, 5), P_2(-3, -2)$

14. $P_1(4, 1), P_2(-1, -2)$

15. $P_1(2, 3), P_2(-1, 3)$

16. $P_1(3, 4), P_2(0, 4)$

17. $P_1(0, 4), P_2(-2, 5)$

18. $P_1(-2, 3), P_2(-2, 5)$

19. $P_1(-3, -1), P_2(-3, 4)$

20. $P_1(-2, -5), P_2(-4, -1)$

21. **Uniform Motion** The graph below shows the relationship between the distance traveled by a motorist and the time of travel. Find the slope of the line between the two points shown on the graph. Write a sentence that states the meaning of the slope.

22. 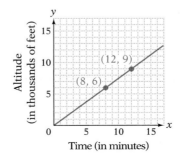 **Aeronautics** The graph below shows how the altitude of an airplane above the runway changes after take-off. Find the slope of the line. Write a sentence that states the meaning of the slope.

23. **Automotive Technology** The graph below shows how the amount of gas in the tank of a car decreases as the car is driven. Find the slope of the line. Write a sentence that states the meaning of the slope.

24. **Meteorology** The troposphere extends from the surface of Earth to an elevation of approximately 11 km. The graph below shows the decrease in temperature of the troposphere as altitude increases. Find the slope of the line. Write a sentence that states the meaning of the slope.

25. Sports Lois and Tanya start from the same place on a jogging course. Lois is jogging at 9 km/h, and Tanya is jogging at 6 km/h. The graphs below show the total distance traveled by each jogger and the total distance between Lois and Tanya. Which lines represent which distances?

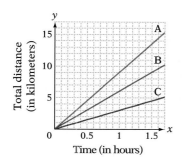

26. Chemistry A chemist is filling two cans from a faucet that releases water at a constant rate. Can 1 has a diameter of 20 mm, and can 2 has a diameter of 30 mm. The depth of the water in each can is measured at 5-second intervals. The graph of the results is shown below. On the graph, which line represents the depth of the water for which can?

27. **Health Science** The American National Standards Institute (ANSI) states that the slope for a wheelchair ramp must not exceed $\frac{1}{12}$.

a. Does a ramp that is 6 in. high and 5 ft long meet the requirements of ANSI?

b. Does a ramp that is 12 in. high and 170 in. long meet the requirements of ANSI?

28. Let l be a line passing through points (a, b) and (c, d). If a, b, c and d are all positive with $a > c$ and $b > d$, does l slant upward to the right or downward to the right?

29. The slope of the line with equation $y = 5x - 3$ is ___?___, and its y-intercept is ___?___.

30. The slope of the line with equation $2x + y = 7$ is ___?___, and its y-intercept is ___?___.

2 **Graph a line given a point and the slope**

Graph by using the slope and the y-intercept.

31. $y = \dfrac{1}{2}x + 2$

32. $y = \dfrac{2}{3}x - 3$

33. $y = -\dfrac{3}{2}x$

34. $y = \dfrac{3}{4}x$

35. $y = -\dfrac{1}{2}x + 2$

36. $y = \dfrac{2}{3}x - 1$

37. $x - 3y = 3$

38. $3x + 2y = 8$

39. $4x + y = 2$

40. Suppose A and B are positive numbers, and C is a negative number. Does the y-intercept of the graph of $Ax + By = C$ lie above or below the x-axis? Does the graph slant upward to the right or downward to the right?

41. Suppose A and C are positive numbers, and B is a negative number. Does the y-intercept of the graph of $Ax + By = C$ lie above or below the x-axis? Does the graph slant upward to the right or downward to the right?

42. Graph the line that passes through the point $(-1, -3)$ and has slope $\dfrac{4}{3}$.

43. Graph the line that passes through the point $(-2, -3)$ and has slope $\dfrac{5}{4}$.

44. Graph the line that passes through the point $(-3, 0)$ and has slope -3.

45. Graph the line that passes through the point $(2, 0)$ and has slope -1.

3.4   **Applying Concepts**

46. Let $f(x)$ be the digit in the nth decimal place of the repeating digit is $0.\overline{387}$. For example, $f(3) = 7$ because 7 is the digit in the third decimal place. Find $f(14)$.

Complete the sentences.

47. If a line has a slope of 2, then the value of y <u>increases/decreases</u> by _____ as the value of x increases by 1.

48. If a line has a slope of -3, then the value of y <u>increases/decreases</u> by _____ as the value of x increases by 1.

49. If a line has a slope of $\frac{1}{2}$, then the value of y <u>increases/decreases</u> by _____ as the value of x increases by 1.

50. If a line has a slope of $-\frac{2}{3}$, then the value of y <u>increases/decreases</u> by _____ as the value of x increases by 1.

Determine the value of k such that the points whose coordinates are given below lie on the same line.

51. $(3, 2), (4, 6), (5, k)$ **52.** $(k, 1), (0, -1), (2, -2)$

53. Match each equation with its graph.

    i. $y = -2x + 4$

    ii. $y = 2x - 4$

    iii. $y = 2$

    iv. $2x + 4y = 0$

    v. $y = \frac{1}{2}x + 4$

    vi. $y = -\frac{1}{4}x - 2$

A.   **B.**   **C.**

D.   **E.**   **F.**

54. Graph $y = 2x + 3$ and $y = 2x - 1$ on the same coordinate system. Explain how the graphs are different and how they are the same. If b is any real number, how is the graph of $y = 2x + b$ related to the two graphs you have drawn?

55. Explain how you can use the slope of a line to determine whether three given points lie on the same line. Then use your procedure to determine whether all of the following points lie on the same line.
    a. $(2, 5), (-1, -1), (3, 7)$ **b.** $(-1, 5), (0, 3), (-3, 4)$

3.5   Finding Equations of Lines

OBJECTIVE 1   **Find the equation of a line given a point and the slope**

When the slope of a line and a point on the line are known, the equation of the line can be determined. If the particular point is the y-intercept, use the slope-intercept form, $y = mx + b$, to find the equation.

■ Find the equation of the line that contains the point $(0, 3)$ and has slope $\frac{1}{2}$.

The known point is the y-intercept, $(0, 3)$.

Use the slope-intercept form. $y = mx + b$

Replace m with $\frac{1}{2}$, the given slope, and replace b $y = \frac{1}{2}x + 3$
with 3, the y-coordinate of the y-intercept.

The equation of the line is $y = \frac{1}{2}x + 3$.

One method of finding the equation of a line when the slope and any point on the line are known involves using the *point-slope formula*. This formula is derived from the formula for the slope of a line.

Let (x_1, y_1) be the given point on the line, and let (x, y) be another point on the line.

Use the formula for the slope of a line. $\dfrac{y - y_1}{x - x_1} = m$

Multiply both sides of the equation by $(x - x_1)$. $\dfrac{y - y_1}{x - x_1}(x - x_1) = m(x - x_1)$

Then simplify. $y - y_1 = m(x - x_1)$

Point-Slope Formula

Let m be the slope of a line, and let (x_1, y_1) be the coordinates of a point on the line. The equation of the line can be found using the **point-slope formula:**

$$y - y_1 = m(x - x_1)$$

Find the equation of the line that contains the point $(4, -1)$ and has slope $-\frac{3}{4}$.

Use the point-slope formula.

$$y - y_1 = m(x - x_1)$$

Substitute the slope, $-\frac{3}{4}$, and the coordinates of the given point, $(4, -1)$, into the point-slope formula. Then simplify.

$$y - (-1) = -\frac{3}{4}(x - 4)$$

$$y + 1 = -\frac{3}{4}x + 3$$

$$y = -\frac{3}{4}x + 2$$

The equation of the line is $y = -\frac{3}{4}x + 2$.

Find the equation of the line that passes through the point whose coordinates are $(4, 3)$ and whose slope is undefined.

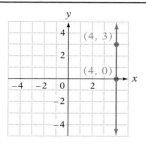

Because the slope is undefined, the point-slope formula cannot be used to find the equation. Instead, recall that when the slope is undefined, the line is vertical and that the equation of a vertical line is $x = a$, where a is the x-coordinate of the x-intercept. Because the line is vertical and passes through $(4, 3)$, the x-intercept is $(4, 0)$.

The equation of the line is $x = 4$.

EXAMPLE 1   Find the equation of the line that contains the point $(-2, 4)$ and has slope 2.

Solution
$$y - y_1 = m(x - x_1)$$
$$y - 4 = 2[x - (-2)]$$
$$y - 4 = 2(x + 2)$$
$$y - 4 = 2x + 4$$
$$y = 2x + 8$$

- **Use the point-slope formula.**
- **Substitute the slope, 2, and the coordinates of the given point, $(-2, 4)$, into the point-slope formula.**

The equation of the line is $y = 2x + 8$.

PROBLEM 1   Find the equation of the line that contains the point $(4, -3)$ and has slope -3.

Solution   See page S8.

OBJECTIVE 2   **Find the equation of a line given two points**

The point-slope formula and the formula for slope are used to find the equation of a line when two points are known.

Find the equation of the line containing the points (3, 2) and (−5, 6).

To use the point-slope formula, we must know the slope. Use the formula for slope to determine the slope of the line between the two given points.

Let $(x_1, y_1) = (3, 2)$ and $(x_2, y_2) = (-5, 6)$.

$$m = \frac{y_2 - y_1}{x_2 - x_1} = \frac{6 - 2}{-5 - 3} = \frac{4}{-8} = -\frac{1}{2}$$

Now use the point-slope formula with $m = -\frac{1}{2}$ and $(x_1, y_1) = (3, 2)$.

$$y - y_1 = m(x - x_1)$$
$$y - 2 = -\frac{1}{2}(x - 3)$$
$$y - 2 = -\frac{1}{2}x + \frac{3}{2}$$
$$y = -\frac{1}{2}x + \frac{7}{2}$$

The equation of the line is $y = -\frac{1}{2}x + \frac{7}{2}$.

EXAMPLE 2   Find the equation of the line containing the points (2, 3) and (4, 1).

Solution $m = \dfrac{y_2 - y_1}{x_2 - x_1} = \dfrac{1 - 3}{4 - 2} = \dfrac{-2}{2} = -1$ • **Find the slope. Let** $(x_1, y_1) = (2, 3)$ **and** $(x_2, y_2) = (4, 1)$.

$y - y_1 = m(x - x_1)$ • **Substitute the slope and the**
$y - 3 = -1(x - 2)$ **coordinates of either one of**
$y - 3 = -x + 2$ **the known points into the**
$y = -x + 5$ **point-slope formula.**

The equation of the line is $y = -x + 5$.

PROBLEM 2   Find the equation of the line containing the points (2, 0) and (5, 3).

Solution   See page S8.

OBJECTIVE 3   **Application problems**

Linear functions can be used to model a variety of applications in science and business. For each application, data are collected and the independent and dependent variables are selected. Then a linear function is determined that models the data.

EXAMPLE 3   In 1950, there were 13 million adults 65 years old or older in the United States. Data from the Census Bureau shows that the population of these adults has been increasing at a constant rate of approximately 0.5 million per year. This rate of increase is expected to continue through the year 2010. Find the equation of the line that approximates the population of adults 65 years old or older in terms of the year. Use your equation to approximate the population of these adults in 2005.

Strategy   Select the independent and dependent variables. Because we want to determine the population of adults 65 years of age or older, that quantity is the *dependent* variable, y. The year is the *independent* variable.

From the data, the ordered pair (1950, 13), where the y-coordinate is in millions of people, is a point on the line. The slope of the line is the *rate* of increase, 0.5 million per year.

Solution   Use the point-slope formula.

$$y - y_1 = m(x - x_1)$$

$$y - 13 = 0.5(x - 1950) \qquad \bullet \ \ m = 0.5, (x_1, y_1) = (1950, 13)$$
$$y - 13 = 0.5x - 975$$
$$y = 0.5x - 962$$

The linear function is $f(x) = 0.5x - 962$.

$$f(x) = 0.5x - 962$$
$$f(2005) = 0.5(2005) - 962 \qquad \bullet \text{ Evaluate the function at 2005 to}$$
$$= 1002.5 - 962 \qquad\qquad\qquad \text{ predict the population in 2005.}$$
$$= 40.5$$

The equation gives an estimate of 40.5 million people 65 years or older in 2005.

PROBLEM 3   Gabriel Daniel Fahrenheit invented the mercury thermometer in 1717. In terms of readings on this thermometer, water freezes at 32°F and boils at 212°F. In 1742 Anders Celsius invented the Celsius temperature scale. On this scale, water freezes at 0°C and boils at 100°C. Find a linear function that can be used to predict the Celsius temperature when the Fahrenheit temperature is known.

Solution   See page S8.

3.5 Concept Review

Identify the following statements as always true, sometimes true, or never true.

1. Increasing the value of m in the equation $y = mx + b$ increases the slope of the line that is the graph of the equation.

2. Decreasing the value of b in the equation $y = mx + b$ decreases the slope of the line that is the graph of the equation.

3. The point-slope formula for the equation of a line is $y = m(x - x_1)$.

4. $x = a$ is the equation for a vertical line.

5. The line represented by the equation $y = 2x - \frac{1}{2}$ has slope $-\frac{1}{2}$ and x-intercept 2.

6. If $y = mx + b$, then m represents the rate of change of y with respect to x.

7. A horizontal line has no slope.

3.5 Exercises

1   Find the equation of a line given a point and the slope

1. In the equation of the line that has slope $-\frac{6}{5}$ and y-intercept $(0, 2)$, m is _____?_____ and b is _____?_____. The equation is $y = $ _____?_____.

2. To find the equation of the line that contains the point $(-4, 5)$ and has slope 2, use the point-slope formula.

$y - y_1 = m(x - x_1)$
$y - 5 = 2(x - (-4))$ • Substitute _____?_____ for y_1, _____?_____ for m, and _____?_____ for x_1.

$y - 5 = 2(x + $ _?_ $)$ • Simplify inside the parentheses.
$y - 5 = $ _?_   • Use the Distributive Property on the right side of the equation.

$y = $ _?_   • Add 5 to each side of the equation.

Find the equation of the line that contains the given point and has the given slope.

3. Point $(0, 5)$, $m = 2$ **4.** Point $(0, 3)$, $m = 1$ **5.** Point $(2, 3)$, $m = \frac{1}{2}$

6. Point $(5, 1)$, $m = \frac{2}{3}$ **7.** Point $(3, 0)$, $m = -\frac{5}{3}$ **8.** Point $(-2, 0)$, $m = \frac{3}{2}$

9. Point $(-1, 7)$, $m = -3$ **10.** Point $(-2, 4)$, $m = -4$ **11.** Point $(0, 0)$, $m = \frac{1}{2}$

12. Point $(0, 0)$, $m = \dfrac{3}{4}$

13. Point $(2, -3)$, $m = 3$

14. Point $(4, -5)$, $m = 2$

15. Point $(3, 5)$, $m = -\dfrac{2}{3}$

16. Point $(5, 1)$, $m = -\dfrac{4}{5}$

17. Point $(0, -3)$, $m = -1$

18. Point $(2, 0)$, $m = \dfrac{5}{6}$

19. Point $(3, -4)$, slope is undefined

20. Point $(-2, 5)$, slope is undefined

21. Point $(-2, -3)$, $m = 0$

22. Point $(-3, -2)$, $m = 0$

23. Point $(4, -5)$, $m = -2$

24. Point $(-3, 5)$, $m = 3$

25. Point $(-5, -1)$, slope is undefined

26. Point $(0, 4)$, slope is undefined

27. A student found the equation of the line containing the points $(-2, 4)$ and $(1, 1)$ to be $y = x + 6$. Sketch the line containing $(-2, 4)$ and $(1, 1)$ and use your sketch to explain why the student's values for m and b cannot be correct.

28. A student found the equation of the line containing the points $(-4, 4)$ and $(4, 6)$ to be $y = \dfrac{1}{4}x + 5$. Sketch the line containing $(-4, 4)$ and $(4,6)$ and use your sketch to explain why the student's values for m and b seem reasonable.

2   Find the equation of a line given two points

Find the equation of the line that contains the given points.

29. $P_1(0, 2)$, $P_2(3, 5)$

30. $P_1(0, 4)$, $P_2(1, 5)$

31. $P_1(0, -3)$, $P_2(-4, 5)$

32. $P_1(0, -2)$, $P_2(-3, 4)$

33. $P_1(-1, 3)$, $P_2(2, 4)$

34. $P_1(-1, 1)$, $P_2(4, 4)$

35. $P_1(0, 3)$, $P_2(2, 0)$

36. $P_1(0, 4)$, $P_2(2, 0)$

37. $P_1(-2, -3)$, $P_2(-1, -2)$

38. $P_1(4, 1)$, $P_2(3, -2)$

39. $P_1(2, 3)$, $P_2(5, 5)$

40. $P_1(7, 2)$, $P_2(4, 4)$

41. $P_1(2, 0)$, $P_2(0, -1)$

42. $P_1(0, 4)$, $P_2(-2, 0)$

43. $P_1(3, -4)$, $P_2(-2, -4)$

44. $P_1(-3, 3)$, $P_2(-2, 3)$

45. $P_1(0, 0)$, $P_2(4, 3)$

46. $P_1(2, -5)$, $P_2(0, 0)$

47. $P_1(-2, 5)$, $P_2(-2, -5)$

48. $P_1(3, 2)$, $P_2(3, -4)$

49. $P_1(2, 1)$, $P_2(-2, -3)$

50. $P_1(-3, -2)$, $P_2(1, -4)$

51. $P_1(0, 3)$, $P_2(3, 0)$

52. $P_1(1, -3)$, $P_2(-2, 4)$

53. A plane takes off from an airport that is 500 ft above sea level. The plane climbs at a rate of 1000 ft/min. If $y = mx + b$ is a linear equation that gives the height y (in feet) of the plane above sea level in terms of the time x (in minutes) after take-off, then $m =$ ___?___ and an ordered pair that is a solution of the equation is (0, ___?___).

54. A plane takes off from an airport that is at sea level and climbs to a height of 12,500 ft in 10 min. If $y = mx + b$ is a linear equation that gives the height y (in feet) of the plane above sea level in terms of the time x (in minutes) after take-off, then two ordered pairs that are solutions of the equation are (0, ___?___) and (10, ___?___).

3   Application problems

55. Aeronautics The pilot of a Boeing 757 jet takes off from Boston's Logan Airport, which is at sea level, and climbs to a cruising altitude of 32,000 ft at a constant rate of 1200 ft/min. Write a linear equation for the height of the plane in terms of the time after take-off. Use your equation to find the height of the plane 11 min after take-off.

56. Physical Fitness A jogger running at 9 mph burns approximately 14 calories per minute. Write a linear equation for the number of calories burned by the jogger in terms of the number of minutes run. Use your equation to find the number of calories burned after jogging for 32 min.

57. Telecommunications A cellular phone company offers several different options for using a cellular telephone. One option, for people who plan on using the phone only in emergencies, costs the user $4.95 per month plus $.59 per minute for each minute the phone is used. Write a linear equation for the monthly cost of the phone in terms of the number of minutes the phone is used. Use your equation to find the monthly cost of using the cellular phone for 13 min in one month.

58. Aeronautics An Airbus 320 plane takes off from Denver International Airport, which is 5200 ft above sea level, and climbs to 30,000 ft at a constant rate of 1000 ft/min. Write a linear equation for the height of the plane in terms of the time after take-off. Use your equation to find the height of the plane 8 min after take-off.

59. Nutrition There are approximately 126 calories in a 2-ounce serving of lean hamburger and approximately 189 calories in a 3-ounce serving. Write a linear equation for the number of calories in lean hamburger in terms of the size of the serving. Use your equation to estimate the number of calories in a 5-ounce serving of lean hamburger.

60. Chemistry At sea level, the boiling point of water is 100°C. At an altitude of 2 km, the boiling point of water is 93°C. Write a linear equation for the boiling point of water in terms of the altitude above sea level. Use your equation to predict the boiling point of water on the top of Mount Everest, which is approximately 8.85 km above sea level. Round to the nearest degree.

61. **History** In 1927, Charles Lindbergh made history by making the first transatlantic flight from New York to Paris. It took Lindbergh approximately 33.5 h to make the trip. In 1997, the Concorde could make the trip in approximately 3.3 h. Write a linear equation of the time, in hours, it takes to cross the Atlantic in terms of the year. Use your equation to predict how long a flight between the two cities would have taken in 1967. Round your answer to the nearest tenth.

62. **Computers** There were 24 million U.S. homes with computers in 1991. From 1991 to 2003, the average annual rate of growth in homes with computers was 7.42 million homes per year. (*Sources:* U.S. Department of Commerce; U.S. Census Bureau) Write a linear equation for the number of homes with computers in terms of the year. Use your equation to predict the number of homes with computers in 2000.

63. Automotive Technology The gas tank of a certain car contains 16 gal when the driver of the car begins a trip. Each mile driven by the driver decreases the amount of gas in the tank by 0.032 gal. Write a linear equation for the number of gallons of gas in the tank in terms of the number of miles driven. Use your equation to find the number of gallons in the tank after driving 150 mi.

64. Oceanography Whales, dolphins, and porpoises communicate using high-pitched sounds that travel through the water. The speed at which the sound travels depends on many factors, one of which is the depth of the water. At approximately 1000 m below sea level, the speed of sound is 1480 m/s. Below 1000 m, the speed of sound increases at a constant rate of 0.017 m/s for each additional meter below 1000 m. Write a linear equation for the speed of sound in terms of the number of meters below sea level. Use your equation to approximate the speed of sound 2500 m below sea level. Round to the nearest meter per second.

3.5 Applying Concepts

65. What is the x-intercept of the graph of $y = mx + b$?

66. A line contains the points $(4, -1)$ and $(2, 1)$. Find the coordinates of three other points that are on this line.

67. Given that f is a linear function for which $f(1) = 3$ and $f(-1) = 5$, determine $f(4)$.

68. Find the equation of the line that passes through the midpoint of the line segment between $P_1(2, 5)$ and $P_2(-4, 1)$ and has slope -2.

69. If $y = mx + b$, where m is a given constant, how does the graph of this equation change as the value of b changes?

70. Explain the similarities and differences between the point-slope formula and the slope-intercept form of a straight line.

71. Explain why the point-slope formula cannot be used to find the equation of a line that is parallel to the y-axis.

3.6 Parallel and Perpendicular Lines

OBJECTIVE 1   Find equations of parallel and perpendicular lines

Two lines that have the same slope do not intersect and are called **parallel lines.**

The slope of each of the lines at the right is $\frac{2}{3}$.

The lines are parallel.

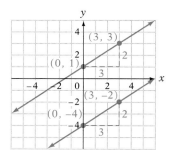

> **Slopes of Parallel Lines**
>
> Two nonvertical lines with slopes of m_1 and m_2 are parallel if and only if $m_1 = m_2$. Any two vertical lines are parallel.

Is the line that contains the points $(-2, 1)$ and $(-5, -1)$ parallel to the line that contains the points $(1, 0)$ and $(4, 2)$?

Find the slope of the line through $(-2, 1)$ and $(-5, -1)$.
$$m_1 = \frac{-1 - 1}{-5 - (-2)} = \frac{-2}{-3} = \frac{2}{3}$$

Find the slope of the line through $(1, 0)$ and $(4, 2)$.
$$m_2 = \frac{2 - 0}{4 - 1} = \frac{2}{3}$$

Because $m_1 = m_2$, the lines are parallel.

EXAMPLE 1   Are the graphs of $y = -\dfrac{3}{2}x - 5$ and $2x + 3y = 6$ parallel?

Solution   Write, if necessary, each equation in the form $y = mx + b$, and then compare the values of m, the slopes of the lines. If the values of m are equal, the graphs are parallel.

The equation $y = -\dfrac{3}{2}x - 5$ is in the form $y = mx + b$.

The slope is $-\dfrac{3}{2}$.

Write the equation $2x + 3y = 6$ in the form $y = mx + b$.

$$2x + 3y = 6$$
$$3y = -2x + 6$$
$$y = -\frac{2}{3}x + 2$$

The slope is $-\dfrac{2}{3}$.

$-\dfrac{2}{3} \neq -\dfrac{3}{2}$. The graphs are not parallel.

PROBLEM 1   Are the graphs of $5x + 2y = 2$ and $5x + 2y = -6$ parallel?

Solution   See page S9.

Find the equation of the line that contains the point $(2, 3)$ and is parallel to the line $y = \dfrac{1}{2}x - 4$.

The slope of the given line is $\dfrac{1}{2}$. Because parallel lines have the same slope, the slope of the unknown line is also $\dfrac{1}{2}$.

Use the point-slope formula.
$$y - y_1 = m(x - x_1)$$

Substitute $m = \dfrac{1}{2}$ and $(x_1, y_1) = (2, 3)$.
$$y - 3 = \frac{1}{2}(x - 2)$$

Solve for y.
$$y - 3 = \frac{1}{2}x - 1$$
$$y = \frac{1}{2}x + 2$$

The equation of the line is $y = \dfrac{1}{2}x + 2$.

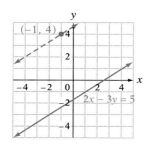

Find the equation of the line that contains the point $(-1, 4)$ and is parallel to the line $2x - 3y = 5$.

Because the lines are parallel, the slope of the unknown line is the same as the slope of the given line. Solve $2x - 3y = 5$ for y and determine its slope.

$$2x - 3y = 5$$
$$-3y = -2x + 5$$
$$y = \frac{2}{3}x - \frac{5}{3}$$

The slope of the given line is $\frac{2}{3}$. Because the lines are parallel, the slope of the unknown line is also $\frac{2}{3}$.

Use the point-slope formula.

$$y - y_1 = m(x - x_1)$$

Substitute $m = \frac{2}{3}$ and $(x_1, y_1) = (-1, 4)$.

$$y - 4 = \frac{2}{3}[x - (-1)]$$

Solve for y.

$$y - 4 = \frac{2}{3}(x + 1)$$

$$y - 4 = \frac{2}{3}x + \frac{2}{3}$$

$$y = \frac{2}{3}x + \frac{14}{3}$$

The equation of the line is $y = \frac{2}{3}x + \frac{14}{3}$.

EXAMPLE 2   Find the equation of the line that contains the point $(3, -1)$ and is parallel to the line $3x - 2y = 4$.

Solution

$$3x - 2y = 4$$
$$-2y = -3x + 4$$
$$y = \frac{3}{2}x - 2$$

• Solve the equation for y to find the slope.

$$m = \frac{3}{2}$$

$$y - y_1 = m(x - x_1)$$

• Use the point-slope formula.

$$y - (-1) = \frac{3}{2}(x - 3)$$

• $m = \frac{3}{2}$, $(x_1, y_1) = (3, -1)$

$$y + 1 = \frac{3}{2}x - \frac{9}{2}$$

$$y = \frac{3}{2}x - \frac{11}{2}$$

PROBLEM 2   Find the equation of the line that contains the point $(4, 1)$ and is parallel to the line $y = \frac{3}{4}x - 1$.

Solution   See page S9.

Two lines that intersect at right angles are **perpendicular lines.**

Any horizontal line is perpendicular to any vertical line. For example, $x = 3$ is perpendicular to $y = -2$, as shown in the graph at the right.

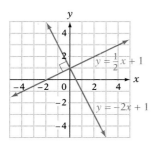

Slopes of Perpendicular Lines

If m_1 and m_2 are the slopes of two lines, neither of which is vertical, then the lines are perpendicular if and only if $m_1 \cdot m_2 = -1$.

A vertical line is perpendicular to a horizontal line.

Solving $m_1 \cdot m_2 = -1$ for m_1 gives $m_1 = -\dfrac{1}{m_2}$. This last equation states that the slopes of perpendicular lines are *negative reciprocals* of each other.

■ Is the line that contains the points $(4, 2)$ and $(-2, 5)$ perpendicular to the line that contains the points $(-4, 3)$ and $(-3, 5)$?

Find the slope of the line that passes through the points $(4, 2)$ and $(-2, 5)$.

$$m_1 = \frac{5 - 2}{-2 - 4} = \frac{3}{-6} = -\frac{1}{2}$$

Find the slope of the line that passes through the points $(-4, 3)$ and $(-3, 5)$.

$$m_2 = \frac{5 - 3}{-3 - (-4)} = \frac{2}{1} = 2$$

Find the product of the two slopes.

$$m_1 \cdot m_2 = -\frac{1}{2}(2) = -1$$

Because $m_1 \cdot m_2 = -1$, the lines are perpendicular.

■

■ Are the graphs of the lines whose equations are $3x + 4y = 8$ and $8x + 6y = 5$ perpendicular?

To determine whether the lines are perpendicular, solve each equation for y and find the slope of each line.

$$3x + 4y = 8$$
$$4y = -3x + 8$$
$$y = -\frac{3}{4}x + 2$$
$$m_1 = -\frac{3}{4}$$

$$8x + 6y = 5$$
$$6y = -8x + 5$$
$$y = -\frac{4}{3}x + \frac{5}{6}$$
$$m_2 = -\frac{4}{3}$$

Then check whether the equation $m_1 \cdot m_2 = -1$ is true.

$$m_1 \cdot m_2 = \left(-\frac{3}{4}\right)\left(-\frac{4}{3}\right) = 1$$

Because $m_1 \cdot m_2 = 1 \neq -1$, the lines are not perpendicular.

■

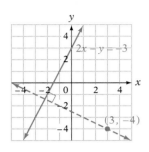

Find the equation of the line that contains the point $(3, -4)$ and is perpendicular to the line $2x - y = -3$.

Determine the slope of the given line by solving the equation for y.

$$2x - y = -3$$
$$-y = -2x - 3$$
$$y = 2x + 3$$

The slope is 2.

The slope of the line perpendicular to the given line is $-\frac{1}{2}$, the negative reciprocal of 2.

Use the point-slope formula.

$$y - y_1 = m(x - x_1)$$

Substitute $m = -\frac{1}{2}$ and $(x_1, y_1) = (3, -4)$.

$$y - (-4) = -\frac{1}{2}(x - 3)$$

Solve for y.

$$y + 4 = -\frac{1}{2}x + \frac{3}{2}$$
$$y = -\frac{1}{2}x - \frac{5}{2}$$

The equation of the perpendicular line is $y = -\frac{1}{2}x - \frac{5}{2}$.

EXAMPLE 3   Are the lines $4x - y = -2$ and $x + 4y = -12$ perpendicular?

Solution $4x - y = -2$
$$-y = -4x - 2$$
$$y = 4x + 2 \qquad m_1 = 4$$

$$x + 4y = -12$$
$$4y = -x - 12$$
$$y = -\frac{1}{4}x - 3 \qquad m_2 = -\frac{1}{4}$$

$$m_1 \cdot m_2 = 4\left(-\frac{1}{4}\right) = -1$$

• Solve each equation for **y** to find the slopes.

• Find the product of the slopes.

Yes, the lines are perpendicular.

PROBLEM 3   Find the equation of the line that contains the point $(-2, 3)$ and is perpendicular to the line $x - 4y = 3$.

Solution   See page S9.

3.6   Concept Review

Determine whether the following statements are always true, sometimes true, or never true.

1. Perpendicular lines have the same y-intercept.

2. Parallel lines have the same slope.

3. The lines given by the equations $y = \frac{3}{2}x + 2$ and $y = -\frac{3}{2}x + 2$ are perpendicular.

4. Two lines are perpendicular if $m_1 \cdot m_2 = 1$.

5. A vertical line is perpendicular to a horizontal line.

6. A line parallel to the y-axis has zero slope.

7. The lines $y = \frac{1}{2}x - 2$ and $y = \frac{1}{2}x - 4$ are parallel.

3.6 Exercises

1   Find equations of parallel and perpendicular lines

1. Given the slopes of two lines, explain how to determine whether the two lines are parallel.

2. Given the slopes of two lines, how can you to determine whether the two lines are perpendicular?

3. The slope of a line is -5. What is the slope of any line parallel to this line?

4. The slope of a line is $\frac{3}{2}$. What is the slope of any line parallel to this line?

5. The slope of a line is 4. What is the slope of any line perpendicular to this line?

6. The slope of a line is $-\frac{4}{5}$. What is the slope of any line perpendicular to this line?

7. Give the slope of any line that is parallel to the line $y = -\frac{1}{3}x + 5$.

8. Give the slope of any line that is perpendicular to the line $y = \frac{3}{5}x + 2$.

9. Is the line $x = -2$ perpendicular to the line $y = 3$?

10. Is the line $y = \frac{1}{2}$ perpendicular to the line $y = -4$?

11. Is the line $x = -3$ parallel to the line $y = \frac{1}{3}$?

12. Is the line $x = 4$ perpendicular to the line $y = -4$?

13. Is the line $y = \frac{2}{3}x - 4$ parallel to the line $y = -\frac{3}{2}x - 4$?

14. Is the line $y = -2x + \frac{2}{3}$ parallel to the line $y = -2x + 3$?

15. Is the line $y = \frac{4}{3}x - 2$ perpendicular to the line $y = -\frac{3}{4}x + 2$?

16. Is the line $y = \frac{1}{2}x + \frac{3}{2}$ perpendicular to the line $y = -\frac{1}{2}x + \frac{3}{2}$?

17. Are the lines $2x + 3y = 2$ and $2x + 3y = -4$ parallel?

18. Are the lines $2x - 4y = 3$ and $2x + 4y = -3$ parallel?

19. Are the lines $x - 4y = 2$ and $4x + y = 8$ perpendicular?

20. Are the lines $4x - 3y = 2$ and $4x + 3y = -7$ perpendicular?

21. Is the line that contains the points $(3, 2)$ and $(1, 6)$ parallel to the line that contains the points $(-1, 3)$ and $(-1, -1)$?

22. Is the line that contains the points $(4, -3)$ and $(2, 5)$ parallel to the line that contains the points $(-2, -3)$ and $(-4, 1)$?

23. Is the line that contains the points $(-3, 2)$ and $(4, -1)$ perpendicular to the line that contains the points $(1, 3)$ and $(-2, -4)$?

24. Is the line that contains the points $(-1, 2)$ and $(3, 4)$ perpendicular to the line that contains the points $(-1, 3)$ and $(-4, 1)$?

25. Is the line that contains the points $(-5, 0)$ and $(0, 2)$ parallel to the line that contains the points $(5, 1)$ and $(0, -1)$?

26. Is the line that contains the points $(3, 5)$ and $(-3, 3)$ perpendicular to the line that contains the points $(2, -5)$ and $(-4, 4)$?

27. Find the equation of the line that contains the point $(-2, -4)$ and is parallel to the line $2x - 3y = 2$.

28. Find the equation of the line that contains the point $(3, 2)$ and is parallel to the line $3x + y = -3$.

29. Find the equation of the line that contains the point $(4, 1)$ and is perpendicular to the line $y = -3x + 4$.

30. Find the equation of the line that contains the point $(2, -5)$ and is perpendicular to the line $y = \frac{5}{2}x - 4$.

31. Find the equation of the line that contains the point $(-1, -3)$ and is perpendicular to the line $3x - 5y = 2$.

32. Find the equation of the line that contains the point $(-1, 3)$ and is perpendicular to the line $2x + 4y = -1$.

33. l is a line with equation $Ax + By = C$ such that A and B are both positive. Does a line parallel to l slant downward to the right or upward to the right?

34. l is a line with equation $Ax + By = C$ such that A is positive and B is negative. Does a line perpendicular to l slant downward to the right or upward to the right?

3.6 Applying Concepts

35. If the graphs of $A_1x + B_1y = C_1$ and $A_2x + B_2y = C_2$ are parallel, express $\dfrac{A_1}{B_1}$ in terms of A_2 and B_2.

36. If the graphs of $A_1x + B_1y = C_1$ and $A_2x + B_2y = C_2$ are perpendicular, express $\dfrac{A_1}{B_1}$ in terms of A_2 and B_2.

For Exercises 37 and 38, suppose a ball is being twirled at the end of a string and the center of rotation is the origin of a coordinate system. If the string breaks, the initial path of the ball is on a line that is perpendicular to the radius of the circle.

37. Suppose the string breaks when the ball is at the point whose coordinates are $P(6, 3)$. Find the equation of the line on which the initial path lies.

38. Suppose the string breaks when the ball is at the point whose coordinates are $P(2, 8)$. Find the equation of the line on which the initial path lies.

39. The graphs of $y = -\frac{1}{2}x + 2$ and $y = \frac{2}{3}x - 5$ intersect at the point whose coordinates are $(6, -1)$. Find the equation of a line whose graph intersects the graphs of the given lines to form a right triangle. (*Hint:* There is more than one answer to this question.)

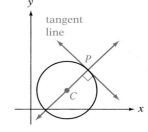

40. **Geometry** A theorem from geometry states that a line passing through the center of a circle and through a point P on the circle is perpendicular to the tangent line at P. (See the figure at the right.)
   a. If the coordinates of P are $(5, 4)$ and the coordinates of C are $(3, 2)$, what is the equation of the tangent line?
   b. What are the x- and y-intercepts of the tangent line?

3.7 Inequalities in Two Variables

OBJECTIVE 1   Graph the solution set of an inequality in two variables

The graph of the linear equation $y = x - 1$ separates the plane into three sets: the set of points on the line, the set of points above the line, and the set of points below the line.

The point whose coordinates are $(2, 1)$ is a solution of $y = x - 1$ and is a point on the line.

The point whose coordinates are $(2, 4)$ is a solution of $y > x - 1$ and is a point above the line.

The point whose coordinates are $(2, -2)$ is a solution of $y < x - 1$ and is a point below the line.

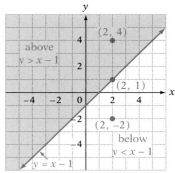

The set of points on the line are the solutions of the equation $y = x - 1$. The set of points above the line are the solutions of the inequality $y > x - 1$. These points form a **half-plane.** The set of points below the line are solutions of the inequality $y < x - 1$. These points also form a half-plane.

An inequality of the form $y > mx + b$ or $Ax + By > C$ is a **linear inequality in two variables.** (The inequality symbol could be replaced by $\geq$, $<$, or $\leq$.) The solution set of a linear inequality in two variables is a half-plane.

The following illustrates the procedure for graphing the solution set of a linear inequality in two variables.

Graph the solution set of $3x - 4y < 12$.

Solve the inequality for y.

$$3x - 4y < 12$$
$$-4y < -3x + 12$$
$$y > \frac{3}{4}x - 3$$

Change the inequality $y > \frac{3}{4}x - 3$ to the equality $y = \frac{3}{4}x - 3$, and graph the line.

If the inequality contains $\leq$ or $\geq$, the line belongs to the solution set and is shown by a *solid line*. If the inequality contains $<$ or $>$, the line is not part of the solution set and is shown by a *dashed line*.

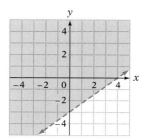

If the inequality contains $>$ or $\geq$, shade the upper half-plane. If the inequality contains $<$ or $\leq$, shade the lower half-plane.

As a check, use the ordered pair (0, 0) to determine whether the correct region of the plane has been shaded. If (0, 0) is a solution of the inequality, then (0, 0) should be in the shaded region. If (0, 0) is not a solution of the inequality, then (0, 0) should not be in the shaded region.

As shown below, (0, 0) is a solution of the inequality in the example above.

$$y > \frac{3}{4}x - 3$$
$$0 > \frac{3}{4}(0) - 3$$
$$0 > 0 - 3$$
$$0 > -3 \qquad \text{True}$$

Because (0, 0) is a solution of the inequality, (0, 0) should be in the shaded region. The solution set as graphed above is correct.

If the line passes through the point (0, 0), another point, such as (0, 1), must be used as a check.

From the graph of $y > \frac{3}{4}x - 3$, note that for a given value of x, more than one value of y can be paired with the value of x. For instance, (4, 1), (4, 3), (5, 1), and $\left(5, \frac{9}{4}\right)$ are all ordered pairs that belong to the graph.

Because there are ordered pairs with the same first component and different second components, the inequality does not represent a function. The inequality is a relation but not a function.

EXAMPLE 1   Graph the solution set of $x + 2y \le 4$.

Solution $x + 2y \le 4$ • **Solve the inequality for _y_.**
$$2y \le -x + 4$$
$$y \le -\frac{1}{2}x + 2$$

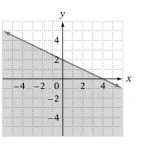

• **Graph $y = -\frac{1}{2}x + 2$ as a solid line. Shade the lower half-plane.**

PROBLEM 1   Graph the solution set of $x + 3y > 6$.

Solution   See page S9.

EXAMPLE 2   Graph the solution set of $x \ge -1$.

Solution

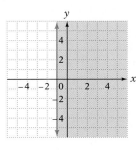

• **Graph $x = -1$ as a solid line.**
• **The point (0, 0) satisfies the inequality. Shade the half-plane to the right of the line.**

PROBLEM 2   Graph the solution set of $y < 2$.

Solution   See page S9.

3.7 Concept Review

Determine whether the following statements are always true, sometimes true, or never true.

1. It is possible to write a linear inequality in two variables that has no solutions.

2. The exponents on the variables in a linear inequality in two variables are 1.

3. The graph of a linear inequality is a half-plane.

4. The graph of a linear inequality in two variables represents a function.

5. The solution of a linear inequality in two variables containing ≤ or ≥ includes the line separating the half-planes.

6. The solution of the inequality $y > x + 2$ is all the points above the line $y = x + 2$.

3.7 Exercises

1 Graph the solution set of an inequality in two variables

1. What is a half-plane?

2. Explain a method that you can use to check that the graph of a linear inequality in two variables has been shaded correctly.

3. Is $(0, 0)$ a solution of $y > 2x - 7$?

4. Is $(0, 0)$ a solution of $y < 5x + 3$?

5. Is $(0, 0)$ a solution of $y \le -\frac{2}{3}x - 8$?

6. Is $(0, 0)$ a solution of $y \ge -\frac{3}{4}x + 9$?

Graph the solution set.

7. $y \le \frac{3}{2}x - 3$

8. $y \ge \frac{4}{3}x - 4$

9. $y < \frac{4}{5}x - 2$

10. $y < \dfrac{3}{5}x - 3$

11. $y < -\dfrac{1}{3}x + 2$

12. $y < -\dfrac{4}{3}x + 3$

13. $x + 3y < 4$

14. $2x - 5y \le 10$

15. $2x + 3y \ge 6$

16. $3x + 2y < 4$

17. $-x + 2y > -8$

18. $-3x + 2y > 2$

19. $y - 4 < 0$

20. $x + 2 \ge 0$

21. $6x + 5y < 15$

22. $3x - 5y < 10$

23. $-5x + 3y \ge -12$

24. $3x + 4y \ge 12$

25. Given that $(0, 0)$ is a point on the graph of the linear inequality $Ax + By > C$, and C is not zero, is C positive or negative?

26. Is $(0, 0)$ a point on the graph of the linear inequality $Ax + By > C$, where C is a positive number?

3.7 Applying Concepts

27. Does the inequality $y < 3x - 1$ represent a function? Explain your answer.

28. Are there any points whose coordinates satisfy both $y \le x + 3$ and $y \ge -\dfrac{1}{2}x + 1$? If so, give the coordinates of three such points. If not, explain why not.

29. Are there any points whose coordinates satisfy both $y \le x - 3$ and $y \ge x + 2$? If so, give the coordinates of three such points. If not, explain why not.

Focus on Problem Solving

Find a Pattern Polya's four recommended problem-solving steps are stated below.

1. Understand the problem.

2. Devise a plan.

3. Carry out the plan.

4. Review your solution

Point of Interest

Carl Friedrich Gauss (1777–1855) has been called the "Prince of Mathematicians" by some historians. He applied his genius to many areas of mathematics and science. A unit of magnetism, the gauss, is named in his honor. Some electronic appliances (televisions, for instance) contain a degausser that controls magnetic fields.

One of the several ways of devising a plan is first to try to find a pattern. Karl Friedrich Gauss supposedly used this method to solve a problem that was given to his math class when he was in elementary school. As the story goes, his teacher wanted to grade some papers while the class worked on a math problem. The problem the teacher gave to the class was to find the sum

$$1 + 2 + 3 + 4 + \cdots + 100$$

Gauss quickly solved the problem by seeing a pattern. Here is what he saw.

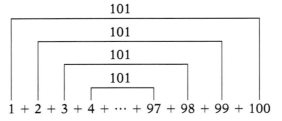

Note that

$$1 + 100 = 101$$
$$2 + 99 = 101$$
$$3 + 98 = 101$$
$$4 + 97 = 101$$

Gauss noted that there were 50 sums of 101. Therefore, the sum of the first 100 natural numbers is

$$1 + 2 + 3 + 4 + \cdots + 97 + 98 + 99 + 100 = 50(101) = 5050$$

Try to solve the following problems by finding a pattern.

1. Find the sum $2 + 4 + 6 + \cdots + 96 + 98 + 100$.

2. Find the sum $1 + 3 + 5 + \cdots + 97 + 99 + 101$.

3. Find another method of finding the sum $1 + 3 + 5 + \cdots + 97 + 99 + 101$ given in the previous exercise.

4. Find the sum $\dfrac{1}{1 \cdot 2} + \dfrac{1}{2 \cdot 3} + \dfrac{1}{3 \cdot 4} + \cdots + \dfrac{1}{49 \cdot 50}$.

   Hint: $\dfrac{1}{1 \cdot 2} = \dfrac{1}{2}, \dfrac{1}{1 \cdot 2} + \dfrac{1}{2 \cdot 3} = \dfrac{2}{3}, \dfrac{1}{1 \cdot 2} + \dfrac{1}{2 \cdot 3} + \dfrac{1}{3 \cdot 4} = \dfrac{3}{4}$

5. The following problem shows that checking a few cases does not always result in a conjecture that is true for *all* cases. Select any two points on a circle and draw a *chord*, the line connecting the points (see the drawing in the left margin). The chord divides the circle into two regions. Now select three different points and draw chords connecting each of the three points with every other point. The chords divide the circle into four regions. Now select four points and connect each of the points with every other point. Make a conjecture about the relationship between the number

2 points, 2 regions

3 points, 4 regions

4 points, 8 regions

5 points, ? regions

of regions and the number of points on the circle. Does your conjecture work for five points? six points?

6. A *polygonal number* is a number that can be represented by arranging that number of dots in rows to form a geometric figure such as a triangle, square, pentagon, or hexagon. For instance, the first four *triangular* numbers, 3, 6, 10, and 15, are given (and shown) below. What are the next two triangular numbers?

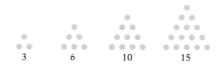

3   6   10   15

Projects & Group Activities

Introduction to Graphing Calculators

There are a variety of computer programs and calculators that can graph an equation. A computer or graphing calculator screen is divided into pixels. Depending on the computer or calculator, there are approximately 6000 to 790,000 pixels available on the screen. The greater the number of pixels, the smoother the graph will appear. A portion of a screen is shown at the left. Each little rectangle represents one pixel.

Calculator Screen

A graphing calculator draws a graph in a manner similar to the way we have shown in this chapter. Values of x are chosen and ordered pairs calculated. Then a graph is drawn through those points by illuminating pixels (an abbreviation for "picture element") on the screen.

Graphing utilities can display only a portion of the xy-plane, called a window. The window [Xmin, Xmax] by [Ymin, Ymax] consists of those points (x, y) that satisfy both of the following:

$$\text{Xmin} \le x \le \text{Xmax} \quad \text{and} \quad \text{Ymin} \le y \le \text{Ymax}$$

The user sets these values before a graph is drawn.

The numbers Xscl and Yscl are the distances between the tick marks that are drawn on the x- and y-axes. If you do not want tick marks on the axes, set Xscl = 0 and Yscl = 0.

The graph at the right is a portion of the graph of $y = \frac{1}{2}x + 1$, as it was drawn with a graphing calculator. The window is

Xmin = −4.7, Xmax = 4.7
Ymin = −3.1, Ymax = 3.1
Xscl = 1 and Yscl = 1

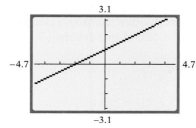

Using interval notation, this is shown as $[-4.7, 4.7]$ by $[-3.1, 3.1]$.

The window $[-4.7, 4.7]$ by $[-3.1, 3.1]$ gives "nice" coordinates in the sense that each time the $\boxed{\blacktriangleright}$ or the $\boxed{\blacktriangleleft}$ is pressed, the change in x is 0.1. The reason for this is that the horizontal distance from the middle of the first pixel to the middle of the last pixel is 94 units. By using Xmin $= -4.7$ and Xmax $= 4.7$, we have[1]

$$\text{Change in } x = \frac{\text{Xmax} - \text{Xmin}}{94} = \frac{4.7 - (-4.7)}{94} = \frac{9.4}{94} = 0.1$$

Similarly, the vertical distance from the middle of the first pixel to the middle of the last pixel is 62 units. Therefore, using Ymin $= -3.1$ and Ymax $= 3.1$ will give nice coordinates in the vertical direction.

Graph each of the following by using a graphing calculator.

<table>
<tr><td>Take Note
The Appendix "Keystroke Guide" contains keystroking suggestions to use with this project.</td><td>1. $y = 2x + 1$</td><td>For $2x$, you may enter $2 \times x$ or just $2x$. The times sign $\times$ is not necessary on many graphing calculators.</td></tr>
</table>

1. $y = 2x + 1$ — For $2x$, you may enter $2 \times x$ or just $2x$. The times sign $\times$ is not necessary on many graphing calculators.

2. $y = -x + 2$ — Many calculators use the $(-)$ key to enter a negative sign.

3. $3x + 2y = 6$ — Solve for y. Then enter the equation.

4. $y = 50x$ — You must adjust the viewing window. Try the window given by $[-4.7, 4.7]$ by $[-250, 250]$ with Yscl $= 50$.

5. $y = \dfrac{2}{3}x - 3$ — You may enter $\frac{2}{3}x$ as $2x/3$ or $(2/3)x$. Although entering $2/3x$ works on some calculators, it is not recommended.

6. $4x + 3y = 75$ — You must adjust the viewing window.

Chapter 3 Summary

Key Words

A **rectangular coordinate system** is formed by two number lines, one horizontal and one vertical, that intersect at the zero point of each line. The number lines that make up a coordinate system are called the **coordinate axes** or simply the **axes**. The **origin** is the point of intersection of the two coordinate axes. Generally, the horizontal axis is labeled the **x-axis**, and the vertical axis is labeled the **y-axis**. A rectangular coordinate system divides the **plane** determined by the axes into four regions called **quadrants**. [3.1.1, p. 128]

Examples

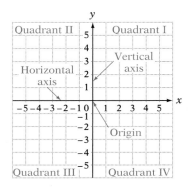

[1]Some calculators have screen widths of 126 pixels. For those calculators, use Xmin $= -6.3$ and Xmax $= 6.3$ to obtain nice coordinates.

An **ordered pair (x, y)** is used to locate a point in a plane. The first number in an ordered pair is called the **abscissa**. The second number in an ordered pair is called the **ordinate**. [3.1.1, p. 128]	(3, 4) is an ordered pair. 3 is the abscissa. 4 is the ordinate.
A **scatter diagram** is a graph of ordered-pair data. [3.1.3, p. 133]	
A **relation** is any set of ordered pairs. [3.2.1, p. 145]	{(2, 3), (2, 4), (3, 4), (5, 7)}
The **domain of a relation** is the set of first coordinates of all the ordered pairs of the relation. The **range of a relation** is the set of second coordinates of all the ordered pairs of the relation. [3.2.1, p. 145]	{(1, 2), (2, 4), (5, 7), (8, 3)} Domain: {1, 2, 5, 8} Range: {2, 3, 4, 7}
A **function** is a set of ordered pairs in which no two ordered pairs have the same first coordinate. [3.2.1, p. 145]	{(2, 3), (3, 5), (5, 7), (6, 9)}
Function notation is used for those equations that represent functions. For the equation at the right, x is the **independent variable** and y is the **dependent variable**. The symbol $f(x)$ is the **value of the function** and represents the value of the dependent variable for a given value of the dependent variable. The process of finding the value of $f(x)$ for a given value of x is called **evaluating the function**. [3.2.1, pp. 147–148]	In function notation, $y = 3x + 7$ is written as $f(x) = 3x + 7$.
The **graph of a function** is the graph of the ordered pairs that belong to the function. A **linear function** is one that can be expressed in the form $f(x) = mx + b$. The graph of a linear function is a straight line. The point at which the graph crosses the x-axis is called the **x-intercept**, and the point at which a graph crosses the y-axis is called the **y-intercept**. [3.2.2, 3.3.1, pp. 151, 165, and 170]	$f(x) = -\dfrac{3}{2}x + 3$
The **slope** of a line is a measure of the slant, or tilt, of a line. The symbol for slope is **m**. A line that slants upward to the right has a **positive slope**, and a line that slants downward to the right has a **negative slope**. [3.4.1, pp. 179–181]	The line $y = 2x - 3$ slants upward to the right. The line $y = -5x + 2$ slants downward to the right.
A horizontal line has **zero slope**. The slope of a vertical line is **undefined**. [3.4.1, p. 181]	$y = 3$ is an equation of a line with zero slope. The slope of the line $x = -3$ is undefined.
An inequality of the form $y > mx + b$ or of the form $Ax + By > C$ is a **linear inequality in two variables**. (The symbol $>$ could be replaced by $\geq$, $<$, or $\leq$.) The solution set of an inequality in two variables is a **half-plane**. [3.7.1, p. 206]	

Essential Rules and Procedures

The **distance formula** $d = \sqrt{(x_2 - x_1)^2 + (y_2 - y_1)^2}$ can be used to find the distance between any two points in a plane. [3.1.2, p. 131]

$(x_1, y_1) = (2, 4), (x_2, y_2) = (-3, 5)$
$d = \sqrt{(-3 - 2)^2 + (5 - 4)^2}$
$\quad = \sqrt{25 + 1}$
$\quad = \sqrt{26}$

The **midpoint formula** $(x_m, y_m) = \left(\dfrac{x_1 + x_2}{2}, \dfrac{y_1 + y_2}{2} \right)$ is used to find the midpoint of a line segment. [3.1.2, p. 132]

$(x_1, y_1) = (2, 3), (x_2, y_2) = (-6, -1)$
$x_m = \dfrac{2 + (-6)}{2} = -2,$
$y_m = \dfrac{3 + (-1)}{2} = 1$
$(x_m, y_m) = (-2, 1)$

The **average rate of change** of y with respect to x is $\dfrac{\text{change in } y}{\text{change in } x}$. [3.1.4, p. 136]

In 1998, 1.7 million households used electronic bill payment. This number increased to 9.9 million in 2002. (*Source:* Yankee Group)

$$\frac{9.9 - 1.7}{2002 - 1998} = 2.05$$

The average annual rate of change in the number of households using electronic bill payment from 1998 to 2002 was 2.05 million.

Vertical line test for the graph of a function If every vertical line intersects a graph at most once, then the graph is the graph of a function. [3.2.3, p. 154]

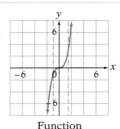

Function   Not a Function

To find the x-intercept of $Ax + By = C$, let $y = 0$. **To find the y-intercept**, let $x = 0$. [3.3.2, p. 170]

$3x + 4y = 12$

Let $y = 0$:   Let $x = 0$:
$3x + 4(0) = 12$ $3(0) + 4y = 12$
$\qquad\quad x = 4$ $\qquad\quad y = 3$

The x-intercept   The y-intercept
is $(4, 0)$.   is $(0, 3)$.

A value of x for which $f(x) = 0$ is called a **zero of the function.** [3.3.2, p. 172]

$f(x) = x + 3$
$\quad 0 = x + 3$
$-3 = x$

The zero of $f(x) = x + 3$ is -3.

The **slope formula** $m = \dfrac{y_2 - y_1}{x_2 - x_1}$, $x_1 \neq x_2$, is used to find the slope of a line when two points on the line are known. [3.4.1, p. 180]

$(x_1, y_1) = (-3, 2)$, $(x_2, y_2) = (1, 4)$

$$m = \frac{4 - 2}{1 - (-3)} = \frac{2}{4} = \frac{1}{2}$$

The equation $y = mx + b$ is called the **slope-intercept form of a straight line**. [3.4.2, p. 183]

$y = -3x + 2$
The slope is -3; the y-intercept is $(0, 2)$.

The **point-slope formula**, $y - y_1 = m(x - x_1)$, is used to find the equation of a line when the slope and a point on the line are known. [3.5.1, p. 190]

The equation of the line that passes through the point $(4, 2)$ and has slope -3 is

$$y - y_1 = m(x - x_1)$$
$$y - 2 = -3(x - 4)$$
$$y - 2 = -3x + 12$$
$$y = -3x + 14$$

Two lines that have the same slope do not intersect and are called **parallel lines**. [3.6.1, p. 198]

$y = 3x - 4$, $m_1 = 3$
$y = 3x + 2$, $m_2 = 3$

Because $m_1 = m_2$, the lines are parallel.

Two lines that intersect at right angles are called **perpendicular lines**. The product of the slopes of two nonvertical perpendicular lines is -1. [3.6.1, p. 201]

$y = \dfrac{1}{2}x - 1$, $m_1 = \dfrac{1}{2}$
$y = -2x + 2$, $m_2 = -2$

Because $m_1 \cdot m_2 = -1$, the lines are perpendicular.

Chapter 3 Review Exercises

1. Determine the ordered-pair solution of $y = \dfrac{x}{x - 2}$ that corresponds to $x = 4$.

2. Find the midpoint and length of the line segment with endpoints $(-2, 4)$ and $(3, 5)$.

3. Graph $f(x) = x^2 - 2$ by evaluating the function when $x = -3, -2, -1, 0, 1, 2,$ and 3. Plot the resulting ordered pairs. Then connect the points to form the graph.

4. Graph: $y = -2$

5. Given $P(x) = 3x + 4$, evaluate $P(-2)$ and $P(a)$.

6. What are the domain and range of the relation? Is the relation a function?
$\{(-1, 0), (0, 2), (1, 2), (2, 0), (5, 3)\}$

7. Find the range of $f(x) = x^2 - 2$ if the domain is $\{-2, -1, 0, 1, 2\}$.

8. Given $f(x) = 3x - 1$, find a number c in the domain of f such that $f(c) = 5$. Write the corresponding ordered pair of the function.

9. Find the x- and y-intercepts and graph $4x - 6y = 12$.

10. Graph: $y = -2x + 2$

11. Graph: $2x - 3y = -6$

12. Find the slope of the line that contains the points $(3, -2)$ and $(-1, 2)$.

13. Graph $3x + 2y = -4$ by using the x- and y-intercepts.

14. Graph the line that passes through the point $(-1, 4)$ and has slope $-\frac{1}{3}$.

15. Find the equation of the line that contains the point $(-3, 4)$ and has slope $\frac{5}{2}$.

16. Find the equation of the line that contains the points $(-2, 4)$ and $(4, -3)$.

17. Find the equation of the line that contains the point $(3, -2)$ and is parallel to the line $y = -3x + 4$.

18. Find the equation of the line that contains the point $(-2, -4)$ and is parallel to the line $2x - 3y = 4$.

19. Find the equation of the line that contains the point $(2, 5)$ and is perpendicular to the line $y = -\frac{2}{3}x + 6$.

20. Find the equation of the line that contains the point $(-3, -1)$ and is perpendicular to the line $4x - 2y = 7$.

21. Find the zero of $f(x) = -3x + 12$.

22. Use the vertical line test to determine whether the graph is the graph of a function.

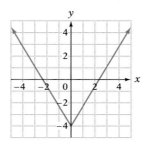

23. Graph the solution set of $y \geq 2x - 3$.

24. Graph the solution set of $3x - 2y < 6$.

25. 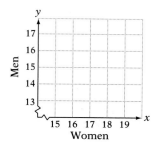 **Life Expectancy** The table below shows the average number of years that women and men were estimated to live beyond age 65 in 1950, 1960, 1970, 1980, 1990, and 2000. (*Source:* 2000 Social Security Trustees Report) Figures are rounded to the nearest whole number. Graph the scatter diagram for these data.

Women, x	15	16	17	18	19	19
Men, y	13	13	13	14	15	16

26. **Demographics** The table below shows the number of foreign-born people living in the United States each decade from 1960 to 2000. (*Source:* U.S. Census Bureau)

a. What was the average annual rate of change in the number of foreign-born people living in the United States from 1980 to 2000? Round to the nearest thousand.

b. Find the average annual rate of change in the number of foreign-born people living in the United States from 1970 to 1980. Was this more than or less than the average annual rate of change in the number of foreign-born people living in the United States from 1980 to 1990?

Year	1960	1970	1980	1990	2000
Number of foreign born (in millions)	9.7	9.6	14.1	19.8	28.4

27. **Uniform Motion** A car is traveling at 55 mph. The equation that describes the distance, d (in miles), traveled is $d = 55t$, where t is the number of hours driven. Use the coordinate axes below to graph this equation for $0 \leq t \leq 6$. The point $(4, 220)$ is on the graph. Write a sentence that describes the meaning of this ordered pair.

28.   **Manufacturing** The graph below shows the relationship between the cost of manufacturing calculators and the number of calculators manufactured. Find the slope of the line between the two points shown on the graph. Write a sentence that states the meaning of the slope.

29. **Construction** A building contractor estimates that the cost to build a new home is $25,000 plus $80 for each square foot of floor space in the house. Determine a linear function that will give the cost to build a house that contains a given number of square feet. Use this model to determine the cost of building a house that contains 2000 ft².

Chapter 3 Test

1. Graph $f(x) = -x^2 + 2$ by evaluating the function when $x = -3, -2, -1, 0, 1, 2,$ and 3. Plot the resulting ordered pairs. Then connect the points to form the graph.

2. Find the ordered-pair solution of $y = 2x + 6$ that corresponds to $x = -3$.

3. Graph: $y = \dfrac{2}{3}x - 4$

4. Graph: $2x + 3y = -3$

5. Find the equation of the vertical line that contains the point $(-2, 3)$.

6. Find the midpoint and length of the line segment with endpoints $(4, 2)$ and $(-5, 8)$.

7. Find the slope of the line that contains the points $(-2, 3)$ and $(4, 2)$.

8. Given $P(x) = 3x^2 - 2x + 1$, evaluate $P(2)$.

9. Graph $2x - 3y = 6$ by using the x- and y-intercepts.

10. Graph the line that passes through the point $(-2, 3)$ and has slope $-\frac{3}{2}$.

11. Find the equation of the line that contains the point $(-5, 2)$ and has slope $\frac{2}{5}$.

12. Given $f(x) = 5x - 2$, find a number c in the domain of f such that $f(c) = 3$. Write the corresponding ordered pair of the function.

13. Find the equation of the line that contains the points $(3, -4)$ and $(-2, 3)$.

14. Find the zero of $s(t) = \frac{4}{3}t - 8$.

15. What are the domain and range of the relation? Is the relation a function?
$\{(-4, 2), (-2, 2), (0, 0), (3, 5)\}$

16. Find the equation of the line that contains the point $(1, 2)$ and is parallel to the line $y = -\frac{3}{2}x - 6$.

17. Find the equation of the line that contains the point $(-2, -3)$ and is perpendicular to the line $y = -\frac{1}{2}x - 3$.

18. Graph the solution set of $3x - 4y > 8$.

19. Use the vertical line test to determine whether the graph is the graph of a function.

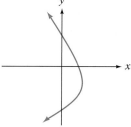

20. **Business** The director of a baseball camp estimates that 100 students will enroll if the tuition is $250. For each $20 increase in tuition, 6 fewer students will enroll. Determine a linear function that will predict the number of students who will enroll at a given tuition. Use this model to predict enrollment when the tuition is $300.

21. **Depreciation** The graph at the right shows the relationship between the value of a rental house and the depreciation allowed for income tax purposes. Find the slope between the two points shown on the graph. Write a sentence that states the meaning of the slope.

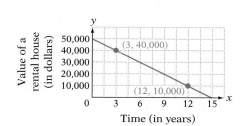

22. **Extra Income** A survey by Transamerica Center for Retirement Studies asked people what they would do with an extra $1000. The table below shows the responses. Graph the scatter diagram for these data.

Response	Percent of respondents
Save it	31%
Pay debt	24%
Spend on essentials	16%
Spend on nonessentials	20%
Give to charity	2%

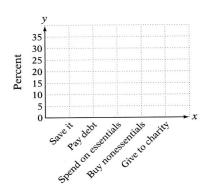

Cumulative Review Exercises

1. Identify the property that justifies the statement. $(x + y) \cdot 2 = 2 \cdot (x + y)$

2. Solve: $3 - \dfrac{x}{2} = \dfrac{3}{4}$

3. Solve: $2[y - 2(3 - y) + 4] = 4 - 3y$

4. Solve: $\dfrac{1 - 3x}{2} + \dfrac{7x - 2}{6} = \dfrac{4x + 2}{9}$

5. Solve: $x - 3 < -4$ or $2x + 2 > 3$

6. Solve: $8 - |2x - 1| = 4$

7. Solve: $|3x - 5| < 5$

8. Simplify: $4 - 2(4 - 5)^3 + 2$

9. Evaluate $(a - b)^2 \div ab$ when $a = 4$ and $b = -2$.

10. Graph: $\{x \,|\, x < -2\} \cup \{x \,|\, x > 0\}$

11. Solve: $3x - 1 < 4$ and $x - 2 > 2$

12. Given $P(x) = x^2 + 5$, evaluate $P(-3)$.

13. Find the ordered-pair solution of $y = -\dfrac{5}{4}x + 3$ that corresponds to $x = -8$.

14. Find the slope of the line that contains the points $(-1, 3)$ and $(3, -4)$.

15. Find the equation of the line that contains the point $(-1, 5)$ and has slope $\dfrac{3}{2}$.

16. Find the equation of the line that contains the points $(4, -2)$ and $(0, 3)$.

17. Find the equation of the line that contains the point $(2, 4)$ and is parallel to the line $y = -\dfrac{3}{2}x + 2$.

18. Find the equation of the line that contains the point $(4, 0)$ and is perpendicular to the line $3x - 2y = 5$.

19. Graph $3x - 5y = 15$ by using the x- and y-intercepts.

20. Graph the line that passes through the point $(-3, 1)$ and has slope $-\frac{3}{2}$.

21. Graph the solution set of $3x - 2y \geq 6$.

22. **Coins** A coin purse contains coins with a value of $1.60. The purse contains nickels and quarters. There are three times as many nickels as quarters. Find the number of nickels in the purse.

23. **Uniform Motion** Two planes are 1800 mi apart and are traveling toward each other. One plane is traveling twice as fast as the other plane. The planes will meet in 3 h. Find the speed of each plane.

24. **Mixture Problem** A grocer combines coffee that costs $8.00 per pound with coffee that costs $3.00 per pound. How many pounds of each should be used to make 80 lb of a blend that costs $5.00 per pound?

25. **Depreciation** The relationship between the depreciated value of a truck for income tax purposes and its age in years is shown in the graph at the right. Write the equation for the line that represents the depreciated value of the truck. Write a sentence that explains the meaning of the slope in the context of this exercise.

4 Systems of Equations and Inequalities

OBJECTIVES

4.1
1 Solve a system of linear equations by graphing
2 Solve a system of linear equations by the substitution method

4.2
1 Solve a system of two linear equations in two variables by the addition method
2 Solve a system of three linear equations in three variables by the addition method

4.3
1 Evaluate determinants
2 Solve systems of linear equations by using Cramer's Rule
3 Solve systems of linear equations by using matrices

4.4
1 Rate-of-wind and water-current problems
2 Application problems

4.5
1 Graph the solution set of a system of linear inequalities

Team sports are a great way to have fun and to get exercise. Informal leagues are formed all over the country for people who want to play a quick game of football or soccer in their free time. Suppose you are the manager of one such soccer league. You have been asked to create a schedule for 12 teams in which each team plays every other team once. How can you calculate how many games must be scheduled? As we learn in the **Focus on Problem Solving on pages 276–277,** one strategy would be to solve an easier problem first. Making connections to other problems you have already solved is an important step toward becoming an excellent problem solver.

DVD

SSM

Online Study Center

Need help? For online student resources, such as section quizzes, visit the Online Study Center at college.hmco.com/info/aufmanndevmathhb.

Prep Test

1. Simplify: $10\left(\dfrac{3}{5}x + \dfrac{1}{2}y\right)$

2. Evaluate $3x + 2y - z$ for $x = -1$, $y = 4$, and $z = -2$.

3. Given $3x - 2z = 4$, find the value of x when $z = -2$.

4. Solve: $3x + 4(-2x - 5) = -5$

5. Solve: $0.45x + 0.06(-x + 4000) = 630$

6. Graph: $y = \dfrac{1}{2}x - 4$

7. Graph: $3x - 2y = 6$

8. Graph: $y > -\dfrac{3}{5}x + 1$

Solving Systems of Linear Equations by Graphing and by the Substitution Method

4.1

OBJECTIVE **1**   **Solve a system of linear equations by graphing**

A **system of equations** is two or more equations considered together. The system at the right is a system of two linear equations in two variables. The graphs of the equations are straight lines.

$$3x + 4y = 7$$
$$2x - 3y = 6$$

A **solution of a system of equations in two variables** is an ordered pair that is a solution of each equation of the system.

Is $(3, -2)$ a solution of the system of equations shown at the right?

$$2x - 3y = 12$$
$$5x + 2y = 11$$

Replace x by 3 and y by -2.

$$
\begin{array}{c|c}
2x - 3y = 12 & 5x + 2y = 11 \\
\hline
2(3) - 3(-2) \mid 12 & 5(3) + 2(-2) \mid 11 \\
6 - (-6) & 15 + (-4) \\
12 = 12 & 11 = 11
\end{array}
$$

Yes, because $(3, -2)$ is a solution of each equation, it is a solution of the system of equations.

A solution of a system of linear equations can be found by graphing the lines that represent the equations of the system on the same set of coordinate axes. Three examples of systems of linear equations in two variables are shown below, along with the graphs of the equations of the systems.

System I	**System II**	**System III**
$x + 2y = 4$	$2x + 3y = 6$	$x - 2y = 4$
$2x + y = -1$	$4x + 6y = -12$	$2x - 4y = 8$

    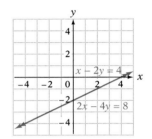

For System I, the two lines intersect at a single point whose coordinates are $(-2, 3)$. Because this point lies on both lines, it is a solution of each equation of the system of equations. We can check this by replacing x by -2 and y by 3. The check is shown below.

Check:

$$\begin{array}{c|c}
x + 2y = 4 \\
\hline
-2 + 2(3) & 4 \\
-2 + 6 & 4 \\
4 = 4
\end{array}
\qquad
\begin{array}{c|c}
2x + y = -1 \\
\hline
2(-2) + 3 & -1 \\
-4 + 3 & -1 \\
-1 = -1
\end{array}$$

• **Replace x by -2 and y by 3.**

The ordered pair $(-2, 3)$ is a solution of System I.

When the graphs of a system of equations intersect at only one point, the system is called an **independent system of equations.** System I is an independent system of equations.

System II above and the graph of the equations of that system are shown again at the right. Note in this case that the graphs of the lines are parallel and do not intersect. Because the graphs do not intersect, there is no point that is on both lines. Therefore, the system of equations has no solution.

$2x + 3y = 6$
$4x + 6y = -12$

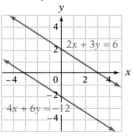

When a system of equations has no solution, it is called an **inconsistent system of equations.** System II is an inconsistent system of equations.

System III from the preceding page and the graph of the equations of that system are shown again at the right. Note that the graph of $x - 2y = 4$ lies directly on top of the graph of $2x - 4y = 8$. Thus the two lines intersect at an infinite number of points. Because the graphs intersect at an infinite number of points, there are an infinite number of solutions of this system of equations. Because each equation represents the same set of points, the solutions of the system of equations can be stated by using the ordered pairs of either one of the equations. Therefore, we can say, "The solutions are the ordered pairs that satisfy $x - 2y = 4$," or we can solve the equation for y and say, "The solutions are the ordered pairs that satisfy $y = \frac{1}{2}x - 2$." We normally state this solution using ordered pairs: "The solutions are the ordered pairs $\left(x, \frac{1}{2}x - 2\right)$."

$$x - 2y = 4$$
$$2x - 4y = 8$$

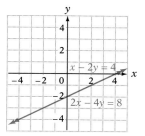

When the two equations in a system of equations represent the same line, the system is called a **dependent system of equations.** System III is a dependent system of equations.

These systems illustrate the three possibilities for a system of linear equations in two variables.

Take Note

Keep in mind the distinction among independent, dependent, and inconsistent systems of equations. You should be able to express your understanding of these terms by using graphs.

1. The graphs intersect at one point.
   The solution of the system of equations is the ordered pair (x, y) whose coordinates are the point of intersection.
   The system of equations is *independent*.

2. The lines are parallel and never intersect.
   There is no solution of the system of equations.
   The system of equations is *inconsistent*.

3. The graphs are the same line, and they intersect at infinitely many points.
   There are an infinite number of solutions of the system of equations.
   The system of equations is *dependent*.

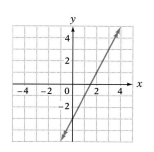

Take Note

The Projects & Group Activities feature at the end of this chapter shows how to use a graphing calculator to solve a system of equations.

Solve by graphing: $2x - y = 3$
$$4x - 2y = 6$$

Graph each line.
The system of equations is dependent.
Solve one of the equations for y.

$$2x - y = 3$$
$$-y = -2x + 3$$
$$y = 2x - 3$$

The solutions are the ordered pairs $(x, 2x - 3)$.

EXAMPLE 1   Solve by graphing: $3x - y = 4$
$3x + y = 2$

Solution

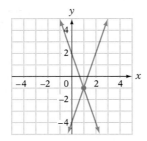

The solution is $(1, -1)$.

PROBLEM 1   Solve by graphing: $x + y = 1$
$2x + y = 0$

Solution   See page S9.

EXAMPLE 2   Solve by graphing

A. $2x + 3y = 6$

$y = -\dfrac{2}{3}x + 1$

B. $x - 2y = 6$

$y = \dfrac{1}{2}x - 3$

Solution   **A.**

B.

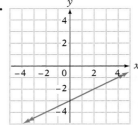

The lines are parallel and therefore do not intersect. The system of equations has no solution. The system of equations is inconsistent.

The system of equations is dependent. The solutions are the ordered pairs

$\left(x, \dfrac{1}{2}x - 3\right)$.

PROBLEM 2   Solve by graphing.

A. $2x + 5y = 10$

$y = -\dfrac{2}{5}x - 2$

B. $3x - 4y = 12$

$y = \dfrac{3}{4}x - 3$

Solution   See page S9.

OBJECTIVE **2**   **Solve a system of linear equations by the substitution method**

A graphical solution of a system of equations is based on approximating the coordinates of a point of intersection. An algebraic method called the **substitution method** can be used to find an exact solution of a system of equations.

To use the substitution method, we must write one of the equations of the system in terms of x or in terms of y.

Solve by the substitution method: $3x + y = 5$
$4x + 5y = 3$

(1)	$3x + y = 5$
(2)	$4x + 5y = 3$

Solve equation (1) for y.
The result is equation (3).   (3)

$3x + y = 5$
$y = -3x + 5$

Use equation (2).
Substitute $-3x + 5$ for y and
solve for x.

$4x + 5y = 3$
$4x + 5(-3x + 5) = 3$
$4x - 15x + 25 = 3$
$-11x = -22$
$x = 2$

Now substitute the value of x
into equation (3) and solve
for y.

$y = -3x + 5$
$y = -3(2) + 5$
$y = -6 + 5$
$y = -1$

The solution is $(2, -1)$.

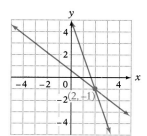

The graph of the system is shown at the left. Note that the graphs intersect at the point whose coordinates are $(2, -1)$, the solution of the system of equations.

Take Note

If, after simplifying, there is no variable in the equation and the resulting equation is *not true*, the system of equations is inconsistent. ($-6 = 2$ is not a true equation.) If the resulting equation is *true*, the system of equations is dependent. ($12 = 12$ is a true equation.)

EXAMPLE 3   Solve by substitution.

A. $3x - 3y = 2$ **B.** $9x + 3y = 12$
    $y = x + 2$ $y = -3x + 4$

Solution   **A.** (1) $3x - 3y = 2$
            (2) $y = x + 2$ • Equation (2) states that $y = x + 2$.
                $3x - 3(x + 2) = 2$ • Substitute $x + 2$ for y in equation (1).
                $3x - 3x - 6 = 2$
                        $-6 = 2$

$-6 = 2$ is not a true equation. The system of equations is inconsistent. The system does not have a solution.

B. (1) $9x + 3y = 12$
    (2) $y = -3x + 4$ • Equation (2) states that
                            $y = -3x + 4$.
        $9x + 3(-3x + 4) = 12$ • Substitute $-3x + 4$ for y in
        $9x - 9x + 12 = 12$ equation (1).
                $12 = 12$

$12 = 12$ is a true equation. The system of equations is dependent. The solutions are the ordered pairs $(x, -3x + 4)$.

PROBLEM 3   Solve by substitution.   **A.** $3x - y = 3$ **B.** $6x - 3y = 6$
                                $6x + 3y = -4$ $2x - y = 2$

Solution   See page S9.

4.1 Concept Review

Determine whether the following statements are always true, sometimes true, or never true.

1. A solution of a system of equations in two variables is an ordered pair that is a solution of every equation in the system.

2. An inconsistent system of equations has no solution.

3. A system of two equations with two unknowns has an infinite number of solutions.

4. A system of two equations with the same slope and different y-intercepts has an infinite number of solutions.

5. When the graphs of a system of equations intersect at only one point, the system of equations is called an independent system of equations.

6. The system $y = \frac{3}{2}x + 2$ and $y = -4x + 2$ has exactly one solution.

4.1 Exercises

1   Solve a system of linear equations by graphing

Determine whether the ordered pair is a solution of the system of equations.

1. $(0, -1)$
$3x - 2y = 2$
$x + 2y = 6$

2. $(2, 1)$
$x + y = 3$
$2x - 3y = 1$

3. $(-3, -5)$
$x + y = -8$
$2x + 5y = -31$

4. $(1, -1)$
$3x - y = 4$
$7x + 2y = -5$

State whether the system of equations is independent, inconsistent, or dependent.

5.

6.

7.

8.

9. Use the graph to solve this system of equations:

$x - 2y = -8$
$3x + y = -3$

The solution is ___?___.

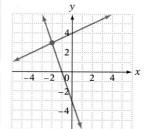

10. An independent system of equations has ___?___ solution(s), an inconsistent system of equations has ___?___ solution(s), and a dependent system of equations has ___?___ solution(s).

Solve by graphing.

11. $x + y = 2$
$x - y = 4$

12. $x + y = 1$
$3x - y = -5$

13. $x - y = -2$
$x + 2y = 10$

14. $2x - y = 5$
$3x + y = 5$

15. $3x - 2y = 6$
$y = 3$

16. $x = 4$
$3x - 2y = 4$

17. $x = 4$
$y = -1$

18. $x + 2 = 0$
$y - 1 = 0$

19. $y = x - 5$
$2x + y = 4$

20. $2x - 5y = 4$
$y = x + 1$

21. $y = \dfrac{1}{2}x - 2$
$x - 2y = 8$

22. $2x + 3y = 6$
$y = -\dfrac{2}{3}x + 1$

23. $2x - 5y = 10$
$y = \dfrac{2}{5}x - 2$

24. $3x - 2y = 6$
$y = \dfrac{3}{2}x - 3$

25. $3x - 4y = 12$
$5x + 4y = -12$

26. $2x - 3y = 6$
$2x - 5y = 10$

In Exercises 27 and 28, A, B, C, and D are nonzero real numbers.

27. Is the following system of equations independent, inconsistent, or dependent?

$y = Ax + C$
$y = Ax + D, D \neq C$

28. Is the following system of equations independent, inconsistent, or dependent?

$x = A$
$y = B$

2   Solve a system of linear equations by the substitution method

29. When you solve a system of equations using the substitution method, how can you tell whether the system of equations is inconsistent?

30. When you solve a system of equations using the substitution method, how can you tell whether the system of equations is dependent?

31. Use this system of equations: (1) $y = 2x - 8$
(2) $x = 3$
To solve the system by substitution, substitute ___?___ for x in equation (1): $y = 2(3) - 8 = $ __?__ .
The solution of the system is (__?__ , __?__).

32. Use this system of equations: (1) $y = x - 1$
(2) $3x + y = 3$
To solve the system by substitution, substitute ___?___ for y in equation (2): $3x + x - 1 = 3$.
Solving the equation $3x + x - 1 = 3$ for x gives $x = $ __?__ .
To find y, substitute this value of x into equation (1): $y = $ __?__ $- 1 = $ __?__ .
The solution of the system is (__?__ , __?__).

Solve by substitution.

33. $3x - 2y = 4$
    $x = 2$

34. $y = -2$
    $2x + 3y = 4$

35. $y = 2x - 1$
    $x + 2y = 3$

36. $y = -x + 1$
    $2x - y = 5$

37. $4x - 3y = 5$
    $y = 2x - 3$

38. $3x + 5y = -1$
    $y = 2x - 8$

39. $x = 2y + 4$
    $4x + 3y = -17$

40. $3x - 2y = -11$
    $x = 2y - 9$

41. $5x + 4y = -1$
    $y = 2 - 2x$

42. $3x + 2y = 4$
    $y = 1 - 2x$

43. $7x - 3y = 3$
    $x = 2y + 2$

44. $3x - 4y = 6$
    $x = 3y + 2$

45. $2x + 2y = 7$
    $y = 4x + 1$

46. $3x + 7y = -5$
    $y = 6x - 5$

47. $3x + y = 5$
    $2x + 3y = 8$

48. $4x + y = 9$
    $3x - 4y = 2$

49. $x + 3y = 5$
    $2x + 3y = 4$

50. $x - 4y = 2$
    $2x - 5y = 1$

51. $3x + 4y = 14$
    $2x + y = 1$

52. $5x + 3y = 8$
    $3x + y = 8$

53. $3x + 5y = 0$
    $x - 4y = 0$

54. $2x - 7y = 0$
    $3x + y = 0$

55. $5x - 3y = -2$
    $-x + 2y = -8$

56. $2x + 7y = 1$
    $-x + 4y = 7$

57. $x + 3y = 4$
    $x = 5 - 3y$

58. $6x + 2y = 7$
    $y = -3x + 2$

59. $2x - 4y = 16$
    $-x + 2y = -8$

60. $3x - 12y = -24$
$\quad\;\; -x + 4y = 8$

61. $3x - y = 10$
$\quad\;\; 6x - 2y = 5$

62. $6x - 4y = 3$
$\quad\;\; 3x - 2y = 9$

63. $y = 3x + 2$
$\quad\;\; y = 2x + 3$

64. $y = 3x - 7$
$\quad\;\; y = 2x - 5$

65. $x = 2y + 1$
$\quad\;\; x = 3y - 1$

66. $x = 4y + 1$
$\quad\;\; x = -2y - 5$

67. $y = 5x - 1$
$\quad\;\; y = 5 - x$

68. $y = 3 - 2x$
$\quad\;\; y = 2 - 3x$

In Exercises 69 and 70, A, B, C, and D are nonzero real numbers.

69. Is the following system of equations independent, inconsistent, or dependent?
$x + By = C$
$x = C - By$

70. Is the following system of equations independent, inconsistent, or dependent?
$Ax + y = C$
$y = D - Ax, D \neq C$

4.1 Applying Concepts

For what values of k will the system of equations be inconsistent?

71. $2x - 2y = 5$
$\quad\;\; kx - 2y = 3$

72. $6x - 3y = 4$
$\quad\;\; 3x - ky = 1$

73. $x = 6y + 6$
$\quad\;\; kx - 3y = 6$

74. $x = 2y + 2$
$\quad\;\; kx - 8y = 2$

Solve using two variables.

75. Number Problem The sum of two numbers is 44. One number is 8 less than the other number. Find the numbers.

76. Number Problem The sum of two numbers is 76. One number is 12 less than the other number. Find the numbers.

77. Number Problem The sum of two numbers is 19. Five less than twice the first number equals the second number. Find the numbers.

78. Number Problem The sum of two numbers is 22. Three times the first plus 2 equals the second number. Find the numbers.

Solve. (*Hint:* These equations are not linear equations. First rewrite the equations as linear equations by substituting x for $\frac{1}{a}$ and y for $\frac{1}{b}$.)

79. $\dfrac{2}{a} + \dfrac{3}{b} = 4$
$\dfrac{4}{a} + \dfrac{1}{b} = 3$

80. $\dfrac{2}{a} + \dfrac{1}{b} = 1$
$\dfrac{8}{a} - \dfrac{2}{b} = 0$

81. $\dfrac{1}{a} + \dfrac{3}{b} = 2$
$\dfrac{4}{a} - \dfrac{1}{b} = 3$

82. $\dfrac{3}{a} + \dfrac{4}{b} = -1$
$\dfrac{1}{a} + \dfrac{6}{b} = 2$

Use a graphing utility to solve each of the following systems of equations. Round answers to the nearest hundredth.

83. $y = -\dfrac{1}{2}x + 2$

$y = 2x - 1$

84. $y = 1.2x + 2$

$y = -1.3x - 3$

85. $y = \sqrt{2}x - 1$

$y = -\sqrt{3}x + 1$

86. $y = \pi x - \dfrac{2}{3}$

$y = -x + \dfrac{\pi}{2}$

87.   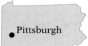 **Demography** Data from the 2000 Census support the following model of the population decline since 1990 of Pittsburgh, Pennsylvania: $y_1 = -0.0036x + 9.559$, where y_1 is the population, in millions, of Pittsburgh in year x. According to data from the same census, Orlando, Florida, has experienced an increase in population that can be modeled by $y_2 = 0.0419x - 82.156$, where y_2 is the population, in millions, of Orlando in year x.

a. Assuming that this model is accurate for future years, will the population of Orlando exceed the population of Pittsburgh in the year 2010?

b. In what year will the population of Orlando first exceed the population of Pittsburgh? Round to the nearest whole number.

c. What does the slope of the line that models Pittsburgh's population mean in the context of this problem?

d. What does the slope of the line that models Orlando's population mean in the context of this problem?

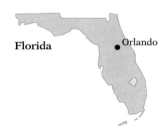

Pennsylvania

Pittsburgh

Florida   Orlando

88. Suppose $\begin{array}{l} a_1x + b_1y = c_1 \\ a_2x + b_2y = c_2 \end{array}$ is a system of equations and $\dfrac{a_1}{b_1} = \dfrac{a_2}{b_2}$. Can the system of equations be independent? Explain your answer.

4.2 # Solving Systems of Linear Equations by the Addition Method

OBJECTIVE **1** ### Solve a system of two linear equations in two variables by the addition method

The **addition method** is an alternative method for solving a system of equations. This method is based on the Addition Property of Equations. Use the addition method when it is not convenient to solve one equation for one variable in terms of another variable.

Note, for the system of equations at the right, the effect of adding equation (2) to equation (1). Because $-3y$ and $3y$ are additive inverses, adding the equations results in an equation with only one variable.

The solution of the resulting equation is the first component of the ordered-pair solution of the system.

(1) $5x - 3y = 14$
(2) $2x + 3y = -7$
$7x + 0y = 7$
$7x = 7$

$7x = 7$
$x = 1$

The second component is found by substituting the value of x into equation (1) or (2) and then solving for y. Equation (1) is used here.

$$(1) \quad 5x - 3y = 14$$
$$5(1) - 3y = 14$$
$$5 - 3y = 14$$
$$-3y = 9$$
$$y = -3$$

The solution is $(1, -3)$.

Point of Interest

There are records of Babylonian mathematicians solving systems of equations 3600 years ago. Here is a system of equations from that time (in our modern notation):

$$\frac{2}{3}x = \frac{1}{2}y + 500$$
$$x + y = 1800$$

We say modern notation *for many reasons. Foremost is the fact that using variables did not become widespread until the 17th century. There are many other reasons, however. The equals sign had not been invented, 2 and 3 did not look like they do today, and zero had not even been considered as a possible number.*

Sometimes adding the two equations does not eliminate one of the variables. In this case, use the Multiplication Property of Equations to rewrite one or both of the equations so that when the equations are added, one of the variables is eliminated. To do this, first choose which variable to eliminate. The coefficients of that variable must be additive inverses. Multiply each equation by a constant that will produce coefficients that are additive inverses.

Solve by the addition method:

$$3x + 4y = 2$$
$$2x + 5y = -1$$

We will number the equations (1) and (2).

$$(1) \quad 3x + 4y = 2$$
$$(2) \quad 2x + 5y = -1$$

Eliminate x. Multiply equation (1) by 2 and equation (2) by -3. Note how the constants are selected. The negative sign is used so that the coefficients will be additive inverses.

$$2 \diagdown (3x + 4y) = 2(2)$$
$$-3 \diagup (2x + 5y) = -3(-1)$$

The coefficients of the x-terms are additive inverses.

$$6x + 8y = 4$$
$$-6x - 15y = 3$$

Add the equations.
Solve for y.

$$-7y = 7$$
$$y = -1$$

Substitute the value of y into one of the equations, and solve for x. Equation (1) is used here.

$$(1) \quad 3x + 4y = 2$$
$$3x + 4(-1) = 2$$
$$3x - 4 = 2$$
$$3x = 6$$
$$x = 2$$

The solution is $(2, -1)$.

Solve by the addition method:

$$\frac{2}{3}x + \frac{1}{2}y = 4$$
$$\frac{1}{4}x - \frac{3}{8}y = -\frac{3}{4}$$

We will number the equations (1) and (2).

$$(1) \quad \frac{2}{3}x + \frac{1}{2}y = 4$$
$$(2) \quad \frac{1}{4}x - \frac{3}{8}y = -\frac{3}{4}$$

Clear the fractions. Multiply each equation by the LCM of the denominators.

$$6\left(\frac{2}{3}x + \frac{1}{2}y\right) = 6(4)$$

$$8\left(\frac{1}{4}x - \frac{3}{8}y\right) = 8\left(-\frac{3}{4}\right)$$

$$4x + 3y = 24$$
$$2x - 3y = -6$$

Eliminate y. Add the equations.
Solve for x.

$$6x = 18$$
$$x = 3$$

Substitute the value of x into equation (1), and solve for y.

$$\frac{2}{3}x + \frac{1}{2}y = 4$$

$$\frac{2}{3}(3) + \frac{1}{2}y = 4$$

$$2 + \frac{1}{2}y = 4$$

$$\frac{1}{2}y = 2$$

$$y = 4$$

The solution is (3, 4).

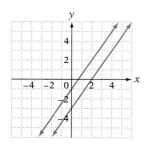

To solve the system of equations at the right, eliminate x. Multiply equation (1) by -2 and add to equation (2).

(1) $3x - 2y = 6$
(2) $6x - 4y = 4$

$$-6x + 4y = -12$$
$$6x - 4y = 4$$

$0 = -8$ is not a true equation.

$$0 = -8$$

The system of equations is inconsistent. The system does not have a solution.

The graph of the equations of the system is shown at the left. Note that the lines are parallel and therefore do not intersect.

EXAMPLE 1 Solve by the addition method.

A. $3x - 2y = 2x + 5$ **B.** $4x - 8y = 36$
$\quad\;\; 2x + 3y = -4$ $\quad\;\; 3x - 6y = 27$

Solution A. (1) $3x - 2y = 2x + 5$
(2) $2x + 3y = -4$

$\quad\quad x - 2y = 5$ • Write equation (1) in the form
$\quad 2x + 3y = -4$ $Ax + By = C$.

$-2(x - 2y) = -2(5)$ • To eliminate x, multiply each side
$\quad 2x + 3y = -4$ of equation (1) by -2.

$-2x + 4y = -10$
$\quad 2x + 3y = -4$

$\quad\quad 7y = -14$ • Add the equations.
$\quad\quad\;\; y = -2$

$$2x + 3y = -4$$
$$2x + 3(-2) = -4$$
$$2x - 6 = -4$$
$$2x = 2$$
$$x = 1$$

• **Replace y in equation (2) by its value.**

The solution is $(1, -2)$.

B. (1) $4x - 8y = 36$
(2) $3x - 6y = 27$

$$3(4x - 8y) = 3(36)$$
$$-4(3x - 6y) = -4(27)$$
$$12x - 24y = 108$$
$$-12x + 24y = -108$$
$$0 = 0$$

• **To eliminate x, multiply each side of equation (1) by 3 and each side of equation (2) by −4.**

• **Add the equations.**

$0 = 0$ is a true equation. The system of equations is dependent. The solutions are the ordered pairs $\left(x, \frac{1}{2}x - \frac{9}{2}\right)$.

Take Note

The result of adding the equations is $0 = 0$. It is not $x = 0$. It is not $y = 0$. There is no variable in the equation $0 = 0$. It does not indicate that the solution is $(0, 0)$. Rather, it indicates a dependent system of equations.

PROBLEM 1   Solve by the addition method.

    A. $2x + 5y = 6$ **B.** $2x + y = 5$
         $3x - 2y = 6x + 2$ $4x + 2y = 6$

■ **Solution**   See page S10.

OBJECTIVE **2** ## Solve a system of three linear equations in three variables by the addition method

An equation of the form $Ax + By + Cz = D$, where A, B, and C are coefficients and D is a constant, is a **linear equation in three variables.** Examples of these equations are shown at the right. The graph of a linear equation in three variables is a plane.

$$2x + 4y - 3z = 7$$
$$x - 6y + z = -3$$

Graphing an equation in three variables requires a third coordinate axis perpendicular to the xy-plane. The third axis is commonly called the z-axis. The result is a three-dimensional coordinate system called the **xyz-coordinate system.** To help visualize a three-dimensional coordinate system, think of a corner of a room: the floor is the xy-plane, one wall is the yz-plane, and the other wall is the xz-plane. A three-dimensional coordinate system is shown at the right.

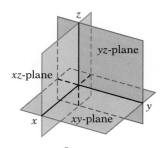

The graph of a point in an xyz-coordinate system is an **ordered triple** (x, y, z). Graphing an ordered triple requires three moves, the first along the x-axis, the second parallel to the y-axis, and the third parallel to the z-axis. The graphs of the points $(-4, 2, 3)$ and $(3, 4, -2)$ are shown at the right.

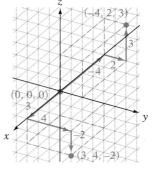

The graph of a linear equation in three variables is a plane. That is, if all the solutions of a linear equation in three variables were plotted in an *xyz*-coordinate system, the graph would look like a large piece of paper extending infinitely. The graph of $x + y + z = 3$ is shown at the right.

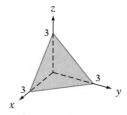

There are different ways in which three planes can be oriented in an *xyz*-coordinate system. The systems of equations represented by the following planes are inconsistent.

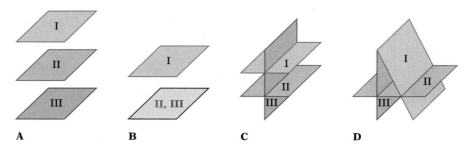

Graphs of Inconsistent Systems of Equations

For a system of three equations in three variables to have a solution, the graphs of the planes must intersect at a single point, they must intersect along a common line, or all equations must have a graph that is the same plane. These situations are shown in the figures that follow.

The three planes shown in Figure E below intersect at a point. A system of equations represented by planes that intersect at a point is independent.

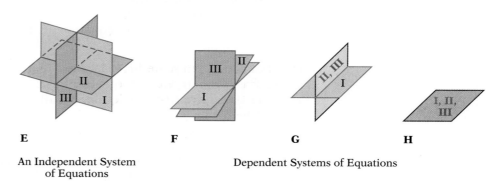

An Independent System
of Equations

Dependent Systems of Equations

The planes shown in Figures F and G above intersect along a common line. The system of equations represented by the planes in Figure H has a graph that is the same plane. The systems of equations represented by these three graphs are dependent.

Just as a solution of an equation in two variables is an ordered pair (x, y), a **solution of an equation in three variables** is an ordered triple (x, y, z). For example, $(2, 1, -3)$ is a solution of the equation $2x - y - 2z = 9$. The ordered triple $(1, 3, 2)$ is not a solution.

A **system of linear equations in three variables** is shown at the right. A **solution of a system of equations in three variables** is an ordered triple that is a solution of each equation of the system.

$$x - 2y + z = 6$$
$$3x + y - 2z = 2$$
$$2x - 3y + 5z = 1$$

A system of linear equations in three variables can be solved by using the addition method. First, eliminate one variable from any two of the given equations. Then eliminate the same variable from any other two equations. The result will be a system of two equations in two variables. Solve this system by the addition method.

Solve: $x + 4y - z = 10$ (1) $x + 4y - z = 10$
         $3x + 2y + z = 4$ (2) $3x + 2y + z = 4$
         $2x - 3y + 2z = -7$ (3) $2x - 3y + 2z = -7$

Eliminate z from equations (1) and (2) by adding the two equations.

$$x + 4y - z = 10$$
$$3x + 2y + z = 4$$
$$(4) \quad 4x + 6y = 14$$

Eliminate z from equations (1) and (3). Multiply equation (1) by 2 and add it to equation (3).

$$2x + 8y - 2z = 20$$
$$2x - 3y + 2z = -7$$
$$(5) \quad 4x + 5y = 13$$

Solve the system of two equations in two variables.

$$(4) \quad 4x + 6y = 14$$
$$(5) \quad 4x + 5y = 13$$

Eliminate x. Multiply equation (5) by -1 and add it to equation (4).

$$4x + 6y = 14$$
$$-4x - 5y = -13$$
$$y = 1$$

Substitute the value of y into equation (4) or (5), and solve for x. Equation (4) is used here.

$$4x + 6y = 14$$
$$4x + 6(1) = 14$$
$$4x + 6 = 14$$
$$4x = 8$$
$$x = 2$$

Substitute the value of y and the value of x into one of the equations in the original system. Equation (2) is used here.

$$3x + 2y + z = 4$$
$$3(2) + 2(1) + z = 4$$
$$6 + 2 + z = 4$$
$$8 + z = 4$$
$$z = -4$$

The solution is $(2, 1, -4)$.

Solve: $2x - 3y - z = 1$ (1) $2x - 3y - z = 1$
         $x + 4y + 3z = 2$ (2) $x + 4y + 3z = 2$
         $4x - 6y - 2z = 5$ (3) $4x - 6y - 2z = 5$

Eliminate x from equations (1) and (2). Multiply equation (2) by -2 and add to equation (1).

$$2x - 3y - z = 1$$
$$-2x - 8y - 6z = -4$$
$$-11y - 7z = -3$$

Eliminate x from equations (1) and (3). Multiply equation (1) by -2 and add to equation (3). This is not a true equation.

$$-4x + 6y + 2z = -2$$
$$\underline{4x - 6y - 2z = 5}$$
$$0 = 3$$

The system is inconsistent.

EXAMPLE 2 Solve: $\begin{aligned} 3x - y + 2z &= 1 \\ 2x + 3y + 3z &= 4 \\ x + y - 4z &= -9 \end{aligned}$

Solution

(1) $3x - y + 2z = 1$
(2) $2x + 3y + 3z = 4$
(3) $x + y - 4z = -9$

$\begin{aligned} 3x - y + 2z &= 1 \\ \underline{x + y - 4z} &= -9 \\ 4x - 2z &= -8 \end{aligned}$

• Eliminate y. Add equations (1) and (3).

(4) $2x - z = -4$

• Multiply each side of the equation by $\frac{1}{2}$.

$\begin{aligned} 9x - 3y + 6z &= 3 \\ \underline{2x + 3y + 3z} &= 4 \\ \end{aligned}$
(5) $11x + 9z = 7$

• Multiply equation (1) by 3 and add to equation (2).

(4) $2x - z = -4$
(5) $11x + 9z = 7$

• Solve the system of two equations.

$\begin{aligned} 18x - 9z &= -36 \\ \underline{11x + 9z} &= 7 \\ 29x &= -29 \\ x &= -1 \end{aligned}$

• Multiply equation (4) by 9 and add to equation (5).

$\begin{aligned} 2x - z &= -4 \\ 2(-1) - z &= -4 \\ -2 - z &= -4 \\ -z &= -2 \\ z &= 2 \end{aligned}$

• Replace x by -1 in equation (4).

$\begin{aligned} x + y - 4z &= -9 \\ -1 + y - 4(2) &= -9 \\ -1 + y - 8 &= -9 \\ -9 + y &= -9 \\ y &= 0 \end{aligned}$

• Replace x by -1 and z by 2 in equation (1), (2), or (3). Equation (3) is used here.

The solution is $(-1, 0, 2)$.

PROBLEM 2 Solve: $\begin{aligned} x - y + z &= 6 \\ 2x + 3y - z &= 1 \\ x + 2y + 2z &= 5 \end{aligned}$

Solution See page S10.

4.2 Concept Review

Determine whether the following statements are always true, sometimes true, or never true.

1. The graph of a linear equation in three variables is a plane.

2. A solution of an equation in three variables is an ordered triple (x, y, z).

3. The solution of a system of linear equations in three variables is a straight line.

4. A system of linear equations in three variables that has an infinite number of solutions is an independent system.

5. When you are solving a system of equations by the addition method and the final result is $0 = 5$, the system is inconsistent and has an infinite number of solutions.

4.2 Exercises

1 Solve a system of two linear equations in two variables by the addition method

1. If you begin to solve the system of equations $\begin{matrix} x + y = 6 \\ x - y = 4 \end{matrix}$ by adding the two equations, the result is $2x = 10$, which means $x = 5$. Does this mean that 5 is a solution of the system of equations? Why or why not?

2. Use this system of equations: (1) $-4x - y = 5$
   (2) $x - 2y = 4$

   a. To eliminate x from the system of equations by using the addition method, multiply each side of equation (___?___) by ___?___.
   b. To eliminate y from the system of equations by using the addition method, multiply each side of equation (___?___) by ___?___.

Solve by the addition method.

3. $x - y = 5$
   $x + y = 7$

4. $x + y = 1$
   $2x - y = 5$

5. $3x + y = 4$
   $x + y = 2$

6. $x - 3y = 4$
   $x + 5y = -4$

7. $3x + y = 7$
   $x + 2y = 4$

8. $x - 2y = 7$
   $3x - 2y = 9$

9. $3x - y = 4$
   $6x - 2y = 8$

10. $x - 2y = -3$
    $-2x + 4y = 6$

11. $2x + 5y = 9$
    $4x - 7y = -16$

12. $8x - 3y = 21$
$4x + 5y = -9$

13. $4x - 6y = 5$
$2x - 3y = 7$

14. $3x + 6y = 7$
$2x + 4y = 5$

15. $3x - 5y = 7$
$x - 2y = 3$

16. $3x + 4y = 25$
$2x + y = 10$

17. $3x + 2y = 16$
$2x - 3y = -11$

18. $2x - 5y = 13$
$5x + 3y = 17$

19. $4x + 4y = 5$
$2x - 8y = -5$

20. $3x + 7y = 16$
$4x - 3y = 9$

21. $5x + 4y = 0$
$3x + 7y = 0$

22. $3x - 4y = 0$
$4x - 7y = 0$

23. $3x - 6y = 6$
$9x - 3y = 8$

24. $4x - 8y = 5$
$8x + 2y = 1$

25. $5x + 2y = 2x + 1$
$2x - 3y = 3x + 2$

26. $3x + 3y = y + 1$
$x + 3y = 9 - x$

27. $\frac{2}{3}x - \frac{1}{2}y = 3$
$\frac{1}{3}x - \frac{1}{4}y = \frac{3}{2}$

28. $\frac{3}{4}x + \frac{1}{3}y = -\frac{1}{2}$
$\frac{1}{2}x - \frac{5}{6}y = -\frac{7}{2}$

29. $\frac{2}{5}x - \frac{1}{3}y = 1$
$\frac{3}{5}x + \frac{2}{3}y = 5$

30. $\frac{5}{6}x + \frac{1}{3}y = \frac{4}{3}$
$\frac{2}{3}x - \frac{1}{2}y = \frac{11}{6}$

31. $\frac{3}{4}x + \frac{2}{5}y = -\frac{3}{20}$
$\frac{3}{2}x - \frac{1}{4}y = \frac{3}{4}$

32. $\frac{2}{5}x - \frac{1}{2}y = \frac{13}{2}$
$\frac{3}{4}x - \frac{1}{5}y = \frac{17}{2}$

33. $4x - 5y = 3y + 4$
$2x + 3y = 2x + 1$

34. $5x - 2y = 8x - 1$
$2x + 7y = 4y + 9$

35. $2x + 5y = 5x + 1$
$3x - 2y = 3y + 3$

36. When you solve a system of equations using the addition method, how can you tell whether the system of equations is inconsistent?

37. When you solve a system of equations using the addition method, how can you tell whether the system of equations is dependent?

In Exercises 38 and 39, A, B, C, and D are nonzero real numbers.

38. Is the following system of equations independent, inconsistent, or dependent?
$Ax + By = 0$
$Cx + Dy = 0, D \neq B$

39. Is the following system of equations independent, inconsistent, or dependent?
$Ax + By = C$
$DAx + DBy = DC$

2 Solve a system of three linear equations in three variables by the addition method

40. Verify that the ordered triple $(-1, -2, 3)$ is a solution of the equation $4x - y + 2z = 4$ by substituting -1 for x, -2 for y, and 3 for z.

41. Look at Exercise 42. State two pairs of equations that can be added together to eliminate the variable z.

Solve by the addition method.

42. $x + 2y - z = 1$
$2x - y + z = 6$
$x + 3y - z = 2$

43. $x + 3y + z = 6$
$3x + y - z = -2$
$2x + 2y - z = 1$

44. $2x - y + 2z = 7$
$x + y + z = 2$
$3x - y + z = 6$

45. $x - 2y + z = 6$
$x + 3y + z = 16$
$3x - y - z = 12$

46. $3x + y = 5$
$3y - z = 2$
$x + z = 5$

47. $2y + z = 7$
$2x - z = 3$
$x - y = 3$

48. $x - y + z = 1$
$2x + 3y - z = 3$
$-x + 2y - 4z = 4$

49. $2x + y - 3z = 7$
$x - 2y + 3z = 1$
$3x + 4y - 3z = 13$

50. $2x + 3z = 5$
$3y + 2z = 3$
$3x + 4y = -10$

51. $3x + 4z = 5$
$2y + 3z = 2$
$2x - 5y = 8$

52. $2x + 4y - 2z = 3$
$x + 3y + 4z = 1$
$x + 2y - z = 4$

53. $x - 3y + 2z = 1$
$x - 2y + 3z = 5$
$2x - 6y + 4z = 3$

54. $2x + y - z = 5$
$x + 3y + z = 14$
$3x - y + 2z = 1$

55. $3x - y - 2z = 11$
$2x + y - 2z = 11$
$x + 3y - z = 8$

56. $3x + y - 2z = 2$
$x + 2y + 3z = 13$
$2x - 2y + 5z = 6$

57. $4x + 5y + z = 6$
$2x - y + 2z = 11$
$x + 2y + 2z = 6$

58. $2x - y + z = 6$
$3x + 2y + z = 4$
$x - 2y + 3z = 12$

59. $3x + 2y - 3z = 8$
$2x + 3y + 2z = 10$
$x + y - z = 2$

60. $3x - 2y + 3z = -4$
$2x + y - 3z = 2$
$3x + 4y + 5z = 8$

61. $3x - 3y + 4z = 6$
$4x - 5y + 2z = 10$
$x - 2y + 3z = 4$

62. $3x - y + 2z = 2$
$4x + 2y - 7z = 0$
$2x + 3y - 5z = 7$

63. $2x + 2y + 3z = 13$
$-3x + 4y - z = 5$
$5x - 3y + z = 2$

64. $2x - 3y + 7z = 0$
$x + 4y - 4z = -2$
$3x + 2y + 5z = 1$

65. $5x + 3y - z = 5$
$3x - 2y + 4z = 13$
$4x + 3y + 5z = 22$

4.2 Applying Concepts

Solve. (*Hint:* First multiply both sides of each equation in the system by a multiple of 10 so that the coefficients and constants are integers.)

66. $0.2x - 0.3y = 0.5$
$0.3x - 0.2y = 0.5$

67. $0.4x - 0.9y = -0.1$
$0.3x + 0.2y = 0.8$

68. $1.25x - 0.25y = -1.5$
$1.5x + 2.5y = 1$

69. $2.25x + 1.5y = 3$
$1.75x + 2.25y = 1.25$

70. $1.5x + 2.5y + 1.5z = 8$
$0.5x - 2y - 1.5z = -1$
$2.5x - 1.5y + 2z = 2.5$

71. $1.6x - 0.9y + 0.3z = 2.9$
$1.6x + 0.5y - 0.1z = 3.3$
$0.8x - 0.7y + 0.1z = 1.5$

Solve.

72. The point of intersection of the graphs of the equations $Ax + 3y = 6$ and $2x + By = -4$ is $(3, -2)$. Find A and B.

73. The point of intersection of the graphs of the equations $Ax + 3y + 2z = 8$, $2x + By - 3z = -12$, and $3x - 2y + Cz = 1$ is $(3, -2, 4)$. Find A, B, and C.

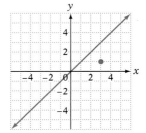

74. The distance between a point and a line is the perpendicular distance from the point to the line. Find the distance between the point $(3, 1)$ and the line $y = x$.

75. **Coin Problem** A coin bank contains only nickels, dimes, and quarters. There is a total of 30 coins in the bank. The value of all the coins is $3.25. Find the number of nickels, dimes, and quarters in the bank. (*Hint:* There is more than one solution.)

The following are not linear systems of equations. However, they can be solved by using a modification of the addition method. Solve each system of equations.

76. $\dfrac{1}{x} - \dfrac{2}{y} = 3$

$\dfrac{2}{x} + \dfrac{3}{y} = -1$

77. $\dfrac{1}{x} + \dfrac{2}{y} = 3$

$\dfrac{1}{x} - \dfrac{3}{y} = -2$

78. $\dfrac{3}{x} + \dfrac{2}{y} = 1$

$\dfrac{2}{x} + \dfrac{4}{y} = -2$

79. $\dfrac{3}{x} - \dfrac{5}{y} = -\dfrac{3}{2}$

$\dfrac{1}{x} - \dfrac{2}{y} = -\dfrac{2}{3}$

80. For Exercise 76, solve each equation of the system for y. Then use a graphing utility to verify the solution you determined algebraically. Note that the graphs are not straight lines.

81. Describe the graph of each of the following equations in an xyz-coordinate system.

a. $x = 3$ **b.** $y = 4$ **c.** $z = 2$ **d.** $y = x$

Solving Systems of Equations by Using Determinants and by Using Matrices

4.3

OBJECTIVE **1**   Evaluate determinants

A **matrix** is a rectangular array of numbers. Each number in the matrix is called an **element** of the matrix. The matrix at the right, with three rows and four columns, is called a 3 × 4 ("3 by 4") matrix.

$$A = \begin{bmatrix} 1 & -3 & 2 & 4 \\ 0 & 4 & -3 & 2 \\ 6 & -5 & 4 & -1 \end{bmatrix}$$

Point of Interest

The word matrix *was first used (in a mathematical context) in 1850. The root of this word is the Latin* mater. *A matrix was thought of as being an object from which something else originates. The idea was that a determinant, discussed at the right, originated (was born) from a matrix. Today, matrices are one of the most widely used tools of applied mathematics.*

A matrix of m rows and n columns is said to be of **order $m \times n$.** Matrix A above has order 3×4. The notation a_{ij} refers to the element of a matrix in the ith row and the jth column. For matrix A, $a_{23} = -3$, $a_{31} = 6$, and $a_{13} = 2$.

A **square matrix** is one that has the same number of rows as columns. A 2×2 matrix and a 3×3 matrix are shown at the right.

$$\begin{bmatrix} -1 & 3 \\ 5 & 2 \end{bmatrix} \qquad \begin{bmatrix} 4 & 0 & 1 \\ 5 & -3 & 7 \\ 2 & 1 & 4 \end{bmatrix}$$

Associated with every square matrix is a number called its **determinant.**

Determinant of a 2 × 2 Matrix

The determinant of a 2×2 matrix $\begin{bmatrix} a_{11} & a_{12} \\ a_{21} & a_{22} \end{bmatrix}$ is written $\begin{vmatrix} a_{11} & a_{12} \\ a_{21} & a_{22} \end{vmatrix}$. The value of this determinant is given by the formula

$$\begin{vmatrix} a_{11} & a_{12} \\ a_{21} & a_{22} \end{vmatrix} = a_{11}a_{22} - a_{21}a_{12}$$

Note that vertical bars are used to represent the determinant and that brackets are used to represent the matrix.

Find the value of the determinant $\begin{vmatrix} 3 & 4 \\ -1 & 2 \end{vmatrix}$.

$$\begin{vmatrix} 3 & 4 \\ -1 & 2 \end{vmatrix} = 3 \cdot 2 - (-1)(4) = 6 - (-4) = 10$$

The value of the determinant is 10.

For a square matrix whose order is 3×3 or greater, the value of the determinant of that matrix is found by using 2×2 determinants.

The **minor of an element** in a 3×3 determinant is the 2×2 determinant that is obtained by eliminating the row and column that contain that element.

Find the minor of -3 for the determinant $\begin{vmatrix} 2 & -3 & 4 \\ 0 & 4 & 8 \\ -1 & 3 & 6 \end{vmatrix}$.

The minor of -3 is the 2×2 determinant created by eliminating the row and column that contain -3.

Eliminate the row and column as shown: $\begin{vmatrix} 2 & -3 & 4 \\ 0 & 4 & 8 \\ -1 & 3 & 6 \end{vmatrix}$

The minor of -3 is $\begin{vmatrix} 0 & 8 \\ -1 & 6 \end{vmatrix}$.

Definition of a Cofactor

The **cofactor** of an element of a determinant is $(-1)^{i+j}$ times the minor of that element, where i is the row number of the element and j is the column number of the element.

For the determinant $\begin{vmatrix} 3 & -2 & 1 \\ 2 & -5 & -4 \\ 0 & 3 & 1 \end{vmatrix}$, find the cofactor of -2 and of -5.

Because -2 is in the first row and the second column, $i = 1$ and $j = 2$. Therefore, $i + j = 1 + 2 = 3$, and $(-1)^{i+j} = (-1)^3 = -1$.

The cofactor of -2 is $(-1)\begin{vmatrix} 2 & -4 \\ 0 & 1 \end{vmatrix}$.

Because -5 is in the second row and the second column, $i = 2$ and $j = 2$. Therefore, $i + j = 2 + 2 = 4$, and $(-1)^{i+j} = (-1)^4 = 1$.

The cofactor of -5 is $1 \cdot \begin{vmatrix} 3 & 1 \\ 0 & 1 \end{vmatrix}$.

Note from this example that the cofactor of an element is -1 times the minor of that element or 1 times the minor of that element, depending on whether the sum $i + j$ is an odd or an even integer.

The value of a 3×3 or larger determinant can be found by **expanding by cofactors** of *any* row or *any* column. The result of expanding by cofactors using the first row of a 3×3 determinant is shown here.

$$\begin{vmatrix} a_{11} & a_{12} & a_{13} \\ a_{21} & a_{22} & a_{23} \\ a_{31} & a_{32} & a_{33} \end{vmatrix} = a_{11}(-1)^{1+1}\begin{vmatrix} a_{22} & a_{23} \\ a_{32} & a_{33} \end{vmatrix} + a_{12}(-1)^{1+2}\begin{vmatrix} a_{21} & a_{23} \\ a_{31} & a_{33} \end{vmatrix} + a_{13}(-1)^{1+3}\begin{vmatrix} a_{21} & a_{22} \\ a_{31} & a_{32} \end{vmatrix}$$

$$= a_{11}\begin{vmatrix} a_{22} & a_{23} \\ a_{32} & a_{33} \end{vmatrix} - a_{12}\begin{vmatrix} a_{21} & a_{23} \\ a_{31} & a_{33} \end{vmatrix} + a_{13}\begin{vmatrix} a_{21} & a_{22} \\ a_{31} & a_{32} \end{vmatrix}$$

Find the value of the determinant $\begin{vmatrix} 2 & -3 & 2 \\ 1 & 3 & -1 \\ 0 & -2 & 2 \end{vmatrix}$.

Expand by cofactors of the first row.

$$\begin{vmatrix} 2 & -3 & 2 \\ 1 & 3 & -1 \\ 0 & -2 & 2 \end{vmatrix} = 2\begin{vmatrix} 3 & -1 \\ -2 & 2 \end{vmatrix} - (-3)\begin{vmatrix} 1 & -1 \\ 0 & 2 \end{vmatrix} + 2\begin{vmatrix} 1 & 3 \\ 0 & -2 \end{vmatrix}$$

$$= 2(6 - 2) - (-3)(2 - 0) + 2(-2 - 0)$$
$$= 2(4) - (-3)(2) + 2(-2) = 8 - (-6) + (-4)$$
$$= 10$$

To illustrate a statement made earlier, the value of this determinant will now be found by expanding by cofactors of the second column.

$$\begin{vmatrix} 2 & -3 & 2 \\ 1 & 3 & -1 \\ 0 & -2 & 2 \end{vmatrix} = -3(-1)^{1+2}\begin{vmatrix} 1 & -1 \\ 0 & 2 \end{vmatrix} + 3(-1)^{2+2}\begin{vmatrix} 2 & 2 \\ 0 & 2 \end{vmatrix} + (-2)(-1)^{3+2}\begin{vmatrix} 2 & 2 \\ 1 & -1 \end{vmatrix}$$

$$= -3(-1)\begin{vmatrix} 1 & -1 \\ 0 & 2 \end{vmatrix} + 3 \cdot 1\begin{vmatrix} 2 & 2 \\ 0 & 2 \end{vmatrix} + (-2)(-1)\begin{vmatrix} 2 & 2 \\ 1 & -1 \end{vmatrix}$$

$$= 3(2 - 0) + 3(4 - 0) + 2(-2 - 2)$$

$$= 3(2) + 3(4) + 2(-4) = 6 + 12 + (-8)$$

$$= 10$$

Note that the value of the determinant is the same whether the first row or the second column is used to expand by cofactors. *Any row or column* can be used to evaluate a determinant by expanding by cofactors.

EXAMPLE 1 Evaluate the determinant. **A.** $\begin{vmatrix} 3 & -2 \\ 6 & -4 \end{vmatrix}$ **B.** $\begin{vmatrix} -2 & 3 & 1 \\ 4 & -2 & 0 \\ 1 & -2 & 3 \end{vmatrix}$

Solution **A.** $\begin{vmatrix} 3 & -2 \\ 6 & -4 \end{vmatrix} = 3(-4) - (6)(-2) = -12 + 12 = 0$

The value of the determinant is 0.

B. $\begin{vmatrix} -2 & 3 & 1 \\ 4 & -2 & 0 \\ 1 & -2 & 3 \end{vmatrix} = -2\begin{vmatrix} -2 & 0 \\ -2 & 3 \end{vmatrix} - 3\begin{vmatrix} 4 & 0 \\ 1 & 3 \end{vmatrix} + 1\begin{vmatrix} 4 & -2 \\ 1 & -2 \end{vmatrix}$

$$= -2(-6 + 0) - 3(12 - 0) + 1(-8 + 2)$$

$$= -2(-6) - 3(12) + 1(-6)$$

$$= 12 - 36 - 6$$

$$= -30$$

The value of the determinant is -30.

PROBLEM 1 Evaluate the determinant.

A. $\begin{vmatrix} -1 & -4 \\ 3 & -5 \end{vmatrix}$ **B.** $\begin{vmatrix} 1 & 4 & -2 \\ 3 & 1 & 1 \\ 0 & -2 & 2 \end{vmatrix}$

Solution See page S11.

OBJECTIVE 2 ## Solve systems of linear equations by using Cramer's Rule

The connection between determinants and systems of equations can be understood by solving a general system of linear equations.

Solve: $a_{11}x + a_{12}y = b_1$ (1) $a_{11}x + a_{12}y = b_1$
       $a_{21}x + a_{22}y = b_2$ (2) $a_{21}x + a_{22}y = b_2$

Eliminate y. Multiply equation (1) by a_{22} and equation (2) by $-a_{12}$.

$$a_{11}a_{22}x + a_{12}a_{22}y = b_1a_{22}$$
$$-a_{21}a_{12}x - a_{12}a_{22}y = -b_2a_{12}$$

Add the equations.

$$(a_{11}a_{22} - a_{21}a_{12})x = b_1a_{22} - b_2a_{12}$$

Assuming $a_{11}a_{22} - a_{21}a_{12} \neq 0$, solve for x.

$$x = \frac{b_1a_{22} - b_2a_{12}}{a_{11}a_{22} - a_{21}a_{12}}$$

The denominator $a_{11}a_{22} - a_{21}a_{12}$ is the determinant of the coefficients of x and y. This is called the **coefficient determinant.**

$$a_{11}a_{22} - a_{21}a_{12} = \begin{vmatrix} a_{11} & a_{12} \\ a_{21} & a_{22} \end{vmatrix}$$

Coefficients of x ⟶
Coefficients of y ⟶

The numerator for x, $b_1a_{22} - b_2a_{12}$, is the determinant obtained by replacing the first column in the coefficient determinant by the constants b_1 and b_2. This is called the **numerator determinant.**

$$b_1a_{22} - b_2a_{12} = \begin{vmatrix} b_1 & a_{12} \\ b_2 & a_{22} \end{vmatrix}$$

Constants of the equations ⟶

Following a similar procedure and eliminating x, we can also express the y-component of the solution in determinant form. These results are summarized in Cramer's Rule.

Cramer's Rule

The solution of the system of equations $\begin{array}{l} a_{11}x + a_{12}y = b_1 \\ a_{21}x + a_{22}y = b_2 \end{array}$ is given by

$$x = \frac{D_x}{D} \text{ and } y = \frac{D_y}{D}, \text{ where}$$

$$D = \begin{vmatrix} a_{11} & a_{12} \\ a_{21} & a_{22} \end{vmatrix}, \quad D_x = \begin{vmatrix} b_1 & a_{12} \\ b_2 & a_{22} \end{vmatrix}, \quad D_y = \begin{vmatrix} a_{11} & b_1 \\ a_{21} & b_2 \end{vmatrix}, \text{ and } D \neq 0.$$

Point of Interest

Cramer's Rule is named after Gabriel Cramer, who used it in a book he published in 1750. However, this rule was published in 1683 by the Japanese mathematician Seki Kown. That publication occurred seven years before Cramer's birth.

EXAMPLE 2   Solve by using Cramer's Rule: $2x - 3y = 8$
                                      $5x + 6y = 11$

Solution $D = \begin{vmatrix} 2 & -3 \\ 5 & 6 \end{vmatrix} = 27$ • Find the value of the coefficient determinant.

$$D_x = \begin{vmatrix} 8 & -3 \\ 11 & 6 \end{vmatrix} = 81$$ • Find the value of each of the numerator determinants.

$$D_y = \begin{vmatrix} 2 & 8 \\ 5 & 11 \end{vmatrix} = -18$$

$$x = \frac{D_x}{D} = \frac{81}{27} = 3$$ • Use Cramer's Rule to write the solutions.

$$y = \frac{D_y}{D} = \frac{-18}{27} = -\frac{2}{3}$$

The solution is $\left(3, -\frac{2}{3}\right)$.

PROBLEM 2   Solve by using Cramer's Rule: $6x - 6y = 5$
$2x - 10y = -1$

Solution   See page S11.

For the system shown at the right, $D = 0$. Therefore, $\dfrac{D_x}{D}$ and $\dfrac{D_y}{D}$ are undefined.

$6x - 9y = 5$
$4x - 6y = 4$

When $D = 0$, the system of equations is dependent if both D_x and D_y are zero. The system of equations is inconsistent if $D = 0$ and either D_x or D_y is not zero.

$D = \begin{vmatrix} 6 & -9 \\ 4 & -6 \end{vmatrix} = 0$

A procedure similar to that followed for two equations in two variables can be used to extend Cramer's Rule to three equations in three variables.

Cramer's Rule for Three Equations in Three Variables

The solution of the system of equations $\begin{aligned} a_{11}x + a_{12}y + a_{13}z &= b_1 \\ a_{21}x + a_{22}y + a_{23}z &= b_2 \\ a_{31}x + a_{32}y + a_{33}z &= b_3 \end{aligned}$ is given

by $x = \dfrac{D_x}{D}$, $y = \dfrac{D_y}{D}$, and $z = \dfrac{D_z}{D}$, where

$$D = \begin{vmatrix} a_{11} & a_{12} & a_{13} \\ a_{21} & a_{22} & a_{23} \\ a_{31} & a_{32} & a_{33} \end{vmatrix}, D_x = \begin{vmatrix} b_1 & a_{12} & a_{13} \\ b_2 & a_{22} & a_{23} \\ b_3 & a_{32} & a_{33} \end{vmatrix}, D_y = \begin{vmatrix} a_{11} & b_1 & a_{13} \\ a_{21} & b_2 & a_{23} \\ a_{31} & b_3 & a_{33} \end{vmatrix},$$

$$D_z = \begin{vmatrix} a_{11} & a_{12} & b_1 \\ a_{21} & a_{22} & b_2 \\ a_{31} & a_{32} & b_3 \end{vmatrix}, \text{ and } D \neq 0.$$

EXAMPLE 3   Solve by using Cramer's Rule: $3x - y + z = 5$
$x + 2y - 2z = -3$
$2x + 3y + z = 4$

Solution $D = \begin{vmatrix} 3 & -1 & 1 \\ 1 & 2 & -2 \\ 2 & 3 & 1 \end{vmatrix} = 28$ • Find the value of the coefficient determinant.

$D_x = \begin{vmatrix} 5 & -1 & 1 \\ -3 & 2 & -2 \\ 4 & 3 & 1 \end{vmatrix} = 28$ • Find the value of each of the numerator determinants.

$D_y = \begin{vmatrix} 3 & 5 & 1 \\ 1 & -3 & -2 \\ 2 & 4 & 1 \end{vmatrix} = 0$

$D_z = \begin{vmatrix} 3 & -1 & 5 \\ 1 & 2 & -3 \\ 2 & 3 & 4 \end{vmatrix} = 56$

$$x = \frac{D_x}{D} = \frac{28}{28} = 1$$

$$y = \frac{D_y}{D} = \frac{0}{28} = 0$$

$$z = \frac{D_z}{D} = \frac{56}{28} = 2$$

• Use Cramer's Rule to write the solution.

The solution is $(1, 0, 2)$.

PROBLEM 3 Solve by using Cramer's Rule:
$$2x - y + z = -1$$
$$3x + 2y - z = 3$$
$$x + 3y + z = -2$$

Solution See page S11.

OBJECTIVE 3 ## Solve systems of linear equations by using matrices

As previously stated in this section, a **matrix** is a rectangular array of numbers. Each number in the matrix is called an **element** of the matrix. The matrix shown below, with 3 rows and 4 columns, is a 3×4 matrix.

$$\begin{bmatrix} 1 & 4 & -3 & 6 \\ -2 & 5 & 2 & 0 \\ -1 & 3 & 7 & -4 \end{bmatrix}$$

The elements $a_{11}, a_{22}, a_{33}, \ldots, a_{nn}$ form the **main diagonal** of a matrix. The elements 1, 5, and 7 form the main diagonal of the matrix above.

By considering only the coefficients and constants for the following system of equations, we can form the corresponding 3×4 **augmented matrix.**

System of Equations   **Augmented Matrix**

$$3x - 2y + z = 2$$
$$x \quad\quad - 3z = -2$$
$$2x - y + 4z = 5$$

$$\begin{bmatrix} 3 & -2 & 1 & 2 \\ 1 & 0 & -3 & -2 \\ 2 & -1 & 4 & 5 \end{bmatrix}$$

Note that when a term is missing from one of the equations of the system, the coefficient of that term is 0, and a 0 is entered in the matrix.

A system of equations can be written from an augmented matrix.

$$\begin{bmatrix} 2 & -1 & 4 & 1 \\ 1 & 1 & 0 & 3 \\ 3 & -2 & -1 & 5 \end{bmatrix}$$
$$2x - y + 4z = 1$$
$$x + y \quad\quad = 3$$
$$3x - 2y - z = 5$$

EXAMPLE 4 Write the augmented matrix for $\begin{array}{l} 2x - 3y = 4 \\ x + 5y = 0 \end{array}$.

Solution The augmented matrix is $\begin{bmatrix} 2 & -3 & 4 \\ 1 & 5 & 0 \end{bmatrix}$.

PROBLEM 4   Write the system of equations that corresponds to the

augmented matrix $\begin{bmatrix} 2 & -3 & 1 & | & 4 \\ 1 & 0 & -2 & | & 3 \\ 0 & 1 & 2 & | & -3 \end{bmatrix}$.

■ **Solution**   See page S11.

A system of equations can be solved by writing the system in matrix form and then performing operations on the matrix similar to those performed on the equations of the system. These operations are called **elementary row operations.**

> ### Elementary Row Operations
>
> **1.** Interchange two rows.
>
> **2.** Multiply all the elements in a row by the same nonzero number.
>
> **3.** Replace a row by the sum of that row and a multiple of any other row.

Each of these elementary row operations has as its basis the operations that can be performed on a system of equations. These operations do not change the solution of the system of equations. Here are some examples of each row operation.

1. Interchange two rows.

Take Note

For each example of a row operation at the right, we are using the same system of equations. The solution of this system of equations is (2, 1). You should verify that (2, 1) is also a solution of the new system of equations. This means that these row operations have not changed the solution.

Original System

$2x - 3y = 1$
$4x + 5y = 13$

The solution is (2, 1).

$\begin{bmatrix} 2 & -3 & | & 1 \\ 4 & 5 & | & 13 \end{bmatrix}$

This notation means to interchange rows 1 and 2.

$R_1 \leftrightarrow R_2$

$\begin{bmatrix} 4 & 5 & | & 13 \\ 2 & -3 & | & 1 \end{bmatrix}$

New System

$4x + 5y = 13$
$2x - 3y = 1$

The solution is (2, 1).

2. Multiply all the elements in a row by the same nonzero number.

Original System

$2x - 3y = 1$
$4x + 5y = 13$

The solution is (2, 1).

$\begin{bmatrix} 2 & -3 & | & 1 \\ 4 & 5 & | & 13 \end{bmatrix}$

This notation means to multiply row 2 by 3.

$3R_2 \rightarrow$

$\begin{bmatrix} 2 & -3 & | & 1 \\ 12 & 15 & | & 39 \end{bmatrix}$

New System

$2x - 3y = 1$
$12x + 15y = 39$

The solution is (2, 1).

Take Note

Note that for the third elementary row operation, the row being multiplied is *not* changed. For the example at the right, row 1 is not changed. The row being added to is replaced by the result of the operation. It is not absolutely necessary to follow this convention, but for consistency, we will always use this method.

3. Replace a row by the sum of that row and a multiple of any other row.

This notation means to replace row 2 by the sum of that row and -2 times row 1.

Original System

$2x - 3y = 1$
$4x + 5y = 13$

$\begin{bmatrix} 2 & -3 & | & 1 \\ 4 & 5 & | & 13 \end{bmatrix} \quad -2R_1 + R_2 \rightarrow \quad \begin{bmatrix} 2 & -3 & | & 1 \\ 0 & 11 & | & 11 \end{bmatrix}$

New System

$2x - 3y = 1$
$11y = 11$

The solution is $(2, 1)$.

The solution is $(2, 1)$.

Note that we replace the row that follows the addition. See the Take Note at the left.

EXAMPLE 5 Let $A = \begin{bmatrix} 1 & 3 & -4 & | & 6 \\ 3 & 2 & 0 & | & -1 \\ -2 & -5 & 3 & | & 4 \end{bmatrix}$. Perform the following elementary row operations on A.

A. $R_1 \leftrightarrow R_3$　　**B.** $-2R_3$　　**C.** $2R_3 + R_1$

Solution　　**A.** $R_1 \leftrightarrow R_3$ means to interchange row 1 and row 3.

$\begin{bmatrix} 1 & 3 & -4 & | & 6 \\ 3 & 2 & 0 & | & -1 \\ -2 & -5 & 3 & | & 4 \end{bmatrix} \quad R_1 \leftrightarrow R_3 \quad \begin{bmatrix} -2 & -5 & 3 & | & 4 \\ 3 & 2 & 0 & | & -1 \\ 1 & 3 & -4 & | & 6 \end{bmatrix}$

B. $-2R_3$ means to multiply row 3 by -2.

$\begin{bmatrix} 1 & 3 & -4 & | & 6 \\ 3 & 2 & 0 & | & -1 \\ -2 & -5 & 3 & | & 4 \end{bmatrix} \quad -2R_3 \rightarrow \quad \begin{bmatrix} 1 & 3 & -4 & | & 6 \\ 3 & 2 & 0 & | & -1 \\ 4 & 10 & -6 & | & -8 \end{bmatrix}$

C. $2R_3 + R_1$ means to multiply row 3 by 2 and then add the result to row 1.

$\begin{bmatrix} 1 & 3 & -4 & | & 6 \\ 3 & 2 & 0 & | & -1 \\ -2 & -5 & 3 & | & 4 \end{bmatrix} \quad 2R_3 + R_1 \rightarrow \quad \begin{bmatrix} -3 & -7 & 2 & | & 14 \\ 3 & 2 & 0 & | & -1 \\ -2 & -5 & 3 & | & 4 \end{bmatrix}$

PROBLEM 5 Let $B = \begin{bmatrix} 1 & 8 & -2 & | & 3 \\ 2 & -3 & 4 & | & 1 \\ 3 & 5 & -7 & | & 3 \end{bmatrix}$. Perform the following elementary row operations on B.

A. $R_2 \leftrightarrow R_3$　　**B.** $3R_2$　　**C.** $-3R_1 + R_3$

Solution　　See page S11.

Elementary row operations are used to solve a system of equations. The goal is to use the elementary row operations to rewrite the augmented matrix with 1's down the main diagonal and 0's to the left of the 1's in all rows except the first. This is called the **row echelon form** of the matrix. Here are some examples of the row echelon form.

$$\begin{bmatrix} 1 & 3 & | & -2 \\ 0 & 1 & | & 3 \end{bmatrix} \qquad \begin{bmatrix} 1 & -2 & 3 & | & 1 \\ 0 & 1 & 2.5 & | & -4 \\ 0 & 0 & 1 & | & 2 \end{bmatrix} \qquad \begin{bmatrix} 1 & 4 & \frac{1}{2} & | & -3 \\ 0 & 1 & 3 & | & 0 \\ 0 & 0 & 1 & | & -\frac{2}{3} \end{bmatrix}$$

We will follow a very definite procedure to rewrite an augmented matrix in row echelon form. For a 2 × 3 augmented matrix, use elementary row operations to

Step 1: Change a_{11} to a 1.
Step 2: Change a_{21} to a 0.
Step 3: Change a_{22} to a 1.

$$\begin{bmatrix} a_{11} & a_{12} & | & a_{13} \\ a_{21} & a_{22} & | & a_{23} \end{bmatrix}$$

Write the matrix $\begin{bmatrix} 3 & -6 & | & 12 \\ 2 & 1 & | & -3 \end{bmatrix}$ in row echelon form.

Step 1: Change a_{11} to 1. One way to do this is to multiply row 1 by the reciprocal of a_{11}.

$$\begin{bmatrix} 3 & -6 & | & 12 \\ 2 & 1 & | & -3 \end{bmatrix} \quad \tfrac{1}{3}R_1 \rightarrow \quad \begin{bmatrix} 1 & -2 & | & 4 \\ 2 & 1 & | & -3 \end{bmatrix}$$

Step 2: Change a_{21} to 0 by multiplying row 1 by the opposite of a_{21} and then adding to row 2.

$$\begin{bmatrix} 1 & -2 & | & 4 \\ 2 & 1 & | & -3 \end{bmatrix} \quad -2R_1 + R_2 \rightarrow \quad \begin{bmatrix} 1 & -2 & | & 4 \\ 0 & 5 & | & -11 \end{bmatrix}$$

Step 3: Change a_{22} to 1 by multiplying by the reciprocal of a_{22}.

$$\begin{bmatrix} 1 & -2 & | & 4 \\ 0 & 5 & | & -11 \end{bmatrix} \quad \tfrac{1}{5}R_2 \rightarrow \quad \begin{bmatrix} 1 & -2 & | & 4 \\ 0 & 1 & | & -\frac{11}{5} \end{bmatrix}$$

A row echelon form of the matrix is $\begin{bmatrix} 1 & -2 & | & 4 \\ 0 & 1 & | & -\frac{11}{5} \end{bmatrix}$.

The row echelon form of a matrix is not unique and depends on the elementary row operations that are used. For instance, suppose we again start with $\begin{bmatrix} 3 & -6 & | & 12 \\ 2 & 1 & | & -3 \end{bmatrix}$ and follow the elementary row operations below.

$$\begin{bmatrix} 3 & -6 & | & 12 \\ 2 & 1 & | & -3 \end{bmatrix} \ -1R_2 + R_1 \rightarrow \ \begin{bmatrix} 1 & -7 & | & 15 \\ 2 & 1 & | & -3 \end{bmatrix} \ -2R_1 + R_2 \rightarrow \ \begin{bmatrix} 1 & -7 & | & 15 \\ 0 & 15 & | & -33 \end{bmatrix} \ \tfrac{1}{15}R_2 \rightarrow \ \begin{bmatrix} 1 & -7 & | & 15 \\ 0 & 1 & | & -\frac{11}{5} \end{bmatrix}$$

The row echelon forms $\begin{bmatrix} 1 & -7 & | & 15 \\ 0 & 1 & | & -\frac{11}{5} \end{bmatrix}$ and $\begin{bmatrix} 1 & -2 & | & 4 \\ 0 & 1 & | & -\frac{11}{5} \end{bmatrix}$ are different.

Row echelon form is not unique.

The order in which the elements in an augmented 3×4 matrix are changed is as follows:

$$\begin{bmatrix} a_{11} & a_{12} & a_{13} & a_{14} \\ a_{21} & a_{22} & a_{23} & a_{24} \\ a_{31} & a_{32} & a_{33} & a_{34} \end{bmatrix}$$

Step 1: Change a_{11} to a 1.

Step 2: Change a_{21} and a_{31} to 0's.
Step 3: Change a_{22} to a 1.
Step 4: Change a_{32} to a 0.
Step 5: Change a_{33} to a 1.

EXAMPLE 6   Write $\begin{bmatrix} 2 & 1 & 3 & -1 \\ 1 & 3 & 5 & -1 \\ -3 & -1 & 1 & 2 \end{bmatrix}$ in row echelon form.

Solution   **Step 1:** Change a_{11} to 1 by interchanging row 1 and row 2.

Note: We could have chosen to multiply row 1 by $\frac{1}{2}$. The sequence of steps to get to row echelon form is not unique.

$$\begin{bmatrix} 2 & 1 & 3 & -1 \\ 1 & 3 & 5 & -1 \\ -3 & -1 & 1 & 2 \end{bmatrix} \quad R_1 \leftrightarrow R_2 \quad \begin{bmatrix} 1 & 3 & 5 & -1 \\ 2 & 1 & 3 & -1 \\ -3 & -1 & 1 & 2 \end{bmatrix}$$

Step 2: Change a_{21} to 0 by multiplying row 1 by the opposite of a_{21} and then adding to row 2.

$$\begin{bmatrix} 1 & 3 & 5 & -1 \\ 2 & 1 & 3 & -1 \\ -3 & -1 & 1 & 2 \end{bmatrix} \quad -2R_1 + R_2 \rightarrow \quad \begin{bmatrix} 1 & 3 & 5 & -1 \\ 0 & -5 & -7 & 1 \\ -3 & -1 & 1 & 2 \end{bmatrix}$$

Change a_{31} to 0 by multiplying row 1 by the opposite of a_{31} and then adding to row 3.

$$\begin{bmatrix} 1 & 3 & 5 & -1 \\ 0 & -5 & -7 & 1 \\ -3 & -1 & 1 & 2 \end{bmatrix} \quad 3R_1 + R_3 \rightarrow \quad \begin{bmatrix} 1 & 3 & 5 & -1 \\ 0 & -5 & -7 & 1 \\ 0 & 8 & 16 & -1 \end{bmatrix}$$

Step 3: Change a_{22} to 1 by multiplying by the reciprocal of a_{22}.

$$\begin{bmatrix} 1 & 3 & 5 & -1 \\ 0 & -5 & -7 & 1 \\ 0 & 8 & 16 & -1 \end{bmatrix} \quad -\frac{1}{5}R_2 \rightarrow \quad \begin{bmatrix} 1 & 3 & 5 & -1 \\ 0 & 1 & \frac{7}{5} & -\frac{1}{5} \\ 0 & 8 & 16 & -1 \end{bmatrix}$$

Step 4: Change a_{32} to 0 by multiplying row 2 by the opposite of a_{32} and then adding to row 3.

$$\begin{bmatrix} 1 & 3 & 5 & -1 \\ 0 & 1 & \frac{7}{5} & -\frac{1}{5} \\ 0 & 8 & 16 & -1 \end{bmatrix} \quad -8R_2 + R_3 \rightarrow \quad \begin{bmatrix} 1 & 3 & 5 & -1 \\ 0 & 1 & \frac{7}{5} & -\frac{1}{5} \\ 0 & 0 & \frac{24}{5} & \frac{3}{5} \end{bmatrix}$$

Step 5: Change a_{33} to 1 by multiplying by the reciprocal of a_{33}.

$$\begin{bmatrix} 1 & 3 & 5 & | & -1 \\ 0 & 1 & \frac{7}{5} & | & -\frac{1}{5} \\ 0 & 0 & \frac{24}{5} & | & \frac{3}{5} \end{bmatrix} \quad \frac{5}{24}R_3 \rightarrow \quad \begin{bmatrix} 1 & 3 & 5 & | & -1 \\ 0 & 1 & \frac{7}{5} & | & -\frac{1}{5} \\ 0 & 0 & 1 & | & \frac{1}{8} \end{bmatrix}$$

A row echelon form of the matrix is $\begin{bmatrix} 1 & 3 & 5 & | & -1 \\ 0 & 1 & \frac{7}{5} & | & -\frac{1}{5} \\ 0 & 0 & 1 & | & \frac{1}{8} \end{bmatrix}$.

PROBLEM 6 Write $\begin{bmatrix} 1 & -3 & 2 & | & 1 \\ -4 & 14 & 0 & | & -2 \\ 2 & -5 & -3 & | & 16 \end{bmatrix}$ in row echelon form.

■ **Solution** See page S11.

If an augmented matrix is in row echelon form, the corresponding system of equations can be solved by substitution. For instance, consider the following matrix in row echelon form and the corresponding system of equations.

$$\begin{bmatrix} 1 & -3 & 4 & | & 7 \\ 0 & 1 & 3 & | & -6 \\ 0 & 0 & 1 & | & -1 \end{bmatrix} \qquad \begin{array}{r} x - 3y + 4z = 7 \\ y + 3z = -6 \\ z = -1 \end{array}$$

From the last equation of the system above, we have $z = -1$. Substitute this value into the second equation and solve for y. Thus $y = -3$.

$$\begin{aligned} y + 3z &= -6 \\ y + 3(-1) &= -6 \\ y - 3 &= -6 \\ y &= -3 \end{aligned}$$

Substitute $y = -3$ and $z = -1$ in the first equation of the system and solve for x. Thus $x = 2$.

$$\begin{aligned} x - 3y + 4z &= 7 \\ x - 3(-3) + 4(-1) &= 7 \\ x + 9 - 4 &= 7 \\ x &= 2 \end{aligned}$$

The solution of the system of equations is $(2, -3, -1)$.

The process of solving a system of equations by using elementary row operations is called the **Gaussian elimination method.**

EXAMPLE 7 Solve by using the Gaussian elimination method:
$$\begin{aligned} 2x - 5y &= 19 \\ 3x + 4y &= -6 \end{aligned}$$

Solution Write the augmented matrix and then use elementary row operations to rewrite the matrix in row echelon form.

$$\begin{bmatrix} 2 & -5 & | & 19 \\ 3 & 4 & | & -6 \end{bmatrix} \xrightarrow[\frac{1}{2}R_1]{\text{Change } a_{11} \text{ to } 1.} \begin{bmatrix} 1 & -\frac{5}{2} & | & \frac{19}{2} \\ 3 & 4 & | & -6 \end{bmatrix}$$

• Note that we multiplied R_1 by the reciprocal of a_{11}.

$$\begin{bmatrix} 1 & -\dfrac{5}{2} & \bigg| & \dfrac{19}{2} \\ 3 & 4 & \bigg| & -6 \end{bmatrix} \xrightarrow[\substack{-3R_1 + R_2}]{\text{Change } a_{21} \text{ to } 0.} \begin{bmatrix} 1 & -\dfrac{5}{2} & \bigg| & \dfrac{19}{2} \\ 0 & \dfrac{23}{2} & \bigg| & -\dfrac{69}{2} \end{bmatrix}$$

- Note that we multiplied R_1 by the opposite of a_{21}.

$$\begin{bmatrix} 1 & -\dfrac{5}{2} & \bigg| & \dfrac{19}{2} \\ 0 & \dfrac{23}{2} & \bigg| & -\dfrac{69}{2} \end{bmatrix} \xrightarrow[\substack{\frac{2}{23}R_2}]{\text{Change } a_{22} \text{ to } 1.} \begin{bmatrix} 1 & -\dfrac{5}{2} & \bigg| & \dfrac{19}{2} \\ 0 & 1 & \bigg| & -3 \end{bmatrix}$$

- This is row echelon form.

(1) $x - \dfrac{5}{2}y = \dfrac{19}{2}$

(2) $y = -3$

- Write the system of equations corresponding to the matrix that is in row echelon form.

$$x - \dfrac{5}{2}(-3) = \dfrac{19}{2}$$

$$x + \dfrac{15}{2} = \dfrac{19}{2}$$

$$x = 2$$

- Substitute -3 for y in equation (1) and solve for x.

The solution is $(2, -3)$.

PROBLEM 7   Solve by using the Gaussian elimination method:
$4x - 5y = 17$
$3x + 2y = 7$

Solution   See page S11.

The Gaussian elimination method can be extended to systems of equations with more than two variables.

EXAMPLE 8   Solve by using the Gaussian elimination method:
$x + 2y - z = 9$
$2x - y + 2z = -1$
$-2x + 3y - 2z = 7$

Solution

$$\begin{bmatrix} 1 & 2 & -1 & \big| & 9 \\ 2 & -1 & 2 & \big| & -1 \\ -2 & 3 & -2 & \big| & 7 \end{bmatrix} \xrightarrow[\substack{-2R_1 + R_2}]{\substack{a_{11} \text{ is } 1. \text{ Change} \\ a_{21} \text{ to } 0.}} \begin{bmatrix} 1 & 2 & -1 & \big| & 9 \\ 0 & -5 & 4 & \big| & -19 \\ -2 & 3 & -2 & \big| & 7 \end{bmatrix}$$

$$\begin{bmatrix} 1 & 2 & -1 & \big| & 9 \\ 0 & -5 & 4 & \big| & -19 \\ -2 & 3 & -2 & \big| & 7 \end{bmatrix} \xrightarrow[\substack{2R_1 + R_3}]{\text{Change } a_{31} \text{ to } 0.} \begin{bmatrix} 1 & 2 & -1 & \big| & 9 \\ 0 & -5 & 4 & \big| & -19 \\ 0 & 7 & -4 & \big| & 25 \end{bmatrix}$$

$$\begin{bmatrix} 1 & 2 & -1 & \big| & 9 \\ 0 & -5 & 4 & \big| & -19 \\ 0 & 7 & -4 & \big| & 25 \end{bmatrix} \xrightarrow[\substack{-\frac{1}{5}R_2}]{\text{Change } a_{22} \text{ to } 1.} \begin{bmatrix} 1 & 2 & -1 & \big| & 9 \\ 0 & 1 & -\dfrac{4}{5} & \big| & \dfrac{19}{5} \\ 0 & 7 & -4 & \big| & 25 \end{bmatrix}$$

$$\begin{bmatrix} 1 & 2 & -1 & \big| & 9 \\ 0 & 1 & -\dfrac{4}{5} & \big| & \dfrac{19}{5} \\ 0 & 7 & -4 & \big| & 25 \end{bmatrix} \xrightarrow[\substack{-7R_2 + R_3}]{\text{Change } a_{32} \text{ to } 0.} \begin{bmatrix} 1 & 2 & -1 & \big| & 9 \\ 0 & 1 & -\dfrac{4}{5} & \big| & \dfrac{19}{5} \\ 0 & 0 & \dfrac{8}{5} & \big| & -\dfrac{8}{5} \end{bmatrix}$$

$$\begin{bmatrix} 1 & 2 & -1 & \bigm| & 9 \\ 0 & 1 & -\dfrac{4}{5} & \bigm| & \dfrac{19}{5} \\ 0 & 0 & \dfrac{8}{5} & \bigm| & -\dfrac{8}{5} \end{bmatrix} \xrightarrow[\tfrac{5}{8}R_2]{\text{Change } a_{33} \text{ to } 1.} \begin{bmatrix} 1 & 2 & -1 & \bigm| & 9 \\ 0 & 1 & -\dfrac{4}{5} & \bigm| & \dfrac{19}{5} \\ 0 & 0 & 1 & \bigm| & -1 \end{bmatrix}$$

• **This is row echelon form.**

(1) $x + 2y - z = 9$

(2) $y - \dfrac{4}{5}z = \dfrac{19}{5}$

(3) $z = -1$

• **Write the system of equations corresponding to the matrix that is in row echelon form.**

$$y - \dfrac{4}{5}(-1) = \dfrac{19}{5}$$

$$y + \dfrac{4}{5} = \dfrac{19}{5}$$

$$y = 3$$

• **Substitute** -1 **for** z **in equation (2) and solve for** y.

$$x + 2y - z = 9$$
$$x + 2(3) - (-1) = 9$$
$$x + 7 = 9$$
$$x = 2$$

• **Substitute** -1 **for** z **and** 3 **for** y **in equation (1) and solve for** x.

The solution is $(2, 3, -1)$.

PROBLEM 8   Solve by using the Gaussian elimination method:
$$2x + 3y + 3z = -2$$
$$x + 2y - 3z = 9$$
$$3x - 2y - 4z = 1$$

■ **Solution**   See page S12.

4.3   Concept Review

Determine whether the following statements are always true, sometimes true, or never true.

1. A 3×3 determinant can be evaluated by expanding about any row or column of the matrix.

2. Cramer's Rule can be used to solve a system of linear equations in three variables.

3. A matrix has the same number of rows and columns.

4. Associated with a matrix is a number called its determinant.

5. A system of two linear equations in two variables has no solution, exactly one solution, or infinitely many solutions.

4.3 Exercises

1 Evaluate determinants

For Exercises 1 to 6, use these matrices:

$$A = \begin{bmatrix} -3 & 0 & 1 \\ 2 & 1 & -4 \end{bmatrix} \quad B = \begin{bmatrix} 1 & -1 \\ 5 & 8 \end{bmatrix} \quad C = \begin{bmatrix} 4 & 1 & -7 \\ 0 & -2 & 6 \\ 5 & 0 & -3 \end{bmatrix}$$

1. In matrix B, element b_{21} is ____?____.

2. Matrix A has ____?____ rows and ____?____ columns, so the order of matrix A is ____?____.

3. Because matrix B has the same number of rows as columns, it is called a ____?____ matrix.

4. Only square matrices have determinants. The matrix above that does *not* have a determinant is matrix ____?____.

5. The determinant of matrix B is written $\begin{vmatrix} 1 & -1 \\ 5 & 8 \end{vmatrix}$.

  The value of this determinant is $(1)(\underline{\ ?\ }) - 5(\underline{\ ?\ }) = \underline{\ ?\ }$.

6. For the determinant of matrix C, the minor of 6 is $\begin{vmatrix} \underline{\ ?\ } & \underline{\ ?\ } \\ \underline{\ ?\ } & \underline{\ ?\ } \end{vmatrix}$.

Evaluate the determinant.

7. $\begin{vmatrix} 2 & -1 \\ 3 & 4 \end{vmatrix}$

8. $\begin{vmatrix} 5 & 1 \\ -1 & 2 \end{vmatrix}$

9. $\begin{vmatrix} 6 & -2 \\ -3 & 4 \end{vmatrix}$

10. $\begin{vmatrix} -3 & 5 \\ 1 & 7 \end{vmatrix}$

11. $\begin{vmatrix} 3 & 6 \\ 2 & 4 \end{vmatrix}$

12. $\begin{vmatrix} 5 & -10 \\ 1 & -2 \end{vmatrix}$

13. $\begin{vmatrix} 1 & -1 & 2 \\ 3 & 2 & 1 \\ 1 & 0 & 4 \end{vmatrix}$

14. $\begin{vmatrix} 4 & 1 & 3 \\ 2 & -2 & 1 \\ 3 & 1 & 2 \end{vmatrix}$

15. $\begin{vmatrix} 3 & -1 & 2 \\ 0 & 1 & 2 \\ 3 & 2 & -2 \end{vmatrix}$

16. $\begin{vmatrix} 4 & 5 & -2 \\ 3 & -1 & 5 \\ 2 & 1 & 4 \end{vmatrix}$

17. $\begin{vmatrix} 4 & 2 & 6 \\ -2 & 1 & 1 \\ 2 & 1 & 3 \end{vmatrix}$

18. $\begin{vmatrix} 3 & 6 & -3 \\ 4 & -1 & 6 \\ -1 & -2 & 3 \end{vmatrix}$

2 Solve systems of linear equations by using Cramer's Rule

For Exercises 19 to 22, use this system of equations:
$$2x - 3y = 5$$
$$-5x + 4y = -2$$

19. a. The coefficient determinant for the system is $D = \begin{vmatrix} \underline{\ ?\ } & \underline{\ ?\ } \\ \underline{\ ?\ } & \underline{\ ?\ } \end{vmatrix}$.

  b. The value of the coefficient determinant is $D = \underline{\ ?\ }$.

20. a. The numerator determinant for x is $D_x = \begin{vmatrix} \dfrac{?}{?} & \dfrac{?}{?} \end{vmatrix}$.

b. The value of the numerator determinant for x is $D_x = \underline{\quad ? \quad}$.

21. a. The numerator determinant for y is $D_y = \begin{vmatrix} \dfrac{?}{?} & \dfrac{?}{?} \end{vmatrix}$.

b. The value of the numerator determinant for y is $D_y = \underline{\quad ? \quad}$.

22. Use your answers to Exercises 19b, 20b, and 21b to find the solution of the system of equations

$$2x - 3y = 5$$
$$-5x + 4y = -2.$$

$$x = \frac{D_x}{D} = \frac{?}{?} = \underline{\quad ? \quad} \text{ and}$$

$$y = \frac{D_y}{D} = \frac{?}{?} = \underline{\quad ? \quad}, \text{ so the solution is } (\underline{\quad ? \quad}, \underline{\quad ? \quad}).$$

Solve by using Cramer's Rule, if possible.

23. $2x - 5y = 26$
$5x + 3y = 3$

24. $3x + 7y = 15$
$2x + 5y = 11$

25. $x - 4y = 8$
$3x + 7y = 5$

26. $5x + 2y = -5$
$3x + 4y = 11$

27. $2x + 3y = 4$
$6x - 12y = -5$

28. $5x + 4y = 3$
$15x - 8y = -21$

29. $2x + 5y = 6$
$6x - 2y = 1$

30. $7x + 3y = 4$
$5x - 4y = 9$

31. $-2x + 3y = 7$
$4x - 6y = 9$

32. $9x + 6y = 7$
$3x + 2y = 4$

33. $2x - 5y = -2$
$3x - 7y = -3$

34. $8x + 7y = -3$
$2x + 2y = 5$

35. $2x - y + 3z = 9$
$x + 4y + 4z = 5$
$3x + 2y + 2z = 5$

36. $3x - 2y + z = 2$
$2x + 3y + 2z = -6$
$3x - y + z = 0$

37. $3x - y + z = 11$
$x + 4y - 2z = -12$
$2x + 2y - z = -3$

38. $x + 2y + 3z = 8$
$2x - 3y + z = 5$
$3x - 4y + 2z = 9$

39. $4x - 2y + 6z = 1$
$3x + 4y + 2z = 1$
$2x - y + 3z = 2$

40. $x - 3y + 2z = 1$
$2x + y - 2z = 3$
$3x - 9y + 6z = -3$

41. $5x - 4y + 2z = 4$
$3x - 5y + 3z = -4$
$3x + y - 5z = 12$

42. $2x + 4y + z = 7$
$x + 3y - z = 1$
$3x + 2y - 2z = 5$

3 Solve systems of linear equations by using matrices

For Exercises 43 to 49, use this augmented matrix for a system of three equations in three variables x, y, and z:

$$\begin{bmatrix} 1 & -2 & 3 & | & 2 \\ 2 & -3 & 1 & | & 1 \\ 3 & -1 & 2 & | & 9 \end{bmatrix}$$

43. The elements of the main diagonal of the augmented matrix are ___?___, ___?___, and ___?___.

44. The coefficient of y in the second equation of the system of equations associated with the augmented matrix is ___?___.

45. The constant for the third equation of the system of equations associated with the augmented matrix is ___?___.

46. Write the matrix that results from interchanging rows 2 and 3 of the augmented matrix ($R_2 \leftrightarrow R_3$):

$$\begin{bmatrix} 1 & -2 & 3 & | & 2 \\ ? & ? & ? & | & ? \\ ? & ? & ? & | & ? \end{bmatrix}$$

47. Write the matrix that results from multiplying row 1 of the augmented matrix by -3 ($-3R_1$):

$$\begin{bmatrix} ? & ? & ? & | & ? \\ 2 & -3 & 1 & | & 1 \\ 3 & -1 & 2 & | & 9 \end{bmatrix}$$

48. When the augmented matrix is in row echelon form, all the elements of the main diagonal will be ___?___. All the elements to the left of the main diagonal will be ___?___.

49. A row echelon form of the matrix is shown below. The equation that corresponds to the first row is ___?___. The equation that corresponds to the second row is ___?___. The equation that corresponds to the third row is ___?___.

$$\begin{bmatrix} 1 & -2 & 3 & | & 2 \\ 0 & 1 & -5 & | & -3 \\ 0 & 0 & 1 & | & 1 \end{bmatrix}$$

50. Is the matrix $\begin{bmatrix} 1 & -2 & 3 & | & 1 \\ 0 & 1 & 2 & | & 8 \\ 0 & 1 & 0 & | & 1 \end{bmatrix}$ in row echelon form? Why or why not?

Write each matrix in row echelon form.

51. $\begin{bmatrix} 2 & -4 & | & 1 \\ 3 & -7 & | & -1 \end{bmatrix}$

52. $\begin{bmatrix} 4 & 2 & | & -2 \\ 7 & 4 & | & -1 \end{bmatrix}$

53. $\begin{bmatrix} 5 & -2 & | & 3 \\ -7 & 3 & | & 1 \end{bmatrix}$

54. $\begin{bmatrix} 2 & 5 & | & -4 \\ 3 & 1 & | & 2 \end{bmatrix}$

55. $\begin{bmatrix} 1 & 4 & 1 & | & -2 \\ 3 & 11 & -1 & | & 2 \\ 2 & 3 & 1 & | & 4 \end{bmatrix}$

56. $\begin{bmatrix} 1 & 2 & 2 & | & -1 \\ -4 & -10 & -1 & | & 3 \\ 3 & 4 & 2 & | & -2 \end{bmatrix}$

57. $\begin{bmatrix} -2 & 6 & -1 & | & 3 \\ 1 & -2 & 2 & | & 1 \\ 3 & -6 & 7 & | & 6 \end{bmatrix}$

58. $\begin{bmatrix} 2 & 6 & 10 & 3 \\ 3 & 8 & 15 & 0 \\ 1 & 2 & 3 & -1 \end{bmatrix}$

59. What is the solution of the system of equations that has $\begin{bmatrix} 1 & -1 & 3 & | & -2 \\ 0 & 1 & -1 & | & 1 \\ 0 & 0 & 1 & | & 3 \end{bmatrix}$ as the row echelon form of the augmented matrix for the system of equations?

60. What is the solution of the system of equations that has $\begin{bmatrix} 1 & -3 & 2 & | & 4 \\ 0 & 1 & -2 & | & 3 \\ 0 & 0 & 1 & | & -1 \end{bmatrix}$ as the row echelon form of the augmented matrix for the system of equations?

Solve by using the Gaussian elimination method.

61. $3x + y = 6$
$2x - y = -1$

62. $2x + y = 3$
$x - 4y = 6$

63. $x - 3y = 8$
$3x - y = 0$

64. $2x + 3y = 16$
$x - 4y = -14$

65. $y = 4x - 10$
$2y = 5x - 11$

66. $2y = 4 - 3x$
$y = 1 - 2x$

67. $2x - y = -4$
$y = 2x - 8$

68. $3x - 2y = -8$
$y = \dfrac{3}{2}x - 2$

69. $4x - 3y = -14$
$3x + 4y = 2$

70. $5x + 2y = 3$
$3x + 4y = 13$

71. $5x + 4y + 3z = -9$
$x - 2y + 2z = -6$
$x - y - z = 3$

72. $x - y - z = 0$
$3x - y + 5z = -10$
$x + y - 4z = 12$

73. $5x - 5y + 2z = 8$
$\quad\;\; 2x + 3y - z = 0$
$\quad\quad\;\; x + 2y - z = 0$

74. $2x + y - 5z = 3$
$\quad\;\; 3x + 2y + z = 15$
$\quad\;\; 5x - y - z = 5$

75. $\quad 2x + 3y + z = 5$
$\quad\; 3x + 3y + 3z = 10$
$\quad\; 4x + 6y + 2z = 5$

76. $\quad x - 2y + 3z = 2$
$\quad\; 2x + y + 2z = 5$
$\quad\; 2x - 4y + 6z = -4$

77. $3x + 2y + 3z = 2$
$\quad\;\; 6x - 2y + z = 1$
$\quad\;\; 3x + 4y + 2z = 3$

78. $2x + 3y - 3z = -1$
$\quad\; 2x + 3y + 3z = 3$
$\quad\; 4x - 4y + 3z = 4$

79. $\quad\; 5x - 5y - 5z = 2$
$\quad\;\; 5x + 5y - 5z = 6$
$\quad 10x + 10y + 5z = 3$

80. $3x - 2y + 2z = 5$
$\quad\; 6x + 3y - 4z = -1$
$\quad\; 3x - y + 2z = 4$

81. $4x + 4y - 3z = 3$
$\quad\; 8x + 2y + 3z = 0$
$\quad\; 4x - 4y + 6z = -3$

4.3 Applying Concepts

Solve for x.

82. $\begin{vmatrix} 3 & 2 \\ 4 & x \end{vmatrix} = -11$

83. $\begin{vmatrix} 1 & 0 & 2 \\ 4 & 3 & -1 \\ 0 & 2 & x \end{vmatrix} = -24$

84. $\begin{vmatrix} -2 & 1 & 3 \\ 0 & x & 4 \\ -1 & 2 & -3 \end{vmatrix} = -24$

Complete.

85. If all the elements in one row or one column of a 2×2 matrix are zeros, the value of the determinant of the matrix is _____.

86. If all the elements in one row or one column of a 3×3 matrix are zeros, the value of the determinant of the matrix is _____.

87. a. The value of the determinant $\begin{vmatrix} x & x & a \\ y & y & b \\ z & z & c \end{vmatrix}$ is _____.

  b. If two columns of a 3×3 matrix contain identical elements, the value of the determinant is _____.

88. Show that $\begin{vmatrix} a & b \\ c & d \end{vmatrix} = -\begin{vmatrix} c & d \\ a & b \end{vmatrix}$.

89. **Surveying** Surveyors use a formula to find the area of a plot of land. The *surveyor's area formula* states that if the vertices (x_1, y_1), (x_2, y_2), (x_3, y_3), ..., (x_n, y_n) of a simple polygon are listed counterclockwise around the perimeter, then the area of the polygon is

$$A = \frac{1}{2}\left\{\begin{vmatrix} x_1 & x_2 \\ y_1 & y_2 \end{vmatrix} + \begin{vmatrix} x_2 & x_3 \\ y_2 & y_3 \end{vmatrix} + \begin{vmatrix} x_3 & x_4 \\ y_3 & y_4 \end{vmatrix} + \cdots + \begin{vmatrix} x_n & x_1 \\ y_n & y_1 \end{vmatrix}\right\}$$

Use the surveyor's area formula to find the area of the polygon with vertices $(9, -3)$, $(26, 6)$, $(18, 21)$, $(16, 10)$, and $(1, 11)$. Measurements given are in feet.

90. Consider the system of equations $\begin{array}{l} 3x - 2y = 12 \\ 2x + 5y = -11 \end{array}$. Graph the equations. Now multiply the second equation by 3, add it to the first equation, and replace the second equation by the new equation. What is the new system of equations? Graph the equations of this system on the same coordinate system. The lines intersect at the same point, so the new system of equations is equivalent to the original system. Explain how this is related to the third elementary row operation.

91. Suppose that applying elementary row operations to an augmented

matrix produces the matrix $\begin{bmatrix} 1 & 2 & -3 & | & 5 \\ 0 & 1 & -2 & | & -2 \\ 0 & 0 & 0 & | & -3 \end{bmatrix}$. Explain why the

original system of equations has no solution.

4.4   Application Problems

OBJECTIVE **1**   **Rate-of-wind and water-current problems**

Motion problems that involve an object moving with or against a wind or current normally require two variables to solve.

Solve: A motorboat traveling with the current can go 24 mi in 2 h. Against the current, it takes 3 h to go the same distance. Find the rate of the motorboat in calm water and the rate of the current.

> **STRATEGY**   **for solving rate-of-wind and water-current problems**
>
> ▶ Choose one variable to represent the rate of the object in calm conditions and a second variable to represent the rate of the wind or current. Using these variables, express the rate of the object with and against the wind or current. Use the equation $rt = d$ to write expressions for the distance traveled by the object. The results can be recorded in a table.

Rate of the boat in calm water: x
Rate of the current: y

	Rate	·	Time	=	Distance
With current	$x + y$	·	2	=	$2(x + y)$
Against current	$x - y$	·	3	=	$3(x - y)$

▶ Determine how the expressions for the distance are related.

The distance traveled with the current is 24 mi.
The distance traveled against the current is 24 mi.

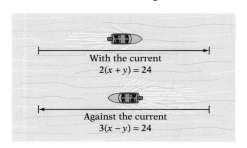

$$2(x + y) = 24$$
$$3(x - y) = 24$$

Solve the system of equations.

$2(x + y) = 24$ ⟶ $\dfrac{1}{2} \cdot 2(x + y) = \dfrac{1}{2} \cdot 24$ ⟶ $x + y = 12$

$3(x - y) = 24$ ⟶ $\dfrac{1}{3} \cdot 3(x - y) = \dfrac{1}{3} \cdot 24$ ⟶ $x - y = 8$

$$2x = 20$$
$$x = 10$$

Replace x by 10 in the equation $x + y = 12$. Solve for y.

$$x + y = 12$$
$$10 + y = 12$$
$$y = 2$$

The rate of the boat in calm water is 10 mph.
The rate of the current is 2 mph.

EXAMPLE 1 Flying with the wind, a plane flew 1000 mi in 5 h. Flying against the wind, the plane could fly only 500 mi in the same amount of time. Find the rate of the plane in calm air and the rate of the wind.

Strategy ▶ Rate of the plane in still air: p
Rate of the wind: w

	Rate	Time	Distance
With wind	$p + w$	5	$5(p + w)$
Against wind	$p - w$	5	$5(p - w)$

▶ The distance traveled with the wind is 1000 mi.
The distance traveled against the wind is 500 mi.

Solution $5(p + w) = 1000$
$5(p - w) = 500$

$p + w = 200$ • **Multiply each side of the equations by $\dfrac{1}{5}$.**
$p - w = 100$

$2p = 300$ • **Add the equations.**
$p = 150$

$$p + w = 200$$
$$150 + w = 200$$
$$w = 50$$

• **Substitute the value of _p_ into one of the equations.**

The rate of the plane in calm air is 150 mph.
The rate of the wind is 50 mph.

PROBLEM 1   A rowing team rowing with the current traveled 18 mi in 2 h. Against the current, the team rowed 10 mi in 2 h. Find the rate of the current.

■ **Solution**   See page S12.

OBJECTIVE 2   ## Application problems

The application problems in this section are varieties of those problems solved earlier in the text. Each of the strategies for the problems in this section will result in a system of equations.

Solve: A store owner purchased twenty 60-watt light bulbs and thirty fluorescent lights for a total cost of $40. A second purchase, at the same prices, included thirty 60-watt bulbs and ten fluorescent lights for a total cost of $25. Find the cost of a 60-watt bulb and of a fluorescent light.

STRATEGY   **for solving an application problem in two variables**

▶ Choose one variable to represent one of the unknown quantities and a second variable to represent the other unknown quantity. Write numerical or variable expressions for all the remaining quantities. These results can be recorded in two tables, one for each of the conditions.

Cost of 60-watt bulb: b
Cost of a fluorescent light: f

First purchase:

	Amount	·	Unit cost	=	Value
60-watt	20	·	b	=	$20b$
Fluorescent	30	·	f	=	$30f$

Second purchase:

	Amount	·	Unit cost	=	Value
60-watt	30	·	b	=	$30b$
Fluorescent	10	·	f	=	$10f$

▶ Determine a system of equations. The strategies presented in Chapter 2 can be used to determine the relationships between the expressions in the tables. Each table will give one equation of the system.

The total of the first purchase was $40. $20b + 30f = 40$
The total of the second purchase was $25. $30b + 10f = 25$

Solve the system of equations.

$20b + 30f = 40$ $\longrightarrow$ $3(20b + 30f) = 3 \cdot 40$ $\longrightarrow$ $60b + 90f = 120$
$30b + 10f = 25$ $-2(30b + 10f) = -2 \cdot 25$ $-60b - 20f = -50$
$$70f = 70$$
$$f = 1$$

Replace f by 1 in the equation $20b + 30f = 40$. $\qquad$ $20b + 30f = 40$
Solve for b. $\qquad$ $20b + 30(1) = 40$
$$20b + 30 = 40$$
$$20b = 10$$
$$b = 0.5$$

The cost of a 60-watt bulb was $.50.
The cost of a fluorescent light was $1.00.

EXAMPLE 2 The total value of the nickels and dimes in a coin bank is $2.50. If the nickels were dimes and the dimes were nickels, the total value of the coins would be $3.05. Find the number of dimes and the number of nickels in the bank.

Strategy ▶ Number of nickels in the bank: n
Number of dimes in the bank: d

Coins in the bank now:

Coin	Number	Value	Total value
Nickels	n	5	$5n$
Dimes	d	10	$10d$

Coins in the bank if the nickels were dimes and the dimes were nickels:

Coin	Number	Value	Total value
Nickels	d	5	$5d$
Dimes	n	10	$10n$

▶ The value of the nickels and dimes in the bank is $2.50.
The value of the nickels and dimes in the bank would be $3.05.

Solution (1) $\quad 5n + 10d = 250$
(2) $\quad 10n + 5d = 305$

$\qquad 10n + 20d = 500$ • **Multiply equation (1) by 2 and equation (2) by −1.**
$\qquad -10n - 5d = -305$
$\qquad\qquad 15d = 195$ • **Add the equations.**
$\qquad\qquad\quad d = 13$

$$5n + 10d = 250$$
$$5n + 10(13) = 250$$
$$5n + 130 = 250$$
$$5n = 120$$
$$n = 24$$

• **Substitute the value of *d* into one of the equations.**

There are 24 nickels and 13 dimes in the bank.

PROBLEM 2   A citrus fruit grower purchased 25 orange trees and 20 grapefruit trees for \$290. The next week, at the same prices, the grower bought 20 orange trees and 30 grapefruit trees for \$330. Find the cost of an orange tree and the cost of a grapefruit tree.

■ **Solution**   See page S12.

Example 3 is an application problem that requires more than two variables. The solution of this problem also illustrates how the substitution method can be used to solve a system of linear equations in three variables.

EXAMPLE 3   An artist is creating a mobile from which three objects will be suspended from a light rod that is 18 in. long as shown at the left. The weight, in ounces, of each object is shown in the diagram. For the mobile to balance, the objects must be positioned so that $w_1d_1 + w_2d_2 = w_3d_3$. The artist wants d_1 to be 1.5 times d_2. Find the distances d_1, d_2, and d_3 so that the mobile will balance.

Strategy   There are three unknowns for this problem. Use the information in the problem to write three equations with d_1, d_2, and d_3 as the variables.

The length of the rod is 18 in. Therefore, $d_1 + d_3 = 18$. Using $w_1d_1 + w_2d_2 = w_3d_3$, we have $2d_1 + 3d_2 = 4d_3$. The artist wants d_1 to be 1.5 times d_2. Thus $d_1 = 1.5d_2$.

Solution   (1) $d_1 + d_3 = 18$
(2) $2d_1 + 3d_2 = 4d_3$
(3) $d_1 = 1.5d_2$

We will solve the system of equations by substitution. Use equation (3) to replace d_1 in equation (1) and in equation (2).

$$1.5d_2 + d_3 = 18$$
$$2(1.5d_2) + 3d_2 = 4d_3$$

(4) $1.5d_2 + d_3 = 18$
(5) $6d_2 = 4d_3$
(6) $1.5d_2 = d_3$ • **Divide each side of equation (5) by 4.**

Replace d_3 by $1.5d_2$ in equation (4) and solve for d_2.

$$1.5d_2 + 1.5d_2 = 18$$
$$3d_2 = 18$$
$$d_2 = 6$$

From equation (6), $d_3 = 1.5d_2 = 1.5(6) = 9$.

Substituting the value of d_3 into equation (1), we have $d_1 = 9$.

The values are $d_1 = 9$ in., $d_2 = 6$ in., and $d_3 = 9$ in.

PROBLEM 3 A science museum charges $10 for an admission ticket, but members receive a discount of $3, and students are admitted for half price. Last Saturday, 750 tickets were sold for a total of $5400. If 20 more student tickets than full-price tickets were sold, how many of each type of ticket were sold?

■ **Solution** See page S13.

4.4 Concept Review

Determine whether the following statements are always true, sometimes true, or never true.

1. The rate of a current in a river is x mph, and the rate of a boat in still water is y mph. The rate of a boat going down the river is $x + y$, and the rate going up the river is $x - y$.

2. The speed of a plane is 500 mph. There is a headwind of 50 mph. The speed of the plane relative to an observer on the ground is 550 mph.

3. A contractor bought 50 yd of nylon carpet for x dollars per yard and bought 100 yd of wool carpet for y dollars per yard. The total cost of the carpet is $50x + 100y$.

4. A coin bank contains nickels and dimes. The total value of the coins is $.70. The bank had 5 dimes and 4 nickels.

4.4 Exercises

1 Rate-of-wind and water-current problems

1. A boat travels down a river for 3 h (traveling with the current), then turns around and takes 5 h to return (traveling against the current). Let b be the rate of the boat, in miles per hour, in calm water and c be the rate of the current, in miles per hour. Complete the following table.

	Rate, r	·	Time, t	=	Distance, d
With current	?	·	?	=	?
Against current	?	·	?	=	?

2. Suppose the distance traveled down the river by the boat in Exercise 1 is 45 mi. Use the expressions in the last column of the table in Exercise 1 to write a system of equations that can be solved to find the rate of the boat in calm water and the rate of the current.

3. ▧ Traveling with the wind, a plane flies m miles in h hours. Traveling against the wind, a plane flies n miles in h hours. Is n less than, equal to, or greater than m?

4. ▧ Traveling against the current, it takes a boat h hours to go m miles. Traveling with the current, the boat takes k hours to go m miles. Is h less than, equal to, or greater than k?

5. Flying with the wind, a small plane flew 320 mi in 2 h. Against the wind, the plane could fly only 280 mi in the same amount of time. Find the rate of the plane in calm air and the rate of the wind.

6. A jet plane flying with the wind went 2100 mi in 4 h. Against the wind, the plane could fly only 1760 mi in the same amount of time. Find the rate of the plane in calm air and the rate of the wind.

7. A cabin cruiser traveling with the current went 48 mi in 3 h. Against the current, it took 4 h to travel the same distance. Find the rate of the cabin cruiser in calm water and the rate of the current.

8. A motorboat traveling with the current went 48 mi in 2 h. Against the current, it took 3 h to travel the same distance. Find the rate of the boat in calm water and the rate of the current.

9. Flying with the wind, a pilot flew 450 mi between two cities in 2.5 h. The return trip against the wind took 3 h. Find the rate of the plane in calm air and the rate of the wind.

10. A turbo-prop plane flying with the wind flew 600 mi in 2 h. Flying against the wind, the plane required 3 h to travel the same distance. Find the rate of the wind and the rate of the plane in calm air.

With the wind
$2(p + w) = 600$

Against the wind
$3(p - w) = 600$

11. A motorboat traveling with the current went 88 km in 4 h. Against the current, the boat could go only 64 km in the same amount of time. Find the rate of the boat in calm water and the rate of the current.

12. A rowing team rowing with the current traveled 18 km in 2 h. Rowing against the current, the team rowed 12 km in the same amount of time. Find the rate of the rowing team in calm water and the rate of the current.

13. A plane flying with a tailwind flew 360 mi in 3 h. Against the wind, the plane required 4 h to fly the same distance. Find the rate of the plane in calm air and the rate of the wind.

14. Flying with the wind, a plane flew 1000 mi in 4 h. Against the wind, the plane required 5 h to fly the same distance. Find the rate of the plane in calm air and the rate of the wind.

15. A motorboat traveling with the current went 54 mi in 3 h. Against the current, it took 3.6 h to travel the same distance. Find the rate of the boat in calm water and the rate of the current.

16. A plane traveling with the wind flew 3625 mi in 6.25 h. Against the wind, the plane required 7.25 h to fly the same distance. Find the rate of the plane in calm air and the rate of the wind.

2   Application problems

17. For one project, a builder buys 200 square feet of hardwood flooring and 300 square feet of wall-to-wall carpet. For another project, a builder buys 350 square feet of hardwood flooring and 100 square feet of wall-to-wall carpet. Let h be the cost per square foot of hardwood flooring and w be the cost per square foot of wall-to-wall carpet. Complete the following tables by replacing the question marks.

First Project	Amount	·	Unit cost	=	Value
Hardwood flooring	?	·	?	=	?
Wall-to-wall carpet	?	·	?	=	?

Second Project	Amount	·	Unit cost	=	Value
Hardwood flooring	?	·	?	=	?
Wall-to-wall carpet	?	·	?	=	?

18. Suppose the builder in Exercise 1 spent $2300 on the flooring and carpet for the first project and $2750 on the flooring and carpet for the second project. Use the expressions in the last column of the tables in Exercise 1 to write a system of equations that can be solved to find the cost per square foot of hardwood flooring and the cost per square foot of wall-to-wall carpet.

Complete Exercises 19 and 20 without actually solving the problems.

19. A coffee merchant mixes 3 lb of dark roast coffee with 1 lb of light roast coffee to create a mixture that cost $6.75 per pound. When he mixes 1 lb of the dark roast coffee with 3 lb of the light roast coffee, the mixture costs $3.50 per pound. Is the cost per pound of the dark roast coffee less than, equal to, or greater than the cost per pound of the light roast coffee?

20. The total value of dimes and quarters in a bank is $2.75. If the dimes were quarters and the quarters were dimes, the total value would be $3.20. Is the number of quarters in the bank less than, equal to, or greater than the number of dimes in the bank?

21. Construction A carpenter purchased 50 ft of redwood and 90 ft of pine for a total cost of $31.20. A second purchase, at the same prices, included

200 ft of redwood and 100 ft of pine for a total cost of $78. Find the cost per foot of redwood and of pine.

22. **Business** A merchant mixed 10 lb of a cinnamon tea with 5 lb of spice tea. The 15-pound mixture cost $40. A second mixture included 12 lb of the cinnamon tea and 8 lb of the spice tea. The 20-pound mixture cost $54. Find the cost per pound of the cinnamon tea and of the spice tea.

23. **Home Economics** During one month, a homeowner used 400 units of electricity and 120 units of gas for a total cost of $147.20. The next month, 350 units of electricity and 200 units of gas were used for a total cost of $144. Find the cost per unit of gas.

24. **Construction** A contractor buys 20 yd^2 of nylon carpet and 28 yd^2 of wool carpet for $1360. A second purchase, at the same prices, includes 15 yd^2 of nylon carpet and 20 yd^2 of wool carpet for $990. Find the cost per square yard of the wool carpet.

25. **Coin Problem** The total value of the quarters and dimes in a coin bank is $6.90. If the quarters were dimes and the dimes were quarters, the total value of the coins would be $7.80. Find the number of quarters in the bank.

26. **Coin Problem** A coin bank contains only nickels and dimes. The total value of the coins in the bank is $2.50. If the nickels were dimes and the dimes were nickels, the total value of the coins would be $3.20. Find the number of nickels in the bank.

27. **Manufacturing** A company manufactures both mountain bikes and trail bikes. The cost of materials for a mountain bike is $70, and the cost of materials for a trail bike is $50. The cost of labor to manufacture a mountain bike is $80, and the cost of labor to manufacture a trail bike is $40. During a week in which the company has budgeted $2500 for materials and $2600 for labor, how many mountain bikes does the company plan to manufacture?

28. **Manufacturing** A company manufactures both liquid crystal display (LCD) and cathode ray tube (CRT) color monitors. The cost of materials for a CRT monitor is $50, whereas the cost of materials for an LCD monitor is $150. The cost of labor to manufacture a CRT monitor is $80, whereas the cost of labor to manufacture an LCD monitor is $130. During a week when the company has budgeted $9600 for materials and $8760 for labor, how many LCD monitors does the company plan to manufacture?

29. **Health Science** A pharmacist has two vitamin-supplement powders. The first powder is 25% vitamin B_1 and 15% vitamin B_2. The second is 15% vitamin B_1 and 20% vitamin B_2. How many milligrams of each of the two powders should the pharmacist use to make a mixture that contains 117.5 mg of vitamin B_1 and 120 mg of vitamin B_2?

30. Chemistry A chemist has two alloys, one of which is 10% gold and 15% lead and the other of which is 30% gold and 40% lead. How many grams of each of the two alloys should be used to make an alloy that contains 60 g of gold and 88 g of lead?

31. Business On Monday, a computer manufacturing company sent out three shipments. The first order, which contained a bill for $114,000, was for 4 Model II, 6 Model VI, and 10 Model IX computers. The second shipment, which contained a bill for $72,000, was for 8 Model II, 3 Model VI, and 5 Model IX computers. The third shipment, which contained a bill for $81,000, was for 2 Model II, 9 Model VI, and 5 Model IX computers. What does the manufacturer charge for a Model VI computer?

32. Health Care A relief organization supplies blankets, cots, and lanterns to victims of fires, floods, and other natural disasters. One week the organization purchased 15 blankets, 5 cots, and 10 lanterns for a total cost of $1250. The next week, at the same prices, the organization purchased 20 blankets, 10 cots, and 15 lanterns for a total cost of $2000. The next week, at the same prices, the organization purchased 10 blankets, 15 cots, and 5 lanterns for a total cost of $1625. Find the cost of one blanket, the cost of one cot, and the cost of one lantern.

33. Investments An investor has a total of $18,000 deposited in three different accounts, which earn annual interest of 9%, 7%, and 5%. The amount deposited in the 9% account is twice the amount in the 5% account. If the three accounts earn total annual interest of $1340, how much money is deposited in each account?

34. Investments An investor has a total of $15,000 deposited in three different accounts, which earn annual interest of 9%, 6%, and 4%. The amount deposited in the 6% account is $2000 more than the amount in the 4% account. If the three accounts earn total annual interest of $980, how much money is deposited in each account?

35. Art A sculptor is creating a mobile from which three objects will be suspended from a light rod that is 15 in. long as shown at the right. The weight, in ounces, of each object is shown in the diagram. For the mobile to balance, the objects must be positioned so that $w_1d_1 = w_2d_2 + w_3d_3$. The artist wants d_3 to be three times d_2. Find the distances d_1, d_2, and d_3 so that the mobile will balance.

36. Art A mobile is made by suspending three objects from a light rod that is 20 in. long as shown at the right. The weight, in ounces, of each object is shown in the diagram. For the mobile to balance, the objects must be positioned so that $w_1d_1 + w_2d_2 = w_3d_3$. The artist wants d_3 to be twice d_2. Find the distances d_1, d_2, and d_3 so that the mobile will balance.

37. Coin Problem A coin bank contains only nickels, dimes, and quarters. The value of the 19 coins in the bank is $2. There are twice as many nickels as dimes. Find the number of each type of coin in the bank.

38. Coin Problem The total value of the nickels, dimes, and quarters in a coin bank is $4. If the nickels were dimes and the dimes were nickels, the total value of the coins would be $3.75. If the quarters were dimes and the dimes were quarters, the total value of the coins would be $6.25. Find the number of nickels, dimes, and quarters in the bank.

39. Investments A financial planner invested $33,000 of a client's money, part at 9%, part at 12%, and the remainder at 8%. The total annual income from these three investments was $3290. The amount invested at 12% was $5000 less than the combined amount invested at 9% and 8%. Find the amount invested at each rate.

40. Education The total number of elementary school students, secondary school students, and students enrolled in colleges in the United States is 71 million. The number enrolled in colleges is equal to the number enrolled in secondary school. The number enrolled in elementary school is 7 million more than the total number of students in secondary schools and colleges. (*Source:* www.infoplease.com) Find the number of students in elementary school, the number in secondary school, and the number enrolled in colleges in the United States.

4.4 Applying Concepts

41. Geometry Two angles are complementary. The larger angle is 9° more than eight times the measure of the smaller angle. Find the measure of the two angles. (Complementary angles are two angles whose sum is 90°.)

42. Geometry Two angles are supplementary. The larger angle is 40° more than three times the measure of the smaller angle. Find the measure of the two angles. (Supplementary angles are two angles whose sum is 180°.)

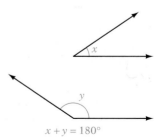

$x + y = 180°$

43. Coin Problem The total value of the nickels, dimes, and quarters in a coin bank is $3.50. If the nickels were dimes and the dimes were nickels, the total value of the coins would be $4.25. If the quarters were dimes and the dimes were quarters, the total value of the coins would be $4.25. Find the number of nickels, dimes, and quarters in the bank.

Solving Systems of Linear Inequalities

OBJECTIVE **1**   **Graph the solution set of a system of linear inequalities**

Two or more inequalities considered together are called a **system of inequalities**. The **solution set of a system of inequalities** is the intersection of the solution sets of the individual inequalities. To graph the solution set of a system of inequalities, first graph the solution set of each inequality. The solution set of the system of inequalities is the region of the plane represented by the intersection of the two shaded areas.

Take Note

You can use a test point to check that the correct region has been denoted as the solution set. We can see from the graph that the point $(2, 4)$ is in the solution set, and as shown below, it is a solution of each inequality in the system. This indicates that the solution set as graphed is correct.

$$2x - y \le 3$$
$$2(2) - (4) \le 3$$
$$0 \le 3 \quad \text{True}$$

$$3x + 2y > 8$$
$$3(2) + 2(4) > 8$$
$$14 > 8 \quad \text{True}$$

■ Graph the solution set: $2x - y \le 3$
$$3x + 2y > 8$$

Solve each equation for y.

$$2x - y \le 3 \qquad\qquad 3x + 2y > 8$$
$$-y \le -2x + 3 \qquad\qquad 2y > -3x + 8$$
$$y \ge 2x - 3 \qquad\qquad y > -\frac{3}{2}x + 4$$

Graph $y = 2x - 3$ as a solid line. Because the inequality is $\ge$, shade above the line.

Graph $y = -\frac{3}{2}x + 4$ as a dashed line. Because the inequality is $>$, shade above the line.

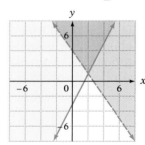

The solution set of the system is the region of the plane represented by the intersection of the solution sets of the individual inequalities.

Point of Interest

Large systems of linear inequalities containing over 100 inequalities have been used to solve application problems in such diverse areas as providing health care and hardening a nuclear missile silo.

■ Graph the solution set: $-x + 2y \ge 4$
$$x - 2y \ge 6$$

Solve each equation for y.

$$-x + 2y \ge 4 \qquad\qquad x - 2y \ge 6$$
$$2y \ge x + 4 \qquad\qquad -2y \ge -x + 6$$
$$y \ge \frac{1}{2}x + 2 \qquad\qquad y \le \frac{1}{2}x - 3$$

Shade above the solid line $y = \frac{1}{2}x + 2$.

Shade below the solid line $y = \frac{1}{2}x - 3$.

Because the solution sets of the two inequalities do not intersect, the solution set of the system is the empty set.

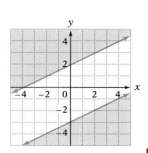

EXAMPLE 1 Graph the solution set.

A. $y \geq x - 1$ **B.** $2x + 3y > 9$
$ y < -2x$ $y < -\dfrac{2}{3}x + 1$

Solution **A.** Shade above the solid line $y = x - 1$.

Shade below the dashed line
$y = -2x$.

The solution set of the system is the
intersection of the solution sets of
the individual inequalities.

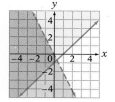

B. Solve $2x + 3y > 9$ for y.

$$2x + 3y > 9$$
$$3y > -2x + 9$$
$$y > -\dfrac{2}{3}x + 3$$

Shade above the dashed line
$y = -\dfrac{2}{3}x + 3$.

Shade below the dashed line
$y = -\dfrac{2}{3}x + 1$.

The intersection of the system is the empty set because
the solution sets of the two inequalities do not intersect.

PROBLEM 1 Graph the solution set.

A. $y \geq 2x - 3$ **B.** $3x + 4y > 12$
$ y > -3x$ $y < \dfrac{3}{4}x - 1$

Solution See page S13.

4.5 Concept Review

Determine whether the following statements are always true, sometimes
true, or never true.

1. The solution set of a system of linear inequalities is an infinite set.

2. The solution set of a system of linear inequalities is the empty set.

3. The solution set of a system of linear inequalities is the intersection of the
solution sets of the individual inequalities.

4.5 Exercises

1 Graph the solution set of a system of linear inequalities

1. Which ordered pair is a solution of the system of inequalities?

$2x - y < 4$
$x - 3y \geq 6$

a. $(5, 1)$ **b.** $(-3, -5)$

2. Which ordered pair is a solution of the system of inequalities?

$3x - 2y \geq 6$
$x + y < 5$

a. $(-2, 3)$ **b.** $(3, -2)$

3. Use the graph showing the four regions of the plane that are determined by the intersecting lines $y = 2x + 2$ and $y = -x + 5$. Complete parts a, b, and c by replacing the question marks with region letters from the graph.
  a. Points in the solution set of the inequality $y \leq 2x + 2$ are located in regions _____?_____ and _____?_____.
  b. Points in the solution set of the inequality $y \geq -x + 5$ are located in regions _____?_____ and _____?_____.
  c. Points in the solution set of the system of inequalities
  $y < 2x + 2$
  $y > -x + 5$
  are located in region _____?_____.

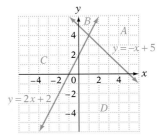

4. Use the graph showing the vertical line through $(2, 0)$ and the horizontal line through $(0, 4)$. Complete parts a and b by replacing the question marks with *greater than* or *less than*.
  a. Points to the right of the vertical line have x-coordinates _____?_____ 2.
  b. Points below the horizontal line have y-coordinates _____?_____ 4.
  c. Write the system of inequalities for which the shaded region is the solution set.

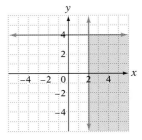

Graph the solution set.

5. $y \leq x - 3$
$y \leq -x + 5$

6. $y > 2x - 4$
$y < -x + 5$

7. $y > 3x - 3$
$y \geq -2x + 2$

8. $y \leq -\dfrac{1}{2}x + 3$
$y \geq x - 3$

9. $2x + y \geq -2$
$6x + 3y \leq 6$

10. $x + y \geq 5$
$3x + 3y \leq 6$

11. $3x - 2y < 6$
$y \leq 3$

12. $x \leq 2$
$3x + 2y > 4$

13. $y > 2x - 6$
$x + y < 0$

14. $x < 3$
$\ y < -2$

15. $x + 1 \geq 0$
$\ y - 3 \leq 0$

16. $5x - 2y \geq 10$
$\ 3x + 2y \geq 6$

17. $2x + y \geq 4$
$\ 3x - 2y < 6$

18. $3x - 4y < 12$
$\ x + 2y < 6$

19. $x - 2y \leq 6$
$\ 2x + 3y \leq 6$

20. $x - 3y > 6$
$\ 2x + y > 5$

21. $x - 2y \leq 4$
$\ 3x + 2y \leq 8$

22. $3x - 2y < 0$
$\ 5x + 3y > 9$

For Exercises 23 to 26, a and b are positive numbers such that $a > b$.
Describe the solution set of each system of inequalities.

23. $x + y < a$
$\ x + y < b$

24. $x + y > a$
$\ x + y < b$

25. $x + y < a$
$\ x + y > b$

26. $x + y > a$
$\ x + y > b$

4.5 Applying Concepts

Graph the solution set.

27. $2x + 3y \leq 15$
$\ 3x - y \leq 6$
$\ \ \ \ \ \ \ y \geq 0$

28. $x + y \leq 6$
$\ x - y \leq 2$
$\ \ \ \ \ x \geq 0$

29. $x - y \leq 5$
$\ 2x - y \geq 6$
$\ \ \ \ \ \ y \geq 0$

30. $x - 3y \leq 6$
$\ 5x - 2y \geq 4$
$\ \ \ \ \ \ \ y \geq 0$

31. $2x - y \leq 4$
$\ 3x + y < 1$
$\ \ \ \ \ \ y \leq 0$

32. $x - y \leq 4$
$\ 2x + 3y > 6$
$\ \ \ \ \ \ x \geq 0$

Focus on Problem Solving

Solve an Easier Problem

 We begin this problem-solving feature with a restatement of the four steps of Polya's recommended problem-solving model.

1. Understand the problem.

2. Devise a plan.

3. Carry out the plan.

4. Review your solution.

One of the several methods of devising a plan is to try to solve an easier problem. Suppose you are in charge of your softball league, which consists of 15 teams. You must devise a schedule in which each team plays every other team once. How many games must be scheduled?

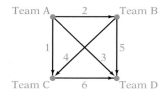

To solve this problem, we will attempt an easier problem first. Suppose that your league contains only a small number of teams. For instance, if there were only 1 team, you would schedule 0 games. If there were 2 teams, you would schedule 1 game. If there were 3 teams, you would schedule 3 games. The diagram at the left shows that 6 games must be scheduled when there are 4 teams in the league.

Here is a table of our results so far. (Remember that making a table is another strategy to be used in problem solving.)

Number of Teams	Number of Games	Possible Pattern
1	0	0
2	1	1
3	3	1 + 2
4	6	1 + 2 + 3

1. Draw a diagram with 5 dots to represent the teams. Draw lines from each dot to a second dot, and determine the number of games required.

2. What is the apparent pattern for the number of games required?

3. Assuming that the pattern continues, how many games must be scheduled for the 15 teams of the original problem?

After solving a problem, good problem solvers ask whether it is possible to solve the problem in a different manner. Here is a possible alternative method of solving the scheduling problem.

Begin with one of the 15 teams (say team A) and ask, "How many games must this team play?" Because there are 14 teams left to play, you must schedule 14 games. Now move to team B. It is already scheduled to play team A, and it does not play itself, so there are 13 teams left for it to play. Consequently, you must schedule 14 + 13 games.

4. Continue this reasoning for the remaining teams and determine the number of games that must be scheduled. Does this answer correspond to the answer you obtained with the first method?

5. Visit **www.allsports.com** to get a listing of the professional sports teams and how they are separated into leagues and divisions. To appreciate how complicated the game schedules can be, try to create a partial schedule where each team in one of the conferences in the National Football League—for instance, the NFC East—plays each other team in that conference twice. An actual schedule would require scheduling an additional eight games for each team in the conference with selected teams in the other conferences.

6. Making connections to other problems you have solved is an important step toward becoming an excellent problem solver. How is the answer to the scheduling of teams related to the triangular numbers discussed in the Focus on Problem Solving in the chapter titled "Linear Functions and Inequalities in Two Variables"?

Projects & Group Activities

Using a Graphing Calculator to Solve a System of Equations

A graphing calculator can be used to solve a system of equations. For this procedure to work on most calculators, it is necessary that the point of intersection be on the screen. This means that you may have to experiment with Xmin, Xmax, Ymin, and Ymax values until the graphs intersect on the screen.

To solve a system of equations graphically, solve each equation for y. Then graph the equations of the system. Their point of intersection is the solution.

For instance, to solve the system of equations

$$4x - 3y = 7$$
$$5x + 4y = 2$$

first solve each equation for y.

$$4x - 3y = 7 \implies y = \frac{4}{3}x - \frac{7}{3}$$

$$5x + 4y = 2 \implies y = -\frac{5}{4}x + \frac{1}{2}$$

The keystrokes needed to solve this system using a TI-83 follow. We are using a viewing window of $[-4.7, 4.7]$ by $[-3.1, 3.1]$. The approximate solution is $(1.096774, -0.870968)$.

| Y= | CLEAR | 4 | X, T, θ, n | ÷ | 3 | − |

7 | ÷ | 3 | ENTER | CLEAR |

(−) | 5 | X, T, θ, n | ÷ | 4 | + | 1 | ÷ |

2 | GRAPH |

Once the calculator has drawn the graphs, use the TRACE feature and move the cursor to the approximate point of intersection. This will give you an approximate solution of the system of equations. A more accurate solution can be found by using the following keystrokes.

2nd | CALC | 5 | ENTER | ENTER | ENTER |

Some of the exercises in the first section of this chapter asked you to solve a system of equations by graphing. Try those exercises again, this time using your graphing calculator.

Chapter 4 Summary

Key Words

Examples

A **system of equations** is two or more equations considered together. A **solution of a system of equations in two variables** is an ordered pair that is a solution of each equation of the system. [4.1.1, p. 223]

The solution of the system
$$x + y = 2$$
$$x - y = 4$$
is the ordered pair $(3, -1)$. $(3, -1)$ is the only ordered pair that is a solution of both equations.

When the graphs of a system of equations intersect at only one point, the system is called an **independent system of equations**. [4.1.1, p. 224]

$3x - 2y = 4$
$5x + 2y = 6$
$8x\ \ \ \ \ = 10$ • **Add the equations.**

When the graphs of a system of equations coincide, the system is called a **dependent system of equations**. [4.1.1, p. 225]

$-3x + 2y = 4$
$3x - 2y = -4$
$0 = 0$ • **Add the equations.**

When the graphs of a system of equations do not intersect, the system has no solution and is called an **inconsistent system of equations**. [4.1.1, p. 224]

$2x - 3y = -2$
$-2x + 3y = 5$
$0 = 3$ • **Add the equations.**

An equation of the form $Ax + By + Cz = D$ is called a **linear equation in three variables**. [4.2.2, p. 235]

$3x + 2y - 5z = 12$ is a linear equation in three variables.

A **solution of a system of equations in three variables** is an ordered triple that is a solution of each equation of the system. [4.2.2, p. 235]

The ordered triple $(1, 2, 1)$ is a solution of the system of equations
$$3x + y - 3z = 2$$
$$-x + 2y + 3z = 6$$
$$2x + 2y - 2z = 4$$

A **matrix** is a rectangular array of numbers. [4.3.1, p. 242]

$\begin{bmatrix} 2 & 3 & 6 \\ -1 & 2 & 4 \end{bmatrix}$ is a 2 × 3 matrix.

A **square matrix** has the same number of rows as columns. [4.3.1, p. 243]

$\begin{bmatrix} 2 & 3 \\ 4 & -1 \end{bmatrix}$ is a square matrix.

A **determinant** is a number associated with a square matrix. [4.3.1, p. 243]

$\begin{vmatrix} 2 & -3 \\ -4 & 5 \end{vmatrix} = 2(5) - (-4)(-3)$
$= 10 - 12$
$= -2$

The **minor of an element** in a 3 × 3 determinant is the 2 × 2 determinant obtained by eliminating the row and column that contain the element. [4.3.1, p. 243]

$$\begin{vmatrix} 2 & 1 & 3 \\ 4 & 6 & 2 \\ 1 & 8 & 3 \end{vmatrix}$$ The minor of 4 is $\begin{vmatrix} 1 & 3 \\ 8 & 3 \end{vmatrix}$.

The **cofactor of an element of a determinant** is $(-1)^{i+j}$ times the minor of the element, where i is the row number of the element and j is its column number. [4.3.1, p. 244]

In the determinant above, 4 is from the second row and the first column. The cofactor of 4 is

$$(-1)^{2+1}\begin{vmatrix} 1 & 3 \\ 8 & 3 \end{vmatrix} = -\begin{vmatrix} 1 & 3 \\ 8 & 3 \end{vmatrix}$$

The evaluation of the determinant of a 3 × 3 or larger matrix is accomplished by **expanding by cofactors**. [4.3.1, p. 244]

Expand by cofactors of the first column.

$$\begin{vmatrix} 2 & 1 & 3 \\ 4 & 6 & 2 \\ 1 & 8 & 3 \end{vmatrix} = 2\begin{vmatrix} 6 & 2 \\ 8 & 3 \end{vmatrix} - 4\begin{vmatrix} 1 & 3 \\ 8 & 3 \end{vmatrix} + 1\begin{vmatrix} 1 & 3 \\ 6 & 2 \end{vmatrix}$$

An **augmented matrix** is one consisting of the coefficients and constants of a system of equations. [4.3.3, p. 248]

The augmented matrix associated with the system

$$4x - 3y + z = 7$$
$$x + y - 5z = 14$$
$$2x + 3z = -4$$

is

$$\begin{bmatrix} 4 & -3 & 1 & | & 7 \\ 1 & 1 & -5 & | & 14 \\ 2 & 0 & 3 & | & -4 \end{bmatrix}$$

The process of solving a system of equations by using elementary row operations is called the **Gaussian elimination method**. [4.3.3, p. 253]

Inequalities considered together are called a **system of inequalities**. The **solution set of a system of inequalities** is the intersection of the solution sets of the individual inequalities. [4.5.1, p. 272]

$$x + y > 3$$
$$x - y > -2$$

Essential Rules and Procedures

A system of equations can be solved by:

a. Graphing [4.1.1, p. 224]

$$y = \frac{1}{2}x + 2$$

$$y = \frac{5}{2}x - 2$$

b. The substitution method [4.1.2, pp. 226–227]

$$\begin{aligned}(1)\quad 2x - 3y &= 4\\ (2)\qquad\quad y &= -x + 2\end{aligned}$$

Substitute the value of y into equation (1).

$$2x - 3(-x + 2) = 4$$

c. The addition method [4.2.1 and 4.2.2, pp. 232, 235]

$$\begin{aligned}-2x + 3y &= 7\\ 2x - 5y &= 2\\ \hline -2y &= 9\qquad\bullet\ \textbf{Add the equations.}\end{aligned}$$

Cramer's Rule [4.3.2, pp. 246, 247]

For two variables: $\begin{aligned}a_{11}x + a_{12}y &= b_1\\ a_{21}x + a_{22}y &= b_2\end{aligned}$

$$x = \frac{D_x}{D}, y = \frac{D_y}{D}, \text{ where } D = \begin{vmatrix}a_{11} & a_{12}\\ a_{21} & a_{22}\end{vmatrix}, D_x = \begin{vmatrix}b_1 & a_{12}\\ b_2 & a_{22}\end{vmatrix},$$

$$D_y = \begin{vmatrix}a_{11} & b_1\\ a_{21} & b_2\end{vmatrix}, \text{ and } D \neq 0.$$

$$\begin{aligned}2x - y &= 6\\ x + 3y &= 4\end{aligned}$$

$$D = \begin{vmatrix}2 & -1\\ 1 & 3\end{vmatrix} = 7, D_x = \begin{vmatrix}6 & -1\\ 4 & 3\end{vmatrix} = 22,$$

$$D_y = \begin{vmatrix}2 & 6\\ 1 & 4\end{vmatrix} = 2$$

$$x = \frac{D_x}{D} = \frac{22}{7}, y = \frac{D_y}{D} = \frac{2}{7}$$

For three variables: $\begin{aligned}a_{11}x + a_{12}y + a_{13}z &= b_1\\ a_{21}x + a_{22}y + a_{23}z &= b_2\\ a_{31}x + a_{32}y + a_{33}z &= b_3\end{aligned}$

$$x = \frac{D_x}{D}, y = \frac{D_y}{D}, \text{ and } z = \frac{D_z}{D}, \text{ where } D = \begin{vmatrix}a_{11} & a_{12} & a_{13}\\ a_{21} & a_{22} & a_{23}\\ a_{31} & a_{32} & a_{33}\end{vmatrix},$$

$$D_x = \begin{vmatrix}b_1 & a_{12} & a_{13}\\ b_2 & a_{22} & a_{23}\\ b_3 & a_{32} & a_{33}\end{vmatrix}, D_y = \begin{vmatrix}a_{11} & b_1 & a_{13}\\ a_{21} & b_2 & a_{23}\\ a_{31} & b_3 & a_{33}\end{vmatrix}, D_z = \begin{vmatrix}a_{11} & a_{12} & b_1\\ a_{21} & a_{22} & b_2\\ a_{31} & a_{32} & b_3\end{vmatrix}, \text{ and }$$

$$D \neq 0$$

$$\begin{aligned}x - y + z &= 2\\ 2x + y - 2z &= -2\\ x - 2y + 3z &= 6\end{aligned}$$

$$D = \begin{vmatrix}1 & -1 & 1\\ 2 & 1 & -2\\ 1 & -2 & 3\end{vmatrix} = 2,$$

$$D_x = \begin{vmatrix}2 & -1 & 1\\ -2 & 1 & -2\\ 6 & -2 & 3\end{vmatrix} = 2,$$

$$D_y = \begin{vmatrix}1 & 2 & 1\\ 2 & -2 & -2\\ 1 & 6 & 3\end{vmatrix} = 4,$$

$$D_z = \begin{vmatrix}1 & -1 & 2\\ 2 & 1 & -2\\ 1 & -2 & 6\end{vmatrix} = 6$$

$$x = \frac{D_x}{D} = \frac{2}{2} = 1, y = \frac{D_y}{D} = \frac{4}{2} = 2,$$

$$z = \frac{D_z}{D} = \frac{6}{2} = 3$$

Elementary row operations to rewrite a matrix in **row echelon form**:
1. Interchange two rows.
2. Multiply all the elements in a row by the same nonzero number.
3. Replace a row by the sum of that row and a multiple of any other row. [4.3.3, p. 249]

$$\begin{bmatrix} 1 & 4 & -2 & 3 \\ 0 & 1 & 3 & -1 \\ 0 & 0 & 1 & 6 \end{bmatrix} \quad \text{Row echelon form}$$

Chapter 4 Review Exercises

1. Solve by substitution: $2x - 6y = 15$
$x = 3y + 8$

2. Solve by substitution: $3x + 12y = 18$
$x + 4y = 6$

3. Solve by the addition method: $3x + 2y = 2$
$x + y = 3$

4. Solve by the addition method: $5x - 15y = 30$
$x - 3y = 6$

5. Solve by the addition method: $3x + y = 13$
$2y + 3z = 5$
$x + 2z = 11$

6. Solve by the addition method:
$3x - 4y - 2z = 17$
$4x - 3y + 5z = 5$
$5x - 5y + 3z = 14$

7. Evaluate the determinant: $\begin{vmatrix} 6 & 1 \\ 2 & 5 \end{vmatrix}$

8. Evaluate the determinant: $\begin{vmatrix} 1 & 5 & -2 \\ -2 & 1 & 4 \\ 4 & 3 & -8 \end{vmatrix}$

9. Solve by using Cramer's Rule: $2x - y = 7$
$3x + 2y = 7$

10. Solve by using Cramer's Rule: $3x - 4y = 10$
$2x + 5y = 15$

11. Solve by using Cramer's Rule: $x + y + z = 0$
$x + 2y + 3z = 5$
$2x + y + 2z = 3$

12. Solve by using Cramer's Rule: $x + 3y + z = 6$
$2x + y - z = 12$
$x + 2y - z = 13$

13. Solve by the addition method: $x - 2y + z = 7$
$3x - z = -1$
$3y + z = 1$

14. Solve by using Cramer's Rule: $3x - 2y = 2$
$-2x + 3y = 1$

15. Solve by using the Gaussian elimination method:
$2x - 2y - 6z = 1$
$4x + 2y + 3z = 1$
$2x - 3y - 3z = 3$

16. Evaluate the determinant: $\begin{vmatrix} 3 & -2 & 5 \\ 4 & 6 & 3 \\ 1 & 2 & 1 \end{vmatrix}$

17. Solve by using Cramer's Rule: $4x - 3y = 17$
$3x - 2y = 12$

18. Solve by using the Gaussian elimination method:
$3x + 2y - z = -1$
$x + 2y + 3z = -1$
$3x + 4y + 6z = 0$

19. Solve by graphing: $x + y = 3$
$3x - 2y = -6$

20. Solve by graphing: $2x - y = 4$
$y = 2x - 4$

21. Graph the solution set: $x + 3y < 6$
$2x - y > 4$

22. Graph the solution set: $2x + 4y \geq 8$
$x + y \leq 3$

23. Uniform Motion   A cabin cruiser traveling with the current went 60 mi in 3 h. Against the current, it took 5 h to travel the same distance. Find the rate of the cabin cruiser in calm water and the rate of the current.

24. Uniform Motion   A plane flying with the wind flew 600 mi in 3 h. Flying against the wind, the plane required 4 h to travel the same distance. Find the rate of the plane in calm air and the rate of the wind.

25. Recreation   At a movie theater, admission tickets are $5 for children and $8 for adults. The receipts for one Friday evening were $2500. The next day there were three times as many children as the preceding evening and only half as many adults as the night before, yet the receipts were still $2500. Find the number of children who attended the movie Friday evening.

26. Investments   An investor has a total of $25,000 deposited in three different accounts, which earn annual interest rates of 8%, 6%, and 4%. The amount deposited in the 8% account is twice the amount in the 6% account. If the three accounts earn total annual interest of $1520, how much money is deposited in each account?

Chapter 4 Test

1. Solve by substitution: $3x + 2y = 4$
$x = 2y - 1$

2. Solve by substitution: $5x + 2y = -23$
$2x + y = -10$

3. Solve by substitution: $y = 3x - 7$
$y = -2x + 3$

4. Solve by using the Gaussian elimination method:
$3x + 4y = -2$
$2x + 5y = 1$

5. Solve by the addition method: $4x - 6y = 5$
$6x - 9y = 4$

6. Solve by the addition method:
$3x - y = 2x + y - 1$
$5x + 2y = y + 6$

7. Solve by the addition method:
$2x + 4y - z = 3$
$x + 2y + z = 5$
$4x + 8y - 2z = 7$

8. Solve by using the Gaussian elimination method:
$x - y - z = 5$
$2x + z = 2$
$3y - 2z = 1$

9. Evaluate the determinant: $\begin{vmatrix} 3 & -1 \\ -2 & 4 \end{vmatrix}$

10. Evaluate the determinant: $\begin{vmatrix} 1 & -2 & 3 \\ 3 & 1 & 1 \\ 2 & -1 & -2 \end{vmatrix}$

11. Solve by using Cramer's Rule: $x - y = 3$
$2x + y = -4$

12. Solve by using Cramer's Rule:
$x - y + z = 2$
$2x - y - z = 1$
$x + 2y - 3z = -4$

13. Solve by using Cramer's Rule:
$3x + 2y + 2z = 2$
$x - 2y - z = 1$
$2x - 3y - 3z = -3$

14. Solve by graphing: $2x - 3y = -6$
$2x - y = 2$

15. Solve by graphing: $x - 2y = -5$
$3x + 4y = -15$

16. Graph the solution set: $2x - y < 3$
$4x + 3y < 11$

17. Graph the solution set: $x + y > 2$
$2x - y < -1$

18. Use a graphing utility to solve the system. Round to the nearest hundredth.
$2x + 3y = 7$
$x - 2y = -5$

19. **Uniform Motion**   A plane flying with the wind went 350 mi in 2 h. The return trip, flying against the wind, took 2.8 h. Find the rate of the plane in calm air and the rate of the wind.

20. **Purchasing**   A clothing manufacturer purchased 60 yd of cotton and 90 yd of wool for a total cost of $1800. Another purchase, at the same prices, included 80 yd of cotton and 20 yd of wool for a total cost of $1000. Find the cost per yard of the cotton and of the wool.

Cumulative Review Exercises

1. Solve: $\dfrac{3}{2}x - \dfrac{3}{8} + \dfrac{1}{4}x = \dfrac{7}{12}x - \dfrac{5}{6}$

2. Find the equation of the line that contains the points $(2, -1)$ and $(3, 4)$.

3. Simplify: $3[x - 2(5 - 2x) - 4x] + 6$

4. Evaluate $a + bc \div 2$ when $a = 4$, $b = 8$, and $c = -2$.

5. Solve: $2x - 3 < 9$ or $5x - 1 < 4$

6. Solve: $|x - 2| - 4 < 2$

7. Solve: $|2x - 3| > 5$

8. Given $f(x) = 3x^3 - 2x^2 + 1$, evaluate $f(-3)$.

9. Find the range of $f(x) = 3x^2 - 2x$ if the domain is $\{-2, -1, 0, 1, 2\}$.

10. Given $F(x) = x^2 - 3$, find $F(2)$.

11. Given $f(x) = 3x - 4$, write $f(2 + h) - f(2)$ in simplest form.

12. Graph: $\{x \,|\, x \leq 2\} \cap \{x \,|\, x > -3\}$

13. Find the equation of the line that contains the point $(-2, 3)$ and has slope $-\dfrac{2}{3}$.

14. Find the equation of the line that contains the point $(-1, 2)$ and is perpendicular to the line $2x - 3y = 7$.

15. Find the distance between the points $(-4, 2)$ and $(2, 0)$.

16. Find the midpoint of the line connecting the points $(-4, 3)$ and $(3, 5)$.

17. Graph $2x - 5y = 10$ by using the slope and y-intercept.

18. Graph the solution set of the inequality $3x - 4y \geq 8$.

19. Solve by substitution: $3x - 2y = 7$
$y = 2x - 1$

20. Solve by the addition method: $3x + 2z = 1$
$2y - z = 1$
$x + 2y = 1$

21. Evaluate the determinant: $\begin{vmatrix} 2 & -5 & 1 \\ 3 & 1 & 2 \\ 6 & -1 & 4 \end{vmatrix}$

22. Solve by graphing: $5x - 2y = 10$
$3x + 2y = 6$

23. Solve by using Cramer's Rule: $4x - 3y = 17$
$3x - 2y = 12$

24. Graph the solution set: $3x - 2y \geq 4$
$x + y < 3$

25. Coins A coin purse contains 40 coins in nickels, dimes, and quarters. There are three times as many dimes as quarters. The total value of the coins is $4.10. How many nickels are in the coin purse?

26. Mixture Problem How many milliliters of pure water must be added to 100 ml of a 4% salt solution to make a 2.5% salt solution?

27. Uniform Motion Flying with the wind, a small plane required 2 h to fly 150 mi. Against the wind, it took 3 h to fly the same distance. Find the rate of the wind.

28. Purchasing A restaurant manager buys 100 lb of hamburger and 50 lb of steak for a total cost of $490. A second purchase, at the same prices, includes 150 lb of hamburger and 100 lb of steak. The total cost is $860. Find the price of one pound of steak.

29. Electronics Find the lower and upper limits of a 12,000-ohm resistor with a 15% tolerance.

30. Compensation The graph below shows the relationship between the monthly income, in dollars, and sales, in thousands of dollars, of an account executive. Find the slope of the line between the two points shown on the graph. Write a sentence that states the meaning of the slope.

CHAPTER

5 Polynomials and Exponents

On May 17, 2002, University of Hawaii astronomers discovered 11 new moons orbiting Jupiter. As telescopes become more powerful and as NASA sends more spacecraft out into the universe, we are able to see faraway objects in more detail. For instance, these new moons of Jupiter are approximately 629,000,000 miles away from Earth. Distances this great are generally expressed in scientific notation, as illustrated in the **Projects and Group Activities on page 363.**

Online Study Center

DVD   SSM

Need help? For online student resources, such as section quizzes, visit the Online Study Center at college.hmco.com/info/aufmanndevmathhb.

Prep Test

1. Simplify: $-4(3y)$

2. Simplify: $(-2)^3$

3. Simplify: $-4a - 8b + 7a$

4. Simplify: $3x - 2[y - 4(x + 1) + 5]$

5. Simplify: $-(x - y)$

6. Write 40 as a product of prime numbers.

7. Find the GCF of 16, 20, and 24.

8. Evaluate $x^3 - 2x^2 + x + 5$ for $x = -2$.

9. Solve: $3x + 1 = 0$

5.1 Exponential Expressions

OBJECTIVE 1 — **Multiply monomials**

Point of Interest

Around A.D. 250, the monomial $3x^2$ shown at the right would have been written *or at least approximately like that. In A.D. 250, the symbol for 3 was not the one we use today.*

A **monomial** is a number, a variable, or a product of a number and variables.

The examples at the right are monomials. The **degree of a monomial** is the sum of the exponents of the variables.

x	degree 1 $(x = x^1)$
$3x^2$	degree 2
$4x^2y$	degree 3
$6x^3y^4z^2$	degree 9
x^n	degree n

The degree of a nonzero constant term is zero.

6	degree 0

The expression $5\sqrt{x}$ is not a monomial because $\sqrt{x}$ cannot be written as a product of variables. The expression $\frac{x}{y}$ is not a monomial because it is a quotient of variables.

The expression x^4 is an exponential expression. The exponent, 4, indicates the number of times the base, x, occurs as a factor.

The product of exponential expressions with the *same* base can be simplified by writing each expression in factored form and writing the result with an exponent.

$$x^3 \cdot x^4 = \overbrace{(x \cdot x \cdot x)}^{3 \text{ factors}} \cdot \overbrace{(x \cdot x \cdot x \cdot x)}^{4 \text{ factors}}$$
$$\underbrace{\qquad\qquad\qquad\qquad}_{7 \text{ factors}}$$
$$= x^7$$

Note that adding the exponents results in the same product.

$$x^3 \cdot x^4 = x^{3+4} = x^7$$

Rule for Multiplying Exponential Expressions

If m and n are positive integers, then $x^m \cdot x^n = x^{m+n}$.

EXAMPLE 1   Simplify: $(5a^2b^4)(2ab^5)$

Solution $(5a^2b^4)(2ab^5)$
$= (5 \cdot 2)(a^2 \cdot a)(b^4 \cdot b^5)$ • Use the Commutative and Associative Properties to rearrange and group factors.

$= 10a^{2+1}b^{4+5}$ • Multiply variables with like bases by adding the exponents.
$= 10a^3b^9$

PROBLEM 1   Simplify: $(7xy^3)(-5x^2y^2)(-xy^2)$

Solution   See page S13.

As shown below, the power of a monomial can be simplified by writing the power in factored form and then using the Rule for Multiplying Exponential Expressions.

Write in factored form. $(a^2)^3 = a^2 \cdot a^2 \cdot a^2$ $(x^3y^4)^2 = (x^3y^4)(x^3y^4)$

Use the Rule for Multiplying Exponential Expressions. $= a^{2+2+2}$ $= x^{3+3}y^{4+4}$
$= a^6$ $= x^6y^8$

It can also be simplified by multiplying each exponent inside the parentheses by the exponent outside the parentheses. $(a^2)^3 = a^{2 \cdot 3} = a^6$ $(x^3y^4)^2 = x^{3 \cdot 2}y^{4 \cdot 2} = x^6y^8$

Rule for Simplifying a Power of an Exponential Expression

If m and n are positive integers, then $(x^m)^n = x^{mn}$.

Rule for Simplifying Powers of Products

If m, n, and p are positive integers, then $(x^my^n)^p = x^{mp}y^{np}$.

EXAMPLE 2   Simplify.

A. $(x^4)^5$ **B.** $(x^2)^n$ **C.** $(2a^3b^4)^3$ **D.** $(2ab)(3a)^2 + 5a(2a^2b)$

Solution   **A.** $(x^4)^5 = x^{4 \cdot 5} = x^{20}$ • Multiply the exponents.

B. $(x^2)^n = x^{2n}$ • Multiply the exponents.

C. $(2a^3b^4)^3 = 2^{1 \cdot 3}a^{3 \cdot 3}b^{4 \cdot 3}$ • Use the Rule for Simplifying Powers of Products.
$= 2^3a^9b^{12}$
$= 8a^9b^{12}$

D. $(2ab)(3a)^2 + 5a(2a^2b) = (2ab)(3^2a^2) + 10a^3b$
$$= (2ab)(9a^2) + 10a^3b$$
$$= 18a^3b + 10a^3b = 28a^3b$$

PROBLEM 2 Simplify.

A. $(y^3)^6$ **B.** $(x^n)^3$ **C.** $(-2ab^3)^4$ **D.** $6a(2a)^2 + 3a(2a^2)$

■ **Solution** See page S13.

OBJECTIVE **2** **Divide monomials and simplify expressions with negative exponents**

The quotient of two exponential expressions with the same base can be simplified by writing each expression in factored form, dividing by common factors, and writing the result with an exponent.

$$\frac{x^5}{x^2} = \frac{\overset{1}{\cancel{x}} \cdot \overset{1}{\cancel{x}} \cdot x \cdot x \cdot x}{\underset{1}{\cancel{x}} \cdot \underset{1}{\cancel{x}}} = x^3$$

Subtracting the exponents gives the same result.

$$\frac{x^5}{x^2} = x^{5-2} = x^3$$

To divide two monomials with the same base, subtract the exponents of the like bases.

Simplify: $\dfrac{z^8}{z^2}$

The bases are the same. Subtract the exponents. $\dfrac{z^8}{z^2} = z^{8-2} = z^6$

Simplify: $\dfrac{a^5b^9}{a^4b}$

Subtract the exponents of the like bases. $\dfrac{a^5b^9}{a^4b} = a^{5-4}b^{9-1} = ab^8$

Consider the expression $\dfrac{x^4}{x^4}$, $x \neq 0$. This expression can be simplified by subtracting exponents or by dividing by common factors.

$$\frac{x^4}{x^4} = x^{4-4} = x^0 \qquad \frac{x^4}{x^4} = \frac{\overset{1}{\cancel{x}} \cdot \overset{1}{\cancel{x}} \cdot \overset{1}{\cancel{x}} \cdot \overset{1}{\cancel{x}}}{\underset{1}{\cancel{x}} \cdot \underset{1}{\cancel{x}} \cdot \underset{1}{\cancel{x}} \cdot \underset{1}{\cancel{x}}} = 1$$

The equations $\dfrac{x^4}{x^4} = x^0$ and $\dfrac{x^4}{x^4} = 1$ suggest the following definition of x^0.

Definition of Zero as an Exponent

If $x \neq 0$, then $x^0 = 1$. The expression 0^0 is not defined.

Take Note

For the example at the right, we indicated that $z \neq 0$. If we try to evaluate $(16z^5)^0$ when $z = 0$, we have $[16(0)^5]^0 = [16(0)]^0 = 0^0$. However, 0^0 is not defined. Therefore, we must assume that $z \neq 0$. To avoid stating this for every example or exercise, we will assume that variables do not have values that result in the expression 0^0.

Point of Interest

In the 15th century, the expression $12\overline{2m}$ was used to mean $12x^{-2}$. The use of $\overline{m}$ reflects an Italian influence, where m was used for minus and p was used for plus. It was understood that $2\overline{m}$ referred to an unnamed variable. Isaac Newton, in the 17th century, advocated the current use of a negative exponent.

Take Note

Note from the example at the right that 2^{-4} is a *positive* number. A negative exponent does not change the sign of a number.

■ Simplify: $(16z^5)^0$, $z \neq 0$

Any nonzero expression to the zero power is 1. $(16z^5)^0 = 1$

■ Simplify: $-(7x^4y^3)^0$

The negative outside the parentheses is not affected by the exponent. $-(7x^4y^3)^0 = -(1) = -1$

Consider the expression $\dfrac{x^4}{x^6}$, $x \neq 0$. This expression can be simplified by subtracting exponents or by dividing by common factors.

$$\frac{x^4}{x^6} = x^{4-6} = x^{-2} \qquad \frac{x^4}{x^6} = \frac{\overset{1}{\cancel{x}} \cdot \overset{1}{\cancel{x}} \cdot \overset{1}{\cancel{x}} \cdot \overset{1}{\cancel{x}}}{\underset{1}{\cancel{x}} \cdot \underset{1}{\cancel{x}} \cdot \underset{1}{\cancel{x}} \cdot \underset{1}{\cancel{x}} \cdot x \cdot x} = \frac{1}{x^2}$$

The equations $\dfrac{x^4}{x^6} = x^{-2}$ and $\dfrac{x^4}{x^6} = \dfrac{1}{x^2}$ suggest that $x^{-2} = \dfrac{1}{x^2}$.

Definition of a Negative Exponent

If $x \neq 0$ and n is a positive integer, then

$$x^{-n} = \frac{1}{x^n} \quad \text{and} \quad \frac{1}{x^{-n}} = x^n$$

■ Evaluate: 2^{-4}

Use the Definition of a Negative Exponent to write the expression with a positive exponent. Then simplify. $2^{-4} = \dfrac{1}{2^4} = \dfrac{1}{16}$

Consider the expression $\left(\dfrac{x^3}{y^4}\right)^2$, $y \neq 0$. This expression can be simplified by squaring $\dfrac{x^3}{y^4}$ or by multiplying each exponent in the quotient by the exponent outside the parentheses.

$$\left(\frac{x^3}{y^4}\right)^2 = \left(\frac{x^3}{y^4}\right)\left(\frac{x^3}{y^4}\right) = \frac{x^3 \cdot x^3}{y^4 \cdot y^4} = \frac{x^{3+3}}{y^{4+4}} = \frac{x^6}{y^8} \qquad \left(\frac{x^3}{y^4}\right)^2 = \frac{x^{3\cdot2}}{y^{4\cdot2}} = \frac{x^6}{y^8}$$

Rule for Simplifying Powers of Quotients

If m, n, and p are integers and $y \neq 0$, then $\left(\dfrac{x^m}{y^n}\right)^p = \dfrac{x^{mp}}{y^{np}}$.

Simplify: $\left(\dfrac{a^2}{b^3}\right)^{-2}$

Use the Rule for Simplifying Powers of Quotients.

$$\left(\dfrac{a^2}{b^3}\right)^{-2} = \dfrac{a^{2(-2)}}{b^{3(-2)}}$$

Use the Definition of a Negative Exponent to write the expression with positive exponents.

$$= \dfrac{a^{-4}}{b^{-6}}$$
$$= \dfrac{b^6}{a^4}$$

An exponential expression is in simplest form when it contains only positive exponents.

Take Note

The exponent on d is -5 (negative 5). The d^{-5} is written in the denominator as d^5. The exponent on 7 is 1 (positive 1). The 7 remains in the numerator.

Also, we indicated that $d \neq 0$. This is done because division by zero is not defined. In this textbook, we will assume that values of the variables are chosen such that division by zero does not occur.

Simplify: $7d^{-5}, d \neq 0$

Use the Definition of a Negative Exponent to rewrite the expression with a positive exponent.

$$7d^{-5} = 7 \cdot \dfrac{1}{d^5} = \dfrac{7}{d^5}$$

Simplify: $\dfrac{2}{5a^{-4}}$

Use the Definition of a Negative Exponent to rewrite the expression with a positive exponent.

$$\left(\dfrac{2}{5a^{-4}}\right) = \dfrac{2}{5} \cdot \dfrac{1}{a^{-4}} = \dfrac{2}{5} \cdot a^4 = \dfrac{2a^4}{5}$$

Now that zero and negative exponents have been defined, a rule for dividing exponential expressions can be stated.

Rules for Dividing Exponential Expressions

If m and n are integers and $x \neq 0$, then $\dfrac{x^m}{x^n} = x^{m-n}$.

Simplify: $\dfrac{x^4}{x^9}$

Use the Rule for Dividing Exponential Expressions. Subtract the exponents, and then use the Definition of a Negative Exponent to rewrite the expression with a positive exponent.

$$\dfrac{x^4}{x^9} = x^{4-9}$$
$$= x^{-5}$$
$$= \dfrac{1}{x^5}$$

The rules for simplifying exponential expressions and powers of exponential expressions are true for all integers. The following rules are restated for convenience.

Rules of Exponents

If m, n, and p are integers, then

$$x^m \cdot x^n = x^{m+n} \qquad\qquad (x^m)^n = x^{mn} \qquad\qquad (x^m y^n)^p = x^{mp} y^{np}$$

$$\frac{x^m}{x^n} = x^{m-n},\ x \neq 0 \qquad \left(\frac{x^m}{y^n}\right)^p = \frac{x^{mp}}{y^{np}},\ y \neq 0 \qquad x^{-n} = \frac{1}{x^n},\ x \neq 0$$

$$x^0 = 1,\ x \neq 0$$

EXAMPLE 3   Simplify.

A. $(3x^2 y^{-3})(6x^{-4} y^5)$ **B.** $\dfrac{x^2 y^{-4}}{x^{-5} y^{-2}}$ **C.** $\left(\dfrac{3a^2 b^{-2} c^{-1}}{27a^{-1} b^2 c^{-4}}\right)^{-2}$

Solution

A. $(3x^2 y^{-3})(6x^{-4} y^5)$

$\quad = 18x^{2+(-4)} y^{-3+5}$

$\quad = 18x^{-2} y^2$

$\quad = \dfrac{18y^2}{x^2}$

- Use the Rule for Multiplying Exponential Expressions.

- Use the Definition of a Negative Exponent to rewrite the expression without negative exponents.

B. $\dfrac{x^2 y^{-4}}{x^{-5} y^{-2}} = x^{2-(-5)} y^{-4-(-2)}$

$\quad = x^7 y^{-2}$

$\quad = \dfrac{x^7}{y^2}$

- Use the Rule for Dividing Exponential Expressions.

- Use the Definition of a Negative Exponent to rewrite the expression without negative exponents.

C. $\left(\dfrac{3a^2 b^{-2} c^{-1}}{27a^{-1} b^2 c^{-4}}\right)^{-2} = \left(\dfrac{a^3 b^{-4} c^3}{9}\right)^{-2}$

$\quad = \dfrac{a^{-6} b^8 c^{-6}}{9^{-2}}$

$\quad = \dfrac{9^2 b^8}{a^6 c^6}$

$\quad = \dfrac{81 b^8}{a^6 c^6}$

- Simplify inside the parentheses by using the Rule for Dividing Exponential Expressions.
- Multiply each exponent inside the parentheses by the exponent outside the parentheses.
- Use the Definition of a Negative Exponent to rewrite the expression without negative exponents.
- Simplify.

PROBLEM 3   Simplify.

A. $(2x^{-5} y)(5x^4 y^{-3})$ **B.** $\dfrac{a^{-1} b^4}{a^{-2} b^{-2}}$ **C.** $\left(\dfrac{2^{-1} x^2 y^{-3}}{4x^{-2} y^{-5}}\right)^{-2}$

Solution   See pages S13–S14.

OBJECTIVE **3**

Scientific notation

**Point
of Interest**

*Astronomers measure the distance
of some stars by using the parsec.
One parsec is approximately
1.92×10^{13} mi.*

Very large and very small numbers are encountered in the fields of science and engineering. For example, the mass of the electron is 0.00000000000000000000000000009 g. Numbers such as this one are difficult to read and write, so a more convenient system for writing them has been developed. It is called **scientific notation.**

To express a number in scientific notation, write the number as the product of a number between 1 and 10 and a power of 10. The form for scientific notation is $a \times 10^n$, where $1 \leq a < 10$ and n is an integer.

Take Note

There are two steps in writing a number in scientific notation: (1) determine the number between 1 and 10, and (2) determine the exponent on 10.

For numbers greater than 10, move the decimal point to the right of the first digit. The exponent n is positive and equal to the number of places the decimal point has been moved.

$$965{,}000 = 9.65 \times 10^5$$
$$3{,}600{,}000 = 3.6 \times 10^6$$
$$92{,}000{,}000{,}000 = 9.2 \times 10^{10}$$

For numbers less than 1, move the decimal point to the right of the first nonzero digit. The exponent n is negative. The absolute value of the exponent is equal to the number of places the decimal point has been moved.

$$0.0002 = 2 \times 10^{-4}$$
$$0.0000000974 = 9.74 \times 10^{-8}$$
$$0.000000000086 = 8.6 \times 10^{-11}$$

EXAMPLE 4   Write 0.000041 in scientific notation.

Solution $0.000041 = 4.1 \times 10^{-5}$ • **The decimal point must be moved 5 places to the right. The exponent is negative.**

PROBLEM 4   Write 942,000,000 in scientific notation.

Solution   See page S14.

Converting a number written in scientific notation to decimal notation requires moving the decimal point.

When the exponent is positive, move the decimal point to the right the same number of places as the exponent.

$$1.32 \times 10^4 = 13{,}200$$
$$1.4 \times 10^8 = 140{,}000{,}000$$

When the exponent is negative, move the decimal point to the left the same number of places as the absolute value of the exponent.

$$1.32 \times 10^{-2} = 0.0132$$
$$1.4 \times 10^{-4} = 0.00014$$

EXAMPLE 5   Write 3.3×10^7 in decimal notation.

Solution $3.3 \times 10^7 = 33{,}000{,}000$ • **Move the decimal point 7 places to the right.**

PROBLEM 5   Write 2.7×10^{-5} in decimal notation.

Solution   See page S14.

Numerical calculations involving numbers that have more digits than a hand-held calculator is able to handle can be performed using scientific notation.

EXAMPLE 6 Simplify: $\dfrac{2{,}400{,}000{,}000 \times 0.0000063}{0.00009 \times 480}$

Solution

$\dfrac{2{,}400{,}000{,}000 \times 0.0000063}{0.00009 \times 480}$

$= \dfrac{2.4 \times 10^9 \times 6.3 \times 10^{-6}}{9 \times 10^{-5} \times 4.8 \times 10^2}$ • **Write the numbers in scientific notation.**

$= \dfrac{(2.4)(6.3) \times 10^{9+(-6)-(-5)-2}}{(9)(4.8)}$ • **Simplify.**

$= 0.35 \times 10^6$

$= 3.5 \times 10^5$ • **Write in scientific notation.**

PROBLEM 6 Simplify: $\dfrac{5{,}600{,}000 \times 0.000000081}{900 \times 0.000000028}$

Solution See page S14.

OBJECTIVE 4 **Application problems**

EXAMPLE 7 How many miles does light travel in 1 day? The speed of light is 186,000 mi/s. Write the answer in scientific notation.

Strategy To find the distance traveled:

▶ Write the speed of light in scientific notation.

▶ Write the number of seconds in 1 day in scientific notation.

▶ Use the equation $d = rt$, where r is the speed of light and t is the number of seconds in 1 day.

Solution $186{,}000 = 1.86 \times 10^5$

$24 \cdot 60 \cdot 60 = 86{,}400 = 8.64 \times 10^4$

$d = rt$
$d = (1.86 \times 10^5)(8.64 \times 10^4)$
$d = 1.86 \times 8.64 \times 10^9$
$d = 16.0704 \times 10^9$
$d = 1.60704 \times 10^{10}$

Light travels 1.60704×10^{10} mi in one day.

PROBLEM 7 A computer can do an arithmetic operation in 1×10^{-7} s. How many arithmetic operations can the computer perform in 1 min? Write the answer in scientific notation.

Solution See page S14.

5.1 Concept Review

Determine whether the following statements are always true, sometimes true, or never true.

1. $2^{-4} = 16$

2. If x is negative, x^{-1} is positive.

3. $(2 + 3)^{-1} = \dfrac{1}{2} + \dfrac{1}{3}$.

4. When multiplying two numbers with the same base, the rule is to multiply the exponents.

5. When adding two numbers with the same base, the rule is to add the exponents.

5.1 Exercises

1 Multiply monomials

1. Of the two expressions $x^4 + y^5$ and x^4y^5, the one that is a monomial is __?__. The degree of this monomial is __?__.

2. a. Use the Rule for Multiplying Exponential Expressions to multiply: $(a^8)(a^5) = $ __?__.
b. Use the Rule for Simplifying a Power of an Exponential Expression to multiply: $(a^8)^5 = $ __?__.
c. Use the Rule for Simplifying Powers of Products to multiply: $(a^8b)^5 = $ __?__.

3. State whether the expression can be simplified using one or more of the rules mentioned in Exercise 2.
a. $(ab)^2$ **b.** $(a + b)^2$ **c.** $(x^2 + y^3)^2$ **d.** $(x^2y^3)^2$

4. a. True or false? $x^3y^4 = xy^{12}$
b. True or false? $x^3y^4 = xy^7$
c. True or false? $(x^3y^4)^2 = x^9y^{16}$
d. True or false? $(x^3 + y^4)^2 = x^6 + y^8$

Simplify.

5. $(ab^3)(a^3b)$ **6.** $(-2ab^4)(-3a^2b^4)$ **7.** $(9xy^2)(-2x^2y^2)$ **8.** $(x^2y)^2$

9. $(x^2y^4)^4$ **10.** $(-2ab^2)^3$ **11.** $(-3x^2y^3)^4$ **12.** $(2^2a^2b^3)^3$

13. $(3^3a^5b^3)^2$ **14.** $(xy)(x^2y)^4$ **15.** $(x^2y^2)(xy^3)^3$ **16.** $[(2x)^4]^2$

17. $[(3x)^3]^2$ **18.** $[(x^2y)^4]^5$ **19.** $[(ab)^3]^6$ **20.** $[(2ab)^3]^2$

21. $[(2xy)^3]^4$ **22.** $[(3x^2y^3)^2]^2$ **23.** $[(2a^4b^3)^3]^2$ **24.** $y^n \cdot y^{2n}$

25. $x^n \cdot x^{n+1}$ **26.** $y^{2n} \cdot y^{4n+1}$ **27.** $y^{3n} \cdot y^{3n-2}$ **28.** $(b^n)^{2n}$

29. $(a^n)^{3n}$ **30.** $(y^{2n})^3$ **31.** $(x^{3n})^5$ **32.** $(b^{2n})^{4n}$

33. $(2xy)(-3x^2yz)(x^2y^3z^3)$

34. $(x^2z^4)(2xyz^4)(-3x^3y^2)$

35. $(3b^5)(2ab^2)(-2ab^2c^2)$

36. $(-c^3)(-2a^2bc)(3a^2b)$

37. $(-2x^2y^3z)(3x^2yz^4)$

38. $(2a^2b)^3(-3ab^4)^2$

39. $(-3ab^3)^3(-2^2a^2b)^2$

40. $(4ab)^2(-2ab^2c^3)^3$

41. $(-2ab^2)(-3a^4b^5)^3$

2 Divide monomials and simplify expressions with negative exponents

42. Explain how to divide two exponential expressions with the same base.

43. If a variable has a negative exponent, how can you rewrite it with a positive exponent?

44. As long as x is not zero, x^0 is defined to be equal to ____?____. Using this definition, $5^0 =$ ____?____, $(2x^2)^0 =$ ____?____, and $-4x^0 =$ ____?____.

45. Simplify $\left(\dfrac{a^{-3}}{a^5}\right)^2$

$\left(\dfrac{a^{-3}}{a^5}\right)^2 = ($ __?__ $)^2$ • **The bases inside the parentheses are the same. Subtract the exponents.**

$\quad = $ __?__ • **Multiply the exponent inside the parentheses by the exponent outside the parentheses.**

$\quad = $ __?__ • **Use the Definition of a Negative Exponent to rewrite the expression with a positive exponent.**

Simplify.

46. $\dfrac{x^3}{x^{12}}$

47. $\dfrac{a^8}{a^5}$

48. $\dfrac{x^3y^6}{x^3y^3}$

49. $\dfrac{a^7b}{a^2b^4}$

50. 2^{-3}

51. $\dfrac{1}{3^{-5}}$

52. $\dfrac{1}{x^{-4}}$

53. $\dfrac{1}{y^{-3}}$

54. $\dfrac{2x^{-2}}{y^4}$

55. $\dfrac{a^3}{4b^{-2}}$

56. $x^{-4}x^4$

57. $x^{-3}x^{-5}$

58. $(3x^{-2})^2$

59. $(5x^2)^{-3}$

60. $\dfrac{x^{-3}}{x^2}$

61. $\dfrac{x^4}{x^{-5}}$

62. $a^{-2} \cdot a^4$

63. $a^{-5} \cdot a^7$

64. $(x^2y^{-4})^2$

65. $(x^3y^5)^{-2}$

66. $(2a^{-1})^{-2}(2a^{-1})^4$

67. $(3a)^{-3}(9a^{-1})^{-2}$

68. $(x^{-2}y)^2(xy)^{-2}$

69. $(x^{-1}y^2)^{-3}(x^2y^{-4})^{-3}$

70. $\dfrac{6^2a^{-2}b^3}{3ab^4}$

71. $\left(\dfrac{x^2y^{-1}}{xy}\right)^{-4}$

72. $\dfrac{-48ab^{10}}{32a^4b^3}$

73. $\dfrac{a^2b^3c^7}{a^6bc^5}$

74. $\dfrac{(-4x^2y^3)^2}{(2xy^2)^3}$

75. $\dfrac{(-3a^2b^3)^2}{(-2ab^4)^3}$

76. $\left(\dfrac{x^{-3}y^{-4}}{x^{-2}y}\right)^{-2}$

77. $\left(\dfrac{a^{-2}b}{a^3b^{-4}}\right)^2$

78. $\dfrac{-x^{5n}}{x^{2n}}$ **79.** $\dfrac{y^{2n}}{-y^{8n}}$ **80.** $\dfrac{a^{3n-2}b^{n+1}}{a^{2n+1}b^{2n+2}}$ **81.** $\dfrac{x^{2n-1}y^{n-3}}{x^{n+4}y^{n+3}}$

82. $\dfrac{(2a^{-3}b^{-2})^3}{(a^{-4}b^{-1})^{-2}}$ **83.** $\dfrac{(3x^{-2}y)^{-2}}{(4xy^{-2})^{-1}}$ **84.** $\left(\dfrac{4^{-2}xy^{-3}}{x^{-3}y}\right)^3\left(\dfrac{8^{-1}x^{-2}y}{x^4y^{-1}}\right)^{-2}$ **85.** $\left(\dfrac{9ab^{-2}}{8a^{-2}b}\right)^{-2}\left(\dfrac{3a^{-2}b}{2a^2b^{-2}}\right)^3$

86. $[(xy^{-2})^3]^{-2}$ **87.** $[(x^{-2}y^{-1})^2]^{-3}$ **88.** $\left[\left(\dfrac{x}{y^2}\right)^{-2}\right]^3$ **89.** $\left[\left(\dfrac{a^2}{b}\right)^{-1}\right]^2$

90. True or false?
   a. $\left(\dfrac{a}{b}\right)^{-1}=\dfrac{b}{a}$ **b.** $(a-b)^{-1}=\dfrac{1}{a}-\dfrac{1}{b}$

91. True or false?
   a. $\dfrac{a^n}{b^m}=\left(\dfrac{a}{b}\right)^{n-m}$ **b.** $\dfrac{a^n}{a^m}=a^{n-m}$

3 Scientific notation

92. A number is in scientific notation if it is written as the product of a number between ___?___ and ___?___ and a power of ___?___.

93. To write the number 0.00000078 in scientific notation, move the decimal point ___?___ places to the ___?___. This means the exponent on 10 is ___?___.

Write in scientific notation.

94. 0.00000467 **95.** 0.00000005 **96.** 0.00000000017

97. 4,300,000 **98.** 200,000,000,000 **99.** 9,800,000,000

Write in decimal notation.

100. 1.23×10^{-7} **101.** 6.2×10^{-12} **102.** 8.2×10^{15}

103. 6.34×10^5 **104.** 3.9×10^{-2} **105.** 4.35×10^9

Simplify. Write the answer in scientific notation.

106. $(3\times10^{-12})(5\times10^{16})$ **107.** $(8.9\times10^{-5})(3.2\times10^{-6})$

108. $(0.0000065)(3,200,000,000,000)$ **109.** $(480,000)(0.0000000096)$

110. $\dfrac{9\times10^{-3}}{6\times10^5}$ **111.** $\dfrac{2.7\times10^4}{3\times10^{-6}}$ **112.** $\dfrac{0.0089}{500,000,000}$

113. $\dfrac{4800}{0.00000024}$ **114.** $\dfrac{0.00056}{0.000000000004}$ **115.** $\dfrac{0.000000346}{0.0000005}$

116. $\dfrac{(3.2 \times 10^{-11})(2.9 \times 10^{15})}{8.1 \times 10^{-3}}$

117. $\dfrac{(6.9 \times 10^{27})(8.2 \times 10^{-13})}{4.1 \times 10^{15}}$

118. $\dfrac{(0.00000004)(84,000)}{(0.0003)(1,400,000)}$

119. $\dfrac{(720)(0.0000000039)}{(26,000,000,000)(0.018)}$

For Exercises 120 and 121, $a \times 10^n$ and $b \times 10^m$ are numbers written in scientific notation. State whether the expression is greater than or less than one.

120. $\dfrac{(a \times 10^n)}{(b \times 10^m)}$, where $n > m$

121. $(a \times 10^n)(b \times 10^m)$, where $n < 0$ and $m < 0$

4 Application problems

122. Write the number of seconds in 5 h in scientific notation:

$$5\text{ h} = (5\text{ h})(\underline{\quad?\quad}\text{ min/h})(\underline{\quad?\quad}\text{ s/min})$$
$$= \underline{\quad?\quad}\text{ s}$$
$$= 1.8 \times 10^{\underline{\;?\;}}.$$

123. The speed of light is 3×10^5 km/s. Use your answer to Exercise 122 to find how many kilometers light travels in 5 h:

$$d = (3 \times 10^5)(1.8 \times 10^4) = \underline{\quad?\quad} \times 10^{\underline{\;?\;}}\text{ km}$$

Solve. Write the answer in scientific notation.

124. Computer Science A computer can do an arithmetic operation in 5×10^{-7} s. How many arithmetic operations can the computer perform in 1 h?

125. Computer Science A computer can do an arithmetic operation in 2×10^{-9} s. How many arithmetic operations can the computer perform in 1 min?

126. Physics How many meters does light travel in 8 h? The speed of light is 3×10^8 m/s.

127. Physics How many meters does light travel in 1 day? The speed of light is 3×10^8 m/s.

128. Physics A high-speed centrifuge makes 4×10^8 revolutions each minute. Find the time in seconds for the centrifuge to make one revolution.

129. Physics The mass of an electron is 9.109×10^{-31} kg. The mass of a proton is 1.673×10^{-27} kg. How many times heavier is a proton than an electron?

130. **Geology** The mass of Earth is 5.9×10^{24} kg. The mass of the sun is 2×10^{30} kg. How many times heavier is the sun than Earth?

131. **Astronomy** It took 11 min for the commands from a computer on Earth to travel to the rover Sojourner on Mars, a distance of 119 million miles. How fast did the signals from Earth to Mars travel? Write the answer in scientific notation.

132. **Astronomy** How long does it take light to travel to Earth from the sun? The sun is 9.3×10^{7} mi from Earth, and light travels 1.86×10^{5} mi/s.

133. **Measurement** The weight of 31 million orchid seeds is 1 oz. Find the weight of one orchid seed.

134. **The Federal Government** In 2005, the gross national debt was approximately 8.1×10^{12} dollars. How much would each American have to pay in order to pay off the debt? Use 3×10^{8} as the number of citizens.

135. **Astronomy** The distance to Saturn is 8.86×10^{8} mi. A satellite leaves Earth traveling at a constant rate of 1×10^{5} mph. How long does it take for the satellite to reach Saturn?

136. **Astronomy** The diameter of Neptune is 3×10^{4} mi. Use the formula $SA = 4\pi r^2$ to find the surface area of Neptune in square miles.

137. **Biology** The radius of a cell is 1.5×10^{-4} mm. Use the formula $V = \frac{4}{3}\pi r^3$ to find the volume of the cell.

138. **Chemistry** One gram of hydrogen contains 6.023×10^{23} atoms. Find the weight of one atom of hydrogen.

139. **Astronomy** Our galaxy is estimated to be 5.6×10^{19} mi across. How long (in hours) would it take a space ship to cross the galaxy traveling at 25,000 mph?

5.1 Applying Concepts

State whether or not the expression is a sum of monomials.

140. $\frac{1}{3}x + 1$

141. $\frac{3}{x} + 1$

142. $5\sqrt{x} + 2$

143. $\sqrt{5}x + 2$

144. $\frac{1}{4y^2} + \frac{1}{3y}$

145. $x + \sqrt{3}$

For what value of k is the given equation an identity?

146. $(2x^3 + 3x^2 + kx + 5) - (x^3 + x^2 - 5x - 2) = x^3 + 2x^2 + 3x + 7$

147. $(6x^3 + kx^2 - 2x - 1) - (4x^3 - 3x^2 + 1) = 2x^3 - x^2 - 2x - 2$

Solve.

148. Geometry The width of a rectangle is x^n. The length of the rectangle is $3x^n$. Find the perimeter of the rectangle in terms of x^n.

149. Geometry The base of an isosceles triangle is $4x^n$. The length of each of the equal sides is $3x^n$. Find the perimeter of the triangle in terms of x^n.

150. Geometry The width of a rectangle is $4ab$. The length is $6ab$. Find the area of the rectangle in terms of a and b.

151. Geometry The height of a triangle is $5xy$. The length of the base of the triangle is $8xy$. Find the area of the triangle in terms of x and y.

Simplify.

152. $\dfrac{4m^4}{n^{-2}} + \left(\dfrac{n^{-1}}{m^2}\right)^{-2}$

153. $\dfrac{5x^3}{y^{-6}} + \left(\dfrac{x^{-1}}{y^2}\right)^{-3}$

154. $\left(\dfrac{3a^{-2}b}{a^{-4}b^{-1}}\right)^2 \div \left(\dfrac{a^{-1}b}{9a^2b^3}\right)^{-1}$

155. $\left(\dfrac{2m^3n^{-2}}{4m^4n}\right)^{-2} \div \left(\dfrac{mn^5}{m^{-1}n^3}\right)^3$

Solve.

156. Use the expressions $(2 + 3)^{-2}$ and $2^{-2} + 3^{-2}$ to show that $(x + y)^{-2} \neq x^{-2} + y^{-2}$.

157. If a and b are real nonzero numbers and $a < b$, is $a^{-1} < b^{-1}$ always a false statement?

158. Correct the error in the following expressions. Explain which rule or property was used incorrectly.
  a. $2x + 3x = 5x^2$
  b. $a - (b - c) = a - b - c$
  c. $x^0 = 0$
  d. $(x^4)^5 = x^9$
  e. $x^2 \cdot x^3 = x^6$
  f. $b^{m+n} = b^m + b^n$

5.2   Introduction to Polynomials

**OBJECTIVE **   ### Evaluate polynomial functions

A **polynomial** is a variable expression in which the terms are monomials.

A polynomial of one term is a **monomial.** $5x$

A polynomial of two terms is a **binomial.** $5x^2y + 6x$

A polynomial of three terms is a **trinomial.** $3x^2 + 9xy - 5y$

Polynomials with more than three terms do not have special names.

The **degree of a polynomial** is the greatest of the degrees of any of its terms.

$3x + 2$	degree 1
$3x^2 + 2x - 4$	degree 2
$4x^3y^2 + 6x^4$	degree 5
$3x^{2n} - 5x^n - 2$	degree $2n$

The terms of a polynomial in one variable are usually arranged so that the exponents of the variable decrease from left to right. This is called **descending order.**

$2x^2 - x + 8$

$3y^3 - 3y^2 + y - 12$

For a polynomial in more than one variable, "descending order" may refer to any one of the variables.

The polynomial at the right is shown first in descending order of the x variable and then in descending order of the y variable.

$2x^2 + 3xy + 5y^2$

$5y^2 + 3xy + 2x^2$

The **linear function** given by $f(x) = mx + b$ is an example of a polynomial function. It is a polynomial function of degree one. A second-degree polynomial function, called a **quadratic function,** is given by the equation $f(x) = ax^2 + bx + c$, $a \neq 0$. A third-degree polynomial function is called a **cubic function.** In general, a **polynomial function** is an expression whose terms are monomials.

To **evaluate a polynomial function**, replace the variable by its value and simplify.

Given $P(x) = x^3 - 3x^2 + 4$, evaluate $P(-3)$.

Substitute -3 for x and simplify.

$$P(x) = x^3 - 3x^2 + 4$$
$$P(-3) = (-3)^3 - 3(-3)^2 + 4$$
$$P(-3) = -27 - 27 + 4$$
$$P(-3) = -50$$

EXAMPLE 1   To overcome the resistance of the wind and the tires on the road, the horsepower (hp), P, required by a cyclist to keep a certain bicycle moving at v mph is given by $P(v) = 0.00003v^3 + 0.00211v$. How much horsepower must the cyclist supply to keep this bicycle moving at 20 mph?

Strategy   To find the horsepower, evaluate the function when $v = 20$.

Solution $P(v) = 0.00003v^3 + 0.00211v$
$P(20) = 0.00003(20)^3 + 0.00211(20)$ • **Replace *v* by 20.**
$= 0.2822$ •   **Simplify.**

The cyclist must supply 0.2822 hp.

PROBLEM 1   The velocity of air that is expelled during a cough can be modeled by $v(r) = 600r^2 - 1000r^3$, where v is the velocity of the air in centimeters per second and r is the radius of the trachea in centimeters. What is the velocity of expelled air during a cough when the radius of the trachea is 0.4 cm?

Solution   See page S14.

The **leading coefficient** of a polynomial function is the coefficient of the variable with the largest exponent. The constant term is the term without a variable.

Find the leading coefficient, the constant term, and the degree of the polynomial function $P(x) = 7x^4 - 3x^2 + 2x - 4$.

The leading coefficient is 7, the constant term is -4, and the degree is 4.

EXAMPLE 2   Find the leading coefficient, the constant term, and the degree of the polynomial $P(x) = 5x^6 - 4x^5 - 3x^2 + 7$.

Solution   The leading coefficient is 5, the constant term is 7, and the degree is 6.

PROBLEM 2   Find the leading coefficient, the constant term, and the degree of the polynomial $R(x) = -3x^4 + 3x^3 + 3x^2 - 2x - 12$.

Solution   See page S14.

The following three functions do not represent polynomial functions.

$f(x) = 3x^2 + 2x^{-1}$ A polynomial function does not have a variable raised to a negative power.

$g(x) = 2\sqrt{x} - 3$ A polynomial function does not have a variable expression within a radical.

$h(x) = \dfrac{x}{x - 1}$ A polynomial function does not have a variable in the denominator of a fraction.

EXAMPLE 3   State whether the function is a polynomial function.
A. $P(x) = 3x^{1/2} + 2x^2 - 3$ **B.** $T(x) = 3\sqrt{x} - 2x^2 - 3x + 2$
C. $R(x) = 14x^3 - \pi x^2 + 3x + 2$

Solution   **A.** This is not a polynomial function. A polynomial function does not have a variable raised to a fractional power.

B. This is not a polynomial function. A polynomial function does not have a variable expression within a radical.

C. This is a polynomial function.

PROBLEM 3   State whether the function is a polynomial function.

A. $R(x) = 5x^{14} - 5$ **B.** $V(x) = -x^{-1} + 2x - 7$
C. $P(x) = 2x - 2\sqrt{x} - 3$

Solution   See page S14.

The graph of a linear function is a straight line and can be found by plotting just two points. The graph of a polynomial function of degree greater than one is a curve. Consequently, many points may have to be found before an accurate graph can be drawn.

Evaluating the quadratic function given by the equation $f(x) = x^2 - x - 6$ when $x = -3, -2, -1, 0, 1, 2, 3,$ and 4 gives the points shown in Figure 1. For instance, $f(-3) = 6$, so $(-3, 6)$ is graphed; $f(2) = -4$, so $(2, -4)$ is graphed; and $f(4) = 6$, so $(4, 6)$ is graphed. Evaluating the function when x is not an integer, such as $x = -\dfrac{3}{2}$ and $x = \dfrac{5}{2}$, produces more points to graph, as shown in Figure 2. Connecting the points with a smooth curve results in Figure 3, which is the graph of f.

Figure 1

Figure 2

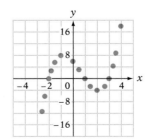

Figure 3

Here is an example of graphing a cubic function, $P(x) = x^3 - 2x^2 - 5x + 6$. Evaluating the function when $x = -2, -1, 0, 1, 2, 3,$ and 4 gives the graph in Figure 4. Evaluating at some noninteger values gives the graph in Figure 5. Finally, connecting the dots with a smooth curve gives the graph in Figure 6.

Figure 4

Figure 5

Figure 6

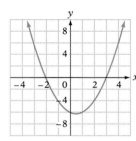

The graphs of
$f(x) = x^2 - x - 6$
(Figure 3) and
$P(x) = x^3 - 2x^2 - 5x + 6$
(Figure 6) are repeated at
right. Note that by the
vertical line test, these
graphs are graphs of
functions.

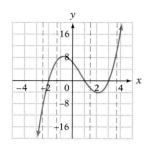

Recall that the domain of a function is the set of first coordinates of the ordered
pairs of a function. Because a polynomial function can be evaluated for any real
number, the domain of a polynomial function is the set of real numbers.

EXAMPLE 4   Graph: $f(x) = x^2 - 2$

Solution

x	$y = f(x)$
-3	7
-2	2
-1	-1
0	-2
1	-1
2	2
3	7

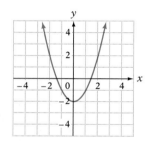

PROBLEM 4   Graph: $f(x) = x^2 - 2x$

Solution   See page S14.

EXAMPLE 5   Graph: $f(x) = x^3 - 1$

Solution

x	$y = f(x)$
-2	-9
-1	-2
0	-1
1	0
2	7

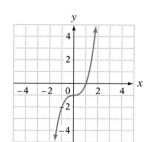

PROBLEM 5   Graph: $F(x) = -x^3 + 1$

Solution   See page S14.

It may be necessary to plot a large number of points before drawing the graph in Example 5. Graphing calculators create graphs by plotting a large number of points and then connecting the points to form a curve. Using a graphing calculator, enter the equation $y = x^3 - 1$. Graph the equation using XMIN = -4.7, XMAX = 4.7, YMIN = -10, YMAX = 10. Now use the TRACE feature to move around the graph and verify that $(-2, -9)$, $(-1, -2)$, $(0, -1)$, $(1, 0)$, and $(2, -7)$ are the coordinates of points on the graph. Follow the same procedure for Problem 5. The point $(2, -7)$ is shown on the graph. For assistance, refer to the Appendix Keystroke Guide.

OBJECTIVE 2   Add or subtract polynomials

Polynomials can be added by combining like terms. Either a vertical or a horizontal format can be used.

Add $(3x^2 + 2x - 7) + (7x^3 - 3 + 4x^2)$. Use a horizontal format.

Use the Commutative and Associative Properties of Addition to rearrange and group like terms.	$(3x^2 + 2x - 7) + (7x^3 - 3 + 4x^2)$ $= 7x^3 + (3x^2 + 4x^2) + 2x + (-7 - 3)$
Combine like terms.	$= 7x^3 + 7x^2 + 2x - 10$

Add $(4x^2 + 5x - 3) + (7x^3 - 7x + 1) + (2x - 3x^2 + 4x^3 + 1)$. Use a vertical format.

Arrange the terms of each polynomial in descending order with like terms in the same column. Add the terms in each column.

$$
\begin{array}{r}
4x^2 + 5x - 3 \\
7x^3 - 7x + 1 \\
4x^3 - 3x^2 + 2x + 1 \\
\hline
11x^3 + x^2 - 1
\end{array}
$$

The additive inverse of the polynomial $x^2 + 5x - 4$ is $-(x^2 + 5x - 4)$.

Take Note

This is the same definition used for subtraction of integers: Subtraction is addition of the opposite.

To simplify the additive inverse of a polynomial, change the sign of every term inside the parentheses.

$$-(x^2 + 5x - 4) = -x^2 - 5x + 4$$

To subtract two polynomials, add the additive inverse of the second polynomial to the first.

Subtract $(3x^2 - 7xy + y^2) - (-4x^2 + 7xy - 3y^2)$. Use a horizontal format.

Rewrite the subtraction as the addition of the additive inverse.

$$(3x^2 - 7xy + y^2) - (-4x^2 + 7xy - 3y^2)$$
$$= (3x^2 - 7xy + y^2) + (4x^2 - 7xy + 3y^2)$$

Combine like terms.

$$= 7x^2 - 14xy + 4y^2$$

Subtract $(6x^3 - 3x + 7) - (3x^2 - 5x + 12)$. Use a vertical format.

Rewrite the subtraction as the addition of the additive inverse.

$$(6x^3 - 3x + 7) - (3x^2 - 5x + 12)$$
$$= (6x^3 - 3x + 7) + (-3x^2 + 5x - 12)$$

Arrange the terms of each polynomial in descending order with like terms in the same column. Add the terms in each column.

$$\begin{array}{r} 6x^3 \qquad - 3x + 7 \\ - 3x^2 + 5x - 12 \\ \hline 6x^3 - 3x^2 + 2x - 5 \end{array}$$

EXAMPLE 6 Add: $(3x^2 - 2x + 5) + (2 - 3x + 4x^3) + (x - 3x^2 - x^3 - 4)$
Use a vertical format.

Solution

$$\begin{array}{r} 3x^2 - 2x + 5 \\ 4x^3 \qquad\quad - 3x + 2 \\ -x^3 - 3x^2 + x - 4 \\ \hline 3x^3 \qquad\quad - 4x + 3 \end{array}$$

• Arrange the terms of each polynomial in descending order with like terms in the same column.

• Combine like terms in each column.

PROBLEM 6 Add: $(5x^2 + 3x - 1) + (2x^2 + 4x - 6) + (8 - 7x + x^2)$
Use a vertical format.

Solution See page S14.

EXAMPLE 7 Subtract: $(3x^2 - 2x + 4) - (7x^2 + 3x - 12)$
Use a vertical format.

Solution

$$(3x^2 - 2x + 4) - (7x^2 + 3x - 12)$$
$$(3x^2 - 2x + 4) + (-7x^2 - 3x + 12)$$

$$\begin{array}{r} 3x^2 - 2x + 4 \\ -7x^2 - 3x + 12 \\ \hline -4x^2 - 5x + 16 \end{array}$$

• Rewrite the subtraction as the addition of the additive inverse.

• Arrange the polynomials in descending order in a vertical format.

• Combine like terms in each column.

PROBLEM 7 Subtract: $(-5x^2 + 2x - 3) - (6x^2 + 3x - 7)$
Use a vertical format.

Solution See page S14.

Functional notation may be used when adding or subtracting polynomials. For instance, if $P(x) = 3x^2 - 2x + 4$ and $R(x) = -5x^3 + 4x + 7$, then

$$P(x) + R(x) = (3x^2 - 2x + 4) + (-5x^3 + 4x + 7)$$
$$= -5x^3 + 3x^2 + 2x + 11$$

$$P(x) - R(x) = (3x^2 - 2x + 4) - (-5x^3 + 4x + 7)$$
$$= (3x^2 - 2x + 4) + (5x^3 - 4x - 7)$$
$$= 5x^3 + 3x^2 - 6x - 3$$

EXAMPLE 8   Given $P(x) = -3x^2 + 2x - 6$ and $R(x) = 4x^3 - 3x + 4$, find $S(x) = P(x) + R(x)$.

Solution $S(x) = P(x) + R(x)$
$$= (-3x^2 + 2x - 6) + (4x^3 - 3x + 4)$$
$$= 4x^3 - 3x^2 - x - 2$$

PROBLEM 8   Given $P(x) = 4x^3 - 3x^2 + 2$ and $R(x) = -2x^2 + 2x - 3$, find $D(x) = P(x) - R(x)$.

Solution   See page S14.

5.2   Concept Review

Determine whether the following statements are always true, sometimes true, or never true.

1. The degree of a polynomial is the greatest of the degrees of its individual terms.

2. The leading coefficient of $4 - 2x - 3x^2$ is 4.

3. Terms with the same variable parts can be added.

4. The additive inverse of a polynomial is a polynomial with every sign changed to the opposite sign.

5. The sum of two trinomials is a trinomial.

6. $f(x) = 3x^2 - 2x + x^{-1}$ is a polynomial function.

5.2   Exercises

1   Evaluate polynomial functions

1. Explain how to determine the degree of a polynomial in one variable. Give two examples of a third-degree polynomial.

2.   Explain how to evaluate a polynomial.

For Exercises 3 and 4, use the polynomial function $P(x) = -3x^2 - 2x + 10$.

3. The degree of P is ___?___. The coefficient -3 is called the ___?___ coefficient. The term 10 is called the ___?___ term.

4. a. To evaluate $P(-2)$, substitute ___?___ for ___?___ in the expression for $P(x)$: $P(\underline{\ \ ?\ \ }) = -3(\underline{\ \ ?\ \ })^2 - 2(\underline{\ \ ?\ \ }) + 10 =$ $\underline{\ \ ?\ \ } + \underline{\ \ ?\ \ } + 10 = \underline{\ \ ?\ \ }$.

b. Use the results of part a to name a point that is on the graph of $y = P(x)$.

State whether the function is a polynomial function. For those that are polynomial functions, identify **a.** the leading coefficient, **b.** the constant term, and **c.** the degree.

5. $P(x) = -x^2 + 3x + 8$

6. $P(x) = 3x^4 - 3x - 7$

7. $R(x) = \dfrac{x}{x + 1}$

8. $R(x) = \dfrac{3x^2 - 2x + 1}{x}$

9. $f(x) = \sqrt{x} - x^2 + 2$

10. $f(x) = x^2 - \sqrt{x + 2} - 8$

11. $g(x) = 3x^5 - 2x^2 + \pi$

12. $g(x) = -4x^5 - 3x^2 + x - \sqrt{7}$

13. $P(x) = 3x^2 - 5x^3 + 2$

14. $P(x) = x^2 - 5x^4 - x^6$

15. $R(x) = 14$

16. $R(x) = \dfrac{1}{x} + 2$

17. Given $P(x) = 3x^2 - 2x - 8$, evaluate $P(3)$.

18. Given $P(x) = -3x^2 - 5x + 8$, evaluate $P(-5)$.

19. Given $R(x) = 2x^3 - 3x^2 + 4x - 2$, evaluate $R(2)$.

20. Given $R(x) = -x^3 + 2x^2 - 3x + 4$, evaluate $R(-1)$.

21. Given $f(x) = x^4 - 2x^2 - 10$, evaluate $f(-1)$.

22. Given $f(x) = x^5 - 2x^3 + 4x$, evaluate $f(2)$.

Graph.

23. $P(x) = x^2 - 1$

24. $P(x) = 2x^2 + 3$

25. $R(x) = x^3 + 2$

26. $R(x) = x^4 + 1$

27. $f(x) = x^3 - 2x$

28. $f(x) = x^2 - x - 2$

29. **Oceanography** The length of a water wave close to land depends on several factors, one of which is the depth of the water. However, the length, L (in meters), of deep-water waves (those far away from land) can be approximated by $L(s) = 0.641s^2$, where s is the speed of the wave in meters per second. Find the length of a deep-water wave that has a speed of 6 m/s. Round to the nearest tenth of a meter.

30. Physics The distance, s (in feet), that an object on the moon will fall in t seconds is given by $s(t) = 2.735t^2$. How far will an object fall on the moon in 3 s?

31. Sports The total number of softball games, T, that must be scheduled in a league that has n teams such that each team plays every other team twice is given by $T(n) = n^2 - n$. What is the total number of games that must be scheduled for a league that has 8 teams?

32. Geometry A diagonal of a polygon is a line from a vertex to a nonadjacent vertex. Seven of the possible diagonals for a decagon (10-sided figure) are shown at the right. The total number, T, of diagonals for an n-sided polygon is given by $T(n) = \frac{1}{2}n^2 - \frac{3}{2}n$. Find the total number of diagonals for a decagon.

33. Food Science Baked Alaska is a dessert that is made by putting a 1-inch meringue coating around a hemisphere of ice cream. The amount of meringue that is needed depends on the radius of the hemisphere of ice cream and is given by $M(r) = 6.14r^2 + 6.14r + 2.094$, where $M(r)$ is the volume of meringue needed (in cubic inches) and r is the radius of the ice cream in inches. Find the amount of meringue that is needed for a baked Alaska that has a mound of ice cream with a 6-inch radius. Round to the nearest whole number.

For Exercises 34 and 35, use the graphs shown below.

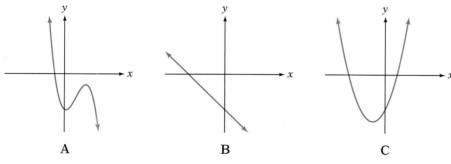

A   B   C

34. Which graph could be the graph of $y = x^2 + 2x - 3$?

35. Which graph could be the graph of $y = x^3 + 3x^2 - x - 3$?

36. Suppose $f(x) = x^2 + 1$ and $g(x) = x^3 + x$. Is $f(x) > g(x)$ or is $f(x) < g(x)$ when $0 < x < 1$? Explain your answer.

2   Add or subtract polynomials

37. The additive inverse of $8x^2 + 3x - 5$ is $-(8x^2 + 3x - 5) = $ ___?___.

38. $(4x^2 + 6x - 1) - (3x^2 - 5x + 2) = (4x^2 + 6x - 1) + ($ ___?___ $)$.

Simplify. Use a vertical format.

39. $(5x^2 + 2x - 7) + (x^2 - 8x + 12)$

40. $(3x^2 - 2x + 7) + (-3x^2 + 2x - 12)$

41. $(x^2 + 8 - 3x) - (2x^2 - 3x + 7)$

42. $(2x^2 + 3x - 7) - (5x^2 - 1 - 8x)$

For Exercises 43–46, simplify using a horizontal format.

43. $(3y^2 - 7y) + (2y^2 - 8y + 2)$

44. $(-2y^2 - 4y - 12) + (5y^2 - 5y)$

45. $(2a^2 - 3a - 7) - (-5a^2 - 2a - 9)$

46. $(3a^2 - 9a) - (-5a^2 + 7a - 6)$

47. Given $P(x) = 3x^3 - 4x^2 - x + 1$ and $R(x) = 2x^3 + 5x - 8$, find $P(x) + R(x)$.

48. Given $P(x) = 5x^3 - 3x - 7$ and $R(x) = 2x^3 - 3x^2 + 8$, find $P(x) - R(x)$.

49. Given $P(x) = x^{2n} + 7x^n - 3$ and $R(x) = -x^{2n} + 2x^n + 8$, find $P(x) + R(x)$.

50. Given $P(x) = 2x^{2n} - x^n - 1$ and $R(x) = 5x^{2n} + 7x^n + 1$, find $P(x) - R(x)$.

51. Given $P(x) = 3x^4 - 3x^3 - x^2$ and $R(x) = 3x^3 - 7x^2 + 2x$, find $S(x) = P(x) + R(x)$.

52. Given $P(x) = 3x^4 - 2x + 1$ and $R(x) = 3x^5 - 5x - 8$, find $S(x) = P(x) + R(x)$.

53. Given $P(x) = x^2 + 2x + 1$ and $R(x) = 2x^3 - 3x^2 + 2x - 7$, find $D(x) = P(x) - R(x)$.

54. Given $P(x) = 2x^4 - 2x^2 + 1$ and $R(x) = 3x^3 - 2x^2 + 3x + 8$, find $D(x) = P(x) - R(x)$.

For Exercises 55 and 56, $P(x) = -ax^2 - bx + c$ and $Q(x) = dx^2 - ex + f$, where $a, b, c, d, e,$ and f are all positive numbers.

55. If $a > d$, $b > e$, and $c > f$, state the sign of the coefficient of each term of $Q(x) - P(x)$.
a. the x^2 term   **b.** the x term   **c.** the constant term

56. If $a > d$, $b < e$, and $c > f$, state the sign of the coefficient of each term of $P(x) - Q(x)$.
a. the x^2 term   **b.** the x term   **c.** the constant term

5.2 Applying Concepts

Two polynomials are equal if the coefficients of like powers are equal. For example,

$$6x^3 - 7x^2 + 2x - 8 = 2x - 7x^2 - 8 + 6x^3$$

In Exercises 57 and 58, use the definition of equality of polynomials to find the value of k that makes the equation an identity.

57. $(2x^3 + 3x^2 + kx + 5) - (x^3 + x^2 - 5x - 2) = x^3 + 2x^2 + 3x + 7$

58. $(6x^3 + kx^2 - 2x - 1) - (4x^3 - 3x^2 + 1) = 2x^3 - x^2 - 2x - 2$

59. If $P(x)$ is a third-degree polynomial and $Q(x)$ is a fourth-degree polynomial, what can be said about the degree of $P(x) + Q(x)$? Give some examples of polynomials that support your answer.

60. If $P(x)$ is a fifth-degree polynomial and $Q(x)$ is a fourth-degree polynomial, what can be said about the degree of $P(x) - Q(x)$? Give some examples of polynomials that support your answer.

61. Sports The deflection, D (in inches), of a beam that is uniformly loaded is given by the polynomial function $D(x) = 0.005x^4 - 0.1x^3 + 0.5x^2$, where x is the distance in feet from one end of the beam. See the figure at the right. The maximum deflection occurs when x is the midpoint of the beam. Determine the maximum deflection for the beam in the diagram.

62. If $P(2) = 3$ and $P(x) = 2x^3 - 4x^2 - 2x + c$, find the value of c.

63. If $P(-1) = -3$ and $P(x) = 4x^4 - 3x^2 + 6x + c$, find the value of c.

64. Graph $f(x) = x^2$, $g(x) = (x - 3)^2$, and $h(x) = (x + 4)^2$ on the same coordinate grid. From the graphs, make a conjecture about the shape and location of $k(x) = (x - 2)^2$. Test your conjecture by graphing k.

65. Graph $f(x) = x^2$, $g(x) = x^2 - 3$, and $h(x) = x^2 + 4$ on the same coordinate grid. From the graphs, make a conjecture about the shape and location of $k(x) = x^2 - 2$. Test your conjecture by graphing k.

66. Engineering Construction of the Golden Gate Bridge, which is a suspension bridge, was completed in 1937. The length of the main span of the bridge is 4200 ft. The height, in feet, of the suspension cables above the roadway varies from 0 ft at the center of the bridge to 525 ft at the towers that support the cables.

Distance from the center of the bridge	Height of the cables above the roadway
0 ft	0 ft
1050 ft	150 ft
2100 ft	525 ft

The function that approximately models the data is $f(x) = \dfrac{1}{8820}x^2 + 25$, where x is the distance from the center of the bridge and $f(x)$ is the height of the cables above the roadway. Use this model to approximate the height of the cables at a distance of **a.** 1000 ft from the center of the bridge and **b.** 1500 ft from the center of the bridge. Round to the nearest tenth.

67. Explain the similarities and differences among the graphs of $f(x) = x^2$, $g(x) = (x - 3)^2$, and $h(x) = x^2 - 3$.

5.3   Multiplication of Polynomials

OBJECTIVE 1   **Multiply a polynomial by a monomial**

To multiply a polynomial by a monomial, use the Distributive Property and the Rule for Multiplying Exponential Expressions.

EXAMPLE 1   Multiply.

A. $-5x(x^2 - 2x + 3)$ **B.** $x^2 - x[3 - x(x - 2) + 3]$

C. $x^n(x^n - x^2 + 1)$

Solution

A. $-5x(x^2 - 2x + 3)$

$= -5x(x^2) - (-5x)(2x) + (-5x)(3)$ • Use the Distributive Property

$= -5x^3 + 10x^2 - 15x$ • Use the Rule for Multiplying Exponential Expressions.

B. $x^2 - x[3 - x(x - 2) + 3]$

$= x^2 - x[3 - x^2 + 2x + 3]$ • Use the Distributive Property to remove the inner grouping symbols.

$= x^2 - x[6 - x^2 + 2x]$ • Combine like terms.

$= x^2 - 6x + x^3 - 2x^2$ • Use the Distributive Property to remove the brackets.

$= x^3 - x^2 - 6x$ • Combine like terms, and write the polynomial in descending order.

C. $x^n(x^n - x^2 + 1)$

$= x^{2n} - x^{n+2} + x^n$ • Use the Distributive Property and the Rule for Multiplying Exponential Expressions.

PROBLEM 1   Multiply.

A. $-4y(y^2 - 3y + 2)$ **B.** $x^2 - 2x[x - x(4x - 5) + x^2]$

C. $y^{n+3}(y^{n-2} - 3y^2 + 2)$

Solution   See page S14.

OBJECTIVE 2   **Multiply two polynomials**

The product of two polynomials is the polynomial obtained by multiplying each term of one polynomial by each term of the other polynomial and then combining like terms.

Multiply: $(2x^2 - 2x + 1)(3x + 2)$

Use the Distributive Property to multiply the trinomial by each term of the binomial.

$(2x^2 - 2x + 1)(3x + 2)$

$= (2x^2 - 2x + 1)(3x) + (2x^2 - 2x + 1)(2)$

Use the Distributive $= (6x^3 - 6x^2 + 3x) + (4x^2 - 4x + 2)$
Property.

Combine like terms. $= 6x^3 - 2x^2 - x + 2$

A more convenient method of multiplying two polynomials is to use a vertical format similar to that used for multiplication of whole numbers.

$$2x^2 - 2x + 1$$
$$\underline{3x + 2}$$

Like terms are written in the $4x^2 - 4x + 2 = 2(2x^2 - 2x + 1)$
same column. $\underline{6x^3 - 6x^2 + 3x} \quad = 3x(2x^2 - 2x + 1)$

Combine like terms. $6x^3 - 2x^2 - \ x + 2$

EXAMPLE 2   Multiply: $(4a^3 - 3a + 7)(a - 5)$

Solution
$$4a^3 - 3a + \ 7$$
$$\underline{a - \ 5}$$
$$-20a^3 \qquad + 15a - 35$$
$$\underline{4a^4 \qquad - 3a^2 + \ 7a}$$
$$4a^4 - 20a^3 - 3a^2 + 22a - 35$$

PROBLEM 2   Multiply: $(-2b^2 + 5b - 4)(-3b + 2)$

Solution   See page S15.

It is frequently necessary to find the product of two binomials. The product can be found by using a method called **FOIL**, which is based on the Distributive Property. The letters FOIL stand for **First**, **Outer**, **Inner**, and **Last**.

> ### Take Note
>
> FOIL is not really a different way of multiplying. It is based on the Distributive Property.
>
> $(3x - 2)(2x + 5)$
> $= 3x(2x + 5) - 2(2x + 5)$
> $= 6x^2 + 15x - 4x - 10$
> $= 6x^2 + 11x - 10$
>
> FOIL is an efficient way to remember how to do binomial multiplication.

Multiply: $(3x - 2)(2x + 5)$

Multiply the **F**irst terms. $(3x - 2)(2x + 5)$ $3x \cdot 2x = 6x^2$

Multiply the **O**uter terms. $(3x - 2)(2x + 5)$ $3x \cdot 5 \ = 15x$

Multiply the **I**nner terms. $(3x - 2)(2x + 5)$ $-2 \cdot 2x = -4x$

Multiply the **L**ast terms. $(3x - 2)(2x + 5)$ $-2 \cdot 5 = -10$

$$\qquad\qquad \mathbf{F} \qquad \mathbf{O} \qquad \mathbf{I} \qquad \mathbf{L}$$

Add the products. $(3x - 2)(2x + 5) \ = \ 6x^2 + 15x - 4x - 10$

Combine like terms. $= \ 6x^2 + 11x - 10$

EXAMPLE 3   Multiply.   **A.** $(6x - 5)(3x - 4)$ **B.** $(a^n - 2b^n)(3a^n - b^n)$

Solution   **A.** $(6x - 5)(3x - 4) = 6x(3x) + 6x(-4) + (-5)(3x) + (-5)(-4)$
$$= 18x^2 - 24x - 15x + 20$$
$$= 18x^2 - 39x + 20$$

B. $(a^n - 2b^n)(3a^n - b^n)$
$$= a^n(3a^n) + a^n(-b^n) + (-2b^n)(3a^n) + (-2b^n)(-b^n)$$
$$= 3a^{2n} - a^n b^n - 6a^n b^n + 2b^{2n}$$
$$= 3a^{2n} - 7a^n b^n + 2b^{2n}$$

> **PROBLEM 3** Multiply.
>
> **A.** $(5a - 3b)(2a + 7b)$ **B.** $(2x^n + y^n)(x^n - 4y^n)$
>
> **Solution** See page S15.

OBJECTIVE 3 Multiply polynomials that have special products

Using FOIL, a pattern can be found for the product of the sum and difference of two terms and for the square of a binomial.

The Sum and Difference of Two Terms

$$(a + b)(a - b) = a^2 - ab + ab - b^2$$
$$= a^2 - b^2$$

Square of the first term ⟶
Square of the second term ⟶

The Square of a Binomial

$$(a + b)^2 = (a + b)(a + b) = a^2 + ab + ab + b^2$$
$$= a^2 + 2ab + b^2$$

Square of the first term ⟶
Twice the product of the two terms ⟶
Square of the second term ⟶

> **EXAMPLE 4** Simplify. **A.** $(4x + 3)(4x - 3)$ **B.** $(2x - 3y)^2$
> **C.** $(x^n + 5)(x^n - 5)$ **D.** $(x^{2n} - 2)^2$
>
> **Solution** **A.** $(4x + 3)(4x - 3) = (4x)^2 - 3^2$ • This is the sum and
> $= 16x^2 - 9$ difference of two terms.
>
> **B.** $(2x - 3y)^2$
> $= (2x)^2 + 2(2x)(-3y) + (-3y)^2$ • This is the square of a
> $= 4x^2 - 12xy + 9y^2$ binomial.
>
> **C.** $(x^n + 5)(x^n - 5) = x^{2n} - 25$
>
> **D.** $(x^{2n} - 2)^2 = x^{4n} - 4x^{2n} + 4$
>
> **PROBLEM 4** Simplify. **A.** $(3x - 7)(3x + 7)$ **B.** $(3x - 4y)^2$
> **C.** $(2x^n + 3)(2x^n - 3)$ **D.** $(2x^n - 8)^2$
>
> **Solution** See page S15.

OBJECTIVE 4 Application problems

> **EXAMPLE 5** The length of a rectangle is $(2x + 3)$ ft. The width is $(x - 5)$ ft. Find the area of the rectangle in terms of the variable x.
>
> **Strategy** To find the area, replace the variables L and W in the equation $A = LW$ by the given values, and solve for A.
>
>
>
> **Solution** $A = LW$
> $A = (2x + 3)(x - 5)$
> $A = 2x^2 - 10x + 3x - 15$
> $A = 2x^2 - 7x - 15$
>
> The area is $(2x^2 - 7x - 15)$ ft^2.

PROBLEM 5   The base of a triangle is $(2x + 6)$ ft. The height is $(x - 4)$ ft. Find the area of the triangle in terms of the variable x.

■ Solution   See page S15.

EXAMPLE 6   The corners are cut from a rectangular piece of cardboard measuring 8 in. by 12 in. The sides are folded up to make a box. Find the volume of the box in terms of the variable x, where x is the length of the side of the square cut from each corner of the rectangle.

Strategy   Length of the box: $12 - 2x$
Width of the box: $8 - 2x$
Height of the box: x
To find the volume, replace the variables L, W, and H in the equation $V = LWH$, and solve for V.

Solution $V = LWH$
$V = (12 - 2x)(8 - 2x)x$
$V = (96 - 24x - 16x + 4x^2)x$
$V = (96 - 40x + 4x^2)x$
$V = 96x - 40x^2 + 4x^3$
$V = 4x^3 - 40x^2 + 96x$

The volume is $(4x^3 - 40x^2 + 96x)$ in^3.

PROBLEM 6   Find the volume of the rectangular solid shown in the diagram. All dimensions are given in feet.

■ Solution   See page S15.

5.3 Concept Review

Determine whether the following statements are always true, sometimes true, or never true.

1. The product of two polynomials is a polynomial.

2. A cubic polynomial is a polynomial that contains three terms.

3. The degree of the product of two polynomials is the sum of the degrees of the polynomials.

4. The product of two binomials is a trinomial.

5. The product of the sum and difference of two different variable terms is a binomial.

6. The Distributive Property is used in multiplying polynomials so that each term of one polynomial multiplies each term of the other polynomial.

5.3 Exercises

1 Multiply a polynomial by a monomial

1. When is the Distributive Property used?

2. Explain how to multiply a monomial and a polynomial by using the Distributive Property.

3. Multiply: $-3y^3(y^2 - 10)$
$-3y^3(y^2 - 10) = \underline{\quad?\quad}(y^2) - (\underline{\quad?\quad})(10)$ • Use the $\underline{\quad?\quad}$ Property to multiply each term of $(y - 10)$ by $-3y^3$.
$= \underline{\quad?\quad} + \underline{\quad?\quad}$ • In the first term, the bases are the same. Add the exponents.

4. Multiply: $a^n(2a^2 + 1)$
$a^n(2a^2 + 1) = (\underline{\quad?\quad})(2a^2) + (\underline{\quad?\quad})(1)$ • Use the Distributive Property to multiply each term of $(2a^2 + 1)$ by a^n.
$= \underline{\quad?\quad} + \underline{\quad?\quad}$ • In the first term, the bases are the same. Add the exponents.

Simplify.

5. $2x(x - 3)$

6. $2a(2a + 4)$

7. $3x^2(2x^2 - x)$

8. $-4y^2(4y - 6y^2)$

9. $3xy(2x - 3y)$

10. $-4ab(5a - 3b)$

11. $x^n(x + 1)$

12. $y^n(y^{2n} - 3)$

13. $x^n(x^n + y^n)$

14. $x - 2x(x - 2)$

15. $2b + 4b(2 - b)$

16. $-2y(3 - y) + 2y^2$

17. $-2a^2(3a^2 - 2a + 3)$

18. $4b(3b^3 - 12b^2 - 6)$

19. $3b(3b^4 - 3b^2 + 8)$

20. $(2x^2 - 3x - 7)(-2x^2)$

21. $-5x^2(4 - 3x + 3x^2 + 4x^3)$

22. $-2y^2(3 - 2y - 3y^2 + 2y^3)$

23. $-2x^2y(x^2 - 3xy + 2y^2)$

24. $3ab^2(3a^2 - 2ab + 4b^2)$

25. $x^n(x^{2n} + x^n + x)$

26. $x^{2n}(x^{2n-2} + x^{2n} + x)$

27. $a^{n+1}(a^n - 3a + 2)$

28. $a^{n+4}(a^{n-2} + 5a^2 - 3)$

29. $2y^2 - y[3 - 2(y - 4) - y]$

30. $3x^2 - x[x - 2(3x - 4)]$

31. $2y - 3[y - 2y(y - 3) + 4y]$ **32.** $4a^2 - 2a[3 - a(2 - a + a^2)]$

33. Which expression(s) are equivalent to $2x - x(5x - 3)$?

   a. $2x - 5x^2 - 3$ **b.** $x(5x - 3)$ **c.** $2x - 5x^2 + 3x$ **d.** $5x^2 - 3x$ **e.** $5x^2 + 5x$ **f.** x **g.** 0

34. Which expression(s) are equivalent to $b^n(b^n - b^3)$?

   a. $b^{2n} - b^{3n}$ **b.** $b^{2n} - b^{n+3}$ **c.** b^{-n} **d.** $b^{n^2} - b^{3n}$

2   Multiply two polynomials

35. For the product $(3x - 2)(x + 5)$:
   The **First** terms are ___?___ and ___?___.
   The **Outer** terms are ___?___ and ___?___.
   The **Inner** terms are ___?___ and ___?___.
   The **Last** terms are ___?___ and ___?___.

36. Use FOIL to multiply $(y + 4)(2y - 7)$:
   The product of the **First** terms is $y \cdot 2y =$ ___?___.
   The product of the **Outer** terms is $y(-7) =$ ___?___.
   The product of the **Inner** terms is $4 \cdot 2y =$ ___?___.
   The product of the **Last** terms is $4(-7) =$ ___?___.
   The sum of these four products is ___?___.

Simplify.

37. $(5x - 7)(3x - 8)$ **38.** $(2x - 3y)(2x + 5y)$ **39.** $(7x - 3y)(2x - 9y)$

40. $(2a - 3b)(5a + 4b)$ **41.** $(3a - 5b)(a + 7b)$ **42.** $(5a + 2b)(3a + 7b)$

43. $(5x + 9y)(3x + 2y)$ **44.** $(3x - 7y)(7x + 2y)$ **45.** $(5x - 9y)(6x - 5y)$

46. $(xy + 4)(xy - 3)$ **47.** $(xy - 5)(2xy + 7)$ **48.** $(2x^2 - 5)(x^2 - 5)$

49. $(x^2 - 4)(x^2 - 6)$ **50.** $(5x^2 - 5y)(2x^2 - y)$ **51.** $(x^2 - 2y^2)(x^2 + 4y^2)$

52. $(x^n + 2)(x^n - 3)$ **53.** $(x^n - 4)(x^n - 5)$ **54.** $(2a^n - 3)(3a^n + 5)$

55. $(5b^n - 1)(2b^n + 4)$ **56.** $(2a^n - b^n)(3a^n + 2b^n)$ **57.** $(3x^n + b^n)(x^n + 2b^n)$

58. $(x - 2)(x^2 - 3x + 7)$ **59.** $(x + 3)(x^2 + 5x - 8)$ **60.** $(x + 5)(x^3 - 3x + 4)$

61. $(a + 2)(a^3 - 3a^2 + 7)$ **62.** $(2a - 3b)(5a^2 - 6ab + 4b^2)$ **63.** $(3a + b)(2a^2 - 5ab - 3b^2)$

64. $(2y^2 - 1)(y^3 - 5y^2 - 3)$ **65.** $(2b^2 - 3)(3b^2 - 3b + 6)$

66. $(2x - 5)(2x^4 - 3x^3 - 2x + 9)$ **67.** $(2a - 5)(3a^4 - 3a^2 + 2a - 5)$

68. $(x^2 + 2x - 3)(x^2 - 5x + 7)$ **69.** $(x^2 - 3x + 1)(x^2 - 2x + 7)$

70. $(a - 2)(2a - 3)(a + 7)$

71. $(b - 3)(3b - 2)(b - 1)$

72. $(x^n + y^n)(x^n - 2x^n y^n + 3y^n)$

73. $(x^n - y^n)(x^{2n} - 3x^n y^n - y^{2n})$

74. Suppose a and b are positive numbers such that $a < b$. Will the coefficient of the x term of the product $(ax - b)(x + 1)$ be positive or negative?

75. If the constant terms of two binomials are both negative, will the constant term of the product of the two binomials also be negative?

3   Multiply polynomials that have special products

76. The product $(a + b)(a - b) = a^2 - b^2$, so
$(2x + 3)(2x - 3) = (\underline{})^2 - (\underline{})^2 = \underline{} - \underline{}$.

77. The product $(a + b)^2 = a^2 + 2ab + b^2$, so
$(4x + 1)^2 = (\underline{})^2 + 2(\underline{})(\underline{}) + (\underline{})^2$
$= \underline{} + \underline{} + \underline{}$.

Simplify.

78. $(a - 4)(a + 4)$

79. $(b - 7)(b + 7)$

80. $(3x - 2)(3x + 2)$

81. $(b - 11)(b + 11)$

82. $(3a + 5b)^2$

83. $(5x - 4y)^2$

84. $(x^2 - 3)^2$

85. $(x^2 + y^2)^2$

86. $(10 + b)(10 - b)$

87. $(2a - 3b)(2a + 3b)$

88. $(5x - 7y)(5x + 7y)$

89. $(x^2 + 1)(x^2 - 1)$

90. $(x^2 + y^2)(x^2 - y^2)$

91. $(2x^n + y^n)^2$

92. $(a^n + 5b^n)^2$

93. $(5a - 9b)(5a + 9b)$

94. $(3x + 7y)(3x - 7y)$

95. $(2x^n - 5)(2x^n + 5)$

96. $(4y + 1)(4y - 1)$

97. $(6 - x)(6 + x)$

98. $(2x^2 - 3y^2)^2$

99. $(3a - 4b)^2$

100. $(2x^2 + 5)^2$

101. $(3x^n + 2)^2$

102. $(4b^n - 3)^2$

103. $(x^n + 3)(x^n - 3)$

104. $(x^n + y^n)(x^n - y^n)$

105. $(x^n - 1)^2$

106. $(a^n - b^n)^2$

107. $(2x^n + 5y^n)^2$

For Exercises 108 to 111, state whether the coefficient of the x term of the product is positive, negative, or zero.

108. $(ax + b)^2$, where $a > 0$ and $b > 0$

109. $(ax + b)(ax - b)$, where $a > 0$ and $b > 0$

110. 🗣 $(ax + b)(ax + b)$, where $a > 0$ and $b < 0$

111. 🗣 $(ax + b)^2$, where $a < 0$ and $b < 0$

4   Application problems

112. Use the figure at the left above, which shows a rectangular piece of cardboard with the corners cut out. The sides can be folded up to make a box. State each dimension of the box in terms of x.
   a. Length of the box = _____?_____
   b. Width of the box = _____?_____
   c. Height of the box = _____?_____

113. a. Use the figure at the right above. We can use the properties of rectangles to show that both unlabeled sides of the figure have length x. The unlabeled vertical side has length $4x - $ ___?___ $= x$. The unlabeled horizontal side has length $x + 3 - $ ___?___ $= x$.
   b. Divide the figure into two rectangles by extending the unlabeled horizontal side. The area of the upper rectangle is $3x($___?___$) = $ ___?___. The area of the lower rectangle is $(x + 3)($___?___$) = $ ___?___. The area of the whole figure is ___?___ $+$ ___?___ $=$ ___?___.

114. **Geometry** The length of a rectangle is $(3x + 3)$ ft. The width is $(x - 4)$ ft. Find the area of the rectangle in terms of the variable x.

115. **Geometry** The base of a triangle is $(x + 2)$ ft. The height is $(2x - 3)$ ft. Find the area of the triangle in terms of the variable x.

116. **Geometry** Find the area of the figure shown below. All dimensions given are in meters.

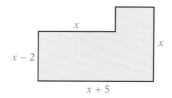

117. **Geometry** Find the area of the figure shown below. All dimensions given are in feet.

118. **Construction** A trough is made from a rectangular piece of metal by folding up the sides as shown in the figure below. What is the volume of the trough in terms of the side folded up?

119. **Construction** A square sheet of cardboard measuring 18 in. by 18 in. is used to make an open box by cutting squares of equal size from the corners and folding up the sides. Find the volume of the box in terms of the variable x, where x is the length of the side of the square cut from the cardboard.

120. **Geometry** The length of the side of a cube is $(x - 2)$ centimeters. Find the volume of the cube in terms of the variable x.

121. **Geometry** The length of a box is $(2x + 3)$ centimeters, the width is $(x - 5)$ centimeters and the height is x centimeters. Find the volume of the box in terms of the variable x.

122. **Geometry** Find the volume of the figure shown below. All dimensions given are in inches.

123. **Geometry** Find the volume of the figure shown below. All dimensions given are in centimeters.

5.3 Applying Concepts

Simplify.

124. $\dfrac{(2x + 1)^5}{(2x + 1)^3}$

125. $\dfrac{(3x - 5)^6}{(3x - 5)^4}$

126. $(a - b)^2 - (a + b)^2$

127. $(x + 2y)^2 + (x + 2y)(x - 2y)$

128. $(4y + 3)^2 - (3y + 4)^2$

129. $2x^2(3x^3 + 4x - 1) - 5x^2(x^2 - 3)$

130. $(2b + 3)(b - 4) + (3 + b)(3 - 2b)$

131. $(3x - 2y)^2 - (2x - 3y)^2$

132. $[x + (y + 1)][x - (y + 1)]$

133. $[x^2(2y - 1)]^2$

For what value of k is the given equation an identity?

134. $(5x - k)(3x + k) = 15x^2 + 4x - k^2$

135. $(kx - 7)(kx + 2) = k^2x^2 + 5x - 14$

Complete.

136. If $m = n + 1$, then $\dfrac{a^m}{a^n} = $ _____.

137. If $m = n + 2$, then $\dfrac{a^m}{a^n} = $ _____.

138. What polynomial when divided by $x - 4$ has a quotient of $2x + 3$?

139. What polynomial when divided by $2x - 3$ has a quotient of $x + 7$?

140. Subtract the product of $4a + b$ and $2a - b$ from $9a^2 - 2ab$.

141. Subtract the product of $5x - y$ and $x + 3y$ from $6x^2 + 12xy - 2y^2$.

142. Find $(3n^4)^3$ if $5(n - 1) = 2(3n - 2)$.

143. Find $(-2n^3)^2$ if $3(2n - 1) = 5(n - 1)$.

5.4 Division of Polynomials

OBJECTIVE 1   Divide a polynomial by a monomial

Note that $\dfrac{9x + 6x}{3}$ can be simplified by first adding the terms in the numerator and then dividing by 3. It can also be simplified by first dividing each term in the numerator by the denominator and then adding the results.

$$\frac{9x + 6x}{3} = \frac{15x}{3} = 5x$$

$$\frac{9x + 6x}{3} = \frac{9x}{3} + \frac{6x}{3} = 3x + 2x = 5x$$

To divide a polynomial by a monomial, divide each term of the numerator by the denominator, and write the sum of the quotients.

$$\frac{a + b}{c} = \frac{a}{b} + \frac{b}{c}$$

Divide each term of the polynomial $8x^3 - 4x^2 + 6x$ by the monomial $2x$. Simplify.

$$\frac{8x^3 - 4x^2 + 6x}{2x} = \frac{8x^3}{2x} - \frac{4x^2}{2x} + \frac{6x}{2x}$$

$$= 4x^2 - 2x + 3$$

EXAMPLE 1   Divide: $\dfrac{6p^4 - 9p^3 - 12p^2}{3p^2}$

Solution $\dfrac{6p^4 - 9p^3 - 12p^2}{3p^2} = \dfrac{6p^4}{3p^2} - \dfrac{9p^3}{3p^2} - \dfrac{12p^2}{3p^2}$ • **Divide each term of the polynomial by $3p^2$.**

$= 2p^2 - 3p - 4$ • **Simplify.**

PROBLEM 1   Divide: $\dfrac{15y^3 + 10y^2 - 25y}{-5y}$

Solution   See page S15.

EXAMPLE 2   Divide: $\dfrac{18a^2b + 27a^2b^2 - 9ab^2}{9a^2b}$

Solution $\dfrac{18a^2b + 27a^2b^2 - 9ab^2}{9a^2b}$

$= \dfrac{18a^2b}{9a^2b} + \dfrac{27a^2b^2}{9a^2b} - \dfrac{9ab^2}{9a^2b}$ • **Divide each term of the polynomial by $9a^2b$.**

$= 2 + 3b - \dfrac{b}{a}$ • **Simplify.**

PROBLEM 2   Divide: $\dfrac{12x^2y^2 - 16xy^2 - 8x}{4x^2y}$

Solution   See page S15.

OBJECTIVE 2   ### Divide polynomials

The division method illustrated in Objective 1 is appropriate only when the divisor is a monomial. To divide two polynomials in which the divisor is not a monomial, use a method similar to that used for division of whole numbers.

To check division of polynomials, use

$$\textbf{Dividend = (quotient × divisor) + remainder}$$

Divide: $(x^2 + 5x - 7) \div (x + 3)$

Step 1
$$x + 3 \overline{)\, x^2 + 5x - 7\,}$$
quotient: x
$$\underline{x^2 + 3x} \quad \downarrow$$
$$2x - 7$$

Think: $x\overline{)x^2} = \dfrac{x^2}{x} = x$

Multiply: $x(x + 3) = x^2 + 3x$
Subtract: $(x^2 + 5x) - (x^2 + 3x) = 2x$
Bring down -7.

Step 2
$$x + 3 \overline{)\, x^2 + 5x - 7\,}$$
quotient: $x + 2$
$$\underline{x^2 + 3x}$$
$$2x - 7$$
$$\underline{2x + 6}$$
$$-13$$

Think: $x\overline{)2x} = \dfrac{2x}{x} = 2$

Multiply: $2(x + 3) = 2x + 6$
Subtract: $(2x - 7) - (2x + 6) = -13$
The remainder is -13.

Check: Dividend $=$ (quotient $\times$ divisor) $+$ remainder

$$(x + 2)(x + 3) + (-13) = x^2 + 3x + 2x + 6 - 13 = x^2 + 5x - 7$$

$$(x^2 + 5x - 7) \div (x + 3) = x + 2 - \frac{13}{x + 3}$$

Divide: $\dfrac{6 - 6x^2 + 4x^3}{2x + 3}$

Arrange the terms in descending order. Note that there is no term of x in $4x^3 - 6x^2 + 6$. Insert a zero as $0x$ for the missing term so that like terms will be in the same columns.

$$
\begin{array}{r}
2x^2 - 6x + 9 \\
2x + 3 \overline{)\,4x^3 - 6x^2 + 0x + 6} \\
\underline{4x^3 + 6x^2} \\
-12x^2 + 0x \\
\underline{-12x^2 - 18x} \\
18x + 6 \\
\underline{18x + 27} \\
-21
\end{array}
$$

$$\frac{4x^3 - 6x^2 + 6}{2x + 3} = 2x^2 - 6x + 9 - \frac{21}{2x + 3}$$

EXAMPLE 3 Divide. **A.** $\dfrac{12x^2 - 11x + 10}{4x - 5}$ **B.** $\dfrac{x^3 + 1}{x + 1}$

Solution **A.**
$$
\begin{array}{r}
3x + 1 \\
4x - 5 \overline{)\,12x^2 - 11x + 10} \\
\underline{12x^2 - 15x} \\
4x + 10 \\
\underline{4x - 5} \\
15
\end{array}
$$

$$\frac{12x^2 - 11x + 10}{4x - 5} = 3x + 1 + \frac{15}{4x - 5}$$

B.
$$
\begin{array}{r}
x^2 - x + 1 \\
x + 1 \overline{)\,x^3 + 0x^2 + 0x + 1} \\
\underline{x^3 + x^2} \\
-x^2 + 0x \\
\underline{-x^2 - x} \\
x + 1 \\
\underline{x + 1} \\
0
\end{array}
$$

$$\frac{x^3 + 1}{x + 1} = x^2 - x + 1$$

PROBLEM 3 Divide. **A.** $\dfrac{15x^2 + 17x - 20}{3x + 4}$ **B.** $\dfrac{3x^3 + 8x^2 - 6x + 2}{3x - 1}$

Solution See page S15.

OBJECTIVE **3**   **Synthetic division**

Synthetic division is a shorter method of dividing a polynomial by a binomial of the form $x - a$. This method of dividing uses only the coefficients of the variable terms and the constant term.

Both long division and synthetic division are used below to simplify the expression $(3x^2 - 10x + 7) \div (x - 2)$.

LONG DIVISION

Compare the coefficients in this problem worked by long division with the coefficients in the same problem worked by synthetic division.

$$
\begin{array}{r}
3x - 4 \\
x - 2 \overline{)3x^2 - 10x + 7} \\
\underline{3x^2 - 6x} \\
-4x + 7 \\
\underline{-4x - 8} \\
-1
\end{array}
$$

$$(3x^2 - 10x + 7) \div (x - 2) = 3x - 4 - \dfrac{1}{x - 2}$$

SYNTHETIC DIVISION

$x - a = x - 2;\, a = 2$

Value of a Coefficients of the dividend

Bring down the 3.

Multiply $2 \cdot 3$ and add the product (6) to -10. The result is -4.

Multiply $2(-4)$ and add the product (-8) to 7. The result is -1.

Coefficients of   Remainder
the quotient

The degree of the first term of the quotient is one degree less than the degree of the first term of the dividend.

$$(3x^2 - 10x + 7) \div (x - 2) = 3x - 4 - \dfrac{1}{x - 2}$$

Check: $(3x - 4)(x - 2) - 1$
$= 3x^2 - 6x - 4x + 8 - 1$
$= 3x^2 - 10x + 7$

Divide: $(2x^3 + 3x^2 - 4x + 8) \div (x + 3)$

Write down the value of a and the coefficients of the dividend.

$x - a = x + 3 = x - (-3)$;
$a = -3$

$$
\begin{array}{r|rrrr}
-3 & 2 & 3 & -4 & 8 \\
   &   & -6 & 9 & -15 \\
\hline
   & 2 & -3 & 5 & -7
\end{array}
$$

Coefficients of the quotient   Remainder

Bring down the 2. Multiply $-3 \cdot 2$ and add the product (-6) to 3. Continue until all the coefficients have been used.

Write the quotient. The degree of the quotient is one degree less than the degree of the dividend.

$$(2x^3 + 3x^2 - 4x + 8) \div (x + 3)$$
$$= 2x^2 - 3x + 5 - \frac{7}{x + 3}$$

EXAMPLE 4 Divide: **A.** $(5x^2 - 3x + 7) \div (x - 1)$

B. $(3x^4 - 8x^2 + 2x + 1) \div (x + 2)$

Solution   **A.**
$$
\begin{array}{r|rrr}
1 & 5 & -3 & 7 \\
  &   & 5 & 2 \\
\hline
  & 5 & 2 & 9
\end{array}
$$

• $x - a = x - 1; a = 1$

$$(5x^2 - 3x + 7) \div (x - 1)$$
$$= 5x + 2 + \frac{9}{x - 1}$$

B.
$$
\begin{array}{r|rrrrr}
-2 & 3 & 0 & -8 & 2 & 1 \\
   &   & -6 & 12 & -8 & 12 \\
\hline
   & 3 & -6 & 4 & -6 & 13
\end{array}
$$

• **Insert a zero for the missing term.**

$x - a = x + 2; a = -2$

$$(3x^4 - 8x^2 + 2x + 1) \div (x + 2)$$
$$= 3x^3 - 6x^2 + 4x - 6 + \frac{13}{x + 2}$$

PROBLEM 4 Divide: **A.** $(6x^2 + 8x - 5) \div (x + 2)$

B. $(2x^4 - 3x^3 - 8x^2 - 2) \div (x - 3)$

Solution See page S15.

OBJECTIVE **4** **Evaluate a polynomial using synthetic division**

A polynomial can be evaluated by using synthetic division. Consider the polynomial $P(x) = 2x^4 - 3x^3 + 4x^2 - 5x + 1$. One way to evaluate the polynomial when $x = 2$ is to replace x by 2 and then simplify the numerical expression.

$$P(x) = 2x^4 - 3x^3 + 4x^2 - 5x + 1$$
$$P(2) = 2(2)^4 - 3(2)^3 + 4(2)^2 - 5(2) + 1$$
$$P(2) = 2(16) - 3(8) + 4(4) - 5(2) + 1$$
$$P(2) = 32 - 24 + 16 - 10 + 1 = 15$$

Now use synthetic division to divide $(2x^4 - 3x^3 + 4x^2 - 5x + 1) \div (x - 2)$.

$$
\begin{array}{r|rrrrr}
2 & 2 & -3 & 4 & -5 & 1 \\
  &   & 4 & 2 & 12 & 14 \\
\hline
  & 2 & 1 & 6 & 7 & 15
\end{array}
$$

Coefficients of the quotient   Remainder

Note that the remainder is 15, which is the same value as $P(2)$. This is not a coincidence. The following theorem states that this situation is always true.

Remainder Theorem

If the polynomial $P(x)$ is divided by $x - a$, the remainder is $P(a)$.

Evaluate $P(x) = x^4 - 3x^2 + 4x - 5$ when $x = -2$ by using the Remainder Theorem.

The value at which the polynomial is evaluated

$$
\begin{array}{r|rrrrr}
-2 & 1 & 0 & -3 & 4 & -5 \\
   &   & -2 & 4 & -2 & -4 \\
\hline
   & 1 & -2 & 1 & 2 & -9
\end{array}
$$
A 0 is inserted for the x^3 term.

← The remainder

$P(-2) = -9$

EXAMPLE 5   Use the Remainder Theorem to evaluate $P(-2)$ when $P(x) = x^3 - 3x^2 + x + 3$.

Solution   Use synthetic division with $a = -2$.

$$
\begin{array}{r|rrrr}
-2 & 1 & -3 & 1 & 3 \\
   &   & -2 & 10 & -22 \\
\hline
   & 1 & -5 & 11 & -19
\end{array}
$$

By the Remainder Theorem, $P(-2) = -19$.

PROBLEM 5   Use the Remainder Theorem to evaluate $P(3)$ when $P(x) = 2x^3 - 4x - 5$.

Solution   See page S16.

5.4   Concept Review

Determine whether the following statements are always true, sometimes true, or never true.

1. The quotient of two monomials is a monomial.

2. Synthetic division is a shorter method of dividing a polynomial by a binomial.

3. In synthetic division, the degree of the quotient is always one less than the degree of the divisor.

4. If a polynomial $P(x)$ is divided by $x - a$, the remainder is $P(a)$.

5.4   Exercises

1   Divide a polynomial by a monomial

1. Replace each question mark to make a true statement.

$$\frac{9y^2 + 6y}{3y} = \frac{9y^2}{?} + \frac{6y}{?}$$
$$= \underline{\ ?\ } + \underline{\ ?\ }$$

2. Replace each question mark to make a true statement.

$$\frac{8x^3 - 12x^2}{4x^2} = \frac{8x^3}{?} - \frac{12x^2}{?}$$
$$= \underline{\ ?\ } - \underline{\ ?\ }$$

Divide.

3. $\dfrac{4a - 8}{4}$

4. $\dfrac{8x - 12y}{2}$

5. $\dfrac{6w^2 + 4w}{2w}$

6. $\dfrac{8z^3 - 6z^2}{-2z}$

7. $\dfrac{3t^3 - 9t^2 + 12t}{3t}$

8. $\dfrac{10a^3 - 20a^2 + 15a}{5a}$

9. $\dfrac{16x^3 - 24x^2 + 48x}{-8x^2}$

10. $\dfrac{12y^2 - 9y + 6}{-3y}$

11. $\dfrac{8v^3 - 6v^2 + 12v}{4v}$

12. $\dfrac{12x^4 - 9x^3 + 8x^2}{6x^2}$

13. $\dfrac{-2xy^2 + 4x^2y}{2xy}$

14. $\dfrac{8a^3b^2 - 12a^2b^3}{4a^2b}$

15. $\dfrac{12x^2y^2 - 16x^2y + 20xy^2}{4x^2y}$

16. $\dfrac{6uv^3 + 9u^2v^2 - 3u^3v}{3uv^2}$

17. $\dfrac{-18x^3y^3 - 12x^2y^2 + 9xy}{3x^2y^2}$

18. $\dfrac{21a^3b^3 - 14a^2b^2 + 28ab}{7a^2b^2}$

19. $\dfrac{6n^2m - 12nm^2 - 9mn}{-3m^2n^2}$

20. $\dfrac{-2xy + 8x^2y - 4xy^2}{-2x^2y^2}$

21. Every division equation has a related multiplication equation. For instance, $\dfrac{12}{3} = 4$ means that $12 = 3 \cdot 4$. What is the related multiplication equation for $\dfrac{12x^2 + 6x}{3x} = 4x + 2$?

22. How can multiplication be used to check that $\dfrac{6x^3 - 12x^2 - 2x}{2x} = 3x^2 - 6x - 1$?

2   Divide polynomials

23. Explain how the degree of the quotient of two polynomials is related to the degrees of the dividend and the divisor.

24. Explain how you can check the result of dividing two polynomials.

Divide by using long division.

25. $(x^2 + 3x - 40) \div (x - 5)$

26. $(x^2 - 14x + 24) \div (x - 2)$

27. $(x^3 - 3x^2 + 2) \div (x - 3)$

28. $(x^3 + 4x^2 - 8) \div (x + 4)$

29. $(6x^2 + 13x + 8) \div (2x + 1)$

30. $(12x^2 + 13x - 14) \div (3x - 2)$

31. $(10x^2 + 9x - 5) \div (2x - 1)$

32. $(18x^2 - 3x + 2) \div (3x + 2)$

33. $(8x^3 - 9) \div (2x - 3)$

34. $(64x^3 + 4) \div (4x + 2)$

35. $(6x^4 - 13x^2 - 4) \div (2x^2 - 5)$

36. $(12x^4 - 11x^2 + 10) \div (3x^2 + 1)$

37. $\dfrac{3x^3 - 8x^2 - 33x - 10}{3x + 1}$

38. $\dfrac{8x^3 - 38x^2 + 49x - 10}{4x - 1}$

39. $\dfrac{4 - 7x + 5x^2 - x^3}{x - 3}$

40. $\dfrac{4 + 6x - 3x^2 + 2x^3}{2x + 1}$

41. $\dfrac{16x^2 - 13x^3 + 2x^4 - 9x + 20}{x - 5}$

42. $\dfrac{x + 3x^4 - x^2 + 5x^3 - 2}{x + 2}$

43. $\dfrac{x^3 - 4x^2 + 2x - 1}{x^2 + 1}$

44. $\dfrac{3x^3 - 2x^2 - 8}{x^2 + 5}$

45. $\dfrac{2x^3 - x + 4 - 3x^2}{x^2 - 1}$

46. $\dfrac{2 - 3x^2 + 5x^3}{x^2 + 3}$

47. $\dfrac{6x^3 + 2x^2 + x + 4}{2x^2 - 3}$

48. $\dfrac{9x^3 + 6x^2 + 2x + 1}{3x^2 + 2}$

49. True or false? When a tenth-degree polynomial is divided by a second-degree polynomial, the quotient is a fifth-degree polynomial.

50. True or false? When a polynomial of degree $3n$ is divided by a polynomial of degree n, the degree of the quotient polynomial is $2n$.

3   Synthetic division

51. Synthetic division is a shorter method of dividing a polynomial by a ___?___ of the form ___?___ .

52. Use this display of the synthetic division of two polynomials in x:

$$
\begin{array}{r|rrr}
-2 & 4 & -1 & 3 \\
   &   & -8 & 18 \\
\hline
   & 4 & -9 & 21
\end{array}
$$

   a. The dividend is the polynomial ___?___ .
   b. The divisor is $x -$ ___?___ $=$ ___?___ .
   c. The "-8" comes from multiplying ___?___ and ___?___ .
   d. The "-9" comes from adding ___?___ and ___?___ .
   e. The quotient is the polynomial ___?___ plus the remainder ___?___ .

Divide by using synthetic division.

53. $(2x^2 - 6x - 8) \div (x + 1)$

54. $(3x^2 + 19x + 20) \div (x + 5)$

55. $(3x^2 - 4) \div (x - 1)$

56. $(4x^2 - 8) \div (x - 2)$

57. $(x^2 - 9) \div (x + 4)$

58. $(x^2 - 49) \div (x + 5)$

59. $(2x^2 + 24) \div (2x + 4)$

60. $(3x^2 - 15) \div (x + 3)$

61. $(2x^3 - x^2 + 6x + 9) \div (x + 1)$

62. $(3x^3 + 10x^2 + 6x - 4) \div (x + 2)$

63. $(x^3 - 6x^2 + 11x - 6) \div (x - 3)$

64. $(x^3 - 4x^2 + x + 6) \div (x + 1)$

65. $(6x - 3x^2 + x^3 - 9) \div (x + 2)$

66. $(5 - 5x + 4x^2 + x^3) \div (x - 3)$

67. $(x^3 + x - 2) \div (x + 1)$

68. $(x^3 + 2x + 5) \div (x - 2)$

69. $(18 + x - 4x^3) \div (2 - x)$

70. $(12 - 3x^2 + x^3) \div (3 + x)$

71. $\dfrac{16x^2 - 13x^3 + 2x^4 - 9x + 20}{x - 5}$

72. $\dfrac{2x^3 - x^2 - 10x + 15 + x^4}{x - 2}$

73. $\dfrac{5 + 5x - 8x^2 + 4x^3 - 3x^4}{2 - x}$

74. $\dfrac{3 - 13x - 5x^2 + 9x^3 - 2x^4}{3 - x}$

75. $\dfrac{3x^4 + 3x^3 - x^2 + 3x + 2}{x + 1}$

76. $\dfrac{4x^4 + 12x^3 - x^2 - x + 2}{x + 3}$

77. $\dfrac{2x^4 - x^2 + 2}{x - 3}$

78. $\dfrac{x^4 - 3x^3 - 30}{x + 2}$

79. $\dfrac{x^3 + 125}{x + 5}$

80. $\dfrac{x^3 + 343}{x + 7}$

81. Suppose you know the number to the left of the vertical line in a synthetic division display of $P(x) \div Q(x)$, and you know the numbers below the horizontal line. Do you have enough information to determine $P(x)$?

82. Suppose you know the number to the left of the vertical line in a synthetic division display of $P(x) \div Q(x)$, and you know the numbers above the horizontal line. Do you have enough information to determine $P(x)$?

4 **Evaluate a polynomial using synthetic division**

83. Finish the synthetic division of $P(x) = 3x^2 - 2x^2 + x - 9$ by $x - 2$.

$$
\begin{array}{c|rrrr}
2 & 3 & -2 & 1 & -9 \\
  &   & 6 & ? & ? \\
\hline
  & 3 & 4 & ? & ?
\end{array}
$$

The value of $P(2)$ is ___?___.

84. Use the synthetic division display to state one point that you know is on the graph of $y = x^3 + x^2 - 9x - 9$.

$$
\begin{array}{c|rrrr}
1 & 1 & 1 & -9 & -9 \\
  &   & 1 & 2 & -7 \\
\hline
  & 1 & 2 & -7 & -16
\end{array}
$$

Use the Remainder Theorem to evaluate the polynomial.

85. $P(x) = 2x^2 - 3x - 1$; $P(3)$

86. $Q(x) = 3x^2 - 5x - 1$; $Q(2)$

87. $R(x) = x^3 - 2x^2 + 3x - 1$; $R(4)$

88. $F(x) = x^3 + 4x^2 - 3x + 2$; $F(3)$

89. $P(z) = 2z^3 - 4z^2 + 3z - 1$; $P(-2)$

90. $R(t) = 3t^3 + t^2 - 4t + 2$; $R(-3)$

91. $Q(x) = x^4 + 3x^3 - 2x^2 + 4x - 9$; $Q(2)$

92. $Y(z) = z^4 - 2z^3 - 3z^2 - z + 7$; $Y(3)$

93. $F(x) = 2x^4 - x^3 - 2x - 5$; $F(-3)$

94. $Q(x) = x^4 - 2x^3 + 4x - 2$; $Q(-2)$

95. $P(x) = x^3 - 3$; $P(5)$

96. $S(t) = 4t^3 + 5$; $S(-4)$

97. $R(t) = 4t^4 - 3t^2 + 5$; $R(-3)$

98. $P(z) = 2z^4 + z^2 - 3$; $P(-4)$

99. $Q(x) = x^5 - 4x^3 - 2x^2 + 5x - 2$; $Q(2)$

100. $T(x) = 2x^5 + 4x^4 - x^2 + 4$; $T(3)$

5.4 Applying Concepts

Divide by using long division.

101. $\dfrac{3x^2 - xy - 2y^2}{3x + 2y}$

102. $\dfrac{12x^2 + 11xy + 2y^2}{4x + y}$

103. $\dfrac{a^3 - b^3}{a - b}$

104. $\dfrac{a^4 + b^4}{a + b}$

105. $\dfrac{x^5 + y^5}{x + y}$

106. $\dfrac{x^6 - y^6}{x - y}$

For what value of k will the remainder be zero?

107. $(x^3 - 3x^2 - x + k) \div (x - 3)$

108. $(x^3 - 2x^2 + x + k) \div (x - 2)$

109. $(x^2 + kx - 6) \div (x - 3)$

110. $(x^3 + kx + k - 1) \div (x - 1)$

111. When $x^2 + x + 2$ is divided by a polynomial, the quotient is $x + 4$, and remainder is 14. Find the polynomial.

5.5 Factoring Polynomials

OBJECTIVE 1   ## Factor a monomial from a polynomial

The GCF of two or more exponential expressions with the same base is the exponential expression with the smallest exponent.

$$2^5 \qquad\qquad x^5$$
$$2^2 \qquad\qquad x^7$$
$$2^9 \qquad\qquad x$$
$$\text{GCF} = 2^2 = 4 \qquad \text{GCF} = x$$

The GCF of two or more monomials is the product of each common factor, with its smallest exponent.

$$16a^4b \;=\; 2^4 \cdot \qquad a^4 \cdot b$$
$$40a^2b^5 = 2^3 \cdot 5 \cdot a^2 \cdot b^5$$
$$\text{GCF} \;\;\;= 2^3 \cdot \qquad a^2 \cdot b = 8a^2b$$

To **factor a polynomial** means to write the polynomial as a product of other polynomials.

> ## Take Note
>
> $3x^2 + 6x$ is a sum. $3x(x + 2)$ is a product. When we factor a polynomial, we write it as a product.

In the example at the right, $3x$ is the GCF of the terms $3x^2$ and $6x$. $3x$ is a **monomial factor** of the terms of the binomial. $x + 2$ is a **binomial factor** of $3x^2 + 6x$.

Polynomial		Factors
$3x^2 + 6x$	$=$	$3x(x + 2)$

EXAMPLE 1 Factor.

A. $4x^3y^2 + 12x^3y + 20xy^2$ **B.** $x^{2n} + x^{n+1} + x^n, n > 0$

Solution **A.** Find the GCF of $4x^3y^2$, $12x^3y$, and $20xy^2$.

$$4x^3y^2 = 2^2 \cdot \qquad x^3 \cdot y^2$$
$$12x^3y = 2^2 \cdot 3 \cdot x^3 \cdot y$$
$$20xy^2 = 2^2 \cdot 5 \cdot x \;\; \cdot y^2$$
$$\text{GCF} = 2^2 \cdot \qquad x \;\; \cdot y = 4xy$$

Rewrite each term of the polynomial as a product with the GCF as one of the factors.

$$4x^3y^2 + 12x^3y + 20xy^2$$
$$= 4xy(x^2y) + 4xy(3x^2) + 4xy(5y)$$
$$= 4xy(x^2y + 3x^2 + 5y)$$

B. Because $n > 0$, $n < 2n$, and $n < n + 1$, the GCF of x^{2n}, x^{n+1}, and x^n is x^n.

$$x^{2n} + x^{n+1} + x^n = x^n(x^n) + x^n(x) + x^n(1)$$
$$= x^n(x^n + x + 1)$$

PROBLEM 1 Factor.   **A.** $3x^3y - 6x^2y^2 - 3xy^3$ **B.** $6t^{2n} - 9t^n$

Solution See page S16.

OBJECTIVE 2   ## Factor by grouping

In the examples at the right, the binomials in parentheses are binomial factors.

$$4x^4(2x - 3)$$
$$-2r^2s(5r + 2s)$$

The Distributive Property is used to factor a common binomial factor from an expression.

Factor: $4a(2b + 3) - 5(2b + 3)$

The common binomial factor is $(2b + 3)$.
Use the Distributive Property to write the
expression as a product of factors.

$$4a(2b + 3) - 5(2b + 3)$$
$$= (2b + 3)(4a - 5)$$

Consider the binomial $y - x$. Factoring -1 from this binomial gives

$$y - x = -(x - y)$$

This equation is sometimes used to factor a common binomial from an expression.

Take Note

For the simplification at the right,

$6r(r - s) - 7(s - r)$
$= 6r(r - s) - 7[(-1)(r - s)]$
$= 6r(r - s) + 7(r - s)$

Factor: $6r(r - s) - 7(s - r)$

Rewrite the expression as a sum of
terms that have a common binomial
factor. Use $s - r = -(r - s)$.

$$6r(r - s) - 7(s - r)$$
$$= 6r(r - s) + 7(r - s)$$

Write the expression as a product of
factors.

$$= (r - s)(6r + 7)$$

Some polynomials can be factored by grouping terms so that a common binomial factor is found.

Factor: $8y^2 + 4y - 6ay - 3a$

Group the first two terms and the last
two terms. Note that
$-6ay - 3a = -(6ay + 3a)$.

$$8y^2 + 4y - 6ay - 3a$$
$$= (8y^2 + 4y) - (6ay + 3a)$$

Factor the GCF from each group.

$$= 4y(2y + 1) - 3a(2y + 1)$$

Write the expression as a product of
factors.

$$= (2y + 1)(4y - 3a)$$

EXAMPLE 2 Factor.   **A.** $3x(y - 4) - 2(4 - y)$ **B.** $xy - 4x - 2y + 8$

Solution   **A.** $3x(y - 4) - 2(4 - y)$
$\qquad = 3x(y - 4) + 2(y - 4)$

- Write the expression as a sum of
  terms that have a common factor.
  Note that $4 - y = -(y - 4)$.

$\qquad = (y - 4)(3x + 2)$

- Write the expression as a product of
  factors.

B. $xy - 4x - 2y + 8$
$\qquad = (xy - 4x) - (2y - 8)$

- Group the first two terms and the
  last two terms.

$\qquad = x(y - 4) - 2(y - 4)$
$\qquad = (y - 4)(x - 2)$

- Factor the GCF from each group.
- Write the expression as the
  product of factors.

PROBLEM 2   Factor.   **A.** $6a(2b - 5) + 7(5 - 2b)$ **B.** $3rs - 2r - 3s + 2$

Solution   See page S16.

OBJECTIVE **3**   ## Factor trinomials of the form $x^2 + bx + c$

A **quadratic trinomial** is a trinomial of the form $ax^2 + bx + c$, where a and b are nonzero coefficients and c is a nonzero constant. The degree of a quadratic trinomial is 2. Here are examples of quadratic trinomials:

$$4x^2 - 3x - 7 \qquad\qquad z^2 + z + 10 \qquad\qquad 2y^2 + 4y - 9$$
$$(a = 4, b = -3, c = -7) \qquad (a = 1, b = 1, c = 10) \qquad (a = 2, b = 4, c = -9)$$

To **factor a quadratic trinomial** means to express the trinomial as the product of two binomials. For example,

Trinomial		Factored Form
$2x^2 - x - 1$	$=$	$(2x + 1)(x - 1)$
$y^2 - 3y + 2$	$=$	$(y - 1)(y - 2)$

In this objective, trinomials of the form $x^2 + bx + c$ $(a = 1)$ will be factored. The next objective deals with trinomials where $a \neq 1$.

The method by which factors of a trinomial are found is based on FOIL. Consider the following binomial products, noting the relationship between the constant terms of the binomials and the terms of the trinomial.

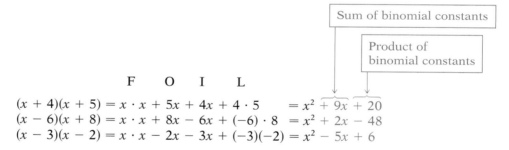

$$\begin{array}{l} \text{F} \quad \text{O} \quad \text{I} \quad \text{L} \\ (x + 4)(x + 5) = x \cdot x + 5x + 4x + 4 \cdot 5 = x^2 + 9x + 20 \\ (x - 6)(x + 8) = x \cdot x + 8x - 6x + (-6) \cdot 8 = x^2 + 2x - 48 \\ (x - 3)(x - 2) = x \cdot x - 2x - 3x + (-3)(-2) = x^2 - 5x + 6 \end{array}$$

Observe two important points from these examples:

1. The constant term of the trinomial is the product of the constant terms of the binomials. The coefficient of x in the trinomial is the sum of the constant terms of the binomials.

2. When the constant term of the trinomial is positive, the constant terms of the binomials have the same sign. When the constant term of the trinomial is negative, the constant terms of the binomials have opposite signs.

Use the points listed above to factor a trinomial. For example, to factor

$$x^2 - 5x - 24$$

find two numbers whose sum is -5 and whose product is -24. Because the constant term of the trinomial is negative (-24), the numbers will have opposite signs.

A systematic method of finding these numbers involves listing the factors of the constant term of the trinomial and the sum of those factors.

Factors of −24	Sum of the Factors
1, −24	$1 + (-24) = -23$
−1, 24	$-1 + 24 = 23$
2, −12	$2 + (-12) = -10$
−2, 12	$-2 + 12 = 10$
3, −8	**$3 + (-8) = -5$**
−3, 8	$-3 + 8 = 5$
4, −6	$4 + (-6) = -2$
−4, 6	$-4 + 6 = 2$

3 and −8 are two numbers whose sum is −5 and whose product is −24. Write the binomial factors of the trinomial.

$$x^2 - 5x - 24 = (x + 3)(x - 8)$$

Check: $(x + 3)(x - 8) = x^2 - 8x + 3x - 24 = x^2 - 5x - 24$

Take Note

You can always check a proposed factorization by multiplying all the factors.

By the Commutative Property of Multiplication, the binomial factors can also be written as

$$x^2 - 5x - 24 = (x - 8)(x + 3)$$

EXAMPLE 3 Factor.

A. $x^2 + 8x + 12$ **B.** $x^2 + 5x - 84$ **C.** $x^2 + 7xy + 12y^2$

Solution **A.** $x^2 + 8x + 12$

Factors of 12	Sum
1, 12	13
2, 6	8
3, 4	7

• Try only positive factors of 12.
• Once the correct pair is found, the other factors need not be tried.

$x^2 + 8x + 12 = (x + 2)(x + 6)$ • Write the factors of the trinomial.

Check: $(x + 2)(x + 6) = x^2 + 6x + 2x + 12$
$= x^2 + 8x + 12$

B. $x^2 + 5x - 84$

$(-7)(12) = -84$
$-7 + 12 = 5$

• The factors must be of opposite signs. Find two factors of −84 whose sum is 5.

$x^2 + 5x - 84 = (x + 12)(x - 7)$

Check: $(x + 12)(x - 7) = x^2 - 7x + 12x - 84$
$= x^2 + 5x - 84$

C. $x^2 + 7xy + 12y^2 = (x + 3y)(x + 4y)$

Check: $(x + 3y)(x + 4y) = x^2 + 4xy + 3xy + 12y^2$
$= x^2 + 7xy + 12y^2$

PROBLEM 3 Factor.

A. $x^2 + 13x + 42$ **B.** $x^2 - x - 20$ **C.** $x^2 + 5xy + 6y^2$

Solution See page S16.

Not all trinomials can be factored using only integers. Consider $x^2 - 3x - 6$.

Factors of -6	Sum
1, −6	−5
−1, 6	5
2, −3	−1
−2, 3	1

Because none of the pairs of factors of -6 has a sum of -3, the trinomial is not factorable. The trinomial $x^3 - 3x - 6$ is a **prime polynomial.** Such a polynomial is said to be **nonfactorable over the integers.** Binomials of the form $x + a$ and $x - a$ are also prime polynomials.

EXAMPLE 4   Factor: $x^2 + 2x - 4$

Solution   The trinomial is nonfactorable over the integers.

• **There are no factors of −4 whose sum is 2.**

PROBLEM 4   Factor: $x^2 + 5x - 1$

Solution   See page S16.

OBJECTIVE ▮4▮   **Factor trinomials of the form $ax^2 + bx + c$**

There are various methods of factoring trinomials of the form $ax^2 + bx + c$, where $a \neq 1$. Factoring by using trial factors and factoring by grouping will be discussed in this objective. Factoring by using trial factors is illustrated first.

To use the trial factor method, use the factors of a and the factors of c to write all the possible binomial factors of the trinomial. Then use FOIL to determine the correct factorization. To reduce the number of trial factors that must be considered, remember the following:

1. Use the signs of the constant term and the coefficient of x in the trinomial to determine the signs of the binomial factors. If the constant term is positive, the signs of the binomial factors will be the same as the sign of the coefficient of x in the trinomial. If the constant term is negative, the constant terms in the binomials will have opposite signs.

2. If the terms of the trinomial do not have a common factor, then the terms in either one of the binomial factors will not have a common factor.

Factor: $4x^2 + 31x - 8$

The terms of the trinomial do not have a common factor; therefore, the binomial factors will not have a common factor.

Because the constant term, c, of the trinomial is negative (-8), the constant terms of the binomial factors will have opposite signs.

Find the factors of a (4) and the factors of c (-8).

Factors of 4	Factors of -8
1, 4	1, -8
2, 2	-1, 8
	2, -4
	-2, 4

Using these factors, write trial factors, and use FOIL to check the middle terms of the trinomial.

Remember that if the terms of the trinomial do not have a common factor, then a binomial factor cannot have a common factor. Such trial factors need not be checked.

Trial Factors	Middle Term
$(x + 1)(4x - 8)$	Common factor
$(x - 1)(4x + 8)$	Common factor
$(x + 2)(4x - 4)$	Common factor
$(x - 2)(4x + 4)$	Common factor
$(2x + 1)(2x - 8)$	Common factor
$(2x - 1)(2x + 8)$	Common factor
$(2x + 2)(2x - 4)$	Common factor
$(2x - 2)(2x + 4)$	Common factor
$(4x + 1)(x - 8)$	$-32x + x = -31x$
$(4x - 1)(x + 8)$	**$32x - x = 31x$**

The correct factors have been found.

$$4x^2 + 31x - 8 = (4x - 1)(x + 8)$$

Other trial factors need not be checked.

The last example illustrates that many of the trial factors may have common factors and thus need not be tried. For the remainder of this chapter, the trial factors with a common factor will not be listed.

EXAMPLE 5   Factor.   **A.** $2x^2 - 21x + 10$ **B.** $6x^2 + 17x - 10$

Solution   **A.** $2x^2 - 21x + 10$

Factors of 2	Factors of 10
1, 2	$-1, -10$
	$-2, -5$

• Use negative factors of 10.

Trial Factors	Middle Term
$(x - 2)(2x - 5)$	$-5x - 4x = -9x$
$(2x - 1)(x - 10)$	$-20x - x = -21x$

• Write trial factors. Use FOIL to check the middle term.

$$2x^2 - 21x + 10 = (2x - 1)(x - 10)$$

B. $6x^2 + 17x - 10$

Factors of 6	Factors of -10
1, 6	1, -10
2, 3	-1, 10
	2, -5
	-2, 5

• Find the factors of a (6) and the factors of c (-10).

Trial Factors	Middle Term
$(x + 2)(6x - 5)$	$-5x + 12x = 7x$
$(x - 2)(6x + 5)$	$5x - 12x = -7x$
$(2x + 1)(3x - 10)$	$-20x + 3x = -17x$
$(2x - 1)(3x + 10)$	$20x - 3x = 17x$

• Write trial factors. Use FOIL to check the middle term.

$$6x^2 + 17x - 10 = (2x - 1)(3x + 10)$$

PROBLEM 5   Factor.   **A.** $4x^2 + 15x - 4$ **B.** $10x^2 + 39x + 14$

Solution   See page S16.

Trinomials of the form $ax^2 + bx + c$ can also be factored by grouping. This method is an extension of the method discussed in Objective 2 of this section.

To factor $ax^2 + bx + c$, first find the factors of $a \cdot c$ whose sum is b. Use the two factors to rewrite the middle term of the trinomial as the sum of two terms. Then factor by grouping to write the factorization of the trinomial.

Factor: $3x^2 + 11x + 8$

Find two positive factors of 24 $(a \cdot c = 3 \cdot 8)$ whose sum is 11, the coefficient of x.

Positive Factors of 24	Sum
1, 24	25
2, 12	14
3, 8	11

The required sum has been found. The remaining factors need not be checked.

Use the factors of 24 whose sum is 11 to write $11x$ as $3x + 8x$. Factor by grouping.

$$\begin{aligned} 3x^2 + 11x + 8 &= 3x^2 + 3x + 8x + 8 \\ &= (3x^2 + 3x) + (8x + 8) \\ &= 3x(x + 1) + 8(x + 1) \\ &= (x + 1)(3x + 8) \end{aligned}$$

Check: $(x + 1)(3x + 8) = 3x^2 + 8x + 3x + 8 = 3x^2 + 11x + 8$

Factor: $4z^2 - 17z - 21$

Find two factors of -84 $[a \cdot c = 4(-21)]$ whose sum is -17, the coefficient of z.

When the required sum is found, the remaining factors need not be checked.

Factors of -84	Sum
1, -84	-83
-1, 84	83
2, -42	-40
-2, 42	40
3, -28	-25
-3, 28	25
4, -21	-17

Use the factors of -84 whose sum is -17 to write $-17z$ as $4z - 21z$. Factor by grouping. Recall that $-21z - 21 = -(21z + 21)$.

$$\begin{aligned} 4z^2 - 17z - 21 &= 4z^2 + 4z - 21z - 21 \\ &= (4z^2 + 4z) - (21z + 21) \\ &= 4z(z + 1) - 21(z + 1) \\ &= (z + 1)(4z - 21) \end{aligned}$$

Factor: $3x^2 - 11x + 4$

Find two negative factors of 12
$(a \cdot c = 3 \cdot 4)$ whose sum is -11.

Because no integer factors of 12
have a sum of -11, $3x^2 - 11x + 4$ is
nonfactorable over the integers.

Factors of 12	Sum
$-1, -12$	-13
$-2, -6$	-8
$-3, -4$	-7

EXAMPLE 6   Factor.   **A.** $2x^2 - 21x + 10$ **B.** $10 - 17x - 6x^2$

Solution   **A.** $2x^2 - 21x + 10$

Factors of 20	Sum
$-1, -20$	-21

• $a \cdot c = 2 \cdot 10 = 20$. Find two factors of 20 whose sum is -21.

$$2x^2 - 21x + 10$$
$$= 2x^2 - 20x - x + 10$$
$$= (2x^2 - 20x) - (x - 10)$$
$$= 2x(x - 10) - (x - 10)$$
$$= (x - 10)(2x - 1)$$

• Rewrite $-21x$ as $-20x - x$.
• Factor by grouping.

B. $10 - 17x - 6x^2$

Factors of -60	Sum
$1, -60$	-59
$-1, 60$	59
$2, -30$	-28
$-2, 30$	28
$3, -20$	-17

• $a \cdot c = -60$. Find two factors of -60 whose sum is -17.

$$10 - 17x - 6x^2$$
$$= 10 - 20x + 3x - 6x^2$$
$$= (10 - 20x) + (3x - 6x^2)$$
$$= 10(1 - 2x) + 3x(1 - 2x)$$
$$= (1 - 2x)(10 + 3x)$$

• Rewrite $-17x$ as $-20x + 3x$.
• Factor by grouping.

PROBLEM 6   Factor.   **A.** $6x^2 + 7x - 20$ **B.** $2 - x - 6x^2$

Solution   See page S16.

Either method of factoring discussed in this objective will always lead to a correct factorization of trinomials of the form $ax^2 + bx + c$ that are factorable.

A polynomial is factored completely when it is written as a product of factors that are nonfactorable over the integers.

Take Note

The first step in *any* factoring problem is to determine whether the terms of the polynomial have a **common factor.** If they do, factor it out first.

Factor: $4x^3 + 12x^2 - 160x$

Factor out the GCF of the terms. The GCF of $4x^3$, $12x^2$, and $160x$ is $4x$.

$$4x^3 + 12x^2 - 160x$$
$$= 4x(x^2 + 3x - 40)$$

Factor the trinomial.

$$= 4x(x + 8)(x - 5)$$

Check: $4x(x + 8)(x - 5) = (4x^2 + 32x)(x - 5) = 4x^3 + 12x^2 - 160x$

EXAMPLE 7 Factor.   **A.** $30y + 2xy - 4x^2y$ **B.** $12x^3y + 14x^2y - 6xy$

Solution **A.** $30y + 2xy - 4x^2y$
$= 2y(15 + x - 2x^2)$
$= 2y(5 + 2x)(3 - x)$

- The GCF of 30y, 2xy, and 4x²y is 2y.
- Factor out the GCF.
- Factor the trinomial.

B. $12x^3y + 14x^2y - 6xy$
$= 2xy(6x^2 + 7x - 3)$
$= 2xy(3x - 1)(2x + 3)$

- The GCF of 12x³y, 14x²y, and 6xy is 2xy.

PROBLEM 7 Factor.   **A.** $3a^3b^3 + 3a^2b^2 - 60ab$ **B.** $40a - 10a^2 - 15a^3$

Solution See page S16.

5.5   Concept Review

Determine whether the following statements are always true, sometimes true, or never true.

1. Factoring reverses the effects of multiplication.

2. A trinomial will factor into the product of two binomials.

3. A trinomial of the form $ax^2 + bx + c$ can be factored by using trial factors.

4. A polynomial with four terms can be factored by grouping.

5.5   Exercises

1   Factor a monomial from a polynomial

1. What is the greatest common factor (GCF) of two monomials? Make up two monomials and name their GCF.

2. What does it mean to factor a polynomial?

3. Of the two expressions $15x^2 - 10x$ and $5x(3x - 2)$, which one is written in *factored form*?

4. The expression $5x(3x - 2)$, has a monomial factor and a binomial factor. The monomial factor is ____?____ and the binomial factor is ____?____.

Factor.

5. $6a^2 - 15a$

6. $32b^2 + 12b$

7. $4x^3 - 3x^2$

8. $12a^5b^2 + 16a^4b$

9. $3a^2 - 10b^3$

10. $9x^2 + 14y^4$

11. $x^5 - x^3 - x$

12. $y^4 - 3y^2 - 2y$

13. $16x^2 - 12x + 24$

14. $2x^5 + 3x^4 - 4x^2$

15. $5b^2 - 10b^3 + 25b^4$

16. $x^2y^4 - x^2y - 4x^2$

17. $x^{2n} - x^n$

18. $a^{5n} + a^{2n}$

19. $x^{3n} - x^{2n}$

20. $y^{4n} + y^{2n}$

21. $a^{2n+2} + a^2$

22. $b^{n+5} - b^5$

23. $12x^2y^2 - 18x^3y + 24x^2y$

24. $14a^4b^4 - 42a^3b^3 + 28a^3b^2$

25. $-16a^2b^4 - 4a^2b^2 + 24a^3b^2$

26. $10x^2y + 20x^2y^2 + 30x^2y^3$

27. $y^{2n+2} + y^{n+2} - y^2$

28. $a^{2n+2} + a^{2n+1} + a^n$

For Exercises 29 to 32, use the polynomial $x^a + x^b + x^c + x^d$, where a, b, c, and d are all positive integers such that $a < b < c < d$.

29. Is the polynomial $x^a + x^b + x^c + x^d$ written in descending order?

30. What is the GCF of the terms of the polynomial $x^a + x^b + x^c + x^d$?

31. Suppose $b = 2a$, $c = 3a$, and $d = 4a$. Write $x^a + x^b + x^c + x^d$ in factored form.

32. Suppose $b = a + 1$, $c = a + 2$, and $d = a + 3$. Write $x^a + x^b + x^c + x^d$ in factored form.

2   Factor by grouping

Factor.

33. $x(a + 2) - 2(a + 2)$

34. $3(x + y) + a(x + y)$

35. $a(x - 2) - b(2 - x)$

36. $3(a - 7) - b(7 - a)$

37. $x^2 + 3x + 2x + 6$

38. $x^2 - 5x + 4x - 20$

39. $xy + 4y - 2x - 8$

40. $ab + 7b - 3a - 21$

41. $ax + bx - ay - by$

42. $2ax - 3ay - 2bx + 3by$

43. $x^2y - 3x^2 - 2y + 6$

44. $a^2b + 3a^2 + 2b + 6$

45. $6 + 2y + 3x^2 + x^2y$

46. $15 + 3b - 5a^2 - a^2b$

47. $2ax^2 + bx^2 - 4ay - 2by$

48. $4a^2x + 2a^2y - 6bx - 3by$

49. $x^ny - 5x^n + y - 5$

50. $a^nx^n + 2a^n + x^n + 2$

51. $x^3 + x^2 + 2x + 2$

52. $y^3 - y^2 + 3y - 3$

53. $2x^3 - x^2 + 4x - 2$

54. $2y^3 - y^2 + 6y - 3$

55. Not all four-term expressions can be factored by grouping. Find the one expression below that can be factored by grouping.

    I. $xy + 6y + 3x - 18$ **II.** $xy - 6y - 3x - 18$ **III.** $xy + 6y - 3x - 18$

56. **a.** Which expression(s) are equivalent to $x^2 - x - 6$?

    I. $x^2 - 5x + 4x - 6$ **II.** $x^2 - 3x + 2x - 6$ **III.** $x^2 - 9x + 8x - 6$

    b. Which expression in part a can be factored by grouping?

3 Factor trinomials of the form $x^2 + bx + c$

57. What is a quadratic trinomial and what does it mean to factor a quadratic trinomial?

58. What does the phrase *nonfactorable over the integers* mean?

59. **a.** Find two numbers whose product is -21 and whose difference is 4.

    b. Find two numbers whose product is 20 and whose sum is -9.

60. To factor a quadratic trinomial of the form $x^2 + bx + c$ into two binomials $(x + n)$ and $(x + m)$, look for constants n and m whose product is ___?___ and whose sum is ___?___.

Factor.

61. $x^2 - 8x + 15$

62. $x^2 + 12x + 20$

63. $a^2 + 12a + 11$

64. $a^2 + a - 72$

65. $b^2 + 2b - 35$

66. $a^2 + 7a + 6$

67. $y^2 - 16y + 39$

68. $y^2 - 18y + 72$

69. $b^2 + 4b - 32$

70. $x^2 + x - 132$

71. $a^2 - 15a + 56$

72. $x^2 + 15x + 50$

73. $y^2 + 13y + 12$

74. $b^2 - 6b - 16$

75. $x^2 + 4x - 5$

76. $a^2 - 3ab + 2b^2$

77. $a^2 + 11ab + 30b^2$

78. $a^2 + 8ab - 33b^2$

79. $x^2 - 14xy + 24y^2$

80. $x^2 + 5xy + 6y^2$

81. $y^2 + 2xy - 63x^2$

82. $y^2 - 13y + 12$

83. $x^2 - 35x - 36$

84. $x^2 + 7x - 18$

85. $a^2 + 13a + 36$

86. $x^2 - 5x + 7$

87. $x^2 - 7x - 12$

88. Suppose b and c are nonzero and n and m are positive constants such that $x^2 + bx + c = (x - n)(x + m)$.
  a. Is c positive or negative?
  b. If b is negative, is n less than, equal to, or greater than m?

89. Suppose b and c are nonzero and n and m are positive constants such that $x^2 + bx + c = (x - n)(x - m)$.
  a. Is c positive or negative?
  b. Is b positive or negative?
  c. Is b less than, equal to, or greater than c?

4 Factor trinomials of the form $ax^2 + bx + c$

In Exercises 90 to 93, information is given about the signs of b and c in $ax^2 + bx + c, a > 0$. If you want to factor $ax^2 + bx + c$ by grouping, you look for factors of ac whose sum is b. In each case, state whether the factors of ac should be two positive numbers, two negative numbers, or one positive and one negative number.

90. $b < 0$ and $c < 0$

91. $b < 0$ and $c > 0$

92. $b > 0$ and $c < 0$

93. $b > 0$ and $c > 0$

Factor.

94. $2x^2 + 7x + 3$
95. $2x^2 - 11x - 40$
96. $6y^2 + 5y - 6$

97. $4y^2 - 15y + 9$
98. $6b^2 - b - 35$
99. $2a^2 + 13a + 6$

100. $3y^2 - 22y + 39$
101. $12y^2 - 13y - 72$
102. $6a^2 - 26a + 15$

103. $5x^2 + 26x + 5$
104. $4a^2 - a - 5$
105. $11x^2 - 122x + 11$

106. $11y^2 - 47y + 12$
107. $12x^2 - 17x + 5$
108. $12x^2 - 40x + 25$

109. $8y^2 - 18y + 9$
110. $4x^2 + 9x + 10$
111. $6a^2 - 5a - 2$

112. $10x^2 - 29x + 10$
113. $2x^2 + 5x + 12$
114. $4x^2 - 6x + 1$

115. $6x^2 + 5xy - 21y^2$
116. $6x^2 + 41xy - 7y^2$
117. $4a^2 + 43ab + 63b^2$

118. $7a^2 + 46ab - 21b^2$
119. $10x^2 - 23xy + 12y^2$
120. $18x^2 + 27xy + 10y^2$

121. $24 + 13x - 2x^2$
122. $6 - 7x - 5x^2$
123. $8 - 13x + 6x^2$

124. $30 + 17a - 20a^2$

125. $15 - 14a - 8a^2$

126. $35 - 6b - 8b^2$

127. $5y^4 - 29y^3 + 20y^2$

128. $30a^2 + 85ab + 60b^2$

129. $4x^3 + 10x^2y - 24xy^2$

130. $8a^4 + 37a^3b - 15a^2b^2$

131. $100 - 5x - 5x^2$

132. $50x^2 + 25x^3 - 12x^4$

133. $320x - 8x^2 - 4x^3$

134. $96y - 16xy - 2x^2y$

135. $20x^2 - 38x^3 - 30x^4$

136. $4x^2y^2 - 32xy + 60$

137. $a^4b^4 - 3a^3b^3 - 10a^2b^2$

138. $2a^2b^4 + 9ab^3 - 18b^2$

139. $90a^2b^2 + 45ab + 10$

140. $3x^3y^2 + 12x^2y - 96x$

141. $4x^4 - 45x^2 + 80$

142. $x^4 + 2x^2 + 15$

143. $2a^5 + 14a^3 + 20a$

144. $3b^6 - 9b^4 - 30b^2$

145. $3x^4y^2 - 39x^2y^2 + 120y^2$

146. $2x^4y - 7x^3y - 30x^2y$

147. $45a^2b^2 + 6ab^2 - 72b^2$

148. $16x^2y^3 + 36x^2y^2 + 20x^2y$

149. $36x^3y + 24x^2y^2 - 45xy^3$

150. $12a^3b - 70a^2b^2 - 12ab^3$

151. $48a^2b^2 - 36ab^3 - 54b^4$

5.5   Applying Concepts

Factor.

152. $2a^3b - ab^3 - a^2b^2$

153. $3x^3y - xy^3 - 2x^2y^2$

154. $2y^3 + 2y^5 - 24y$

155. $9b^3 + 3b^5 - 30b$

Find all integers k such that the trinomial can be factored over the integers.

156. $x^2 + kx + 8$

157. $x^2 + kx - 6$

158. $2x^2 - kx + 3$

159. $2x^2 - kx - 5$

160. $3x^2 + kx + 5$

161. $2x^2 + kx - 3$

162. **Geometry** Write the area of the shaded region in factored form.

a.

b.

c.
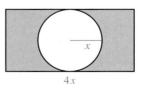

5.6 Special Factoring

OBJECTIVE **1**   **Factor the difference of two perfect squares and factor perfect-square trinomials**

The product of a term and itself is called a **perfect square.** The exponents on variables of perfect squares are always even numbers.

Term		Perfect Square
5	$5 \cdot 5 =$	25
x	$x \cdot x =$	x^2
$3y^4$	$3y^4 \cdot 3y^4 =$	$9y^8$
x^n	$x^n \cdot x^n =$	x^{2n}

The **square root of a perfect square** is one of the two equal factors of the perfect square. $\sqrt{}$ is the symbol for square root. To find the exponent of the square root of a variable term, divide the exponent by 2. For the examples at the right, assume that x and y represent positive numbers.

$\sqrt{25} = 5$
$\sqrt{x^2} = x$
$\sqrt{9y^8} = 3y^4$
$\sqrt{x^{2n}} = x^n$

Take Note

$(a + b)$ is the sum of the two terms a and b. $(a - b)$ is the difference of the two terms a and b. a and b are the square roots of a^2 and b^2.

The factors of the difference of two perfect squares are the sum and difference of the square roots of the perfect squares.

Factors of the Difference of Two Perfect Squares

$$a^2 - b^2 = (a + b)(a - b)$$

The *sum* of two perfect squares, $a^2 + b^2$, is nonfactorable over the integers.

EXAMPLE 1   Factor: $25x^2 - 1$

   Solution $25x^2 - 1 = (5x)^2 - 1^2$ • Write the binomial as the difference of two perfect squares.

               $= (5x + 1)(5x - 1)$ • The factors are the sum and difference of the square roots of the perfect squares.

PROBLEM 1   Factor: $x^2 - 36y^4$

   Solution   See page S17.

A perfect-square trinomial is the square of a binomial.

Factors of a Perfect-Square Trinomial

$$a^2 + 2ab + b^2 = (a + b)^2$$
$$a^2 - 2ab + b^2 = (a - b)^2$$

In factoring a perfect-square trinomial, remember that the terms of the binomial are the square roots of the perfect squares of the trinomial. The sign in the binomial is the sign of the middle term of the trinomial.

Factor: $4x^2 - 12x + 9$

Because $4x^2$ is a perfect square and 9 is a perfect square, try factoring $4x^2 - 12x + 9$ as the square of a binomial.

$$4x^2 - 12x + 9 \stackrel{?}{=} (2x - 3)^2$$

Check:
$(2x - 3)^2 = (2x - 3)(2x - 3) = 4x^2 - 6x - 6x + 9 = 4x^2 - 12x + 9$

The factorization checks. Thus $4x^2 - 12x + 9 = (2x - 3)^2$.

It is important to check a proposed factorization as we did above. The next example illustrates the importance of this check.

Factor: $x^2 + 13x + 36$

Because x^2 is a perfect square and 36 is a perfect square, try factoring $x^2 + 13x + 36$ as the square of a binomial.

$$x^2 + 13x + 36 \stackrel{?}{=} (x + 6)^2$$

Check: $(x + 6)^2 = (x + 6)(x + 6) = x^2 + 6x + 6x + 36 = x^2 + 12x + 36$

In this case, the proposed factorization of $x^2 + 13x + 36$ does *not* check. Try another factorization. The numbers 4 and 9 are factors of 36 whose sum is 13.

$$x^2 + 13x + 36 = (x + 4)(x + 9)$$

EXAMPLE 2   Factor: $4x^2 - 20x + 25$

Solution $4x^2 - 20x + 25 = (2x - 5)^2$

PROBLEM 2   Factor: $9x^2 + 12x + 4$

Solution   See page S17.

OBJECTIVE 2   **Factor the sum or the difference of two cubes**

The product of the same three factors is called a **perfect cube**. The exponents on variables of perfect cubes are always divisible by 3.

Term		Perfect Cube
2	$2 \cdot 2 \cdot 2 =$	8
$3y$	$3y \cdot 3y \cdot 3y =$	$27y^3$
x^2	$x^2 \cdot x^2 \cdot x^2 =$	x^6
x^n	$x^n \cdot x^n \cdot x^n =$	x^{3n}

The **cube root** of a perfect cube is one of the three equal factors of the perfect cube. $\sqrt[3]{}$ is the symbol for cube root. To find the exponent of the cube root of a perfect-cube variable term, divide the exponent by 3.

$$\sqrt[3]{8} = 2$$
$$\sqrt[3]{27y^3} = 3y$$
$$\sqrt[3]{x^6} = x^2$$
$$\sqrt[3]{x^{3n}} = x^n$$

The following rules are used to factor the sum or difference of two perfect cubes.

Factoring the Sum or Difference of Two Perfect Cubes

$$a^3 + b^3 = (a + b)(a^2 - ab + b^2)$$
$$a^3 - b^3 = (a - b)(a^2 + ab + b^2)$$

To factor $8x^3 - 27$:

Write the binomial as the difference of two perfect cubes.

$$8x^3 - 27 = (2x)^3 - 3^3$$

The terms of the binomial factor are the cube roots of the perfect cubes. The sign of the binomial factor is the same sign as in the given binomial. The trinomial factor is obtained from the binomial factor.

$$= (2x - 3)(4x^2 + 6x + 9)$$

Square of the first term

Opposite of the product of the two terms

Square of the last term

EXAMPLE 3   Factor.   **A.** $x^3y^3 - 1$ **B.** $(x + y)^3 - x^3$

Solution   **A.** $x^3y^3 - 1$
$= (xy)^3 - 1^3$ • Write the binomial as the difference of two perfect cubes.
$= (xy - 1)(x^2y^2 + xy + 1)$

B. $(x + y)^3 - x^3$ • This is a difference of two perfect cubes.
$= [(x + y) - x][(x + y)^2 + x(x + y) + x^2]$
$= y(x^2 + 2xy + y^2 + x^2 + xy + x^2)$ • Simplify.
$= y(3x^2 + 3xy + y^2)$

PROBLEM 3   Factor.   **A.** $8x^3 + y^3z^3$ **B.** $(x - y)^3 + (x + y)^3$

Solution   See page S17.

OBJECTIVE 3   ## Factor trinomials that are quadratic in form

Certain trinomials can be expressed as quadratic trinomials by making suitable variable substitutions. A trinomial is **quadratic in form** if it can be written as

$$au^2 + bu + c$$

If we let $x^2 = u$, the trinomial $x^4 + 5x^2 + 6$ can be written as shown at the right.

$x^4 + 5x^2 + 6$
$= (x^2)^2 + 5(x^2) + 6$
$= u^2 + 5u + 6$

The trinomial is quadratic in form.

If we let $xy = u$, the trinomial $2x^2y^2 + 3xy - 9$ can be written as shown at the right.

$2x^2y^2 + 3xy - 9$
$= 2(xy)^2 + 3(xy) - 9$
$= 2u^2 + 3u - 9$

The trinomial is quadratic in form.

When a trinomial that is quadratic in form is factored, the variable part of the first term in each binomial factor will be u. For example, because $x^4 + 5x^2 + 6$ is quadratic in form when $x^2 = u$, the first term in each binomial factor will be x^2.

$$x^4 + 5x^2 + 6 = (x^2)^2 + 5(x^2) + 6$$
$$= (x^2 + 2)(x^2 + 3)$$

The trinomial $x^2y^2 - 2xy - 15$ is quadratic in form when $xy = u$. The first term in each binomial factor will be xy.

$$x^2y^2 - 2xy - 15 = (xy)^2 - 2(xy) - 15$$
$$= (xy + 3)(xy - 5)$$

EXAMPLE 4 Factor.   **A.** $6x^2y^2 - xy - 12$ **B.** $2x^4 + 5x^2 - 12$

Solution **A.** $6x^2y^2 - xy - 12$
$= (3xy + 4)(2xy - 3)$

• The trinomial is quadratic in form when $xy = u$.

B. $2x^4 + 5x^2 - 12$
$= (x^2 + 4)(2x^2 - 3)$

• The trinomial is quadratic in form when $x^2 = u$.

PROBLEM 4 Factor.   **A.** $6x^2y^2 - 19xy + 10$ **B.** $3x^4 + 4x^2 - 4$

Solution See page S17.

OBJECTIVE **4**   **Factor completely**

Take Note

Remember that you may have to factor more than once in order to write the polynomial as a product of *prime* factors.

When factoring a polynomial completely, ask the following questions about the polynomial.

1. Is there a common factor? If so, factor out the GCF.

2. If the polynomial is a binomial, is it the difference of two perfect squares, the sum of two perfect cubes, or the difference of two perfect cubes? If so, factor.

3. If the polynomial is a trinomial, is it a perfect-square trinomial or the product of two binomials? If so, factor.

4. If the polynomial has four terms, can it be factored by grouping? If so, factor.

5. Is each factor nonfactorable over the integers? If not, factor.

EXAMPLE 5 Factor. **A.** $x^2y + 2x^2 - y - 2$ **B.** $x^{4n} - y^{4n}$

Solution **A.** $x^2y + 2x^2 - y - 2$
$= (x^2y + 2x^2) - (y + 2)$ • Factor by grouping.
$= x^2(y + 2) - (y + 2)$
$= (y + 2)(x^2 - 1)$
$= (y + 2)(x + 1)(x - 1)$ • Factor the difference of two perfect squares.

B. $x^{4n} - y^{4n}$
$= (x^{2n})^2 - (y^{2n})^2$ • Factor the difference of
$= (x^{2n} + y^{2n})(x^{2n} - y^{2n})$ two perfect squares.
$= (x^{2n} + y^{2n})[(x^n)^2 - (y^n)^2]$ • Factor the difference of
$= (x^{2n} + y^{2n})(x^n + y^n)(x^n - y^n)$ two perfect squares.

PROBLEM 5 Factor. **A.** $4x - 4y - x^3 + x^2y$ **B.** $x^{4n} - x^{2n}y^{2n}$

Solution See page S17.

5.6 Concept Review

Determine whether the following statements are always true, sometimes true, or never true.

1. $a^2b^2c^2$ is an example of a perfect-square trinomial.

2. The factors of $a^3 + b^3$ are $(a + b)(a + b)(a + b)$.

3. The difference of two perfect cubes is not factorable.

4. Factoring out the GCF is the first thing to try in factoring polynomials.

5. The polynomial $b^3 + 1$ is not factorable.

5.6 Exercises

1 **Factor the difference of two perfect squares and factor perfect-square trinomials**

Which of the expressions are perfect squares?

1. $4; 8; 25x^6; 12y^{10}; 100x^4y^4$ **2.** $9; 18; 15a^8; 49b^{12}; 64a^{16}b^2$

Name the square root of the expression.

3. $16z^8$ **4.** $36d^{10}$ **5.** $81a^4b^6$ **6.** $25m^2n^{12}$

7. a. The binomial $16x^2 - 1$ is in the form $a^2 - b^2$, where $a = \underline{}$ and $b = \underline{}$.
b. Use the formula $a^2 - b^2 = (a + b)(a - b)$ to factor $16x^2 - 1$:
$16x^2 - 1 = (\underline{})(\underline{})$.

8. a. The trinomial $25y^2 - 20y + 4$ is in the form $a^2 - 2ab + b^2$, where $a = \underline{}$ and $b = \underline{}$.
b. Use the formula $a^2 - 2ab + b^2 = (a - b)^2$ to factor $25y^2 - 20y + 4$:
$25y^2 - 20y + 4 = (\underline{})^2$.

9. Explain how to factor the difference of two perfect squares.

10. What is a perfect-square trinomial?

Factor.

11. $x^2 - 16$

12. $y^2 - 49$

13. $4x^2 - 1$

14. $81x^2 - 4$

15. $b^2 - 2b + 1$

16. $a^2 + 14a + 49$

17. $16x^2 - 40x + 25$

18. $49x^2 + 28x + 4$

19. $x^2y^2 - 100$

20. $a^2b^2 - 25$

21. $x^2 + 4$

22. $a^2 + 16$

23. $x^2 + 6xy + 9y^2$

24. $4x^2y^2 + 12xy + 9$

25. $4x^2 - y^2$

26. $49a^2 - 16b^4$

27. $a^{2n} - 1$

28. $b^{2n} - 16$

29. $a^2 + 4a + 4$

30. $b^2 - 18b + 81$

31. $x^2 - 12x + 36$

32. $y^2 - 6y + 9$

33. $16x^2 - 121$

34. $49y^2 - 36$

35. $1 - 9a^2$

36. $16 - 81y^2$

37. $4a^2 + 4a - 1$

38. $9x^2 + 12x - 4$

39. $b^2 + 7b + 14$

40. $y^2 - 5y + 25$

41. $25 - a^2b^2$

42. $64 - x^2y^2$

43. $25a^2 - 40ab + 16b^2$

44. $4a^2 - 36ab + 81b^2$

45. $x^{2n} + 6x^n + 9$

46. $y^{2n} - 16y^n + 64$

47. Which expressions are equivalent to $x^{16} - 81$?
a. $(x^4 + 9)(x^4 - 9)$ **b.** $(x^8 + 9)(x^8 - 9)$ **c.** $(x^4 + 9)(x^2 + 3)(x^2 - 3)$
d. $(x^8 + 9)(x^4 + 3)(x^4 - 3)$

48. Given that a and b are positive numbers, which expressions can be factored?
a. $a^2x^2 - 2abx + b^2$ **b.** $-a^2x^2 - 2abx - b^2$ **c.** $-a^2x^2 + 2abx - b^2$
d. $a^2x^2 - 2abx - b^2$

2   Factor the sum or the difference of two cubes

Which of the expressions are perfect cubes?

49. $4; 8; x^9; a^8b^8; 27c^{15}d^{18}$

50. $9; 27; y^{12}; m^3n^6; 64mn^9$

Name the cube root of the expression.

51. $8x^9$

52. $27y^{15}$

53. $64a^6b^{18}$

54. $125c^{12}d^3$

55. a. The binomial $125x^3 + 8$ is in the form $a^3 + b^3$, where $a = $ __?__ and $b = $ __?__ .
  b. Use the formula $a^3 + b^3 = (a + b)(a^2 - ab + b^2)$ to factor $125x^3 + 8$: $125x^3 + 8 = ($__?__$)($__?__$)$.

56. a and b are positive numbers. Which expressions can be factored?
  a. $a^3x^3 - b^3y^3$ **b.** $a^9x^3 + b^9y^3$ **c.** $a^8x^3 + b^8y^3$
  d. $a^6x^3 - b^3y^6$

Factor.

57. $x^3 - 27$

58. $y^3 + 125$

59. $8x^3 - 1$

60. $64a^3 + 27$

61. $x^3 - y^3$

62. $x^3 - 8y^3$

63. $m^3 + n^3$

64. $27a^3 + b^3$

65. $64x^3 + 1$

66. $1 - 125b^3$

67. $27x^3 - 8y^3$

68. $64x^3 + 27y^3$

69. $x^3y^3 + 64$

70. $8x^3y^3 + 27$

71. $16x^3 - y^3$

72. $27x^3 - 8y^3$

73. $8x^3 - 9y^3$

74. $27a^3 - 16$

75. $(a - b)^3 - b^3$

76. $a^3 + (a + b)^3$

77. $x^{6n} + y^{3n}$

78. $x^{3n} + y^{3n}$

3   Factor trinomials that are quadratic in form

79. The trinomial $5x^4y^2 - 17x^2y - 12$ can be written in the quadratic form $5u^2 - 17u - 12$, where $u = $ __?__ .

80. The trinomial $8x^{4n} + 2x^{2n} - 3$ can be written in the quadratic form $8u^2 + 2u - 3$, where $u = $ __?__ .

81. What does it mean for a polynomial to be quadratic in form?

82. Do all polynomials that are quadratic in form factor? If not, give an example of one that does not factor.

Factor.

83. $x^2y^2 - 8xy + 15$

84. $x^2y^2 - 8xy - 33$

85. $x^2y^2 - 17xy + 60$

86. $a^2b^2 + 10ab + 24$

87. $x^4 - 9x^2 + 18$

88. $y^4 - 6y^2 - 16$

89. $b^4 - 13b^2 - 90$

90. $a^4 + 14a^2 + 45$

91. $x^4y^4 - 8x^2y^2 + 12$

92. $a^4b^4 + 11a^2b^2 - 26$

93. $x^{2n} + 3x^n + 2$

94. $a^{2n} - a^n - 12$

95. $3x^2y^2 - 14xy + 15$

96. $5x^2y^2 - 59xy + 44$

97. $6a^2b^2 - 23ab + 21$

98. $10a^2b^2 + 3ab - 7$

99. $2x^4 - 13x^2 - 15$

100. $3x^4 + 20x^2 + 32$

101. $2x^{2n} - 7x^n + 3$

102. $4x^{2n} + 8x^n - 5$

103. $6a^{2n} + 19a^n + 10$

4 Factor completely

104. When factoring a polynomial, you should look first for a ___?___ factor.

105. To factor a polynomial with four terms, try factoring by ___?___.

Factor.

106. $5x^2 + 10x + 5$

107. $12x^2 - 36x + 27$

108. $3x^4 - 81x$

109. $27a^4 - a$

110. $7x^2 - 28$

111. $20x^2 - 5$

112. $y^4 - 10y^3 + 21y^2$

113. $y^5 + 6y^4 - 55y^3$

114. $x^4 - 16$

115. $16x^4 - 81$

116. $8x^5 - 98x^3$

117. $16a - 2a^4$

118. $x^3y^3 - x^3$

119. $x^3 + 2x^2 - x - 2$

120. $2x^3 - 3x^2 - 8x + 12$

121. $2x^3 + 4x^2 - 3x - 6$

122. $3x^3 - 3x^2 + 4x - 4$

123. $x^3 + x^2 - 16x - 16$

124. $4x^3 + 8x^2 - 9x - 18$

125. $a^3b^6 - b^3$

126. $x^6y^6 - x^3y^3$

127. $x^4 - 2x^3 - 35x^2$

128. $x^4 + 15x^3 - 56x^2$

129. $4x^2 + 4x - 1$

130. $8x^4 - 40x^3 + 50x^2$

131. $6x^5 + 74x^4 + 24x^3$

132. $x^4 - y^4$

133. $16a^4 - b^4$

134. $x^6 + y^6$

135. $x^4 - 5x^2 - 4$

136. $a^4 - 25a^2 - 144$

137. $3b^5 - 24b^2$

138. $16a^4 - 2a$

139. $x^4y^2 - 5x^3y^3 + 6x^2y^4$

140. $a^4b^2 - 8a^3b^3 - 48a^2b^4$

141. $16x^3y + 4x^2y^2 - 42xy^3$

142. $24a^2b^2 - 14ab^3 - 90b^4$

143. $x^3 - 2x^2 - x + 2$

144. $x^3 - 2x^2 - 4x + 8$

145. $8xb - 8x - 4b + 4$

146. $4xy + 8x + 4y + 8$

147. $4x^2y^2 - 4x^2 - 9y^2 + 9$

148. $4x^4 - x^2 - 4x^2y^2 + y^2$

149. $x^5 - 4x^3 - 8x^2 + 32$

150. $x^6y^3 + x^3 - x^3y^3 - 1$

151. $a^{2n+2} - 6a^{n+2} + 9a^2$

152. $x^{2n+1} + 2x^{n+1} + x$

153. $2x^{n+2} - 7x^{n+1} + 3x^n$

154. $3b^{n+2} + 4b^{n+1} - 4b^n$

155. The factored form of a polynomial $P(x)$ is $x^n(x - a)(x + b)$. What is the degree of the polynomial P?

156. The factored form of a polynomial $P(x)$ is $x^{2n}(x^n + a)(x^n + b)$. What is the degree of the polynomial P?

5.6   Applying Concepts

Find all integers k such that the trinomial is a perfect-square trinomial.

157. $4x^2 - kx + 25$

158. $9x^2 - kx + 1$

159. $16x^2 + kxy + y^2$

160. $49x^2 + kxy + 64y^2$

Factor.

161. $ax^3 + b - bx^3 - a$

162. $xy^2 - 2b - x + 2by^2$

163. $y^{8n} - 2y^{4n} + 1$

164. $x^{6n} - 1$

Solve.

165. Number Problem The product of two numbers is 63. One of the two numbers is a perfect square. The other is a prime number. Find the sum of the two numbers.

166. Number Problem What is the smallest whole number by which 250 can be multiplied so that the product will be a perfect square?

167. Number Problem Palindromic numbers are natural numbers that remain unchanged when their digits are written in reverse order. Find all perfect squares less than 500 that are palindromic numbers.

168. **Food Science** A large circular cookie is cut from a square piece of dough. The diameter of the cookie is x cm. The piece of dough is x cm on a side and 1 cm deep. In terms of x, how many cubic centimeters of dough are left over? Use the approximation 3.14 for π.

169. Factor $x^4 + 64$. (*Suggestion:* Add and subtract $16x^2$ so that the expression becomes $(x^4 + 16x^2 + 64) - 16x^2$. Now factor the difference of two squares.)

170. Using the strategy of Exercise 169, factor $x^4 + 4$. (*Suggestion:* Add and subtract $4x^2$.)

171. Can a third-degree polynomial have factors $x - 1$, $x + 1$, $x - 3$, and $x + 4$? Why or why not?

5.7   Solving Equations by Factoring

OBJECTIVE 1   **Solve equations by factoring**

Consider the equation $ab = 0$. If a is not zero, then b must be zero. Conversely, if b is not zero, then a must be zero. This is summarized in the Principle of Zero Products.

> **Principle of Zero Products**
>
> If the product of two factors is zero, then at least one of the factors must be zero.
>
> $$\text{If } ab = 0, \text{ then } a = 0 \text{ or } b = 0.$$

The Principle of Zero Products is used to solve equations.

Solve: $(x - 4)(x + 2) = 0$

By the Principle of Zero Products, if $(x - 4)(x + 2) = 0$, then $x - 4 = 0$ or $x + 2 = 0$.

$$x - 4 = 0 \qquad\qquad x + 2 = 0$$
$$x = 4 \qquad\qquad\quad x = -2$$

Check:

$$\begin{array}{c|c}
(x - 4)(x + 2) = 0 & (x - 4)(x + 2) = 0 \\
\hline
(4 - 4)(4 + 2) \mid 0 & (-2 - 4)(-2 + 2) \mid 0 \\
0 \cdot 6 \mid 0 & -6 \cdot 0 \mid 0 \\
0 = 0 & 0 = 0
\end{array}$$

-2 and 4 check as solutions. The solutions are -2 and 4.

An equation of the form $ax^2 + bx + c = 0$, $a \neq 0$, is a **quadratic equation.** A quadratic equation is in **standard form** when the polynomial is written in descending order and is equal to zero.

Some quadratic equations can be solved by factoring and then using the Principle of Zero Products.

Solve: $2x^2 - x = 1$

<table>
<tr><td></td><td>$2x^2 - x = 1$</td></tr>
</table>

Write the equation in standard form. $2x^2 - x = 1$
$2x - x - 1 = 0$

Factor the trinomial. $(2x + 1)(x - 1) = 0$

Use the Principle of Zero Products. $2x + 1 = 0 \quad x - 1 = 0$

Solve each equation for x. $2x = -1 \quad x = 1$
$x = -\dfrac{1}{2}$

The solutions check.   The solutions are $-\dfrac{1}{2}$ and 1.

Take Note

Note the steps involved in solving a quadratic equation by factoring:

1. Write in standard form.
2. Factor.
3. Set each factor equal to 0.
4. Solve each equation.
5. Check the solutions.

The Principle of Zero Products can be extended to more than two factors. For example, if $abc = 0$, then $a = 0$, $b = 0$, or $c = 0$.

Solve: $x^3 - x^2 - 4x + 4 = 0$

Factor by grouping.
$$x^3 - x^2 - 4x + 4 = 0$$
$$(x^3 - x^2) - (4x - 4) = 0$$
$$x^2(x - 1) - 4(x - 1) = 0$$
$$(x - 1)(x^2 - 4) = 0$$
$$(x - 1)(x + 2)(x - 2) = 0$$

Use the Principle of Zero Products. $x - 1 = 0 \quad x + 2 = 0 \quad x - 2 = 0$

Solve each equation for x. $x = 1 \quad x = -2 \quad x = 2$

The solutions are -2, 1, and 2.

EXAMPLE 1 Solve.

A. $3x^2 + 5x = 2$ B. $(x + 4)(x - 3) = 8$
C. $x^3 - x^2 - 25x + 25 = 0$

Solution A. $3x^2 + 5x = 2$
$3x^2 + 5x - 2 = 0$ • Write the equation in standard form.

$(3x - 1)(x + 2) = 0$ • Factor the trinomial.
$3x - 1 = 0 \quad x + 2 = 0$ • Let each factor equal zero (the Principle of Zero Products).

$3x = 1 \quad x = -2$ • Solve each equation for x.
$x = \dfrac{1}{3}$

The solutions are $\dfrac{1}{3}$ and -2.   • Write the solutions.

B. $(x + 4)(x - 3) = 8$
$x^2 + x - 12 = 8$
- Write the equation in standard form by first multiplying the binomials.

$x^2 + x - 20 = 0$
- Subtract 8 from each side of the equation.

$(x + 5)(x - 4) = 0$
$x + 5 = 0 \quad x - 4 = 0$
$x = -5 \quad\quad x = 4$
- Factor the trinomial.
- Let each factor equal zero.
- Solve each equation for x.

The solutions are -5 and 4.
- Write the solutions.

C. $x^3 - x^2 - 25x + 25 = 0$
$(x^3 - x^2) - (25x - 25) = 0$
$x^2(x - 1) - 25(x - 1) = 0$
$(x^2 - 25)(x - 1) = 0$
$(x + 5)(x - 5)(x - 1) = 0$
$x + 5 = 0 \quad x - 5 = 0 \quad x - 1 = 0$
- Factor by grouping.

- Let each factor equal zero.

$x = -5 \quad\quad x = 5 \quad\quad x = 1$
- Solve each equation for x.

The solutions are -5, 1, and 5.
- Write the solutions.

PROBLEM 1 Solve.
A. $4x^2 + 11x = 3$ **B.** $(x - 2)(x + 5) = 8$
C. $x^3 + 4x^2 - 9x - 36 = 0$

Solution See page S17.

The Principle of Zero Products is used to find elements in the domain of a quadratic function that correspond to a given element in the range.

Take Note

You can check the values of c by evaluating the function.

$f(x) = x^2 - 3x - 5$
$f(4) = 4^2 - 3(4) - 5$
$\quad\quad = -1 \checkmark$

$f(-1) = (-1)^2 - 3(-1) - 5$
$\quad\quad\quad = -1 \checkmark$

EXAMPLE 2 Given that -1 is in the range of the function defined by $f(x) = x^2 - 3x - 5$, find two values of c for which $f(c) = -1$.

Solution
$f(c) = -1$
$c^2 - 3c - 5 = -1$
$c^2 - 3c - 4 = 0$
$(c - 4)(c + 1) = 0$
- $f(c) = c^2 - 3c - 5$
- Write in standard form.
- Solve for c by factoring.

$c - 4 = 0 \quad c + 1 = 0$
$c = 4 \quad\quad c = -1$

The values of c are -1 and 4.

PROBLEM 2 Given that 4 is in the range of the function defined by $s(t) = t^2 - t - 2$, find two values of c for which $s(c) = 4$.

Solution See page S17.

In Example 2, there are two values in the domain that can be paired with the range element -1. The two values are -1 and 4. Two ordered pairs that belong to the function are $(-1, -1)$ and $(4, -1)$. *Remember:* A function can have different first elements paired with the same second element. A function cannot have the same first element paired with different second elements.

The graph of $f(x) = x^2 - 3x - 5$ is shown at the left.

Recall that a *zero* of a function f is a number c for which $f(c) = 0$. The zeros of some quadratic functions can be found by using the Principle of Zero Products. Finding the zeros is similar to Example 2, where the range element is 0.

EXAMPLE 3	Find the zeros of $f(x) = x^2 - 2x - 8$.
Solution	We must find the values of c for which $f(c) = 0$.

$$f(c) = 0$$
$$c^2 - 2c - 8 = 0 \quad \bullet\ \textbf{\textit{f}(x)} = \textbf{\textit{x}}^2 - \textbf{2\textit{x}} - \textbf{8. Thus \textit{f}(\textit{c})} = \textbf{\textit{c}}^2 - \textbf{2\textit{c}} - \textbf{8.}$$
$$(c + 2)(c - 4) = 0 \quad \bullet\ \textbf{Factor and use the Principle of Zero Products.}$$

$$c + 2 = 0 \qquad c - 4 = 0$$
$$c = -2 \qquad\quad c = 4$$

The zeros of f are -2 and 4.

y

$(-2, 0)$ $(4, 0)$

$f(x) = x^2 - 2x - 8$

As mentioned earlier in the text, the x-coordinates of the x-intercepts of the graph of a function are zeros of the function. See the graph at the left.

PROBLEM 3	Find the zeros of $s(t) = t^2 + 5t - 14$.
Solution	See page S17.

OBJECTIVE **2**   ## Application problems

EXAMPLE 4	An architect wants to design a fountain to be placed on the front lawn of a new art museum. The base of the fountain is to be 30 ft by 40 ft with a uniform brick walkway around the fountain. The total area of the fountain and the walkway is 2576 ft². How wide is the walkway?
Strategy	Let x represent the width of the brick walkway. Then the width of the fountain and walkway is $30 + 2x$, and the length of the fountain and walkway is $40 + 2x$. Use the formula $A = LW$, where $A = 2576$, to write an equation.
Solution	

$$A = LW$$
$$2576 = (40 + 2x)(30 + 2x) \quad \bullet\ \textbf{Replace \textit{A}, \textit{L}, and \textit{W} by their values.}$$
$$2576 = 1200 + 140x + 4x^2 \quad \bullet\ \textbf{Multiply.}$$
$$0 = 4x^2 + 140x - 1376$$
$$0 = x^2 + 35x - 344 \quad \bullet\ \textbf{Divide each side by 4.}$$
$$0 = (x - 8)(x + 43) \quad \bullet\ \textbf{Factor and use the Principle of Zero Products.}$$

$$x - 8 = 0 \qquad x + 43 = 0$$
$$x = 8 \qquad\qquad x = -43$$

A walkway -43 ft wide would not make sense.

The walkway must be 8 ft wide.

PROBLEM 4	A diagonal of a polygon is a line from one vertex of the polygon to a nonadjacent vertex. The number of diagonals, D, of a polygon with n sides is given by $D = \dfrac{n(n - 3)}{2}$. Find the number of sides for a polygon that has 20 diagonals.
Solution	See page S17.

5.7 Concept Review

Determine whether the following statements are always true, sometimes true, or never true.

1. The Principle of Zero Products can be stated as follows: If $ab = 0$, then $a = 0$ or $b = 0$.

2. One side of an equation must be zero in order for us to solve the equation by factoring.

3. Two solutions of an equation are found when solving an equation by the Principle of Zero Products.

4. The Principle of Zero Products can be used to solve a second-degree equation.

5. If n is an integer, then $n + 1$ and $n + 3$ represent odd integers.

6. By the Principle of Zero Products, if $(x + 2)(x + 3) = 4$, then $x + 2 = 4$ or $x + 3 = 4$.

5.7 Exercises

1 Solve equations by factoring

1. ✎ What is a quadratic equation? How does it differ from a linear equation? Give an example of each type of equation.

2. The Principle of Zero Products states that if the product of two factors is ___?___, then at least one of the factors is ___?___.

3. Of the two quadratic equations $0 = 5x^2 + 2x - 3$ and $x^2 - 4x = 3$, the one that is in standard form is ___?___.

4. Solve: $3x^2 - 5x - 2 = 0$

$$3x^2 - 5x - 2 = 0$$

• The equation is in ___?___ form.

$$(x - \underline{\quad?\quad})(3x + \underline{\quad?\quad}) = 0$$

• Factor the trinomial.

$$x - 2 = \underline{\quad?\quad} \qquad 3x + 1 = \underline{\quad?\quad}$$

• Use the Principle of Zero Products to set each factor equal to 0.

$$x = \underline{\quad?\quad} \qquad x = \underline{\quad?\quad}$$

• Solve each equation for x.

5. Let $f(x) = x^2 + x - 15$. To find two values of c for which $f(c) = 5$, solve the equation $x^2 + x - 15 = \underline{\quad?\quad}$.

6. How is the Principle of Zero Products used to solve some quadratic equations?

Solve.

7. $(y + 4)(y + 6) = 0$

8. $(a - 5)(a - 2) = 0$

9. $x(x - 7) = 0$

10. $b(b + 8) = 0$

11. $3z(2z + 5) = 0$

12. $4y(3y - 2) = 0$

13. $(2x + 3)(x - 7) = 0$

14. $(4a - 1)(a + 9) = 0$

15. $b^2 - 49 = 0$

16. $4z^2 - 1 = 0$

17. $9t^2 - 16 = 0$

18. $x^2 + x - 6 = 0$

19. $y^2 + 4y - 5 = 0$

20. $a^2 - 8a + 16 = 0$

21. $2b^2 - 5b - 12 = 0$

22. $t^2 - 8t = 0$

23. $x^2 - 9x = 0$

24. $2y^2 - 10y = 0$

25. $3a^2 - 12a = 0$

26. $b^2 - 4b = 32$

27. $z^2 - 3z = 28$

28. $2x^2 - 5x = 12$

29. $3t^2 + 13t = 10$

30. $4y^2 - 19y = 5$

31. $5b^2 - 17b = -6$

32. $6a^2 + a = 2$

33. $8x^2 - 10x = 3$

34. $z(z - 1) = 20$

35. $y(y - 2) = 35$

36. $t(t + 1) = 42$

37. $x(x - 12) = -27$

38. $x(2x - 5) = 12$

39. $y(3y - 2) = 8$

40. $2b^2 - 6b = b - 3$

41. $3a^2 - 4a = 20 - 15a$

42. $2t^2 + 5t = 6t + 15$

43. $(y + 5)(y - 7) = -20$

44. $(x + 2)(x - 6) = 20$

45. $(b + 5)(b + 10) = 6$

46. $(a - 9)(a - 1) = -7$

47. $(t - 3)^2 = 1$

48. $(y - 4)^2 = 4$

49. $(3 - x)^2 + x^2 = 5$

50. $(2 - b)^2 + b^2 = 10$

51. $(a - 1)^2 = 3a - 5$

52. $2x^3 + x^2 - 8x - 4 = 0$

53. $x^3 + 4x^2 - x - 4 = 0$

54. $12x^3 - 8x^2 - 3x + 2 = 0$

Find the values c in the domain of f for which $f(c)$ is the indicated value.

55. $f(x) = x^2 - 3x + 3; f(c) = 1$

56. $f(x) = x^2 + 4x - 2; f(c) = 3$

57. $f(x) = 2x^2 - x - 5; f(c) = -4$

58. $f(x) = 6x^2 - 5x - 9; f(c) = -3$

59. $f(x) = 4x^2 - 4x + 3; f(c) = 2$

60. $f(x) = x^2 - 6x + 12; f(c) = 3$

Find the zeros of the function.

61. $f(x) = x^2 + 3x - 4$

62. $g(x) = x^2 + 2x - 15$

63. $s(t) = t^2 - 4t - 12$

64. $f(t) = t^2 + 3x - 18$

65. $f(x) = 2x^2 - 5x + 3$

66. $g(x) = 3x^2 - 7x - 6$

67. $p(x) = x^2 + 6x + 9$

68. $f(x) = 4x^2 - 4x + 1$

2   Application problems

69. Let x represent a positive integer. Then the next consecutive positive integer is ___?___, and an expression that represents the sum of the squares of the two integers is ___?___.

70. Suppose you are given the following problem: "The sum of the squares of two consecutive positive integers is 61. Find the two integers." The equation you solve to determine the answer has solutions -6 and 5. Which solution should be eliminated and why?

71. Number Problem The sum of a number and its square is 90. Find the number.

72. Number Problem The sum of a number and its square is 132. Find the number.

73. Number Problem The sum of the squares of two consecutive positive integers is equal to 145. Find the two integers.

74. Number Problem The sum of the squares of two consecutive odd integers is equal to 290. Find the two integers.

75. Number Problem The sum of the cube of a number and the product of the number and twelve is equal to seven times the square of the number. Find the number.

76. Number Problem The sum of the cube of a number and the product of the number and seven is equal to eight times the square of the number. Find the number.

77. Geometry The length of a rectangle is 5 in. more than twice the width. The area is 168 in². Find the width and length of the rectangle.

78. Geometry The width of a rectangle is 5 ft less than the length. The area of the rectangle is 300 ft². Find the length and width of the rectangle.

79. Construction A trough is made from a rectangular piece of metal by folding up the sides as shown in the figure at the right. What should the value of x be so that the volume is 72 m³?

80. Geometry The number of possible diagonals, D, in a polygon with n sides is given by $D = \frac{n(n-3)}{2}$. Find the number of sides for a polygon with 54 diagonals.

81. Space Science A small rocket is launched with an acceleration of 10 m/s². The velocity, v, of the rocket after it has traveled s meters is given by $v^2 = 20s$. Find the velocity of this rocket after it has traveled 500 m.

82. Construction A pole is being secured with two guy wires, as shown in the figure at the right. What is the value of x so that the 20-foot guy wire will attach as shown?

83. Geometry The length of the base of a triangle is three times the height. The area of the triangle is 24 cm². Find the base and height of the triangle.

84. Geometry The height of a triangle is 4 cm more than twice the length of the base. The area of the triangle is 35 cm². Find the height of the triangle.

85. Physics An object is thrown downward, with an initial speed of 16 ft/s, from the top of a building 480 ft high. How many seconds later will the object hit the ground? Use the equation $d = vt + 16t^2$, where d is the distance in feet, v is the initial speed in feet per second, and t is the time in seconds.

86. Physics A stone is thrown into an empty well with an initial speed of 8 ft/s. The well is 624 ft deep. How many seconds later will the stone hit the bottom of the well? Use the equation $d = vt + 16t^2$, where d is the distance in feet, v is the initial speed in feet per second, and t is the time in seconds.

87. Geometry The length of a rectangle is 6 cm, and the width is 3 cm. If both the length and the width are increased by equal amounts, the area of the rectangle is increased by 70 cm². Find the length and width of the larger rectangle.

88. Geometry The width of a rectangle is 4 cm, and the length is 8 cm. If both the width and the length are increased by equal amounts, the area of the rectangle is increased by 64 cm². Find the length and width of the larger rectangle.

5.7 Applying Concepts

89. Find $3n^2 + 2n - 1$ if $n(n + 6) = 16$.

90. Find $4y^2 - y + 3$ if $(y - 1)(y + 2) = 4$.

91. Find $-a^2 + 5a - 2$ if $6a(a - 1) = 36$.

Find the values c in the domain of f for which $f(c)$ is the indicated value.

92. $f(x) = x^3 + 9x^2 - x - 14; f(c) = -5$ **93.** $f(x) = x^3 + 3x^2 - 4x - 11; f(c) = 1$

94. Geometry The perimeter of a rectangular garden is 44 m. The area of the garden is 120 m². Find the length and width of the garden.

95. Construction A rectangular piece of cardboard is 10 in. longer than it is wide. Squares 2 in. on a side are to be cut from each corner and then the sides folded up to make an open box with a volume of 112 in³. Find the length and width of the piece of cardboard.

96. Geometry The sides of a rectangular box have areas of 16 cm², 20 cm², and 80 cm². Find the volume of the box.

97. Write an equation whose solutions are 3, 2, and −1.

98. The following seems to show that $1 = 2$. Explain the error.

$$a = b$$
$$a^2 = ab$$
$$a^2 - b^2 = ab - b^2$$
$$(a - b)(a + b) = b(a - b)$$
$$a + b = b$$
$$b + b = b$$
$$2b = b$$
$$2 = 1$$

- **Multiply each side of the equation by *a*.**
- **Subtract *b²* from each side of the equation.**
- **Factor.**
- **Divide each side by *a − b*.**
- **Because *a = b*, substitute *b* for *a*.**

- **Divide both sides by *b*.**

Focus on Problem Solving

Find a Counterexample   When you are faced with an assertion, it may be that the assertion is false. For instance, consider the statement "Every prime number is an odd number." This assertion is false because the prime number 2 is an even number.

Finding an example that illustrates that an assertion is false is called finding a *counterexample*. The number 2 is a counterexample to the assertion that every prime number is an odd number.

If you are given an unfamiliar problem, one strategy to consider as a means of solving the problem is to find a counterexample. For each of the following problems, answer *true* if the assertion is always true. If the assertion is not true, answer *false* and give a counterexample. If terms are used that you do not understand, consult a reference to find their meaning.

1. If x is a real number, then x^2 is always positive.

2. The product of an odd integer and an even integer is an even integer.

3. If m is a positive integer, then $2m + 1$ is always a positive odd integer.

4. If $x < y$, then $x^2 < y^2$.

5. Given any three positive numbers a, b, and c, it is possible to construct a triangle whose sides have lengths a, b, and c.

6. The product of two irrational numbers is an irrational number.

7. If n is a positive integer greater than 2, then $(1 \cdot 2 \cdot 3 \cdot 4 \cdot \cdots \cdot n) + 1$ is a prime number.

8. Draw a polygon with more than three sides. Select two different points inside the polygon and join the points with a line segment. The line segment always lies completely inside the polygon.

9. Let A, B, and C be three points in the plane that are not collinear. Let d_1 be the distance from A to B, and let d_2 be the distance from A to C. Then the distance between B and C is less than $d_1 + d_2$.

10. Consider the line segment AB shown at the left. Two points, C and D, are randomly selected on the line segment, and three new segments are formed: AC, CD, and DB. The three new line segments can always be connected to form a triangle.

It may not be easy to establish that an assertion is true or to find a counterexample to the assertion. For instance, consider the assertion that every positive integer greater than 3 can be written as the sum of two primes. For example, $9 = 2 + 7$, $6 = 3 + 3$, and $8 = 3 + 5$. Is this assertion always true? (*Note:* This assertion, called **Goldbach's conjecture,** has never been proved, nor has a counterexample ever been found!)

Projects & Group Activities

Astronomical Distances and Scientific Notation

Astronomers have units of measurement that are useful for measuring vast distances in space. Two of these units are the astronomical unit and the light-year. An **astronomical unit** is the average distance between Earth and the sun. A **light-year** is the distance a ray of light travels in 1 year.

1. Light travels at a speed of 1.86×10^5 mi/s. Find the measure of 1 light-year in miles. Use a 365-day year.

2. The distance between Earth and the star Alpha Centauri is approximately 25 trillion miles. Find the distance between Earth and Alpha Centauri in light-years. Round to the nearest hundredth.

3. The Coma cluster of galaxies is approximately 2.8×10^8 light-years from Earth. Find the distance, in miles, from the Coma Cluster to Earth. Write the answer in scientific notation.

4. One astronomical unit (A.U.) is 9.3×10^7 mi. The star Pollux in the constellation Gemini is 1.8228×10^{12} mi from Earth. Find the distance from Pollux to Earth in astronomical units.

5. One light-year is equal to approximately how many astronomical units? Round to the nearest thousand.

Shown below are data on the planets in our solar system. The planets are listed in alphabetical order.

Gemini

Planet	Distance from the Sun (in kilometers)	Mass (in kilograms)
Earth	1.50×10^8	5.97×10^{24}
Jupiter	7.79×10^8	1.90×10^{27}
Mars	2.28×10^8	6.42×10^{23}
Mercury	5.79×10^7	3.30×10^{23}
Neptune	4.50×10^9	1.02×10^{26}
Pluto	5.87×10^9	1.25×10^{22}
Saturn	1.43×10^9	5.68×10^{26}
Uranus	2.87×10^9	8.68×10^{25}
Venus	1.08×10^8	4.87×10^{24}

6. Arrange the planets in order from closest to the sun to farthest from the sun.

7. Arrange the planets in order from the one with the least mass to the one with the greatest mass.

8. Write a rule for ordering numbers written in scientific notation.

Chapter 5 Summary

Key Words	*Examples*
A **monomial** is a number, a variable, or a product of numbers and variables. [5.1.1, p. 287]	$2, x, 3x, -4x^2, 23x^2y^3$ are monomials.
The **degree of a polynomial** is the greatest of the degrees of any of its terms. [5.2.1, p. 301]	The degree of the polynomial $x^3 + 3x^2y^2 - 4xy - 3$ is 4.
A **polynomial** is a variable expression in which the terms are monomials. [5.2.1, p. 301]	$x^4 - 2xy - 32x + 8$ is a polynomial. The terms are x^4, $-2xy$, $-32x$, and 8.
A polynomial of two terms is a **binomial**. [5.2.1, p. 301]	$3x - y$ is a binomial.
A polynomial of three terms is a **trinomial**. [5.2.1, p. 301]	$x^2 - 2x + 4$ is a trinomial.
Synthetic division is a shorter method of dividing a polynomial by a binomial of the form $x - a$. This method uses only the coefficients of the variable terms. [5.4.3, p. 324]	$$\begin{array}{r} 2 \,\rfloor\, \begin{array}{rrrr} 3 & 0 & -9 & -5 \\ & 6 & 12 & 6 \\ \hline 3 & 6 & 3 & 1 \end{array} \end{array}$$ $(3x^3 - 9x - 5) \div (x - 2)$ $= 3x^2 + 6x + 3 + \dfrac{1}{x - 2}$
A number written in **scientific notation** is a number written in the form $a \times 10^n$, where $1 \le a < 10$. [5.1.3, p. 293]	$0.000000023 = 2.3 \times 10^{-8}$
To **factor a polynomial** means to write the polynomial as the product of other polynomials. [5.5.1, p. 332]	$x^2 + 5x + 6 = (x + 2)(x + 3)$
A **quadratic trinomial** is a polynomial of the form $ax^2 + bx + c$, where a and b are nonzero coefficients and c is a nonzero constant. [5.5.3, p. 334]	$3x^2 - 2x + 8, a = 3, b = -2, c = 8$
To **factor a quadratic trinomial** means to express the trinomial as the product of two binomials. [5.5.3, p. 334]	$3x^2 + 10x - 8 = (3x - 2)(x + 4)$
A polynomial is **nonfactorable over the integers** if it does not factor using only integers. [5.5.3, p. 336]	$x^2 + x + 1$ is nonfactorable.
The product of a term and itself is a **perfect square**. [5.6.1, p. 345]	$(5x)(5x) = 25x^2$; $25x^2$ is a perfect square.
The **square root of a perfect square** is one of the two equal factors of the perfect square. [5.6.1, p. 345]	$\sqrt{25x^2} = 5x$
The product of three factors is called a **perfect cube**. [5.6.2, p. 346]	$(2x)(2x)(2x) = 8x^3$; $8x^3$ is a perfect cube.

The **cube root** of a perfect cube is one of the three equal factors of the perfect cube.   [5.6.2, p. 347]

$$\sqrt[3]{8x^3} = 2x$$

A **quadratic equation** is an equation of the form

$$ax^2 + bx + c = 0, \text{ where } a \neq 0$$

A quadratic equation is in standard form when the polynomial is in descending order and equal to zero.   [5.7.1, p. 355]

$3x^2 + 3x + 8 = 0$ is a quadratic equation in standard form.

Essential Rules and Procedures

Rule for Multiplying Exponential Expressions
If m and n are integers, then $x^m \cdot x^n = x^{m+n}$.   [5.1.1, p. 288]

$x^2 \cdot x^5 = x^{2+5} = x^7$

Rule for Simplifying a Power of an Exponential Expression
If m and n are integers, then $(x^m)^n = x^{mn}$.   [5.1.1, p. 288]

$(x^4)^3 = x^{4 \cdot 3} = x^{12}$

Rule for Dividing Exponential Expressions
If m and n are integers and $x \neq 0$, then $\dfrac{x^m}{x^n} = x^{m-n}$.

[5.1.2, p. 291]

$\dfrac{x^{12}}{x^7} = x^{12-7} = x^5$

Rule for Simplifying Powers of Products
If m, n, and p are integers, then $(x^m y^n)^p = x^{mp} y^{np}$.
[5.1.1, p. 288]

$(x^2 y^5)^3 = x^{2 \cdot 3} y^{5 \cdot 3} = x^6 y^{15}$

Rule for Simplifying Powers of Quotients
If m, n, and p are integers and $y \neq 0$, then $\left(\dfrac{x^m}{y^n}\right)^p = \dfrac{x^{mp}}{y^{np}}$.

[5.1.2, p. 290]

$\left(\dfrac{x^2}{y^4}\right)^5 = \dfrac{x^{2 \cdot 5}}{y^{4 \cdot 5}} = \dfrac{x^{10}}{y^{20}}$

Definition of a Negative Exponent
If $n > 0$ and $x \neq 0$, then $x^{-n} = \dfrac{1}{x^n}$ and $\dfrac{1}{x^{-n}} = x^n$.   [5.1.2, p. 290]

$x^{-3} = \dfrac{1}{x^3} \qquad \dfrac{1}{x^{-4}} = x^4$

Definition of Zero as an Exponent
If $x \neq 0$, then $x^0 = 1$.   [5.1.2, p. 289]

$5^0 = 1 \qquad (2xy^4)^0 = 1$

To divide a polynomial by a monomial, divide each term of the polynomial by the monomial.   [5.4.1, p. 321]

$$\dfrac{12x^5 + 8x^3 - 6x}{4x^2} = 3x^3 + 2x - \dfrac{3}{2x}$$

Remainder Theorem
If the polynomial $P(x)$ is divided by $x - a$, the remainder is $P(a)$.
[5.4.4, p. 326]

$P(x) = x^3 - x^2 + x - 1$

```
-2 | 1  -1   1    -1
   |     -2   6   -14
   ------------------
     1  -3   7   -15
```

$P(-2) = -15$

Factors of the Difference of Two Perfect Squares
$a^2 - b^2 = (a - b)(a + b)$ [5.6.1, p. 345]

$x^2 - 9 = (x - 3)(x + 3)$

Factors of a Perfect-Square Trinomial
$a^2 + 2ab + b^2 = (a + b)^2$ [5.6.1, p. 345]

$4x^2 + 12x + 9 = (2x + 3)^2$

Factoring the Sum or Difference of Two Cubes
$a^3 + b^3 = (a + b)(a^2 - ab + b^2)$
$a^3 - b^3 = (a - b)(a^2 + ab + b^2)$ [5.6.2, p. 347]

$x^3 + 64 = (x + 4)(x^2 - 4x + 16)$
$8b^3 - 1 = (2b - 1)(4b^2 + 2b + 1)$

The Principle of Zero Products
If $ab = 0$, then $a = 0$ or $b = 0$. [5.7.1, p. 354]

$(x - 4)(x + 2) = 0$
$x - 4 = 0$ $x + 2 = 0$

Chapter 5 Review Exercises

1. Add: $(3x^2 - 2x - 6) + (-x^2 - 3x + 4)$

2. Subtract: $(5x^2 - 8xy + 2y^2) - (x^2 - 3y^2)$

3. Multiply: $(5x^2yz^4)(2xy^3z^{-1})(7x^{-2}y^{-2}z^3)$

4. Multiply: $(2x^{-1}y^2z^5)^4(-3x^3yz^{-3})$

5. Simplify: $\dfrac{3x^4yz^{-1}}{-12xy^3z^2}$

6. Simplify: $\dfrac{(2a^4b^{-3}c^2)^3}{(2a^3b^2c^{-1})^4}$

7. Write 93,000,000 in scientific notation.

8. Write 2.54×10^{-3} in decimal notation.

9. Simplify: $\dfrac{3 \times 10^{-3}}{1.5 \times 10^3}$

10. Given $P(x) = 2x^3 - x + 7$, evaluate $P(-2)$.

11. Graph: $y = x^2 + 1$

12. Identify **a.** the leading coefficient, **b.** the constant term, and **c.** the degree of the polynomial $P(x) = 3x^5 - 3x^2 + 7x + 8$.

13. Use the Remainder Theorem to evaluate $P(x) = -2x^3 + 2x^2 - 4$ when $x = -3$.

14. Divide: $\dfrac{6x^2y^3 - 18x^3y^2 + 12x^4y}{3x^2y}$

15. Divide: $\dfrac{15x^2 + 2x - 2}{3x - 2}$

16. Divide: $\dfrac{12x^2 - 16x - 7}{6x + 1}$

17. Divide: $\dfrac{4x^3 + 27x^2 + 10x + 2}{x + 6}$

18. Divide: $\dfrac{x^4 - 4}{x - 4}$

19. Multiply: $4x^2y(3x^3y^2 + 2xy - 7y^3)$

20. Multiply: $a^{2n+3}(a^n - 5a + 2)$

21. Simplify: $5x^2 - 4x[x - (3x + 2) + x]$

22. Multiply: $(x^{2n} - x)(x^{n+1} - 3)$

23. Multiply: $(x + 6)(x^3 - 3x^2 - 5x + 1)$

24. Multiply: $(x - 4)(3x + 2)(2x - 3)$

25. Multiply: $(5a + 2b)(5a - 2b)$

26. Simplify: $(4x - 3y)^2$

27. Factor: $18a^5b^2 - 12a^3b^3 + 30a^2b$

28. Factor: $5x^{n+5} + x^{n+3} + 4x^2$

29. Factor: $x(y - 3) + 4(3 - y)$

30. Factor: $2ax + 4bx - 3ay - 6by$

31. Factor: $x^2 + 12x + 35$

32. Factor: $12 + x - x^2$

33. Factor: $x^2 - 16x + 63$

34. Factor: $6x^2 - 31x + 18$

35. Factor: $24x^2 + 61x - 8$

36. Factor: $x^2y^2 - 9$

37. Factor: $4x^2 + 12xy + 9y^2$

38. Factor: $x^{2n} - 12x^n + 36$

39. Factor: $36 - a^{2n}$

40. Factor: $64a^3 - 27b^3$

41. Factor: $8 - y^{3n}$

42. Factor: $15x^4 + x^2 - 6$

43. Factor: $36x^8 - 36x^4 + 5$

44. Factor: $21x^4y^4 + 23x^2y^2 + 6$

45. Factor: $3a^6 - 15a^4 - 18a^2$

46. Factor: $x^{4n} - 8x^{2n} + 16$

47. Factor: $3a^4b - 3ab^4$

48. Solve: $x^3 - x^2 - 6x = 0$

49. Solve: $6x^2 + 60 = 39x$

50. Solve: $x^3 - 16x = 0$

51. Solve: $y^3 + y^2 - 36y - 36 = 0$

52. Find the zeros of $f(x) = x^2 - 5x - 6$.

53. Astronomy The most distant object visible from Earth without the aid of a telescope is the Great Galaxy of Andromeda. It takes light from the Great Galaxy of Andromeda 2.2×10^6 years to travel to Earth. Light travels about 5.9×10^{12} mph. How far from Earth is the Great Galaxy of Andromeda?

54. Solar Power Light from the sun supplies Earth with 2.4×10^{14} horsepower. Earth receives only 2.2×10^{-7} of the power generated by the sun. How much power is generated by the sun?

55. Geometry The length of a rectangle is $(5x + 3)$ cm. The width is $(2x - 7)$ cm. Find the area of the rectangle in terms of the variable x.

56. Geometry The length of the side of a cube is $(3x - 1)$ ft. Find the volume of the cube in terms of the variable x.

57. Geometry Find the area of the figure shown at the right. All dimensions given are in inches.

58. Integer Problem The sum of the squares of two consecutive even integers is 52. Find the two integers.

59. Integer Problem The sum of a number and its square is 56. Find the number.

60. Geometry The length of a rectangle is 2 m more than twice the width. The area of the rectangle is 60 m². Find the length of the rectangle.

Chapter 5 Test

1. Subtract:
$(6x^3 - 7x^2 + 6x - 7) - (4x^3 - 3x^2 + 7)$

2. Simplify: $(-4a^2b)^3(-ab^4)$

3. Simplify: $\dfrac{(2a^{-4}b^2)^3}{4a^{-2}b^{-1}}$

4. Write the number 0.000000501 in scientific notation.

5. Write the number of seconds in 1 week in scientific notation.

6. Simplify: $(2x^{-3}y)^{-4}$

7. Simplify: $-5x[3 - 2(2x - 4) - 3x]$

8. Multiply: $(3a + 4b)(2a - 7b)$

9. Multiply: $(3t^3 - 4t^2 + 1)(2t^2 - 5)$

10. Simplify: $(3z - 5)^2$

11. Divide: $\dfrac{25x^2y^2 - 15x^2y + 20xy^2}{5x^2y}$

12. Divide: $(4x^3 + x - 15) \div (2x - 3)$

13. Divide: $(x^3 - 5x^2 + 5x + 5) \div (x - 3)$

14. Given $P(x) = 3x^2 - 8x + 1$, evaluate $P(2)$.

15. Use the Remainder Theorem to evaluate $P(x) = -x^3 + 4x - 8$ when $x = -2$.

16. Factor: $6a^4 - 13a^2 - 5$

17. Factor: $12x^3 + 12x^2 - 45x$

18. Factor: $16x^2 - 25$

19. Factor: $16t^2 + 24t + 9$

20. Factor: $27x^3 - 8$

21. Factor: $6x^2 - 4x - 3xa + 2a$

22. Find the zeros of $g(x) = 2x^2 - 5x - 12$.

23. Solve: $6x^2 = x + 1$

24. Solve: $6x^3 + x^2 - 6x - 1 = 0$

25. Geometry The length of a rectangle is $(5x + 1)$ ft. The width is $(2x - 1)$ ft. Find the area of the rectangle in terms of the variable x.

26. Space Travel A space vehicle travels 2.4×10^5 mi from Earth to the moon at an average velocity of 2×10^4 mph. How long does it take the space vehicle to reach the moon?

Cumulative Review Exercises

1. Simplify: $8 - 2[-3 - (-1)]^2 + 4$

2. Evaluate $\dfrac{2a - b}{b - c}$ when $a = 4, b = -2$, and $c = 6$.

3. Identify the property that justifies the statement $2x + (-2x) = 0$.

4. Simplify: $2x - 4[x - 2(3 - 2x) + 4]$

5. Solve: $\dfrac{2}{3} - y = \dfrac{5}{6}$

6. Solve: $8x - 3 - x = -6 + 3x - 8$

7. Divide: $\dfrac{x^3 - 3}{x - 3}$

8. Solve: $3 - |2 - 3x| = -2$

9. Given $P(x) = 3x^2 - 2x + 2$, evaluate $P(-2)$.

10. What values of x are excluded from the domain of the function $f(x) = \dfrac{x + 1}{x + 2}$?

11. Find the range of the function given by $F(x) = 3x^2 - 4$ if the domain is $\{-2, -1, 0, 1, 2\}$.

12. Find the slope of the line that contains the points $(-2, 3)$ and $(4, 2)$.

13. Find the equation of the line that contains the point $(-1, 2)$ and has slope $-\dfrac{3}{2}$.

14. Find the equation of the line that contains the point $(-2, 4)$ and is perpendicular to the line $3x + 2y = 4$.

15. Solve by using Cramer's Rule: $\begin{aligned} 2x - 3y &= 2 \\ x + y &= -3 \end{aligned}$

16. Solve by the addition method:
$$\begin{aligned} x - y + z &= 0 \\ 2x + y - 3z &= -7 \\ -x + 2y + 2z &= 5 \end{aligned}$$

17. Graph $3x - 4y = 12$ by using the x- and y-intercepts.

18. Graph the solution set of $-3x + 2y < 6$.

19. Solve by graphing: $\begin{aligned} x - 2y &= 3 \\ -2x + y &= -3 \end{aligned}$

20. Graph the solution set: $\begin{aligned} 2x + y &< 3 \\ -6x + 3y &\geq 4 \end{aligned}$

21. Simplify: $(4a^{-2}b^3)(2a^3b^{-1})^{-2}$

22. Simplify: $\dfrac{(5x^3y^{-3}z)^{-2}}{y^4z^{-2}}$

23. Simplify: $3 - (3 - 3^{-1})^{-1}$

24. Multiply: $(2x + 3)(2x^2 - 3x + 1)$

25. Factor: $-4x^3 + 14x^2 - 12x$

26. Factor: $a(x - y) - b(y - x)$

27. Factor: $x^4 - 16$

28. Factor: $2x^3 - 16$

29. **Integer Problem** The sum of two integers is twenty-four. The difference between four times the smaller integer and nine is three less than twice the larger integer. Find the integers.

30. **Metallurgy** How many ounces of pure gold that costs $360 per ounce must be mixed with 80 oz of an alloy that costs $120 per ounce to make a mixture that costs $200 per ounce?

31. **Uniform Motion** Two cyclists are 25 mi apart and are traveling toward each other. One cyclist is traveling at $\frac{2}{3}$ the rate of the other cyclist. They pass in 2 h. Find the rate of each cyclist.

32. Investments If $3000 is invested at an annual simple interest rate of 7.5%, how much additional money must be invested at an annual simple interest rate of 10% so that the total interest earned is 9% of the total investment?

33. Travel The graph below shows the relationship between the distance traveled in miles and the time of travel in hours. Find the slope of the line between the two points on the graph. Write a sentence that states the meaning of the slope.

6 Rational Expressions

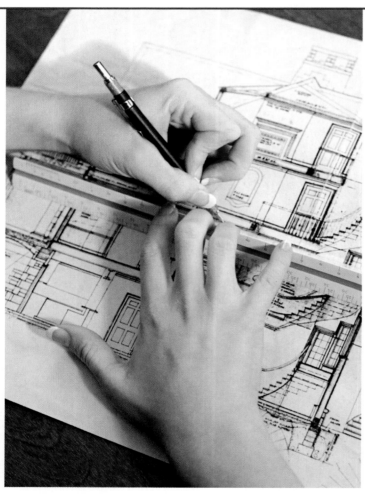

Designing architectural plans such as these requires a great deal of skill and concentration. This architect is creating a scale drawing, in which each dimension is carefully produced using ratios and proportions. These drawings must be very accurate and consistent, since contractors will depend on them to create the real building. You will have a chance to work with scale drawings in **Exercise 19 on page 418,** which asks you to determine the dimensions of a room if one-quarter inch on paper represents one foot in real life.

Online Study Center

DVD **SSM**

Need help? For online student resources, such as section quizzes, visit the Online Study Center at college.hmco.com/info/aufmanndevmathhb.

Prep Test

1. Find the LCM of 10 and 25.

For Exercises 2 to 5, add, subtract, multiply, or divide.

2. $-\dfrac{3}{8} \cdot \dfrac{4}{9}$

3. $-\dfrac{4}{5} \div \dfrac{8}{15}$

4. $-\dfrac{5}{6} + \dfrac{7}{8}$

5. $-\dfrac{3}{8} - \left(-\dfrac{7}{12}\right)$

6. Simplify: $\dfrac{\dfrac{2}{3} - \dfrac{1}{4}}{\dfrac{1}{8} - 2}$

7. Evaluate $\dfrac{2x - 3}{x^2 - x + 1}$ for $x = 2$.

8. Solve: $4(2x + 1) = 3(x - 2)$

9. Solve: $10\left(\dfrac{t}{2} + \dfrac{t}{5}\right) = 10(1)$

10. Two planes start from the same point and fly in opposite directions. The first plane is flying 20 mph slower than the second plane. In 2 h, the planes are 480 mi apart. Find the rate of each plane.

6.1 Introduction to Rational Functions

OBJECTIVE **1**   **Find the domain of a rational function**

An expression in which the numerator and denominator are polynomials is called a **rational expression.** Examples of rational expressions are shown at the right.

$$\dfrac{9}{z} \qquad \dfrac{3x + 4}{2x^2 + 1} \qquad \dfrac{x^3 - x + 1}{x^2 - 3x - 5}$$

The expression $\dfrac{\sqrt{x} + 3}{x}$ is not a rational expression because $\sqrt{x} + 3$ is not a polynomial.

A function that is written in terms of a rational expression is a **rational function.** Each of the following equations represents a rational function.

$$f(x) = \dfrac{x^2 + 3}{2x - 1} \qquad g(t) = \dfrac{3}{t^2 - 4} \qquad R(z) = \dfrac{z^2 + 3z - 1}{z^2 + z - 12}$$

To evaluate a rational function, replace the variable by its value. Then simplify.

EXAMPLE 1   Given $f(x) = \dfrac{3x - 4}{x^2 - 2x + 1}$, find $f(-3)$.

Solution $f(x) = \dfrac{3x - 4}{x^2 - 2x + 1}$

$f(-3) = \dfrac{3(-3) - 4}{(-3)^2 - 2(-3) + 1}$ • **Substitute** -3 **for** x.

$f(-3) = \dfrac{-9 - 4}{9 + 6 + 1}$

$f(-3) = \dfrac{-13}{16}$

$f(-3) = -\dfrac{13}{16}$

PROBLEM 1   Given $f(x) = \dfrac{3 - 5x}{x^2 + 5x + 6}$, find $f(2)$.

Solution   See page S18.

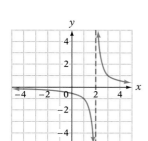

The graph of $f(x) = \dfrac{1}{x - 2}$ is shown at the left. Note that the graph never intersects the line $x = 2$ (shown as a dashed line). This value of x is excluded from the domain of $f(x) = \dfrac{1}{x - 2}$.

Because division by zero is not defined, the domain of a rational function must exclude those numbers for which the value of the polynomial in the denominator is zero.

Determine the domain of $g(x) = \dfrac{x^2 + 4}{3x - 6}$.

The domain of g must exclude values of x for which the denominator is zero.

Set the denominator equal to zero. $3x - 6 = 0$

Solve for x. $3x = 6$

This value must be *excluded* from the domain. $x = 2$

The domain of g is $\{x \mid x \neq 2\}$.

EXAMPLE 2   Find the domain of $f(x) = \dfrac{2x - 6}{x^2 - 3x - 4}$.

Solution   The domain must exclude values of x for which $x^2 - 3x - 4 = 0$. Solve this equation for x. Because $x^2 - 3x - 4$ factors over the integers, solve the equation by using the Principle of Zero Products.

Take Note

In Chapter 8, we will discuss how to solve this problem when the polynomial does not factor.

$$x^2 - 3x - 4 = 0$$
$$(x + 1)(x - 4) = 0$$

$$x + 1 = 0 \qquad x - 4 = 0$$
$$x = -1 \qquad x = 4$$

When $x = -1$ and $x = 4$, the value of the denominator is zero. Therefore, these values must be excluded from the domain of f.

The domain is $\{x \mid x \neq -1, 4\}$.

PROBLEM 2   Find the domain of $g(x) = \dfrac{5 - x}{x^2 - 4}$.

■   **Solution**   See page S18.

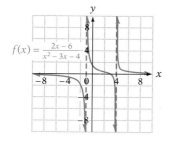

$f(x) = \dfrac{2x - 6}{x^2 - 3x - 4}$

The graph of the function in Example 2 is shown at the left. Note that the graph never intersects the lines $x = -1$ and $x = 4$ (shown as dashed lines). These are the two values of x excluded from the domain of f.

EXAMPLE 3   Find the domain of $f(x) = \dfrac{3x + 2}{x^2 + 1}$.

Solution   The domain must exclude values of x for which $x^2 + 1 = 0$. It is not possible for $x^2 + 1 = 0$, because $x^2 \geq 0$, and a positive number added to a number equal to or greater than zero cannot equal zero. Therefore, there are no real numbers that must be excluded from the domain of f.

The domain is $\{x \mid x \in \text{real numbers}\}$.

PROBLEM 3   Find the domain of $p(x) = \dfrac{6x}{x^2 + 4}$.

■   **Solution**   See page S18.

$f(x) = \dfrac{3x + 2}{x^2 + 1}$

The graph of the function in Example 3 is shown at the left. Because the domain of f is all real numbers, there are points on the graph for all values of x.

OBJECTIVE **2**   **Simplify rational expressions**

A rational expression is in **simplest form** when the numerator and denominator have no common factors other than 1. The Multiplication Property of One is used to write a rational expression in simplest form.

■

Simplify: $\dfrac{x^2 - 25}{x^2 + 13x + 40}$

$$\frac{x^2 - 25}{x^2 + 13x + 40} = \frac{(x - 5)(x + 5)}{(x + 8)(x + 5)} = \frac{(x - 5)}{(x + 8)} \cdot \frac{(x + 5)}{(x + 5)} = \frac{x - 5}{x + 8} \cdot 1 = \frac{x - 5}{x + 8},$$

$$x \neq -8, -5$$

The requirement $x \neq -8, -5$ must be included because division by 0 is not allowed.

■

The simplification above is usually shown with slashes to indicate that a common factor has been removed:

$$\frac{x^2 - 25}{x^2 + 13x + 40} = \frac{(x - 5)\cancel{(x + 5)}}{(x + 8)\cancel{(x + 5)}} = \frac{x - 5}{x + 8}, x \neq -8, -5$$

We will show a simplification with slashes. We will also omit the restrictions that prevent division by zero. Nonetheless, those restrictions *always* are implied.

EXAMPLE 4   Simplify.

    A. $\dfrac{x^2 - 16}{x^2 + 11x + 28}$ **B.** $\dfrac{12 + 5x - 2x^2}{2x^2 - 3x - 20}$ **C.** $\dfrac{x^{2n} + x^n - 2}{x^{2n} - 1}$

Solution   **A.** $\dfrac{x^2 - 16}{x^2 + 11x + 28} = \dfrac{(x + 4)(x - 4)}{(x + 4)(x + 7)}$ • Factor the numerator and the denominator.

$$= \frac{\cancel{(x + 4)}^{1}(x - 4)}{\cancel{(x + 4)}_{1}(x + 7)}$$ • Divide by the common factors.

$$= \frac{x - 4}{x + 7}$$ • Write the answer in simplest form.

B. $\dfrac{12 + 5x - 2x^2}{2x^2 - 3x - 20} = \dfrac{(4 - x)(3 + 2x)}{(x - 4)(2x + 5)}$ • Factor the numerator and the denominator.

$$= \frac{\cancel{(4 - x)}^{-1}(3 + 2x)}{\cancel{(x - 4)}_{1}(2x + 5)}$$ • Divide by the common factors. Remember that $4 - x = -(x - 4)$. Therefore, $\dfrac{4 - x}{x - 4} = \dfrac{-(x - 4)}{x - 4} = \dfrac{-1}{1} = -1$.

$$= -\frac{2x + 3}{2x + 5}$$ • Write the answer in simplest form.

C. $\dfrac{x^{2n} + x^n - 2}{x^{2n} - 1} = \dfrac{(x^n - 1)(x^n + 2)}{(x^n - 1)(x^n + 1)}$ • Factor the numerator and the denominator.

$$= \frac{\cancel{(x^n - 1)}^{1}(x^n + 2)}{\cancel{(x^n - 1)}_{1}(x^n + 1)}$$ • Divide by the common factors.

$$= \frac{x^n + 2}{x^n + 1}$$

PROBLEM 4   Simplify.

    A. $\dfrac{6x^4 - 24x^3}{12x^3 - 48x^2}$ **B.** $\dfrac{20x - 15x^2}{15x^3 - 5x^2 - 20x}$

    C. $\dfrac{x^{2n} + x^n - 12}{x^{2n} - 3x^n}$

Solution   See page S18.

Take Note

Recall that

$$(b - a) = -(a - b)$$

Therefore,

$$(4 - x) = -(x - 4)$$

In general,

$$\frac{b - a}{a - b} = \frac{\cancel{-(a - b)}^{1}}{\cancel{a - b}_{1}} = -1$$

6.1 Concept Review

Determine whether the following statements are always true, sometimes true, or never true.

1. $\dfrac{x^2 + 2x + 1}{x^{\frac{1}{2}} - 2x + 4}$ is a rational expression.

2. A rational expression with a variable in the denominator will have restrictions on the value of x.

3. When simplifying rational expressions, divide the numerator and denominator by the GCF of the numerator and denominator.

4. If $x \neq y$, the rational expression $\dfrac{x - y}{y - x}$ can be reduced to -1.

5. $\dfrac{a + 4}{a^2 + 6a + 8} = \dfrac{a + 4}{(a + 4)(a + 2)} = \dfrac{\cancel{a + 4}}{\cancel{(a + 4)}(a + 2)} = \dfrac{0}{a + 2} = 0$

6. For all values of a, $\dfrac{a(a + 4)}{a} = a + 4$.

6.1 Exercises

1 Find the domain of a rational function

1. What is a rational function? Give an example of a rational function.

2. What values are excluded from the domain of a rational function?

Complete Exercises 3 and 4 by replacing the question marks. Use the rational function $f(x) = \dfrac{x + 2}{1 - 2x}$.

3. To find $f(-3)$, substitute -3 for x: $f(-3) = \dfrac{\underline{} + 2}{1 - 2(\underline{})} = \dfrac{\underline{}}{1 + \underline{}}$

   $= \underline{}$.

4. Find the domain of the function. The domain must exclude values of x for which the denominator is $\underline{}$.

   $1 - 2x = \underline{}$.   • Set the denominator equal to zero.

   $-2x = \underline{}$.   • Subtract 1 from each side of the equation.

   $x = \underline{}$.   • Divide each side of the equation by -2.

   The domain must exclude the value $\underline{}$, so the domain is $\{x \mid x \neq \underline{}\}$.

5. Given $f(x) = \dfrac{2}{x - 3}$, find $f(4)$.

6. Given $f(x) = \dfrac{-7}{5 - x}$, find $f(-2)$.

7. Given $f(x) = \dfrac{x - 2}{x + 4}$, find $f(-2)$.

8. Given $f(x) = \dfrac{x - 3}{2x - 1}$, find $f(3)$.

9. Given $f(x) = \dfrac{1}{x^2 - 2x + 1}$, find $f(-2)$.

10. Given $f(x) = \dfrac{-3}{x^2 - 4x + 2}$, find $f(-1)$.

11. Given $f(x) = \dfrac{x - 2}{2x^2 + 3x + 8}$, find $f(3)$.

12. Given $f(x) = \dfrac{x^2}{3x^2 - 3x + 5}$, find $f(4)$.

13. Given $f(x) = \dfrac{x^2 - 2x}{x^3 - x + 4}$, find $f(-1)$.

14. Given $f(x) = \dfrac{8 - x^2}{x^3 - x^2 + 4}$, find $f(-3)$.

Find the domain of the function.

15. $H(x) = \dfrac{4}{x - 3}$

16. $G(x) = \dfrac{-2}{x + 2}$

17. $f(x) = \dfrac{x}{x + 4}$

18. $g(x) = \dfrac{3x}{x - 5}$

19. $R(x) = \dfrac{5x}{3x + 9}$

20. $p(x) = \dfrac{-2x}{6 - 2x}$

21. $q(x) = \dfrac{4 - x}{(x - 4)(x + 2)}$

22. $h(x) = \dfrac{2x + 1}{(x + 1)(x + 5)}$

23. $V(x) = \dfrac{x^2}{(2x + 5)(3x - 6)}$

24. $F(x) = \dfrac{x^2 - 1}{(4x + 8)(3x - 1)}$

25. $f(x) = \dfrac{x^2 + 1}{x}$

26. $g(x) = \dfrac{2x^3 - x - 1}{x^2}$

27. $k(x) = \dfrac{x + 1}{x^2 + 1}$

28. $P(x) = \dfrac{2x + 3}{2x^2 + 3}$

29. $f(x) = \dfrac{2x - 1}{x^2 + x - 6}$

30. $G(x) = \dfrac{3 - 4x}{x^2 + 4x - 5}$

31. $A(x) = \dfrac{5x + 2}{x^2 + 2x - 24}$

32. $h(x) = \dfrac{3x}{x^2 - 4}$

33. $f(x) = \dfrac{4x - 7}{3x^2 + 12}$

34. $g(x) = \dfrac{x^2 + x + 1}{5x^2 + 1}$

35. $G(x) = \dfrac{x^2 + 1}{6x^2 - 13x + 6}$

36. $A(x) = \dfrac{5x - 7}{x(x - 2)(x - 3)}$

37. $f(x) = \dfrac{x^2 + 8x + 4}{2x^3 + 9x^2 - 5x}$

38. $H(x) = \dfrac{x^4 - 1}{2x^3 + 2x^2 - 24x}$

39. The graph of the function $f(x) = -\dfrac{1}{x + 1}$ never crosses the vertical line $x = -1$. Is the portion of the graph that is to the right of the vertical line $x = -1$ above the x-axis or below the x-axis?

40. The graph of the function $f(x) = \dfrac{1}{(x-1)(x+2)}$ never crosses the vertical lines $x = 1$ and $x = -2$. Is the portion of the graph that is in between the vertical lines $x = 1$ and $x = -2$ above the x-axis or below the x-axis?

2 Simplify rational expressions

41. When is a rational expression in simplest form?

42. Are the rational expressions $\dfrac{x(x-2)}{2(x-2)}$ and $\dfrac{x}{2}$ equal for all values of x? Why or why not?

43. To simplify a rational expression, first write the numerator and denominator in ___?___ form. Then simplify the rational expression by dividing its numerator and denominator by any ___?___ factors.

44. Simplify: $\dfrac{x^2 - 1}{3x^2 + 3x}$

$$\dfrac{x^2 - 1}{3x^2 + 3x} = \dfrac{(x - \underline{\ ?\ })(x + \underline{\ ?\ })}{(\underline{\ ?\ })(x + 1)}$$

• Factor the numerator and denominator.

$$= \dfrac{\underline{\ ?\ }}{\underline{\ ?\ }}$$

• Divide the numerator and denominator by the common factor ___?___.

Simplify.

45. $\dfrac{4 - 8x}{4}$

46. $\dfrac{8y + 2}{2}$

47. $\dfrac{6x^2 - 2x}{2x}$

48. $\dfrac{3y - 12y^2}{3y}$

49. $\dfrac{8x^2(x - 3)}{4x(x - 3)}$

50. $\dfrac{16y^4(y + 8)}{12y^3(y + 8)}$

51. $\dfrac{2x - 6}{3x - x^2}$

52. $\dfrac{3a^2 - 6a}{12 - 6a}$

53. $\dfrac{6x^3 - 15x^2}{12x^2 - 30x}$

54. $\dfrac{-36a^2 - 48a}{18a^3 + 24a^2}$

55. $\dfrac{a^2 + 4a}{4a - 16}$

56. $\dfrac{3x - 6}{x^2 + 2x}$

57. $\dfrac{16x^3 - 8x^2 + 12x}{4x}$

58. $\dfrac{3x^3y^3 - 12x^2y^2 + 15xy}{3xy}$

59. $\dfrac{-10a^4 - 20a^3 + 30a^2}{-10a^2}$

60. $\dfrac{-7a^5 - 14a^4 + 21a^3}{-7a^3}$

61. $\dfrac{3x^{3n} - 9x^{2n}}{12x^{2n}}$

62. $\dfrac{8a^n}{4a^{2n} - 8a^n}$

63. $\dfrac{x^2 - 7x + 12}{x^2 - 9x + 20}$

64. $\dfrac{x^2 - x - 20}{x^2 - 2x - 15}$

65. $\dfrac{x^2 - xy - 2y^2}{x^2 - 3xy + 2y^2}$

66. $\dfrac{2x^2 + 7xy - 4y^2}{4x^2 - 4xy + y^2}$

67. $\dfrac{6 - x - x^2}{3x^2 - 10x + 8}$

68. $\dfrac{3x^2 + 10x - 8}{8 - 14x + 3x^2}$

69. $\dfrac{14 - 19x - 3x^2}{3x^2 - 23x + 14}$

70. $\dfrac{x^2 + x - 12}{x^2 - x - 12}$

71. $\dfrac{a^2 - 7a + 10}{a^2 + 9a + 14}$

72. $\dfrac{x^2 - 2x}{x^2 + 2x}$

73. $\dfrac{a^2 - b^2}{a^3 + b^3}$

74. $\dfrac{x^4 - y^4}{x^2 + y^2}$

75. $\dfrac{x^3 + y^3}{3x^3 - 3x^2y + 3xy^2}$

76. $\dfrac{3x^3 + 3x^2 + 3x}{9x^3 - 9}$

77. $\dfrac{x^3 - 4xy^2}{3x^3 - 2x^2y - 8xy^2}$

78. $\dfrac{4a^2 - 8ab + 4b^2}{4a^2 - 4b^2}$

79. $\dfrac{4x^3 - 14x^2 + 12x}{24x + 4x^2 - 8x^3}$

80. $\dfrac{6x^3 - 15x^2 - 75x}{150x + 30x^2 - 12x^3}$

81. $\dfrac{x^2 - 4}{a(x + 2) - b(x + 2)}$

82. $\dfrac{x^2(a - 2) - a + 2}{ax^2 - ax}$

83. $\dfrac{x^4 + 3x^2 + 2}{x^4 - 1}$

84. $\dfrac{x^4 - 2x^2 - 3}{x^4 + 2x^2 + 1}$

85. $\dfrac{x^2y^2 + 4xy - 21}{x^2y^2 - 10xy + 21}$

86. $\dfrac{6x^2y^2 + 11xy + 4}{9x^2y^2 + 9xy - 4}$

87. $\dfrac{a^{2n} - a^n - 2}{a^{2n} + 3a^n + 2}$

88. $\dfrac{a^{2n} + a^n - 12}{a^{2n} - 2a^n - 3}$

89. True or false? $\dfrac{4x^2 - 8x}{16 - 8x} = \dfrac{x^2}{4}$

90. True or false? $\dfrac{4x + 1}{8x + 2} = \dfrac{1}{2}$

6.1 Applying Concepts

91. Evaluate $h(x) = \dfrac{x + 2}{x - 3}$ when $x = 2.9$, 2.99, 2.999, and 2.9999. On the basis of your evaluations, complete the following sentence. As x becomes closer to 3, the values of $h(x)$ ———.

92. Evaluate $h(x) = \dfrac{x + 2}{x - 3}$ when $x = 3.1, 3.01, 3.001,$ and 3.0001. On the basis of your evaluations, complete the following sentence. As x becomes closer to 3, the values of $h(x)$ _____ .

93. Photography The focal length of a camera lens is the distance from the lens to the point where parallel rays of light come to a focus.

|—Focal length—|

The relationship among the focal length (F), the distance between the object and the lens (x, in meters), and the distance between the lens and the film (y, in millimeters) is given by $\dfrac{1}{F} = \dfrac{1}{x} + \dfrac{1}{y}$. A camera used by a professional photographer has a dial that allows the focal length to be set at a constant value. Suppose a photographer chooses a focal length of 50 mm. Substituting this value into the equation, solving for y, and using $y = f(x)$ notation yield $f(x) = \dfrac{50x}{x - 50}$.

  a. Graph this equation for $50 < x \le 6000$.
  b. The point whose coordinates are (2000, 51), to the nearest integer, is on the graph of the function. Give an interpretation of this ordered pair.
  c. Give a reason for choosing the domain such that $x > 50$.
  d. Photographers refer to depth of field as a range of distances in which an object remains in focus. Use the graph to explain why the depth of field is larger for objects that are far from the lens than for objects that are close to the lens.

94. Suppose that $F(x) = \dfrac{g(x)}{h(x)}$ and that, for some real number a, $g(a) = 0$ and $h(a) = 0$. Is $F(x)$ in simplest form? Explain your answer.

95. Why can the numerator and denominator of a rational expression be divided by their common factors? What conditions must be placed on the value of the variables when a rational expression is simplified?

6.2 Operations on Rational Expressions

OBJECTIVE 1 **Multiply and divide rational expressions**

The product of two fractions is a fraction whose numerator is the product of the numerators of the two fractions and whose denominator is the product of the denominators of the two fractions.

$$\frac{a}{b} \cdot \frac{c}{d} = \frac{ac}{bd}$$

$$\frac{5}{a+2} \cdot \frac{b-3}{3} = \frac{5(b-3)}{(a+2)3} = \frac{5b-15}{3a+6}$$

The product of two rational expressions can often be simplified by factoring the numerator and the denominator.

Simplify: $\dfrac{x^2-2x}{2x^2+x-15} \cdot \dfrac{2x^2-x-10}{x^2-4}$

$$\frac{x^2-2x}{2x^2+x-15} \cdot \frac{2x^2-x-10}{x^2-4}$$

Factor the numerator and denominator of each fraction.

$$= \frac{x(x-2)}{(x+3)(2x-5)} \cdot \frac{(x+2)(2x-5)}{(x+2)(x-2)}$$

Multiply.

$$= \frac{x(x-2)(x+2)(2x-5)}{(x+3)(2x-5)(x+2)(x-2)}$$

Divide by the common factors.

$$= \frac{x \overset{1}{\cancel{(x-2)}} \overset{1}{\cancel{(x+2)}} \overset{1}{\cancel{(2x-5)}}}{(x+3)\underset{1}{\cancel{(2x-5)}}\underset{1}{\cancel{(x+2)}}\underset{1}{\cancel{(x-2)}}}$$

Write the answer in simplest form.

$$= \frac{x}{x+3}$$

EXAMPLE 1 Multiply.

A. $\dfrac{2x^2-6x}{3x-6} \cdot \dfrac{6x-12}{8x^3-12x^2}$ **B.** $\dfrac{6x^2+x-2}{6x^2+7x+2} \cdot \dfrac{2x^2+9x+4}{4-7x-2x^2}$

Solution **A.** $\dfrac{2x^2-6x}{3x-6} \cdot \dfrac{6x-12}{8x^3-12x^2} = \dfrac{2x(x-3)}{3(x-2)} \cdot \dfrac{6(x-2)}{4x^2(2x-3)}$

$$= \frac{12x(x-3)\overset{1}{\cancel{(x-2)}}}{12x^2\underset{1}{\cancel{(x-2)}}(2x-3)} = \frac{x-3}{x(2x-3)}$$

B. $\dfrac{6x^2+x-2}{6x^2+7x+2} \cdot \dfrac{2x^2+9x+4}{4-7x-2x^2}$

$$= \frac{(2x-1)(3x+2)}{(3x+2)(2x+1)} \cdot \frac{(2x+1)(x+4)}{(1-2x)(4+x)}$$

$$= \frac{\overset{-1}{\cancel{(2x-1)}}\overset{1}{\cancel{(3x+2)}}\overset{1}{\cancel{(2x+1)}}\overset{1}{\cancel{(x+4)}}}{\underset{1}{\cancel{(3x+2)}}\underset{1}{\cancel{(2x+1)}}\underset{1}{\cancel{(1-2x)}}\underset{1}{\cancel{(x+4)}}} = -1$$

PROBLEM 1   Multiply.

A. $\dfrac{12 + 5x - 3x^2}{x^2 + 2x - 15} \cdot \dfrac{2x^2 + x - 45}{3x^2 + 4x}$

B. $\dfrac{2x^2 - 13x + 20}{x^2 - 16} \cdot \dfrac{2x^2 + 9x + 4}{6x^2 - 7x - 5}$

■   **Solution**   See page S18.

The **reciprocal of a rational expression** is the rational expression with the numerator and denominator interchanged.

Rational expression $\left\{ \begin{array}{cc} \dfrac{a}{b} & \dfrac{b}{a} \\ a^2 - 2y & 4 \\ \dfrac{}{4} & \dfrac{}{a^2 - 2y} \end{array} \right\}$ Reciprocal

To divide two rational expressions, multiply by the reciprocal of the divisor.

$$\frac{a}{b} \div \frac{c}{d} = \frac{a}{b} \cdot \frac{d}{c} = \frac{ad}{bc}$$

$$\frac{2}{a} \div \frac{5}{b} = \frac{2}{a} \cdot \frac{b}{5} = \frac{2b}{5a}$$

$$\frac{x + y}{2} \div \frac{x - y}{5} = \frac{x + y}{2} \cdot \frac{5}{x - y} = \frac{(x + y)5}{2(x - y)} = \frac{5x + 5y}{2x - 2y}$$

EXAMPLE 2   Divide.

A. $\dfrac{12x^2y^2 - 24xy^2}{5z^2} \div \dfrac{4x^3y - 8x^2y}{3z^4}$

B. $\dfrac{3y^2 - 10y + 8}{3y^2 + 8y - 16} \div \dfrac{2y^2 - 7y + 6}{2y^2 + 5y - 12}$

Solution   A. $\dfrac{12x^2y^2 - 24xy^2}{5z^2} \div \dfrac{4x^3y - 8x^2y}{3z^4}$

$$= \frac{12x^2y^2 - 24xy^2}{5z^2} \cdot \frac{3z^4}{4x^3y - 8x^2y}$$

$$= \frac{12xy^2(x - 2)}{5z^2} \cdot \frac{3z^4}{4x^2y(x - 2)}$$

$$= \frac{36xy^2z^4\overset{1}{\cancel{(x-2)}}}{20x^2yz^2\underset{1}{\cancel{(x-2)}}} = \frac{9yz^2}{5x}$$

B. $\dfrac{3y^2 - 10y + 8}{3y^2 + 8y - 16} \div \dfrac{2y^2 - 7y + 6}{2y^2 + 5y - 12}$

$$= \frac{3y^2 - 10y + 8}{3y^2 + 8y - 16} \cdot \frac{2y^2 + 5y - 12}{2y^2 - 7y + 6}$$

$$= \frac{(y-2)(3y-4)}{(3y-4)(y+4)} \cdot \frac{(y+4)(2y-3)}{(y-2)(2y-3)}$$

$$= \frac{\overset{1}{\cancel{(y-2)}}\overset{1}{\cancel{(3y-4)}}\overset{1}{\cancel{(y+4)}}\overset{1}{\cancel{(2y-3)}}}{\underset{1}{\cancel{(3y-4)}}\underset{1}{\cancel{(y+4)}}\underset{1}{\cancel{(y-2)}}\underset{1}{\cancel{(2y-3)}}} = 1$$

PROBLEM 2   Divide.

A. $\dfrac{6x^2 - 3xy}{10ab^4} \div \dfrac{16x^2y^2 - 8xy^3}{15a^2b^2}$

B. $\dfrac{6x^2 - 7x + 2}{3x^2 + x - 2} \div \dfrac{4x^2 - 8x + 3}{5x^2 + x - 4}$

■   **Solution**   See page S18.

OBJECTIVE **2**   **Add and subtract rational expressions**

When adding rational expressions in which the denominators are the same, add the numerators. The denominator of the sum is the common denominator. Write the answer in simplest form.

$$\frac{a}{c} + \frac{b}{c} = \frac{a+b}{c}$$

$$\frac{4x}{15} + \frac{8x}{15} = \frac{4x + 8x}{15} = \frac{12x}{15} = \frac{4x}{5}$$

$$\frac{a}{a^2 - b^2} + \frac{b}{a^2 - b^2} = \frac{a+b}{a^2 - b^2} = \frac{a+b}{(a-b)(a+b)} = \frac{\overset{1}{\cancel{(a+b)}}}{(a-b)\underset{1}{\cancel{(a+b)}}} = \frac{1}{a-b}$$

When subtracting rational expressions in which the denominators are the same, subtract the numerators. The denominator of the difference is the common denominator. Write the answer in simplest form.

$$\frac{y}{y-3} - \frac{3}{y-3} = \frac{y-3}{y-3} = \frac{\overset{1}{\cancel{(y-3)}}}{\underset{1}{\cancel{(y-3)}}} = 1$$

Take Note

Be careful with signs when subtracting algebraic fractions. Note that we must subtract the entire numerator.

$(7x - 12) - (3x - 6) =$
            $7x - 12 - 3x + 6$

$$\frac{7x - 12}{2x^2 + 5x - 12} - \frac{3x - 6}{2x^2 + 5x - 12} = \frac{(7x - 12) - (3x - 6)}{2x^2 + 5x - 12}$$

$$= \frac{7x - 12 - 3x + 6}{2x^2 + 5x - 12}$$

$$= \frac{4x - 6}{2x^2 + 5x - 12}$$

$$= \frac{2(2x - 3)}{(2x - 3)(x + 4)}$$

$$= \frac{2\overset{1}{\cancel{(2x-3)}}}{\underset{1}{\cancel{(2x-3)}}(x + 4)} = \frac{2}{x + 4}$$

Before two rational expressions with different denominators can be added or subtracted, both rational expressions must be expressed in terms of a common denominator. This common denominator is the LCM of the denominators of the rational expressions.

The LCM of two or more polynomials is the simplest polynomial that contains the factors of each polynomial. To find the LCM, first factor each polynomial completely. The LCM is the product of each factor the greatest number of times it occurs in any one factorization.

To find the LCM of $3x^2 + 15x$ and $6x^4 + 24x^3 - 30x^2$, factor each polynomial.

$$3x^2 + 15x = 3x(x + 5)$$
$$6x^4 + 24x^3 - 30x^2 = 6x^2(x^2 + 4x - 5) = 6x^2(x - 1)(x + 5)$$

The LCM is the product of the LCM of the numerical coefficients and each variable factor the greatest number of times it occurs in any one factorization.

$$\text{LCM} = 6x^2(x - 1)(x + 5)$$

Write the fractions $\dfrac{x + 2}{x^2 - 2x}$ and $\dfrac{5x}{3x - 6}$ in terms of the LCM of the denominators.

Find the LCM of the denominators.
The LCM is $3x(x - 2)$.

For each fraction, multiply the numerator and denominator by the factor whose product with the denominator is the LCM.

$$\frac{x + 2}{x^2 - 2x} = \frac{x + 2}{x(x - 2)} \cdot \frac{3}{3} = \frac{3x + 6}{3x(x - 2)}$$

$$\frac{5x}{3x - 6} = \frac{5x}{3(x - 2)} \cdot \frac{x}{x} = \frac{5x^2}{3x(x - 2)}$$

Add: $\dfrac{3x}{2x - 3} + \dfrac{3x + 6}{2x^2 + x - 6}$

The LCM of $2x - 3$ and $2x^2 + x - 6$ is $(2x - 3)(x + 2)$.

$$\frac{3x}{2x - 3} + \frac{3x + 6}{2x^2 + x - 6}$$

Rewrite each fraction in terms of the LCM of the denominators.

$$= \frac{3x}{2x - 3} \cdot \frac{x + 2}{x + 2} + \frac{3x + 6}{(2x - 3)(x + 2)}$$

$$= \frac{3x^2 + 6x}{(2x - 3)(x + 2)} + \frac{3x + 6}{(2x - 3)(x + 2)}$$

Add the fractions.

$$= \frac{(3x^2 + 6x) + (3x + 6)}{(2x - 3)(x + 2)}$$

$$= \frac{3x^2 + 9x + 6}{(2x - 3)(x + 2)}$$

Factor the numerator to determine whether there are common factors in the numerator and denominator.

$$= \frac{3(x^2 + 3x + 2)}{(2x - 3)(x + 2)}$$

$$= \frac{3(x + 2)(x + 1)}{(2x - 3)(x + 2)}$$

$$= \frac{3\overset{1}{\cancel{(x + 2)}}(x + 1)}{(2x - 3)\underset{1}{\cancel{(x + 2)}}} = \frac{3(x + 1)}{2x - 3}$$

EXAMPLE 3 Subtract: $\dfrac{x}{2x-4} - \dfrac{4-x}{x^2-2x}$

Solution

$\dfrac{x}{2x-4} - \dfrac{4-x}{x^2-2x}$

$= \dfrac{x}{2(x-2)} \cdot \dfrac{x}{x} - \dfrac{4-x}{x(x-2)} \cdot \dfrac{2}{2}$ • Write each fraction in terms of the LCM. The LCM is $2x(x-2)$.

$= \dfrac{x^2}{2x(x-2)} - \dfrac{8-2x}{2x(x-2)}$ • Subtract the fractions.

$= \dfrac{x^2 - (8-2x)}{2x(x-2)}$

$= \dfrac{x^2 + 2x - 8}{2x(x-2)}$

$= \dfrac{(x+4)(x-2)}{2x(x-2)}$

$= \dfrac{\overset{1}{(x+4)\cancel{(x-2)}}}{2x\underset{1}{\cancel{(x-2)}}} = \dfrac{x+4}{2x}$ • Divide by the common factors.

PROBLEM 3 Add: $\dfrac{a-3}{a^2-5a} + \dfrac{a-9}{a^2-25}$

Solution See page S19.

EXAMPLE 4 Simplify: $\dfrac{6x-23}{2x^2+x-6} + \dfrac{3x}{2x-3} - \dfrac{5}{x+2}$

Solution

$\dfrac{6x-23}{2x^2+x-6} + \dfrac{3x}{2x-3} - \dfrac{5}{x+2}$

$= \dfrac{6x-23}{(2x-3)(x+2)} + \dfrac{3x}{2x-3} \cdot \dfrac{x+2}{x+2} - \dfrac{5}{x+2} \cdot \dfrac{2x-3}{2x-3}$

$= \dfrac{6x-23}{(2x-3)(x+2)} + \dfrac{3x^2+6x}{(2x-3)(x+2)} - \dfrac{10x-15}{(2x-3)(x+2)}$

$= \dfrac{(6x-23) + (3x^2+6x) - (10x-15)}{(2x-3)(x+2)}$

$= \dfrac{6x-23+3x^2+6x-10x+15}{(2x-3)(x+2)}$

$= \dfrac{3x^2+2x-8}{(2x-3)(x+2)} = \dfrac{(3x-4)(x+2)}{(2x-3)(x+2)} = \dfrac{3x-4}{2x-3}$

PROBLEM 4 Simplify: $\dfrac{x-1}{x-2} - \dfrac{7-6x}{2x^2-7x+6} + \dfrac{4}{2x-3}$

Solution See page S19.

6.2   Concept Review

Determine whether the following statements are always true, sometimes true, or never true.

1. To divide an expression by a nonzero rational number, multiply the expression by the reciprocal of the divisor.

2. To multiply rational expressions, multiply the numerators and multiply the denominators.

3. $\dfrac{3}{x+y} + \dfrac{2}{x+y} = \dfrac{3+2}{(x+y)+(x+y)} = \dfrac{5}{2x+2y}$

4. $\dfrac{2x}{x(x+4)} - \dfrac{2}{x+4} = \dfrac{2\cancel{x}}{\cancel{x}(x+4)} - \dfrac{2}{x+4} = \dfrac{2}{x+4} - \dfrac{2}{x+4} = 0$

6.2   Exercises

1   Multiply and divide rational expressions

1. Explain how to multiply two rational expressions.

2. Explain how to divide two rational expressions.

Multiply or divide.

3. $\dfrac{27a^2b^5}{16xy^2} \cdot \dfrac{20x^2y^3}{9a^2b}$

4. $\dfrac{15x^2y^4}{24ab^3} \cdot \dfrac{28a^2b^4}{35xy^4}$

5. $\dfrac{3x-15}{4x^2-2x} \cdot \dfrac{20x^2-10x}{15x-75}$

6. $\dfrac{2x^2+4x}{8x^2-40x} \cdot \dfrac{6x^3-30x^2}{3x^2+6x}$

7. $\dfrac{x^2y^3}{x^2-4x-5} \cdot \dfrac{2x^2-13x+15}{x^4y^3}$

8. $\dfrac{2x^2-5x+3}{x^6y^3} \cdot \dfrac{x^4y^4}{2x^2-x-3}$

9. $\dfrac{x^2-3x+2}{x^2-8x+15} \cdot \dfrac{x^2+x-12}{8-2x-x^2}$

10. $\dfrac{x^2+x-6}{12+x-x^2} \cdot \dfrac{x^2+x-20}{x^2-4x+4}$

11. $\dfrac{x^{n+1}+2x^n}{4x^2-6x} \cdot \dfrac{8x^2-12x}{x^{n+1}-x^n}$

12. $\dfrac{x^{2n}+2x^n}{x^{n+1}+2x} \cdot \dfrac{x^2-3x}{x^{n+1}-3x^n}$

13. $\dfrac{12+x-6x^2}{6x^2+29x+28} \cdot \dfrac{2x^2+x-21}{4x^2-9}$

14. $\dfrac{x^2+5x+4}{4+x-3x^2} \cdot \dfrac{3x^2+2x-8}{x^2+4x}$

15. $\dfrac{x^{2n} - x^n - 6}{x^{2n} + x^n - 2} \cdot \dfrac{x^{2n} - 5x^n - 6}{x^{2n} - 2x^n - 3}$

16. $\dfrac{x^{2n} + 3x^n + 2}{x^{2n} - x^n - 6} \cdot \dfrac{x^{2n} + x^n - 12}{x^{2n} - 1}$

17. $\dfrac{x^3 - y^3}{2x^2 + xy - 3y^2} \cdot \dfrac{2x^2 + 5xy + 3y^2}{x^2 + xy + y^2}$

18. $\dfrac{x^4 - 5x^2 + 4}{3x^2 - 4x - 4} \cdot \dfrac{3x^2 - 10x - 8}{x^2 - 4}$

19. $\dfrac{6x^2y^4}{35a^2b^5} \div \dfrac{12x^3y^3}{7a^4b^5}$

20. $\dfrac{12a^4b^7}{13x^2y^2} \div \dfrac{18a^5b^6}{26xy^3}$

21. $\dfrac{2x - 6}{6x^2 - 15x} \div \dfrac{4x^2 - 12x}{18x^3 - 45x^2}$

22. $\dfrac{4x^2 - 4y^2}{6x^2y^2} \div \dfrac{3x^2 + 3xy}{2x^2y - 2xy^2}$

23. $\dfrac{2x^2 - 2y^2}{14x^2y^4} \div \dfrac{x^2 + 2xy + y^2}{35xy^3}$

24. $\dfrac{8x^3 + 12x^2y}{4x^2 - 9y^2} \div \dfrac{16x^2y^2}{4x^2 - 12xy + 9y^2}$

25. $\dfrac{2x^2 - 5x - 3}{2x^2 + 7x + 3} \div \dfrac{2x^2 - 3x - 20}{2x^2 - x - 15}$

26. $\dfrac{3x^2 - 10x - 8}{6x^2 + 13x + 6} \div \dfrac{2x^2 - 9x + 10}{4x^2 - 4x - 15}$

27. $\dfrac{x^2 - 8x + 15}{x^2 + 2x - 35} \div \dfrac{15 - 2x - x^2}{x^2 + 9x + 14}$

28. $\dfrac{2x^2 + 13x + 20}{8 - 10x - 3x^2} \div \dfrac{6x^2 - 13x - 5}{9x^2 - 3x - 2}$

29. $\dfrac{x^{2n} + x^n}{2x - 2} \div \dfrac{4x^n + 4}{x^{n+1} - x^n}$

30. $\dfrac{x^{2n} - 4}{4x^n + 8} \div \dfrac{x^{n+1} - 2x}{4x^3 - 12x^2}$

31. $\dfrac{2x^2 - 13x + 21}{2x^2 + 11x + 15} \div \dfrac{2x^2 + x - 28}{3x^2 + 4x - 15}$

32. $\dfrac{2x^2 - 13x + 15}{2x^2 - 3x - 35} \div \dfrac{6x^2 + x - 12}{6x^2 + 13x - 28}$

33. $\dfrac{14 + 17x - 6x^2}{3x^2 + 14x + 8} \div \dfrac{4x^2 - 49}{2x^2 + 15x + 28}$

34. $\dfrac{16x^2 - 9}{6 - 5x - 4x^2} \div \dfrac{16x^2 + 24x + 9}{4x^2 + 11x + 6}$

35. $\dfrac{2x^{2n} - x^n - 6}{x^{2n} - x^n - 2} \div \dfrac{2x^{2n} + x^n - 3}{x^{2n} - 1}$

36. $\dfrac{x^{4n} - 1}{x^{2n} + x^n - 2} \div \dfrac{x^{2n} + 1}{x^{2n} + 3x^n + 2}$

37. $\dfrac{6x^2 + 6x}{3x + 6x^2 + 3x^3} \div \dfrac{x^2 - 1}{1 - x^3}$

38. $\dfrac{x^3 + y^3}{2x^3 + 2x^2y} \div \dfrac{3x^3 - 3x^2y + 3xy^2}{6x^2 - 6y^2}$

39. Which expression is *not* equivalent to $\dfrac{x^2 + 4x - 5}{x^2 - x - 6}$?

    a. $\dfrac{x - 1}{x + 2} \div \dfrac{x - 3}{x + 5}$ **b.** $\dfrac{x - 1}{x - 3} \cdot \dfrac{x + 5}{x + 2}$

    c. $\dfrac{x - 3}{x - 1} \div \dfrac{x + 5}{x + 2}$ **d.** $\dfrac{x + 5}{2x - 6} \cdot \dfrac{2x - 2}{x + 2}$

40. The simplified form of the product $\left(\dfrac{x - 1}{x}\right)^8 \cdot \left(\dfrac{x^5}{x - 5}\right)^2$ has a factor in the form x^n in the numerator. What is n?

2   Add and subtract rational expressions

41. To find the LCM of $x^2 - 6x + 9$ and $x^2 - 9$, first factor each polynomial:

$x^2 - 6x + 9 =$ ___?___   • **$x^2 - 6x + 9$ factors as a perfect-square trinomial.**
$x^2 - 9 =$ ___?___   • **$x^2 - 9$ factors as the difference of two perfect squares.**

The LCM will use the factor $x - 3$ ___?___ time(s) and the factor $x + 3$ ___?___ time(s). The LCM is ___?___.

42. True or false? The LCM of $(xy)^3$ and xy^3 is $(xy)^3$.

43. How many factors of $x - 4$ are in the LCM of each pair of expressions?

a. $x^2 - x - 12$ and $x^2 - 8x + 16$ **b.** $x^2 + x - 12$ and $x^2 + 8x + 16$
c. $x^2 - 16$ and $x^2 - x - 12$

44. How many factors of a are in the LCM of $(a^2b)^3$ and a^4b^4? How many factors of b?

Write each fraction in terms of the LCM of the denominators.

45. $\dfrac{3}{4x^2y}, \dfrac{17}{12xy^4}$

46. $\dfrac{5}{16a^3b^3}, \dfrac{7}{30a^5b}$

47. $\dfrac{3x}{2x - 3}, \dfrac{5x}{2x + 3}$

48. $\dfrac{2}{7y - 3}, \dfrac{-3}{7y + 3}$

49. $\dfrac{2x}{x^2 - 9}, \dfrac{x + 1}{x - 3}$

50. $\dfrac{3x}{x^2 - 16}, \dfrac{2x}{4x - 16}$

51. $\dfrac{3x}{x^2 - 1}, \dfrac{5x}{x^2 - 2x + 1}$

52. $\dfrac{2x}{x^2 + x - 6}, \dfrac{-4x}{x^2 + 5x + 6}$

53. Subtract: $\dfrac{5}{x - 4} - \dfrac{2}{x + 3}$

$\dfrac{5}{x - 4} - \dfrac{2}{x + 3}$ • **The LCM of the denominators is ___?___.**

$= \dfrac{5}{x - 4} \cdot \dfrac{x + 3}{x + 3} - \dfrac{2}{x + 3} \cdot \dfrac{x - 4}{x - 4}$ • **Multiply the numerator and denominator of each fraction by the factor whose product with the denominator is the LCM.**

$= \dfrac{?}{(x - 4)(x + 3)} - \dfrac{?}{(x - 4)(x + 3)}$

$= \dfrac{(\underline{\ ?\ }) - (\underline{\ ?\ })}{(x - 4)(x + 3)} = \dfrac{5x + 15 - \underline{\ ?\ } + \underline{\ ?\ }}{(x - 4)(x + 3)}$

$= \dfrac{\underline{\ ?\ } + \underline{\ ?\ }}{(x - 4)(x + 3)}$

54. 🗣 True or false? $\dfrac{1}{x-3} + \dfrac{1}{3-x} = 0$

Add or subtract.

55. $\dfrac{3}{2xy} - \dfrac{7}{2xy} - \dfrac{9}{2xy}$

56. $-\dfrac{3}{4x^2} + \dfrac{8}{4x^2} - \dfrac{3}{4x^2}$

57. $\dfrac{x}{x^2-3x+2} - \dfrac{2}{x^2-3x+2}$

58. $\dfrac{3x}{3x^2+x-10} - \dfrac{5}{3x^2+x-10}$

59. $\dfrac{3}{2x^2y} - \dfrac{8}{5x} - \dfrac{9}{10xy}$

60. $\dfrac{2}{5ab} - \dfrac{3}{10a^2b} + \dfrac{4}{15ab^2}$

61. $\dfrac{2}{3x} - \dfrac{3}{2xy} + \dfrac{4}{5xy} - \dfrac{5}{6x}$

62. $\dfrac{3}{4ab} - \dfrac{2}{5a} + \dfrac{3}{10b} - \dfrac{5}{8ab}$

63. $\dfrac{2x-1}{12x} - \dfrac{3x+4}{9x}$

64. $\dfrac{3x-4}{6x} - \dfrac{2x-5}{4x}$

65. $\dfrac{3x+2}{4x^2y} - \dfrac{y-5}{6xy^2}$

66. $\dfrac{2y-4}{5xy^2} + \dfrac{3-2x}{10x^2y}$

67. $\dfrac{2x}{x-3} - \dfrac{3x}{x-5}$

68. $\dfrac{3a}{a-2} - \dfrac{5a}{a+1}$

69. $\dfrac{3}{2a-3} + \dfrac{2a}{3-2a}$

70. $\dfrac{x}{2x-5} - \dfrac{2}{5x-2}$

71. $\dfrac{3}{x+5} + \dfrac{2x+7}{x^2-25}$

72. $\dfrac{x}{4-x} - \dfrac{4}{x^2-16}$

73. $\dfrac{2}{x} - 3 - \dfrac{10}{x-4}$

74. $\dfrac{6a}{a-3} - 5 + \dfrac{3}{a}$

75. $\dfrac{1}{2x-3} - \dfrac{5}{2x} + 1$

76. $\dfrac{5}{x} - \dfrac{5x}{5-6x} + 2$

77. $\dfrac{3}{x^2-1} + \dfrac{2x}{x^2+2x+1}$

78. $\dfrac{1}{x^2-6x+9} - \dfrac{1}{x^2-9}$

79. $\dfrac{x}{x+3} - \dfrac{3-x}{x^2-9}$

80. $\dfrac{1}{x+2} - \dfrac{3x}{x^2+4x+4}$

81. $\dfrac{2x-3}{x+5} - \dfrac{x^2-4x-19}{x^2+8x+15}$

82. $\dfrac{-3x^2+8x+2}{x^2+2x-8} - \dfrac{2x-5}{x+4}$

83. $\dfrac{x^n}{x^{2n} - 1} - \dfrac{2}{x^n + 1}$

84. $\dfrac{2}{x^n - 1} + \dfrac{x^n}{x^{2n} - 1}$

85. $\dfrac{2x - 2}{4x^2 - 9} - \dfrac{5}{3 - 2x}$

86. $\dfrac{x^2 + 4}{4x^2 - 36} - \dfrac{13}{x + 3}$

87. $\dfrac{x - 2}{x + 1} - \dfrac{3 - 12x}{2x^2 - x - 3}$

88. $\dfrac{3x - 4}{4x + 1} + \dfrac{3x + 6}{4x^2 + 9x + 2}$

89. $\dfrac{x + 1}{x^2 + x - 6} - \dfrac{x + 2}{x^2 + 4x + 3}$

90. $\dfrac{x + 1}{x^2 + x - 12} - \dfrac{x - 3}{x^2 + 7x + 12}$

91. $\dfrac{x - 1}{2x^2 + 11x + 12} + \dfrac{2x}{2x^2 - 3x - 9}$

92. $\dfrac{x - 2}{4x^2 + 4x - 3} + \dfrac{3 - 2x}{6x^2 + x - 2}$

93. $\dfrac{x}{x - 3} - \dfrac{2}{x + 4} - \dfrac{14}{x^2 + x - 12}$

94. $\dfrac{x^2}{x^2 + x - 2} + \dfrac{3}{x - 1} - \dfrac{4}{x + 2}$

95. $\dfrac{x^2 + 6x}{x^2 + 3x - 18} - \dfrac{2x - 1}{x + 6} + \dfrac{x - 2}{3 - x}$

96. $\dfrac{2x^2 - 2x}{x^2 - 2x - 15} - \dfrac{2}{x + 3} + \dfrac{x}{5 - x}$

97. $\dfrac{4 - 20x}{6x^2 + 11x - 10} - \dfrac{4}{2 - 3x} + \dfrac{x}{2x + 5}$

98. $\dfrac{x}{4x - 1} + \dfrac{2}{2x + 1} + \dfrac{6}{8x^2 + 2x - 1}$

99. $\dfrac{2x^2}{x^4 - 1} - \dfrac{1}{x^2 - 1} + \dfrac{1}{x^2 + 1}$

100. $\dfrac{x^2 - 12}{x^4 - 16} + \dfrac{1}{x^2 - 4} - \dfrac{1}{x^2 + 4}$

6.2 Applying Concepts

Simplify.

101. $\dfrac{(x + 1)^2}{1 - 2x} \cdot \dfrac{2x - 1}{x + 1}$

102. $\left(\dfrac{2m}{3}\right)^2 \div \left(\dfrac{m^2}{6} + \dfrac{m}{2}\right)$

103. $\left(\dfrac{y - 2}{x^2}\right)^3 \cdot \left(\dfrac{x}{2 - y}\right)^2$

104. $\dfrac{b + 3}{b - 1} \div \dfrac{b + 3}{b - 2} \cdot \dfrac{b - 1}{b + 4}$

105. $\left(\dfrac{y+1}{y-1}\right)^2 - 1$

106. $\left(\dfrac{1}{3} - \dfrac{2}{a}\right) \div \left(\dfrac{3}{a} - 2 + \dfrac{a}{4}\right)$

107. $\dfrac{3x^2+6x}{4x^2-16} \cdot \dfrac{2x+8}{x^2+2x} \div \dfrac{3x-9}{5x-20}$

108. $\dfrac{5y^2-20}{3y^2-12y} \cdot \dfrac{9y^3+6y^2}{2y^2-4y} \div \dfrac{y^3+2y^2}{2y^2-8y}$

109. $\dfrac{a^2+a-6}{4+11a-3a^2} \cdot \dfrac{15a^2-a-2}{4a^2+7a-2} \div \dfrac{6a^2-7a-3}{4-17a+4a^2}$

110. $\dfrac{25x-x^3}{x^4-1} \cdot \dfrac{3-x-4x^2}{2x^2+7x-15} \div \dfrac{4x^3-23x^2+15x}{3-5x+2x^2}$

111. $\left(\dfrac{x+1}{2x-1} - \dfrac{x-1}{2x+1}\right) \cdot \left(\dfrac{2x-1}{x} - \dfrac{2x-1}{x^2}\right)$

112. $\left(\dfrac{y-2}{3y+1} - \dfrac{y+2}{3y-1}\right) \cdot \left(\dfrac{3y+1}{y} - \dfrac{3y-1}{y^2}\right)$

Solve.

113. Use $x = 3$ and $y = 5$ to show that $\dfrac{1}{x} + \dfrac{1}{y} \neq \dfrac{1}{x+y}$.

114. Use $x = 3$ and $y = 5$ to show that $\dfrac{1}{x} - \dfrac{1}{y} \neq \dfrac{1}{x-y}$.

Rewrite the expression as the sum of two fractions in simplest form.

115. $\dfrac{3x+6y}{xy}$

116. $\dfrac{5a+8b}{ab}$

117. $\dfrac{4a^2+3ab}{a^2b^2}$

118. **Manufacturing** Manufacturers who package their product in cans would like to design the can so that the minimum amount of aluminum is needed. If a soft drink can contains 12 oz (355 cm³), the function that relates the surface area of the can (the amount of aluminum needed) to the radius of the bottom of the can is given by the equation $f(r) = 2\pi r^2 + \dfrac{710}{r}$, where r is measured in centimeters.

a. Express the right side of this equation with a common denominator.

b. Graph the equation for $0 < r \le 7.5$.

c. The point whose coordinates are (7, 409), to the nearest integer, is on the graph of f. Write a sentence that gives an interpretation of this ordered pair.

d. Use a graphing utility to determine the radius of the can that has a minimum surface area. Round to the nearest tenth.

e. The height of the can is determined from $h = \frac{355}{\pi r^2}$. Use the answer to part d to determine the height of the can that has a minimum surface area. Round to the nearest tenth.

f. Determine the minimum surface area. Round to the nearest tenth.

119. **Manufacturing** A manufacturer wants to make square tissues and package them in a box. The manufacturer has determined that to be competitive, the box needs to hold 175 tissues, which means that the volume of the box will be 132 in^3. The amount of cardboard (surface area) that will be necessary to build this box is given by $f(x) = 2x^2 + \frac{528}{x}$, where x is the height of the box in inches.

a. Express the right side of this equation with a common denominator.

b. Graph the equation for $1.5 < x \le 10$.

c. The point whose coordinates are (4, 164) is on the graph. Write a sentence that explains the meaning of this point.

d. With a graphing utility, determine, to the nearest tenth, the height of the box that uses the minimum amount of cardboard.

e. Determine the minimum amount of cardboard. Round to the nearest tenth.

120. For adding or subtracting fractions, any common denominator will do. Explain the advantages and disadvantages of using the LCM of the denominators.

121. A student incorrectly tried to add the fractions $\frac{1}{5}$ and $\frac{2}{3}$ by adding the the numerators and the denominators. The procedure was shown as

$$\frac{1}{5} + \frac{2}{3} = \frac{1+2}{5+3} = \frac{3}{8}$$

Write the fractions $\frac{1}{5}, \frac{2}{3}$, and $\frac{3}{8}$ in order from smallest to largest. Now take any two other fractions, add the numerators and the denominators, and then write the fractions in order from smallest to largest. Do you see a pattern? If so, explain it. If not, try a few more examples until you find a pattern.

6.3 Complex Fractions

OBJECTIVE **1** **Simplify complex fractions**

A **complex fraction** is a fraction whose numerator or denominator contains one or more fractions. Examples of complex fractions are shown below.

$$\frac{5}{2 + \dfrac{1}{2}} \qquad \frac{5 + \dfrac{1}{y}}{5 - \dfrac{1}{y}} \qquad \frac{x + 4 + \dfrac{1}{x + 2}}{x - 2 + \dfrac{1}{x + 2}}$$

Simplify: $\dfrac{\dfrac{1}{x} + \dfrac{1}{y}}{\dfrac{1}{x} - \dfrac{1}{y}}$

Multiply the numerator and denominator of the complex fraction by the LCM of the denominators. The LCM of x and y is xy.

$$\frac{\dfrac{1}{x} + \dfrac{1}{y}}{\dfrac{1}{x} - \dfrac{1}{y}} = \frac{\dfrac{1}{x} + \dfrac{1}{y}}{\dfrac{1}{x} - \dfrac{1}{y}} \cdot \frac{xy}{xy} = \frac{\dfrac{1}{x} \cdot xy + \dfrac{1}{y} \cdot xy}{\dfrac{1}{x} \cdot xy - \dfrac{1}{y} \cdot xy} = \frac{y + x}{y - x}$$

Note that after the numerator and denominator of the complex fraction have been multiplied by the LCM of the denominators, no fraction remains in the numerator or denominator.

The method shown above of simplifying a complex fraction by multiplying the numerator and denominator by the LCM of the denominators is used in Example 1. However, a different approach is to rewrite the numerator and denominator of the complex fraction as single fractions and then divide the numerator by the denominator. Here the example shown above is simplified by using this alternative method.

Rewrite the numerator and denominator of the complex fraction as single fractions.

$$\frac{\dfrac{1}{x} + \dfrac{1}{y}}{\dfrac{1}{x} - \dfrac{1}{y}} = \frac{\dfrac{1}{x} \cdot \dfrac{y}{y} + \dfrac{1}{y} \cdot \dfrac{x}{x}}{\dfrac{1}{x} \cdot \dfrac{y}{y} - \dfrac{1}{y} \cdot \dfrac{x}{x}} = \frac{\dfrac{y}{xy} + \dfrac{x}{xy}}{\dfrac{y}{xy} - \dfrac{x}{xy}} = \frac{\dfrac{y + x}{xy}}{\dfrac{y - x}{xy}}$$

Take Note

Recall that the fraction bar can be read "divided by."

Divide the numerator of the complex fraction by the denominator.

$$= \frac{y + x}{xy} \div \frac{y - x}{xy} = \frac{y + x}{xy} \cdot \frac{xy}{y - x}$$

Multiply the fractions. Simplify.

$$= \frac{(y + x)xy}{xy(y - x)} = \frac{y + x}{y - x}$$

Note that this is the same result we got before.

EXAMPLE 1 Simplify. **A.** $\dfrac{2 - \dfrac{11}{x} + \dfrac{15}{x^2}}{3 - \dfrac{5}{x} - \dfrac{12}{x^2}}$ **B.** $\dfrac{2x - 1 + \dfrac{7}{x + 4}}{3x - 8 + \dfrac{17}{x + 4}}$

Solution **A.** $\dfrac{2 - \dfrac{11}{x} + \dfrac{15}{x^2}}{3 - \dfrac{5}{x} - \dfrac{12}{x^2}} = \dfrac{2 - \dfrac{11}{x} + \dfrac{15}{x^2}}{3 - \dfrac{5}{x} - \dfrac{12}{x^2}} \cdot \dfrac{x^2}{x^2}$ • **The LCM of the denominators is x^2.**

$$= \dfrac{2 \cdot x^2 - \dfrac{11}{x} \cdot x^2 + \dfrac{15}{x^2} \cdot x^2}{3 \cdot x^2 - \dfrac{5}{x} \cdot x^2 - \dfrac{12}{x^2} \cdot x^2}$$

$$= \dfrac{2x^2 - 11x + 15}{3x^2 - 5x - 12}$$

$$= \dfrac{(2x - 5)(x - 3)}{(3x + 4)(x - 3)} = \dfrac{2x - 5}{3x + 4}$$

B. $\dfrac{2x - 1 + \dfrac{7}{x + 4}}{3x - 8 + \dfrac{17}{x + 4}} = \dfrac{2x - 1 + \dfrac{7}{x + 4}}{3x - 8 + \dfrac{17}{x + 4}} \cdot \dfrac{x + 4}{x + 4}$ • **The LCM of the denominators is $x + 4$.**

$$= \dfrac{(2x - 1)(x + 4) + \dfrac{7}{x + 4}(x + 4)}{(3x - 8)(x + 4) + \dfrac{17}{x + 4}(x + 4)}$$

$$= \dfrac{2x^2 + 7x - 4 + 7}{3x^2 + 4x - 32 + 17}$$

$$= \dfrac{2x^2 + 7x + 3}{3x^2 + 4x - 15}$$

$$= \dfrac{(2x + 1)(x + 3)}{(3x - 5)(x + 3)} = \dfrac{2x + 1}{3x - 5}$$

PROBLEM 1 **A.** $\dfrac{3 + \dfrac{16}{x} + \dfrac{16}{x^2}}{6 + \dfrac{5}{x} - \dfrac{4}{x^2}}$ **B.** $\dfrac{2x + 5 + \dfrac{14}{x - 3}}{4x + 16 + \dfrac{49}{x - 3}}$

Solution See page S19.

6.3 Concept Review

Determine whether the following statements are always true, sometimes true, or never true.

1. The numerator of a complex fraction contains one or more fractions.

2. We can simplify a complex fraction by multiplying the numerator and denominator of the complex fraction by the LCM of the denominators.

3. The LCM of the denominators in the complex fraction $\dfrac{1 - \dfrac{3}{x-3}}{\dfrac{2}{x} + 1}$ is $x(x-3)$.

4. $\dfrac{c^{-1}}{a^{-1} + b^{-1}} = \dfrac{a+b}{c}$

6.3 Exercises

1 Simplify complex fractions

1. What is a complex fraction?

2. What is the general goal of simplifying a complex fraction?

For Exercises 3 to 6, use the complex fraction $\dfrac{1 - \dfrac{2}{a}}{1 + \dfrac{1}{a^2}}$.

3. To simplify the complex fraction, multiply the numerator and denominator of the complex fraction by the LCM of the denominators of the fractions ___?___ and ___?___. The LCM is ___?___.

4. When you multiply the numerator of the complex fraction by a^2, the numerator of the complex fraction simplifies to ___?___.

5. When you multiply the denominator of the complex fraction by a^2, the denominator of the complex fraction simplifies to ___?___.

6. The simplified form of the complex fraction is ___?___.

Simplify.

7. $\dfrac{2 - \dfrac{1}{3}}{4 + \dfrac{11}{3}}$

8. $\dfrac{3 + \dfrac{5}{2}}{8 - \dfrac{7}{2}}$

9. $\dfrac{3 - \dfrac{2}{3}}{5 + \dfrac{5}{6}}$

10. $\dfrac{1 + \dfrac{1}{x}}{1 - \dfrac{1}{x^2}}$

11. $\dfrac{\dfrac{1}{y^2} - 1}{1 + \dfrac{1}{y}}$

12. $\dfrac{a - 2}{\dfrac{4}{a} - a}$

13. $\dfrac{\dfrac{25}{a} - a}{5 + a}$

14. $\dfrac{\dfrac{1}{a^2} - \dfrac{1}{a}}{\dfrac{1}{a^2} + \dfrac{1}{a}}$

15. $\dfrac{\dfrac{1}{b} + \dfrac{1}{2}}{\dfrac{4}{b^2} - 1}$

16. $\dfrac{2 - \dfrac{4}{x + 2}}{5 - \dfrac{10}{x + 2}}$

17. $\dfrac{4 + \dfrac{12}{2x - 3}}{5 + \dfrac{15}{2x - 3}}$

18. $\dfrac{\dfrac{3}{2a - 3} + 2}{\dfrac{-6}{2a - 3} - 4}$

19. $\dfrac{\dfrac{-5}{b - 5} - 3}{\dfrac{10}{b - 5} + 6}$

20. $\dfrac{\dfrac{x}{x + 1} - \dfrac{1}{x}}{\dfrac{x}{x + 1} + \dfrac{1}{x}}$

21. $\dfrac{\dfrac{2a}{a - 1} - \dfrac{3}{a}}{\dfrac{1}{a - 1} + \dfrac{2}{a}}$

22. $\dfrac{\dfrac{3}{x}}{\dfrac{9}{x^2}}$

23. $\dfrac{\dfrac{x}{3x - 2}}{\dfrac{x}{9x^2 - 4}}$

24. $\dfrac{\dfrac{a^2 - b^2}{4a^2 b}}{\dfrac{a + b}{16ab^2}}$

25. $\dfrac{1 - \dfrac{1}{x} - \dfrac{6}{x^2}}{1 - \dfrac{4}{x} + \dfrac{3}{x^2}}$

26. $\dfrac{1 - \dfrac{3}{x} - \dfrac{10}{x^2}}{1 + \dfrac{11}{x} + \dfrac{18}{x^2}}$

27. $\dfrac{\dfrac{15}{x^2} - \dfrac{2}{x} - 1}{\dfrac{4}{x^2} - \dfrac{5}{x} + 4}$

28. $\dfrac{1 - \dfrac{2x}{3x - 4}}{x - \dfrac{32}{3x - 4}}$

29. $\dfrac{1 - \dfrac{12}{3x + 10}}{x - \dfrac{8}{3x + 10}}$

30. $\dfrac{x - 1 + \dfrac{2}{x - 4}}{x + 3 + \dfrac{6}{x - 4}}$

31. $\dfrac{x - 5 - \dfrac{18}{x + 2}}{x + 7 + \dfrac{6}{x + 2}}$

32. $\dfrac{x - 4 + \dfrac{9}{2x + 3}}{x + 3 - \dfrac{5}{2x + 3}}$

33. $\dfrac{\dfrac{1}{a} - \dfrac{3}{a - 2}}{\dfrac{2}{a} + \dfrac{5}{a - 2}}$

34. $\dfrac{\dfrac{2}{b} - \dfrac{5}{b + 3}}{\dfrac{3}{b} + \dfrac{3}{b + 3}}$

35. $\dfrac{\dfrac{1}{y^2} - \dfrac{1}{xy} - \dfrac{2}{x^2}}{\dfrac{1}{y^2} - \dfrac{3}{xy} + \dfrac{2}{x^2}}$

36. $\dfrac{\dfrac{2}{b^2} - \dfrac{5}{ab} - \dfrac{3}{a^2}}{\dfrac{2}{b^2} + \dfrac{7}{ab} + \dfrac{3}{a^2}}$

37. $\dfrac{\dfrac{x-1}{x+1} - \dfrac{x+1}{x-1}}{\dfrac{x-1}{x+1} + \dfrac{x+1}{x-1}}$

38. $\dfrac{\dfrac{y}{y+2} - \dfrac{y}{y-2}}{\dfrac{y}{y+2} + \dfrac{y}{y-2}}$

39. $4 - \dfrac{2}{2 - \dfrac{3}{x}}$

40. Is the expression the reciprocal of the complex fraction $\dfrac{1}{1 - \dfrac{1}{a}}$?

a. $\dfrac{a}{a-1}$ **b.** $\dfrac{a-1}{a}$ **c.** $1 - \dfrac{1}{a}$

41. The denominator of a certain complex fraction is the reciprocal of its numerator. Which of the following is the simplified form of this complex fraction?
a. 1
b. the square of the complex fraction
c. the square of the numerator of the complex fraction
d. the reciprocal of the complex fraction

6.3 Applying Concepts

Simplify.

42. $\dfrac{x^{-1} + y^{-1}}{x^{-1} - y^{-1}}$

43. $\dfrac{x^{-1}}{y^{-1}} + \dfrac{y}{x}$

44. $\dfrac{x^{-1} + y}{x^{-1} - y}$

45. $\dfrac{x - \dfrac{1}{x}}{1 + \dfrac{1}{x}}$

46. $1 - \dfrac{1}{1 - \dfrac{1}{b-2}}$

47. $2 - \dfrac{2}{2 - \dfrac{2}{c-1}}$

48. $3 - \dfrac{2}{1 - \dfrac{2}{3 - \dfrac{2}{x}}}$

49. $a + \dfrac{a}{2 + \dfrac{1}{1 - \dfrac{2}{a}}}$

50. $a - \dfrac{1}{2 - \dfrac{2}{2 - \dfrac{2}{a}}}$

51. $\dfrac{\dfrac{1}{x+h} - \dfrac{1}{x}}{h}$

52. $\dfrac{\dfrac{1}{(x+h)^2} - \dfrac{1}{x^2}}{h}$

53. Find the sum of the reciprocals of three consecutive even integers.

54. **Electronics** The total resistance, R, of three resistors in parallel is given by the formula $R = \dfrac{1}{\dfrac{1}{R_1} + \dfrac{1}{R_2} + \dfrac{1}{R_3}}$. Find the total parallel resistance when

$R_1 = 2$ ohms, $R_2 = 4$ ohms, and $R_3 = 8$ ohms.

55. **Car Loans** The interest rate on a loan to purchase a car affects the monthly payment. The function that relates the monthly payment for a 5-year loan (60-month loan) to the monthly interest rate is given by

$$P(x) = \frac{Cx}{\left[1 - \dfrac{1}{(x+1)^{60}}\right]}$$

where x is the monthly interest rate (as a decimal), C is the loan amount for the car, and $P(x)$ is the monthly payment.
a. Simplify the complex fraction.
b. Graph this equation for $0 < x \le 0.025$ and $C = \$20{,}000$.
c. What is the interval of *annual* interest rates for the domain in part b?
d. The point whose coordinates are approximately (0.005, 386.66) is on the graph of this equation. Write a sentence that gives an interpretation of this ordered pair.
e. Use a graphing utility to determine the monthly payment for a car with a loan amount of $20,000 and an annual interest rate of 8%. Round to the nearest dollar.

6.4   Rational Equations

OBJECTIVE 1   **Solve fractional equations**

To solve an equation containing fractions, **clear denominators** by multiplying each side of the equation by the LCM of the denominators. Then solve for the variable.

Solve: $\dfrac{3x}{x-5} = 5 - \dfrac{5}{x-5}$

$$\frac{3x}{x-5} = 5 - \frac{5}{x-5}$$

Multiply each side of the equation by the LCM of the denominators.

$$(x-5)\left(\frac{3x}{x-5}\right) = (x-5)\left(5 - \frac{5}{x-5}\right)$$

$$3x = (x-5)5 - (x-5)\left(\frac{5}{x-5}\right)$$

Simplify.

$$3x = 5x - 25 - 5$$
$$3x = 5x - 30$$

Solve the equation for x.

$$-2x = -30$$
$$x = 15$$

15 checks as a solution.
The solution is 15.

Occasionally, a value of the variable that appears to be a solution will make one of the denominators zero. In this case, the equation has no solution for that value of the variable.

Solve: $\dfrac{3x}{x-3} = 2 + \dfrac{9}{x-3}$

Multiply each side of the equation by the LCM of the denominators.

$$\dfrac{3x}{x-3} = 2 + \dfrac{9}{x-3}$$

$$(x-3)\left(\dfrac{3x}{x-3}\right) = (x-3)\left(2 + \dfrac{9}{x-3}\right)$$

Use the Distributive Property.

$$3x = (x-3)2 + (x-3)\left(\dfrac{9}{x-3}\right)$$

$$3x = 2x - 6 + 9$$
$$3x = 2x + 3$$
$$x = 3$$

Substituting 3 into the equation results in division by zero. Because division by zero is not defined, the equation has no solution.

$$\dfrac{3x}{x-3} = 2 + \dfrac{9}{x-3}$$

$$\dfrac{3(3)}{3-3} = 2 + \dfrac{9}{3-3}$$

$$\dfrac{9}{0} = 2 + \dfrac{9}{0}$$

Multiplying each side of an equation by a variable expression may produce an equation with different solutions from the original equation. Thus, any time you multiply each side of an equation by a variable expression, you must check the resulting solution.

EXAMPLE 1   Solve.   **A.** $\dfrac{1}{4} = \dfrac{5}{x+5}$ **B.** $\dfrac{2x}{x-2} = \dfrac{1}{3x-4} + 2$

Solution   A. $\dfrac{1}{4} = \dfrac{5}{x+5}$

$$4(x+5)\dfrac{1}{4} = 4(x+5)\dfrac{5}{x+5}$$ • Multiply each side of the equation by the LCM of the denominators.

$$x+5 = 4(5)$$
$$x+5 = 20$$
$$x = 15$$

15 checks as a solution.
The solution is 15.

B. $\dfrac{2x}{x-2} = \dfrac{1}{3x-4} + 2$

$$(x-2)(3x-4)\dfrac{2x}{x-2} = (x-2)(3x-4)\left(\dfrac{1}{3x-4} + 2\right)$$

$$(3x-4)2x = (x-2)(3x-4)\left(\dfrac{1}{3x-4}\right) + (x-2)(3x-4)2$$

$$6x^2 - 8x = x - 2 + 6x^2 - 20x + 16$$
$$6x^2 - 8x = 6x^2 - 19x + 14$$
$$11x = 14$$
$$x = \frac{14}{11}$$

$\frac{14}{11}$ checks as a solution.

The solution is $\frac{14}{11}$.

PROBLEM 1 Solve. **A.** $\dfrac{5}{2x - 3} = \dfrac{-2}{x + 1}$ **B.** $\dfrac{4x + 1}{2x - 1} = 2 + \dfrac{3}{x - 3}$

Solution See page S19.

OBJECTIVE **2**

Point of Interest

The following problem was recorded in the Jiuzhang, a Chinese text that dates to the Han dynasty (about 200 B.C. to A.D. 200). "A reservoir has 5 channels bringing water to it. The first channel can fill the reservoir in $\frac{1}{3}$ day, the second in 1 day, the third in $2\frac{1}{2}$ days, the fourth in 3 days, and the fifth in 5 days. If all channels are open, how long does it take to fill the reservoir?" This problem is the earliest known work problem.

Work problems

Rate of work is that part of a task that is completed in one unit of time. If a mason can build a retaining wall in 12 h, then in 1 h the mason can build $\frac{1}{12}$ of the wall. The mason's rate of work is $\frac{1}{12}$ of the wall each hour. If an apprentice can build the wall in x hours, the rate of work for the apprentice is $\frac{1}{x}$ of the wall each hour.

In solving a work problem, the goal is to determine the time it takes to complete a task. The basic equation that is used to solve work problems is

Rate of work × Time worked = Part of task completed

For example, if a pipe can fill a tank in 5 h, then in 2 h the pipe will fill $\frac{1}{5} \times 2 = \frac{2}{5}$ of the tank. In t hours, the pipe will fill $\frac{1}{5} \times t = \frac{t}{5}$ of the tank.

Solve: A mason can build a wall in 10 h. An apprentice can build a wall in 15 h. How long would it take them to build the wall if they worked together?

STRATEGY	for solving a work problem

▶ For each person or machine, write a numerical or variable expression for the rate of work, the time worked, and the part of the task completed. The results can be recorded in a table.

Unknown time to build the wall working together: t

	Rate of work	·	Time worked	=	Part of task completed
Mason	$\dfrac{1}{10}$	·	t	=	$\dfrac{t}{10}$
Apprentice	$\dfrac{1}{15}$	·	t	=	$\dfrac{t}{15}$

▶ Determine how the parts of the task completed are related. Use the fact that the sum of the parts of the task completed must equal 1, the complete task.

The sum of the part of the task completed by the mason and the part of the task completed by the apprentice is 1.

$$\frac{t}{10} + \frac{t}{15} = 1$$

$$30\left(\frac{t}{10} + \frac{t}{15}\right) = 30(1)$$

$$3t + 2t = 30$$
$$5t = 30$$
$$t = 6$$

Working together, they would build the wall in 6 h.

EXAMPLE 2 An electrician requires 12 h to wire a house. The electrician's apprentice can wire a house in 16 h. After working alone on one job for 4 h, the electrician quits, and the apprentice completes the task. How long does it take the apprentice to finish wiring the house?

Strategy ▶ Time required for the apprentice to finish wiring the house: t

	Rate	Time	Part
Electrician	$\frac{1}{12}$	4	$\frac{4}{12}$
Apprentice	$\frac{1}{16}$	t	$\frac{t}{16}$

▶ The sum of the part of the task completed by the electrician and the part of the task completed by the apprentice is 1.

Solution
$$\frac{4}{12} + \frac{t}{16} = 1$$

$$\frac{1}{3} + \frac{t}{16} = 1$$

$$48\left(\frac{1}{3} + \frac{t}{16}\right) = 48(1)$$

$$16 + 3t = 48$$
$$3t = 32$$
$$t = \frac{32}{3}$$

It takes the apprentice $10\frac{2}{3}$ h to finish wiring the house.

Fills tank
in x hours

Fills tank
in 9 hours

Fills $\frac{1}{x}$ of the
tank each hour

Fills $\frac{1}{9}$ of the
tank each hour

PROBLEM 2   Two water pipes can fill a tank with water in 6 h. The larger
pipe working alone can fill the tank in 9 h. How long would
it take the smaller pipe, working alone, to fill the tank?

Solution   See page S20.

OBJECTIVE **3**   Uniform motion problems

A car that travels constantly in a straight line at 55 mph is in uniform motion.
Uniform motion means that the speed of an object does not change.

The basic equation used to solve uniform motion problems is

$$\textbf{Distance = Rate} \times \textbf{Time}$$

An alternative form of this equation can be written by solving the equation for
time. This form of the equation is used to solve the following problem.

$$\frac{\textbf{Distance}}{\textbf{Rate}} = \textbf{Time}$$

50 mi
r

150 mi
3r

Solve: A motorist drove 150 mi on country roads before driving 50 mi on
mountain roads. The rate of speed on the country roads was three times the
rate on the mountain roads. The time spent traveling the 200 mi was 5 h. Find
the rate of the motorist on the country roads.

> **STRATEGY**   for solving a uniform motion problem
>
> ▶ For each object, write a numerical or variable expression for the
> distance, rate, and time. The results can be recorded in a table.

The unknown rate of speed on the mountain roads: r
Rate of speed on the country roads: $3r$

	Distance	÷	Rate	=	Time
Country roads	150	÷	$3r$	=	$\dfrac{150}{3r}$
Mountain roads	50	÷	r	=	$\dfrac{50}{r}$

> ▶ Determine how the times traveled by each object are related. For
> example, it may be known that the times are equal, or the total time
> may be known.

The total time for the trip is 5 h.

$$\frac{150}{3r} + \frac{50}{r} = 5$$

$$\frac{50}{r} + \frac{50}{r} = 5$$

$$r\left(\frac{50}{r} + \frac{50}{r}\right) = r(5)$$

$$50 + 50 = 5r$$
$$100 = 5r$$
$$20 = r$$

The rate of speed on the country roads was 3r. Replace r with 20 and evaluate.

$$3r = 3(20) = 60$$

The rate of speed on the country roads was 60 mph.

EXAMPLE 3   A marketing executive traveled 810 mi on a corporate jet in the same amount of time that it took to travel an additional 162 mi by helicopter. The rate of the jet was 360 mph greater than the rate of the helicopter. Find the rate of the jet.

Strategy   ▶ Rate of the helicopter: r
Rate of the jet: $r + 360$

	Distance	Rate	Time
Jet	810	$r + 360$	$\frac{810}{r + 360}$
Helicopter	162	r	$\frac{162}{r}$

▶ The time traveled by jet is equal to the time traveled by helicopter.

Solution

$$\frac{810}{r + 360} = \frac{162}{r}$$

$$r(r + 360)\left(\frac{810}{r + 360}\right) = r(r + 360)\left(\frac{162}{r}\right)$$

$$810r = (r + 360)162$$
$$810r = 162r + 58{,}320$$
$$648r = 58{,}320$$
$$r = 90$$

• The rate of the helicopter was 90 mph.

$$r + 360 = 90 + 360 = 450$$

• Substitute the value of r into the variable expression for the rate of the jet.

The rate of the jet was 450 mph.

PROBLEM 3 A plane can fly at a rate of 150 mph in calm air. Traveling with the wind, the plane flew 700 mi in the same amount of time it took to fly 500 mi against the wind. Find the rate of the wind.

■ **Solution** See page S20.

6.4 Concept Review

Determine whether the following statements are always true, sometimes true, or never true.

1. $\dfrac{3x}{x-2} + \dfrac{4}{x} - 3$ is a rational equation.

2. Multiplying both sides of an equation by the same variable expression produces an equivalent equation.

3. -2 and 5 cannot be solutions of the equation $\dfrac{1}{x+2} - 3 = \dfrac{x-2}{x-5}$.

4. An equation that contains a variable in a denominator can be simplified to an equivalent equation with no variables in the denominator.

5. If it takes 3 h to fill a tub with water, then $\dfrac{1}{3}$ of the tub can be filled in 1 h.

6.4 Exercises

1 Solve fractional equations

For Exercises 1 to 4, use the equation $\dfrac{8}{x} = \dfrac{5}{x+3}$.

1. The first step in solving the equation is to clear denominators by multiplying each side of the equation by the LCM of the denominators _____?_____ and _____?_____. The LCM is _____?_____.

2. **a.** When you multiply the left side of the equation by the LCM $x(x+3)$, the left side simplifies to _____?_____.
   b. When you multiply the right side of the equation by the LCM $x(x+3)$, the right side simplifies to _____?_____.

3. Use your answers to Exercise 2 to write the equation that results from clearing denominators: _____?_____ = _____?_____. The solution of this equation is _____?_____.

4. The solution of a rational equation must be checked in the original equation. To check the solution you found in Exercise 3 in the original equation, substitute ____?____ for x and simplify:

$\dfrac{8}{-8} = \dfrac{5}{-8+3}$ simplifies to ____?____ = ____?____, which shows that the solution checks.

Solve.

5. $\dfrac{x}{2} + \dfrac{5}{6} = \dfrac{x}{3}$

6. $\dfrac{x}{5} - \dfrac{2}{9} = \dfrac{x}{15}$

7. $1 - \dfrac{3}{y} = 4$

8. $7 + \dfrac{6}{y} = 5$

9. $\dfrac{8}{2x-1} = 2$

10. $3 = \dfrac{18}{3x-4}$

11. $\dfrac{4}{x-4} = \dfrac{2}{x-2}$

12. $\dfrac{x}{3} = \dfrac{x+1}{7}$

13. $\dfrac{x-2}{5} = \dfrac{1}{x+2}$

14. $\dfrac{x+4}{10} = \dfrac{6}{x-3}$

15. $\dfrac{3}{x-2} = \dfrac{4}{x}$

16. $\dfrac{5}{x} = \dfrac{2}{x+3}$

17. $\dfrac{3}{x-4} + 2 = \dfrac{5}{x-4}$

18. $\dfrac{5}{y+3} - 2 = \dfrac{7}{y+3}$

19. $\dfrac{8}{x-5} = \dfrac{3}{x}$

20. $\dfrac{16}{2-x} = \dfrac{4}{x}$

21. $5 + \dfrac{8}{a-2} = \dfrac{4a}{a-2}$

22. $\dfrac{-4}{a-4} = 3 - \dfrac{a}{a-4}$

23. $\dfrac{x}{2} + \dfrac{20}{x} = 7$

24. $3x = \dfrac{4}{x} - \dfrac{13}{2}$

25. $\dfrac{6}{x-5} = \dfrac{1}{x}$

26. $\dfrac{8}{x-2} = \dfrac{4}{x+1}$

27. $\dfrac{x}{x+2} = \dfrac{6}{x+5}$

28. $\dfrac{x}{x-2} = \dfrac{3}{x-4}$

29. $-\dfrac{5}{x+7} + 1 = \dfrac{4}{x+7}$

30. $5 - \dfrac{2}{2x-5} = \dfrac{3}{2x-5}$

31. $\dfrac{2}{4y^2-9} + \dfrac{1}{2y-3} = \dfrac{3}{2y+3}$

32. $\dfrac{5}{x-2} - \dfrac{2}{x+2} = \dfrac{3}{x^2-4}$

33. $\dfrac{5}{x^2-7x+12} = \dfrac{2}{x-3} + \dfrac{5}{x-4}$

34. $\dfrac{9}{x^2+7x+10} = \dfrac{5}{x+2} - \dfrac{3}{x+5}$

When a proposed solution of a rational equation does not check in the original equation, it is because it results in an expression involving division by zero. For each equation, state the values of x that, when substituted into the original equation, would result in division by zero.

35. $\dfrac{x^2+24}{x^2+x-12} + \dfrac{x}{4} = \dfrac{2x}{x-3}$

36. $\dfrac{1}{x-2} - 1 = \dfrac{2}{x^2-2x}$

2   Work problems

37. If one person can complete a task in 2 h and another person can complete the same task in 3 h, will it take more or less than 2 h to complete the task when both people are working? Explain your answer.

38. If a gardener can mow a lawn in 20 min, what portion of the lawn can the gardener mow in 1 min?

39. It takes the hot water hose 6 min to fill a washing machine. It takes the cold water hose 4 min to fill the machine. Let t represent the amount of time the hot and cold water hoses together take to fill the machine with warm water. Complete the following table.

	Rate of work	·	Time worked	=	Part of task completed
Hot water hose	?	·	?	=	?
Cold water hose	?	·	?	=	?

40. Refer to Exercise 39. When the washing machine is full, the "part of task completed" is the whole task, so the sum of the parts completed by the hot water hose and by the cold water hose is ___?___. Use this fact and the expressions in the table in Exercise 39 to write an equation that can be solved to find the amount of time it takes to fill the washer with warm water: ___?___ + ___?___ = ___?___ .

41. A large biotech firm uses two computers to process the daily results of its research studies. One computer can process the data in 2 h; the other computer takes 3 h to do the same job. How long would it take to process the data if both computers were used?

42. Two college students have started their own business building computers from kits. Working alone, one student can build a computer in 20 h. When the second student helps, they can build a computer in 7.5 h. How long would it take the second student, working alone, to build the computer?

43. One solar heating panel can raise the temperature of water 1 degree in 30 min. A second solar heating panel can raise the temperature 1 degree in 45 min. How long would it take to raise the temperature of the water 1 degree with both solar panels operating?

44. One member of a gardening team can landscape a new lawn in 36 h. The other member of the team can do the job in 45 h. How long would it take to landscape a lawn if both gardeners worked together?

45. One member of a telephone crew can wire new telephone lines in 5 h. It takes 7.5 h for the other member of the crew to do the job. How long would it take to wire new telephone lines if both members of the crew worked together?

46. As the spring flood waters began to recede in Texas, a young family was faced with pumping the water from their basement. One pump they were using could dispose of 9000 gal in 3 h. A second pump could dispose of the same number of gallons in 4.5 h. How many hours would it take to dispose of 9000 gal if both pumps were working?

47. A new machine can package transistors four times as fast as an older machine. Working together, the machines can package the transistors in 8 h. How long would it take the new machine, working alone, to package the transistors?

48. A ski resort can "manufacture" enough snow to open its steepest run in 12 h, whereas naturally falling snow would have to last for 36 h to provide enough snow. If the resort makes snow at the same time as it is snowing naturally, how long will it be before the run can be opened?

49. The larger of two printers being used to print the payroll for a major corporation requires 40 min to print the payroll. After both printers have been operating for 10 min, the larger printer malfunctions. The smaller printer requires 50 more minutes to complete the payroll. How long would it take the smaller printer, working alone, to print the payroll?

50. An experienced bricklayer can work twice as fast as an apprentice bricklayer. After they worked together on a job for 8 h, the experienced bricklayer quit. The apprentice required 12 more hours to finish the job. How long would it take the experienced bricklayer, working alone, to do the job?

51. A roofer requires 12 h to shingle a roof. After the roofer and an apprentice work on a roof for 3 h, the roofer moves on to another job. The apprentice requires 12 more hours to finish the job. How long would it take the apprentice, working alone, to do the job?

52. A welder requires 25 h to do a job. After the welder and an apprentice work on a job for 10 h, the welder quits. The apprentice finishes the job in 17 h. How long would it take the apprentice, working alone, to do the job?

53. Two clerks are addressing envelopes for a mayoral candidate's political campaign. One clerk can address one envelope every 30 s, whereas it takes 40 s for the second clerk to address one envelope. How many minutes will it take them, working together, to address 140 envelopes?

54. Three machines are filling water bottles. The machines can fill the daily quota of water bottles in 12 h, 15 h, and 20 h, respectively. How long would it take to fill the daily quota of water bottles with all three machines working?

55. With both hot and cold water running, a bathtub can be filled in 10 min. The drain will empty the tub in 15 min. A child turns both faucets on and leaves the drain open. How long will it be before the bathtub starts to overflow?

56. The inlet pipe can fill a water tank in 30 min. The outlet pipe can empty the tank in 20 min. How long would it take to empty a full tank with both pipes open?

57. An oil tank has two inlet pipes and one outlet pipe. One inlet pipe can fill the tank in 12 h, and the other inlet pipe can fill the tank in 20 h. The outlet pipe can empty the tank in 10 h. How long would it take to fill the tank with all three pipes open?

58. Water from a tank is being used for irrigation at the same time as the tank is being filled. The two inlet pipes can fill the tank in 6 h and 12 h, respectively. The outlet pipe can empty the tank in 24 h. How long would it take to fill the tank with all three pipes open?

59. It takes Jane n minutes to weed a row of the garden, and it takes Paul m minutes to weed a row of the garden, where $m > n$. Let t be the amount of time it takes Jane and Paul to weed a row of the garden together. Is t less than n, between n and m, or greater than m?

60. Ernie and Mike painted a fence together in a hours. It would have taken Ernie b hours to paint the fence by himself. What fraction of the fence did Ernie paint? What fraction of the fence did Mike paint?

3   Uniform motion problems

61. a. A plane can fly 470 mph in calm air. In the time it takes the plane to fly 1320 mi against a headwind, it could fly 1500 mi if it were flying with the wind. Let w represent the rate of the wind. Complete the following table.

	Distance	÷	Rate	=	Time
Against the wind	_____?_____	÷	_____?_____	=	_____?_____
With the wind	_____?_____	÷	_____?_____	=	_____?_____

b. Use the relationship between the expressions in the last column of the table to write an equation that can be solved to find the rate of the wind: _____?_____ = _____?_____.

62. Use the equation from part b of Exercise 61. The first step in solving this equation is to multiply each side of the equation by _____?_____.

63. Two skaters take off for an afternoon of rollerblading in Central Park. The first skater can cover 15 mi in the same time it takes the second skater, traveling 3 mph slower than the first skater, to cover 12 mi. Find the rate of each rollerblader.

64. A commercial jet travels 1620 mi in the same amount of time it takes a corporate jet to travel 1260 mi. The rate of the commercial jet is 120 mph greater than the rate of the corporate jet. Find the rate of each jet.

Bethesda Fountain in Central Park

65. A passenger train travels 295 mi in the same amount of time it takes a freight train to travel 225 mi. The rate of the passenger train is 14 mph greater than the rate of the freight train. Find the rate of each train.

66. The rate of a bicyclist is 7 mph more than the rate of a long-distance runner. The bicyclist travels 30 mi in the same amount of time it takes the runner to travel 16 mi. Find the rate of the runner.

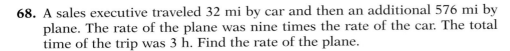

67. A cyclist rode 40 mi before having a flat tire and then walking 5 mi to a service station. The cycling rate was four times the walking rate. The time spent cycling and walking was 5 h. Find the rate at which the cyclist was riding.

68. A sales executive traveled 32 mi by car and then an additional 576 mi by plane. The rate of the plane was nine times the rate of the car. The total time of the trip was 3 h. Find the rate of the plane.

69. A motorist drove 72 mi before running out of gas and then walking 4 mi to a gas station. The driving rate of the motorist was twelve times the walking rate. The time spent driving and walking was 2.5 h. Find the rate at which the motorist walks.

70. An insurance representative traveled 735 mi by commercial jet and then an additional 105 mi by helicopter. The rate of the jet was four times the rate of the helicopter. The entire trip took 2.2 h. Find the rate of the jet.

71. A business executive can travel the 480 ft between two terminals of an airport by walking on a moving sidewalk in the same time required to walk 360 ft without using the moving sidewalk. If the rate of the moving sidewalk is 2 ft/s, find the rate at which the executive can walk.

72. A cyclist and a jogger start from a town at the same time and head for a destination 18 mi away. The rate of the cyclist is twice the rate of the jogger. The cyclist arrives 1.5 h before the jogger. Find the rate of the cyclist.

73. A single-engine plane and a commercial jet leave an airport at 10 A.M. and head for an airport 960 mi away. The rate of the jet is four times the rate of the single-engine plane. The single-engine plane arrives 4 h after the jet. Find the rate of each plane.

74. Marlys can row a boat 3 mph faster than she can swim. She is able to row 10 mi in the same time it takes her to swim 4 mi. Find Marlys's rate swimming.

75. A cruise ship can sail 28 mph in calm water. Sailing with the Gulf Stream, the ship can sail 170 mi in the same amount of time as it takes to sail 110 mi against the Gulf Stream. Find the rate of the Gulf Stream.

76. A commercial jet can fly 500 mph in calm air. Traveling with the jet stream, the plane flew 2420 mi in the same amount of time as it takes to fly 1580 mi against the jet stream. Find the rate of the jet stream.

77. A tour boat used for river excursions can travel 7 mph in calm water. The amount of time it takes to travel 20 mi with the current is the same amount of time it takes to travel 8 mi against the current. Find the rate of the current.

78. A canoe can travel 8 mph in still water. Traveling with the current of a river, the canoe can travel 15 mi in the same amount of time it takes to travel 9 mi against the current. Find the rate of the current.

6.4 Applying Concepts

79. Number Problem The denominator of a fraction is 4 more than the numerator. If both the numerator and the denominator of the fraction are increased by 3, the new fraction is $\frac{5}{6}$. Find the original fraction.

80. Work Problem One pipe can fill a tank in 3 h, a second pipe can fill the tank in 4 h, and a third pipe can fill the tank in 6 h. How long would it take to fill the tank with all three pipes operating?

81. Work Problem One printer can print a company's paychecks in 24 min, a second printer can print the checks in 16 min, and a third printer can do the job in 12 min. How long would it take to print the checks with all three printers operating?

82. Uniform Motion Problem By increasing your speed by 10 mph, you can drive the 200-mile trip to your hometown in 40 min less time than the trip usually takes you. How fast do you usually drive?

83. Uniform Motion Problem Because of weather conditions, a bus driver reduced the usual speed along a 165-mile bus route by 5 mph. The bus arrived only 15 min later than its usual arrival time. How fast does the bus usually travel?

84. Work Problem If a pump can fill a pool in A hours and a second pump can fill the pool in B hours, find a formula, in terms of A and B, for the time it takes both pumps, working together, to fill the pool.

85. Uniform Motion Problem If a parade is 1 mi long and is proceeding at 3 mph, how long will it take a runner, jogging at 5 mph, to run from the beginning of the parade to the end and then back to the beginning?

86. ✎ Write a report on the Rhind Papyrus.

87. ✎ What is a unit fraction? What role did unit fractions play in early Egyptian mathematics?

6.5 Proportions and Variation

OBJECTIVE 1 **Proportions**

Quantities such as 3 feet, 5 liters, and 2 miles are number quantities written with units. In these examples, the units are feet, liters, and miles.

A **ratio** is the quotient of two quantities that have the same unit.

The weekly wages of a painter are $800. The painter spends $150 a week for food. The ratio of wages spent for food to the total weekly wages is written as shown below.

$\dfrac{\$150}{\$800} = \dfrac{150}{800} = \dfrac{3}{16}$ A ratio is in simplest form when the two numbers do not have a common factor. The units are not written.

A **rate** is the quotient of two quantities that have different units.

A car travels 120 mi on 3 gal of gas. The miles-to-gallon rate is written as shown below.

$\dfrac{120\text{ mi}}{3\text{ gal}} = \dfrac{40\text{ mi}}{1\text{ gal}}$ A rate is in simplest form when the two numbers do not have a common factor. The units are written as part of the rate.

A **proportion** is an equation that states that two ratios or rates are equal. For example, $\dfrac{90\text{ km}}{4\text{ L}} = \dfrac{45\text{ km}}{2\text{ L}}$ and $\dfrac{3}{4} = \dfrac{x+2}{16}$ are proportions.

Note that a proportion is a special kind of fractional equation. Many application problems can be solved by using proportions.

The sales tax on a car that costs $24,000 is $1320. Find the sales tax on a car that costs $29,000.

Write a proportion using x to represent the sales tax.

$$\dfrac{1320}{24,000} = \dfrac{x}{29,000}$$

To solve the proportion, multiply each side of the equation by the denominators.

$$\dfrac{11}{200} = \dfrac{x}{29,000}$$

$$(200)(29,000)\left(\dfrac{11}{200}\right) = (200)(29,000)\left(\dfrac{x}{29,000}\right)$$

$$(29,000)(11) = 200x$$
$$319,000 = 200x$$
$$1595 = x$$

The sales tax on the $29,000 car is $1595.

EXAMPLE 1   A stock investment of 50 shares pays a dividend of $106. At this rate, how many aditional shares are needed to earn a dividend of $424?

Strategy   To find the additional number of shares that are required, write and solve a proportion using x to represent the additional number of shares. Then $50 + x$ is the total number of shares of stock.

Solution
$$\frac{106}{50} = \frac{424}{50 + x}$$

$$\frac{53}{25} = \frac{424}{50 + x}$$

$$25(50 + x)\frac{53}{25} = 25(50 + x)\frac{424}{50 + x}$$

$$(50 + x)53 = (25)424$$
$$2650 + 53x = 10{,}600$$
$$53x = 7950$$
$$x = 150$$

An additional 150 shares of stock are required.

PROBLEM 1   Two pounds of cashews cost $5.80. At this rate, how much would 15 lb of cashews cost?

Solution   See page S20.

OBJECTIVE ② Variation problems

A **direct variation** is a special function that can be expressed as the equation $y = kx$, where k is a constant. The equation $y = kx$ is read "y varies directly as x" or "y is proportional to x." The constant k is called the **constant of variation** or the **constant of proportionality.**

The circumference (C) of a circle varies directly as the diameter (d). The direct variation equation is written $C = \pi d$. The constant of variation is π.

A nurse earns $28 per hour. The nurse's total wage (w) is directly proportional to the number of hours (h) worked. The equation of variation is $w = 28h$. The constant of proportionality is 28.

In general, a direct variation equation can be written in the form $y = kx^n$, where n is a positive number. For example, the equation $y = kx^2$ is read "y varies directly as the square of x."

The area (A) of a circle varies directly as the square of the radius (r) of the circle. The direct variation equation is $A = \pi r^2$.

Given that V varies directly as r and that $V = 20$ when $r = 4$, the constant of variation can be found by writing the basic direct variation equation, replacing V and r by the given values, and solving for the constant of variation.

$$V = kr$$
$$20 = k \cdot 4$$
$$5 = k$$

The direct variation equation can then be written by substituting the value of k into the basic direct variation equation.

$$V = 5r$$

The graph of $V = 5r$

The tension (T) in a spring varies directly as the distance (x) it is stretched. If $T = 8$ lb when $x = 2$ in., find T when $x = 4$ in.

Write the basic direct variation equation.	$T = kx$
Replace T and x by the given values.	$8 = k \cdot 2$
Solve for the constant of variation.	$4 = k$
Write the direct variation equation.	$T = 4x$
To find T when $x = 4$ in., substitute 4 for x in the direct variation equation and solve for T.	$T = 4x$ $T = 4 \cdot 4$ $T = 16$

When $x = 4$ in., the tension is 16 lb.

The graph of $T = 4x$

EXAMPLE 2   The amount (A) of medication prescribed for a person varies directly with the person's weight (W). For a person who weighs 50 kg, 2 ml of medication are prescribed. How many milliliters of medication are required for a person who weighs 75 kg?

Strategy   To find the required amount of medication:

▶ Write the basic direct variation equation, replace the variables by the given values, and solve for k.

▶ Write the direct variation equation, replacing k by its value. Substitute 75 for W, and solve for A.

Solution

$$A = kW$$
$$2 = k \cdot 50$$
$$\frac{1}{25} = k$$

$$A = \frac{1}{25}W \qquad \bullet \textbf{ This is the direct variation equation.}$$

$$A = \frac{1}{25} \cdot 75 = 3 \qquad \bullet \textbf{ Replace } \boldsymbol{W} \textbf{ by 75.}$$

The required amount of medication is 3 ml.

PROBLEM 2   The distance (s) a body falls from rest varies directly as the square of the time (t) of the fall. An object falls 64 ft in 2 s. How far will it fall in 5 s?

Solution   See page S20.

A **joint variation** is a variation in which a variable varies directly as the product of two or more other variables. A joint variation can be expressed as the equation $z = kxy$, where k is a constant. The equation $z = kxy$ is read "z varies jointly as x and y."

The area (A) of a triangle varies jointly as the base (b) and the height (h). The joint variation equation is written $A = \frac{1}{2}bh$. The constant of variation is $\frac{1}{2}$.

An **inverse variation** is a function that can be expressed as the equation $y = \dfrac{k}{x}$, where k is a constant. The equation $y = \dfrac{k}{x}$ is read "y varies inversely as x" or "y is inversely proportional to x."

In general, an inverse variation equation can be written $y = \dfrac{k}{x^n}$, where n is a positive number. For example, the equation $y = \dfrac{k}{x^2}$ is read "y varies inversely as the square of x."

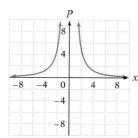

The graph of $P = \dfrac{20}{x^2}$

Given that P varies inversely as the square of x and that $P = 5$ when $x = 2$, the variation constant can be found by writing the basic inverse variation equation, replacing P and x by the given values, and solving for the constant variation.

$$P = \dfrac{k}{x^2}$$
$$5 = \dfrac{k}{2^2}$$
$$5 = \dfrac{k}{4}$$
$$20 = k$$

The inverse variation equation can then be found by substituting the value of k into the basic inverse variation equation.

$$P = \dfrac{20}{x^2}$$

The length (L) of a rectangle with fixed area is inversely proportional to the width (w). If $L = 6$ ft when $w = 2$ ft, find L when $w = 3$ ft.

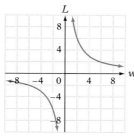

The graph of $L = \dfrac{12}{w}$

Write the basic inverse variation equation. $L = \dfrac{k}{w}$

Replace L and w by the given values. $6 = \dfrac{k}{2}$

Solve for the constant of variation. $12 = k$

Write the inverse variation equation. $L = \dfrac{12}{w}$

To find L when $w = 3$ ft, substitute 3 for w in the inverse variation equation and solve for L.

$$L = \dfrac{12}{w}$$
$$L = \dfrac{12}{3}$$
$$L = 4$$

When $w = 3$ ft, the length is 4 ft.

EXAMPLE 3   A company that produces personal computers has determined that the number of computers it can sell (s) is inversely proportional to the price (P) of the computer. Two thousand computers can be sold when the price is $2500. How many computers can be sold when the price of a computer is $2000?

Strategy   To find the number of computers:

▶ Write the basic inverse variation equation, replace the variables by the given values, and solve for k.

▶ Write the inverse variation equation, replacing k by its value. Substitute 2000 for P, and solve for s.

Solution

$$s = \frac{k}{P}$$

$$2000 = \frac{k}{2500}$$

$$5{,}000{,}000 = k$$

$$s = \frac{5{,}000{,}000}{P} \qquad \bullet \text{ This is the inverse variation equation.}$$

$$s = \frac{5{,}000{,}000}{2000} = 2500 \qquad \bullet \text{ Replace } P \text{ by } 2000.$$

At a price of \$2000, 2500 computers can be sold.

PROBLEM 3   The resistance (R) to the flow of electric current in a wire of fixed length is inversely proportional to the square of the diameter (d) of the wire. If a wire of diameter 0.01 cm has a resistance of 0.5 ohm, what is the resistance in a wire that is 0.02 cm in diameter?

Solution   See page S20.

A **combined variation** is a variation in which two or more types of variation occur at the same time. For example, in chemistry, the volume (V) of a gas varies directly as the temperature (T) and inversely as the pressure (P). This combined variation is written $V = \frac{kT}{P}$.

EXAMPLE 4   The pressure (P) of a gas varies directly as the temperature (T) and inversely as the volume (V). When $T = 50°$ and $V = 275$ in^3, $P = 20$ lb/in^2. Find the pressure of a gas when $T = 60°$ and $V = 250$ in^3.

Strategy   To find the pressure:

▶ Write the basic combined variation equation, replace the variables by the given values, and solve for k.

▶ Write the combined variation equation, replacing k by its value. Substitute 60 for T and 250 for V, and solve for P.

Solution

$$P = \frac{kT}{V}$$

$$20 = \frac{k(50)}{275}$$

$$110 = k$$

$$P = \frac{110T}{V} \qquad \bullet \text{ This is the combined variation equation.}$$

$$P = \frac{110(60)}{250} = 26.4 \qquad \bullet \text{ Replace } T \text{ by } 60 \text{ and } V \text{ by } 250.$$

The pressure is 26.4 lb/in^2.

PROBLEM 4   The strength (s) of a rectangular beam varies jointly as its width (W) and as the square of its depth (d) and inversely as its length (L). If the strength of a beam 2 in. wide, 12 in. deep, and 12 ft long is 1200 lb, find the strength of a beam 4 in. wide, 8 in. deep, and 16 ft long.

Solution   See page S21.

6.5   Concept Review

Determine whether the following statements are always true, sometimes true, or never true.

1. If x varies inversely as y, then when x is doubled, y is doubled.

2. If a varies inversely as b, then ab is a constant.

3. If a varies jointly as b and c, then $a = \dfrac{kb}{c}$.

4. If the length of a rectangle is held constant, then the area of the rectangle varies directly as the width.

5. If the area of a rectangle is held constant, then the length varies directly as the width.

6. The circumference of a circle varies directly as the diameter. If the diameter of a circle is doubled, then the circumference of the circle will be doubled.

6.5   Exercises

1   Proportions

1. How does a ratio differ from a rate?

2. What is a proportion?

3. The scale on a map shows that a distance of 2 cm on the map represents an actual distance of 5 mi. This rate can be expressed as the quotient

$$\dfrac{?}{?} \text{ or as the quotient } \dfrac{?}{?}.$$

4. Let x be the distance (in miles) represented by 13 cm on the map described in Exercise 3. Use a proportion to find x.

$$\frac{5}{2} = \frac{?}{\underline{\quad ? \quad}}$$

• Write the proportion so that each side is the ratio of miles to centimeters.

$$(2)(13)\left(\frac{5}{2}\right) = (2)(13)\left(\frac{x}{13}\right)$$

• Multiply each side of the proportion by $\underline{\quad ? \quad}$ and $\underline{\quad ? \quad}$.

$$\underline{\quad ? \quad} = (\underline{\quad ? \quad})x$$

• Simplify.

$$\underline{\quad ? \quad} = x$$

• Divide each side of the equation by $\underline{\quad ? \quad}$.

13 cm on the map represents $\underline{\quad ? \quad}$ mi.

Solve the proportion.

5. $\dfrac{x + 1}{10} = \dfrac{2}{5}$

6. $\dfrac{4}{x + 2} = \dfrac{3}{4}$

7. $\dfrac{x}{4} = \dfrac{x - 2}{8}$

8. $\dfrac{8}{x - 5} = \dfrac{3}{x}$

9. $\dfrac{8}{x - 2} = \dfrac{4}{x + 1}$

10. $\dfrac{4}{x - 4} = \dfrac{2}{x - 2}$

11. $\dfrac{8}{3x - 2} = \dfrac{2}{2x + 1}$

12. $\dfrac{x - 2}{x - 5} = \dfrac{2x}{2x + 5}$

13. 🗿 True or false? If $\dfrac{a}{b} = \dfrac{c}{d}$, then $\dfrac{b}{a} = \dfrac{d}{c}$.

14. 🗿 True or false? If $\dfrac{a}{b} = \dfrac{c}{d}$, then $\dfrac{a}{c} = \dfrac{b}{d}$.

15. **Environmental Science** In a wildlife preserve, 60 ducks are captured, tagged, and then released. Later, 200 ducks are examined, and three of the 200 ducks are found to have tags. Estimate the number of ducks in the preserve.

16. **Political Science** A pre-election survey showed that 7 out of every 12 voters would vote in an election. At this rate, how many people would be expected to vote in a city of 210,000?

17. **Food Service** A caterer estimates that 2 gal of fruit punch will serve 30 people. How much additional punch is necessary to serve 75 people?

18. **Nutrition** If a 56-gram serving of pasta contains 7 g of protein, how many grams of protein are in a 454-gram box of the pasta?

19. **Architecture** On an architectural drawing, $\frac{1}{4}$ in. represents 1 ft. Find the dimensions of a room that measures $4\frac{1}{4}$ in. by $5\frac{1}{2}$ in. on the drawing.

20. **Construction** A contractor estimated that 15 ft² of window space will be allowed for every 160 ft² of floor space. Using this estimate, how much window space will be allowed for 3200 ft² of floor space?

21. Energy Walking 4 mi in 2 h will use 650 calories. Walking at the same rate, how many miles would a person need to walk to lose 1 pound? (The burning of 3500 calories is equivalent to the loss of 1 pound.) Round to the nearest hundredth.

22. Construction To tile 24 ft² of area, 120 ceramic tiles are needed. At this rate, how many tiles are needed to tile 300 ft²?

23. Health Science Three-fourths of an ounce of a medication are required for a 120-pound adult. At the same rate, how many additional ounces of medication are required for a 200-pound adult?

24. Physics An object that weighs 100 lb on Earth would weigh 90.5 lb on Venus. At this rate, what is the weight on Venus of an object that weighs 150 lb on Earth?

25. Environmental Science Six ounces of an insecticide are mixed with 15 gal of water to make a spray for spraying an orange grove. At the same rate, how much additional insecticide is required to be mixed with 100 gal of water?

26. Ecology In an attempt to estimate the number of Siberian tigers in a preserve, a wildlife management team captured, tagged, and released 50 Siberian tigers. A few months later, they captured 150 Siberian tigers of which 30 had tags. Estimate the number of Siberian tigers in the region.

27. Internet Speeds A certain wireless Internet connection will download a 4-megabyte file in 60 s. At this rate, how many seconds would it take to download a 5-megabyte file?

28. Construction A contractor estimated that 30 ft³ of cement is required to make a concrete floor that measures 90 ft². Using this estimate, find how many additional cubic feet of cement would be required to make a concrete floor that measures 120 ft².

29. Graphic Arts The accompanying picture of a whale uses a scale of 1 in. represents 48 ft. Estimate the actual length of the whale.

30. Graphic Arts The accompanying picture of an elephant uses a scale of 1 in. represents 12 ft. Estimate the actual height of the elephant.

2 **Variation problems**

31.   What is a direct variation?

32. What is an inverse variation?

33. A ball whose circumference is 30 cm weighs 250 g. An 800-gram ball made of the same material has a circumference of 96 cm. Is the relationship between the circumference of a ball made of this material and its weight a direct variation or an indirect variation?

34. A person who weighs 150 lb on Earth weighs only 149.25 lb at 10 mi above Earth and 148.5 lb at 20 mi above Earth. Is the relationship between weight and distance above Earth a direct variation or an indirect variation?

35. **Scuba Diving** The pressure (p) on a diver in the water varies directly as the depth (d). If the pressure is 3.6 lb/in² when the depth is 8 ft, what is the pressure when the depth is 30 ft?

36. **Physics** The distance (d) a spring will stretch varies directly as the force (f) applied to the spring. If a force of 5 lb is required to stretch a spring 2 in., what force is required to stretch the spring 5 in.?

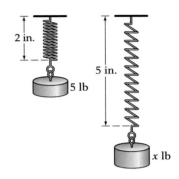

37. **Business** The profit (P) realized by a company varies directly as the number of products it sells (s). If a company makes a profit of $2500 on the sale of 20 products, what is the profit when the company sells 300 products?

38. **Farming** The number of bushels of wheat (b) produced by a farm is directly proportional to the number of acres (A) planted in wheat. If a 25-acre farm yields 1125 bushels of wheat, what is the yield of a farm that has 220 acres of wheat?

39. **Art** Leonardo da Vinci observed that the length of a person's face varies directly as the length of the person's chin. If a person whose face length is 9 in. has a chin length of 1.5 in., what is the length of a person's face whose chin length is 1.7 in.?

40. **Art** Leonardo da Vinci observed that a person's height varies directly as the width of the person's shoulders. If a person 70 in. tall has a shoulder width of 17.5 in., what is the height of a person whose shoulder width is 16 in.?

41. **Optics** The distance (d) a person can see to the horizon from a point above the surface of Earth varies directly as the square root of the height (H). If, for a height of 500 ft, the horizon is 19 mi away, how far is the horizon from a point that is 800 ft high? Round to the nearest hundredth.

42. **Physics** The period (p) of a pendulum, or the time it takes for the pendulum to make one complete swing, varies directly as the square root of the length (L) of the pendulum. If the period of a pendulum is 1.5 s when the length is 2 ft, find the period when the length is 4.5 ft. Round to the nearest hundredth.

43. **Physics** The distance (s) a ball will roll down an inclined plane is directly proportional to the square of the time (t). If the ball rolls 5 ft in 1 s, how far will it roll in 4 s?

44. Automotive Technology The stopping distance (*s*) of a car varies directly as the square of its speed (*v*). If a car traveling 30 mph requires 60 ft to stop, find the stopping distance for a car traveling 55 mph. Round to the nearest tenth.

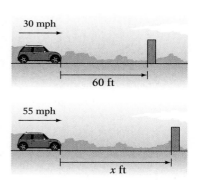

30 mph

60 ft

45. Chemistry For a constant temperature, the pressure (*P*) of a gas varies inversely as the volume (*V*). If the pressure is 25 lb/in² when the volume is 400 ft³, find the pressure when the volume is 150 ft³.

55 mph

x ft

46. Physics The pressure (*p*) in a liquid varies directly as the product of the depth (*d*) and the density (*D*) of the liquid. If the pressure is 37.5 lb/in² when the depth is 100 in. and the density is 1.2 lb/in², find the pressure when the density remains the same and the depth is 60 in.

47. Mechanical Engineering The speed (*v*) of a gear varies inversely as the number of teeth (*t*). If a gear that has 48 teeth makes 20 revolutions per minute, how many revolutions per minute will a gear that has 30 teeth make?

48. Electricity The current (*I*) in a wire varies directly as the voltage (*v*) and inversely as the resistance (*r*). If the current is 27.5 amps when the voltage is 110 volts and the resistance is 4 ohms, find the current when the voltage is 195 volts and the resistance is 12 ohms.

49. Magnetism The repulsive force (*f*) between the north poles of two magnets is inversely proportional to the square of the distance (*d*) between them. If the repulsive force is 18 lb when the distance is 3 in., find the repulsive force when the distance is 1.2 in.

50. Physics The intensity (*I*) of a light source is inversely proportional to the square of the distance (*d*) from the source. If the intensity is 8 lumens at a distance of 6 m, what is the intensity when the distance is 4 m?

51. Electricity The resistance (*R*) of a wire varies directly as the length (*L*) of the wire and inversely as the square of the diameter (*d*). If the resistance is 9 ohms in 50 ft of wire that has a diameter of 0.05 in., find the resistance in 50 ft of a similar wire that has a diameter of 0.02 in.

52. Music The frequency of vibration (*f*) of a guitar string varies directly as the square root of the tension (*T*) and inversely as the length (*L*) of the string. If the frequency is 40 vibrations per second when the tension is 25 lb and the length of the string is 3 ft, find the frequency when the tension is 36 lb and the string is 4 ft long.

53. Sailing The wind force (*w*) on a vertical surface varies directly as the product of the area (*A*) of the surface and the square of the wind velocity (*v*). When the wind is blowing at 30 mph, the force on an area of 10 ft² is 45 lb. Find the force on this area when the wind is blowing at 60 mph.

54. Electricity The power (*P*) in an electric circuit is directly proportional to the product of the current (*I*) and the square of the resistance (*R*). If the power is 100 watts when the current is 4 amps and the resistance is 5 ohms, find the power when the current is 2 amps and the resistance is 10 ohms.

6.5 Applying Concepts

55. a. Graph $y = kx$ when $k = 2$.
   b. What kind of function does the graph represent?

56. a. Graph $y = kx$ when $k = \dfrac{1}{2}$.
   b. What kind of function does the graph represent?

57. a. Graph $y = \dfrac{k}{x}$ when $k = 2$ and $x > 0$.
   b. Is this the graph of a function?

58. a. Graph $y = \dfrac{k}{x^2}$ when $k = 2$ and $x > 0$.
   b. Is this the graph of a function?

59. In the inverse variation equation $y = \dfrac{k}{x}$, what is the effect on x when y doubles?

60. In the direct variation equation $y = kx$, what is the effect on y when x doubles?

Complete using the word *directly* or *inversely*.

61. If a varies directly as b and inversely as c, then c varies _____ as b and _____ as a.

62. If a varies _____ as b and c, then abc is constant.

63. If the width of a rectangle is held constant, the area of the rectangle varies _____ as the length.

64. If the area of a rectangle is held constant, the length of the rectangle varies _____ as the width.

65. A number h is the harmonic mean of the numbers a and b if the reciprocal of h is equal to the average of the reciprocals of a and b.
   a. Write an expression for the harmonic mean of a and b.
   b. Find the harmonic mean of 10 and 15.

66. Write a report on financial ratios used by stock market analysts. Include the price-earnings ratio, current ratio, quick ratio, percent yield, and ratio of stockholders' equity to liabilities.

6.6   Literal Equations

OBJECTIVE **1**   **Solve literal equations**

A **literal equation** is an equation that contains more than one variable. Examples of literal equations are shown at the right.

$$3x - 2y = 4$$
$$v^2 = v_0^2 + 2as$$

Formulas are used to express relationships among physical quantities. A **formula** is a literal equation that states a rule about measurement. Examples of formulas are shown below.

$$s = vt - 16t^2 \qquad \text{(Physics)}$$
$$c^2 = a^2 + b^2 \qquad \text{(Geometry)}$$
$$A = P(1 + r)^t \qquad \text{(Business)}$$

The Addition and Multiplication Properties of Equations can be used to solve a literal equation for one of the variables. The goal is to rewrite the equation so that the variable being solved for is alone on one side of the equation, and all the other numbers and variables are on the other side.

Solve $C = \dfrac{5}{9}(F - 32)$ for F.

$$C = \frac{5}{9}(F - 32)$$

Use the Distributive Property to remove parentheses.

$$C = \frac{5}{9}F - \frac{160}{9}$$

Multiply each side of the equation by the LCM of the denominators.

$$9C = 5F - 160$$

Add 160 to each side of the equation.

$$9C + 160 = 5F$$

Divide each side of the equation by the coefficient 5.

$$\frac{9C + 160}{5} = F$$

EXAMPLE 1   **A.** Solve $A = P + Prt$ for P.   **B.** Solve $\dfrac{S}{S - C} = R$ for C.

Solution   **A.**
$$A = P + Prt$$
$$A = (1 + rt)P$$

• Factor P from P + Prt.

$$\frac{A}{1 + rt} = \frac{(1 + rt)P}{1 + rt}$$

• Divide each side of the equation by 1 + rt.

$$\frac{A}{1 + rt} = P$$

B.
$$\frac{S}{S - C} = R$$

$$(S - C)\frac{S}{S - C} = (S - C)R$$

• Multiply each side of the equation by S − C.

$$S = SR - CR$$
$$CR + S = SR$$

• Add CR to each side of the equation.

$$CR = SR - S$$

- Subtract S from each side of the equation.
- Divide each side of the equation by R.

$$C = \frac{SR - S}{R}$$

PROBLEM 1   A. Solve $\dfrac{1}{R_1} + \dfrac{1}{R_2} = \dfrac{1}{R}$ for R.   **B.** Solve $t = \dfrac{r}{r+1}$ for r.

■ **Solution**   See page S21.

6.6 Concept Review

Determine whether the following statements are always true, sometimes true, or never true.

1. A formula is a literal equation that states a rule about measurement.

2. A literal equation contains two variables.

3. The formula $\dfrac{1}{R_1} + \dfrac{1}{R_2} = \dfrac{1}{R}$ is taken from physics. When we solve for R_2, we get $R_2 = R - R_1$.

4. Consider the formula $P = 2L + 2W$. When we double the perimeter, the length and width will both be doubled.

6.6 Exercises

1   Solve literal equations

1. Solve $P = \dfrac{R - C}{n}$ for C.

$$P = \frac{R - C}{n}$$

$$(\underline{\quad ? \quad})P = (\underline{\quad ? \quad})\left(\frac{R - C}{n}\right)$$

- Multiply each side of the equation by $\underline{\quad ? \quad}$.

$$nP = \underline{\quad ? \quad}$$

- Simplify.

$$nP - R = -C$$

- Subtract $\underline{\quad ? \quad}$ from each side.

$$\underline{\quad ? \quad} = C$$

- Multiply each side by -1.

2. Only two steps are needed to solve $P = \dfrac{R - C}{n}$ for n. The first step is to

____?____ each side of the equation by ____?____. The second step is to

____?____ each side of the equation by ____?____. The result is $n = $ ____?____.

Solve the formula for the variable given.

3. $P = 2L + 2W$; W (Geometry)

4. $F = \dfrac{9}{5}C + 32$; C (Temperature conversion)

5. $S = C - rC$; C (Business)

6. $A = P + Prt$; t (Business)

7. $PV = nRT$; R (Chemistry)

8. $A = \dfrac{1}{2}bh$; h (Geometry)

9. $F = \dfrac{Gm_1m_2}{r^2}$; m_2 (Physics)

10. $\dfrac{P_1V_1}{T_1} = \dfrac{P_2V_2}{T_2}$; P_2 (Chemistry)

11. $I = \dfrac{E}{R + r}$; R (Physics)

12. $S = V_0t - 16t^2$; V_0 (Physics)

13. $A = \dfrac{1}{2}h(b_1 + b_2)$; b_2 (Geometry)

14. $V = \dfrac{1}{3}\pi r^2h$; h (Geometry)

15. $\dfrac{1}{R} = \dfrac{1}{R_1} + \dfrac{1}{R_2}$; R_2 (Physics)

16. $\dfrac{1}{f} = \dfrac{1}{a} + \dfrac{1}{b}$; b (Physics)

17. $a_n = a_1 + (n - 1)d$; d (Mathematics)

18. $P = \dfrac{R - C}{n}$; R (Business)

19. $S = 2WH + 2WL + 2LH$; H (Geometry)

20. $S = 2\pi r^2 + 2\pi rH$; H (Geometry)

Solve for x.

21. $ax + by + c = 0$

22. $x = ax + b$

23. $ax + b = cx + d$

24. $y - y_1 = m(x - x_1)$

25. $\dfrac{a}{x} = \dfrac{b}{c}$

26. $\dfrac{1}{x} + \dfrac{1}{a} = b$

27. $\dfrac{1}{a} + \dfrac{1}{b} = \dfrac{1}{x}$

28. $a(a - x) = b(b - x)$

29. When asked to solve $ax + b = cx$ for x, one student's result was $x = \dfrac{b}{c - a}$. Another student's result was $x = -\dfrac{b}{a - c}$. Are their answers equivalent?

30. When asked to solve $I = \dfrac{E}{R + r}$ for r, one student's result was $r = \dfrac{E}{I} - R$. Another student's result was $r = \dfrac{E - IR}{I}$. Are their answers equivalent?

6.6   Applying Concepts

Solve for x.

31. $\dfrac{x - y}{y} = \dfrac{x + 5}{2y}$

32. $\dfrac{x - 2}{y} = \dfrac{x + 2}{5y}$

33. $\dfrac{x}{x + y} = \dfrac{2x}{4y}$

34. $\dfrac{2x}{x - 2y} = \dfrac{x}{2y}$

35. $\dfrac{x - y}{2x} = \dfrac{x - 3y}{5y}$

36. $\dfrac{x - y}{x} = \dfrac{2x}{9y}$

Solve for the given variable.

37. $\dfrac{w_1}{w_2} = \dfrac{f_2 - f}{f - f_1}; f$

38. $v = \dfrac{v_1 + v_2}{1 + \dfrac{v_1 v_2}{c^2}}; v_1$

Focus on Problem Solving

Implication   Sentences that are constructed using "If…, then…" occur frequently in problem-solving situations. These sentences are called **implications.** The sentence "If it rains, then I will stay home" is an implication. The phrase *it rains* is called the **antecedent** of the implication. The phrase *I will stay home* is the **consequent** of the implication.

The sentence "If $x = 4$, then $x^2 = 16$" is a true sentence. The **contrapositive** of an implication is formed by switching the antecedent and the consequent and then negating each one. The contrapositive of "If $x = 4$, then $x^2 = 16$" is "If $x^2 \neq 16$, then $x \neq 4$." This sentence is also true. It is a principle of logic that an implication and its contrapositive are either both true or both false.

The **converse** of an implication is formed by switching the antecedent and the consequent. The converse of "If $x = 4$, then $x^2 = 16$" is "If $x^2 = 16$, then $x = 4$." Note that the converse is not a true statement, because if $x^2 = 16$, then x could equal -4. The converse of an implication may or may not be true.

Those statements for which the implication and the converse are both true are very important. They can be stated in the form "x if and only if y." For instance, a number is divisible by 5 if and only if the last digit of the number is 0 or 5. The implication "If a number is divisible by 5, then it ends in 0 or 5" and the converse "If a number ends in 0 or 5, then it is divisible by 5" are both true.

For each of the following, state the contrapositive and the converse of the implication. If the converse and the implication are both true statements, write a sentence using the phrase "if and only if."

1. If I live in Chicago, then I live in Illinois.

2. If today is June 1, then yesterday was May 31.

3. If today is not Thursday, then tomorrow is not Friday.

4. If a number is divisible by 8, then it is divisible by 4.

5. If a number is an even number, then it is divisible by 2.

6. If a number is a multiple of 6, then it is a multiple of 3.

7. If $4z = 20$, then $z = 5$.

8. If an angle measures $90°$, then it is a right angle.

9. If p is a prime number greater than 2, then p is an odd number.

10. If the equation of a graph is $y = mx + b$, then the graph of the equation is a straight line.

11. If $a = 0$ or $b = 0$, then $ab = 0$.

12. If the coordinates of a point are $(5, 0)$, then the point is on the x-axis.

13. If a quadrilateral is a square, then the quadrilateral has four sides of equal length.

14. If $x = y$, then $x^2 = y^2$.

Projects & Group Activities

Continued Fractions   The following complex fraction is called a **continued fraction.**

$$1 + \cfrac{1}{1 + \cfrac{1}{1 + \cfrac{1}{1 + \cfrac{1}{1 + \cdots}}}}$$

The dots indicate that the pattern continues to repeat forever.

A **convergent** for a continued fraction is an approximation of the repeated pattern. For instance,

$$c_2 = 1 + \cfrac{1}{1 + \cfrac{1}{1 + 1}} \qquad c_3 = 1 + \cfrac{1}{1 + \cfrac{1}{1 + \cfrac{1}{1 + 1}}} \qquad c_4 = 1 + \cfrac{1}{1 + \cfrac{1}{1 + \cfrac{1}{1 + \cfrac{1}{1 + 1}}}}$$

1. Calculate c_5 for the continued fraction above.

The fraction above is related to the golden rectangle, which has been used in architectural designs as diverse as the Parthenon in Athens, built around 440 B.C., and the United Nations building. A golden rectangle is one for which

$$\frac{\text{length}}{\text{width}} = \frac{\text{length} + \text{width}}{\text{length}}$$

An example of a golden rectangle is shown below.

Here is another continued fraction, which was discovered by Leonhard Euler (1707–1793). Calculating the convergents of this continued fraction yields approximations that are closer and closer to π.

$$\pi = 3 + \cfrac{1^2}{6 + \cfrac{3^2}{6 + \cfrac{5^2}{6 + \cfrac{7^2}{6 + \cdots}}}}$$

2. Calculate $c_5 = 3 + \cfrac{1^2}{6 + \cfrac{3^2}{6 + \cfrac{5^2}{6 + \cfrac{7^2}{6 + \cfrac{9^2}{6 + 11^2}}}}}$

Chapter 6 Summary

Key Words

A fraction in which the numerator and denominator are polynomials is called a **rational expression**. [6.1.1, p. 373]

A rational expression is in **simplest form** when the numerator and denominator have no common factors. [6.1.2, p. 375]

The **reciprocal of a rational expression** is the rational expression with the numerator and denominator interchanged. [6.2.1, p. 383]

The **least common multiple (LCM) of two or more polynomials** is the simplest polynomial that contains the factors of each polynomial. [6.2.2, p. 385]

A **complex fraction** is a fraction whose numerator or denominator contains one or more fractions. [6.3.1, p. 394]

A **ratio** is the quotient of two quantities that have the same unit. When a ratio is in simplest form, the units are not written. [6.5.1, p. 412]

A **rate** is the quotient of two quantities that have different units. [6.5.1, p. 412]

A **proportion** is an equation that states the equality of two ratios or rates. [6.5.1, p. 412]

Direct variation is a special function that can be expressed as the equation $y = kx^n$, where k is a constant called the **constant of variation** or the **constant of proportionality**. [6.5.2, p. 413]

Examples

$\dfrac{x^2 + 2x + 1}{x - 3}$ is a rational expression.

$\dfrac{x^2 + 3x + 2}{(x + 1)^2} = \dfrac{(x + 1)(x + 2)}{(x + 1)(x + 1)} = \dfrac{x + 2}{x + 1}$

The reciprocal of $\dfrac{a^2 - b^2}{x - y}$ is $\dfrac{x - y}{a^2 - b^2}$.

$4x^2 - 12x = 4x(x - 3)$
$3x^3 - 21x^2 + 36x = 3x(x - 3)(x - 4)$
LCM $= 12x(x - 3)(x - 4)$

$\dfrac{\dfrac{1}{x} + \dfrac{1}{y}}{\dfrac{1}{x}}$ is a complex fraction.

$\dfrac{\$35}{\$100}$ written as a ratio in simplest form is $\dfrac{7}{20}$.

$\dfrac{65 \text{ mi}}{2 \text{ gal}}$ is a rate.

$\dfrac{75}{3} = \dfrac{x}{42}$ is a proportion.

$E = mc^2$ is Einstein's formula relating energy and mass. c^2 is the constant of proportionality.

Joint variation is a variation in which a variable varies directly as the product of two or more variables. A joint variation can be expressed as the equation $z = kxy$, where k is a constant. [6.5.2, p. 414]

$C = kAT$ is a formula for the cost of insulation, where A is the area to be insulated and T is the thickness of the insulation.

Inverse variation is a function that can be expressed as the equation $y = \dfrac{k}{x^n}$, where k is a constant. [6.5.2, p. 415]

$I = \dfrac{k}{d^2}$ gives the intensity of a light source at a distance d from the source.

Combined variation is a variation in which two or more types of variation occur at the same time. [6.5.2, p. 416]

$V = \dfrac{kT}{P}$ is a formula that states that the volume of a gas is directly proportional to the temperature and inversely proportional to the pressure.

A **formula** is a literal equation that states rules about measurements. [6.6.1, p. 423]

$P = 2L + 2W$ is the formula for the perimeter of a rectangle.

Essential Rules and Procedures

To multiply fractions

$\dfrac{a}{b} \cdot \dfrac{c}{d} = \dfrac{ac}{bd}$ [6.2.1, p. 382]

$$\dfrac{x^2 + 2x - 8}{x^2 - 2x} \cdot \dfrac{3x - 12}{x^2 - 16}$$
$$= \dfrac{(x + 4)(x - 2)}{x(x - 2)} \cdot \dfrac{3(x - 4)}{(x + 4)(x - 4)}$$
$$= \dfrac{(x + 4)(x - 2) \cdot 3(x - 4)}{x(x - 2)(x + 4)(x - 4)}$$
$$= \dfrac{3}{x}$$

To divide fractions

$\dfrac{a}{b} \div \dfrac{c}{d} = \dfrac{a}{b} \cdot \dfrac{d}{c}$ [6.2.1, p. 383]

$$\dfrac{3x}{x - 5} \div \dfrac{3}{x + 4} = \dfrac{3x}{x - 5} \cdot \dfrac{x + 4}{3}$$
$$= \dfrac{3x(x + 4)}{3(x - 5)} = \dfrac{x(x + 4)}{x - 5}$$
$$= \dfrac{x^2 + 4x}{x - 5}$$

To add fractions

$\dfrac{a}{c} + \dfrac{b}{c} = \dfrac{a + b}{c}$ [6.2.2, p. 384]

$$\dfrac{2x - 7}{x^2 + 4} + \dfrac{x + 2}{x^2 + 4} = \dfrac{(2x - 7) + (x + 2)}{x^2 + 4}$$
$$= \dfrac{3x - 5}{x^2 + 4}$$

To subtract fractions

$\dfrac{a}{c} - \dfrac{b}{c} = \dfrac{a - b}{c}$ [6.2.2, p. 384]

$$\dfrac{5x - 6}{x + 2} - \dfrac{2x + 4}{x + 2} = \dfrac{(5x - 6) - (2x + 4)}{x + 2}$$
$$= \dfrac{3x - 10}{x + 2}$$

Equation for Work Problems
Rate of work × Time worked = Part of task completed
[6.4.2, p. 401]

A roofer requires 24 h to shingle a roof. An apprentice can shingle the roof in 36 h. How long would it take to shingle the roof if both roofers worked together?

$$\frac{t}{24} + \frac{t}{36} = 1$$

Equation for Uniform Motion Problems

$$\text{Distance} = \text{Rate} \times \text{Time} \quad \text{or} \quad \frac{\text{Distance}}{\text{Rate}} = \text{Time} \ [6.4.3, \text{p. } 403]$$

A motorcycle travels 195 mi in the same amount of time it takes a car to travel 159 mi. The rate of the motorcycle is 12 mph greater than the rate of the car. Find the rate of the car.

$$\frac{195}{r + 12} = \frac{159}{r}$$

Chapter 6 Review Exercises

1. Given $P(x) = \dfrac{x}{x - 3}$, find $P(4)$.

2. Given $P(x) = \dfrac{x^2 - 2}{3x^2 - 2x + 5}$, find $P(-2)$.

3. Find the domain of $g(x) = \dfrac{2x}{x - 3}$.

4. Find the domain of $f(x) = \dfrac{2x - 7}{3x^2 + 3x - 18}$.

5. Find the domain of $F(x) = \dfrac{x^2 - x}{3x^2 + 4}$.

6. Simplify: $\dfrac{6a^{5n} + 4a^{4n} - 2a^{3n}}{2a^{3n}}$

7. Simplify: $\dfrac{16 - x^2}{x^3 - 2x^2 - 8x}$

8. Simplify: $\dfrac{x^3 - 27}{x^2 - 9}$

9. Multiply: $\dfrac{a^6b^4 + a^4b^6}{a^5b^4 - a^4b^4} \cdot \dfrac{a^2 - b^2}{a^4 - b^4}$

10. Multiply: $\dfrac{x^3 - 8}{x^3 + 2x^2 + 4x} \cdot \dfrac{x^3 + 2x^2}{x^2 - 4}$

11. Multiply: $\dfrac{16 - x^2}{6x - 6} \cdot \dfrac{x^2 + 5x + 6}{x^2 - 8x + 16}$

12. Divide: $\dfrac{x^{2n} - 5x^n + 4}{x^{2n} - 2x^n - 8} \div \dfrac{x^{2n} - 4x^n + 3}{x^{2n} + 8x^n + 12}$

13. Divide: $\dfrac{27x^3 - 8}{9x^3 + 6x^2 + 4x} \div \dfrac{9x^2 - 12x + 4}{9x^2 - 4}$

14. Divide: $\dfrac{3 - x}{x^2 + 3x + 9} \div \dfrac{x^2 - 9}{x^3 - 27}$

15. Add: $\dfrac{5}{3a^2b^3} + \dfrac{7}{8ab^4}$

16. Subtract: $\dfrac{3x^2 + 2}{x^2 - 4} - \dfrac{9x - x^2}{x^2 - 4}$

17. Simplify: $\dfrac{8}{9x^2 - 4} + \dfrac{5}{3x - 2} - \dfrac{4}{3x + 2}$

18. Simplify: $\dfrac{6x}{3x^2 - 7x + 2} - \dfrac{2}{3x - 1} + \dfrac{3x}{x - 2}$

19. Simplify: $\dfrac{x}{x - 3} - 4 - \dfrac{2x - 5}{x + 2}$

20. Simplify: $\dfrac{x - 6 + \dfrac{6}{x - 1}}{x + 3 - \dfrac{12}{x - 1}}$

21. Simplify: $\dfrac{x + \dfrac{3}{x - 4}}{3 + \dfrac{x}{x - 4}}$

22. Solve: $\dfrac{5x}{2x - 3} + 4 = \dfrac{3}{2x - 3}$

23. Solve: $\dfrac{x}{x - 3} = \dfrac{2x + 5}{x + 1}$

24. Solve: $\dfrac{6}{x - 3} - \dfrac{1}{x + 3} = \dfrac{51}{x^2 - 9}$

25. Solve: $\dfrac{30}{x^2 + 5x + 4} + \dfrac{10}{x + 4} = \dfrac{4}{x + 1}$

26. Solve $I = \dfrac{1}{R}V$ for R.

27. Solve $Q = \dfrac{N - S}{N}$ for N.

28. Solve $S = \dfrac{a}{1 - r}$ for r.

29. **Fuel Efficiency** A car uses 4 tanks of fuel to travel 1800 mi. At this rate, how many tanks of fuel would be required for a trip of 3000 mi?

30. **Cartography** On a certain map, 2.5 in. represents 10 mi. How many miles would be represented by 12 in.?

31. **Work Problem** An electrician requires 65 min to install a ceiling fan. The electrician and an apprentice, working together, take 40 min to install the fan. How long would it take the apprentice, working alone, to install the ceiling fan?

32. **Work Problem** The inlet pipe can fill a tub in 24 min. The drain pipe can empty the tub in 15 min. How long would it take to empty a full tub with both pipes open?

33. **Work Problem** Three students can paint a dormitory room in 8 h, 16 h, and 16 h, respectively. How long would it take to do the job if all three students worked together?

34. Uniform Motion A canoeist can travel 10 mph in calm water. The amount of time it takes to travel 60 mi with the current is the same amount of time it takes to travel 40 mi against the current. Find the rate of the current.

35. Uniform Motion A bus and a cyclist leave a school at 8 A.M. and head for a stadium 90 mi away. The rate of the bus is three times the rate of the cyclist. The cyclist arrives 4 h after the bus. Find the rate of the bus.

36. Uniform Motion A tractor travels 10 mi in the same amount of time it takes a car to travel 15 mi. The rate of the tractor is 15 mph less than the rate of the car. Find the rate of the tractor.

37. Physics The pressure (p) of wind on a flat surface varies jointly as the area (A) of the surface and the square of the wind's velocity (v). If the pressure on 22 ft^2 is 10 lb when the wind's velocity is 10 mph, find the pressure on the same surface when the wind's velocity is 20 mph.

38. Light The illumination (I) produced by a light varies inversely as the square of the distance (d) from the light. If the illumination produced 10 ft from a light is 12 lumens, find the illumination 2 ft from the light.

39. Electricity The electrical resistance (r) of a cable varies directly as its length (l) and inversely as the square of its diameter (d). If a cable 16,000 ft long and $\frac{1}{4}$ in. in diameter has a resistance of 3.2 ohms, what is the resistance of a cable that is 8000 ft long and $\frac{1}{2}$ in. in diameter?

Chapter 6 Test

1. Simplify: $\dfrac{v^3 - 4v}{2v^2 - 5v + 2}$

2. Simplify: $\dfrac{2a^2 - 8a + 8}{4 + 4a - 3a^2}$

3. Multiply: $\dfrac{3x^2 - 12}{5x - 15} \cdot \dfrac{2x^2 - 18}{x^2 + 5x + 6}$

4. Given $P(x) = \dfrac{3 - x^2}{x^3 - 2x^2 + 4}$, find $P(-1)$.

5. Divide: $\dfrac{2x^2 - x - 3}{2x^2 - 5x + 3} \div \dfrac{3x^2 - x - 4}{x^2 - 1}$

6. Multiply: $\dfrac{x^{2n} - x^n - 2}{x^{2n} + x^n} \cdot \dfrac{x^{2n} - x^n}{x^{2n} - 4}$

7. Simplify: $\dfrac{2}{x^2} + \dfrac{3}{y^2} - \dfrac{5}{2xy}$

8. Simplify: $\dfrac{3x}{x - 2} - 3 + \dfrac{4}{x + 2}$

9. Find the domain of $f(x) = \dfrac{3x^2 - x + 1}{x^2 - 9}$.

10. Subtract: $\dfrac{x + 2}{x^2 + 3x - 4} - \dfrac{2x}{x^2 - 1}$

11. Simplify: $\dfrac{1 - \dfrac{1}{x} - \dfrac{12}{x^2}}{1 + \dfrac{6}{x} + \dfrac{9}{x^2}}$

12. Simplify: $\dfrac{1 - \dfrac{1}{x + 2}}{1 - \dfrac{3}{x + 4}}$

13. Solve: $\dfrac{3}{x + 1} = \dfrac{2}{x}$

14. Solve: $\dfrac{4x}{2x - 1} = 2 - \dfrac{1}{2x - 1}$

15. Solve $ax = bx + c$ for x.

16. Work Problem The inlet pipe can fill a water tank in 48 min. The outlet pipe can empty the tank in 30 min. How long would it take to empty a full tank with both pipes open?

17. Wall Papering An interior designer uses two rolls of wallpaper for every 45 ft² of wall space in an office. At this rate, how many rolls of wallpaper are needed for an office that has 315 ft² of wall space?

18. Work Problem One landscaper can till the soil for a lawn in 30 min, whereas it takes a second landscaper 15 min to do the same job. How long would it take to till the soil for the lawn if both landscapers worked together?

19. Unform Motion A cyclist travels 20 mi in the same amount of time it takes a hiker to walk 6 mi. The rate of the cyclist is 7 mph greater than the rate of the hiker. Find the rate of the cyclist.

20. Physics The stopping distance (s) of a car varies directly as the square of the speed (v) of the car. For a car traveling at 50 mph, the stopping distance is 170 ft. Find the stopping distance of a car that is traveling at 30 mph.

Cumulative Review Exercises

1. Simplify: $8 - 4[-3 - (-2)]^2 \div 5$

2. Solve: $\dfrac{2x - 3}{6} - \dfrac{x}{9} = \dfrac{x - 4}{3}$

3. Solve: $5 - |x - 4| = 2$

4. Find the domain of $f(x) = \dfrac{x}{x - 3}$.

5. Given $P(x) = \dfrac{x-1}{2x-3}$, find $P(-2)$.

6. Write 0.000000035 in scientific notation.

7. Solve: $\dfrac{x}{x+1} = 1$

8. Solve: $(9x - 1)(x - 4) = 0$

9. Simplify: $\dfrac{(2a^{-2}b^3)}{(4a)^{-1}}$

10. Solve: $x - 3(1 - 2x) \geq 1 - 4(2 - 2x)$

11. Multiply: $(2a^2 - 3a + 1)(-2a^2)$

12. Factor: $2x^{2n} + 3x^n - 2$

13. Factor: $x^3y^3 - 27$

14. Simplify: $\dfrac{x^4 + x^3y - 6x^2y^2}{x^3 - 2x^2y}$

15. Find the equation of the line that contains the point $(-2, -1)$ and is parallel to the line $3x - 2y = 6$.

16. Simplify: $(x - x^{-1})^{-1}$

17. Graph $-3x + 5y = -15$ by using the x- and y-intercepts.

18. Graph the solution set: $\begin{aligned} x + y &\leq 3 \\ -2x + y &> 4 \end{aligned}$

19. Divide: $\dfrac{4x^3 + 2x^2 - 10x + 1}{x - 2}$

20. Divide: $\dfrac{16x^2 - 9y^2}{16x^2y - 12xy^2} \div \dfrac{4x^2 - xy - 3y^2}{12x^2y^2}$

21. Find the domain of $f(x) = \dfrac{x^2 + 6x + 7}{3x^2 + 5}$.

22. Subtract: $\dfrac{5x}{3x^2 - x - 2} - \dfrac{2x}{x^2 - 1}$

23. Evaluate the determinant: $\begin{vmatrix} 6 & 5 \\ 2 & -3 \end{vmatrix}$

24. Simplify: $\dfrac{x - 4 + \dfrac{5}{x+2}}{x + 2 - \dfrac{1}{x+2}}$

25. Solve: $\begin{aligned} x + y + z &= 3 \\ -2x + y + 3z &= 2 \\ 2x - 4y + z &= -1 \end{aligned}$

26. Given $f(x) = x^2 - 3x + 3$ and $f(c) = 1$, find c.

27. Solve the proportion: $\dfrac{2}{x-3} = \dfrac{5}{2x-3}$

28. Solve: $\dfrac{3}{x^2-36} = \dfrac{2}{x-6} - \dfrac{5}{x+6}$

29. Multiply: $(a+5)(a^3-3a+4)$

30. Solve $I = \dfrac{E}{R+r}$ for r.

31. Are the graphs of $4x+3y=12$ and $3x+4y=16$ perpendicular?

32. Graph: $f(x) = 1 - x + x^3$

33. Integer Problem The sum of two integers is 15. Five times the smaller integer is five more than twice the larger integer. Find the integers.

34. Food Mixture How many pounds of almonds that cost $5.40 per pound must be mixed with 50 lb of peanuts that cost $2.60 per pound to make a mixture that costs $4.00 per pound?

35. Elections A pre-election survey showed that three out of five voters would vote in an election. At this rate, how many people would be expected to vote in a city of 125,000?

36. Work Problem A new computer can work six times as fast as an older computer. Working together, the computers can complete a job in 12 min. How long would it take the new computer, working alone, to do the job?

37. Uniform Motion A plane can fly at a rate of 300 mph in calm air. Traveling with the wind, the plane flew 900 mi in the same amount of time it took to fly 600 mi against the wind. Find the rate of the wind.

38. Music The frequency of vibration (f) in an open pipe organ varies inversely as the length (L) of the pipe. If the air in a pipe 2 m long vibrates 60 times per minute, find the frequency in a pipe that is 1.5 m long.

7 Rational Exponents and Radicals

DVD **SSM**

Online Study Center

Need help? For online student resources, such as section quizzes, visit the Online Study Center at college.hmco.com/info/aufmanndevmathhb.

Satellite phones, satellite radios, and satellite TV are just three examples of the many ways satellites are now being used in everyday life. Thousands of man-made satellites have been launched into space and are now orbiting Earth. The speed at which a satellite orbits Earth is a function of its height above Earth's surface. The height at which it orbits Earth is dependent on the satellite's purpose. The relationship between a satellite's speed and its height above Earth can be modeled by a radical equation, such as the one used in **Exercise 85 on page 475.**

Prep Test

1. Complete: $48 = ? \cdot 3$

For Exercises 2 to 7, simplify.

2. 2^5

3. $6\left(\dfrac{3}{2}\right)$

4. $\dfrac{1}{2} - \dfrac{2}{3} + \dfrac{1}{4}$

5. $(3 - 7x) - (4 - 2x)$

6. $\dfrac{3x^5y^6}{12x^4y}$

7. $(3x - 2)^2$

For Exercises 8 and 9, multiply.

8. $(2 + 4x)(5 - 3x)$

9. $(6x - 1)(6x + 1)$

10. Solve: $x^2 - 14x - 5 = 10$

7.1 Rational Exponents and Radical Expressions

OBJECTIVE 1

Simplify expressions with rational exponents

Point of Interest

Nicolas Chuquet (ca. 1475), a French physician, wrote an algebra text in which he used a notation for expressions with fractional exponents. He wrote $R^2 6$ to mean $6^{1/2}$ and $R^3 15$ to mean $15^{1/3}$. This was an improvement over earlier notations that used words for these expressions.

In this section, the definition of an exponent is extended beyond integers so that any rational number can be used as an exponent. The definition is expressed in such a way that the Rules of Exponents hold true for rational exponents.

Consider the expression $\left(a^{\frac{1}{n}}\right)^n$ for $a > 0$ and n a positive integer. Now simplify, assuming that the Rule for Simplifying a Power of an Exponential Expression is true.

$$\left(a^{\frac{1}{n}}\right)^n = a^{\frac{1}{n} \cdot n} = a^1 = a$$

Because $\left(a^{\frac{1}{n}}\right)^n = a$, the number $a^{\frac{1}{n}}$ **is the number whose nth power is a.**

$$25^{\frac{1}{2}} = 5 \text{ because } (5)^2 = 25.$$
$$8^{\frac{1}{3}} = 2 \text{ because } (2)^3 = 8.$$

In the expression $a^{\frac{1}{n}}$, if a is a negative number and n is a positive even integer, then $a^{\frac{1}{n}}$ is not a real number.

$(-4)^{\frac{1}{2}}$ is not a real number, because there is no real number whose second power is -4.

When n is a positive odd integer, a can be a positive or a negative number.

$$(-27)^{\frac{1}{3}} = -3 \text{ because } (-3)^3 = -27.$$

Using the definition of $a^{\frac{1}{n}}$ and the Rules of Exponents, it is possible to define any exponential expression that contains a rational exponent.

Definition of $a^{\frac{m}{n}}$

If m and n are positive integers and $a^{\frac{1}{n}}$ is a real number, then

$$a^{\frac{m}{n}} = \left(a^{\frac{1}{n}}\right)^m$$

> **Take Note**
>
> Although we can simplify an expression by rewriting $a^{\frac{m}{n}}$ in the form $(a^m)^{\frac{1}{n}}$, it is usually easier to simplify $\left(a^{\frac{1}{n}}\right)^m$. For instance, simplifying $\left(27^{\frac{1}{3}}\right)^2$ is easier than simplifying $(27^2)^{\frac{1}{3}}$.

The expression $a^{\frac{m}{n}}$ can also be written $a^{\frac{m}{n}} = a^{m \cdot \frac{1}{n}} = (a^m)^{\frac{1}{n}}$. However, rewriting $a^{\frac{m}{n}}$ as $(a^m)^{\frac{1}{n}}$ is not as useful as rewriting it as $\left(a^{\frac{1}{n}}\right)^m$. See the Take Note at the left.

As shown above, expressions that contain rational exponents do not always represent real numbers when the base of the exponential expression is a negative number. For this reason, all variables in this chapter represent positive numbers unless otherwise stated.

> **Take Note**
>
> Note that $32^{-\frac{2}{5}} = \frac{1}{4}$, a positive number. A negative exponent does not affect the sign of a number.

EXAMPLE 1   Simplify.   **A.** $27^{\frac{2}{3}}$ **B.** $32^{-\frac{2}{5}}$ **C.** $(-49)^{\frac{3}{2}}$

Solution   **A.** $27^{\frac{2}{3}} = (3^3)^{\frac{2}{3}}$ • **Rewrite 27 as 3^3.**

$\qquad\qquad = 3^{3\left(\frac{2}{3}\right)}$ • **Use the Rule for Simplifying a Power of an Exponential Expression.**

$\qquad\qquad = 3^2$

$\qquad\qquad = 9$ • **Simplify.**

B. $32^{-\frac{2}{5}} = (2^5)^{-\frac{2}{5}}$ • **Rewrite 32 as 2^5.**

$\qquad\qquad = 2^{-2}$ • **Use the Rule for Simplifying a Power of an Exponential Expression.**

$\qquad\qquad = \dfrac{1}{2^2}$ • **Use the Rule of Negative Exponents.**

$\qquad\qquad = \dfrac{1}{4}$ • **Simplify.**

C. $(-49)^{\frac{3}{2}}$ • **The base of the exponential expression is a negative number, while the denominator of the exponent is a positive even number.**

$(-49)^{\frac{3}{2}}$ is not a real number.

PROBLEM 1   Simplify.   **A.** $64^{\frac{2}{3}}$ **B.** $16^{-\frac{3}{4}}$ **C.** $(-81)^{\frac{3}{4}}$

Solution   See page S21.

EXAMPLE 2   Simplify.   **A.** $b^{\frac{1}{2}} \cdot b^{\frac{2}{3}} \cdot b^{-\frac{1}{4}}$ **B.** $(x^6 y^4)^{\frac{3}{2}}$ **C.** $\left(\dfrac{8a^3 b^{-4}}{64a^{-9}b^2}\right)^{\frac{2}{3}}$

Solution   **A.** $b^{\frac{1}{2}} \cdot b^{\frac{2}{3}} \cdot b^{-\frac{1}{4}} = b^{\frac{1}{2}+\frac{2}{3}-\frac{1}{4}}$ • Use the Rule for Multiplying
$$= b^{\frac{6}{12}+\frac{8}{12}-\frac{3}{12}}$$ Exponential Expressions.
$$= b^{\frac{11}{12}}$$

B. $(x^6 y^4)^{\frac{3}{2}} = x^{6\left(\frac{3}{2}\right)} y^{4\left(\frac{3}{2}\right)}$ • Use the Rule for Simplifying Powers of
$$= x^9 y^6$$ Products.

C. $\left(\dfrac{8a^3 b^{-4}}{64a^{-9}b^2}\right)^{\frac{2}{3}} = \left(\dfrac{a^{12}}{8b^6}\right)^{\frac{2}{3}}$ • Use the Rule for Dividing Exponential
    Expressions.
$$= \left(\dfrac{a^{12}}{2^3 b^6}\right)^{\frac{2}{3}}$$ • Rewrite 8 as 2^3.
$$= \dfrac{a^8}{2^2 b^4}$$ • Use the Rule for Simplifying Powers of
    Quotients.
$$= \dfrac{a^8}{4b^4}$$

PROBLEM 2   Simplify.   **A.** $\dfrac{x^{\frac{1}{2}} y^{-\frac{5}{4}}}{x^{-\frac{4}{3}} y^{\frac{1}{3}}}$ **B.** $\left(x^{\frac{3}{4}} y^{\frac{1}{2}} z^{-\frac{2}{3}}\right)^{-\frac{4}{3}}$ **C.** $\left(\dfrac{16a^{-2}b^{\frac{4}{3}}}{9a^4 b^{-\frac{2}{3}}}\right)^{-\frac{1}{2}}$

Solution   See page S21.

OBJECTIVE 2   **Write exponential expressions as radical expressions and radical expressions as exponential expressions**

As stated in the previous objective, $a^{\frac{1}{n}}$ is the number whose nth power is a. This can be stated as $a^{\frac{1}{n}}$ is the **nth root** of a. The expression $\sqrt[n]{a}$ is another symbol for the nth root of a.

Alternative Notation for the nth Root of a

If a is a real number and n is a positive integer, then $\sqrt[n]{a} = a^{\frac{1}{n}}$.

In the expression $\sqrt[n]{a}$, the symbol $\sqrt{}$ is called a **radical**, n is the **index** of the radical, and a is the **radicand**. When $n = 2$, the radical expression represents a square root and the index 2 is usually not written.

An exponential expression with a rational exponent can be written as a radical expression.

Definition of the nth Root of a^m

If $a^{\frac{1}{n}}$ is a real number, then $a^{\frac{m}{n}} = a^{m \cdot \frac{1}{n}} = (a^m)^{\frac{1}{n}} = \sqrt[n]{a^m}$.

The expression $a^{\frac{m}{n}}$ can also be written $a^{\frac{m}{n}} = a^{\frac{1}{n} \cdot m} = \left(\sqrt[n]{a}\right)^m$.

The exponential expression at the right has been written as a radical expression.

$$y^{\frac{2}{3}} = (y^2)^{\frac{1}{3}} = \sqrt[3]{y^2}$$

The radical expressions at the right have been written as exponential expressions.

$$\sqrt[5]{x^6} = (x^6)^{\frac{1}{5}} = x^{\frac{6}{5}}$$

$$\sqrt{17} = (17)^{\frac{1}{2}} = 17^{\frac{1}{2}}$$

Write $(5x)^{\frac{2}{5}}$ as a radical expression.

The denominator of the rational exponent is the index of the radical. The numerator is the power of the radicand.

$$(5x)^{\frac{2}{5}} = \sqrt[5]{(5x)^2}$$

Simplify.

$$= \sqrt[5]{25x^2}$$

Write $\sqrt[3]{x^4}$ as an exponential expression with a rational exponent.

The index of the radical is the denominator of the rational exponent. The power of the radicand is the numerator of the rational exponent.

$$\sqrt[3]{x^4} = (x^4)^{\frac{1}{3}} = x^{\frac{4}{3}}$$

EXAMPLE 3   Rewrite the exponential expression as a radical expression.
   A. $(3x)^{\frac{2}{3}}$ **B.** $-2x^{\frac{2}{3}}$

Solution   **A.** $(3x)^{\frac{2}{3}} = \sqrt[3]{(3x)^2}$ • The denominator of the rational exponent is the
                $= \sqrt[3]{9x^2}$ index of the radical. The numerator is the
                                            power of the radicand.

   B. $-2x^{\frac{2}{3}} = -2(x^2)^{\frac{1}{3}}$ • The -2 is not raised to the power.
          $= -2\sqrt[3]{x^2}$

PROBLEM 3   Rewrite the exponential expression as a radical expression.
   A. $(2x^3)^{\frac{3}{4}}$ **B.** $-5a^{\frac{5}{6}}$

Solution   See page S21.

EXAMPLE 4   Rewrite the radical expression as an exponential expression.
   A. $\sqrt[7]{x^5}$ **B.** $\sqrt[3]{a^3 + b^3}$

Solution   **A.** $\sqrt[7]{x^5} = (x^5)^{\frac{1}{7}} = x^{\frac{5}{7}}$ • The index of the radical is the
                                                        denominator of the rational exponent.
                                                        The power of the radicand is the
                                                        numerator of the rational exponent.

   B. $\sqrt[3]{a^3 + b^3} = (a^3 + b^3)^{\frac{1}{3}}$ • Note that $(a^3 + b^3)^{\frac{1}{3}} \neq a + b$.

PROBLEM 4   Rewrite the radical expression as an exponential expression.
   A. $\sqrt[3]{3ab}$ **B.** $\sqrt[4]{x^4 + y^4}$

Solution   See page S21.

OBJECTIVE   **3**   **Simplify radical expressions that are roots of perfect powers**

Every positive number has two square roots, one a positive and one a negative number. For example, because $(5)^2 = 25$ and $(-5)^2 = 25$, there are two square roots of 25: 5 and -5.

The symbol $\sqrt{}$ is used to indicate the positive or **principal square root.** To indicate the negative square root of a number, a negative sign is placed in front of the radical. $\sqrt{25} = 5$

$-\sqrt{25} = -5$

The square root of zero is zero. $\sqrt{0} = 0$

The square root of a negative number is not a real number, because the square of a real number must be positive. $\sqrt{-25}$ is not a real number.

The square root of a squared negative number is a positive number. $\sqrt{(-5)^2} = \sqrt{25} = 5$

For any real number a, $\sqrt{a^2} = |a|$ and $-\sqrt{a^2} = -|a|$. If a is a positive real number, then $\sqrt{a^2} = a$ and $(\sqrt{a})^2 = a$.

The cube root of a positive number is positive. $\sqrt[3]{8} = 2$, because $2^3 = 8$.

The cube root of a negative number is negative. $\sqrt[3]{-8} = -2$, because $(-2)^3 = -8$.

For any real number a, $\sqrt[3]{a^3} = a$.

The following holds true for finding the nth root of a real number.

If n is an even integer, then $\sqrt[n]{a^n} = |a|$ and $-\sqrt[n]{a^n} = -|a|$. If n is an odd integer, then $\sqrt[n]{a^n} = a$.

For example,

$$\sqrt[6]{y^6} = |y| \qquad -\sqrt[12]{x^{12}} = -|x| \qquad \sqrt[5]{b^5} = b$$

For the remainder of this chapter, we will assume that variable expressions inside a radical represent positive numbers. Therefore, it is not necessary to use the absolute value signs.

> ### Take Note
>
> Note that when the index is an even natural number, the nth root requires absolute value symbols.
>
> $\sqrt[6]{y^6} = |y|$ but $\sqrt[5]{y^5} = y$
>
> Because we stated that variables within radicals represent *positive* numbers, we will omit the absolute value symbols when writing an answer.

■   Simplify: $\sqrt[4]{x^4 y^8}$

The radicand is a perfect fourth power because the exponents on the variables are divisible by 4. Write the radical expression as an exponential expression. $\sqrt[4]{x^4 y^8} = (x^4 y^8)^{\frac{1}{4}}$

Use the Rule for Simplifying Powers of Products. $= xy^2$

Simplify: $\sqrt[3]{125c^9d^6}$

The radicand is a perfect cube because 125 is a perfect cube ($125 = 5^3$) and all the exponents on the variables are divisible by 3.

$$\sqrt[3]{125c^9d^6} = (5^3c^9d^6)^{\frac{1}{3}}$$

Use the Rule for Simplifying Powers of Products.

$$= 5c^3d^2$$

Note that a variable expression is a perfect power if the exponents on the factors are evenly divisible by the index of the radical.

The chart below shows roots of perfect powers. Knowledge of these roots is very helpful in simplifying radical expressions.

Square Roots		Cube Roots	Fourth Roots	Fifth Roots
$\sqrt{1} = 1$	$\sqrt{36} = 6$	$\sqrt[3]{1} = 1$	$\sqrt[4]{1} = 1$	$\sqrt[5]{1} = 1$
$\sqrt{4} = 2$	$\sqrt{49} = 7$	$\sqrt[3]{8} = 2$	$\sqrt[4]{16} = 2$	$\sqrt[5]{32} = 2$
$\sqrt{9} = 3$	$\sqrt{64} = 8$	$\sqrt[3]{27} = 3$	$\sqrt[4]{81} = 3$	$\sqrt[5]{243} = 3$
$\sqrt{16} = 4$	$\sqrt{81} = 9$	$\sqrt[3]{64} = 4$	$\sqrt[4]{256} = 4$	
$\sqrt{25} = 5$	$\sqrt{100} = 10$	$\sqrt[3]{125} = 5$	$\sqrt[4]{625} = 5$	

Take Note

From the chart, $\sqrt[5]{243} = 3$, which means that $3^5 = 243$. From this we know that $(-3)^5 = -243$, which means $\sqrt[5]{-243} = -3$.

Simplify: $\sqrt[5]{-243x^5y^{15}}$

From the chart, 243 is a perfect fifth power, and each exponent is divisible by 5. Therefore, the radicand is a perfect fifth power.

$$\sqrt[5]{-243x^5y^{15}} = -3xy^3$$

EXAMPLE 5   Simplify.

    A. $\sqrt{49x^2y^{12}}$ **B.** $\sqrt[3]{-125a^6b^9}$ **C.** $-\sqrt[4]{16a^4b^8}$

Solution   **A.** $\sqrt{49x^2y^{12}} = 7xy^6$ • The radicand is a perfect square. Divide each exponent by 2.

    B. $\sqrt[3]{-125a^6b^9} = -5a^2b^3$ • The radicand is a perfect cube. Divide each exponent by 3.

    C. $-\sqrt[4]{16a^4b^8} = -2ab^2$ • The radicand is a perfect fourth power. Divide each exponent by 4.

PROBLEM 5   Simplify.

    A. $\sqrt{121x^{10}y^4}$ **B.** $\sqrt[3]{-8x^{12}y^3}$ **C.** $-\sqrt[4]{81x^{12}y^8}$

Solution   See page S21.

7.1 Concept Review

Determine whether the following statements are always true, sometimes true, or never true.

1. For real numbers, $\sqrt{x^2} = x$.

2. $\sqrt{(-2)^2} = -2$

3. $\sqrt[3]{(-3)^3} = -3$

4. For positive integers a and n, $\sqrt[n]{a} = a^{\frac{1}{n}}$.

5. For positive integers a, m, and n, $(a^m)^{\frac{1}{n}} = a^{\frac{m}{n}}$.

6. The nth root of a negative number is negative.

7.1 Exercises

1 Simplify expressions with rational exponents

1. $125^{\frac{1}{3}}$ is the number whose ___?___ power is ___?___, so $125^{\frac{1}{3}} = $ ___?___.

2. $16^{\frac{1}{4}}$ is the number whose ___?___ power is ___?___, so $16^{\frac{1}{4}} = $ ___?___.

3. Simplify: $64^{-\frac{3}{2}}$

$64^{-\frac{3}{2}} = ($ ___?___ $^2)^{-\frac{3}{2}}$ • Write 64 as ___?___ ^{2}.

$= 8^{\frac{?}{}}$ • Use the Rule for Simplifying the Power of an Exponential Expression: multiply the exponents.

$= \dfrac{1}{\underline{\quad?\quad}}$ • Use the Definition of a Negative Exponent: $a^{-n} = \dfrac{1}{a^n}$.

$= $ ___?___ • Evaluate.

4. Simplify: $\left(a^{\frac{1}{3}} \cdot a^{\frac{1}{2}}\right)^2$

$\left(a^{\frac{1}{3}} \cdot a^{\frac{1}{2}}\right)^2 = (a^{\frac{?}{}})^2$ • Use the Rule for Multiplying Exponential Expressions: add the exponents.

$= a^{\frac{?}{}}$ • Use the Rule for Simplifying the Power of an Exponential Expression: multiply the exponents.

5. Which of the following is undefined?

a. $-25^{\frac{1}{2}}$ **b.** $25^{-\frac{1}{2}}$ **c.** $-25^{-\frac{1}{2}}$ **d.** $(-25)^{\frac{1}{2}}$

6. Which of the following is (are) equivalent to $16^{-\frac{1}{2}}$?

    a. -8 **b.** $\dfrac{1}{4}$ **c.** -4 **d.** 4^{-1}

Simplify.

7. $8^{\frac{1}{3}}$

8. $16^{\frac{1}{2}}$

9. $9^{\frac{3}{2}}$

10. $25^{\frac{3}{2}}$

11. $27^{-\frac{2}{3}}$

12. $64^{-\frac{1}{3}}$

13. $32^{\frac{2}{5}}$

14. $16^{\frac{3}{4}}$

15. $(-25)^{\frac{5}{2}}$

16. $(-36)^{\frac{1}{4}}$

17. $\left(\dfrac{25}{49}\right)^{-\frac{3}{2}}$

18. $\left(\dfrac{8}{27}\right)^{-\frac{2}{3}}$

19. $x^{\frac{1}{2}}x^{\frac{1}{2}}$

20. $a^{\frac{1}{3}}a^{\frac{5}{3}}$

21. $y^{-\frac{1}{4}}y^{\frac{3}{4}}$

22. $x^{\frac{2}{5}} \cdot x^{-\frac{4}{5}}$

23. $x^{-\frac{2}{3}} \cdot x^{\frac{3}{4}}$

24. $x \cdot x^{-\frac{1}{2}}$

25. $a^{\frac{1}{3}} \cdot a^{\frac{3}{4}} \cdot a^{-\frac{1}{2}}$

26. $y^{-\frac{1}{6}} \cdot y^{\frac{2}{3}} \cdot y^{\frac{1}{2}}$

27. $\dfrac{a^{\frac{1}{2}}}{a^{\frac{3}{2}}}$

28. $\dfrac{b^{\frac{1}{3}}}{b^{\frac{4}{3}}}$

29. $\dfrac{y^{-\frac{3}{4}}}{y^{\frac{1}{4}}}$

30. $\dfrac{x^{-\frac{3}{5}}}{x^{\frac{1}{5}}}$

31. $\dfrac{y^{\frac{2}{3}}}{y^{-\frac{5}{6}}}$

32. $\dfrac{b^{\frac{3}{4}}}{b^{-\frac{3}{2}}}$

33. $(x^2)^{-\frac{1}{2}}$

34. $(a^8)^{-\frac{3}{4}}$

35. $\left(x^{-\frac{2}{3}}\right)^6$

36. $\left(y^{-\frac{5}{6}}\right)^{12}$

37. $\left(a^{-\frac{1}{2}}\right)^{-2}$

38. $\left(b^{-\frac{2}{3}}\right)^{-6}$

39. $\left(x^{-\frac{3}{8}}\right)^{-\frac{4}{5}}$

40. $\left(y^{-\frac{3}{2}}\right)^{-\frac{2}{9}}$

41. $\left(a^{\frac{1}{2}} \cdot a\right)^2$

42. $\left(b^{\frac{2}{3}} \cdot b^{\frac{1}{6}}\right)^6$

43. $\left(x^{-\frac{1}{2}} \cdot x^{\frac{3}{4}}\right)^{-2}$

44. $\left(a^{\frac{1}{2}} \cdot a^{-2}\right)^3$

45. $\left(y^{-\frac{1}{2}} \cdot y^{\frac{3}{2}}\right)^{\frac{2}{3}}$

46. $\left(b^{-\frac{2}{3}} \cdot b^{\frac{1}{4}}\right)^{-\frac{4}{3}}$

47. $(x^8y^2)^{\frac{1}{2}}$

48. $(a^3b^9)^{\frac{2}{3}}$

49. $(x^4y^2z^6)^{\frac{3}{2}}$

50. $(a^8b^4c^4)^{\frac{3}{4}}$

51. $(x^{-3}y^6)^{-\frac{1}{3}}$

52. $(a^2b^{-6})^{-\frac{1}{2}}$

53. $\left(x^{-2}y^{\frac{1}{3}}\right)^{-\frac{3}{4}}$

54. $\left(a^{-\frac{2}{3}}b^{\frac{2}{3}}\right)^{\frac{3}{2}}$

55. $\left(\dfrac{x^{\frac{1}{2}}}{y^{-2}}\right)^4$

56. $\left(\dfrac{b^{-\frac{3}{4}}}{a^{-\frac{1}{2}}}\right)^8$

57. $\dfrac{x^{\frac{1}{4}} \cdot x^{-\frac{1}{2}}}{x^{\frac{2}{3}}}$

58. $\dfrac{b^{\frac{1}{2}} \cdot b^{-\frac{3}{4}}}{b^{\frac{1}{4}}}$

59. $\left(\dfrac{y^{\frac{2}{3}} \cdot y^{-\frac{5}{6}}}{y^{\frac{1}{9}}}\right)^9$

60. $\left(\dfrac{a^{\frac{1}{3}} \cdot a^{-\frac{2}{3}}}{a^{\frac{1}{2}}}\right)^4$

61. $\left(\dfrac{b^2 \cdot b^{-\frac{3}{4}}}{b^{-\frac{1}{2}}}\right)^{-\frac{1}{2}}$

62. $\dfrac{\left(x^{-\frac{5}{6}} \cdot x^3\right)^{-\frac{2}{3}}}{x^{\frac{4}{3}}}$

63. $\left(a^{\frac{2}{3}}b^2\right)^6 \left(a^3b^3\right)^{\frac{1}{3}}$

64. $\left(x^3 y^{-\frac{1}{2}}\right)^{-2} \left(x^{-3}y^2\right)^{\frac{1}{6}}$

65. $(16m^{-2}n^4)^{-\frac{1}{2}}\left(mn^{\frac{1}{2}}\right)$

66. $(27m^3n^{-6})^{\frac{1}{3}}\left(m^{-\frac{1}{3}}n^{\frac{5}{6}}\right)^6$

67. $\left(\dfrac{x^{\frac{1}{2}}y^{-\frac{3}{4}}}{y^{\frac{2}{3}}}\right)^{-6}$

68. $\left(\dfrac{x^{\frac{1}{2}}y^{-\frac{5}{4}}}{y^{-\frac{3}{4}}}\right)^{-4}$

69. $\left(\dfrac{2^{-6}b^{-3}}{a^{-\frac{1}{2}}}\right)^{-\frac{2}{3}}$

70. $\left(\dfrac{49c^{\frac{5}{3}}}{a^{-\frac{1}{4}}b^{\frac{5}{6}}}\right)^{-\frac{3}{2}}$

71. $\dfrac{(x^{-2}y^4)^{\frac{1}{2}}}{\left(x^{\frac{1}{2}}\right)^4}$

72. $\dfrac{(x^{-3})^{\frac{1}{3}}}{(x^9y^6)^{\frac{1}{6}}}$

73. $a^{-\frac{1}{4}}\left(a^{\frac{5}{4}} - a^{\frac{9}{4}}\right)$

74. $x^{\frac{4}{3}}\left(x^{\frac{2}{3}} + x^{-\frac{1}{3}}\right)$

75. $y^{\frac{2}{3}}\left(y^{\frac{1}{3}} + y^{-\frac{2}{3}}\right)$

76. $b^{-\frac{2}{5}}\left(b^{-\frac{3}{5}} - b^{\frac{7}{5}}\right)$

77. $a^{\frac{1}{6}}\left(a^{\frac{5}{6}} - a^{-\frac{7}{6}}\right)$

78. $\left(x^{\frac{n}{3}}\right)^{3n}$

79. $\left(a^{\frac{2}{n}}\right)^{-5n}$

80. $x^n \cdot x^{\frac{n}{2}}$

81. $a^{\frac{n}{2}} \cdot a^{-\frac{n}{3}}$

82. $\dfrac{y^{\frac{n}{2}}}{y^{-n}}$

83. $\dfrac{b^{\frac{m}{3}}}{b^m}$

84. $\left(x^{\frac{2}{n}}\right)^n$

85. $(x^{5n})^{2n}$

86. $\left(x^{\frac{n}{4}}y^{\frac{n}{8}}\right)^8$

87. $\left(x^{\frac{n}{2}}y^{\frac{n}{3}}\right)^6$

2   ## Write exponential expressions as radical expressions and radical expressions as exponential expressions

88. In the radical expression $\sqrt[n]{a}$, n is called the ____?____ and a is called the ____?____.

89. To rewrite $\sqrt[5]{a^4}$ as an exponential expression, find the exponent for the base a. The rational exponent will be $\dfrac{\text{power on the radicand}}{\text{index}} = \dfrac{?}{?} \cdot \sqrt[5]{a^4} = a^{\frac{?}{}}$.

90. True or false? $8x^{\frac{1}{3}} = 2\sqrt[3]{x}$

91. True or false? $\sqrt[4]{x^3} = (\sqrt[4]{x})^3$

Rewrite the exponential expression as a radical expression.

92. $3^{\frac{1}{4}}$

93. $5^{\frac{1}{2}}$

94. $a^{\frac{3}{2}}$

95. $b^{\frac{4}{3}}$

96. $(2t)^{\frac{5}{2}}$

97. $(3x)^{\frac{2}{3}}$

98. $-2x^{\frac{2}{3}}$

99. $-3a^{\frac{2}{5}}$

100. $(a^2b)^{\frac{2}{3}}$

101. $(x^2y^3)^{\frac{3}{4}}$

102. $(a^2b^4)^{\frac{3}{5}}$

103. $(a^3b^7)^{\frac{3}{2}}$

104. $(4x + 3)^{\frac{3}{4}}$

105. $(3x - 2)^{\frac{1}{3}}$

106. $x^{-\frac{2}{3}}$

Rewrite the radical expression as an exponential expression.

107. $\sqrt{14}$

108. $\sqrt{7}$

109. $\sqrt[3]{x}$

110. $\sqrt[4]{y}$

111. $\sqrt[3]{x^4}$

112. $\sqrt[4]{a^3}$

113. $\sqrt[5]{b^3}$

114. $\sqrt[4]{b^5}$

115. $\sqrt[3]{2x^2}$

116. $\sqrt[5]{4y^7}$

117. $-\sqrt{3x^5}$

118. $-\sqrt[4]{4x^5}$

119. $3x\sqrt[3]{y^2}$

120. $2y\sqrt{x^3}$

121. $\sqrt{a^2 + 2}$

3   Simplify radical expressions that are roots of perfect powers

122. $16x^{12}y^{20}$ is a perfect fourth power because $16 = ($ ___?___ $)^4$, $x^{12} = ($ ___?___ $)^4$, and $y^{20} = ($ ___?___ $)^4$.

123. $32a^{10}b^{15}$ is a perfect fifth power because $32 = ($ ___?___ $)^5$, $a^{10} = ($ ___?___ $)^5$, and $b^{15} = ($ ___?___ $)^5$.

For Exercises 124 to 127, state whether the expression simplifies to a positive number, a negative number, or a number that is not a real number.

124. $-\sqrt[3]{8x^{15}}$

125. $-\sqrt{9x^8}$

126. $\sqrt{-4x^{12}}$

127. $-\sqrt[3]{-27x^9}$

Simplify.

128. $\sqrt{x^{16}}$

129. $\sqrt{y^{14}}$

130. $-\sqrt{x^8}$

131. $-\sqrt{a^6}$

132. $\sqrt{x^2y^{10}}$

133. $\sqrt{a^{14}b^6}$

134. $\sqrt{25x^6}$

135. $\sqrt{121y^{12}}$

136. $\sqrt[3]{x^3y^9}$

137. $\sqrt[3]{a^6b^{12}}$

138. $-\sqrt[3]{x^{15}y^3}$

139. $-\sqrt[3]{a^9b^9}$

140. $\sqrt[3]{27a^9}$

141. $\sqrt[3]{125b^{15}}$

142. $\sqrt[3]{-8x^3}$

143. $\sqrt[3]{-a^6b^9}$

144. $\sqrt{16a^4b^{12}}$

145. $\sqrt{25x^8y^2}$

146. $\sqrt{-16x^4y^2}$

147. $\sqrt{-9a^6b^8}$

148. $\sqrt[3]{27x^9}$

149. $\sqrt[3]{8a^{21}b^6}$

150. $\sqrt[3]{-64x^9y^{12}}$

151. $\sqrt[3]{-27a^3b^{15}}$

152. $\sqrt[4]{x^{16}}$

153. $\sqrt[4]{y^{12}}$

154. $\sqrt[4]{16x^{12}}$

155. $\sqrt[4]{81a^{20}}$

156. $-\sqrt[4]{x^8y^{12}}$

157. $-\sqrt[4]{a^{16}b^4}$

158. $\sqrt[5]{x^{20}y^{10}}$

159. $\sqrt[5]{a^5b^{25}}$

160. $\sqrt[4]{81x^4y^{20}}$

161. $\sqrt[4]{16a^8b^{20}}$

162. $\sqrt[5]{32a^5b^{10}}$

163. $\sqrt[5]{-32x^{15}y^{20}}$

164. $\sqrt[5]{243x^{10}y^{40}}$

165. $\sqrt{\dfrac{16x^2}{y^{14}}}$

166. $\sqrt{\dfrac{49a^4}{b^{24}}}$

167. $\sqrt[3]{\dfrac{27b^3}{a^9}}$

168. $\sqrt[3]{\dfrac{64x^{15}}{y^6}}$

169. $\sqrt{(2x+3)^2}$

170. $\sqrt{(4x+1)^2}$

171. $\sqrt{x^2+2x+1}$

172. $\sqrt{x^2+4x+4}$

7.1 Applying Concepts

Simplify.

173. $\sqrt[3]{\sqrt{x^6}}$

174. $\sqrt{\sqrt[3]{y^6}}$

175. $\sqrt[5]{\sqrt[3]{b^{15}}}$

176. $\sqrt{\sqrt{16x^{12}}}$

177. $\sqrt[5]{\sqrt{a^{10}b^{20}}}$

178. $\sqrt[3]{\sqrt{64x^{36}y^{30}}}$

For what value of p is the given equation true?

179. $y^py^{\frac{2}{5}}=y$

180. $\dfrac{y^p}{y^{\frac{3}{4}}}=y^{\frac{1}{2}}$

181. $x^px^{-\frac{1}{2}}=x^{\frac{1}{4}}$

Operations on Radical Expressions

OBJECTIVE 1 **Simplify radical expressions**

Point of Interest

The Latin expression for irrational numbers was numerus surdus, *which means "inaudible number." A prominent 16th-century mathematician wrote of irrational numbers, "just as an infinite number is not a number, so an irrational number is not a true number, but lies hidden in some sort of cloud of infinity." In 1872, Richard Dedekind wrote a paper that established the first logical treatment of irrational numbers.*

If a number is not a perfect power, its root can only be approximated; examples include $\sqrt{5}$ and $\sqrt[3]{3}$. These numbers are **irrational numbers.** Their decimal representations never terminate or repeat.

$$\sqrt{5} = 2.2360679... \qquad \sqrt[3]{3} = 1.4422495...$$

A radical expression is not in simplest form when the radicand contains a factor greater than 1 that is a perfect power. The Product Property of Radicals is used to simplify radical expressions whose radicands are not perfect powers.

Product Property of Radicals

If $\sqrt[n]{a}$ and $\sqrt[n]{b}$ are positive real numbers, then

$$\sqrt[n]{ab} = \sqrt[n]{a} \cdot \sqrt[n]{b} \quad \text{and} \quad \sqrt[n]{a} \cdot \sqrt[n]{b} = \sqrt[n]{ab}$$

Simplify: $\sqrt{48}$

Write the radicand as the product of a perfect square and a factor that does not contain a perfect square.	$\sqrt{48} = \sqrt{16 \cdot 3}$
Use the Product Property of Radicals to write the expression as a product.	$= \sqrt{16}\sqrt{3}$
Simplify $\sqrt{16}$.	$= 4\sqrt{3}$

Note that 48 must be written as the product of a perfect square and *a factor that does not contain a perfect square.* Therefore, it would not be correct to rewrite $\sqrt{48}$ as $\sqrt{4 \cdot 12}$ and simplify the expression as shown at the right. Although 4 is a perfect-square factor of 48, 12 contains a perfect square $(12 = 4 \cdot 3)$ and $\sqrt{12}$ can be simplified. Remember to find the largest perfect power that is a factor of the radicand.

$$\sqrt{48} = \sqrt{4 \cdot 12}$$
$$= \sqrt{4}\sqrt{12}$$
$$= 2\sqrt{12}$$

Not in simplest form

Simplify: $\sqrt[3]{x^7}$

Write the radicand as the product of a perfect cube and a factor that does not contain a perfect cube.	$\sqrt[3]{x^7} = \sqrt[3]{x^6 \cdot x}$
Use the Product Property of Radicals to write the expression as a product.	$= \sqrt[3]{x^6}\sqrt[3]{x}$
Simplify.	$= x^2\sqrt[3]{x}$

EXAMPLE 1 Simplify: $\sqrt[4]{32x^7}$

Solution $\sqrt[4]{32x^7} = \sqrt[4]{16x^4(2x^3)}$

• Write the radicand as the product of a perfect fourth power and factors that do not contain a perfect fourth power.

$\qquad\qquad = \sqrt[4]{16x^4}\,\sqrt[4]{2x^3}$

• Use the Product Property of Radicals to write the expression as a product.

$\qquad\qquad = 2x\sqrt[4]{2x^3}$

• Simplify.

PROBLEM 1 Simplify: $\sqrt[5]{128x^7}$

Solution See page S21.

OBJECTIVE 2 Add and subtract radical expressions

The Distributive Property is used to simplify the sum or difference of radical expressions that have the same radicand and the same index. For example,

$$3\sqrt{5} + 8\sqrt{5} = (3 + 8)\sqrt{5} = 11\sqrt{5}$$
$$2\sqrt[3]{3x} - 9\sqrt[3]{3x} = (2 - 9)\sqrt[3]{3x} = -7\sqrt[3]{3x}$$

Radical expressions that are in simplest form and have unlike radicands or different indices cannot be simplified by the Distributive Property. The following expressions cannot be simplified by the Distributive Property.

$$3\sqrt[4]{2} - 6\sqrt[4]{3}$$ • **The radicands are different.**
$$2\sqrt[4]{4x} + 3\sqrt[3]{4x}$$ • **The indices are different.**

Simplify: $3\sqrt{32x^2} - 2x\sqrt{2} + \sqrt{128x^2}$

First simplify each term. Then combine like terms by using the Distributive Property.

$$3\sqrt{32x^2} - 2x\sqrt{2} + \sqrt{128x^2} = 3\sqrt{16x^2}\sqrt{2} - 2x\sqrt{2} + \sqrt{64x^2}\sqrt{2}$$
$$= 3 \cdot 4x\sqrt{2} - 2x\sqrt{2} + 8x\sqrt{2}$$
$$= 12x\sqrt{2} - 2x\sqrt{2} + 8x\sqrt{2}$$
$$= 18x\sqrt{2}$$

EXAMPLE 2 Subtract.

A. $5b\sqrt[4]{32a^7b^5} - 2a\sqrt[4]{162a^3b^9}$ **B.** $5\sqrt[5]{2x^7y^{11}} - y\sqrt[5]{64^7y^6}$

Solution **A.** $5b\sqrt[4]{32a^7b^5} - 2a\sqrt[4]{162a^3b^9}$
$$= 5b\sqrt[4]{16a^4b^4}\sqrt[4]{2a^3b} - 2a\sqrt[4]{81b^8}\sqrt[4]{2a^3b}$$
$$= 5b \cdot 2ab\sqrt[4]{2a^3b} - 2a \cdot 3b^2\sqrt[4]{2a^3b}$$
$$= 10ab^2\sqrt[4]{2a^3b} - 6ab^2\sqrt[4]{2a^3b}$$
$$= 4ab^2\sqrt[4]{2a^3b}$$

B. $5\sqrt[5]{2x^7y^{11}} - y\sqrt[5]{64^7y^6} = 5\sqrt[5]{x^5y^{10}}\sqrt[5]{2x^2y} - y\sqrt[5]{32x^5y^5}\sqrt[5]{2x^2y}$
$$= 5 \cdot xy^2\sqrt[5]{2x^2y} - y \cdot 2xy\sqrt[5]{2x^2y}$$
$$= 5xy^2\sqrt[5]{2x^2y} - 2xy^2\sqrt[5]{2x^2y}$$
$$= 3xy^2\sqrt[5]{2x^2y}$$

PROBLEM 2 Add or subtract.

A. $3xy\sqrt[3]{81x^5y} - \sqrt[3]{192x^8y^4}$ **B.** $4a\sqrt[3]{54a^7b^9} + a^2b\sqrt[3]{128a^4b^6}$

Solution See page S21.

O B J E C T I V E   **3**   **Multiply radical expressions**

The Product Property of Radicals is used to multiply radical expressions with the same index.

$$\sqrt{3x} \cdot \sqrt{5y} = \sqrt{3x \cdot 5y} = \sqrt{15xy}$$

Multiply: $\sqrt[3]{2a^5b}\ \sqrt[3]{16a^2b^2}$

Use the Product Property of Radicals to multiply the radicands. Then simplify.

$$\begin{aligned}\sqrt[3]{2a^5b}\ \sqrt[3]{16a^2b^2} &= \sqrt[3]{32a^7b^3} \\ &= \sqrt[3]{8a^6b^3}\ \sqrt[3]{4a} \\ &= 2a^2b\sqrt[3]{4a}\end{aligned}$$

Multiply: $\sqrt{2x}\left(\sqrt{8x} - \sqrt{3}\right)$

Use the Distributive Property to remove parentheses. Then simplify.

$$\begin{aligned}\sqrt{2x}\left(\sqrt{8x} - \sqrt{3}\right) &= \sqrt{16x^2} - \sqrt{6x} \\ &= 4x - \sqrt{6x}\end{aligned}$$

EXAMPLE 3   Multiply: $\sqrt{3x}\left(\sqrt{27x^2} - \sqrt{3x}\right)$

Solution $$\begin{aligned}\sqrt{3x}\left(\sqrt{27x^2} - \sqrt{3x}\right) &= \sqrt{81x^3} - \sqrt{9x^2} \\ &= \sqrt{81x^2}\sqrt{x} - \sqrt{9x^2} \\ &= 9x\sqrt{x} - 3x\end{aligned}$$

PROBLEM 3   Multiply: $\sqrt{5b}\left(\sqrt{3b} - \sqrt{10}\right)$

Solution   See page S22.

To multiply $\left(\sqrt[3]{x} - 1\right)\left(\sqrt[3]{x} + 7\right)$, use the FOIL method. Then combine like terms.

$$\begin{aligned}\left(\sqrt[3]{x} - 1\right)\left(\sqrt[3]{x} + 7\right) &= \sqrt[3]{x^2} + 7\sqrt[3]{x} - \sqrt[3]{x} - 7 \\ &= \sqrt[3]{x^2} + 6\sqrt[3]{x} - 7\end{aligned}$$

The expressions $a + b$ and $a - b$, which are the sum and difference of two terms, are called **conjugates** of each other. The product of conjugates of the form $(a + b)(a - b)$ is $a^2 - b^2$.

$$\left(\sqrt{x} - 3\right)\left(\sqrt{x} + 3\right) = \left(\sqrt{x}\right)^2 - 3^2 = x - 9$$

Take Note

The concept of conjugate is used in a number of different instances. Make sure you understand this idea.

The conjugate of $\sqrt{3} - 4$ is $\sqrt{3} + 4$.

The conjugate of $\sqrt{3} + 4$ is $\sqrt{3} - 4$.

The conjugate of $\sqrt{5a} + \sqrt{b}$ is $\sqrt{5a} - \sqrt{b}$.

EXAMPLE 4   Multiply.
  A. $\left(2\sqrt[3]{x} - 3\right)\left(3\sqrt[3]{x} - 4\right)$ **B.** $\left(\sqrt{xy} - 2\right)\left(\sqrt{xy} + 2\right)$

Solution   **A.** $\left(2\sqrt[3]{x} - 3\right)\left(3\sqrt[3]{x} - 4\right)$ • **Use the FOIL method.**
  $$\begin{aligned}&= 6\sqrt[3]{x^2} - 8\sqrt[3]{x} - 9\sqrt[3]{x} + 12 \\ &= 6\sqrt[3]{x^2} - 17\sqrt[3]{x} + 12\end{aligned}$$

  B. $\left(\sqrt{xy} - 2\right)\left(\sqrt{xy} + 2\right)$ • **Use $(a - b)(a + b) = a^2 - b^2$.**
  $$\begin{aligned}&= \left(\sqrt{xy}\right)^2 - 2^2 \\ &= xy - 4\end{aligned}$$

PROBLEM 4   Multiply.
  A. $\left(2\sqrt[3]{2x} - 3\right)\left(\sqrt[3]{2x} - 5\right)$ **B.** $\left(2\sqrt{x} - 3\right)\left(2\sqrt{x} + 3\right)$

Solution   See page S22.

OBJECTIVE **4**   **Divide radical expressions**

The Quotient Property of Radicals is used to divide radical expressions with the same index.

Quotient Property of Radicals

If $\sqrt[n]{a}$ and $\sqrt[n]{b}$ are real numbers, and $b \neq 0$, then

$$\sqrt[n]{\frac{a}{b}} = \frac{\sqrt[n]{a}}{\sqrt[n]{b}} \quad \text{and} \quad \frac{\sqrt[n]{a}}{\sqrt[n]{b}} = \sqrt[n]{\frac{a}{b}}$$

Simplify: $\sqrt[3]{\dfrac{81x^5}{y^6}}$

Use the Quotient Property of Radicals. Then simplify each radical expression.

$$\sqrt[3]{\frac{81x^5}{y^6}} = \frac{\sqrt[3]{81x^5}}{\sqrt[3]{y^6}}$$

$$= \frac{\sqrt[3]{27x^3}\,\sqrt[3]{3x^2}}{\sqrt[3]{y^6}}$$

$$= \frac{3x\sqrt[3]{3x^2}}{y^2}$$

Simplify: $\dfrac{\sqrt{5a^4b^7c^2}}{\sqrt{ab^3c}}$

Use the Quotient Property of Radicals. Then simplify the radicand.

$$\frac{\sqrt{5a^4b^7c^2}}{\sqrt{ab^3c}} = \sqrt{\frac{5a^4b^7c^2}{ab^3c}}$$

$$= \sqrt{5a^3b^4c}$$
$$= \sqrt{a^2b^4}\,\sqrt{5ac}$$
$$= ab^2\sqrt{5ac}$$

Simplest Form of a Radical Expression

A radical expression is in simplest form when *all* of the following conditions are met.

1. The radicand contains no factor greater than 1 that is a perfect power of the index.

2. There is no fraction under the radical sign.

3. No radical remains in the denominator of the radical expression.

The procedure used to remove a radical from a denominator is called **rationalizing the denominator.** This is illustrated in the next example.

Simplify: $\dfrac{2}{\sqrt{x}}$

Multiply the expression by 1 in the form $\dfrac{\sqrt{x}}{\sqrt{x}}$.

$$\dfrac{2}{\sqrt{x}} = \dfrac{2}{\sqrt{x}} \cdot \dfrac{\sqrt{x}}{\sqrt{x}} = \dfrac{2\sqrt{x}}{\sqrt{x^2}} = \dfrac{2\sqrt{x}}{x}$$

Then simplify.

EXAMPLE 5   Simplify.   **A.** $\dfrac{5}{\sqrt{5x}}$ **B.** $\dfrac{3x}{\sqrt[3]{4x}}$

Solution   **A.** $\dfrac{5}{\sqrt{5x}} = \dfrac{5}{\sqrt{5x}} \cdot \dfrac{\sqrt{5x}}{\sqrt{5x}}$ • **Multiply the expression by** $\dfrac{\sqrt{5x}}{\sqrt{5x}}$.

$\qquad = \dfrac{5\sqrt{5x}}{\sqrt{25x^2}}$

$\qquad = \dfrac{5\sqrt{5x}}{5x}$

$\qquad = \dfrac{\sqrt{5x}}{x}$

B. $\dfrac{3x}{\sqrt[3]{4x}} = \dfrac{3x}{\sqrt[3]{4x}} \cdot \dfrac{\sqrt[3]{2x^2}}{\sqrt[3]{2x^2}}$ • **Multiply the expression by** $\dfrac{\sqrt[3]{2x^2}}{\sqrt[3]{2x^2}}$.
$\sqrt[3]{4x} \cdot \sqrt[3]{2x^2} = \sqrt[3]{8x^3}$.
$8x^3$ is a perfect cube.

$\qquad = \dfrac{3x\sqrt[3]{2x^2}}{\sqrt[3]{8x^3}}$

$\qquad = \dfrac{3x\sqrt[3]{2x^2}}{2x}$

$\qquad = \dfrac{3\sqrt[3]{2x^2}}{2}$

PROBLEM 5   Simplify.   **A.** $\dfrac{y}{\sqrt{3y}}$ **B.** $\dfrac{3}{\sqrt[3]{3x^2}}$

Solution   See page S22.

> ### Take Note
> Note that multiplying by $\dfrac{\sqrt[3]{4x}}{\sqrt[3]{4x}}$ will not rationalize the denominator of $\dfrac{3x}{\sqrt[3]{4x}}$.
>
> $\dfrac{3x}{\sqrt[3]{4x}} \cdot \dfrac{\sqrt[3]{4x}}{\sqrt[3]{4x}} = \dfrac{3x\sqrt[3]{4x}}{\sqrt[3]{16x^2}}$
>
> Because $16x^2$ is not a perfect cube, the denominator still contains a radical expression.

To simplify a fraction that has a square-root radical expression with two terms in the denominator, multiply the numerator and denominator by the conjugate of the denominator. Then simplify. This is illustrated in the two examples that follow.

> ### Take Note
> Here are two examples of using a conjugate to simplify a radical expression.

$$\dfrac{3}{5 - \sqrt{7}} = \dfrac{3}{5 - \sqrt{7}} \cdot \dfrac{5 + \sqrt{7}}{5 + \sqrt{7}} = \dfrac{15 + 3\sqrt{7}}{25 - 7} = \dfrac{3(5 + \sqrt{7})}{18} = \dfrac{5 + \sqrt{7}}{6}$$

$$\dfrac{\sqrt{x} - \sqrt{y}}{\sqrt{x} + \sqrt{y}} = \dfrac{\sqrt{x} - \sqrt{y}}{\sqrt{x} + \sqrt{y}} \cdot \dfrac{\sqrt{x} - \sqrt{y}}{\sqrt{x} - \sqrt{y}} = \dfrac{\sqrt{x^2} - \sqrt{xy} - \sqrt{xy} + \sqrt{y^2}}{(\sqrt{x})^2 - (\sqrt{y})^2}$$

$$= \dfrac{x - 2\sqrt{xy} + y}{x - y}$$

EXAMPLE 6 Simplify. **A.** $\dfrac{2 - \sqrt{5}}{3 + \sqrt{2}}$ **B.** $\dfrac{\sqrt{3} + \sqrt{y}}{\sqrt{3} - \sqrt{y}}$

Solution **A.** $\dfrac{2 - \sqrt{5}}{3 + \sqrt{2}} = \dfrac{2 - \sqrt{5}}{3 + \sqrt{2}} \cdot \dfrac{3 - \sqrt{2}}{3 - \sqrt{2}} = \dfrac{6 - 2\sqrt{2} - 3\sqrt{5} + \sqrt{10}}{9 - 2}$

$$= \dfrac{6 - 2\sqrt{2} - 3\sqrt{5} + \sqrt{10}}{7}$$

B. $\dfrac{\sqrt{3} + \sqrt{y}}{\sqrt{3} - \sqrt{y}} = \dfrac{\sqrt{3} + \sqrt{y}}{\sqrt{3} - \sqrt{y}} \cdot \dfrac{\sqrt{3} + \sqrt{y}}{\sqrt{3} + \sqrt{y}}$

$$= \dfrac{\sqrt{9} + \sqrt{3y} + \sqrt{3y} + \sqrt{y^2}}{(\sqrt{3})^2 - (\sqrt{y})^2} = \dfrac{3 + 2\sqrt{3y} + y}{3 - y}$$

PROBLEM 6 Simplify. **A.** $\dfrac{4 + \sqrt{2}}{3 - \sqrt{3}}$ **B.** $\dfrac{\sqrt{2} + \sqrt{x}}{\sqrt{2} - \sqrt{x}}$

Solution See page S22.

7.2 Concept Review

Determine whether the following statements are always true, sometimes true, or never true.

1. If a is a real number, then $\sqrt{a}$ represents a real number.

2. If b is a real number, then $\sqrt[3]{b}$ represents a real number.

3. For positive integers x and y, $\sqrt[a]{x} \cdot \sqrt[b]{y} = \sqrt[ab]{xy}$.

4. The conjugate of $\sqrt{a} + \sqrt{b}$ is found by replacing b with its opposite.

5. If $x < 0$, then $\sqrt{x^2} = -x$.

6. For positive integers x and y, $\sqrt[a]{x} \cdot \sqrt[a]{y} = \sqrt[a]{xy}$.

7.2 Exercises

1 Simplify radical expressions

1. Simplify: $\sqrt{50}$

$\sqrt{50} = \sqrt{\underline{\quad ? \quad} \cdot 2}$

• Write 50 as the product of a perfect-square factor and a factor that does not contain a perfect square.

$= \sqrt{\underline{\quad ? \quad}} \sqrt{\underline{\quad ? \quad}}$

• Use the Product Property of Radicals to write the expression as the product of two square roots.

$= \underline{\quad ? \quad} \sqrt{2}$

• Simplify $\sqrt{25}$.

2. Simplify: $\sqrt[3]{16x^{14}}$

$\sqrt[3]{16x^{14}} = \sqrt[3]{(\underline{\ \ ?\ \ })(2x^2)}$ • Write $16x^4$ as the product of a perfect cube and a factor that does not contain a perfect cube.

$= \sqrt[3]{\underline{\ \ ?\ \ }}\ \sqrt[3]{2x^2}$ • Use the Product Property of Radicals.

$= \underline{\ \ ?\ \ }\ \sqrt[3]{2x^2}$ • Simplify.

3. State whether the number is rational or irrational.
a. $\sqrt{19}$ **b.** $-\sqrt{81}$ **c.** $\sqrt[3]{25}$ **d.** $\sqrt[3]{-27}$

4. State whether the expression is in simplest form.
a. $2\sqrt[5]{x^7}$ **b.** $\sqrt[3]{36y^2}$ **c.** $9a^2\sqrt{54ab}$ **d.** $2b\sqrt[4]{8b^3}$

Explain why the simplification is incorrect.

5. $\sqrt{32} = \sqrt{4\cdot8} = \sqrt{4}\sqrt{8} = 2\sqrt{8}$

6. $\sqrt[3]{128} = \sqrt[3]{8\cdot16} = \sqrt[3]{8}\sqrt[3]{16} = 2\sqrt[3]{16}$

Simplify.

7. $\sqrt{18}$ **8.** $\sqrt{40}$ **9.** $\sqrt{98}$ **10.** $\sqrt{128}$

11. $\sqrt[3]{72}$ **12.** $\sqrt[3]{54}$ **13.** $\sqrt[3]{16}$ **14.** $\sqrt[3]{128}$

15. $\sqrt{x^4y^3z^5}$ **16.** $\sqrt{x^3y^6z^9}$ **17.** $\sqrt{8a^3b^8}$

18. $\sqrt{24a^9b^6}$ **19.** $\sqrt{45x^2y^3z^5}$ **20.** $\sqrt{60xy^7z^{12}}$

21. $\sqrt[3]{-125x^2y^4}$ **22.** $\sqrt[4]{16x^9y^5}$ **23.** $\sqrt[3]{-216x^5y^9}$

24. $\sqrt[3]{a^8b^{11}c^{15}}$ **25.** $\sqrt[3]{a^5b^8}$ **26.** $\sqrt[4]{64x^8y^{10}}$

2   Add and subtract radical expressions

27. The Distributive Property can be used to add or subtract radicals that have the same ___?___ and the same ___?___.

28. Simplify: $5\sqrt[5]{x^{12}} + 2x\sqrt[5]{x^7}$

$5\sqrt[5]{x^{12}} + 2x\sqrt[5]{x^7} = 5\sqrt[5]{\underline{\ ?\ }}\sqrt[5]{x^2} + 2x\sqrt[5]{\underline{\ ?\ }}\sqrt[5]{x^2}$

$= 5(\underline{\ ?\ })\sqrt[5]{x^2} + 2x(\underline{\ ?\ })\sqrt[5]{x^2}$ • Simplify the perfect fifth roots.

$= 5x^2\sqrt[5]{x^2} + \underline{\ ?\ }\sqrt[5]{x^2}$ • Multiply.

$= (\underline{\ ?\ } + \underline{\ ?\ })\sqrt[5]{x^2}$ • Use the Distributive Property.

$= \underline{\ ?\ }\sqrt[5]{x^2}$ • Add.

29. State whether the expression can be simplified.

    a. $5x\sqrt{x} + x\sqrt[3]{x}$ **b.** $\sqrt[5]{10y} - \sqrt[5]{y}$

    c. $\sqrt[3]{2+a} + \sqrt[3]{2+a}$ **d.** $\sqrt{8x^2} + \sqrt{2}$

30. Which expressions are equivalent to $\sqrt{ab} + \sqrt{ab}$?

    a. $2\sqrt{ab}$ **b.** $\sqrt{2ab}$ **c.** $2ab$ **d.** $\sqrt{4ab}$

Simplify

31. $\sqrt{2} + \sqrt{2}$ **32.** $\sqrt{5} - \sqrt{5}$

33. $4\sqrt[3]{7} - \sqrt[3]{7}$ **34.** $3\sqrt[3]{11} - 8\sqrt[3]{11}$

35. $2\sqrt{x} - 8\sqrt{x}$ **36.** $3\sqrt{y} + 12\sqrt{y}$

37. $\sqrt{8} - \sqrt{32}$ **38.** $\sqrt{27} - \sqrt{75}$

39. $\sqrt{128x} - \sqrt{98x}$ **40.** $\sqrt{48x} + \sqrt{147x}$

41. $\sqrt{27a} - \sqrt{8a}$ **42.** $\sqrt{18b} + \sqrt{75b}$

43. $2\sqrt{2x^3} + 4x\sqrt{8x}$ **44.** $5y\sqrt{8y} + 2\sqrt{50y^3}$

45. $x\sqrt{75xy} - \sqrt{27x^3y}$ **46.** $3\sqrt{8x^2y^3} - 2x\sqrt{32y^3}$

47. $2\sqrt{32x^2y^3} - xy\sqrt{98y}$ **48.** $6y\sqrt{x^3y} - 2\sqrt{x^3y^3}$

49. $7b\sqrt{a^5b^3} - 2ab\sqrt{a^3b^3}$ **50.** $2a\sqrt{27ab^5} + 3b\sqrt{3a^3b}$

51. $\sqrt[3]{128} + \sqrt[3]{250}$ **52.** $\sqrt[3]{16} - \sqrt[3]{54}$

53. $2\sqrt[3]{3a^4} - 3a\sqrt[3]{81a}$ **54.** $2b\sqrt[3]{16b^2} + \sqrt[3]{128b^5}$

55. $3\sqrt[3]{x^5y^7} - 8xy\sqrt[3]{x^2y^4}$ **56.** $3\sqrt[4]{32a^5} - a\sqrt[4]{162a}$

57. $2a\sqrt[4]{16ab^5} + 3b\sqrt[4]{256a^5b}$ **58.** $2\sqrt{50} - 3\sqrt{125} + \sqrt{98}$

59. $3\sqrt{108} - 2\sqrt{18} - 3\sqrt{48}$ **60.** $\sqrt{9b^3} - \sqrt{25b^3} + \sqrt{49b^3}$

61. $\sqrt{4x^7y^5} + 9x^2\sqrt{x^3y^5} - 5xy\sqrt{x^5y^3}$ **62.** $2x\sqrt{8xy^2} - 3y\sqrt{32x^3} + \sqrt{8x^3y^2}$

63. $5a\sqrt{3a^3b} + 2a^2\sqrt{27ab} - 4\sqrt{75a^5b}$ **64.** $\sqrt[3]{54xy^3} - 5\sqrt[3]{2xy^3} + \sqrt[3]{128xy^3}$

3 Multiply radical expressions

65. Multiply: $\sqrt{3}(\sqrt{6} - 6\sqrt{x})$

    $\sqrt{3}(\sqrt{6} - 6\sqrt{x}) = \sqrt{3} \cdot \sqrt{6} - \sqrt{3} \cdot 6\sqrt{x}$ • **Use the Distributive Property.**

                         $= \sqrt{\underline{\ \ ?\ \ }} - 6\sqrt{\underline{\ \ ?\ \ }}$ • **The indices are the same.**

                                          Multiply the radicands.

                         $= \underline{\ \ ?\ \ }\sqrt{2} - 6\sqrt{3x}$ • **Simplify $\sqrt{18}$.**

66. a. Two expressions in the form $a + b$ and $a - b$ are called ___?___.
b. The conjugate of $\sqrt{y} - 5$ is ___?___.
c. The product of conjugates of the form $a + b$ and $a - b$ is ___?___.
d. $(\sqrt{y} - 5)(\sqrt{y} + 5) = ($___?___$)^2 - ($___?___$)^2 = $ ___?___ $-$ ___?___.

Multiply.

67. $\sqrt{8}\sqrt{32}$

68. $\sqrt{14}\sqrt{35}$

69. $\sqrt[3]{4}\sqrt[3]{8}$

70. $\sqrt[3]{6}\sqrt[3]{36}$

71. $\sqrt{x^2y^5}\sqrt{xy}$

72. $\sqrt{a^3b}\sqrt{ab^4}$

73. $\sqrt{2x^2y}\sqrt{32xy}$

74. $\sqrt{5x^3y}\sqrt{10x^3y^4}$

75. $\sqrt[3]{x^2y}\sqrt[3]{16x^4y^2}$

76. $\sqrt[3]{4a^2b^3}\sqrt[3]{8ab^5}$

77. $\sqrt[4]{12ab^3}\sqrt[4]{4a^5b^2}$

78. $\sqrt[4]{36a^2b^4}\sqrt[4]{12a^5b^3}$

79. $\sqrt{3}(\sqrt{27} - \sqrt{3})$

80. $\sqrt{10}(\sqrt{10} - \sqrt{5})$

81. $\sqrt{x}(\sqrt{x} - \sqrt{2})$

82. $\sqrt{y}(\sqrt{y} - \sqrt{5})$

83. $\sqrt{2x}(\sqrt{8x} - \sqrt{32})$

84. $\sqrt{3a}(\sqrt{27a^2} - \sqrt{a})$

85. $(\sqrt{x} - 3)^2$

86. $(\sqrt{2x} + 4)^2$

87. $(4\sqrt{5} + 2)^2$

88. $2\sqrt{3x^2} \cdot 3\sqrt{12xy^3} \cdot \sqrt{6x^3y}$

89. $2\sqrt{14xy} \cdot 4\sqrt{7x^2y} \cdot 3\sqrt{8xy^2}$

90. $\sqrt[3]{8ab}\sqrt[3]{4a^2b^3}\sqrt[3]{9ab^4}$

91. $\sqrt[3]{2a^2b}\sqrt[3]{4a^3b^2}\sqrt[3]{8a^5b^6}$

92. $(\sqrt{2} - 3)(\sqrt{2} + 4)$

93. $(\sqrt{5} - 5)(2\sqrt{5} + 2)$

94. $(\sqrt{y} - 2)(\sqrt{y} + 2)$

95. $(\sqrt{x} - y)(\sqrt{x} + y)$

96. $(\sqrt{2x} - 3\sqrt{y})(\sqrt{2x} + 3\sqrt{y})$

97. $(2\sqrt{3x} - \sqrt{y})(2\sqrt{3x} + \sqrt{y})$

98. $(\sqrt{a} - 2)(\sqrt{a} - 3)$

99. $(\sqrt{x} + 4)(\sqrt{x} - 7)$

100. $(\sqrt[3]{a} + 2)(\sqrt[3]{a} + 3)$

101. $(\sqrt[3]{x} - 4)(\sqrt[3]{x} + 5)$

102. $(2\sqrt{x} - \sqrt{y})(3\sqrt{x} + \sqrt{y})$

103. True or false? $(\sqrt{a} - 1)(\sqrt{a} + 1) > a$

104. True or false? $\sqrt{a}(\sqrt{a} - a) = a(1 - \sqrt{a})$

4 Divide radical expressions

105. Divide: $\dfrac{\sqrt[4]{80x^{10}}}{\sqrt[4]{5x}}$

$\dfrac{\sqrt[4]{80x^{10}}}{\sqrt[4]{5x}} = \sqrt[4]{\dfrac{80x^{10}}{5x}}$ • Use the ___?___ Property of Radicals.

$= \sqrt[4]{16x^{-?}}$ • Simplify the radicand.

$= \sqrt[4]{16x^{-?}}\,\sqrt[4]{x}$

$= \underline{\quad?\quad}\,\sqrt[4]{x}$ • Simplify the perfect fourth power.

106. When is a radical expression in simplest form?

107. State whether the expression is in simplest form.

a. $\dfrac{\sqrt[3]{a^2}}{b}$ b. $\dfrac{\sqrt{a^3}}{b}$ c. $\sqrt[4]{\dfrac{a}{b}}$ d. $\dfrac{\sqrt{a}}{\sqrt{a}+b}$

108. By what expression should the numerator and denominator be multiplied in order to rationalize the denominator?

a. $\dfrac{1}{\sqrt{6}}$ b. $\dfrac{7}{\sqrt[3]{2y^5}}$ c. $\dfrac{8x}{\sqrt[4]{27x}}$ d. $\dfrac{4}{\sqrt{3}-x}$

Simplify.

109. $\dfrac{\sqrt{32x^2}}{\sqrt{2x}}$

110. $\dfrac{\sqrt{60y^4}}{\sqrt{12y}}$

111. $\dfrac{\sqrt{42a^3b^5}}{\sqrt{14a^2b}}$

112. $\dfrac{\sqrt{65ab^4}}{\sqrt{5ab}}$

113. $\dfrac{1}{\sqrt{5}}$

114. $\dfrac{1}{\sqrt{2}}$

115. $\dfrac{1}{\sqrt{2x}}$

116. $\dfrac{2}{\sqrt{3y}}$

117. $\dfrac{5}{\sqrt{5x}}$

118. $\dfrac{9}{\sqrt{3a}}$

119. $\sqrt{\dfrac{x}{5}}$

120. $\sqrt{\dfrac{y}{2}}$

121. $\dfrac{3}{\sqrt[3]{2}}$

122. $\dfrac{5}{\sqrt[3]{9}}$

123. $\dfrac{3}{\sqrt[3]{4x^2}}$

124. $\dfrac{5}{\sqrt[3]{3y}}$

125. $\dfrac{\sqrt{40x^3y^2}}{\sqrt{80x^2y^3}}$

126. $\dfrac{\sqrt{15a^2b^5}}{\sqrt{30a^5b^3}}$

127. $\dfrac{\sqrt{24a^2b}}{\sqrt{18ab^4}}$

128. $\dfrac{\sqrt{12x^3y}}{\sqrt{20x^4y}}$

129. $\dfrac{2}{\sqrt{5}+2}$

130. $\dfrac{5}{2 - \sqrt{7}}$

131. $\dfrac{3}{\sqrt{y} - 2}$

132. $\dfrac{-7}{\sqrt{x} - 3}$

133. $\dfrac{\sqrt{2} - \sqrt{3}}{\sqrt{2} + \sqrt{3}}$

134. $\dfrac{\sqrt{3} + \sqrt{4}}{\sqrt{2} + \sqrt{3}}$

135. $\dfrac{4 - \sqrt{2}}{2 - \sqrt{3}}$

136. $\dfrac{3 - \sqrt{x}}{3 + \sqrt{x}}$

137. $\dfrac{\sqrt{3} - \sqrt{5}}{\sqrt{2} + \sqrt{5}}$

138. $\dfrac{\sqrt{2} + \sqrt{3}}{\sqrt{3} - \sqrt{2}}$

139. $\dfrac{3}{\sqrt[4]{8x^3}}$

140. $\dfrac{-3}{\sqrt[4]{27y^2}}$

141. $\dfrac{4}{\sqrt[5]{16a^2}}$

142. $\dfrac{a}{\sqrt[5]{81a^4}}$

143. $\dfrac{2x}{\sqrt[5]{64x^3}}$

144. $\dfrac{3y}{\sqrt[4]{32y^2}}$

145. $\dfrac{\sqrt{a} + a\sqrt{b}}{\sqrt{a} - a\sqrt{b}}$

146. $\dfrac{\sqrt{3} - 3\sqrt{y}}{\sqrt{3} + 3\sqrt{y}}$

147. $\dfrac{3\sqrt{xy} + 2\sqrt{xy}}{\sqrt{x} - \sqrt{y}}$

148. $\dfrac{2\sqrt{x} + 3\sqrt{y}}{\sqrt{x} - 4\sqrt{y}}$

7.2 Applying Concepts

Simplify.

149. $\left(\sqrt{8} - \sqrt{2}\right)^3$

150. $\left(\sqrt{27} - \sqrt{3}\right)^3$

151. $\left(\sqrt{2} - 3\right)^3$

152. $\left(\sqrt{5} + 2\right)^3$

153. $\dfrac{3}{\sqrt{y + 1} + 1}$

154. $\dfrac{2}{\sqrt{x + 4} + 2}$

Rewrite as an expression with a single radical.

155. $\dfrac{\sqrt[3]{(x + y)^2}}{\sqrt{x + y}}$

156. $\dfrac{\sqrt[4]{(a + b)^3}}{\sqrt{a + b}}$

157. $\sqrt[4]{2y}\sqrt{x + 3}$

158. $\sqrt[4]{2x}\sqrt{y - 2}$

159. $\sqrt{a}\sqrt[3]{a + 3}$

160. $\sqrt{b}\sqrt[3]{b - 1}$

Write in exponential form and then simplify.

161. $\sqrt{16^{\frac{1}{2}}}$

162. $\sqrt[3]{4^{\frac{3}{2}}}$

163. $\sqrt[4]{32^{-\frac{4}{5}}}$

164. $\sqrt{243^{-\frac{4}{5}}}$

165. 🥧 **National Debt** The approximate national debt, in trillions of dollars, for every other year from 1994 to 2006 is given in the table at the right. (*Source:* www.publicdebt.treas.gov/opd/opdpenny.htm) A function that models this data is $D(x) = 3.06x^{0.3}$, where $x = 2$ corresponds to the year 1992 and $D(x)$ is the national debt in trillions of dollars.
  a. Write this function in radical form.
  b. Find the value of the national debt predicted by the model for the year 1995.
  c. Find the value of the national debt predicted by the model for the year 2003.

Year	National Debt
1994	4.69
1996	5.22
1998	5.53
2000	5.67
2002	6.23
2004	7.38
2006	8.39

166. ✏️ By what factor must you multiply a number in order to double its square root? to triple its square root? to double its cube root? to triple its cube root? Explain.

7.3 Radical Functions

OBJECTIVE 1   **Find the domain of a radical function**

A **radical function** is one that contains a fractional exponent or a variable underneath a radical. Examples of radical functions are shown at the right.

$$f(x) = 3^4\sqrt{x^5} - 7$$
$$g(x) = 3x - 2x^{\frac{1}{2}} + 5$$

Note that these are *not* polynomial functions because polynomial functions do not contain variables raised to a fractional power or variable radical expressions.

The domain of a radical function is a set of real numbers for which the radical expression is a real number. For example, -9 is one number that would be excluded from the domain of $f(x) = \sqrt{x + 5}$ because

$$f(-9) = \sqrt{-9 + 5} = \sqrt{-4},$$ which is not a real number.

State the domain of $f(x) = \sqrt{x + 5}$ in set-builder notation.

The value of $\sqrt{x + 5}$ is a real number when $x + 5$ is greater than or equal to zero: $x + 5 \geq 0$. Solving this inequality for x results in $x \geq -5$.

The domain of f is $\{x \mid x \geq -5\}$.

State the domain of $F(x) = \sqrt[3]{2x - 6}$.

Because the cube root of a real number is a real number, $\sqrt[3]{2x - 6}$ is a real number for all values of x. [For instance, $F(-1) = \sqrt[3]{2(-1) - 6} = \sqrt[3]{-8} = -2$.] Therefore, the domain of F is all real numbers.

These last two examples suggest the following:

> If the index of a radical expression is an even number, the radicand must be greater than or equal to zero to ensure that the value of the expression will be a real number. If the index of a radical expression is an odd number, the radicand may be a positive or a negative number.

EXAMPLE 1 State the domain of each function in set-builder notation.
A. $V(x) = \sqrt[4]{6 - 4x}$ **B.** $R(x) = \sqrt[5]{x + 4}$

Solution   **A.** $6 - 4x \geq 0$

$-4x \geq -6$

$x \leq \dfrac{3}{2}$

• *V* contains an even root. Therefore, the radicand must be greater than or equal to zero.

The domain is $\left\{x \mid x \leq \dfrac{3}{2}\right\}$.

B. $\{x \mid x \in \text{real numbers}\}$

• Because *R* contains an odd root, the radicand may be positive or negative.

PROBLEM 1 State the domain of each function in interval notation.
A. $Q(x) = \sqrt[3]{6x + 12}$ **B.** $T(x) = (3x + 9)^{\frac{1}{2}}$

Solution   See page S22.

OBJECTIVE 2

Graph a radical function

The graph of a radical function is produced in the same manner as the graph of any other function. The function is evaluated at several values in the domain of the function, and the resulting ordered pairs are graphed. Ordered pairs must be graphed until an accurate graph can be made.

Take Note

By first determining the domain of the function, you discover the possible values of *x* to use when evaluating the function. Any value of *x* in the domain can be used. We used "nice" values—values of *x* that result in a perfect-square radicand. However, any value of *x* can be used. For instance, if *x* = 3, then

$f(3) = \sqrt{5} \approx 2.24$

and the ordered pair (3, 2.24) belongs to the graph. This ordered pair is just a little more difficult to graph.

Graph: $f(x) = \sqrt{x + 2}$

Because *f* contains an even root, the radicand must be positive. To determine the domain of *f*, solve the inequality $x + 2 \geq 0$. The solution is $x \geq -2$, so the domain is $\{x \mid x \geq -2\}$. Now determine ordered pairs of the function by choosing values of *x* from the domain. Some possible choices are shown in the following table.

x	$f(x) = \sqrt{x + 2}$	y
-2	$f(-2) = \sqrt{-2 + 2} = \sqrt{0} = 0$	0
-1	$f(-1) = \sqrt{-1 + 2} = \sqrt{1} = 1$	1
2	$f(2) = \sqrt{2 + 2} = \sqrt{4} = 2$	2
7	$f(7) = \sqrt{7 + 2} = \sqrt{9} = 3$	3

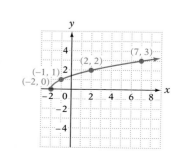

EXAMPLE 2 Graph: $H(x) = \sqrt[3]{x}$

Solution Because H contains only an odd root, the domain of H is all real numbers. Choose some values of x in the domain of H, and evaluate the function for those values. Some possible choices are given in the following table.

x	$H(x) = \sqrt[3]{x}$	y
-8	$H(-8) = \sqrt[3]{-8} = -2$	-2
-1	$H(-1) = \sqrt[3]{-1} = -1$	-1
0	$H(0) = \sqrt[3]{0} = 0$	0
1	$H(1) = \sqrt[3]{1} = 1$	1
8	$H(8) = \sqrt[3]{8} = 2$	2

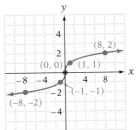

PROBLEM 2 Graph: $F(x) = \sqrt{x - 2}$

Solution See page S22.

The graph of $f(x) = \sqrt{x + 2}$ and $H(x) = \sqrt[3]{x}$ are shown below. Note that each graph satisfies the vertical line test for the graph of a function.

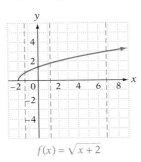

$f(x) = \sqrt{x + 2}$

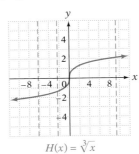

$H(x) = \sqrt[3]{x}$

A graphing utility can be used to graph radical functions. See the Appendix for instructions on how to enter a radical function on a graphing utility.

EXAMPLE 3 Graph: $Z(x) = 4 + (8 - 6x)^{\frac{1}{2}}$

Solution Because Z involves an even root, the radicand must be positive. The domain is $\left\{ x \mid x \le \dfrac{4}{3} \right\}$.

PROBLEM 3   Graph: $y(x) = 2 - \sqrt[3]{x} - 1$

■ **Solution**   See page S22.

7.3 Concept Review

Determine whether the following statements are always true, sometimes true, or never true.

1. The number 5 is not in the domain of $f(x) = \sqrt{4 - x}$.

2. The domain of $f(x) = \sqrt[3]{x} - 2$ is the set of all real numbers.

3. The domain of $f(x) = \dfrac{3}{x^2 + 4}$ is all the real numbers except -2 and 2.

4. If x is a real number, the expression $f(x) = \sqrt{-x^2}$ represents a radical function.

7.3 Exercises

1 Find the domain of a radical function

1. What is a radical function?

2. What is the difference between a radical function and a polynomial function?

3. a. When n is an even number, the domain of $f(x) = x^{1/n}$ is $\{x \mid x \underline{\quad ? \quad}\}$.
b. When n is an odd number, the domain of $f(x) = x^{1/n}$ is $\{x \mid x \underline{\quad ? \quad}\}$.

4. To find the domain of $f(x) = 8 + \sqrt[4]{2x} - 1$, note that the index of the radical is even, so the function is defined only when $\underline{\quad ? \quad} \geq 0$. Solving this inequality for x gives $x \geq \underline{\quad ? \quad}$. In interval notation, the domain of f is $[\underline{\quad ? \quad}, \underline{\quad ? \quad})$.

5. State whether the domain of f is $(-\infty, 0]$, $[0, \infty)$, all real numbers, or the empty set.
a. $f(x) = \sqrt{-x}$
b. $f(x) = \sqrt{-x^2}$
c. $f(x) = -\sqrt{x^2}$
d. $f(x) = \sqrt{(-x)^2}$

6. 🗣 **a.** True or false? The functions $f(x) = \sqrt[4]{3x - 4}$ and $g(x) = \sqrt[3]{3x - 4}$ have the same domain.
b. True or false? $f(x) = \sqrt{3}\,x^2$ is a radical function.

State the domain of each function in set-builder notation.

7. $f(x) = 2x^{\frac{1}{3}}$

8. $r(x) = -3\sqrt[5]{2x}$

9. $g(x) = -2\sqrt{x + 1}$

10. $h(x) = 3x^{\frac{1}{4}} - 2$

11. $f(x) = 2x\sqrt{x} - 3$

12. $y(x) = -3\sqrt[3]{1 + x}$

13. $C(x) = -3x^{\frac{3}{4}} + 1$

14. $G(x) = 6x^{\frac{2}{5}} + 5$

15. $F(x) = 4(3x - 6)^{\frac{1}{2}}$

State the domain of each function in interval notation.

16. $f(x) = -2(4x - 12)^{\frac{1}{2}}$

17. $g(x) = 2(2x - 10)^{\frac{2}{3}}$

18. $J(x) = 4 - (3x - 3)^{\frac{2}{5}}$

19. $V(x) = x - \sqrt{12 - 4x}$

20. $Y(x) = -6 + \sqrt{6 - x}$

21. $h(x) = 3\sqrt[4]{(x - 2)^3}$

22. $g(x) = \frac{2}{3}\sqrt[4]{(4 - x)^3}$

23. $f(x) = x - (4 - 6x)^{\frac{1}{2}}$

24. $F(x) = (9 + 12x)^{\frac{1}{2}} - 4$

2 **Graph a radical function**

For Exercises 25 to 28, use the function $f(x) = -\sqrt{x - 5}$.

25. The domain of f is $\{x \mid x\underline{\quad ?\quad}\}$.

26. For what value of x will the radicand be equal to the perfect square 9?

27. $f(14) = -\sqrt{\underline{\quad ?\quad} - 5} = -\sqrt{\underline{\quad ?\quad}} = \underline{\quad ?\quad}$

28. Use the results of Exercise 27 to state a point that is on the graph of $f(x) = -\sqrt{x - 5}$.

Graph.

29. $F(x) = \sqrt{x}$

30. $G(x) = -\sqrt{x}$

31. $h(x) = -\sqrt[3]{x}$

32. $K(x) = \sqrt[3]{x + 1}$

33. $f(x) = -\sqrt{x + 2}$

34. $g(x) = \sqrt{x - 1}$

35. $S(x) = -\sqrt[4]{x}$

36. $C(x) = (x + 2)^{\frac{1}{4}}$

37. $F(x) = (x - 2)^{\frac{1}{2}}$

38. $f(x) = -(x - 1)^{\frac{1}{2}}$

39. $Q(x) = (x - 3)^{\frac{1}{3}}$

40. $H(x) = (-x)^{\frac{1}{3}}$

Graph.

41. $f(x) = 2x^{\frac{2}{5}} - 1$

42. $h(x) = 3x^{\frac{2}{5}} + 2$

43. $g(x) = 3 - (5 - 2x)^{\frac{1}{2}}$

44. $y(x) = 1 + (4 - 8x)^{\frac{1}{2}}$

45. $V(x) = \sqrt[5]{(x - 2)^2}$

46. $A(x) = x\sqrt{3x - 9}$

47. $F(x) = 2x - 3\sqrt[3]{x} - 1$

48. $f(x) = 2x - \sqrt{x} - 1$

49. $f(x) = 3x\sqrt{4x + 8}$

50. **a.** Which graph below could be the graph of $f(x) = -x^{1/2}$?
    b. Which graph below could be the graph of $f(x) = (-x)^{1/2}$?
  c. Which graph below could be the graph of $f(x) = -(-x)^{1/2}$?
  d. Which graph below could be the graph of $f(x) = x^{1/2}$?

A.

B.

C.

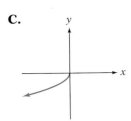

D.

51. State whether the graph of the given function will be above the x-axis, below the x-axis, or both above and below the x-axis.
  a. $f(x) = -x^{1/3}$ **b.** $f(x) = -\sqrt{x} + 2$ **c.** $f(x) = \sqrt[4]{3x}$
  d. $f(x) = (-2x)^{1/2}$

7.3 Applying Concepts

52. **Sports** Many major league baseball parks have a symmetric design as shown in the figure at the right. One decision that the designer must make is the shape of the outfield. One possible design uses the function

$$f(x) = k + (400 - k)\sqrt{1 - \frac{x^2}{a^2}}$$

to determine the shape of the outfield.
  a. Graph this equation for $k = 0$, $a = 287$, and $-240 \le x \le 240$.
  b. What is the maximum value of this function for the given interval?
  c. The equation of the right-field foul line is $y = x$. Where does the foul line intersect the graph of f? That is, find the point on the graph of f for which $y = x$.
  d. If the units on the axes are feet, what is the distance from home plate along the foul line to the base of the right-field wall?

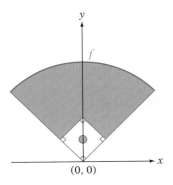

53. ⬤ ◣   **Currency** According to the Bureau of Engraving and Printing, the average life span of different denominations of currency is as shown in the table at the right. The function that approximately models these data is $f(x) = 1.38x^{\frac{2}{5}}$, where x is the denomination of the bill and $f(x)$ is the average life span in years.

Currency	Average Life Span
$1 bill	1.8 years
$5 bill	2 years
$10 bill	3 years
$20 bill	4 years
$50 bill	9 years
$100 bill	9 years

  a. In the context of the problem, what is the domain of the function $f(x) = 1.38x^{\frac{2}{5}}$? Why is 0 not in the domain? Why are negative numbers not in the domain?

  b. If 2 were in the domain of the function, what life span would the model predict for the $2 bill? Round to the nearest tenth. Do you think this estimate is reasonable?

54. ◣   Writing the fraction $\frac{2}{4}$ in lowest terms as $\frac{1}{2}$, it appears that $(x^2)^{\frac{1}{4}} = x^{\frac{1}{2}}$.

  Using $-10 \le x \le 10$, graph $f(x) = (x^2)^{\frac{1}{4}}$ and then graph $g(x) = x^{\frac{1}{2}}$.

Are the graphs the same? If they are, try graphing $g(x) = x^{\frac{1}{2}}$ first and then $f(x) = (x^2)^{\frac{1}{4}}$. Explain why the graphs are not the same. In your explanation, include why $x^{\frac{2}{4}} = x^{\frac{1}{2}}$ is not always a true statement.

7.4 Solving Equations Containing Radical Expressions

OBJECTIVE 1   Solve equations containing one or more radical expressions

An equation that contains a variable expression in a radicand is a **radical equation**.

$$\left. \begin{array}{l} \sqrt[3]{2x - 5} + x = 7 \\ \sqrt{x + 1} - \sqrt{x} = 4 \end{array} \right\} \begin{array}{l} \text{Radical} \\ \text{equations} \end{array}$$

The following property is used to solve a radical equation.

Take Note

You might assume that the converse of this is also true. That is, if $a^2 = b^2$, then $a = b$. But this is not the case. For example, if $a = -4$ and $b = 4$, then $(-4)^2 = 4^2$ but $-4 \ne 4$.

Property of Raising Each Side of an Equation to a Power

If two numbers are equal, then the same powers of the numbers are equal.

$$\text{If } a = b, \text{ then } a^n = b^n.$$

Solve: $\sqrt{x-2} - 6 = 0$

Rewrite the equation with the radical on one side of the equation and the constant on the other side.

$$\sqrt{x-2} - 6 = 0$$
$$\sqrt{x-2} = 6$$

Square each side of the equation.

$$(\sqrt{x-2})^2 = 6^2$$

Solve the resulting equation.

$$x - 2 = 36$$
$$x = 38$$

Check the solution.

Check: $\sqrt{x-2} - 6 = 0$

$$\begin{array}{c|c} \sqrt{38-2} - 6 & 0 \\ \sqrt{36} - 6 & 0 \\ 6 - 6 & 0 \\ & 0 = 0 \end{array}$$

38 checks as a solution.
The solution is 38.

EXAMPLE 1   Solve.   **A.** $\sqrt{3x-2} - 8 = -3$ **B.** $\sqrt[3]{3x-1} = -4$

Solution   **A.** $\sqrt{3x-2} - 8 = -3$

$$\sqrt{3x-2} = 5$$

- Rewrite the equation so that the radical is alone on one side of the equation.

$$(\sqrt{3x-2})^2 = 5^2$$
$$3x - 2 = 25$$
$$3x = 27$$
$$x = 9$$

- Square each side of the equation.
- Solve the resulting equation.

Check:

- Check the solution.

$$\sqrt{3x-2} - 8 = -3$$

$$\begin{array}{c|c} \sqrt{3 \cdot 9 - 2} - 8 & -3 \\ \sqrt{27-2} - 8 & -3 \\ \sqrt{25} - 8 & -3 \\ 5 - 8 & -3 \\ -3 & = -3 \end{array}$$

The solution is 9.

B. $\sqrt[3]{3x-1} = -4$
$$(\sqrt[3]{3x-1})^3 = (-4)^3$$
$$3x - 1 = -64$$
$$3x = -63$$
$$x = -21$$

- Cube each side of the equation.
- Solve the resulting equation.

Check:

- Check the solution.

$$\sqrt[3]{3x-1} = -4$$

$$\begin{array}{c|c} \sqrt[3]{3(-21)-1} & -4 \\ \sqrt[3]{-63-1} & -4 \\ \sqrt[3]{-64} & -4 \\ -4 & = -4 \end{array}$$

The solution is -21.

PROBLEM 1 Solve.   **A.** $\sqrt{4x+5}-12=-5$ **B.** $\sqrt[4]{x-8}=3$

Solution See page S22.

When you raise both sides of an equation to an even power, the resulting equation may have a solution that is not a solution of the original equation. Therefore, it is necessary to check the solution of a radical equation.

EXAMPLE 2 Solve.   **A.** $x+2\sqrt{x-1}=9$ **B.** $\sqrt{x+7}=\sqrt{x}+1$

Solution **A.** $x+2\sqrt{x-1}=9$

$2\sqrt{x-1}=9-x$

• Rewrite the equation with the radical on one side of the equation.

$(2\sqrt{x-1})^2=(9-x)^2$
• Square each side of the equation.
$4(x-1)=81-18x+x^2$
$4x-4=81-18x+x^2$
$0=x^2-22x+85$

• Write the quadratic equation in standard form.

$0=(x-5)(x-17)$ • Factor.

$x-5=0 \qquad x-17=0$ • Use the Principle of Zero
$x=5 \qquad\qquad x=17$ Products.

Check:
$$x+2\sqrt{x-1}=9 \qquad x+2\sqrt{x-1}=9$$

$5+2\sqrt{5-1}$	9	$17+2\sqrt{17-1}$	9
$5+2\sqrt{4}$	9	$17+2\sqrt{16}$	9
$5+2\cdot2$	9	$17+2\cdot4$	9
$5+4$	9	$17+8$	9
$9=9$		$25\neq9$	

17 does not check as a solution. It is called an **extraneous solution** of the equation.

The solution is 5.

B. $\sqrt{x+7}=\sqrt{x}+1$
• A radical appears on each side of the equation.
$(\sqrt{x+7})^2=(\sqrt{x}+1)^2$
• Square each side of the equation.
$x+7=x+2\sqrt{x}+1$
$6=2\sqrt{x}$ • Simplify the resulting equation.
$3=\sqrt{x}$ • The equation contains a radical.
$3^2=(\sqrt{x})^2$ • Square each side of the equation.
$9=x$

Check: • Check the solution.
$$\sqrt{x+7}=\sqrt{x}+1$$
$\sqrt{9+7}$	$\sqrt{9}+1$
$\sqrt{16}$	$3+1$
$4=4$	

The solution is 9.

PROBLEM 2 Solve.   **A.** $x+3\sqrt{x+2}=8$ **B.** $\sqrt{x+5}=5-\sqrt{x}$

Solution See pages S22–S23.

OBJECTIVE **2**   **Application problems**

A right triangle contains one 90° angle. The side opposite the 90° angle is called the **hypotenuse.** The other two sides are called **legs.**

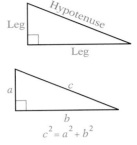

Pythagoras, a Greek mathematician, is credited with the discovery that the square of the hypotenuse of a right triangle is equal to the sum of the squares of the two legs. This is called the Pythagorean Theorem.

Pythagoras
(c. 580 B.C.–529 B.C.)

$$c^2 = a^2 + b^2$$

Pythagorean Theorem

The square of the hypotenuse, c, of a right triangle is equal to the sum of the squares of the two legs, a and b.

$$c^2 = a^2 + b^2$$

EXAMPLE 3   A ladder 20 ft long is leaning against a building. How high on the building will the ladder reach when the bottom of the ladder is 8 ft from the building? Round to the nearest tenth.

Strategy   To find the distance, use the Pythagorean Theorem. The hypotenuse is the length of the ladder. One leg is the distance from the bottom of the ladder to the base of the building. The distance along the building from the ground to the top of the ladder is the unknown leg.

Solution
$$c^2 = a^2 + b^2$$
$$20^2 = 8^2 + b^2$$
$$400 = 64 + b^2$$
$$336 = b^2$$
$$(336)^{\frac{1}{2}} = (b^2)^{\frac{1}{2}}$$
$$\sqrt{336} = b$$
$$18.3 \approx b$$

The distance is 18.3 ft.

PROBLEM 3   Find the diagonal of a rectangle that is 6 cm in length and 3 cm in width. Round to the nearest tenth.

Solution   See page S23.

7.4   Concept Review

Determine whether the following statements are always true, sometimes true, or never true.

1. If $a^n = b^n$, then $a = b$.

2. When you raise both sides of an equation to an even power, the resulting equation has a solution that is not a solution of the original equation.

3. If two sides of a triangle are known, the third side can be found by using the Pythagorean Theorem.

4. The solution of $\sqrt[3]{-x} = 8$ is -512.

7.4   Exercises

1   **Solve equations containing one or more radical expressions**

1. Which of the equations $\sqrt{2}\,x + 1 = 7$ and $\sqrt{2x + 1} = 7$ is a radical equation?

2. Solve: $\sqrt[3]{x} - 3 = -4$

$$\sqrt[3]{x} - 3 = -4$$
$$(\sqrt[3]{x} - 3)^{\underline{?}} = (-4)^{\underline{?}}$$ • **Cube each side of the equation.**
$$\underline{\quad ? \quad} = \underline{\quad ? \quad}$$ • **Simplify.**
$$x = \underline{\quad ? \quad}$$ • **Add** $\underline{\quad ? \quad}$ **to each side of the equation.**

3. What is the first step when solving $\sqrt{x} + 3 = 9$?

4. Why is it necessary to check the proposed solutions of a radical equation?

Solve.

5. $\sqrt{x} = 5$ 　　　　　　　　 **6.** $\sqrt{y} = 2$ 　　　　　　　　 **7.** $\sqrt[3]{a} = 3$

8. $\sqrt[3]{y} = 5$ 　　　　　　　　 **9.** $\sqrt{3x} = 12$ 　　　　　　　　 **10.** $\sqrt{5x} = 10$

11. $\sqrt[3]{4x} = -2$ 　　　　　　　 **12.** $\sqrt[3]{6x} = -3$ 　　　　　　　 **13.** $\sqrt{2x} = -4$

14. $\sqrt{5x} = -5$ 　　　　　　　 **15.** $\sqrt{3x - 2} = 5$ 　　　　　　 **16.** $\sqrt{5x - 4} = 9$

$3 - 2x = 7$

18. $\sqrt{9 - 4x} = 4$

19. $7 = \sqrt{1 - 3x}$

$5 = \sqrt{8 - 7x}$

21. $\sqrt[3]{4x - 1} = 2$

22. $\sqrt[3]{5x + 2} = 3$

$\sqrt[3]{1 - 2x} = -3$

24. $\sqrt[3]{3 - 2x} = -2$

25. $\sqrt[3]{9x + 1} = 4$

6. $\sqrt{3x + 9} - 12 = 0$

27. $\sqrt{4x - 3} - 5 = 0$

28. $\sqrt{x - 2} = 4$

29. $\sqrt[3]{x - 3} + 5 = 0$

30. $\sqrt[3]{x - 2} = 3$

31. $\sqrt[3]{2x - 6} = 4$

32. $\sqrt[4]{4x + 1} = 2$

33. $\sqrt[4]{2x - 9} = 3$

34. $\sqrt{2x - 3} - 2 = 1$

35. $\sqrt{3x - 5} - 5 = 3$

36. $\sqrt[3]{2x - 3} + 5 = 2$

37. $\sqrt[3]{x - 4} + 7 = 5$

38. $\sqrt{5x - 16} + 1 = 4$

39. $\sqrt{3x - 5} - 2 = 3$

40. $\sqrt{2x - 1} - 8 = -5$

41. $\sqrt{7x + 2} - 10 = -7$

42. $\sqrt[3]{4x - 3} - 2 = 3$

43. $\sqrt[3]{1 - 3x} + 5 = 3$

44. $1 - \sqrt{4x + 3} = -5$

45. $7 - \sqrt{3x + 1} = -1$

46. $\sqrt{x + 1} = 2 - \sqrt{x}$

47. $\sqrt{2x + 4} = 3 - \sqrt{2x}$

48. $\sqrt{x^2 + 3x - 2} - x = 1$

49. $\sqrt{x^2 - 4x - 1} + 3 = x$

50. $\sqrt{x^2 - 3x - 1} = 3$

51. $\sqrt{x^2 - 2x + 1} = 3$

52. $\sqrt{2x + 5} - \sqrt{3x - 2} = 1$

53. $\sqrt{4x + 1} - \sqrt{2x + 4} = 1$

54. $\sqrt{5x - 1} - \sqrt{3x - 2} = 1$

54. $\sqrt{5x + 4} - \sqrt{3x + 1} = 1$

56. $\sqrt[4]{x^2 + 2x + 8} - 2 = 0$

57. $\sqrt[4]{x^2 + x - 1} - 1 = 0$

58. $4\sqrt{x + 1} - x = 1$

59. $3\sqrt{x - 2} + 2 = x$

60. $x + 3\sqrt{x - 2} = 12$

61. $x + 2\sqrt{x + 1} = 7$

62. Without actually solving the equations, identify which equation has no solution.

a. $\sqrt{4x - 8} = -5$ **b.** $\sqrt[3]{4x - 8} = -5$

c. $\sqrt{4x - 8} = -5$ **d.** $-\sqrt{4x - 8} = -5$

63. How many times will the Property of Raising Each Side of an Equation to a Power be used to solve the equation? Do not solve.

a. $\sqrt{x - 8} = \sqrt{2x - 1}$ **b.** $\sqrt{x - 8} = \sqrt{2x} - 1$

2 Application problems

64. The equation $v = 8\sqrt{d}$ gives the speed v, in feet per second, of a dropped object after the object has fallen d feet. A stone is dropped from a bridge. To find the distance the stone has fallen when it reaches a speed of 56 ft/s, replace ___?___ with 56 and solve for ___?___.

65. A 15-foot ladder leans against the side of a building with its bottom d feet from the building. The ladder reaches a height of h feet. Which of the following distances is *not* a possible value for h?
   a. 2 ft   **b.** 8 ft   **c.** 14 ft   **d.** 20 ft

66. Sports The equation $s = 16.97\sqrt[9]{n}$ can be used to predict the maximum speed, s (in feet per second), of n rowers on a scull. Find, to the nearest whole number, how many rowers are needed to travel at 20 ft/s. Does doubling the number of rowers double the maximum speed of the scull?

67. Meteorology The sustained wind velocity, v (in meters per second), in a hurricane is given by $v = 6.3\sqrt{1013 - p}$, where p is the air pressure in millibars (mb). If the velocity of the wind in a hurricane is 64 m/s, what is the air pressure? Round to the nearest tenth. What happens to wind speed in a hurricane as air pressure decreases?

68. Astronomy The time, T (in days), that it takes a planet to revolve around the sun can be approximated by the equation $T = 0.407\sqrt{d^3}$, where d is the mean distance of the planet from the sun in millions of miles. It takes Venus approximately 226 days to complete one revolution of the sun. To the nearest million miles, what is the mean distance of Venus from the sun?

69. Astronomy The time, T (in days), that it takes a moon of Saturn to revolve around Saturn can be approximated by the equation $T = 0.373\sqrt{d^3}$, where d is the mean distance of the moon from Saturn in units of 100,000 km. It takes the moon Tethys approximately 1.89 days to complete one revolution of Saturn. To the nearest 1000 km, what is the mean distance of Tethys from Saturn?

70. Construction The maximum velocity of a roller coaster depends on the vertical drop from the top of the highest hill to the bottom of that hill. The formula $v = 8\sqrt{h}$ gives the relationship between maximum velocity, v (in feet per second), and height, h (in feet). The maximum velocity of the Magnum XL-200 roller coaster in Sandusky, Ohio, is approximately 114 ft/s. How tall, to the nearest foot, is the highest hill for this roller coaster?

71. Health Science The number of calories an animal uses per day (called the metabolic rate of the animal) can be approximated by $M = 126.4\sqrt[4]{W^3}$, where M is the metabolic rate and W is the weight of the animal in pounds. Find, to the nearest hundred pounds, the weight of an elephant whose metabolic rate is 60,000 calories per day.

72. Construction A 12-foot ladder is leaning against a building. How high on the building will the ladder reach when the bottom of the ladder is 4 ft from the building? Round to the nearest tenth.

73. Construction A 26-foot ladder is leaning against a building. How far is the bottom of the ladder from the wall when the ladder reaches a height of 24 ft on the building?

74. Uniform Motion Two joggers start from the same point and travel in the directions shown in the figure at the right. One jogger is traveling 8 ft/s, and the second jogger is traveling 9 ft/s. What is the distance between the joggers after 1 min? Round to the nearest tenth.

75. Uniform Motion Two joggers leave the same point at the same time, one jogging east at 3 m/s and the other jogging south at 3.5 m/s. What is the distance between the joggers after 3 min? Round to the nearest hundredth.

76. Geometry The diagonal of a rectangle is a line drawn from one vertex to the opposite vertex. Find the length of the diagonal in the rectangle shown at the right. Round to the nearest tenth.

3 m

9 m

77. Geometry The diagonal of a rectangle is a line drawn from one vertex to the opposite vertex. Find the length of the diagonal in the rectangle shown at the right. Round to the nearest tenth.

2.5 cm

8.5 cm

78. Oceanography How far would a submarine periscope have to be above the water to locate a ship 3.2 mi away? The equation for the distance in miles that the lookout can see is $d = \sqrt{1.5h}$, where h is the height in feet above the surface of the water. Round to the nearest hundredth.

79. Oceanography How far would a submarine periscope have to be above the water to locate a ship 3.5 mi away? The equation for the distance in miles that the lookout can see is $d = \sqrt{1.5h}$, where h is in height in feet above the surface of the water. Round to the nearest hundredth.

80. Physics An object is dropped from a bridge. Find the distance the object has fallen when the speed reaches 80 ft/s. Use the equation $v = 8\sqrt{d}$, where v is the speed of the object and d is the distance.

81. Physics An object is dropped from a high building. Find the distance the object has fallen when the speed reaches 120 ft/s. Use the equation $v = 8\sqrt{d}$, where v is the speed of the object and d is the distance.

82. Automotive Technology Find the distance required for a car to reach a velocity of 60 m/s when the acceleration is 10 m/s². Use the equation $v = \sqrt{2as}$, where v is the velocity, a is the acceleration, and s is the distance.

83. Automotive Technology Find the distance required for a car to reach a velocity of 48 ft/s when the acceleration is 12 ft/s². Use the equation $v = \sqrt{2as}$, where v is the velocity, a is the acceleration, and s is the distance.

84. Clocks Find the length of a pendulum that makes one swing in 3 s. The equation for the time of one swing of a pendulum is $T = 2\pi\sqrt{\dfrac{L}{32}}$, where T is the time in seconds and L is the length in feet. Round to the nearest hundredth.

2.4 s

85. Satellites At what height above Earth's surface is a satellite in orbit if it is

traveling at a speed of 7500 m/s? Use the equation $v = \sqrt{\dfrac{4 \times 10^{14}}{h + 6.4 \times 10^6}}$,

where v is the speed of the satellite in meters per second and h is the height above Earth's surface in meters. Round to the nearest thousand.

7.4 Applying Concepts

Solve.

86. $x^{\frac{3}{4}} = 8$

87. $x^{\frac{2}{3}} = 9$

88. $x^{\frac{5}{4}} = 32$

Solve the formula for the given variable.

89. $v = \sqrt{64d}$; d

90. $a^2 + b^2 = c^2$; a

91. $V = \pi r^2 h$; r

92. $V = \dfrac{4}{3} \pi r^3$; r

Solve.

93. $\sqrt{3x - 2} = \sqrt{2x - 3} + \sqrt{x - 1}$

94. $\sqrt{2x + 3} + \sqrt{x + 2} = \sqrt{x + 5}$

95. Geometry A box has a base that measures 4 in. by 6 in. The height of the box is 3 in. Find the greatest distance between two corners. Round to the nearest hundredth.

96. Number Problem Find three odd integers a, b, and c such that $a^2 + b^2 = c^2$.

97. Geometry Find the length of the side labeled x.

98. If a and b are nonnegative real numbers, is the equation always true, sometimes true, or never true?

$$\sqrt{a^2 + b^2} = a + b$$

Write a paragraph that supports your answer.

99. If a and b are both positive real numbers and $a > b$, is a^b less than, equal to, or greater than b^a? Does your answer depend on a and b?

Complex Numbers

OBJECTIVE **1**   **Simplify complex numbers**

The radical expression $\sqrt{-4}$ is not a real number because there is no real number whose square is -4. However, the solution of an algebraic equation is sometimes the square root of a negative number.

For example, the equation $x^2 + 1 = 0$ does not have a real number solution, because there is no real number whose square is a negative number.

$$x^2 + 1 = 0$$
$$x^2 = -1$$

During the late 17th century, a new number, called an **imaginary number,** was defined so that a negative number would have a square root. The letter i was chosen to represent the number whose square is -1.

$$i^2 = -1$$

An imaginary number is defined in terms of i.

Definition of $\sqrt{-a}$

If a is a positive real number, then the principal square root of negative a is the imaginary number $i\sqrt{a}$.

$$\sqrt{-a} = i\sqrt{a}$$

Here are some examples:

$$\sqrt{-16} = i\sqrt{16} = 4i$$
$$\sqrt{-12} = i\sqrt{12} = 2i\sqrt{3}$$
$$\sqrt{-21} = i\sqrt{21}$$
$$\sqrt{-1} = i\sqrt{1} = i$$

It is customary to write i in front of a radical to avoid confusing $\sqrt{a}\,i$ with $\sqrt{ai}$.

The real numbers and imaginary numbers make up the complex numbers.

Definition of a Complex Number

A **complex number** is a number of the form $a + bi$, where a and b are real numbers and $i = \sqrt{-1}$. The number a is the **real part** of $a + bi$, and b is the **imaginary part.**

Take Note

The *imaginary part* of a complex number is a real number. As another example, the imaginary part of $6 - 8i$ is -8.

Examples of complex numbers are shown at the right.

Real part⌐   ⌐Imaginary part
        ↓   ↓
     $a + bi$
     $3 + 2i$
     $8 - 10i$

Complex numbers — $a + bi$
┌ Real numbers
│ $a + 0i$ A **real number** is a complex number in which $b = 0$.
│
└ Imaginary numbers
    $0 + bi$ An **imaginary number** is a complex number in which $a = 0$.

EXAMPLE 1   Simplify: $\sqrt{-80}$

Solution $\sqrt{-80} = i\sqrt{80} = i\sqrt{16 \cdot 5} = 4i\sqrt{5}$

PROBLEM 1   Simplify: $\sqrt{-45}$

Solution   See page S23.

Simplify: $\sqrt{20} - \sqrt{-50}$

Write the complex number in the form $a + bi$.

$$\sqrt{20} - \sqrt{-50} = \sqrt{20} - i\sqrt{50}$$

Use the Product Property of Radicals to simplify each radical.

$$= \sqrt{4 \cdot 5} - i\sqrt{25 \cdot 2}$$
$$= 2\sqrt{5} - 5i\sqrt{2}$$

EXAMPLE 2   Simplify: $\sqrt{25} + \sqrt{-40}$

Solution $\sqrt{25} + \sqrt{-40} = \sqrt{25} + i\sqrt{40} = \sqrt{25} + i\sqrt{4 \cdot 10}$
$$= 5 + 2i\sqrt{10}$$

PROBLEM 2   Simplify: $\sqrt{98} - \sqrt{-60}$

Solution   See page S23.

OBJECTIVE 2   **Add and subtract complex numbers**

Addition and Subtraction of Complex Numbers

To add two complex numbers, add the real parts and add the imaginary parts. To subtract two complex numbers, subtract the real parts and subtract the imaginary parts.

$$(a + bi) + (c + di) = (a + c) + (b + d)i$$
$$(a + bi) - (c + di) = (a - c) + (b - d)i$$

EXAMPLE 3   Add: $(3 + 2i) + (6 - 5i)$

Solution $(3 + 2i) + (6 - 5i)$
$$= (3 + 6) + (2 - 5)i$$ • **Add the real parts and add the imaginary parts.**
$$= 9 - 3i$$

PROBLEM 3 Subtract: $(-4 + 2i) - (6 - 8i)$

Solution See page S23.

Add: $\left(3 + \sqrt{-12}\right) + \left(7 - \sqrt{-27}\right)$

Write each complex number in the form $a + bi$.	$\left(3 + \sqrt{-12}\right) + \left(7 - \sqrt{-27}\right)$ $= \left(3 + i\sqrt{12}\right) + \left(7 - i\sqrt{27}\right)$
Use the Product Property of Radicals to simplify each radical.	$= \left(3 + i\sqrt{4 \cdot 3}\right) + \left(7 - i\sqrt{9 \cdot 3}\right)$ $= \left(3 + 2i\sqrt{3}\right) + \left(7 - 3i\sqrt{3}\right)$
Add the complex numbers.	$= 10 - i\sqrt{3}$

EXAMPLE 4 Subtract: $\left(9 - \sqrt{-8}\right) - \left(5 + \sqrt{-32}\right)$

Solution $\left(9 - \sqrt{-8}\right) - \left(5 + \sqrt{-32}\right)$
$$= \left(9 - i\sqrt{8}\right) - \left(5 + i\sqrt{32}\right)$$

- Write each complex number in the form $a + bi$.

$$= \left(9 - i\sqrt{4 \cdot 2}\right) - \left(5 + i\sqrt{16 \cdot 2}\right)$$
$$= \left(9 - 2i\sqrt{2}\right) - \left(5 + 4i\sqrt{2}\right)$$

- Simplify each radical.

$$= 4 - 6i\sqrt{2}$$

- Subtract.

PROBLEM 4 Subtract: $\left(16 - \sqrt{-45}\right) - \left(3 + \sqrt{-20}\right)$

Solution See page S23.

OBJECTIVE **3** **Multiply complex numbers**

When we multiply complex numbers, the term i^2 is frequently a part of the product. Recall that $i^2 = -1$.

Multiply: $2i \cdot 3i$

Multiply the imaginary numbers.	$2i \cdot 3i = 6i^2$
Replace i^2 by -1. Then simplify.	$= 6(-1) = -6$

When multiplying square roots of negative numbers, first rewrite the radical expressions using i.

Multiply: $\sqrt{-6} \cdot \sqrt{-24}$

Write each radical as the product of a real number and i.	$\sqrt{-6} \cdot \sqrt{-24} = i\sqrt{6} \cdot i\sqrt{24}$
Multiply the imaginary numbers.	$= i^2\sqrt{144}$
Replace i^2 by -1.	$= -\sqrt{144}$
Simplify.	$= -12$

Take Note

This example illustrates an important point. When working with a number that has a square root of a negative number, always rewrite the number with i before continuing.

Note from this example that it would have been incorrect to multiply the radicands of the two radical expressions. To illustrate,

$$\sqrt{-6} \cdot \sqrt{-24} = \sqrt{(-6)(-24)} = \sqrt{144} = 12, \ not \ -12$$

Multiply: $4i(3 - 2i)$

Use the Distributive Property to remove parentheses.

$4i(3 - 2i) = 12i - 8i^2$

Replace i^2 by -1.

$= 12i - 8(-1)$

Write the answer in the form $a + bi$.

$= 8 + 12i$

EXAMPLE 5 Multiply: $\sqrt{-8}(\sqrt{6} - \sqrt{-2})$

Solution $\sqrt{-8}(\sqrt{6} - \sqrt{-2})$
$= i\sqrt{8}(\sqrt{6} - i\sqrt{2})$

• Write each complex number in the form $a + bi$.

$= i\sqrt{48} - i^2\sqrt{16}$

• Use the Distributive Property.

$= i\sqrt{16 \cdot 3} - (-1)\sqrt{16}$

• Simplify each radical. Replace i^2 by -1.

$= 4i\sqrt{3} + 4$

$= 4 + 4i\sqrt{3}$

• Write the answer in the form $a + bi$.

PROBLEM 5 Multiply: $\sqrt{-3}(\sqrt{27} - \sqrt{-6})$

Solution See page S23.

The product of two complex numbers can be found by using the FOIL method. For example,

$$(2 + 4i)(3 - 5i) = 6 - 10i + 12i - 20i^2$$
$$= 6 + 2i - 20i^2$$
$$= 6 + 2i - 20(-1)$$
$$= 26 + 2i$$

The conjugate of $a + bi$ is $a - bi$.

The product of conjugates of the form $(a + bi)(a - bi)$ is $a^2 + b^2$.

$$(a + bi)(a - bi) = a^2 - b^2i^2 = a^2 - b^2(-1) = a^2 + b^2$$

For example, $(2 + 3i)(2 - 3i) = 2^2 + 3^2 = 4 + 9 = 13$.

Note that the product of a complex number and its conjugate is a real number.

EXAMPLE 6 Multiply.

A. $(3 - 4i)(2 + 5i)$ **B.** $\left(\dfrac{9}{10} + \dfrac{3}{10}i\right)\left(1 - \dfrac{1}{3}i\right)$

C. $(4 + 5i)(4 - 5i)$ **D.** $(6 + i)^2$

Solution **A.** $(3 - 4i)(2 + 5i)$
$= 6 + 15i - 8i - 20i^2$

• Use the FOIL method.

$= 6 + 7i - 20i^2$

• Combine like terms.

$= 6 + 7i - 20(-1)$

• Replace i^2 by -1.

$= 26 + 7i$

• Write the answer in the form $a + bi$.

B. $\left(\dfrac{9}{10} + \dfrac{3}{10}i\right)\left(1 - \dfrac{1}{3}i\right)$

$= \dfrac{9}{10} - \dfrac{3}{10}i + \dfrac{3}{10}i - \dfrac{1}{10}i^2$ • **Use the FOIL method.**

$= \dfrac{9}{10} - \dfrac{1}{10}i^2$ • **Combine like terms.**

$= \dfrac{9}{10} - \dfrac{1}{10}(-1)$ • **Replace i^2 by -1.**

$= \dfrac{9}{10} + \dfrac{1}{10} = 1$ • **Simplify.**

C. $(4 + 5i)(4 - 5i) = 4^2 + 5^2$ • **The product of conjugates of**
$= 16 + 25$ **the form $(a + bi)(a - bi)$ is**
$= 41$ **$a^2 + b^2$.**

D. $(6 + i)^2 = 36 + 12i + i^2$ • **$(6 + i)^2 = (6 + i)(6 + i)$**
$= 36 + 12i + (-1)$
$= 35 + 12i$

PROBLEM 6 Multiply.

    A. $(4 - 3i)(2 - i)$ **B.** $(3 - i)\left(\dfrac{3}{10} + \dfrac{1}{10}i\right)$

    C. $(3 + 6i)(3 - 6i)$ **D.** $(1 + 5i)^2$

    ■ **Solution** See page S23.

OBJECTIVE 4 **Divide complex numbers**

A fraction containing one or more complex numbers is in simplest form when no imaginary number remains in the denominator.

Simplify: $\dfrac{4 - 5i}{2i}$

Multiply the expression by 1 in the form $\dfrac{i}{i}$. $\dfrac{4 - 5i}{2i} = \dfrac{4 - 5i}{2i} \cdot \dfrac{i}{i}$

$= \dfrac{4i - 5i^2}{2i^2}$

Replace i^2 by -1. $= \dfrac{4i - 5(-1)}{2(-1)}$

Simplify. $= \dfrac{5 + 4i}{-2}$

Write the answer in the form $a + bi$. $= -\dfrac{5}{2} - 2i$

EXAMPLE 7 Simplify: $\dfrac{5 + 4i}{3i}$

Solution $\dfrac{5 + 4i}{3i} = \dfrac{5 + 4i}{3i} \cdot \dfrac{i}{i} = \dfrac{5i + 4i^2}{3i^2} = \dfrac{5i + 4(-1)}{3(-1)} = \dfrac{-4 + 5i}{-3}$

$= \dfrac{4}{3} - \dfrac{5}{3}i$

PROBLEM 7 Simplify: $\dfrac{2 - 3i}{4i}$

■ **Solution** See page S23.

Simplify: $\dfrac{3 + 2i}{1 + i}$

To simplify a fraction that has a complex number in the denominator, multiply the numerator and denominator by the conjugate of the complex number. The conjugate of $1 + i$ is $1 - i$.

$$\dfrac{3 + 2i}{1 + i} = \dfrac{(3 + 2i)}{(1 + i)} \cdot \dfrac{(1 - i)}{(1 - i)}$$

$$= \dfrac{3 - 3i + 2i - 2i^2}{1^2 + 1^2}$$

$$= \dfrac{3 - i - 2(-1)}{2}$$

$$= \dfrac{5 - i}{2} = \dfrac{5}{2} - \dfrac{1}{2}i$$

EXAMPLE 8 Simplify: $\dfrac{5 - 3i}{4 + 2i}$

Solution $\dfrac{5 - 3i}{4 + 2i} = \dfrac{(5 - 3i)}{(4 + 2i)} \cdot \dfrac{(4 - 2i)}{(4 - 2i)} = \dfrac{20 - 10i - 12i + 6i^2}{4^2 + 2^2}$

$$= \dfrac{20 - 22i + 6(-1)}{20}$$

$$= \dfrac{14 - 22i}{20}$$

$$= \dfrac{7 - 11i}{10}$$

$$= \dfrac{7}{10} - \dfrac{11}{10}i$$

PROBLEM 8 Simplify: $\dfrac{2 + 5i}{3 - 2i}$

■ **Solution** See page S23.

7.5 Concept Review

Determine whether the following statements are always true, sometimes true, or never true.

1. The product of two imaginary numbers is a real number.

2. The sum of two complex numbers is a real number.

3. A complex number is a number of the form $a + bi$, where a and b are real numbers and $\sqrt{-1} = i$.

4. The product of two complex numbers is a real number.

7.5 Exercises

1 Simplify complex numbers

1. ✎ What is an imaginary number? What is a complex number?

2. ✎ Are all real numbers also complex numbers? Are all complex numbers also real numbers?

3. $\sqrt{-1} = i$, so $i^2 = $ __?__ .

4. **a.** The real part of the complex number $7 - 9i$ is __?__ .
   b. The imaginary part of the complex number $7 - 9i$ is __?__ .

5. Simplify: $\sqrt{-54}$
   $$\sqrt{-54} = \underline{\ ?\ }\ \sqrt{54} = i\sqrt{(\underline{\ ?\ })(\underline{\ ?\ })} = \underline{\ ?\ }\ \sqrt{6}$$

6. Simplify: $\sqrt{-100x^{16}}$
   $$\sqrt{-100x^{16}} = \underline{\ ?\ }\ \sqrt{100x^{16}} = \underline{\ ?\ }\ i$$

7. ✎ Is $10 - 3i$ equivalent to $10 + \sqrt{-9}$ or to $10 - \sqrt{-9}$?

8. ✎ Which of the following are equivalent to $\sqrt{25} + \sqrt{-25}$?
   a. $5 - 5i$ **b.** $5 + 5i$ **c.** $\sqrt{25} + i\sqrt{25}$ **d.** $\sqrt{25} - i\sqrt{25}$

Simplify.

9. $\sqrt{-4}$

10. $\sqrt{-64}$

11. $\sqrt{-98}$

12. $\sqrt{-72}$

13. $\sqrt{-27}$

14. $\sqrt{-75}$

15. $\sqrt{16} + \sqrt{-4}$

16. $\sqrt{25} + \sqrt{-9}$

17. $\sqrt{12} - \sqrt{-18}$

18. $\sqrt{60} - \sqrt{-48}$

19. $\sqrt{160} - \sqrt{-147}$

20. $\sqrt{96} - \sqrt{-125}$

21. $\sqrt{-4a^2}$

22. $\sqrt{-16b^6}$

23. $\sqrt{-49x^{12}}$

24. $\sqrt{-32x^3y^2}$

25. $\sqrt{-144a^3b^5}$

26. $\sqrt{-18a^{10}b^9}$

27. $\sqrt{4a} + \sqrt{-12a^2}$

28. $\sqrt{25b} - \sqrt{-48b^2}$

29. $\sqrt{18b^5} - \sqrt{-27b^3}$

30. $\sqrt{a^5b^2} - \sqrt{-a^5b^2}$

31. $\sqrt{-50x^3y^3} + x\sqrt{25x^4y^3}$

32. $\sqrt{-121xy} + \sqrt{60x^2y^2}$

33. $\sqrt{-49a^5b^2} - ab\sqrt{-25a^3}$

34. $\sqrt{-16x^2y} - x\sqrt{-49y}$

35. $\sqrt{12a^3} + \sqrt{-27b^3}$

2 Add and subtract complex numbers

36. Add: $(7 - 9i) + (-3 + 4i)$

$(7 - 9i) + (-3 + 4i)$

$= (7 + \underline{\quad?\quad}) + (-9 + \underline{\quad?\quad})i$ • Add the real parts. Add the imaginary parts.

$= \underline{\quad?\quad}$ • Simplify.

37. Subtract: $12 - (6 - \sqrt{-64})$

$12 - (6 - \sqrt{-64}) = 12 - (6 - \underline{\quad?\quad}i)$ • Write the complex number in the form $a + bi$.

$= (12 - \underline{\quad?\quad}) - (\underline{\quad?\quad})$ • Subtract the real parts. Subtract the imaginary part.

$= \underline{\quad?\quad} + \underline{\quad?\quad}$ • Simplify.

Add or subtract.

38. $(2 + 4i) + (6 - 5i)$ **39.** $(6 - 9i) + (4 + 2i)$

40. $(-2 - 4i) - (6 - 8i)$ **41.** $(3 - 5i) + (8 - 2i)$

42. $(8 - \sqrt{-4}) - (2 + \sqrt{-16})$ **43.** $(5 - \sqrt{-25}) - (11 - \sqrt{-36})$

44. $(12 - \sqrt{-50}) + (7 - \sqrt{-8})$ **45.** $(5 - \sqrt{-12}) - (9 + \sqrt{-108})$

46. $(\sqrt{8} + \sqrt{-18}) + (\sqrt{32} - \sqrt{-72})$ **47.** $(\sqrt{40} - \sqrt{-98}) - (\sqrt{90} + \sqrt{-32})$

48. $(5 - 3i) + 2i$ **49.** $(6 - 8i) + 4i$

50. $(7 + 2i) + (-7 - 2i)$ **51.** $(8 - 3i) + (-8 + 3i)$

52. $(9 + 4i) + 6$ **53.** $(4 + 6i) + 7$

For Exercises 54 to 57, use the complex numbers $m = a + bi$ and $n = c - di$, where $a, b, c,$ and d are all positive real numbers.

54. True or false? If $a = c$ and $b = d$, then $m - n = 2bi$.

55. True or false? If $m - n$ is a real number, then $b + d = 0$.

56. Suppose $a > c$ and $b > d$. Is the imaginary part of $m + n$ positive or negative?

57. Suppose $a < c$ and $b < d$. Is the real part of $m - n$ positive or negative?

3 **Multiply complex numbers**

Multiply.

58. $(7i)(-9i)$

59. $(-6i)(-4i)$

60. $\sqrt{-2}\,\sqrt{-8}$

61. $\sqrt{-5}\,\sqrt{-45}$

62. $\sqrt{-3}\,\sqrt{-6}$

63. $\sqrt{-5}\,\sqrt{-10}$

64. $2i(6 + 2i)$

65. $-3i(4 - 5i)$

66. Multiply: $-7i(5 - \sqrt{-64})$

$$-7i(5 - \sqrt{-64}) = -7i(5 - \underline{\quad ?\quad}\,i)$$
• Rewrite $\sqrt{-64}$ in terms of i.
$$= (\underline{\quad ?\quad})(5) - (\underline{\quad ?\quad})(8i)$$
• Use the Distributive Property.
$$= \underline{\quad ?\quad} + \underline{\quad ?\quad}\,i^2$$
• Simplify.
$$= -35i + 56(\underline{\quad ?\quad})$$
• $i^2 = \underline{\quad ?\quad}$
$$= \underline{\quad ?\quad}$$
• Write the answer in $a + bi$ form.

67. Multiply: $(1 + 9i)(1 - 9i)$

$$(1 + 9i)(1 - 9i) = (\underline{\quad ?\quad})^2 + (\underline{\quad ?\quad})^2$$
• $(a + bi)(a - bi) = a^2 + b^2$
$$= \underline{\quad ?\quad} + \underline{\quad ?\quad} = \underline{\quad ?\quad}$$
• Simplify.

68. $\sqrt{-2}(\sqrt{8} + \sqrt{-2})$

69. $\sqrt{-3}(\sqrt{12} - \sqrt{-6})$

70. $(5 - 2i)(3 + i)$

71. $(2 - 4i)(2 - i)$

72. $(6 + 5i)(3 + 2i)$

73. $(4 - 7i)(2 + 3i)$

74. $(1 - i)\left(\dfrac{1}{2} + \dfrac{1}{2}i\right)$

75. $\left(\dfrac{4}{5} - \dfrac{2}{5}i\right)\left(1 + \dfrac{1}{2}i\right)$

76. $\left(\dfrac{6}{5} + \dfrac{3}{5}i\right)\left(\dfrac{2}{3} - \dfrac{1}{3}i\right)$

77. $(2 - i)\left(\dfrac{2}{5} + \dfrac{1}{5}i\right)$

78. $(4 - 3i)(4 + 3i)$

79. $(8 - 5i)(8 + 5i)$

80. $(3 - i)(3 + i)$

81. $(7 - i)(7 + i)$

82. $(6 + i)^2$

83. $(4 - 3i)^2$

84. $(5 - 2i)^2$

85. $(-1 + i)^2$

86. True or false? For all real numbers a and b, the product $(a + bi)(a - bi)$ is a positive real number.

87. True or false? The product of two imaginary numbers is always a negative real number.

4   **Divide complex numbers**

88. Simplify: $\dfrac{1 - 2i}{-5i}$

$\dfrac{1 - 2i}{-5i} = \dfrac{1 - 2i}{-5i} \cdot \dfrac{?}{?}$ • To remove i from the denominator, multiply the expression by 1 in the form $\dfrac{i}{i}$.

$= \dfrac{i - \dfrac{?}{}}{-5i^2}$ • Multiply the numerators. Multiply the denominators.

$= \dfrac{i - 2(\underline{})}{-5(\underline{})}$ • Replace i^2 by -1.

$= \dfrac{i + \dfrac{?}{}}{?}$ • Simplify.

$= \underline{} + \underline{}\,i$ • Write in the form $a + bi$.

89. To simplify $\dfrac{2i}{2 - 3i}$, multiply the numerator and denominator by $\underline{}$.

Simplify.

90. $\dfrac{3}{i}$

91. $\dfrac{4}{5i}$

92. $\dfrac{2 - 3i}{-4i}$

93. $\dfrac{16 + 5i}{-3i}$

94. $\dfrac{4}{5 + i}$

95. $\dfrac{6}{5 + 2i}$

96. $\dfrac{2}{2 - i}$

97. $\dfrac{5}{4 - i}$

98. $\dfrac{1 - 3i}{3 + i}$

99. $\dfrac{2 + 12i}{5 + i}$

100. $\dfrac{\sqrt{-10}}{\sqrt{8} - \sqrt{-2}}$

101. $\dfrac{\sqrt{-2}}{\sqrt{12} - \sqrt{-8}}$

102. $\dfrac{2 - 3i}{3 + i}$

103. $\dfrac{3 + 5i}{1 - i}$

104. True or false? The quotient of two imaginary numbers is an imaginary number.

105. True or false? The reciprocal of an imaginary number is an imaginary number.

7.5 Applying Concepts

Note the pattern when successive powers of i are simplified. Use the pattern for Exercises 106 to 114.

$i^1 = i$ $i^5 = i \cdot i^4 = i(1) = i$
$i^2 = -1$ $i^6 = i^2 \cdot i^4 = -1$
$i^3 = i^2 \cdot i = -i$ $i^7 = i^3 \cdot i^4 = -i$
$i^4 = i^2 \cdot i^2 = (-1)(-1) = 1$ $i^8 = i^4 \cdot i^4 = 1$

106.   When the exponent on i is a multiple of 4, the power equals _____.

107. i^6 **108.** i^9 **109.** i^{57} **110.** i^{65}

111. i^{-6} **112.** i^{-34} **113.** i^{-58} **114.** i^{-180}

115. a. Is $3i$ a solution of $2x^2 + 18 = 0$?   **116. a.** Is $1 + 3i$ a solution of $x^2 - 2x - 10 = 0$?
   b. Is $-3i$ a solution of $2x^2 + 18 = 0$?   **b.** Is $1 - 3i$ a solution of $x^2 - 2x - 10 = 0$?

117. Solve the following equations. Describe the solution by using the following terms: integer, rational number, irrational number, real number, and imaginary number. Note that more than one term may be used to describe the answer.

a. $x^2 + 3 = 7$ **b.** $x^2 + 1 = 0$

c. $\dfrac{5}{8}x = \dfrac{2}{3}$ **d.** $x^2 + 1 = 9$

e. $x^{\frac{3}{4}} = 8$ **f.** $\sqrt[3]{x} = -27$

Focus on Problem Solving

Another Look at Polya's Four-Step Process   Polya's four general steps to follow when attempting to solve a problem are to understand the problem, devise a plan, carry out the plan, and review the solution. (See the Focus on Problem Solving in the chapter titled Review of Real Numbers.) In the process of devising a plan (Step 2), it may be appropriate to write a mathematical expression or an equation. We will illustrate this with the following problem.

Number the letters of the alphabet in sequence from 1 to 26. (See the list on the next page.) Find a word for which the product of the numerical values of the letters of the word equals 1,000,000. We will agree that a "word" is any sequence of letters that contains at least one vowel but is not necessarily in the dictionary.

Understand the Problem   Consider REZB. The product of the letters is $18 \cdot 5 \cdot 26 \cdot 2 = 4680$. This "word" is a sequence of letters with at least one vowel. However, the product of the numerical values of the letters is not 1,000,000. Thus this word does not solve our problem.

Devise a Plan   Actually, we should have known that the product of the letters in REZB could not equal 1,000,000. The letter R has a factor of 9, and the letter Z has a factor of 13. Neither of these two numbers is a factor of 1,000,000. Consequently, R and Z cannot be letters in the word we are trying to find. This observation leads to an important observation: each of the letters that make up our word must be factors of 1,000,000. To find these letters, consider the prime factorization of 1,000,000.

A = 1	N = 14
B = 2	O = 15
C = 3	P = 16
D = 4	Q = 17
E = 5	R = 18
F = 6	S = 19
G = 7	T = 20
H = 8	U = 21
I = 9	V = 22
J = 10	W = 23
K = 11	X = 24
L = 12	Y = 25
M = 13	Z = 26

$$1{,}000{,}000 = 2^6 \cdot 5^6$$

Looking at the prime factorization, we note that only letters that contain only 2 or 5 as factors are possible candidates. These letters are B, D, E, H, J, P, T, and Y. One additional point: Because 1 times any number is the number, A can be part of any word we construct.

Our task is now to construct a word from these letters such that the product is 1,000,000. From the prime factorization above, we must have 2 as a factor 6 times and 5 as a factor 6 times.

Carry Out the Plan   We must construct a word with the characteristics described in our plan. Here is a possibility:

THEBEYE

Review the Solution   You should multiply the values of all of the letters and verify that the product is 1,000,000. To ensure that you have an understanding of the problem, try to find other "words" that satisfy the condition of the problem.

Projects & Group Activities

Solving Radical Equations with a Graphing Calculator   The radical equation $\sqrt{x-2} - 6 = 0$ was solved algebraically at the beginning of Section 7.4. To solve $\sqrt{x-2} - 6 = 0$ with a graphing calculator, use the left side of the equation and write an equation in two variables.

$$y = \sqrt{x-2} - 6$$

The graph of $y = \sqrt{x-2} - 6$ is shown on the following page. The solution set of the equation $y = \sqrt{x-2} - 6$ is the set of ordered pairs (x, y) whose coordinates make the equation a true statement. The x-coordinate where $y = 0$ is the solution of the equation $\sqrt{x-2} - 6 = 0$. The solution is the x-intercept of the curve given by the equation $y = \sqrt{x-2} - 6$. The solution is 38.

The solution of the radical equation $\sqrt[3]{x} - 2 = -0.8$ is 1.488. A graphing calculator can be used to find any rational or irrational solution to a predetermined degree of accuracy. The graph of $y = \sqrt[3]{x} - 2 + 0.8$ is shown below. The graph intersects the x-axis at $x = 1.488$.

To graph the equation $y = \sqrt[3]{x} - 2 + 0.8$ on a TI-83/83 Plus or TI-84 Plus, press

| Y= | | MATH | 4 | X, T, θ, n | − | 2 |) | + | .8 | ZOOM | 6 |

Press 2nd CALC 2 to find the x-intercept of the equation.

You were to solve Exercises 5 to 61 in Section 7.4 by algebraic means. Try some of those exercises again, this time using a graphing calculator.

Use a graphing calculator to find the solution of the following equations. Round to the nearest thousandth.

1. $\sqrt{x + 0.3} = 1.3$

2. $\sqrt[3]{x + 1.2} = -1.1$

3. $\sqrt[4]{3x - 1.5} = 1.4$

Chapter 7 Summary

Key Words

The **nth root of a** is $a^{\frac{1}{n}}$. The expression $\sqrt[n]{a}$ is another symbol for the nth root of a. In the expression $\sqrt[n]{a}$, the symbol $\sqrt{}$ is called a **radical**, n is the **index** of the radical, and a is the **radicand**. [7.1.2, p. 440]

Examples

$125^{\frac{1}{3}} = \sqrt[3]{125} = 5$

The index is 3 and the radicand is 125.

If $a^{\frac{1}{n}}$ is a real number, then $a^{\frac{m}{n}} = \sqrt[n]{a^m} = (\sqrt[n]{a})^m$. [7.1.2, p. 440]

$8^{\frac{2}{3}} = (\sqrt[3]{8})^2 = 2^2 = 4$

The symbol $\sqrt{}$ is used to indicate the positive square root, or **principal square root**, of a number. [7.1.3, p. 442]

$\sqrt{16} = 4$
$-\sqrt{16} = -4$

The expressions $a + b$ and $a - b$ are called **conjugates** of each other. The product of conjugates of the form $(a + b)(a - b)$ is $a^2 - b^2$. [7.2.3, p. 451]

$(x - 3)(x + 3) = x^2 - 3^2 = x^2 - 9$

The procedure used to remove a radical from the denominator of a radical expression is called **rationalizing the denominator**. [7.2.4, p. 452]

$$\frac{2}{1 - \sqrt{3}} = \frac{2}{1 - \sqrt{3}} \cdot \frac{1 + \sqrt{3}}{1 + \sqrt{3}}$$
$$= \frac{2(1 + \sqrt{3})}{(1 - \sqrt{3})(1 + \sqrt{3})}$$
$$= \frac{2 + 2\sqrt{3}}{1 - 3} = -1 - \sqrt{3}$$

A **radical equation** is an equation that contains a variable expression in a radicand. [7.4.1, p. 467]

$\sqrt{x - 2} - 3 = 6$ is a radical equation.

A **complex number** is a number of the form $a + bi$, where a and b are real numbers and $i = \sqrt{-1}$. For the complex number $a + bi$, a is the **real part** of the complex number, and b is the **imaginary part** of the complex number. [7.5.1, p. 476]

$3 + 2i$ is a complex number.

Essential Rules and Procedures

Definition of $a^{\frac{m}{n}}$
If m and n are positive integers and $a^{\frac{1}{n}}$ is a real number, then $a^{\frac{m}{n}} = \left(a^{\frac{1}{n}}\right)^m$. [7.1.1, p. 439]

$8^{\frac{2}{3}} = \left(8^{\frac{1}{3}}\right)^2 = 2^2 = 4$

Definition of the nth root of a
If a is a real number, then $a^{\frac{1}{n}} = \sqrt[n]{a}$. [7.1.2, p. 440]

$x^{\frac{1}{3}} = \sqrt[3]{x}$

Definition of the nth root of a^m
If $a^{\frac{1}{n}}$ is a real number, then $a^{\frac{m}{n}} = \sqrt[n]{a^m}$. [7.1.2, p. 440]

$b^{\frac{3}{4}} = \sqrt[4]{b^3}$

Product Property of Radicals
If $\sqrt[n]{a}$ and $\sqrt[n]{b}$ are positive real numbers, then $\sqrt[n]{ab} = \sqrt[n]{a}\,\sqrt[n]{b}$. [7.2.1, p. 449]

$\sqrt{9 \cdot 7} = \sqrt{9}\sqrt{7} = 3\sqrt{7}$

Quotient Property of Radicals
If $\sqrt[n]{a}$ and $\sqrt[n]{b}$ are positive real numbers, and $b \neq 0$, then $\sqrt[n]{\dfrac{a}{b}} = \dfrac{\sqrt[n]{a}}{\sqrt[n]{b}}$. [7.2.4, p. 452]

$\sqrt[3]{\dfrac{5}{27}} = \dfrac{\sqrt[3]{5}}{\sqrt[3]{27}} = \dfrac{\sqrt[3]{5}}{3}$

Property of Raising Both Sides of an Equation to a Power
If a and b are real numbers and $a = b$, then $a^n = b^n$.
[7.4.1, p. 467]

If $x = 4$, then $x^2 = 4^2$.

Pythagorean Theorem
$c^2 = a^2 + b^2$ [7.4.2, p. 470]

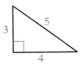

$3^2 + 4^2 = 5^2$

Principal Square Root of a Negative Number
If a is a positive real number, then $\sqrt{-a} = i\sqrt{a}$. [7.5.1, p. 476]

$\sqrt{-8} = i\sqrt{8} = 2i\sqrt{2}$

Addition Property of Complex Numbers
If $a + bi$ and $c + di$ are complex numbers, then
$(a + bi) + (c + di) = (a + c) + (b + d)i$. [7.5.2, p. 477]

$(2 + 4i) + (3 + 6i) = (2 + 3) + (4 + 6)i$
$= 5 + 10i$

Subtraction Property of Complex Numbers
If $a + bi$ and $c + di$ are complex numbers, then
$(a + bi) - (c + di) = (a - c) + (b - d)i$. [7.5.2, p. 477]

$(4 + 3i) - (7 + 4i) = (4 - 7) + (3 - 4)i$
$= -3 - i$

Chapter 7 Review Exercises

1. Simplify: $81^{-\frac{1}{4}}$

2. Simplify: $\dfrac{x^{-\frac{3}{2}}}{x^{\frac{7}{2}}}$

3. Simplify: $(a^{16})^{-\frac{5}{8}}$

4. Simplify: $(16x^{-4}y^{12})(100x^6y^{-2})^{\frac{1}{2}}$

5. Rewrite $3x^{\frac{3}{4}}$ as a radical expression.

6. Rewrite $7y\sqrt[3]{x^2}$ as an exponential expression.

7. Simplify: $\sqrt[4]{81a^8b^{12}}$

8. Simplify: $-\sqrt{49x^6y^{16}}$

9. Simplify: $\sqrt[3]{-8a^6b^{12}}$

10. Simplify: $\sqrt{18a^3b^6}$

11. Simplify: $\sqrt[5]{-64a^8b^{12}}$

12. Simplify: $\sqrt[4]{x^6y^8z^{10}}$

13. Add: $\sqrt{54} + \sqrt{24}$

14. Subtract: $\sqrt{48x^5y} - x\sqrt{80x^3y}$

15. Subtract: $\sqrt{50a^4b^3} - ab\sqrt{18a^2b}$

16. Simplify: $4x\sqrt{12x^2y} + \sqrt{3x^4y} - x^2\sqrt{27y}$

17. Multiply: $\sqrt{32}\,\sqrt{50}$

18. Multiply: $\sqrt[3]{16x^4y}\,\sqrt[3]{4xy^5}$

19. Multiply: $\sqrt{3x}(3 + \sqrt{3x})$

20. Multiply: $(5 - \sqrt{6})^2$

21. Multiply: $(\sqrt{3} + 8)(\sqrt{3} - 2)$

22. Simplify: $\dfrac{\sqrt{125x^6}}{\sqrt{5x^3}}$

23. Simplify: $\dfrac{8}{\sqrt{3y}}$

24. Simplify: $\dfrac{x+2}{\sqrt{x}+\sqrt{2}}$

25. Simplify: $\dfrac{\sqrt{x}+\sqrt{y}}{\sqrt{x}-\sqrt{y}}$

26. Simplify: $\sqrt{-36}$

27. Simplify: $\sqrt{-50}$

28. Simplify: $\sqrt{49}-\sqrt{-16}$

29. Simplify: $\sqrt{200}+\sqrt{-12}$

30. Add: $(5+2i)+(4-3i)$

31. Subtract: $(-8+3i)-(4-7i)$

32. Add: $\left(9-\sqrt{-16}\right)+\left(5+\sqrt{-36}\right)$

33. Subtract: $\left(\sqrt{50}+\sqrt{-72}\right)-\left(\sqrt{162}-\sqrt{-8}\right)$

34. Add: $(3-9i)+7$

35. Multiply: $(8i)(2i)$

36. Multiply: $i(3-7i)$

37. Multiply: $\sqrt{-12}\,\sqrt{-6}$

38. Multiply: $(6-5i)(4+3i)$

39. Simplify: $\dfrac{-6}{i}$

40. Simplify: $\dfrac{5+2i}{3i}$

41. Simplify: $\dfrac{7}{2-i}$

42. Simplify: $\dfrac{\sqrt{16}}{\sqrt{4}-\sqrt{-4}}$

43. Simplify: $\dfrac{5+9i}{1-i}$

44. Solve: $\sqrt[3]{9x}=-6$

45. State the domain of $f(x)=\sqrt[4]{3x-2}$ in set-builder notation.

46. State the domain of $f(x)=\sqrt[3]{x-5}$ in set-builder notation.

47. Graph: $g(x)=3x^{\frac{1}{3}}$

48. Graph: $f(x)=\sqrt{x-3}$

49. Solve: $\sqrt[3]{3x-5}=2$

50. Solve: $\sqrt{4x+9}+10=11$

51. Geometry Find the width of a rectangle that has a diagonal of 13 in. and a length of 12 in.

52. Wind Power The velocity of the wind determines the amount of power generated by a windmill. A typical equation for this relationship is $v=4.05\sqrt[3]{P}$, where v is the velocity in miles per hour and P is the power in watts. Find the amount of power generated by a wind of 20 mph. Round to the nearest whole number.

53. Physics Find the distance required for a car to reach a velocity of 88 ft/s when the acceleration is 16 ft/s². Use the equation $v=\sqrt{2as}$, where v is the velocity, a is the acceleration, and s is the distance.

54. Home Maintenance A 12-ft ladder is leaning against a building. How far from the building is the bottom of the ladder when the top of the ladder touches the building 10 ft above the ground? Round to the nearest hundredth.

Chapter 7 Test

1. Simplify: $\dfrac{r^{\frac{2}{3}}r^{-1}}{r^{-\frac{1}{2}}}$

2. Simplify: $\dfrac{\left(2x^{\frac{1}{3}}y^{-\frac{2}{3}}\right)^6}{(x^{-4}y^8)^{\frac{1}{4}}}$

3. Simplify: $\left(\dfrac{4a^4}{b^2}\right)^{-\frac{3}{2}}$

4. Rewrite $3y^{\frac{2}{5}}$ as a radical expression.

5. Rewrite $\frac{1}{2}\sqrt[4]{x^3}$ as an exponential expression.

6. State the domain of $f(x) = \sqrt{4 - x}$ in set-builder notation.

7. State the domain of $f(x) = (2x - 3)^{\frac{1}{3}}$ in interval notation.

8. Simplify: $\sqrt[3]{27a^4b^3c^7}$

9. Add: $\sqrt{18a^3} + a\sqrt{50a}$

10. Subtract: $\sqrt[3]{54x^7y^3} - x\sqrt[3]{128x^4y^3} - x^2\sqrt[3]{2xy^3}$

11. Multiply: $\sqrt{3x}\left(\sqrt{x} - \sqrt{25x}\right)$

12. Multiply: $\left(2\sqrt{3} + 4\right)\left(3\sqrt{3} - 1\right)$

13. Multiply: $\left(\sqrt{a} - 3\sqrt{b}\right)\left(2\sqrt{a} + 5\sqrt{b}\right)$

14. Multiply: $\left(2\sqrt{x} + \sqrt{y}\right)^2$

15. Simplify: $\dfrac{\sqrt{32x^5y}}{\sqrt{2xy^3}}$

16. Simplify: $\dfrac{4 - 2\sqrt{5}}{2 - \sqrt{5}}$

17. Simplify: $\dfrac{\sqrt{x}}{\sqrt{x} - \sqrt{y}}$

18. Multiply: $\left(\sqrt{-8}\right)\left(\sqrt{-2}\right)$

19. Subtract: $(5 - 2i) - (8 - 4i)$

20. Multiply: $(2 + 5i)(4 - 2i)$

21. Simplify: $\dfrac{2 + 3i}{1 - 2i}$

22. Add: $(2 + i) + (2 - i)$

23. Solve: $\sqrt{x + 12} - \sqrt{x} = 2$

24. Solve: $\sqrt[3]{2x - 2} + 4 = 2$

25. Guy Wires A guy wire is attached to a point 30 ft above the ground on a lamppost. The wire is anchored to the ground at a point 6 ft from the base of the post. Find the length of the guy wire. Round to the nearest tenth.

30 ft

6 ft

Cumulative Review Exercises

1. Identify the property that justifies the statement. $(a + 2)b = ab + 2b$

2. Simplify: $2x - 3[x - 2(x - 4) + 2x]$

3. Find $A \cap B$ given $A = \{2, 4, 6\}$ and $B = \{1, 3, 5\}$.

4. Solve: $\sqrt[3]{2x - 5} + 3 = 6$

5. Solve: $5 - \dfrac{2}{3}x = 4$

6. Solve: $2[4 - 2(3 - 2x)] = 4(1 - x)$

7. Solve: $3x - 4 \le 8x + 1$
Write the solution set in set-builder notation.

8. Solve: $5 < 2x - 3 < 7$
Write the solution set in set-builder notation.

9. Solve: $|7 - 3x| > 1$

10. Factor: $64a^2 - b^2$

11. Factor: $x^5 + 2x^3 - 3x$

12. Solve: $3x^2 + 13x - 10 = 0$

13. Graph: $g(x) = \sqrt{1 - x}$

14. Is the line $x - 2y = 4$ perpendicular to the line $2x + y = 4$?

15. Simplify: $(3^{-1}x^3y^{-5})(3^{-1}y^{-2})^{-2}$

16. Simplify: $\left(\dfrac{x^{-\frac{1}{2}}y^{\frac{3}{4}}}{y^{-\frac{5}{4}}} \right)^4$

17. Subtract: $\sqrt{20x^3} - x\sqrt{45x}$

18. Multiply: $(\sqrt{5} - 3)(\sqrt{5} - 2)$

19. Simplify: $\dfrac{\sqrt[3]{4x^5y^4}}{\sqrt[3]{8x^2y^5}}$

20. Simplify: $\dfrac{3i}{2 - i}$

21. Graph: $\{x \mid x > -1\} \cap \{x \mid x \le 3\}$

22. State the domain of $g(x) = \sqrt[5]{2x + 5}$ in set-builder notation.

23. Given $f(x) = 3x^2 - 2x + 1$, evaluate $f(-3)$.

24. Find an equation of the line that passes through the points $(2, 3)$ and $(-1, 2)$.

25. Evaluate the determinant: $\begin{vmatrix} 1 & 2 & -3 \\ 0 & -1 & 2 \\ 3 & 1 & -2 \end{vmatrix}$

26. Solve by using Cramer's Rule: $\begin{aligned} 2x - y &= 4 \\ -2x + 3y &= 5 \end{aligned}$

27. Find the slope and y-intercept of the equation $3x - 2y = -6$ and then graph the line.

28. Graph the solution set of $3x + 2y \le 4$.

29. Stamps A collection of thirty stamps consists of 13¢ stamps and 18¢ stamps. The total value of the stamps is $4.85. Find the number of 18¢ stamps.

30. Investments An investment of $2500 is made at an annual simple interest rate of 7.2%. How much additional money must be invested at an annual simple interest rate of 8.4% so that the total interest earned is $516?

31. Geometry The width of a rectangle is 6 ft less than the length. The area of the rectangle is 72 ft². Find the length and width of the rectangle.

32. Uniform Motion A sales executive traveled 25 mi by car and then an additional 625 mi by plane. The rate by plane was five times the rate by car. The total time of the trip was 3 h. Find the rate of the plane.

33. Astronomy How long does it take light to travel to Earth from the moon when the moon is 232,500 mi from Earth? Light travels 1.86×10^5 mi/s.

34. Periscopes How far would a submarine periscope have to be above the water to locate a ship 7 mi away? The equation for the distance in miles that the lookout can see is $d = \sqrt{1.5h}$, where h is the height in feet above the surface of the water. Round to the nearest tenth.

35. Investments The graph shows the amount invested and the annual interest income from an investment. Find the slope of the line between the two points shown on the graph. Then write a sentence that states the meaning of the slope.

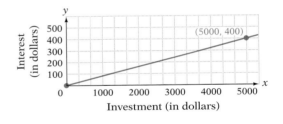

CHAPTER

8 Quadratic Equations and Inequalities

DVD   **SSM**

Online Study Center

Need help? For online student resources, such as section quizzes, visit the Online Study Center at college.hmco.com/info/aufmanndevmathhb.

The H. J. Heinz Company may be known for its ketchup, but it also produces a number of different brands of condiments, sauces, meals, and snacks. Offering a number of different items increases the chance that people will buy at least one Heinz product, thereby increasing the company's profit. Profit is the difference between a company's revenue (the total amount of money the company earns by selling its products or services) and its costs (the total amount of money the company spends in doing business). Quadratic functions are used in **Exercises 29 and 30 on page 562** to determine the maximum profit or revenue a company can earn.

Prep Test

1. Simplify: $\sqrt{18}$

2. Simplify: $\sqrt{-9}$

3. Simplify: $\dfrac{3x - 2}{x - 1} - 1$

4. Evaluate $b^2 - 4ac$ when $a = 2$, $b = -4$, and $c = 1$.

5. Is $4x^2 + 28x + 49$ a perfect-square trinomial?

6. Factor: $4x^2 - 4x + 1$

7. Factor: $9x^2 - 4$

8. Graph $\{x \mid x < -1\} \cap \{x \mid x < 4\}$

9. Solve: $x(x - 1) = x + 15$

10. Solve: $\dfrac{4}{x - 3} = \dfrac{16}{x}$

8.1 Solving Quadratic Equations by Factoring or by Taking Square Roots

OBJECTIVE 1 Solve quadratic equations by factoring

A **quadratic equation** is an equation of the form $ax^2 + bx + c = 0$, where a and b are coefficients, c is a constant, and $a \neq 0$.

$$3x^2 - x + 2 = 0, \quad a = 3, \quad b = -1, \quad c = 2$$
$$-x^2 + 4 = 0, \quad a = -1, \quad b = 0, \quad c = 4$$
$$6x^2 - 5x = 0, \quad a = 6, \quad b = -5, \quad c = 0$$

A quadratic equation is in **standard form** when the polynomial is in descending order and equal to zero.

Because the degree of the polynomial $ax^2 + bx + c$ is 2, a quadratic equation is also called a **second-degree equation.**

In the chapter entitled "Polynomials and Exponents," the Principle of Zero Products was used to solve some quadratic equations. That procedure is reviewed here.

Principle of Zero Products

If the product of two factors is zero, then at least one of the factors must be zero.

If $ab = 0$, then $a = 0$ or $b = 0$.

The Principle of Zero Products states that if the product of two factors is zero, then at least one of the factors must be zero.

Take Note

Recall that the steps involved in solving a quadratic equation by factoring are

1. Write the equation in standard form.

2. Factor.

3. Use the Principle of Zero Products to set each factor equal to 0.

4. Solve each equation.

5. Check the solutions.

Solve by factoring: $x^2 - 6x = -9$

Write the equation in standard form.	$x^2 - 6x = -9$
	$x^2 - 6x + 9 = 0$
Factor.	$(x - 3)(x - 3) = 0$
Use the Principle of Zero Products.	$x - 3 = 0 \qquad x - 3 = 0$
Solve each equation.	$x = 3 \qquad\qquad x = 3$
	3 checks as a solution.
Write the solutions.	The solution is 3.

When a quadratic equation has two solutions that are the same number, the solution is called a **double root** of the equation. The solution 3 is a double root of the equation $x^2 - 6x = -9$.

EXAMPLE 1   Solve for x by factoring: $x^2 - 4ax - 5a^2 = 0$

Solution $x^2 - 4ax - 5a^2 = 0$ • This is a literal equation. Solve for x in terms of a.

$(x + a)(x - 5a) = 0$ • Factor.

$x + a = 0 \qquad x - 5a = 0$

$\qquad x = -a \qquad\qquad x = 5a$

The solutions are $-a$ and $5a$.

PROBLEM 1   Solve for x by factoring: $x^2 - 3ax - 4a^2 = 0$

Solution   See page S23.

OBJECTIVE 2   Write a quadratic equation given its solutions

As shown below, the solutions of the equation $(x - r_1)(x - r_2) = 0$ are r_1 and r_2.

$(x - r_1)(x - r_2) = 0$

$x - r_1 = 0 \qquad x - r_2 = 0$

$\qquad x = r_1 \qquad\qquad x = r_2$

Check:

$(x - r_1)(x - r_2) = 0$		$(x - r_1)(x - r_2) = 0$	
$(r_1 - r_1)(r_1 - r_2)$	0	$(r_2 - r_1)(r_2 - r_2)$	0
$0 \cdot (r_1 - r_2)$		$(r_2 - r_1) \cdot 0$	
	$0 = 0$		$0 = 0$

Using the equation $(x - r_1)(x - r_2) = 0$ and the fact that r_1 and r_2 are solutions of this equation, it is possible to write a quadratic equation given its solutions.

Write a quadratic equation that has solutions 4 and -5.

	$(x - r_1)(x - r_2) = 0$
Replace r_1 by 4 and r_2 by -5.	$(x - 4)[x - (-5)] = 0$
Simplify.	$(x - 4)(x + 5) = 0$
Multiply.	$x^2 + x - 20 = 0$

EXAMPLE 2 Write a quadratic equation that has integer coefficients and has solutions $\frac{2}{3}$ and $\frac{1}{2}$.

Solution

$$(x - r_1)(x - r_2) = 0$$

$$\left(x - \frac{2}{3}\right)\left(x - \frac{1}{2}\right) = 0 \qquad \bullet \text{ Replace } r_1 \text{ by } \frac{2}{3} \text{ and } r_2 \text{ by } \frac{1}{2}.$$

$$x^2 - \frac{7}{6}x + \frac{1}{3} = 0 \qquad \bullet \text{ Multiply.}$$

$$6\left(x^2 - \frac{7}{6}x + \frac{1}{3}\right) = 6 \cdot 0 \qquad \bullet \text{ Multiply each side of the equation by the LCM of the denominators.}$$

$$6x^2 - 7x + 2 = 0$$

PROBLEM 2 Write a quadratic equation that has integer coefficients and has solutions $-\frac{2}{3}$ and $\frac{1}{6}$.

Solution See page S24.

OBJECTIVE 3 **Solve quadratic equations by taking square roots**

The solution of the quadratic equation $x^2 = 16$ is shown at the right.

$$x^2 = 16$$
$$x^2 - 16 = 0$$
$$(x + 4)(x - 4) = 0$$

$$x + 4 = 0 \qquad x - 4 = 0$$
$$x = -4 \qquad x = 4$$

Note that the solution is the positive or the negative square root of 16, 4 or -4.

The solution can also be found by taking the square root of each side of the equation. Recall that if x is a real number, then $\sqrt{x^2} = |x|$. This fact is used to solve some quadratic equations by taking square roots.

Solve by taking square roots: $x^2 = 16$

Take the square root of each side of the equation.

$$x^2 = 16$$
$$\sqrt{x^2} = \sqrt{16}$$

$\sqrt{x^2} = |x|$. $\sqrt{16} = 4$.

$$|x| = 4$$

Solve the absolute value equation. The notation $x = \pm 4$ means $x = 4$ or $x = -4$.

$$x = \pm 4$$

The solutions are -4 and 4.

Solving a quadratic equation by taking the square root of each side of the equation can lead to solutions that contain radicals.

Solve by taking square roots: $3x^2 = 54$

Solve for x^2.

$$3x^2 = 54$$
$$x^2 = 18$$

Take the square root of each side of the equation.

$$\sqrt{x^2} = \sqrt{18}$$

Simplify.

$$|x| = 3\sqrt{2}$$
$$x = \pm 3\sqrt{2}$$

The solutions are $-3\sqrt{2}$ and $3\sqrt{2}$.

This method can also be used when the solutions are complex numbers.

Solve by taking square roots: $2x^2 + 18 = 0$

Solve for x^2.

$$2x^2 + 18 = 0$$
$$2x^2 = -18$$
$$x^2 = -9$$

Take the square root of each side of the equation.

$$\sqrt{x^2} = \sqrt{-9}$$

Simplify.

$$|x| = 3i$$
$$x = \pm 3i$$

The solutions are $-3i$ and $3i$.

An equation containing the square of a binomial can be solved by taking square roots.

EXAMPLE 3   Solve by taking square roots: $3(x - 2)^2 + 12 = 0$

Solution

$$3(x - 2)^2 + 12 = 0$$
$$3(x - 2)^2 = -12$$ • Solve for $(x - 2)^2$.
$$(x - 2)^2 = -4$$
$$\sqrt{(x - 2)^2} = \sqrt{-4}$$ • Take the square root of each side of the equation. Then simplify.
$$|x - 2| = 2i$$
$$x - 2 = \pm 2i$$

$x - 2 = 2i$ $\qquad x - 2 = -2i$ • Solve for x.
$x = 2 + 2i$ $\qquad x = 2 - 2i$

The solutions are $2 + 2i$ and $2 - 2i$.

PROBLEM 3   Solve by taking square roots: $2(x + 1)^2 + 24 = 0$

Solution   See page S24.

8.1 Concept Review

Determine whether the following statements are always true, sometimes true, or never true.

1. A quadratic equation has two real roots.

2. A quadratic equation is also called a second-degree equation.

3. If $(x - 3)(x + 5) = 8$, then $x - 3 = 8$ or $x + 5 = 8$.

4. A quadratic equation has one root.

8.1 Exercises

1 Solve quadratic equations by factoring

1. Explain why the restriction that $a \neq 0$ is given in the definition of a quadratic equation.

2. What does the Principle of Zero Products state? How is it used to solve a quadratic equation?

Write the quadratic equation in standard form and with the coefficient of x^2 positive. Name the values of a, b, and c.

3. $2x^2 - 4x = 5$ **4.** $x^2 = 3x + 1$ **5.** $5x = 4x^2 - 6$ **6.** $3x^2 = 7$

7. Solve: $x^2 - 49 = 0$

$x^2 - 49 = 0$
$(\underline{\ ?\ })(\underline{\ ?\ }) = 0$

$x + 7 = \underline{\ ?\ }$ $x - 7 = \underline{\ ?\ }$

$x = \underline{\ ?\ }$ $x = \underline{\ ?\ }$

- The equation is in $\underline{\ ?\ }$ form.
- Factor the difference of two perfect squares.
- Use the Principle of $\underline{\ ?\ }$ to set each factor equal to 0.
- Solve each equation.

8. Solve for x: $x^2 + ax - 6a^2 = 0$

$x^2 + ax - 6a^2 = 0$

$(x - \underline{\ ?\ })(x + \underline{\ ?\ }) = 0$

$\underline{\ ?\ } = 0$ $\underline{\ ?\ } = 0$

$x = \underline{\ ?\ }$ $x = \underline{\ ?\ }$

- The equation is a literal equation. Treat a as a constant.
- Factor the trinomial.
- Use the Principle of Zero Products to set each factor equal to 0.
- Solve each equation for x in terms of a.

Solve by factoring.

9. $x^2 - 4x = 0$

10. $y^2 + 6y = 0$

11. $t^2 - 25 = 0$

12. $p^2 - 81 = 0$

13. $s^2 - s - 6 = 0$

14. $v^2 + 4v - 5 = 0$

15. $y^2 - 6y + 9 = 0$

16. $x^2 + 10x + 25 = 0$

17. $9z^2 - 18z = 0$

18. $4y^2 + 20y = 0$

19. $r^2 - 3r = 10$

20. $p^2 + 5p = 6$

21. $v^2 + 10 = 7v$

22. $t^2 - 16 = 15t$

23. $2x^2 - 9x - 18 = 0$

24. $3y^2 - 4y - 4 = 0$

25. $4z^2 - 9z + 2 = 0$

26. $2s^2 - 9s + 9 = 0$

27. $3w^2 + 11w = 4$

28. $2r^2 + r = 6$

29. $6x^2 = 23x + 18$

30. $6x^2 = 7x - 2$

31. $4 - 15u - 4u^2 = 0$

32. $3 - 2y - 8y^2 = 0$

33. $x + 18 = x(x - 6)$

34. $t + 24 = t(t + 6)$

35. $4s(s + 3) = s - 6$

36. $3v(v - 2) = 11v + 6$

37. $u^2 - 2u + 4 = (2u - 3)(u + 2)$

38. $(3v - 2)(2v + 1) = 3v^2 - 11v - 10$

39. $(3x - 4)(x + 4) = x^2 - 3x - 28$

Solve for x by factoring.

40. $x^2 + 14ax + 48a^2 = 0$

41. $x^2 - 9bx + 14b^2 = 0$

42. $x^2 + 9xy - 36y^2 = 0$

43. $x^2 - 6cx - 7c^2 = 0$

44. $x^2 - ax - 20a^2 = 0$

45. $2x^2 + 3bx + b^2 = 0$

46. $3x^2 - 4cx + c^2 = 0$

47. $3x^2 - 14ax + 8a^2 = 0$

48. $3x^2 - 11xy + 6y^2 = 0$

49. Given that $ax^2 + bx + c = 0$ is a quadratic equation that can be solved by factoring, state whether the equation has two positive solutions, two negative solutions, or one positive and one negative solution.
 a. $a > 0, b < 0, c < 0$ **b.** $a > 0, b > 0, c > 0$ **c.** $a > 0, b < 0, c > 0$

50. Which equation has a double root?

 a. $x^2 = a^2$ **b.** $x^2 + 2ax = a^2$
 c. $x^2 + 2ax = -a^2$ **d.** $x^2 - 2ax = a^2$

2 Write a quadratic equation given its solutions

51. If r is a solution of $ax^2 + bx + c = 0$, then _____?_____ is a factor of $ax^2 + bx + c$.

52. a. The factored form of a quadratic equation that has solutions -4 and 7 is (___?___)(___?___) = 0.
   b. The standard form of the equation in part a is _____?_____ = 0.

Write a quadratic equation that has integer coefficients and has as solutions the given pair of numbers.

53. 2 and 5

54. 3 and 1

55. -2 and -4

56. -1 and -3

57. 6 and -1

58. -2 and 5

59. 3 and -3

60. 5 and -5

61. 4 and 4

62. 2 and 2

63. 0 and 5

64. 0 and -2

65. 0 and 3

66. 0 and -1

67. 3 and $\dfrac{1}{2}$

68. 2 and $\dfrac{2}{3}$

69. $-\dfrac{3}{4}$ and 2

70. $-\dfrac{1}{2}$ and 5

71. $-\dfrac{5}{3}$ and -2

72. $-\dfrac{3}{2}$ and -1

73. $-\dfrac{2}{3}$ and $\dfrac{2}{3}$

74. $-\dfrac{1}{2}$ and $\dfrac{1}{2}$

75. $\dfrac{1}{2}$ and $\dfrac{1}{3}$

76. $\dfrac{3}{4}$ and $\dfrac{2}{3}$

77. $\dfrac{6}{5}$ and $-\dfrac{1}{2}$

78. $\dfrac{3}{4}$ and $-\dfrac{3}{2}$

79. $-\dfrac{1}{4}$ and $-\dfrac{1}{2}$

80. $-\dfrac{5}{6}$ and $-\dfrac{2}{3}$

81. $\dfrac{3}{5}$ and $-\dfrac{1}{10}$

82. $\dfrac{7}{2}$ and $-\dfrac{1}{4}$

For Exercises 83 to 86, r_1 and r_2 are solutions of the equation $ax^2 + bx + c = 0$, where a is positive. In each case, state whether b is positive or negative, and whether c is positive or negative.

83. $r_1 < 0, r_2 < 0$

84. $r_1 > 0, r_2 < 0, r_1 > |r_2|$

85. $r_1 > 0, r_2 < 0, r_1 < |r_2|$

86. $r_1 > 0, r_2 > 0$

3   Solve quadratic equations by taking square roots

87. The notation $x = \pm 6$ means $x = $ ___?___ or $x = $ ___?___ .

88. Solve by taking square roots: $4x^2 + 100 = 0$.
   $4x^2 + 100 = 0$

   $4x^2 = $ ___?___   • Subtract ___?___ from each side of the equation.

   $x^2 = $ ___?___   • Divide each side of the equation by ___?___ .

   $\sqrt{x^2} = \sqrt{-25}$ • Take the ___?___ of each side of the equation.

   $|x| = $ ___?___   • Simplify $\sqrt{-25}$.

   $x = \pm$ ___?___   • Solve for x.

Solve by taking square roots.

89. $y^2 = 49$ **90.** $x^2 = 64$ **91.** $z^2 = -4$ **92.** $v^2 = -16$

93. $s^2 - 4 = 0$ **94.** $r^2 - 36 = 0$ **95.** $4x^2 - 81 = 0$ **96.** $9x^2 - 16 = 0$

97. $y^2 + 49 = 0$ **98.** $z^2 + 16 = 0$ **99.** $v^2 - 48 = 0$ **100.** $s^2 - 32 = 0$

101. $r^2 - 75 = 0$ **102.** $u^2 - 54 = 0$ **103.** $z^2 + 18 = 0$

104. $t^2 + 27 = 0$ **105.** $(x - 1)^2 = 36$ **106.** $(x + 2)^2 = 25$

107. $3(y + 3)^2 = 27$ **108.** $4(s - 2)^2 = 36$ **109.** $5(z + 2)^2 = 125$

110. $(x - 2)^2 = -4$ **111.** $(x + 5)^2 = -25$ **112.** $(x - 8)^2 = -64$

113. $3(x - 4)^2 = -12$ **114.** $5(x + 2)^2 = -125$ **115.** $3(x - 9)^2 = -27$

116. $2(y - 3)^2 = 18$ **117.** $\left(v - \dfrac{1}{2}\right)^2 = \dfrac{1}{4}$ **118.** $\left(r + \dfrac{2}{3}\right)^2 = \dfrac{1}{9}$

119. $\left(x - \dfrac{2}{5}\right)^2 = \dfrac{9}{25}$ **120.** $\left(y + \dfrac{1}{3}\right)^2 = \dfrac{4}{9}$ **121.** $\left(a + \dfrac{3}{4}\right)^2 = \dfrac{9}{16}$

122. $4\left(x - \dfrac{1}{2}\right)^2 = 1$ **123.** $3\left(x - \dfrac{5}{3}\right)^2 = \dfrac{4}{3}$ **124.** $2\left(x + \dfrac{3}{5}\right)^2 = \dfrac{8}{25}$

125. $(x + 5)^2 - 6 = 0$ **126.** $(t - 1)^2 - 15 = 0$ **127.** $(s - 2)^2 - 24 = 0$

128. $(y + 3)^2 - 18 = 0$ **129.** $(z + 1)^2 + 12 = 0$ **130.** $(r - 2)^2 + 28 = 0$

131. $(v - 3)^2 + 45 = 0$ **132.** $(x + 5)^2 + 32 = 0$ **133.** $\left(u + \dfrac{2}{3}\right)^2 - 18 = 0$

134. $\left(z - \dfrac{1}{2}\right)^2 - 20 = 0$ **135.** $\left(x + \dfrac{1}{2}\right)^2 + 40 = 0$ **136.** $\left(r - \dfrac{3}{2}\right)^2 + 48 = 0$

For Exercises 137 to 140, a and b are positive real numbers. In each case, state how many real or complex number solutions the equation has.

137. $(x - a)^2 + b = 0$

138. $x^2 + a = 0$

139. $(x - a)^2 = 0$

140. $(x - a)^2 - b = 0$

8.1 Applying Concepts

Write a quadratic equation that has as solutions the given pair of numbers.

141. $\sqrt{2}$ and $-\sqrt{2}$

142. $\sqrt{5}$ and $-\sqrt{5}$

143. i and $-i$

144. $2i$ and $-2i$

145. $2\sqrt{2}$ and $-2\sqrt{2}$

146. $3\sqrt{2}$ and $-3\sqrt{2}$

147. $2\sqrt{3}$ and $-2\sqrt{3}$

148. $i\sqrt{2}$ and $-i\sqrt{2}$

149. $2i\sqrt{3}$ and $-2i\sqrt{3}$

Solve for x.

150. $2a^2x^2 = 32b^2$

151. $5y^2x^2 = 125z^2$

152. $(x + a)^2 - 4 = 0$

153. $2(x - y)^2 - 8 = 0$

154. $(2x - 1)^2 = (2x + 3)^2$

155. $(x - 4)^2 = (x + 2)^2$

Solve.

156. Show that the solutions of the equation $ax^2 + bx = 0$ are 0 and $-\dfrac{b}{a}$.

157. Show that the solutions of the equation $ax^2 + c = 0$, $a > 0$, $c > 0$, are $\dfrac{\sqrt{ca}}{a}i$ and $-\dfrac{\sqrt{ca}}{a}i$.

158. **Chemistry** A chemical reaction between carbon monoxide and water vapor is used to increase the ratio of hydrogen gas in certain gas mixtures. In the process, carbon dioxide is also formed. For a certain reaction, the concentration of carbon dioxide, x, in moles per liter, is given by $0.58 = \dfrac{x^2}{(0.02 - x)^2}$. Solve this equation for x. Round to the nearest ten-thousandth.

159. Show that if the complex number $z_1 + z_2i$ is a solution of the equation $ax^2 + bx + c = 0$, where a, b, and c are real numbers and $a \neq 0$, then $z_1 - z_2i$, the complex conjugate, is also a solution of the equation.

Solving Quadratic Equations by Completing the Square and by Using the Quadratic Formula

OBJECTIVE 1   ## Solve quadratic equations by completing the square

Recall that a perfect-square trinomial is the square of a binomial. Some examples of perfect-square trinomials follow.

Perfect-square trinomial		Square of a binomial
$x^2 + 8x + 16$	$=$	$(x + 4)^2$
$x^2 - 10x + 25$	$=$	$(x - 5)^2$
$x^2 + 2ax + a^2$	$=$	$(x + a)^2$

For each perfect-square trinomial, the square of $\frac{1}{2}$ the coefficient of x equals the constant term.

$$\left(\frac{1}{2} \text{ coefficient of } x\right)^2 = \text{Constant term}$$

$$x^2 + 8x + 16, \qquad \left(\frac{1}{2} \cdot 8\right)^2 = 16$$

$$x^2 - 10x + 25, \qquad \left[\frac{1}{2}(-10)\right]^2 = 25$$

$$x^2 + 2ax + a^2, \qquad \left(\frac{1}{2} \cdot 2a\right)^2 = a^2$$

To complete the square on $x^2 + bx$, add $\left(\frac{1}{2}b\right)^2$ to $x^2 + bx$.

■ Complete the square on $x^2 - 12x$. Write the resulting perfect-square trinomial as the square of a binomial.

Find the constant term.

$$\left[\frac{1}{2}(-12)\right]^2 = (-6)^2 = 36$$

Complete the square on $x^2 - 12x$ by adding the constant term.

$$x^2 - 12x + 36$$

Write the resulting perfect-square trinomial as the square of a binomial.

$$x^2 - 12x + 36 = (x - 6)^2$$

■ Complete the square on $z^2 + 3z$. Write the resulting perfect-square trinomial as the square of a binomial.

Find the constant term.

$$\left(\frac{1}{2} \cdot 3\right)^2 = \left(\frac{3}{2}\right)^2 = \frac{9}{4}$$

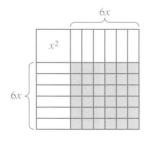

Complete the square on $z^2 + 3z$ by adding the constant term.

$$z^2 + 3z + \frac{9}{4}$$

Write the resulting perfect-square trinomial as the square of a binomial.

$$z^2 + 3z + \frac{9}{4} = \left(z + \frac{3}{2}\right)^2$$

Not all quadratic equations can be solved by factoring, but any quadratic equation can be solved by completing the square. Add to each side of the equation the term that completes the square. Rewrite the equation in the form $(x + a)^2 = b$. Then take the square root of each side of the equation.

Solve by completing the square: $x^2 - 4x - 14 = 0$

$$x^2 - 4x - 14 = 0$$

Add 14 to each side of the equation.

$$x^2 - 4x = 14$$

Add the constant term that completes the square on $x^2 - 4x$ to each side of the equation.

$$x^2 - 4x + 4 = 14 + 4$$

$$\left[\frac{1}{2}(-4)\right]^2 = 4$$

Factor the perfect-square trinomial.

$$(x - 2)^2 = 18$$

Take the square root of each side of the equation.

$$\sqrt{(x-2)^2} = \sqrt{18}$$

Simplify.

$$|x - 2| = 3\sqrt{2}$$

Solve for x.

$$x - 2 = \pm 3\sqrt{2}$$

$$x - 2 = 3\sqrt{2} \qquad x - 2 = -3\sqrt{2}$$
$$x = 2 + 3\sqrt{2} \qquad x = 2 - 3\sqrt{2}$$

Check:

$$x^2 - 4x - 14 = 0$$
$$\begin{array}{c|c}(2 + 3\sqrt{2})^2 - 4(2 + 3\sqrt{2}) - 14 & 0 \\ 4 + 12\sqrt{2} + 18 - 8 - 12\sqrt{2} - 14 & 0 \\ 0 = 0 \end{array}$$

$$x^2 - 4x - 14 = 0$$
$$\begin{array}{c|c}(2 - 3\sqrt{2})^2 - 4(2 - 3\sqrt{2}) - 14 & 0 \\ 4 - 12\sqrt{2} + 18 - 8 + 12\sqrt{2} - 14 & 0 \\ 0 = 0 \end{array}$$

Write the solutions.

The solutions are $2 + 3\sqrt{2}$ and $2 - 3\sqrt{2}$.

As shown on the previous page, the solutions of the equation $x^2 - 4x - 14 = 0$ are $2 + 3\sqrt{2}$ and $2 - 3\sqrt{2}$. These are the exact solutions. However, in some situations it may be preferable to have decimal approximations of the solutions to a quadratic equation. Approximate solutions can be found by using a calculator and then rounding to the desired degree of accuracy.

$$2 + 3\sqrt{2} \approx 6.243 \text{ and } 2 - 3\sqrt{2} \approx -2.243$$

To the nearest thousandth, the approximate solutions of the equation $x^2 - 4x - 14 = 0$ are 6.243 and −2.243.

When a, the coefficient of the x^2 term, is not 1, divide each side of the equation by a before completing the square.

Solve $2x^2 - x - 2 = 0$. Find the exact solutions and approximate the solutions to the nearest thousandth.

$$2x^2 - x - 2 = 0$$
$$2x^2 - x = 2$$

Divide each side of the equation by the coefficient of x^2.

$$\frac{2x^2 - x}{2} = \frac{2}{2}$$

The coefficient of the x^2 term is now 1.

$$x^2 - \frac{1}{2}x = 1$$

Add the term that completes the square on $x^2 - \frac{1}{2}x$ to each side of the equation. Factor the perfect-square trinomial.

$$x^2 - \frac{1}{2}x + \frac{1}{16} = 1 + \frac{1}{16}$$
$$\left(x - \frac{1}{4}\right)^2 = \frac{17}{16}$$

Take the square root of each side of the equation.

$$\sqrt{\left(x - \frac{1}{4}\right)^2} = \sqrt{\frac{17}{16}}$$

Simplify.

$$\left|x - \frac{1}{4}\right| = \frac{\sqrt{17}}{4}$$

$$x - \frac{1}{4} = \pm\frac{\sqrt{17}}{4}$$

Solve for x.

$$x - \frac{1}{4} = \frac{\sqrt{17}}{4} \qquad x - \frac{1}{4} = -\frac{\sqrt{17}}{4}$$
$$x = \frac{1}{4} + \frac{\sqrt{17}}{4} \qquad x = \frac{1}{4} - \frac{\sqrt{17}}{4}$$

Check the solutions.

$$\frac{1 + \sqrt{17}}{4} \text{ and } \frac{1 - \sqrt{17}}{4} \text{ check as solutions.}$$

$$\frac{1 + \sqrt{17}}{4} \approx 1.281 \qquad \frac{1 - \sqrt{17}}{4} \approx -0.781$$

Write the solutions.   The exact solutions are $\dfrac{1 + \sqrt{17}}{4}$ and $\dfrac{1 - \sqrt{17}}{4}$. To the nearest thousandth, the solutions are 1.281 and -0.781.

EXAMPLE 1   Solve by completing the square.

A. $4x^2 - 8x + 1 = 0$ **B.** $x^2 + 4x + 5 = 0$

Solution   **A.** $4x^2 - 8x + 1 = 0$

$$4x^2 - 8x = -1$$
• Subtract 1 from each side of the equation.

$$\frac{4x^2 - 8x}{4} = \frac{-1}{4}$$
• The coefficient of the x^2 term must be 1. Divide each side of the equation by 4.

$$x^2 - 2x = -\frac{1}{4}$$

$$x^2 - 2x + 1 = -\frac{1}{4} + 1$$
• Complete the square. $\left[\frac{1}{2}(-2)\right]^2 = 1$

$$(x - 1)^2 = \frac{3}{4}$$
• Factor the perfect-square trinomial.

$$\sqrt{(x - 1)^2} = \sqrt{\frac{3}{4}}$$
• Take the square root of each side of the equation.

$$|x - 1| = \frac{\sqrt{3}}{2}$$

$$x - 1 = \pm\frac{\sqrt{3}}{2}$$
• Simplify.

$$x - 1 = \frac{\sqrt{3}}{2} \qquad x - 1 = -\frac{\sqrt{3}}{2}$$
• Solve for x.

$$x = 1 + \frac{\sqrt{3}}{2} \qquad x = 1 - \frac{\sqrt{3}}{2}$$

$$x = \frac{2 + \sqrt{3}}{2} \qquad x = \frac{2 - \sqrt{3}}{2}$$

The solutions are $\dfrac{2 + \sqrt{3}}{2}$ and $\dfrac{2 - \sqrt{3}}{2}$.

B. $x^2 + 4x + 5 = 0$

$$x^2 + 4x = -5$$
• Subtract 5 from each side of the equation.

$$x^2 + 4x + 4 = -5 + 4$$
• Complete the square.

$$(x + 2)^2 = -1$$
• Factor the perfect-square trinomial.

$$\sqrt{(x + 2)^2} = \sqrt{-1}$$
• Take the square root of each side of the equation. Simplify.

$$|x + 2| = i$$

$$x + 2 = \pm i$$

$$x + 2 = i \qquad x + 2 = -i$$
• Solve for x.

$$x = -2 + i \qquad x = -2 - i$$

The solutions are $-2 + i$ and $-2 - i$.

| **PROBLEM 1**   Solve by completing the square.

  A. $4x^2 - 4x - 1 = 0$ **B.** $2x^2 + x - 5 = 0$

  Solution   See page S24.

OBJECTIVE **2**   ## Solve quadratic equations by using the quadratic formula

A general formula known as the **quadratic formula** can be derived by applying the method of completing the square to the standard form of a quadratic equation. This formula can be used to solve any quadratic equation.

The solution of the equation $ax^2 + bx + c = 0$ by completing the square is shown below.

$$ax^2 + bx + c = 0$$

Subtract the constant term from each side of the equation.

$$ax^2 + bx + c - c = 0 - c$$
$$ax^2 + bx = -c$$

Divide each side of the equation by a, the coefficient of x^2.

$$\frac{ax^2 + bx}{a} = \frac{-c}{a}$$
$$x^2 + \frac{b}{a}x = -\frac{c}{a}$$

Complete the square by adding $\left(\frac{1}{2}\cdot\frac{b}{a}\right)^2$ to each side of the equation.

$$x^2 + \frac{b}{a}x + \left(\frac{1}{2}\cdot\frac{b}{a}\right)^2 = \left(\frac{1}{2}\cdot\frac{b}{a}\right)^2 - \frac{c}{a}$$
$$x^2 + \frac{b}{a}x + \frac{b^2}{4a^2} = \frac{b^2}{4a^2} - \frac{c}{a}$$

Simplify the right side of the equation.

$$x^2 + \frac{b}{a}x + \frac{b^2}{4a^2} = \frac{b^2}{4a^2} - \left(\frac{c}{a}\cdot\frac{4a}{4a}\right)$$
$$x^2 + \frac{b}{a}x + \frac{b^2}{4a^2} = \frac{b^2}{4a^2} - \frac{4ac}{4a^2}$$
$$x^2 + \frac{b}{a}x + \frac{b^2}{4a^2} = \frac{b^2 - 4ac}{4a^2}$$

Factor the perfect-square trinomial on the left side of the equation.

$$\left(x + \frac{b}{2a}\right)^2 = \frac{b^2 - 4ac}{4a^2}$$

Take the square root of each side of the equation.

$$\sqrt{\left(x + \frac{b}{2a}\right)^2} = \sqrt{\frac{b^2 - 4ac}{4a^2}}$$
$$\left|x + \frac{b}{2a}\right| = \frac{\sqrt{b^2 - 4ac}}{2a}$$
$$x + \frac{b}{2a} = \pm\frac{\sqrt{b^2 - 4ac}}{2a}$$

Solve for x.

$$x + \frac{b}{2a} = \frac{\sqrt{b^2 - 4ac}}{2a} \qquad\qquad x + \frac{b}{2a} = -\frac{\sqrt{b^2 - 4ac}}{2a}$$

$$x = -\frac{b}{2a} + \frac{\sqrt{b^2 - 4ac}}{2a} \qquad\qquad x = -\frac{b}{2a} - \frac{\sqrt{b^2 - 4ac}}{2a}$$

$$= \frac{-b + \sqrt{b^2 - 4ac}}{2a} \qquad\qquad = \frac{-b - \sqrt{b^2 - 4ac}}{2a}$$

Point of Interest

Although mathematicians have studied quadratic equations since around 500 B.C., it was not until the 18th century that the formula was written as it is today. Of further note, the word quadratic has the same Latin root as does the word square.

Quadratic Formula

The solutions of $ax^2 + bx + c = 0$, $a \neq 0$, are

$$\frac{-b + \sqrt{b^2 - 4ac}}{2a} \quad \text{and} \quad \frac{-b - \sqrt{b^2 - 4ac}}{2a}$$

The quadratic formula is frequently written in the form

$$x = \frac{-b \pm \sqrt{b^2 - 4ac}}{2a}$$

Solve by using the quadratic formula: $2x^2 + 5x + 3 = 0$

The equation $2x^2 + 5x + 3 = 0$ is in standard form. $a = 2$, $b = 5$, $c = 3$
Replace a, b, and c in the quadratic formula with these values.

$$x = \frac{-b \pm \sqrt{b^2 - 4ac}}{2a}$$

$$= \frac{-(5) \pm \sqrt{(5)^2 - 4(2)(3)}}{2(2)}$$

$$= \frac{-5 \pm \sqrt{25 - 24}}{4}$$

$$= \frac{-5 \pm \sqrt{1}}{4} = \frac{-5 \pm 1}{4}$$

Take Note

The solutions of this quadratic equation are rational numbers. When this happens, the equation could have been solved by factoring and using the Principle of Zero Products. This may be easier than using the quadratic formula.

$$x = \frac{-5 + 1}{4} = \frac{-4}{4} = -1 \qquad x = \frac{-5 - 1}{4} = \frac{-6}{4} = -\frac{3}{2}$$

The solutions are -1 and $-\dfrac{3}{2}$.

Solve $3x^2 = 4x + 6$ by using the quadratic formula. Find the exact solutions, and approximate the solutions to the nearest thousandth.

Write the equation in standard form by subtracting $4x$ and 6 from each side of the equation.

$$3x^2 = 4x + 6$$
$$3x^2 - 4x - 6 = 0$$

$a = 3$, $b = -4$, $c = -6$

$$x = \frac{-b \pm \sqrt{b^2 - 4ac}}{2a}$$

Replace a, b, and c in the quadratic formula with these values.

$$= \frac{-(-4) \pm \sqrt{(-4)^2 - 4(3)(-6)}}{2(3)}$$

$$= \frac{4 \pm \sqrt{16 - (-72)}}{6}$$

$$= \frac{4 \pm \sqrt{88}}{6} = \frac{4 \pm 2\sqrt{22}}{6}$$

$$= \frac{\cancel{2}(2 \pm \sqrt{22})}{\cancel{2} \cdot 3} = \frac{2 \pm \sqrt{22}}{3}$$

Check:

$$3x^2 = 4x + 6$$

$$3\left(\frac{2 + \sqrt{22}}{3}\right)^2 \,\bigg|\, 4\left(\frac{2 + \sqrt{22}}{3}\right) + 6$$

$$3\left(\frac{4 + 4\sqrt{22} + 22}{9}\right) \,\bigg|\, \frac{8}{3} + \frac{4\sqrt{22}}{3} + \frac{18}{3}$$

$$3\left(\frac{26 + 4\sqrt{22}}{9}\right) \,\bigg|\, \frac{26}{3} + \frac{4\sqrt{22}}{3}$$

$$\frac{26 + 4\sqrt{22}}{3} = \frac{26 + 4\sqrt{22}}{3}$$

$$3x^2 = 4x + 6$$

$$3\left(\frac{2 - \sqrt{22}}{3}\right)^2 \,\bigg|\, 4\left(\frac{2 - \sqrt{22}}{3}\right) + 6$$

$$3\left(\frac{4 - 4\sqrt{22} + 22}{9}\right) \,\bigg|\, \frac{8}{3} - \frac{4\sqrt{22}}{3} + \frac{18}{3}$$

$$3\left(\frac{26 - 4\sqrt{22}}{9}\right) \,\bigg|\, \frac{26}{3} - \frac{4\sqrt{22}}{3}$$

$$\frac{26 - 4\sqrt{22}}{3} = \frac{26 - 4\sqrt{22}}{3}$$

The exact solutions are $\frac{2 + \sqrt{22}}{3}$ and $\frac{2 - \sqrt{22}}{3}$.

$$\frac{2 + \sqrt{22}}{3} \approx 2.230 \qquad \frac{2 - \sqrt{22}}{3} \approx -0.897$$

To the nearest thousandth, the solutions are 2.230 and −0.897.

Solve by using the quadratic formula: $4x^2 = 8x - 13$

Write the equation in standard form.

$$4x^2 = 8x - 13$$
$$4x^2 - 8x + 13 = 0$$
$$a = 4, b = -8, c = 13$$

Replace a, b, and c in the quadratic formula by their values.

$$x = \frac{-b \pm \sqrt{b^2 - 4ac}}{2a}$$
$$= \frac{-(-8) \pm \sqrt{(-8)^2 - 4 \cdot 4 \cdot 13}}{2 \cdot 4}$$

Simplify.

$$= \frac{8 \pm \sqrt{64 - 208}}{8}$$
$$= \frac{8 \pm \sqrt{-144}}{8}$$

Write the answer in the form $a + bi$.

$$= \frac{8 \pm 12i}{8} = \frac{2 \pm 3i}{2} = 1 \pm \frac{3}{2}i$$

Check:

$$4x^2 = 8x - 13$$

$$4\left(1 + \frac{3}{2}i\right)^2 \,\bigg|\, 8\left(1 + \frac{3}{2}i\right) - 13$$

$$4\left(1 + 3i - \frac{9}{4}\right) \,\bigg|\, 8 + 12i - 13$$

$$4\left(-\frac{5}{4} + 3i\right) \,\bigg|\, -5 + 12i$$

$$-5 + 12i = -5 + 12i$$

$$4x^2 = 8x - 13$$

$$4\left(1 - \frac{3}{2}i\right)^2 \,\bigg|\, 8\left(1 - \frac{3}{2}i\right) - 13$$

$$4\left(1 - 3i - \frac{9}{4}\right) \,\bigg|\, 8 - 12i - 13$$

$$4\left(-\frac{5}{4} - 3i\right) \,\bigg|\, -5 - 12i$$

$$-5 - 12i = -5 - 12i$$

The solutions are $1 + \frac{3}{2}i$ and $1 - \frac{3}{2}i$.

EXAMPLE 2 Solve by using the quadratic formula.
A. $4x^2 + 12x + 9 = 0$ **B.** $2x^2 - x + 5 = 0$

Solution **A.** $4x^2 + 12x + 9 = 0$ • $a = 4, b = 12, c = 9$

$$x = \frac{-b \pm \sqrt{b^2 - 4ac}}{2a}$$ • Replace a, b, and c in the quadratic formula by their values. Then simplify.

$$= \frac{-12 \pm \sqrt{12^2 - 4 \cdot 4 \cdot 9}}{2 \cdot 4}$$

$$= \frac{-12 \pm \sqrt{144 - 144}}{8}$$

$$= \frac{-12 \pm \sqrt{0}}{8} = \frac{-12}{8} = -\frac{3}{2}$$ • The equation has a double root.

The solution is $-\frac{3}{2}$.

B. $2x^2 - x + 5 = 0$ • $a = 2, b = -1, c = 5$

$$x = \frac{-b \pm \sqrt{b^2 - 4ac}}{2a}$$ • Replace a, b, and c in the quadratic formula by their values. Then simplify.

$$= \frac{-(-1) \pm \sqrt{(-1)^2 - 4 \cdot 2 \cdot 5}}{2 \cdot 2}$$

$$= \frac{1 \pm \sqrt{1 - 40}}{4}$$

$$= \frac{1 \pm \sqrt{-39}}{4} = \frac{1 \pm i\sqrt{39}}{4}$$

The solutions are $\frac{1}{4} + \frac{\sqrt{39}}{4}i$ and $\frac{1}{4} - \frac{\sqrt{39}}{4}i$.

PROBLEM 2 Solve by using the quadratic formula.
A. $x^2 + 6x - 9 = 0$ **B.** $4x^2 = 4x - 1$

Solution See page S24.

In Example 2A, the solution of the equation is a double root, and in Example 2B, the solutions are complex numbers.

In the quadratic formula, the quantity $b^2 - 4ac$ is called the **discriminant.** When a, b, and c are real numbers, the discriminant determines whether a quadratic equation will have a double root, two real number solutions that are not equal, or two complex number solutions.

Effect of the Discriminant on the Solutions of a Quadratic Equation

1. If $b^2 - 4ac = 0$, the equation has one real number solution, a double root.

2. If $b^2 - 4ac > 0$, the equation has two real number solutions that are not equal.

3. If $b^2 - 4ac < 0$, the equation has two complex number solutions.

The equation $x^2 - 4x - 5 = 0$ has two real number solutions because the discriminant is greater than zero.

$a = 1, b = -4, c = -5$

$b^2 - 4ac = (-4)^2 - 4(1)(-5)$
$= 16 + 20$
$= 36$

$36 > 0$

EXAMPLE 3   Use the discriminant to determine whether $4x^2 - 2x + 5 = 0$ has one real number solution, two real number solutions, or two complex number solutions.

Solution $b^2 - 4ac = (-2)^2 - 4(4)(5)$ • $a = 4, b = -2, c = 5$
$= 4 - 80$
$= -76$
$-76 < 0$ • **The discriminant is less than 0.**

The equation has two complex number solutions.

PROBLEM 3   Use the discriminant to determine whether $3x^2 - x - 1 = 0$ has one real number solution, two real number solutions, or two complex number solutions.

Solution   See page S25.

8.2   Concept Review

Determine whether the following statements are always true, sometimes true, or never true.

1. A quadratic equation can be solved by completing the square.

2. The expression $b^2 - 4ac$ is called the discriminant.

3. If $b^2 > 4ac$, the quadratic equation has two complex number solutions.

4. The quadratic formula can be used to solve quadratic equations that have irrational roots.

5. $x^2 + 5x + 25$ is a perfect-square trinomial.

6. To complete the square on $3x^2 + 6x$, add 9.

8.2   Exercises

1   Solve quadratic equations by completing the square

1. a. To complete the square on $x^2 + 14x$, find the constant c that makes $x^2 + 14x + c$ a ___?___ trinomial.

The constant term c will be the square of half the coefficient of

_____?_____, so $c = \left[\dfrac{1}{2}(\underline{\quad ? \quad})\right]^2 = (\underline{\quad ? \quad})$.

b. Complete the square on $x^2 + 14x$ and write the result as the square of a binomial:

$x^2 + 14x + \underline{\quad ? \quad} = (\underline{\quad ? \quad})^2$

2. Rewrite the equation $3x^2 - 6x + 2 = 0$ in the form $(x - m)^2 = n$.

$3x^2 - 6x + 2 = 0$

$\quad\quad 3x^2 - 6x = \underline{\quad ? \quad}$ • Subtract 2 from each side of the equation.

$\quad x^2 - (\underline{\quad ? \quad})x = \underline{\quad ? \quad}$ • To make the coefficient of x^2 equal to 1, divide each side of the equation by 3.

$x^2 - 2x + \underline{\quad ? \quad} = -\dfrac{2}{3} + \underline{\quad ? \quad}$ • Add $\left[\dfrac{1}{2}(\underline{\quad ? \quad})\right]^2$ to each side of the equation.

$\quad (x - \underline{\quad ? \quad})^2 = \underline{\quad ? \quad}$ • Factor the left side of the equation. Simplify the right side of the equation.

3. What is the next step when using completing the square to solve $x^2 + 6x = 4$?

4. Are there some quadratic equations that cannot be solved by completing the square? Why or why not?

Solve by completing the square.

5. $x^2 - 4x - 5 = 0$ **6.** $y^2 + 6y + 5 = 0$ **7.** $v^2 + 8v - 9 = 0$

8. $w^2 - 2w - 24 = 0$ **9.** $z^2 - 6z + 9 = 0$ **10.** $u^2 + 10u + 25 = 0$

11. $r^2 + 4r - 7 = 0$ **12.** $s^2 + 6s - 1 = 0$ **13.** $x^2 - 6x + 7 = 0$

14. $y^2 + 8y + 13 = 0$ **15.** $z^2 - 2z + 2 = 0$ **16.** $t^2 - 4t + 8 = 0$

First try to solve by factoring. If you are unable to solve the equation by factoring, solve the equation by completing the square.

17. $t^2 - t - 1 = 0$ **18.** $u^2 - u - 7 = 0$ **19.** $y^2 - 6y = 4$

20. $w^2 + 4w = 2$ **21.** $x^2 = 8x - 15$ **22.** $z^2 = 4z - 3$

23. $v^2 = 4v - 13$ **24.** $x^2 = 2x - 17$ **25.** $p^2 + 6p = -13$

26. $x^2 + 4x = -20$ **27.** $y^2 - 2y = 17$ **28.** $x^2 + 10x = 7$

29. $z^2 = z + 4$ **30.** $r^2 = 3r - 1$ **31.** $x^2 + 13 = 2x$

32. $x^2 + 27 = 6x$

33. $2y^2 + 3y + 1 = 0$

34. $2t^2 + 5t - 3 = 0$

35. $4r^2 - 8r = -3$

36. $4u^2 - 20u = -9$

37. $6y^2 - 5y = 4$

38. $6v^2 - 7v = 3$

39. $4x^2 - 4x + 5 = 0$

40. $4t^2 - 4t + 17 = 0$

41. $9x^2 - 6x + 2 = 0$

42. $9y^2 - 12y + 13 = 0$

43. $2s^2 = 4s + 5$

44. $3u^2 = 6u + 1$

45. $2r^2 = 3 - r$

46. $2x^2 = 12 - 5x$

47. $y - 2 = (y - 3)(y + 2)$

48. $8s - 11 = (s - 4)(s - 2)$

49. $6t - 2 = (2t - 3)(t - 1)$

50. $2z + 9 = (2z + 3)(z + 2)$

51. $(x - 4)(x + 1) = x - 3$

52. $(y - 3)^2 = 2y + 10$

Solve by completing the square. Approximate the solutions to the nearest thousandth.

53. $z^2 + 2z = 4$

54. $t^2 - 4t = 7$

55. $2x^2 = 4x - 1$

56. $3y^2 = 5y - 1$

57. $4z^2 + 2z - 1 = 0$

58. $4w^2 - 8w = 3$

59. True or false? If $c > 4$, the solutions of $x^2 + 4x + c = 0$ are real numbers.

60. True or false? If $c = b^2$, $x^2 + 2bx = -c$ has one real solution.

2   Solve quadratic equations by using the quadratic formula

61. Write the quadratic formula. What does each variable in the formula represent?

62. Write the expression that appears under the radical symbol in the quadratic formula. What is this quantity called? What can it be used to determine?

63. Suppose you must solve the quadratic equation $x^2 = 3x + 5$. Does it matter whether you rewrite the equation as $x^2 - 3x - 5 = 0$ or as $0 = -x^2 + 3x + 5$ before you begin?

64. Which method of solving a quadratic equation do you prefer: completing the square or using the quadratic formula? Why?

65. To write the equation $x^2 = 6x - 10$ in standard form, subtract ___?___ from and add ___?___ to each side of the equation. The resulting equation is ___?___ $= 0$. Then $a = $ ___?___, $b = $ ___?___, $c = $ ___?___.

66. Use the values of a, b, and c that you found in Exercise 65 to evaluate the discriminant for the equation $x^2 = 6x - 10$: $b^2 - 4ac = ($___?___$)^2$
$- 4($___?___$)($___?___$) = $ ___?___ $- $ ___?___ $= $ ___?___.

67. Based on the value of the discriminate you found in Exercise 66, the equation $x^2 = 6x - 10$ must have two ___?___ number solutions.

68. Using the quadratic formula to solve $x^2 = 6x - 10$ leads to the result $\dfrac{6 \pm \sqrt{-4}}{2}$. Simplify this result.

$$\dfrac{6 \pm \sqrt{-4}}{2} = \dfrac{6 \pm \underline{\ ?\ }}{2}$$ • Rewrite $\sqrt{-4}$ as the imaginary number ___?___ .

$$= \underline{\ ?\ } \pm \underline{\ ?\ }$$ • Divide each term of the numerator by the denominator.

Solve by using the quadratic formula.

69. $x^2 - 3x - 10 = 0$

70. $z^2 - 4z - 8 = 0$

71. $y^2 + 5y - 36 = 0$

72. $z^2 - 3z - 40 = 0$

73. $w^2 = 8w + 72$

74. $t^2 = 2t + 35$

75. $v^2 = 24 - 5v$

76. $x^2 = 18 - 7x$

77. $2y^2 + 5y - 3 = 0$

78. $4p^2 - 7p + 3 = 0$

79. $8s^2 = 10s + 3$

80. $12t^2 = 5t + 2$

First try to solve by factoring. If you are unable to solve the equation by factoring, solve the equation by using the quadratic formula.

81. $v^2 - 2v - 7 = 0$

82. $t^2 - 2t - 11 = 0$

83. $y^2 - 8y - 20 = 0$

84. $x^2 = 14x - 24$

85. $v^2 = 12v - 24$

86. $2z^2 - 2z - 1 = 0$

87. $4x^2 - 4x - 7 = 0$

88. $2p^2 - 8p + 5 = 0$

89. $2s^2 - 3s + 1 = 0$

90. $4w^2 - 4w - 1 = 0$

91. $3x^2 + 10x + 6 = 0$

92. $3v^2 = 6v - 2$

93. $6w^2 = 19w - 10$

94. $z^2 + 2z + 2 = 0$

95. $p^2 - 4p + 5 = 0$

96. $y^2 - 2y + 5 = 0$

97. $x^2 + 6x + 13 = 0$

98. $s^2 - 4s + 13 = 0$

99. $t^2 - 6t + 10 = 0$

100. $2w^2 - 2w + 5 = 0$

101. $4v^2 + 8v + 3 = 0$

102. $2x^2 + 6x + 5 = 0$

103. $2y^2 + 2y + 13 = 0$

104. $4t^2 - 6t + 9 = 0$

105. $3v^2 + 6v + 1 = 0$

106. $2r^2 = 4r - 11$

107. $3y^2 = 6y - 5$

108. $2x(x - 2) = x + 12$

109. $10y(y + 4) = 15y - 15$

110. $(3s - 2)(s + 1) = 2$

111. $(2t + 1)(t - 3) = 9$

Solve by using the quadratic formula. Approximate the solutions to the nearest thousandth.

112. $x^2 - 6x - 6 = 0$

113. $p^2 - 8p + 3 = 0$

114. $r^2 - 2r = 4$

115. $w^2 + 4w = 1$

116. $3t^2 = 7t + 1$

117. $2y^2 = y + 5$

Use the discriminant to determine whether the quadratic equation has one real number solution, two real number solutions, or two complex number solutions.

118. $2z^2 - z + 5 = 0$

119. $3y^2 + y + 1 = 0$

120. $9x^2 - 12x + 4 = 0$

121. $4x^2 + 20x + 25 = 0$

122. $2v^2 - 3v - 1 = 0$

123. $3w^2 + 3w - 2 = 0$

124. $2p^2 + 5p + 1 = 0$

125. $2t^2 + 9t + 3 = 0$

126. $5z^2 + 2 = 0$

127. True or false? If $a > 0$ and $c < 0$, the solutions of $ax^2 + bx + c = 0$ are real numbers.

128. True or false? If $a > 0$, $b = 0$, and $c > 0$, the solutions of $ax^2 + bx + c = 0$ are real numbers.

Classify each equation as linear or quadratic.

129. $2x^2 + 3x = 1$

130. $2x = 3x - 1$

131. $4x - 2 = 5$

132. $4x^2 - 2x = 5$

133. $6x(x - 2) = 7$

134. $6x - 2 = 7$

8.2 Applying Concepts

Solve.

135. $\sqrt{2}y^2 + 3y - 2\sqrt{2} = 0$

136. $\sqrt{3}z^2 + 10z - 3\sqrt{3} = 0$

137. $\sqrt{2}x^2 + 5x - 3\sqrt{2} = 0$

138. $\sqrt{3}w^2 + w - 2\sqrt{3} = 0$

139. $t^2 - t\sqrt{3} + 1 = 0$

140. $y^2 + y\sqrt{7} + 2 = 0$

Solve for x.

141. $x^2 - ax - 2a^2 = 0$

142. $x^2 - ax - 6a^2 = 0$

143. $2x^2 + 3ax - 2a^2 = 0$

144. $2x^2 - 7ax + 3a^2 = 0$

145. $x^2 - 2x - y = 0$

146. $x^2 - 4xy - 4 = 0$

For what values of p does the quadratic equation have two real number solutions that are not equal? Write the answer in set-builder notation.

147. $x^2 - 6x + p = 0$

148. $x^2 + 10x + p = 0$

For what values of p does the quadratic equation have two complex number solutions? Write the answer in set-builder notation.

149. $x^2 - 2x + p = 0$

150. $x^2 + 4x + p = 0$

Solve.

151. Find all values of x that satisfy the equation $x^2 + ix + 2 = 0$.

152. Show that the equation $2x^2 + bx - 2 = 0$ always has real number solutions regardless of the value of b.

153. Sports The height, h (in feet), of a baseball above the ground t seconds after it is hit can be approximated by the equation $h = -16t^2 + 70t + 4$. Using this equation, determine when the ball will hit the ground. Round to the nearest hundredth. (*Hint:* The ball hits the ground when $h = 0$.)

154. Sports After a baseball is hit, there are two equations that can be considered. One gives the height, h (in feet), the ball is above the ground t seconds after it is hit. The second is the distance, s (in feet), the ball is from home plate t seconds after it is hit. A model of this situation is given by $h = -16t^2 + 70t + 4$ and $s = 44.5t$. Using this model, determine whether the ball will clear a fence 325 ft from home plate. Round to the nearest tenth.

155. Conservation The National Forest Management Act of 1976 specifies that harvesting timber in national forests must be accomplished in conjunction with environmental considerations. One such consideration is providing a habitat for the spotted owl. One model of the survival of the spotted owl requires the solution of the equation $x^2 - s_a x - s_j s_s f = 0$ for x. Different values of s_a, s_j, s_s, and f are given in the table at the right. (*Source:* Charles Biles and Barry Noon, "The Spotted Owl!" from *The Journal of Undergraduate Mathematics and Its Application*, Vol. 11, No. 2, 1990. Reprinted with permission.) The values are particularly important because they relate to the survival of the owl. If $x > 1$, then the model predicts a growth in the population; if $x = 1$, the population remains steady; if $x < 1$, the population decreases. The important solution of the equation is the larger of the two roots of the equation.

	U.S. Forest Service	Lande
s_j	0.34	0.11
s_s	0.97	0.71
s_a	0.97	0.94
f	0.24	0.24

a. Determine the larger root of this equation for values provided by the U.S. Forest Service. Round to the nearest hundredth. Does it predict that the population will increase, remain steady, or decrease?

b. Determine the larger root of this equation for the values provided by R. Lande in *Oecologia* (Vol. 75, 1988). Round to the nearest hundredth. Does it predict that the population will increase, remain steady, or decrease?

156. Agriculture An agricultural research group determined that the amount of grass harvested from a pasture could be modeled by the equation $A = -0.001532x^2 + 0.3358x - 7.5323$, where x is the amount, in 100,000 kg per hectare, of a fertilizer that is applied to the pasture. According to this model, how many kilograms per hectare of fertilizer must be applied to a pasture to produce 800,000 kg per hectare of grass? Round to the nearest thousand.

157. Here is an outline for an alternative method for deriving the quadratic formula. Fill in the details of this derivation. Begin with the equation $ax^2 + bx + c = 0$. Subtract c from each side of the equation. Multiply each side of the equation by $4a$. Now add b^2 to each side. Supply the remaining steps until you have reached the quadratic formula.

158. Explain how to complete the square of $x^2 + bx$.

8.3 Equations That Are Reducible to Quadratic Equations

OBJECTIVE 1   **Equations that are quadratic in form**

Certain equations that are not quadratic equations can be expressed in quadratic form by making suitable substitutions. An equation is **quadratic in form** if it can be written as $au^2 + bu + c = 0$.

To see that the equation at the right is quadratic in form, let $x^2 = u$. Replace x^2 by u. The equation is quadratic in form.

$$x^4 - 4x^2 - 5 = 0$$
$$(x^2)^2 - 4(x^2) - 5 = 0$$
$$u^2 - 4u - 5 = 0$$

To see that the equation at the right is quadratic in form, let $y^{\frac{1}{2}} = u$. Replace $y^{\frac{1}{2}}$ by u. The equation is quadratic in form.

$$y - y^{\frac{1}{2}} - 6 = 0$$
$$\left(y^{\frac{1}{2}}\right)^2 - \left(y^{\frac{1}{2}}\right) - 6 = 0$$
$$u^2 - u - 6 = 0$$

The key to recognizing equations that are quadratic in form is that when the equation is written in standard form, the exponent on one variable term is $\frac{1}{2}$ the exponent on the other variable term.

Solve: $z + 7z^{\frac{1}{2}} - 18 = 0$

The equation $z + 7z^{\frac{1}{2}} - 18 = 0$ is quadratic in form.

To solve this equation, let $z^{\frac{1}{2}} = u$.

Solve for u by factoring.

Replace u by $z^{\frac{1}{2}}$.

Solve for z by squaring each side of the equation.

$$z + 7z^{\frac{1}{2}} - 18 = 0$$
$$\left(z^{\frac{1}{2}}\right)^2 + 7\left(z^{\frac{1}{2}}\right) - 18 = 0$$
$$u^2 + 7u - 18 = 0$$
$$(u - 2)(u + 9) = 0$$

$u - 2 = 0 \qquad u + 9 = 0$
$u = 2 \qquad u = -9$
$z^{\frac{1}{2}} = 2 \qquad z^{\frac{1}{2}} = -9$

$\left(z^{\frac{1}{2}}\right)^2 = 2^2 \qquad \left(z^{\frac{1}{2}}\right)^2 = (-9)^2$
$z = 4 \qquad z = 81$

Check the solution. When each side of the equation has been squared, the resulting equation may have an extraneous solution.

Check: $\quad z + 7z^{\frac{1}{2}} - 18 = 0$
$4 + 7(4)^{\frac{1}{2}} - 18 \mid 0$
$4 + 7 \cdot 2 - 18$
$4 + 14 - 18$
$0 = 0$

$$\frac{z + 7z^{\frac{1}{2}} - 18 = 0}{\begin{array}{l|l} 81 + 7(81)^{\frac{1}{2}} - 18 & 0 \\ 81 + 7 \cdot 9 - 18 & \\ 81 + 63 - 18 & \\ \qquad\qquad 126 \neq 0 \end{array}}$$

4 checks as a solution, but 81 does not.

Write the solution.   The solution is 4.

EXAMPLE 1 Solve: **A.** $x^4 + x^2 - 12 = 0$ **B.** $x^{\frac{2}{3}} - 2x^{\frac{1}{3}} - 3 = 0$

Solution **A.** $x^4 + x^2 - 12 = 0$ • **The equation is quadratic**
$(x^2)^2 + (x^2) - 12 = 0$ **in form.**
$u^2 + u - 12 = 0$ • **Let $x^2 = u$.**
$(u - 3)(u + 4) = 0$ • **Solve for u by factoring.**

$u - 3 = 0 \qquad u + 4 = 0$
$u = 3 \qquad\quad u = -4$

$\quad x^2 = 3 \qquad\qquad x^2 = -4$ • **Replace u by x^2.**
$\sqrt{x^2} = \sqrt{3} \qquad \sqrt{x^2} = \sqrt{-4}$ • **Solve for x by taking**
$\quad x = \pm\sqrt{3} \qquad\quad x = \pm 2i$ **square roots.**

The solutions are $\sqrt{3}$, $-\sqrt{3}$, $2i$, and $-2i$.

B. $x^{\frac{2}{3}} - 2x^{\frac{1}{3}} - 3 = 0$ • **The equation is quadratic**
$\left(x^{\frac{1}{3}}\right)^2 - 2\left(x^{\frac{1}{3}}\right) - 3 = 0$ **in form.**
$u^2 - 2u - 3 = 0$ • **Let $x^{\frac{1}{3}} = u$.**
$(u - 3)(u + 1) = 0$ • **Solve for u by factoring.**

$u - 3 = 0 \qquad u + 1 = 0$
$u = 3 \qquad\quad u = -1$

$x^{\frac{1}{3}} = 3 \qquad\qquad x^{\frac{1}{3}} = -1$ • **Replace u by $x^{\frac{1}{3}}$.**
$\left(x^{\frac{1}{3}}\right)^3 = 3^3 \qquad \left(x^{\frac{1}{3}}\right)^3 = (-1)^3$ • **Solve for x by cubing both**
$x = 27 \qquad\qquad x = -1$ **sides of the equation.**

The solutions are 27 and -1.

PROBLEM 1 Solve.   **A.** $x - 5x^{\frac{1}{2}} + 6 = 0$ **B.** $4x^4 + 35x^2 - 9 = 0$

Solution See page S25.

OBJECTIVE **2**   ## Radical equations

Certain equations containing a radical can be solved by first solving the equation for the radical expression and then squaring each side of the equation.

Remember that when each side of an equation has been squared, the resulting equation may have an extraneous solution. Therefore, the solutions of a radical equation must be checked.

Solve: $\sqrt{x + 2} + 4 = x$

Solve for the radical expression.	$\sqrt{x + 2} + 4 = x$
	$\sqrt{x + 2} = x - 4$
Square each side of the equation.	$\left(\sqrt{x + 2}\right)^2 = (x - 4)^2$
Simplify.	$x + 2 = x^2 - 8x + 16$
Write the equation in standard form.	$0 = x^2 - 9x + 14$
Solve for x by factoring.	$0 = (x - 7)(x - 2)$

$$x - 7 = 0 \qquad x - 2 = 0$$
$$x = 7 \qquad\quad x = 2$$

Check the solution.

Check:
$$\sqrt{x + 2} + 4 = x \qquad\qquad \sqrt{x + 2} + 4 = x$$
$$\dfrac{\sqrt{7 + 2} + 4}{\;} \Big|\; 7 \qquad\qquad \dfrac{\sqrt{2 + 2} + 4}{\;} \Big|\; 2$$
$$\sqrt{9} + 4 \qquad\qquad\quad \sqrt{4} + 4$$
$$3 + 4 \qquad\qquad\qquad 2 + 4$$
$$7 = 7 \qquad\qquad\qquad\quad 6 \neq 2$$

2 does not check as a solution.

Write the solution.   The solution is 7.

EXAMPLE 2   Solve: $\sqrt{7y - 3} + 3 = 2y$

Solution
$$\sqrt{7y - 3} + 3 = 2y$$
$$\sqrt{7y - 3} = 2y - 3$$
$$\left(\sqrt{7y - 3}\right)^2 = (2y - 3)^2$$
$$7y - 3 = 4y^2 - 12y + 9$$
$$0 = 4y^2 - 19y + 12$$

$$0 = (4y - 3)(y - 4)$$

$$4y - 3 = 0 \qquad y - 4 = 0$$
$$4y = 3 \qquad\quad y = 4$$
$$y = \dfrac{3}{4}$$

- Solve for the radical expression.
- Square each side of the equation.
- Write the equation in standard form.
- Solve for y by factoring.

- 4 checks as a solution.

  $\dfrac{3}{4}$ does not check as a solution.

The solution is 4.

PROBLEM 2   Solve: $\sqrt{2x + 1} + x = 7$

Solution   See page S25.

If an equation contains more than one radical, the procedure of solving for the radical expression and squaring each side of the equation may have to be repeated.

EXAMPLE 3   Solve: $\sqrt{2y + 1} - \sqrt{y} = 1$

Solution
$$\sqrt{2y + 1} - \sqrt{y} = 1$$
$$\sqrt{2y + 1} = \sqrt{y} + 1$$
$$\left(\sqrt{2y + 1}\right)^2 = \left(\sqrt{y} + 1\right)^2$$

- Solve for one of the radical expressions.
- Square each side of the equation.

$$2y + 1 = y + 2\sqrt{y} + 1$$
$$y = 2\sqrt{y}$$
$$y^2 = \left(2\sqrt{y}\right)^2$$
$$y^2 = 4y$$
$$y^2 - 4y = 0$$
$$y(y - 4) = 0$$

- Solve for the radical expression.
- Square each side of the equation.

- Write the equation in standard form.

$$y = 0 \qquad y - 4 = 0$$
$$y = 4$$

- 0 and 4 check as solutions.

The solutions are 0 and 4.

PROBLEM 3   Solve: $\sqrt{2x - 1} + \sqrt{x} = 2$

Solution   See page S25.

OBJECTIVE 3   **Fractional equations**

After each side of a fractional equation has been multiplied by the LCM of the denominators, the resulting equation is sometimes a quadratic equation. The solutions to the resulting equation must be checked, because multiplying each side of an equation by a variable expression may produce an equation that has a solution that is not a solution of the original equation.

Solve: $\dfrac{1}{r} + \dfrac{1}{r + 1} = \dfrac{3}{2}$

$$\frac{1}{r} + \frac{1}{r + 1} = \frac{3}{2}$$

Multiply each side of the equation by the LCM of the denominators.

$$2r(r + 1)\left(\frac{1}{r} + \frac{1}{r + 1}\right) = 2r(r + 1) \cdot \frac{3}{2}$$
$$2(r + 1) + 2r = r(r + 1) \cdot 3$$
$$2r + 2 + 2r = (r^2 + r) \cdot 3$$
$$4r + 2 = 3r^2 + 3r$$

Write the equation in standard form.

$$0 = 3r^2 - r - 2$$
$$0 = (3r + 2)(r - 1)$$

Solve for r by factoring.

$$3r + 2 = 0 \qquad r - 1 = 0$$
$$3r = -2 \qquad\quad r = 1$$
$$r = -\frac{2}{3}$$

$-\dfrac{2}{3}$ and 1 check as solutions.

Write the solutions.

The solutions are $-\dfrac{2}{3}$ and 1.

EXAMPLE 4   Solve: $\dfrac{18}{2a - 1} + 3a = 17$

Solution

$$\frac{18}{2a - 1} + 3a = 17$$

- The LCM of the denominators is $2a - 1$.

$$(2a - 1)\left(\frac{18}{2a - 1} + 3a\right) = (2a - 1)17$$

$$(2a - 1)\frac{18}{2a - 1} + (2a - 1)(3a) = (2a - 1)17$$

$$18 + 6a^2 - 3a = 34a - 17$$
$$6a^2 - 37a + 35 = 0$$

• Write the equation in standard form.

$$(6a - 7)(a - 5) = 0$$

• Solve for *a* by factoring.

$$6a - 7 = 0 \qquad a - 5 = 0$$
$$6a = 7 \qquad\qquad a = 5$$
$$a = \frac{7}{6}$$

The solutions are $\frac{7}{6}$ and 5.

PROBLEM 4   Solve: $3y + \dfrac{25}{3y - 2} = -8$

Solution   See page S25.

8.3   Concept Review

Determine whether the following statements are always true, sometimes true, or never true.

1. An equation that is quadratic in form can be solved by the quadratic formula.

2. Squaring both sides of a radical equation produces an extraneous root.

3. $x + 3\sqrt{x} - 8 = 0$ is quadratic in form.

4. $\sqrt[4]{x} + 2\sqrt{3x} - 8 = 0$ is quadratic in form.

8.3   Exercises

1   Equations that are quadratic in form

1. The equation $x^8 + 4x^4 - 5 = 0$ is equivalent to the quadratic equation $u^2 + 4u - 5 = 0$, where $u = \underline{\quad ? \quad}$.

2. The equation $p - 2p^{\frac{1}{2}} - 8 = 0$ is equivalent to the quadratic equation $u^2 - 2u - 8 = 0$, where $u = \underline{\quad ? \quad}$.

3. What does it mean for an equation to be quadratic in form?

4. Explain how to show that $x^4 - 2x^2 - 3 = 0$ is quadratic in form.

Solve.

5. $x^4 - 13x^2 + 36 = 0$

6. $y^4 - 5y^2 + 4 = 0$

7. $z^4 - 6z^2 + 8 = 0$

8. $t^4 - 12t^2 + 27 = 0$

9. $p - 3p^{\frac{1}{2}} + 2 = 0$

10. $v - 7v^{\frac{1}{2}} + 12 = 0$

11. $x - x^{\frac{1}{2}} - 12 = 0$

12. $w - 2w^{\frac{1}{2}} - 15 = 0$

13. $z^4 + 3z^2 - 4 = 0$

14. $y^4 + 5y^2 - 36 = 0$

15. $x^4 + 12x^2 - 64 = 0$

16. $x^4 - 81 = 0$

17. $p + 2p^{\frac{1}{2}} - 24 = 0$

18. $v + 3v^{\frac{1}{2}} - 4 = 0$

19. $y^{\frac{2}{3}} - 9y^{\frac{1}{3}} + 8 = 0$

20. $z^{\frac{2}{3}} - z^{\frac{1}{3}} - 6 = 0$

21. $x^6 - 9x^3 + 8 = 0$

22. $y^6 + 9y^3 + 8 = 0$

23. $z^8 - 17z^4 + 16 = 0$

24. $v^4 - 15v^2 - 16 = 0$

25. $p^{\frac{2}{3}} + 2p^{\frac{1}{3}} - 8 = 0$

26. $w^{\frac{2}{3}} + 3w^{\frac{1}{3}} - 10 = 0$

27. $2x - 3x^{\frac{1}{2}} + 1 = 0$

28. $3y - 5y^{\frac{1}{2}} - 2 = 0$

29. Which equations can be solved by solving the quadratic equation $u^2 - 8u - 20 = 0$?
   a. $x^{10} - 8x^5 - 20 = 0$ **b.** $x^{16} - 8x^4 - 20 = 0$
   c. $x^{1/10} - 8x^{1/5} - 20 = 0$ **d.** $x^{2/5} - 8x^{1/5} - 20 = 0$

30. Each equation can be solved by solving the quadratic equation $u^2 + 5u + 6 = 0$. Which equations could possibly end up with extraneous solutions?
   a. $x^{1/4} + 5x^{1/8} + 6 = 0$ **b.** $x^8 + 5x^4 + 6 = 0$
   c. $x + 5x^{1/2} + 6 = 0$ **d.** $x^{2/3} + 5x^{1/3} + 6 = 0$

2   Radical equations

31. The first step in the solution of the equation $\sqrt{a + 1} + 7 = a + 2$ is to solve for __?__ by subtracting __?__ from each side of the equation. The second step is to __?__ each side of the equation.

32. Solving the equation given in Exercise 31 yields $a = 8$ and $a = 3$. Checking these solutions in the original equation shows that the solution __?__ is extraneous.

33. Look at the equations to be solved in Exercises 35 to 52. List the exercise numbers of the equations for which the first step of the solution will be to square both sides of the equation.

34. Look at the equations to be solved in Exercises 35 to 52. List the exercise numbers of the equations whose solutions will require squaring both sides two separate times.

Solve.

35. $\sqrt{x+1} + x = 5$

36. $\sqrt{x-4} + x = 6$

37. $x = \sqrt{x+6}$

38. $\sqrt{2y-1} = y - 2$

39. $\sqrt{3w+3} = w + 1$

40. $\sqrt{2s+1} = s - 1$

41. $\sqrt{4y+1} - y = 1$

42. $\sqrt{3s+4} + 2s = 12$

43. $\sqrt{10x+5} - 2x = 1$

44. $\sqrt{t+8} = 2t + 1$

45. $\sqrt{p+11} = 1 - p$

46. $x - 7 = \sqrt{x-5}$

47. $\sqrt{x-1} - \sqrt{x} = -1$

48. $\sqrt{y+1} = \sqrt{y+5}$

49. $\sqrt{2x-1} = 1 - \sqrt{x-1}$

50. $\sqrt{x+6} + \sqrt{x+2} = 2$

51. $\sqrt{t+3} + \sqrt{2t+7} = 1$

52. $\sqrt{5-2x} = \sqrt{2-x} + 1$

3   Fractional equations

53. Use the equation $\dfrac{4}{y} = \dfrac{y-6}{y-4}$.

   a. The first step in solving the equation is to clear denominators by multiplying each side of the equation by the LCM of the denominators ___?___ and ___?___. The LCM is ___?___.

   b. When you multiply the left side of the equation by the LCM $y(y-4)$, the left side simplifies to ___?___.

   c. When you multiply the right side of the equation by the LCM $y(y-4)$, the right side simplifies to ___?___.

   d. Use your answers to parts b and c to write the equation that results from clearing denominators: ___?___ = ___?___.

54. a. Using the results of Exercise 53, we know we can solve the rational equation $\dfrac{4}{y} = \dfrac{y-6}{y-4}$ by solving the quadratic equation $4y - 16 = y^2 - 6y$. Written in standard form, this equation is $0 =$ ___?___.

   b. Solve $0 = y^2 - 10y + 16$ by factoring: $0 = ($___?___$)($___?___$)$, so $y =$ ___?___ or $y =$ ___?___.

   c. Both solutions from part b check in the original equation, because neither solution makes one of the denominators equal to ___?___.

Solve.

55. $x = \dfrac{10}{x-9}$

56. $z = \dfrac{5}{z-4}$

57. $\dfrac{t}{t+1} = \dfrac{-2}{t-1}$

58. $\dfrac{2v}{v-1} = \dfrac{5}{v+2}$

59. $\dfrac{y-1}{y+2} + y = 1$

60. $\dfrac{2p-1}{p-2} + p = 8$

61. $\dfrac{3r + 2}{r + 2} - 2r = 1$

62. $\dfrac{2v + 3}{v + 4} + 3v = 4$

63. $\dfrac{2}{2x + 1} + \dfrac{1}{x} = 3$

64. $\dfrac{3}{s} - \dfrac{2}{2s - 1} = 1$

65. $\dfrac{16}{z - 2} + \dfrac{16}{z + 2} = 6$

66. $\dfrac{2}{y + 1} + \dfrac{1}{y - 1} = 1$

67. $\dfrac{t}{t - 2} + \dfrac{2}{t - 1} = 4$

68. $\dfrac{4t + 1}{t + 4} + \dfrac{3t - 1}{t + 1} = 2$

69. $\dfrac{5}{2p - 1} + \dfrac{4}{p + 1} = 2$

70. $\dfrac{3w}{2w + 3} + \dfrac{2}{w + 2} = 1$

71. $\dfrac{2v}{v + 2} + \dfrac{3}{v + 4} = 1$

72. $\dfrac{x + 3}{x + 1} - \dfrac{x - 2}{x + 3} = 5$

8.3 Applying Concepts

73. $\dfrac{x^2}{4} + \dfrac{x}{2} = 6$

74. $3\left(\dfrac{x + 1}{2}\right)^2 = 54$

75. $\dfrac{x + 2}{3} + \dfrac{2}{x - 2} = 3$

76. $\dfrac{x^4}{4} + 1 = \dfrac{5x^2}{4}$

77. $\dfrac{x^4}{3} - \dfrac{8x^2}{3} = 3$

78. $\dfrac{x^2}{4} + \dfrac{x}{2} + \dfrac{1}{8} = 0$

79. $\dfrac{x^4}{8} + \dfrac{x^2}{4} = 3$

80. $\sqrt{x^4 - 2} = x$

81. $\sqrt{x^4 + 4} = 2x$

82. $\left(\sqrt{x} - 2\right)^2 - 5\sqrt{x} + 14 = 0$ (*Hint:* Let $u = \sqrt{x} - 2$.)

83. $\left(\sqrt{x} + 3\right)^2 - 4\sqrt{x} - 17 = 0$ (*Hint:* $u = \sqrt{x} + 3$.)

84. **Sports** According to the Compton's Interactive Encyclopedia, the minimum dimensions of a football used in the National Football Association games are 10.875 in. long and 20.75 in. in circumference at the center. A possible model for the cross section of a football is given by

$y = \pm 3.3041 \sqrt{1 - \dfrac{x^2}{29.7366}}$, where x is the distance from the center of the football and y is the radius of the football at x.

a. What is the domain of the equation?

b. Graph $y = 3.3041 \sqrt{1 - \dfrac{x^2}{29.7366}}$ and $y = -3.3041 \sqrt{1 - \dfrac{x^2}{29.7366}}$ on the same coordinate axes. Explain why the $\pm$ symbol occurs in the equation.

c. Determine the radius of the football when x is 3 in. Round to the nearest ten-thousandth.

8.4

Applications of Quadratic Equations

OBJECTIVE 1 **Application problems**

The application problems in this section are similar to those problems that were solved earlier in the text. Each of the strategies for the problems in this section will result in a quadratic equation.

Solve: A small pipe takes 16 min longer to empty a tank than does a larger pipe. Working together, the pipes can empty the tank in 6 min. How long would it take each pipe, working alone, to empty the tank?

> **STRATEGY** **for solving an application problem**
>
> ▶ Determine the type of problem. Is it a uniform motion problem, a geometry problem, an integer problem, or a work problem?

The problem is a work problem.

> ▶ Choose a variable to represent the unknown quantity. Write numerical or variable expressions for all the remaining quantities. These results can be recorded in a table.

The unknown time of the larger pipe: t
The unknown time of the smaller pipe: $t + 16$

	Rate of work	·	Time worked	=	Part of task completed
Larger pipe	$\dfrac{1}{t}$	·	6	=	$\dfrac{6}{t}$
Smaller pipe	$\dfrac{1}{t + 16}$	·	6	=	$\dfrac{6}{t + 16}$

> ▶ Determine how the quantities are related. If necessary, review the strategies presented in earlier chapters.

The sum of the parts of the task completed must equal 1.

$$\frac{6}{t} + \frac{6}{t + 16} = 1$$

$$t(t + 16)\left(\frac{6}{t} + \frac{6}{t + 16}\right) = t(t + 16) \cdot 1$$
$$(t + 16)6 + 6t = t^2 + 16t$$
$$6t + 96 + 6t = t^2 + 16t$$

$$0 = t^2 + 4t - 96$$
$$0 = (t + 12)(t - 8)$$

$$t + 12 = 0 \qquad t - 8 = 0$$
$$t = -12 \qquad\quad t = 8$$

The solution $t = -12$ is not possible because time cannot be a negative number.

The time for the smaller pipe is $t + 16$. Replace t by 8 and evaluate.

$$t + 16 = 8 + 16 = 24$$

The larger pipe requires 8 min to empty the tank.
The smaller pipe requires 24 min to empty the tank.

EXAMPLE 1   In 8 h, two campers rowed 15 mi down a river and then rowed back to their campsite. The rate of the river's current was 1 mph. Find the rate at which the campers row in calm water.

Strategy   ▶ This is a uniform motion problem.

▶ Unknown rowing rate of the campers: r

	Distance	÷	Rate	=	Time
Down river	15	÷	$r + 1$	=	$\dfrac{15}{r + 1}$
Up river	15	÷	$r - 1$	=	$\dfrac{15}{r - 1}$

▶ The total time of the trip was 8 h.

Solution
$$\frac{15}{r + 1} + \frac{15}{r - 1} = 8$$
$$(r + 1)(r - 1)\left(\frac{15}{r + 1} + \frac{15}{r - 1}\right) = (r + 1)(r - 1)8$$
$$(r - 1)15 + (r + 1)15 = (r^2 - 1)8$$
$$15r - 15 + 15r + 15 = 8r^2 - 8$$
$$30r = 8r^2 - 8$$
$$0 = 8r^2 - 30r - 8$$
$$0 = 2(4r^2 - 15r - 4)$$
$$0 = 2(4r + 1)(r - 4)$$

$$4r + 1 = 0 \qquad r - 4 = 0$$
$$4r = -1 \qquad\quad r = 4$$
$$r = -\frac{1}{4}$$

• The solution $r = -\frac{1}{4}$ is not possible because the rate cannot be a negative number.

The rowing rate is 4 mph.

PROBLEM 1   The length of a rectangle is 3 m more than the width. The area is 54 m². Find the length of the rectangle.

Solution   See page S26.

8.4   Concept Review

Determine whether the following statements are always true, sometimes true, or never true.

1. Let x be an integer. Then x^2 and $(x + 2)^2$ represent the squares of two consecutive odd integers.

2. Let x be an integer. Then x^2, $(x + 1)^2$, and $(x + 2)^2$ represent the squares of three consecutive integers.

3. If t is the time to complete an amount of work, then $\frac{1}{t}$ is the rate of doing work.

4. Let r be the rate of rowing a boat in calm water. If the river has a current of 2 mph, then the rate of rowing down the river is $r + 2$, and the rate of rowing up the river is $r - 2$.

8.4   Exercises

1   Application problems

1. The length of a rectangle is 4 ft less than twice the width. Let w be the width of the rectangle.
   a. In terms of w, the length of the rectangle is ____?____ ft.
   b. In terms of w, the area of the rectangle is ____?____ ft².
   c. The area of the rectangle is 96 ft². Use your answer to part b and the fact that the area of the rectangle is 96 ft² to write an equation that can be solved to find the width of the rectangle: ____?____ = ____?____.

2. **a.** Solve the equation from part c of Exercise 1.

$$w(2w - 4) = 96$$
$$\underline{\quad?\quad} - \underline{\quad?\quad} = 96 \qquad \bullet \text{ Use the Distributive Property.}$$
$$2w^2 - 4w - 96 = 0 \qquad \bullet \text{ Subtract } \underline{\quad?\quad} \text{ from each side of the equation.}$$
$$w^2 - 2w - 48 = 0 \qquad \bullet \text{ Divide each side of the equation by } \underline{\quad?\quad}.$$
$$(w - \underline{\quad?\quad})(w + \underline{\quad?\quad}) = 0 \qquad \bullet \text{ Factor the left side.}$$
$$\underline{\quad?\quad} = 0 \qquad \underline{\quad?\quad} = 0 \qquad \bullet \text{ Use the Principle of Zero Products.}$$
$$w = \underline{\quad?\quad} \qquad w = \underline{\quad?\quad} \qquad \bullet \text{ Solve for } w.$$

   b. Only one solution from part a makes sense as the width of the rectangle described in Exercise 1. The width of the rectangle is ____?____. The length of the rectangle is ____?____.

Complete Exercises 3 and 4 *without* writing and solving an equation. Use this situation: A small pipe takes 6 h longer to fill a tank than a large pipe. Working together, the pipes can fill the tank in 2 h.

3. 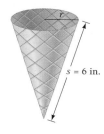 True or false? The amount of time that it takes the large pipe, working alone to fill the tank is less than 2 h.

4. True or false? The amount of time that it takes the small pipe, working alone to fill the tank is greater than 8 h.

Solve.

5. Farming A rectangular corral is constructed in a pasture. The length of the rectangle is 8 ft more than twice the width. The area of the rectangle is to be 640 ft^2. What are the length and width of the rectangle?

6. Manufacturing The surface area of the ice cream cone shown at the right is given by $A = \pi r^2 + \pi rs$, where r is the radius of the circular top of the ice cream cone and s is the slant height of the cone. If the area of the cone is 11.25π in^2 and the slant height of the cone is 6 in., find the radius of the cone.

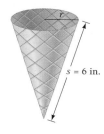

$s = 6$ in.

7. Geometry The length of a rectangle is 2 ft less than three times the width of the rectangle. The area of the rectangle is 65 ft^2. Find the length and width of the rectangle.

8. Geometry The length of a rectangle is 2 cm less than twice the width. The area of the rectangle is 180 cm^2. Find the length and width of the rectangle.

9. Geometry A square piece of cardboard is formed into a box by cutting 10-centimeter squares from each of the four corners and then folding up the sides, as shown in the figure. If the volume of the box is to be 49,000 cm^3, what size square piece of cardboard is needed?

10 cm

10 cm

10. Geography The state of Colorado is almost perfectly rectangular, with its north border 111 mi longer than its west border. The state encompasses 104,000 mi^2. Estimate the dimensions of Colorado. Round to the nearest mile.

Colorado

11. Transportation An 18-wheeler left a grain depot with a load of wheat and traveled 550 mi to deliver the wheat before returning to the depot. Because of the lighter load on the return trip, the average speed of the truck returning was 5 mph faster than its average speed going. Find the rate returning if the entire trip, not counting unloading time or rest stops, was 21 h.

12. Racing The *Tour de France* is a bicycle race that begins in Dublin, Ireland but is primarily a race through France. On each day, racers cover a certain distance depending on the steepness of the terrain. Suppose that on one particular day, the racers must complete 210 mi. One cyclist, traveling 10 mph faster than a second cyclist, covers this distance in 2.4 h less time than the second cyclist. Find the rate of the first cyclist.

13. **Physics** The height of a projectile fired upward is given by the formula $s = v_0t - 16t^2$, where s is the height, v_0 is the initial velocity, and t is the time. Find the time for a projectile to return to Earth if it has an initial velocity of 200 ft/s.

14. **Physics** The height of a projectile fired upward is given by the formula $s = v_0t - 16t^2$, where s is the height, v_0 is the initial velocity, and t is the time. Find the times at which a projectile with an initial velocity of 128 ft/s will be 64 ft above the ground. Round to the nearest hundredth of a second.

15. **Automotive Technology** In Germany, there are no speed limits on some portions of the autobahn (highway). Other portions have a speed limit of 180 km/h (approximately 112 mph). The distance, d (in meters), required to stop a car traveling at v kilometers per hour is $d = 0.019v^2 + 0.69v$. Approximate, to the nearest tenth, the maximum speed a driver can be going and still be able to stop within 150 m.

German Autobahn System

16. **Sports** A penalty kick in soccer is made from a penalty mark that is 36 ft from a goal that is 8 ft high. A possible equation for the flight of a penalty kick is $h = -0.002x^2 + 0.35x$, where h is the height (in feet) of the ball x feet from the penalty mark. Assuming that the flight of the kick is toward the goal and that it is not touched by the goalie, will the ball land in the net?

17. **Aeronautics** A model rocket is launched with an initial velocity of 200 ft/s. The height, h, of the rocket t seconds after the launch is given by $h = -16t^2 + 200t$. How many seconds after launch will the rocket be 300 ft above the ground? Round to the nearest hundredth of a second.

18. **Sports** A diver jumps from a platform that is 10 m high. The height of the diver t seconds after the beginning of the dive is given by $h = -4.9t^2 + 3.2t + 10.5$. To the nearest hundredth of a second, how long after the beginning of the dive will the diver enter the water?

19. **Petroleum Engineering** A small pipe can fill an oil tank in 6 min more time than it takes a larger pipe to fill the same tank. Working together, both pipes can fill the tank in 4 min. How long would it take each pipe, working alone, to fill the tank?

20. **Metallurgy** A small heating unit takes 8 h longer to melt a piece of iron than does a larger unit. Working together, the heating units can melt the iron in 3 h. How long would it take each heating unit, working alone, to melt the iron?

21. **Recreation** A cruise ship made a trip of 100 mi in 8 h. The ship traveled the first 40 mi at a constant rate before increasing its speed by 5 mph. Another 60 mi was traveled at the increased speed. Find the rate of the cruise ship for the first 40 mi.

22. **Sports** A cyclist traveled 60 mi at a constant rate before reducing the speed by 2 mph. Another 40 mi was traveled at the reduced speed. The total time for the 100-mile trip was 9 h. Find the rate during the first 60 mi.

23. **Aeronautics** The rate of a single-engine plane in calm air is 100 mph. Flying with the wind, the plane can fly 240 mi in 1 h less time than is required to make the return trip of 240 mi. Find the rate of the wind.

24. **Transportation** A car travels 120 mi. A second car, traveling 10 mph faster than the first car, makes the same trip in 1 h less time. Find the speed of each car.

25. **Sports** To prepare for an upcoming race, a sculling crew rowed 16 mi down a river and back in 6 h. If the rate of the river's current is 2 mph, find the sculling crew's rate of rowing in calm water.

26. **Sports** A fishing boat traveled 30 mi down a river and then returned. The total time for the round trip was 4 h, and the rate of the river's current was 4 mph. Find the rate of the boat in still water.

8.4   **Applying Concepts**

Solve.

27. **Number Problem** The numerator of a fraction is 3 less than the denominator. The sum of the fraction and four times its reciprocal is $\frac{17}{2}$. Find the fraction.

28. **Integer Problem** Find two consecutive even integers whose cubes differ by 488.

29. **Geometry** An open box is formed from a rectangular piece of cardboard whose length is 8 cm more than its width by cutting squares whose sides are 2 cm in length from each corner and then folding up the sides. Find the dimensions of the box if its volume is 256 cm^3.

30. **Construction** The height of an arch is given by the equation

$$h(x) = -\frac{3}{64}x^2 + 27, \quad -24 \le x \le 24$$

where $|x|$ is the distance in feet from the center of the arch.
a. What is the maximum height of the arch?
b. What is the height of the arch 8 ft to the right of center?
c. How far from the center is the arch 8 ft tall?

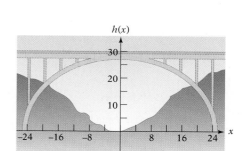

31. **Physics** Using Torricelli's Principle, it can be shown that the depth d, in centimeters, of a liquid in a bottle with a hole of area 0.5 cm^2 in its side can be approximated by $d = 0.0034t^2 - 0.52518t + 20$, where t is the time, in seconds, since a stopper was removed from the hole. When will the depth be 10 cm? Round to the nearest tenth.

32. Geometry The volumes of two spheres differ by 372π cm³. The radius of the larger sphere is 3 cm more than the radius of the smaller sphere. Find the radius of the larger sphere. $\left(\textit{Hint: } \text{The formula for the volume of a sphere is } V = \frac{4}{3}\pi r^3.\right)$

33. Geometry A perfectly spherical scoop of mint chocolate chip ice cream is placed in a cone as shown at the right. How far is the bottom of the scoop of ice cream from the bottom of the cone? (*Hint:* A line segment from the center of the scoop of ice cream to the point at which the ice cream touches the cone is perpendicular to the edge of the cone.)

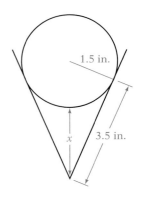

8.5   Nonlinear Inequalities

OBJECTIVE 1   **Solve nonlinear inequalities**

A **quadratic inequality in one variable** is one that can be written in the form $ax^2 + bx + c < 0$ or $ax^2 + bx + c > 0$, where $a \neq 0$. The symbols $\leq$ and $\geq$ can also be used.

Quadratic inequalities can be solved by algebraic means. However, it is often easier to use a graphical method to solve these inequalities. The graphical method is used in the example that follows.

Solve and graph the solution set of $x^2 - x - 6 < 0$.

Factor the trinomial.

$$x^2 - x - 6 < 0$$
$$(x - 3)(x + 2) < 0$$

On a number line, draw vertical lines at the numbers that make each factor equal to zero.

$$x - 3 = 0 \qquad x + 2 = 0$$
$$x = 3 \qquad\quad x = -2$$

For each factor, place plus signs above the number line for those regions where the factor is positive and place negative signs where the factor is negative. $x - 3$ is positive for $x > 3$, and $x + 2$ is positive for $x > -2$.

Because $x^2 - x - 6 < 0$, the solution set will be the regions where one factor is positive and the other factor is negative.

Write the solution set.

$\{x\,|-2 < x < 3\}$

The graph of the solution set of the inequality $x^2 - x - 6 < 0$ is shown at the right.

$$\begin{array}{c} \longleftrightarrow \!\!\!+\!\!+\!\!+\!\!(\!+\!\!+\!\!+\!\!+\!\!+\!)\!\!+\!\!+ \\ -5\ -4\ -3\ -2\ -1\ \ 0\ \ 1\ \ 2\ \ 3\ \ 4\ \ 5 \end{array}$$

This method of solving quadratic inequalities can be used on any polynomial that can be factored into linear factors.

Solve and graph the solution set of $x^3 - 4x^2 - 4x + 16 > 0$.

Factor the polynomial by grouping.

$$x^3 - 4x^2 - 4x + 16 > 0$$
$$x^2(x - 4) - 4(x - 4) > 0$$
$$(x^2 - 4)(x - 4) > 0$$
$$(x - 2)(x + 2)(x - 4) > 0$$

On a number line, identify for each factor the regions where the factor is positive and where the factor is negative.

There are two regions where the product of the three factors is positive.

Write the solution set.

$\{x\,|-2 < x < 2 \text{ or } x > 4\}$

The graph of the solution set of the inequality $x^3 - 4x^2 - 4x + 16 > 0$ is shown at the right.

$$\begin{array}{c} \longleftrightarrow \!\!\!+\!\!+\!\!+\!\!(\!+\!\!+\!\!+\!\!)\!\!+\!\!+\!\!(\!+ \\ -5\ -4\ -3\ -2\ -1\ \ 0\ \ 1\ \ 2\ \ 3\ \ 4\ \ 5 \end{array}$$

EXAMPLE 1   Solve and graph the solution set of $2x^2 - x - 3 \ge 0$.

Solution
$$2x^2 - x - 3 \ge 0$$
$$(2x - 3)(x + 1) \ge 0$$

$$\left\{x\,|\,x \le -1 \text{ or } x \ge \dfrac{3}{2}\right\}$$

PROBLEM 1   Solve and graph the solution set of $2x^2 - x - 10 \le 0$.

Solution   See page S26.

The graphical method can be used to solve rational inequalities.

Solve: $\dfrac{2x - 5}{x - 4} \le 1$

$$\dfrac{2x - 5}{x - 4} \le 1$$

Rewrite the inequality so that 0 appears on the right side of the inequality.

$$\dfrac{2x - 5}{x - 4} - 1 \le 0$$

Then simplify.

$$\dfrac{2x - 5}{x - 4} - \dfrac{x - 4}{x - 4} \le 0$$

$$\dfrac{x - 1}{x - 4} \le 0$$

On a number line, identify for each factor of the numerator and each factor of the denominator the regions where the factor is positive and where the factor is negative.

The region where the quotient of the two factors is negative is between 1 and 4.

Write the solution set.

$$\{x \mid 1 \le x < 4\}$$

Note that 1 is part of the solution set, but 4 is not part of the solution set because the denominator of the rational expression is zero when $x = 4$.

EXAMPLE 2   Solve and graph the solution set of $\dfrac{x + 4}{x - 3} \ge 0$.

Solution $\dfrac{x + 4}{x - 3} \ge 0$

$\{x \mid x > 3 \text{ or } x \le -4\}$

PROBLEM 2   Solve and graph the solution set of $\dfrac{x}{x - 2} \le 0$.

Solution   See page S26.

8.5 Concept Review

Determine whether the following statements are always true, sometimes true, or never true.

1. The endpoints of a solution set of a quadratic inequality are not included in the solution set.

2. The solution set of $(x - 3)(x - 2)(x + 2) > 0$ is 3, 2, and -2.

3. The solution set of a quadratic inequality is an infinite set.

4. The solution set of $\dfrac{1}{x - 1} > 0$ is $\{x \mid x > 1\}$.

8.5 Exercises

1 **Solve nonlinear inequalities**

1. For the nonlinear inequality $\dfrac{x - 2}{x - 3} \geq 1$, is 3 a possible element of the solution set? Why or why not?

2. To use a number line diagram to solve the inequality $(x + 3)(x - 8) > 0$, begin by drawing vertical lines through ____?____ and ____?____.

3. When x is between -4 and 7, the numerator of $\dfrac{x - 7}{x + 4}$ is negative and the denominator is ____?____. The quotient of a negative number and a positive number is ____?____, so the expression $\dfrac{x - 7}{x + 4}$ is ____?____ for all values of x between -4 and 7.

4. If $(x - 3)(x - 5) > 0$, what must be true of the values of $x - 3$ and $x - 5$?

Solve and graph the solution set.

5. $(x - 4)(x + 2) > 0$ 　　　　　　　　　　**6.** $(x + 1)(x - 3) > 0$

7. $x^2 - 3x + 2 \geq 0$ 　　　　　　　　　　**8.** $x^2 + 5x + 6 > 0$

9. $x^2 - x - 12 < 0$

10. $x^2 + x - 20 < 0$

11. $(x - 1)(x + 2)(x - 3) < 0$

12. $(x + 4)(x - 2)(x - 1) \geq 0$

13. $\dfrac{x - 4}{x + 2} > 0$

14. $\dfrac{x + 2}{x - 3} > 0$

15. $\dfrac{x - 3}{x + 1} \leq 0$

16. $\dfrac{x - 1}{x} > 0$

17. $\dfrac{(x - 1)(x + 2)}{x - 3} \leq 0$

18. $\dfrac{(x + 3)(x - 1)}{x - 2} \geq 0$

19. Which inequalities can be solved using this diagram?

a. $x(x + 3)(x - 4) > 0$ **b.** $x + 3 < x(x - 4)$

c. $0 > \dfrac{x}{3 - x}$ **d.** $\dfrac{x + 3}{x(x - 4)} < 0$

20. $a, b,$ and c are positive numbers such that $a < b < c$. In which of the following intervals is the product $(x - a)(x - b)(x - c)$ always negative?
a. $\{x \mid a < x < c\}$ **b.** $\{x \mid x > c\}$
c. $\{x \mid x < a\}$ **d.** $\{x \mid b < x < c\}$

Solve.

21. $x^2 - 16 > 0$

22. $x^2 - 4 \geq 0$

23. $x^2 - 4x + 4 > 0$

24. $x^2 + 6x + 9 > 0$

25. $x^2 - 9x \leq 36$

26. $x^2 + 4x > 21$

27. $2x^2 - 5x + 2 \geq 0$

28. $4x^2 - 9x + 2 < 0$

29. $4x^2 - 8x + 3 < 0$

30. $2x^2 + 11x + 12 \geq 0$

31. $(x - 6)(x + 3)(x - 2) \leq 0$

32. $(x + 5)(x - 2)(x - 3) > 0$

33. $(2x - 1)(x - 4)(2x + 3) > 0$

34. $(x - 2)(3x - 1)(x + 2) \leq 0$

35. $x^3 + 3x^2 - x - 3 \leq 0$

36. $x^3 + x^2 - 9x - 9 < 0$

37. $x^3 - x^2 - 4x + 4 \geq 0$

38. $2x^3 + 3x^2 - 8x - 12 \geq 0$

39. $\dfrac{3x}{x - 2} > 1$

40. $\dfrac{2x}{x + 1} < 1$

41. $\dfrac{2}{x + 1} \geq 2$

42. $\dfrac{3}{x - 1} < 2$

43. $\dfrac{x}{(x - 1)(x + 2)} \geq 0$

44. $\dfrac{x - 2}{(x + 1)(x - 1)} \leq 0$

45. $\dfrac{1}{x} < 2$

46. $\dfrac{x}{2x - 1} \geq 1$

8.5 Applying Concepts

Graph the solution set.

47. $(x + 2)(x - 3)(x + 1)(x + 4) > 0$

48. $(x - 1)(x + 3)(x - 2)(x - 4) \geq 0$

49. $(x^2 + 2x - 8)(x^2 - 2x - 3) < 0$

50. $(x^2 + 2x - 3)(x^2 + 3x + 2) \geq 0$

51. $(x^2 + 1)(x^2 - 3x + 2) > 0$

52. $(x^2 - 9)(x^2 + 5x + 6) \leq 0$

53. $\dfrac{x^2(3 - x)(2x + 1)}{(x + 4)(x + 2)} \geq 0$

54. $\dfrac{1}{x} + x > 2$

55. $3x - \dfrac{1}{x} \leq 2$

56. $x^2 - x < \dfrac{1 - x}{x}$

8.6 | **Properties of Quadratic Functions**

OBJECTIVE **1**   ### Graph a quadratic function

Recall that a linear function is one that can be expressed by the equation $f(x) = mx + b$. The graph of a linear function has certain characteristics. It is a straight line with slope m and y-intercept $(0, b)$. A **quadratic function** is one that can be expressed by the equation $f(x) = ax^2 + bx + c, a \neq 0$. The graph of this function, which is called a **parabola**, also has certain characteristics. The graph of a quadratic function can be drawn by finding ordered pairs that belong to the function.

Take Note

Sometimes the value of the independent variable is called the **input** because it is *put in* place of the independent variable. The result of evaluating the function is called the **output**.

An **input/output table** shows the results of evaluating a function for various values of the independent variable. An input/output table for $f(x) = x^2 - 2x - 3$ is shown at the right.

■   Graph: $f(x) = x^2 - 2x - 3$

By evaluating the function for various values of x, find enough ordered pairs to determine the shape of the graph.

x	$f(x) = x^2 - 2x - 3$	$f(x)$	(x, y)
-2	$f(-2) = (-2)^2 - 2(-2) - 3$	5	$(-2, 5)$
-1	$f(-1) = (-1)^2 - 2(-1) - 3$	0	$(-1, 0)$
0	$f(0) = (0)^2 - 2(0) - 3$	-3	$(0, -3)$
1	$f(1) = (1)^2 - 2(1) - 3$	-4	$(1, -4)$
2	$f(2) = (2)^2 - 2(2) - 3$	-3	$(2, -3)$
3	$f(3) = (3)^2 - 2(3) - 3$	0	$(3, 0)$
4	$f(4) = (4)^2 - 2(4) - 3$	5	$(4, 5)$

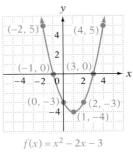

Because the value of $f(x) = x^2 - 2x - 3$ is a real number for all values of x, the domain of f is all real numbers. From the graph, it appears that no value of y is less than -4. Thus the range is $\{y \mid y \geq -4\}$. The range can also be determined algebraically, as shown below, by completing the square.

$$f(x) = x^2 - 2x - 3$$

Group the variable terms. $f(x) = (x^2 - 2x) - 3$

Complete the square of $x^2 - 2x$. Add and $f(x) = (x^2 - 2x + 1) - 1 - 3$
subtract $\left[\frac{1}{2}(-2)\right]^2 = 1$ to $x^2 - 2x$.

Factor and combine like terms. $f(x) = (x - 1)^2 - 4$

The square of a number is always positive. $(x - 1)^2 \geq 0$

Subtract 4 from each side of the inequality. $(x - 1)^2 - 4 \geq -4$

Replace $(x - 1)^2 - 4$ with $f(x)$. $f(x) \geq -4$
                                                  $y \geq -4$

Take Note

In completing the square, 1 is both added and subtracted. Because $1 - 1 = 0$, the expression $x^2 - 2x - 3$ is not changed. Note that

$(x - 1)^2 - 4$
$= (x^2 - 2x + 1) - 4$
$= x^2 - 2x - 3$

which is the original expression.

From the last inequality, the range is $\{y \mid y \geq -4\}$.

In general, the graph of $f(x) = ax^2 + bx + c, a \neq 0$, resembles a "cup" shape as shown on the next page. The parabola opens up when $a > 0$ and opens down when $a < 0$. The **vertex** of the parabola is the point with the smallest y-coordinate when $a > 0$ and is the point with the largest y-coordinate when $a < 0$.

$a > 0$

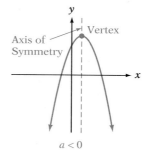

$a < 0$

The **axis of symmetry** is a line that passes through the vertex of the parabola and is parallel to the y-axis. To understand the axis of symmetry, think of folding the graph along that line. The two portions of the graph will match up.

The vertex and axis of symmetry of a parabola can be found by completing the square.

Find the vertex and the axis of symmetry of the graph of $F(x) = x^2 + 4x + 3$.

To find the coordinates of the vertex, complete the square. Group the variable terms.

$F(x) = x^2 + 4x + 3$

$F(x) = (x^2 + 4x) + 3$

Complete the square of $x^2 + 4x$. Add and subtract $\left[\frac{1}{2}(4)\right]^2 = 4$ to and from $x^2 + 4x$.

$F(x) = (x^2 + 4x + 4) - 4 + 3$

Factor and combine like terms.

$F(x) = (x + 2)^2 - 1$

Because a, the coefficient of x^2, is positive ($a = 1$), the parabola opens up and the vertex is the point with the least y-coordinate. Because $(x + 2)^2 \geq 0$ for all values of x, the least y-coordinate occurs when $(x + 2)^2 = 0$. When $x = -2$, this expression equals zero.

The x-coordinate of the vertex is -2.

To find the y-coordinate of the vertex, evaluate the function at $x = -2$.

$F(x) = (x + 2)^2 - 1$
$F(-2) = (-2 + 2)^2 - 1 = -1$

The y-coordinate of the vertex is -1.

From these results, the coordinates of the vertex are $(-2, -1)$. The axis of symmetry is the line whose equation is $x = -2$.

By following the process illustrated in the last example and completing the square of $f(x) = ax^2 + bx + c$, we can find a formula for the coordinates of the vertex of a parabola.

Vertex and Axis of Symmetry of a Parabola

Let $f(x) = ax^2 + bx + c$ be the equation of a parabola. The coordinates of the vertex are $\left(-\dfrac{b}{2a}, f\left(-\dfrac{b}{2a}\right)\right)$. The equation of the axis of symmetry is $x = -\dfrac{b}{2a}$.

The coordinates of the vertex and the axis of symmetry can be used to graph a parabola.

Graph $y = x^2 + 2x - 3$ using the vertex and the axis of symmetry.

Find the x-coordinate of the vertex. $a = 1$ and $b = 2$.

$$x = -\frac{b}{2a} = -\frac{2}{2(1)} = -1$$

Find the y-coordinate of the vertex by replacing x with -1 and solving for y.

$$\begin{aligned} y &= x^2 + 2x - 3 \\ y &= (-1)^2 + 2(-1) - 3 \\ y &= 1 - 2 - 3 \\ y &= -4 \end{aligned}$$

The vertex is $(-1, -4)$.

The axis of symmetry is the line $x = -1$.

Find some ordered-pair solutions of the equation and record these in a table. Because the graph is symmetric to the line $x = -1$, choose values of x greater than -1.

x	y
0	-3
1	0
2	5

Graph the ordered-pair solutions on a rectangular coordinate system. Use symmetry to locate points of the graph on the other side of the axis of symmetry. Remember that corresponding points on the graph are the same distance from the axis of symmetry.

Draw a parabola through the points.

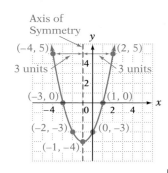

Using a graphing utility, graph the equation $y = x^2 + 2x - 3$ with a domain of $[-4.7, 4.7]$. Trace along the graph and verify that $(-1, -4)$ are the coordinates of the vertex.

EXAMPLE 1   Find the vertex and the axis of symmetry of the parabola whose equation is $y = -3x^2 + 6x + 1$. Then sketch its graph.

Solution $x = -\dfrac{b}{2a} = -\dfrac{6}{2(-3)} = 1$

$y = -3x^2 + 6x + 1$
$y = -3(1)^2 + 6(1) + 1$
$y = 4$

• Find the *x*-coordinate of the vertex.
$a = -3$ and $b = 6$.
• Find the *y*-coordinate of the vertex by replacing *x* by 1 and solving for *y*.

The vertex is (1, 4).

The axis of symmetry is the line $x = 1$.

• The axis of symmetry is the line $x = -\dfrac{b}{2a}$.

• Because *a* is negative, the parabola opens down. Find a few ordered pairs, and use symmetry to sketch the graph.

PROBLEM 1   Find the vertex and the axis of symmetry of the parabola whose equation is $y = x^2 - 2$. Then sketch its graph.

Solution   See page S26.

EXAMPLE 2   Graph $f(x) = -2x^2 - 4x + 3$. State the domain and range of the function.

Solution   Because *a* is negative ($a = -2$), the graph of *f* will open down. The *x*-coordinate of the vertex is

$x = -\dfrac{b}{2a} = -\dfrac{-4}{2(-2)} = -1.$

The *y*-coordinate of the vertex is
$f(-1) = -2(-1)^2 - 4(-1) + 3 = 5$. The vertex is (−1, 5).

Evaluate $f(x)$ for various values of x, and use symmetry to draw the graph.

Because $f(x) = -2x^2 - 4x + 3$ is a real number for all values of x, the domain of the function is $\{x \,|\, x \in \text{real numbers}\}$. The vertex of the parabola is the highest point on the graph. Because the *y*-coordinate at that point is 5, the range is $\{y \,|\, y \le 5\}$.

PROBLEM 2   Graph $g(x) = x^2 + 4x - 2$. State the domain and range of the function.

Solution   See page S26.

Take Note

Once the coordinates of the vertex are found, the range of the quadratic function can be determined.

OBJECTIVE **2**   ## Find the *x*-intercepts of a parabola

Recall that a point at which a graph crosses the *x*- or *y*-axis is called an *intercept* of the graph. The *x*-intercepts of the graph of an equation occur when $y = 0$; the *y*-intercepts occur when $x = 0$.

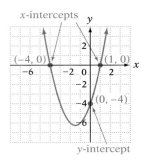

The graph of $y = x^2 + 3x - 4$ is shown at the right. The points whose coordinates are $(-4, 0)$ and $(1, 0)$ are *x*-intercepts of the graph.

Find the *x*-intercepts for the parabola whose equation is $y = 4x^2 - 4x + 1$.

To find *x*-intercepts, let $y = 0$.	$y = 4x^2 - 4x + 1$ $0 = 4x^2 - 4x + 1$
Solve for *x* by factoring and using the Principle of Zero Products.	$0 = (2x - 1)(2x - 1)$

$$2x - 1 = 0 \qquad\qquad 2x - 1 = 0$$
$$2x = 1 \qquad\qquad 2x = 1$$
$$x = \frac{1}{2} \qquad\qquad x = \frac{1}{2}$$

The *x*-intercept is $\left(\frac{1}{2}, 0\right)$.

In this last example, the parabola has only one *x*-intercept. In this case, the parabola is said to be *tangent* to the *x*-axis at $x = \frac{1}{2}$.

Find the *x*-intercepts of $y = 2x^2 - x - 6$.

To find the *x*-intercepts, let $y = 0$.	$y = 2x^2 - x - 6$ $0 = 2x^2 - x - 6$
Solve for *x* by factoring and using the Principle of Zero Products.	$0 = (2x + 3)(x - 2)$

$$2x + 3 = 0 \qquad\qquad x - 2 = 0$$
$$x = -\frac{3}{2} \qquad\qquad x = 2$$

The *x*-intercepts are $\left(-\frac{3}{2}, 0\right)$ and $(2, 0)$.

Take Note

We are being careful in this discussion to say *real zero*, by which we mean a zero that is a real number. Later in this section, we will discuss complex number zeros.

If the equation $y = 2x^2 - x - 6$ were written in function notation as $f(x) = 2x^2 - x - 6$, then to find the *x*-intercepts you would let $f(x) = 0$ and solve for *x*. Recall that a value of *x* for which $f(x) = 0$ is a *zero* of the function.

Thus, $-\frac{3}{2}$ and 2 are zeros of $f(x) = 2x^2 - x - 6$.

Find the zeros of $f(x) = x^2 - 2x - 1$.

To find the zeros, let $f(x) = 0$ and solve for x.

Because $x^2 - 2x - 1$ does not easily factor, use the quadratic formula to solve for x.

$a = 1$, $b = -2$, and $c = -1$.

$$f(x) = x^2 - 2x - 1$$
$$0 = x^2 - 2x - 1$$
$$x = \frac{-b \pm \sqrt{b^2 - 4ac}}{2a}$$
$$= \frac{-(-2) \pm \sqrt{(-2)^2 - 4(1)(-1)}}{2(1)}$$
$$= \frac{2 \pm \sqrt{4 + 4}}{2}$$
$$= \frac{2 \pm \sqrt{8}}{2}$$
$$= \frac{2 \pm 2\sqrt{2}}{2}$$
$$= 1 \pm \sqrt{2}$$

The zeros of the function are $1 - \sqrt{2}$ and $1 + \sqrt{2}$.

The graph of $f(x) = x^2 - 2x - 1$ is shown at the right. Note that the zeros are the x-intercepts of the graph of f.

$(1 - \sqrt{2}, 0)$ $(1 + \sqrt{2}, 0)$

The preceding example demonstrates that the x-coordinate of an x-intercept of the graph of a function is a real zero of the function, and a real zero of a function is the x-coordinate of an x-intercept of the graph of the function.

As mentioned in the Take Note on page 544, a function may have complex number zeros.

Find the zeros of $f(x) = -x^2 + 2x - 2$.

To find the zeros, let $f(x) = 0$ and solve for x.

Because $-x^2 + 2x - 1$ does not easily factor, use the quadratic formula to solve for x.

$a = -1$, $b = 2$, $c = -2$

$$f(x) = -x^2 + 2x - 2$$
$$0 = -x^2 + 2x - 2$$
$$x = \frac{-b \pm \sqrt{b^2 - 4ac}}{2a}$$
$$= \frac{-2 \pm \sqrt{2^2 - 4(-1)(-2)}}{2(-1)}$$
$$= \frac{-2 \pm \sqrt{4 - 8}}{-2}$$
$$= \frac{-2 \pm \sqrt{-4}}{-2} = \frac{-2 \pm 2i}{-2}$$
$$= 1 \pm i$$

The complex zeros of the function are $1 - i$ and $1 + i$.

The graph of $f(x) = -x^2 + 2x - 2$ is shown at the right. Note that the graph does not cross the x-axis.

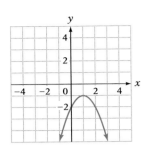

This example shows that a function can have a zero without crossing the x-axis. The zero of the function, in this case, is a complex number. If the graph of a quadratic function crosses the x-axis, it has a real zero. If the graph never crosses the x-axis, it has only complex zeros. See the Applying Concept exercises for functions that have both real and complex zeros.

EXAMPLE 3   Find the x-intercepts of the parabola given by each equation.

   A. $y = x^2 + 2x - 2$ **B.** $y = 4x^2 + 4x + 1$

Solution   **A.** $y = x^2 + 2x - 2$

   $0 = x^2 + 2x - 2$ • Let $y = 0$.

   $x = \dfrac{-b \pm \sqrt{b^2 - 4ac}}{2a}$ • The equation is nonfactorable over the integers. Use the quadratic formula to solve for x.

   $= \dfrac{-(2) \pm \sqrt{(2)^2 - 4(1)(-2)}}{2 \cdot 1}$

   $= \dfrac{-2 \pm \sqrt{4 + 8}}{2}$

   $= \dfrac{-2 \pm \sqrt{12}}{2}$

   $= \dfrac{-2 \pm 2\sqrt{3}}{2} = -1 \pm \sqrt{3}$

   The x-intercepts are $\left(-1 + \sqrt{3}, 0\right)$ and $\left(-1 - \sqrt{3}, 0\right)$.

   B. $y = 4x^2 + 4x + 1$

   $0 = 4x^2 + 4x + 1$ • Let $y = 0$.

   $0 = (2x + 1)(2x + 1)$ • Solve for x by factoring.

   $2x + 1 = 0 \qquad 2x + 1 = 0$

   $ 2x = -1 \qquad 2x = -1$

   $ x = -\dfrac{1}{2} \qquad x = -\dfrac{1}{2}$ • The equation has a double root.

   The x-intercept is $\left(-\dfrac{1}{2}, 0\right)$.

PROBLEM 3   Find the x-intercepts of the parabola given by each equation.

   A. $y = 2x^2 - 5x + 2$ **B.** $y = x^2 + 4x + 4$

Solution   See page S26.

The zeros of a quadratic function can always be determined exactly by solving a quadratic equation. However, it is possible to approximate the real zeros by graphing the function and determining the x-intercepts.

EXAMPLE 4 Graph $f(x) = 2x^2 - x - 5$. Estimate the real zeros of the function to the nearest tenth.

Solution Graph the function. Then use the features of a graphing utility to estimate the zeros.

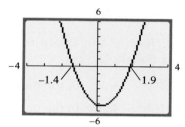

The approximate values of the zeros are -1.4 and 1.9.

PROBLEM 4 Graph $f(x) = -x^2 - 4x + 6$. Estimate the real zeros of the function to the nearest tenth.

Solution See page S26.

In Examples 3 and 4, we found values of x in the domain of a function f for which $f(x) = 0$. We can extend this to finding values in the domain for which $f(x) = c$, where c is a real number.

EXAMPLE 5 Find two values of x in the domain of $f(x) = x^2 + 2x - 1$ for which $f(x) = 3$.

Solution

$$f(x) = x^2 + 2x - 1$$
$$3 = x^2 + 2x - 1$$
$$0 = x^2 + 2x - 4$$

• We are trying to find x for which $f(x) = 3$. Replace $f(x)$ by 3 and solve for x.

$$x = \frac{-b \pm \sqrt{b^2 - 4ac}}{2a}$$

$$= \frac{-2 \pm \sqrt{2^2 - 4(1)(-4)}}{2(1)}$$

$$= \frac{-2 \pm \sqrt{4 + 16}}{2}$$

$$= \frac{-2 \pm \sqrt{20}}{2}$$

$$= \frac{-2 \pm 2\sqrt{5}}{2}$$

$$= -1 \pm \sqrt{5}$$

• Because $x^2 + 2x - 4$ does not easily factor, use the quadratic formula to solve for x. $a = 1, b = 2, c = -4$.

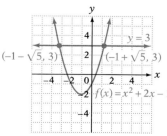

The values of x for which $f(x) = 3$ are $-1 - \sqrt{5}$ and $-1 + \sqrt{5}$. The graph of $f(x) = x^2 + 2x - 1$ is shown above. Note that the graph crosses the line $y = 3$ when $x = -1 - \sqrt{5}$ and $x = -1 + \sqrt{5}$.

PROBLEM 5   Find two values of x in the domain of $f(x) = -x^2 - 4x + 2$ for which $f(x) = -4$.

Solution   See pages S26–S27.

Recall that the discriminant of $ax^2 + bx + c$ is the expression $b^2 - 4ac$ and that this expression can be used to determine whether $ax^2 + bx + c = 0$ has zero, one, or two real number solutions. Because there is a connection between the solutions of $ax^2 + bx + c = 0$ and the x-intercepts of the graph of $y = ax^2 + bx + c$, the discriminant can be used to determine the number of x-intercepts of a parabola.

> **Effect of the Discriminant on the Number of x-Intercepts of a Parabola**
>
> 1. If $b^2 - 4ac = 0$, the parabola has one x-intercept.
>
> 2. If $b^2 - 4ac > 0$, the parabola has two x-intercepts.
>
> 3. If $b^2 - 4ac < 0$, the parabola has no x-intercepts.

Use the discriminant to determine the number of x-intercepts of the parabola whose equation is $y = 2x^2 - x + 2$.

$$a = 2, b = -1, c = 2$$

Evaluate the discriminant.

$$b^2 - 4ac = (-1)^2 - 4(2)(2)$$
$$= 1 - 16$$
$$= -15$$

$$-15 < 0$$

The discriminant is less than zero, so the parabola has no x-intercepts.

EXAMPLE 6   Use the discriminant to determine the number of x-intercepts of the parabola whose equation is $y = x^2 - 6x + 9$.

Solution $b^2 - 4ac = (-6)^2 - 4(1)(9)$ • $a = 1, b = -6, c = 9$
$$= 36 - 36$$
$$= 0$$ • The discriminant is equal to zero.

The parabola has one x-intercept.

PROBLEM 6   Use the discriminant to determine the number of x-intercepts of the parabola whose equation is $y = x^2 - x - 6$.

Solution   See page S27.

8.6   Concept Review

Determine whether the following statements are always true, sometimes true, or never true.

1. The axis of symmetry of a parabola goes through the origin.

2. The vertex is the lowest point on the graph of a quadratic function.

3. A parabola has two x-intercepts.

4. If the discriminant for a quadratic function is zero, the graph of the function has one x-intercept.

5. The graph of a quadratic function has one y-intercept.

6. The domain of a quadratic function is the set of real numbers.

8.6   Exercises

1   Graph a quadratic function

1. What is a quadratic function?

2. What are the vertex and axis of symmetry of the graph of a parabola?

3. The axis of symmetry of a parabola is the line $x = -5$. What is the x-coordinate of the vertex of the parabola?

4. The axis of symmetry of a parabola is the line $x = 8$. What is the x-coordinate of the vertex of the parabola?

5. The vertex of a parabola is $(7, -9)$. What is the equation of the axis of symmetry of the parabola?

6. The vertex of a parabola is $(-4, 10)$. What is the equation of the axis of symmetry of the parabola?

7. Use the quadratic function $f(x) = 3x^2 - 1$.
  a. The function is in the standard form $f(x) = ax^2 + bx + c$, where
  $a = \underline{\quad?\quad}$, $b = \underline{\quad?\quad}$, and $c = \underline{\quad?\quad}$.
  b. The graph of the function is a $\underline{\quad?\quad}$. Because $a > 0$, the graph
  opens $\underline{\quad?\quad}$.
  c. The x-coordinate of the vertex is $x = -\dfrac{b}{2a} = -\dfrac{\underline{\quad?\quad}}{2(\underline{\quad?\quad})} = \underline{\quad?\quad}$.
  d. The y-coordinate of the vertex is $f(0) = 3(\underline{\quad?\quad})^2 - 1 = \underline{\quad?\quad}$.
  The vertex of the parabola is $(\underline{\quad?\quad}, \underline{\quad?\quad})$.

8. Use the results of Exercise 7.
  a. The axis of symmetry of the graph of $f(x) = 3x^2 - 1$ is the vertical line
  $x = \underline{\quad?\quad}$.
  b. One point on the graph of $f(x) = 3x^2 - 1$ is (2, 11). This point is
  $\underline{\quad?\quad}$ units to the right of the axis of symmetry. The corresponding
  point 2 units to the left of the axis of the symmetry is $(\underline{\quad?\quad}, \underline{\quad?\quad})$.

Find the vertex and axis of symmetry of the parabola given by each equation.
Then sketch its graph.

9. $y = x^2$

10. $y = -x^2$

11. $y = x^2 - 2$

12. $y = x^2 + 2$

13. $y = -x^2 + 3$

14. $y = -x^2 - 1$

15. $y = \dfrac{1}{2}x^2$

16. $y = 2x^2$

17. $y = 2x^2 - 1$

18. $y = -\dfrac{1}{2}x^2 + 2$

19. $y = x^2 - 2x$

20. $y = x^2 + 2x$

21. $y = -2x^2 + 4x$

22. $y = \dfrac{1}{2}x^2 - x$

23. $y = x^2 - x - 2$

24. $y = x^2 - 3x + 2$

25. $y = 2x^2 - x - 5$

26. $y = 2x^2 - x - 3$

Graph the function. State the domain and range of the function.

27. $f(x) = 2x^2 - 4x - 5$

28. $f(x) = 2x^2 + 8x + 3$

29. $f(x) = -2x^2 - 3x + 2$

30. $f(x) = 2x^2 - 7x + 3$

31. $f(x) = x^2 - 4x + 4$

32. $f(x) = -x^2 + 6x - 9$

33. $f(x) = x^2 + 4x - 3$

34. $f(x) = x^2 - 2x - 2$

35. $f(x) = -x^2 - 4x - 5$

36. $f(x) = -x^2 + 4x + 1$

For Exercises 37 to 40, use the quadratic function $f(x) = ax^2 + bx + c$.

37. True or false? If $a < 0$, then the range of f is $\left\{ y \mid y \geq f\left(-\dfrac{b}{2a}\right) \right\}$.

38. True or false? If $b = 0$, then the axis of symmetry is the y-axis.

39. If $a > 0$ and $b < 0$, is the axis of symmetry is to the left or to the right of the y-axis?

40. True or false? If $b = 2a$, then the point with x-coordinate -2 has the same y-coordinate as the point with x-coordinate 0.

2 Find the x-intercepts of a parabola

41. If 3 is a zero of the function $y = f(x)$, then $f(\underline{\quad ? \quad}) = \underline{\quad ? \quad}$, and $(\underline{\quad ? \quad}, \underline{\quad ? \quad})$ is an $\underline{\quad ? \quad}$-intercept of the graph of $y = f(x)$.

42. Use the equation $y = 2x^2 - 3x + 5$. The discriminant is $b^2 - 4ac = (\underline{\quad ? \quad})^2 - 4(\underline{\quad ? \quad})(\underline{\quad ? \quad}) = \underline{\quad ? \quad} - \underline{\quad ? \quad} = \underline{\quad ? \quad}$. Because the discriminant is negative, the graph of $y = 2x^2 - 3x + 5$ has $\underline{\quad ? \quad}$ x-intercepts.

43. How can you find the x-intercepts for the graph of a quadratic function?

44. How can the discriminant be used to determine the number of x-intercepts for the graph of a quadratic function?

Find the x-intercepts of the parabola given by each equation.

45. $y = x^2 - 4$

46. $y = x^2 - 9$

47. $y = 2x^2 - 4x$

48. $y = 3x^2 + 6x$

49. $y = x^2 - x - 2$

50. $y = x^2 - 2x - 8$

51. $y = 2x^2 - 5x - 3$

52. $y = 4x^2 + 11x + 6$

53. $y = 3x^2 - 19x - 14$

54. $y = 6x^2 + 7x + 2$

55. $y = 3x^2 - 19x + 20$

56. $y = 3x^2 + 19x + 28$

57. $y = 9x^2 - 12x + 4$

58. $y = x^2 - 2$

59. $y = 9x^2 - 2$

60. $y = 2x^2 - x - 1$

61. $y = 4x^2 - 4x - 15$

62. $y = x^2 + 2x - 1$

63. $y = x^2 + 4x - 3$

64. $y = x^2 + 6x + 10$

65. $y = -x^2 - 4x - 5$

66. $y = x^2 - 2x - 2$

67. $y = -x^2 - 2x + 1$

68. $y = -x^2 + 4x + 1$

Find the zeros of the function.

69. $f(x) = x^2 + 3x + 2$

70. $f(x) = x^2 - 6x + 9$

71. $f(x) = -x^2 + 4x - 5$

72. $f(x) = -x^2 + 3x + 8$

73. $f(x) = 2x^2 - 3x$

74. $f(x) = -3x^2 + 4x$

75. $f(x) = 2x^2 - 4$

76. $f(x) = 3x^2 + 6$

77. $f(x) = 2x^2 + 3x + 2$

78. $f(x) = 3x^2 - x + 4$

79. $f(x) = -3x^2 + 4x - 1$

80. $f(x) = -2x^2 + x + 5$

81. The zeros of the function $f(x) = x^2 - 2x - 3$ are -1 and 3. What are the x-intercepts of the graph of the equation $y = x^2 - 2x - 3$?

82. The zeros of the function $f(x) = x^2 - x - 20$ are -4 and 5. What are the x-intercepts of the graph of the equation $y = x^2 - x - 20$?

Graph the function. Estimate the real zeros of the function to the nearest tenth.

83. $f(x) = x^2 + 3x - 1$

84. $f(x) = x^2 - 2x - 4$

85. $f(x) = 2x^2 - 3x - 7$

86. $f(x) = -2x^2 - x + 2$

87. $f(x) = x^2 + 6x + 12$

88. $f(x) = x^2 - 3x + 9$

89. Find two values of x in the domain of $f(x) = x^2 - 10x - 5$ for which $f(x) = 2$.

90. Find two values of x in the domain of $f(x) = x^2 - 4x - 20$ for which $f(x) = 3$.

91. Find two values of x in the domain of $f(x) = x^2 - 2x - 10$ for which $f(x) = 7$.

92. Find two values of x in the domain of $f(x) = x^2 - 2x + 2$ for which $f(x) = 6$.

93. Show that there are no values of x in the domain of $f(x) = x^2 - 2x + 11$ for which $f(x) = 2$.

94. Show that there are no values of x in the domain of $f(x) = x^2 - 4x + 5$ for which $f(x) = -17$.

Use the discriminant to determine the number of x-intercepts of the graph of the parabola.

95. $y = 2x^2 + x + 1$

96. $y = 2x^2 + 2x - 1$

97. $y = -x^2 - x + 3$

98. $y = -2x^2 + x + 1$

99. $y = x^2 - 8x + 16$

100. $y = x^2 - 10x + 25$

101. $y = -3x^2 - x - 2$

102. $y = -2x^2 + x - 1$

103. $y = 4x^2 - x - 2$

104. $y = 2x^2 + x + 4$

105. $y = -2x^2 - x - 5$

106. $y = -3x^2 + 4x - 5$

107. $y = x^2 + 8x + 16$

108. $y = x^2 - 12x + 36$

109. $y = x^2 + x - 3$

For Exercises 110 to 113, $f(x) = ax^2 + bx + c$ is a quadratic function whose graph is a parabola that has only one x-intercept, $(n, 0)$.

110. True or false? $(n, 0)$ is also the vertex of the parabola.

111. True or false? $ax^2 + bx + c$ is a perfect-square trinomial.

112. True or false? If $a > 0$, then for all real numbers x, $f(x) \geq 0$.

113. True or false? The point with x-coordinate $n - m$ has the same y-coordinate as the point with x-coordinate $n + m$.

8.6 Applying Concepts

Find the value of k such that the graph of the equation contains the given point.

114. $y = x^2 - 3x + k$; $(2, 5)$

115. $y = x^2 + 2x + k$; $(-3, 1)$

116. $y = 2x^2 + kx - 3$; $(4, -3)$

117. $y = 3x^2 + kx - 6$; $(-2, 4)$

For Exercises 118 to 121, find the zeros of the function. Graph the equation and verify that the x-coordinates of the x-intercepts are the real zeros of the function. These functions are examples of functions with both real and complex zeros.

118. $f(x) = x^3 - 3x^2 + x - 3$

119. $f(x) = x^3 + x^2 + 4x + 4$

120. $f(x) = x^4 - 3x^2 - 4$

121. $f(x) = x^4 + 3x^2 - 4$

Solve.

122. One root of the quadratic equation $2x^2 - 5x + k = 0$ is 4. What is the other root?

123. What is the value of k if the vertex of the parabola $y = x^2 - 8x + k$ is a point on the x-axis?

124. The zeros of the function $f(x) = mx^2 + nx + 6$ are -2 and 3. What are the zeros of the function $g(x) = nx^2 + mx - 6$?

125. The point (x_1, y_1) lies in quadrant I and is a solution of the equation $y = 3x^2 - 2x - 1$. Given $y_1 = 5$, find x_1.

126. The point (x_1, y_1) lies in quadrant II and is a solution of the equation $y = 2x^2 + 5x - 3$. Given $y_1 = 9$, find x_1.

127. Match each equation with its graph.

    i. $f(x) = x^2$
    ii. $f(x) = x^2 - 1$
    iii. $f(x) = -x^2$
    iv. $f(x) = -x^2 + 3$
    v. $f(x) = x^2 + 3x - 2$
    vi. $f(x) = -x^2 - 3x + 2$

A.

B.

C.

D.

E.

F.

Physics The drag force F, in pounds, on a certain bicyclist is given by $F(v) = 0.151v^2$, where v is the velocity of the bicyclist in miles per hour.

128. Find the vertex of the parabola given by $F(v) = 0.151v^2$, and state what the vertex means in the context of this problem.

129. Find the drag force on the bicyclist when she or he is traveling 15 mph.

130. Graph the equation for the interval $[0, 30]$.

An equation of the form $y = ax^2 + bx + c$ can be written in the form $y = a(x - h)^2 + k$, where (h, k) are the coordinates of the vertex of the parabola. Use the process of completing the square to rewrite the equation in the form $y = a(x - h)^2 + k$. Find the vertex. (*Hint:* Review the example at the bottom of page 540.)

131. $y = x^2 - 4x + 7$

132. $y = x^2 - 2x - 2$

133. $y = x^2 + x + 2$

134. $y = x^2 - x - 3$

Using $y = a(x - h)^2 + k$ as the equation of a parabola with the vertex at (h, k), find the equation of the parabola that has the given characteristics. Write the final equation in the form $y = ax^2 + bx + c$.

135. Vertex $(1, 2)$; the graph passes through $P(2, 5)$

136. Vertex $(0, -3)$; the graph passes through $P(3, -2)$

8.7 Applications of Quadratic Functions

OBJECTIVE 1   Minimum and maximum problems

The graph of $f(x) = x^2 - 2x + 3$ is shown at the right. Because a is positive, the parabola opens up. The vertex of the parabola is the lowest point on the parabola. It is the point that has the minimum y-coordinate. Therefore, the value of the function at this point is a **minimum.**

The graph of $f(x) = -x^2 + 2x + 1$ is shown at the right. Because a is negative, the parabola opens down. The vertex of the parabola is the highest point on the parabola. It is the point that has the maximum y-coordinate. Therefore, the value of the function at this point is a **maximum.**

To find the minimum or maximum value of a quadratic function, first find the x-coordinate of the vertex. Then evaluate the function at that value.

EXAMPLE 1   Find the maximum or minimum value of the function $f(x) = -2x^2 + 4x + 3$.

Solution $x = -\dfrac{b}{2a} = -\dfrac{4}{2(-2)} = 1$ • Find the x-coordinate of the vertex. $a = -2, b = 4$.

$f(x) = -2x^2 + 4x + 3$ • Evaluate the function at $x = 1$.
$f(1) = -2(1)^2 + 4(1) + 3$
$f(1) = 5$

Because $a < 0$, the graph of f opens down. Therefore, the function has a maximum value.

The maximum value of the function is 5.

PROBLEM 1   Find the maximum or minimum value of $f(x) = 2x^2 - 3x + 1$.

Solution   See page S27.

$f(x) = -2x^2 + 4x + 3$

OBJECTIVE 2   Applications of minimum and maximum

A mason is forming a rectangular floor for a storage shed. The perimeter of the rectangle is 44 ft. What dimensions of the rectangle would give the floor a maximum area? What is the maximum area?

Point of Interest

Calculus is a branch of mathematics that demonstrates, among other things, how to find the maximum or minimum of functions other than quadratic functions. These are very important problems in applied mathematics. For instance, an automotive engineer wants to design a car whose shape will minimize the effect of air flow. The same engineer tries to maximize the efficiency of a car's engine. Similarly, an economist may try to determine what business practices will minimize cost and maximize profit.

We are given the perimeter of the rectangle, and we want to find the dimensions of the rectangle that will yield the maximum area for the floor. Use the equation for the perimeter of a rectangle.

$$P = 2L + 2W$$

$P = 44$

Divide both sides of the equation by 2.

Solve the equation for W.

$$44 = 2L + 2W$$
$$22 = L + W$$
$$22 - L = W$$

Now use the equation for the area of a rectangle. Use substitution to express the area in terms of L.

$$A = LW$$

From the equation above, $W = 22 - L$.
Substitute $22 - L$ for W.

$$A = L(22 - L)$$
$$A = 22L - L^2$$

The area of the rectangle is $22L - L^2$. To find the length of the rectangle, find the L-coordinate of the vertex of the function $f(L) = -L^2 + 22L$.

For the function $f(L) = -L^2 + 22L$,

$$L = -\frac{b}{2a} = -\frac{22}{2(-1)} = 11$$

$a = -1$ and $b = 22$.

The length of the rectangle is 11 ft.

To find the width, replace L in $22 - L$ by the L-coordinate of the vertex and evaluate.

$$W = 22 - L$$
$$W = 22 - 11 = 11$$

The width of the rectangle is 11 ft.

The dimensions of the rectangle that would give the floor a maximum area are 11 ft by 11 ft.

To find the maximum area of the floor, evaluate the function $f(L) = -L^2 + 22L$ at the L-coordinate of the vertex.

$$f(L) = -L^2 + 22L$$
$$f(11) = -(11)^2 + 22(11)$$
$$= -121 + 242 = 121$$

The maximum area of the floor is 121 ft².

The graph of the function $f(L) = -L^2 + 22L$ is shown at the right. Note that the vertex of the parabola is (11, 121). For any value of L less than 11, the area of the floor will be less than 121 ft². For any value of L greater than 11, the area of the floor will be less than 121 ft². 121 is the maximum value of the function, and the maximum value occurs when $L = 11$.

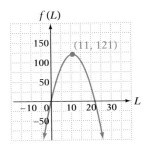

EXAMPLE 2 A mining company has determined that the cost in dollars (*c*) per ton of mining a mineral is given by

$$c(x) = 0.2x^2 - 2x + 12$$

where x is the number of tons of the mineral that is mined. Find the number of tons of the mineral that should be mined to minimize the cost. What is the minimum cost?

Strategy ▶ To find the number of tons that will minimize the cost, find the x-coordinate of the vertex.

▶ To find the minimum cost, evaluate the function at the x-coordinate of the vertex.

Solution $x = -\dfrac{b}{2a} = -\dfrac{-2}{2(0.2)} = 5$

To minimize the cost, 5 tons should be mined.

$c(x) = 0.2x^2 - 2x + 12$
$c(5) = 0.2(5)^2 - 2(5) + 12 = 5 - 10 + 12 = 7$

The minimum cost per ton is $7.

Note: The graph of the function $c(x) = 0.2x^2 - 2x + 12$ is shown at the left. The vertex of the parabola is $(5, 7)$. For any value of x less than 5, the cost per ton is greater than $7. For any value of x greater than 5, the cost per ton is greater than $7. 7 is the minimum value of the function, and the minimum value occurs when $x = 5$.

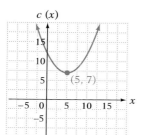

$c(x)$

$(5, 7)$

PROBLEM 2   The height in feet (s) of a ball thrown straight up is given by $s(t) = -16t^2 + 64t$, where t is the time in seconds. Find the time it takes the ball to reach its maximum height. What is the maximum height?

Solution   See page S27.

EXAMPLE 3   Find two numbers whose difference is 10 and whose product is a minimum.

Strategy   Let x represent one number. Because the difference between the two numbers is 10, $x + 10$ represents the other number. Then their product is represented by $x(x + 10) = x^2 + 10x$.

▶ To find one of the two numbers, find the x-coordinate of the vertex of $f(x) = x^2 + 10x$.

▶ To find the other number, replace x in $x + 10$ by the x-coordinate of the vertex and evaluate.

Solution $x = -\dfrac{b}{2a} = -\dfrac{10}{2(1)} = -5$
$x + 10 = -5 + 10 = 5$

The numbers are -5 and 5.

PROBLEM 3   A rectangular fence is being constructed along a stream to enclose a picnic area. If 100 ft of fence is available, what dimensions of the rectangle will produce the maximum area for picnicking?

Solution   See page S27.

8.7   Concept Review

Determine whether the following statements are always true, sometimes true, or never true.

1. A quadratic function has a minimum value.

2. The y-coordinate of the vertex of a quadratic function is the minimum value of the function.

3. The maximum or minimum of a quadratic function is the value of the function evaluated at the x-coordinate of the vertex.

4. The x-value of the vertex of $y = ax^2 + bx + c$, $a \neq 0$, is given by $-\frac{b}{2a}$.

5. The maximum value of a quadratic function is a positive number.

6. The function $f(x) = -x^2 + 3x - 2$ will have a maximum value.

8.7   Exercises

1   Minimum and maximum problems

1. What is the minimum value or the maximum value of a quadratic function?

2. Describe how to find the minimum or maximum value of a quadratic function.

For Exercises 3 and 4, use the quadratic function $f(x) = -8x^2 + 8x$.

3. Because $a = $ ___?___ , the graph of f opens ___?___. The vertex is the highest point on the graph, so its ___?___-coordinate is the maximum value of $f(x)$.

4. The vertex of the graph of f occurs at $x = -\dfrac{b}{2a} = -\dfrac{?}{2(\underline{})} = \underline{}$.
The maximum value of $f(x)$ is $f(\underline{}) = -8(\underline{})^2 + 8(\underline{})$
$= \underline{} + \underline{} = \underline{}$.

5. Does the function have a minimum or a maximum value?
   a. $f(x) = -x^2 + 6x - 1$ **b.** $f(x) = 2x^2 - 4$ **c.** $f(x) = -5x^2 + x$

6. Does the function have a minimum or a maximum value?
   a. $f(x) = 3x^2 - 2x + 4$ **b.** $f(x) = -x^2 + 9$ **c.** $f(x) = 6x^2 - 3x$

Find the minimum or maximum value of the quadratic function.

7. $f(x) = x^2 - 2x + 3$

8. $f(x) = 2x^2 + 4x$

9. $f(x) = -2x^2 + 4x - 3$

10. $f(x) = -2x^2 + 4x - 5$

11. $f(x) = -2x^2 - 3x + 4$

12. $f(x) = -2x^2 - 3x$

13. $f(x) = 2x^2 + 3x - 8$

14. $f(x) = 3x^2 + 3x - 2$

15. $f(x) = -3x^2 + x - 6$

16. $f(x) = -x^2 - x + 2$

17. $f(x) = x^2 - 5x + 3$

18. $f(x) = 3x^2 + 5x + 2$

19. Which of the following parabolas has the highest minimum value?
a. $y = x^2 - 2x - 3$ **b.** $y = x^2 - 10x + 20$ **c.** $y = 3x^2 - 6$

20. Which of the following parabolas has the highest maximum value?
a. $y = -2x^2 + 2x - 1$ **b.** $y = -x^2 + 8x - 2$ **c.** $y = -4x^2 + 3$

21. The vertex of a parabola that opens up is $(-4, 7)$. Does the function have a maximum or a minimum value? What is the maximum or minimum value of the function?

22. The vertex of a parabola that opens down is $(3, -5)$. Does the function have a maximum or a minimum value? What is the maximum or minimum value of the function?

Complete Exercises 23 and 24 given that the vertex of the graph of the function $f(x) = x^2 + bx + c$ is (n, m) and the vertex of the graph of the function $g(x) = -x^2 + dx + e$ is (p, q).

23. True or false? If $m > q$, then for all values of x, $f(x) > g(x)$.

24. True or false? If $m < q$, then for all values of x, $f(x) < g(x)$.

2 Applications of minimum and maximum

Complete Exercises 25 and 26 given that the approximate height h, in meters, of a ball t seconds after it is thrown vertically upward from a height of 2 m, at an initial speed of 30 m/s, is given by the function $h(t) = -5t^2 + 30t + 2$.

25. To find out after how many seconds the ball reaches its maximum height, find the ____?____-coordinate of the vertex of the graph of h:
$$t = -\frac{b}{2a} = \frac{?}{-2(\underline{\ ?\ })} = \underline{\ ?\ }.$$ The ball reaches its maximum height after ____?____ s.

26. Use the result of Exercise 25. To find the maximum height of the ball, evaluate $h(\underline{\ ?\ }) = -5(\underline{\ ?\ })^2 + 30(\underline{\ ?\ }) + 2 = \underline{\ ?\ } + \underline{\ ?\ }$
$+ 2 = \underline{\ ?\ }$. The maximum height of the ball is ____?____ m.

Solve.

27. Physics The height s, in feet, of a rock thrown upward at an initial speed of 64 ft/s from a cliff 50 ft above an ocean beach is given by the function $s(t) = -16t^2 + 64t + 50$, where t is the time in seconds. Find the maximum height above the beach that the rock will attain.

28. **Sports** An event in the Summer Olympics is 10-meter springboard diving. In this event, the height s, in meters, of a diver above the water t seconds after jumping is given by $s(t) = -4.9t^2 + 7.8t + 10$. What is the maximum height that the diver will be above the water? Round to the nearest tenth.

29. Business A tour operator believes that the profit P, in dollars, from selling x tickets is given by $P(x) = 40x - 0.25x^2$. Using this model, find the maximum profit that the tour operator can expect.

30. Manufacturing A manufacturer of microwave ovens believes that the revenue R, in dollars, that the company receives is related to the price P, in dollars, of an oven by the function $R(P) = 125P - 0.25P^2$. What price will give the maximum revenue?

31. Chemistry A pool is treated with a chemical to reduce the amount of algae. The amount of algae in the pool t days after the treatment can be approximated by the function $A(t) = 40t^2 - 400t + 500$. How many days after treatment will the pool have the least amount of algae?

32. Structural Engineering The suspension cable that supports a small footbridge hangs in the shape of a parabola. The height h, in feet, of the cable above the bridge is given by the function $h(x) = 0.25x^2 - 0.8x + 25$, where x is the distance in feet from one end of the bridge. What is the minimum height of the cable above the bridge?

33. **Telescopes** An equation of the thickness h, in inches, of the mirror at the Palomar Mountain Observatory is given by

$$h(x) = 0.000379x^2 - 0.0758x + 24,$$

where x is measured from the edge of the mirror. Find the minimum thickness of the mirror.

34. **Art** The Buckingham Fountain in Chicago shoots water from a nozzle at the base of the fountain. The height h, in feet, of the water above the ground t seconds after it leaves the nozzle is given by the function $h(t) = -16t^2 + 90t + 15$. What is the maximum height of the water? Round to the nearest tenth.

35. Fire Science The height s, in feet, of water squirting from a fire hose nozzle is given by the equation $s(x) = -\frac{1}{30}x^2 + 2x + 5$, where x is the horizontal distance from the nozzle. How high on a building 40 ft from the fire hose will the water land?

50 ft

24 in.

x h

200 in.

Not to scale

40 ft

s

5 ft

36. **Automotive Technology** On wet concrete, the stopping distance s, in feet, of a car traveling v miles per hour is given by $s(v) = 0.055v^2 + 1.1v$. At what speed could a car be traveling and still stop at a stop sign 44 ft away?

37. **Number Problem** Find two numbers whose sum is 20 and whose product is a maximum.

38. **Number Problem** Find two numbers whose difference is 14 and whose product is a minimum.

39. **Ranching** A rancher has 200 ft of fencing to build a rectangular corral alongside an existing fence. Determine the dimensions of the corral that will maximize the enclosed area.

8.7 Applying Concepts

40. Show that the minimum value of
$$S(x) = (2 - x)^2 + (5 - x)^2 + (4 - x)^2 + (7 - x)^2$$
occurs when x is the average of the numbers 2, 5, 4, and 7.

Use a graphing utility to find the minimum or maximum value of the function. Round to the nearest tenth. See the Graphing Calculator Appendix for assistance.

41. $f(x) = x^4 - 2x^2 + 4$ **42.** $f(x) = x^4 + 2x^3 + 1$

43. $f(x) = -x^6 + x^4 - x^3 + x$ **44.** $f(x) = -x^8 + x^6 - x^4 + 5x^2 + 7$

45. On the basis of Exercises 41–44, make a conjecture about the relationship between the sign of the leading coefficient of a polynomial function of even degree and whether that function will have a minimum or a maximum value.

Solve.

46. **Traffic Control** Traffic engineers try to determine the effect a traffic light has at an intersection. By gathering data about the intersection, engineers can determine the approximate number of cars that enter the intersection in the horizontal direction and those that enter in the vertical direction. The engineers would also collect information on the time it takes a stopped car to regain the normal posted speed limit. One model of this situation is $T = \left(\frac{H + V}{2}\right)R^2 + (0.08H - 1.08V)R + 0.58V$, where H is the number of cars arriving at the intersection from the horizontal direction, V is the number of cars arriving at the intersection from the vertical direction, and R is the percent of time the light is red in the horizontal direction. T is the total delay time for all cars and is measured as the number of times the traffic light changes from red to green and back to red.
a. Graph this equation for $H = 100$, $V = 150$, and $0 \le R \le 1$.
b. Write a sentence that explains why the graph is drawn only for $0 \le R \le 1$.
c. What percent of the time should the traffic light remain red in the horizontal direction to minimize T? Round to the nearest whole percent.

47. Write a paper on the history of higher-degree equations. Include discoveries made by del Ferro, Ferrari, and Ruffini.

Focus on Problem Solving

Inductive and Deductive Reasoning

Consider the following sums of odd positive integers.

$$1 + 3 = 4 = 2^2$$ Sum of the first two odd numbers is 2^2.

$$1 + 3 + 5 = 9 = 3^2$$ Sum of the first three odd numbers is 3^2.

$$1 + 3 + 5 + 7 = 16 = 4^2$$ Sum of the first four odd numbers is 4^2.

$$1 + 3 + 5 + 7 + 9 = 25 = 5^2$$ Sum of the first five odd numbers is 5^2.

1. Make a conjecture about the value of the sum

$$1 + 3 + 5 + 7 + 9 + 11 + 13 + 15$$

without adding the numbers.

If the pattern continues, a possible conjecture is that the sum of the first eight odd positive integers is $8^2 = 64$. By adding the numbers, you can verify that this is correct. Inferring that the pattern established by a few cases is valid for all cases is an example of **inductive reasoning.**

2. Use inductive reasoning to find the next figure in the sequence below.

       ?

The fact that a pattern appears to be true does not *prove* that it is true for all cases. For example, consider the polynomial $n^2 - n + 41$. If we begin substituting positive integer values for n and evaluating the expression, we produce the following table.

n	$n^2 - n + 41$	
1	$1^2 - 1 + 41 = 41$	41 is a prime number.
2	$2^2 - 2 + 41 = 43$	43 is a prime number.
3	$3^2 - 3 + 41 = 47$	47 is a prime number.
4	$4^2 - 4 + 41 = 53$	53 is a prime number.

Even if we try a number like 30, we have $30^2 - 30 + 41 = 911$, and 911 is a prime number. Thus it appears that the value of this polynomial is a prime number for any value of n. However, the conjecture is not true. For instance, if $n = 41$, we have $41^2 - 41 + 41 = 41^2 = 1681$, which is not a prime number because it is divisible by 41. This illustrates that inductive reasoning may lead to incorrect conclusions and that an inductive proof must be available to prove conjectures. There is such a proof, called *mathematical induction*, that you may study in a future math course.

Now consider the true statement that the sum of the measures of the interior angles of a triangle is 180°. The figure on the left is a triangle; therefore, the sum of the measures of the interior angles must be 180°. This is an example of *deductive reasoning*. **Deductive reasoning** uses a rule or statement of fact to reach a conclusion.

$\angle A + \angle B + \angle C = 180°$

3. Use deductive reasoning to complete the following: "All even numbers are divisible by 2. Because 41,386 is an even number, . . ."

4. a. Use the pattern given below to find the three missing terms in
   — — — 64.

   A 2 3 4 B 6 7 8 C 10 11 12 D 14 15 16 ...

   b. Is this inductive or deductive reasoning?

5. a. Draw the next figure in the sequence:

   b. Is this inductive or deductive reasoning?

6. a. If ◊◊◊◊◊ = ‡‡‡ and ‡‡‡ = ∇∇∇∇, how many ◊'s equal ∇∇∇∇∇∇∇∇?

   b. Is this inductive or deductive reasoning?

7. a. If ♠♠ = ♦♦♦♦♦♦, and ♦♦♦ = ♣♣, and ♣♣♣♣ = ♥, how many ♥'s equal ♠♠♠♠♠♠?

   b. Is this inductive or deductive reasoning?

For Exercises 8 to 11, determine whether inductive or deductive reasoning is being used.

8. The Atlanta Braves have won eight games in a row. Therefore, the Atlanta Braves will win their next game.

9. All quadrilaterals have four sides. A square is a quadrilateral. Therefore, a square has four sides.

10. Every English setter likes to hunt. Duke is an English setter, so Duke likes to hunt.

11. All kitchen remodeling jobs cost more than the contractor's estimate. The contractor estimated the cost of remodeling my kitchen at $35,000. Therefore, it will cost more than $35,000 to have my kitchen remodeled.

Projects & Group Activities

**Using a Graphing
Calculator to Solve a
Quadratic Equation**

Recall that an x-intercept of the graph of an equation is a point at which the graph crosses the x-axis. For the graph in Figure 1 below, the x-intercepts are $(-2, 0)$ and $(3, 0)$.

Recall also that to find the x-intercept of a graph, set $y = 0$ and then solve for x. For the equation in Figure 1, if we set $y = 0$, the resulting equation is $0 = x^2 - x - 6$, which is a quadratic equation. Solving this equation by factoring, we have

$$0 = x^2 - x - 6$$
$$0 = (x + 2)(x - 3)$$

$$x + 2 = 0 \qquad x - 3 = 0$$
$$x = -2 \qquad x = 3$$

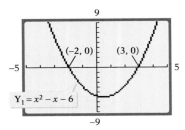

Figure 1

Thus the solutions of the equation are the x-coordinates of the x-intercepts of the graph.

This connection between the solutions of an equation and the x-intercepts of a graph allows us to find approximations of the real number solutions of an equation graphically. For example, to use a TI-83/83 Plus or TI-84 Plus to approximate the solutions of $2x^2 + 5x - 1 = 0$ graphically, use the following keystrokes to graph $y = 2x^2 + 5x - 1$ and find the decimal approximations of the x-coordinates of the x-intercepts. Use the window shown in the graph in Figure 2.

Use the arrow keys to move to the left of the leftmost x-intercept. Press ENTER. Use the arrow keys to move to a point just to the right of the leftmost x-intercept. Press ENTER twice. The x-coordinate at the bottom of the screen is the approximation of one solution of the equation. To find the other solution, use the same procedure but move the cursor first to the left and then to the right of the rightmost x-intercept.

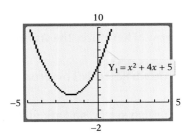

Figure 2

Attempting to find the solutions of an equation graphically will not necessarily yield all the solutions. Because the x-coordinates of the x-intercepts of a graph are *real* numbers, only real number solutions can be found. For instance, consider the equation $x^2 + 4x + 5 = 0$. The graph of $y = x^2 + 4x + 5$ is shown in Figure 3. Note that the graph has no x-intercepts and that consequently it has no real number solutions. However, $x^2 + 4x + 5 = 0$ does have complex number solutions that can be obtained by using the quadratic formula. They are $-2 + i$ and $-2 - i$.

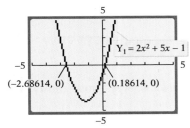

Figure 3

Use a graphing calculator to approximate the solutions of the equation.

1. $x^2 + 6x + 1 = 0$

2. $-x^2 + x + 3 = 0$

3. $2x^2 + 4x - 1 = 0$

4. $x^2 + 4x + 5 = 0$

Finding the Maximum or Minimum of a Function Using a Graphing Calculator

Recall that for a quadratic function, the maximum or minimum value of the function is the y-coordinate of the vertex of the graph of the function. We determined algebraically that the coordinates of the vertex are $\left(-\dfrac{b}{2a}, f\left(-\dfrac{b}{2a}\right)\right)$. It is also possible to use a graphing calculator to approximate a maximum or minimum value. The method used to find the value depends on the calculator model. However, it is generally true for most calculators that the point at which the function has a maximum or minimum must be shown on the screen. If it is not, you must select a different viewing window.

$f(x) = 4x^2 + 4x + 1$

Minimum
X=-.5   Y=0

For a TI-83/83 Plus or TI-84 Plus graphing calculator, press 2nd CALC 3 to determine a minimum value or 2nd CALC 4 to determine a maximum value. Move the cursor to a point on the curve that is to the left of the minimum (or maximum). Press ENTER. Move the cursor to a point on the curve that is to the right of the minimum (or maximum). Press ENTER twice. The minimum (or maximum) value is shown as the y-coordinate at the bottom of the screen.

1. Find the maximum or minimum value of $f(x) = -x^2 - 3x + 2$ by using a graphing calculator.

2. Find the maximum or minimum value of $f(x) = x^2 - 4x - 2$ by using a graphing calculator.

3. Find the maximum or minimum value of $f(x) = -\sqrt{2}x^2 - \pi x + 2$ by using a graphing calculator.

4. Find the maximum or minimum value of $f(x) = \dfrac{x^2}{\sqrt{5}} - \sqrt{7}x - \sqrt{11}$ by using a graphing calculator.

5. **Manufacturing** A manufacturer of camera lenses estimated that the average monthly cost C of production is given by the function $C(x) = 0.1x^2 - 20x + 2000$, where x is the number of lenses produced each month. Find the number of lenses the company should produce in order to minimize the average cost.

6. **Income** The net annual income I, in dollars, of a family physician can be modeled by the equation $I(x) = -290(x - 48)^2 + 148,000$, where x is the age of the physician and $27 \le x \le 70$. Find (a) the age at which the physician's income will be a maximum and (b) the maximum income.

Chapter 8 Summary

Key Words	*Examples*
A **quadratic equation** is an equation of the form $ax^2 + bx + c = 0$, where $a \neq 0$. A quadratic equation is also called a **second-degree equation**. [8.1.1, p. 496]	$3x^2 + 4x - 7 = 0$ and $x^2 - 1 = 0$ are quadratic equations.
A quadratic equation is in **standard form** when the polynomial is in descending order and equal to zero. [8.1.1, p. 496]	$x^2 - 5x + 6 = 0$ is a quadratic equation in standard form.

When a quadratic equation has two solutions that are the same number, the solution is called a **double root** of the equation. [8.1.1, p. 497]

$$x^2 - 4x + 4 = 0$$
$$(x - 2)(x - 2) = 0$$

$$x - 2 = 0 \qquad x - 2 = 0$$
$$x = 2 \qquad\qquad x = 2$$

2 is a double root.

For an equation of the form $ax^2 + bx + c = 0$, the quantity $b^2 - 4ac$ is called the **discriminant**. [8.2.2, p. 513]

$$2x^2 - 3x + 2 = 0$$
$$a = 2, b = -3, c = 2$$
$$b^2 - 4ac = (-3)^2 - 4(2)(2)$$
$$= 9 - 16 = -7$$

A **quadratic inequality in one variable** is one that can be written in the form $ax^2 + bx + c > 0$ or $ax^2 + bx + c < 0$, where $a \neq 0$. The symbols $\leq$ and $\geq$ can also be used. [8.5.1, p. 534]

$3x^2 + 5x - 8 \leq 0$ is a quadratic inequality.

The **x-coordinate of the vertex of a parabola** is given by $-\dfrac{b}{2a}$. [8.6.1, p. 542]

$y = 2x^2 - 8x + 5$ $a = 2, b = -8$
The x-coordinate of the vertex is

$$-\frac{-8}{2(2)} = 2.$$

The **x-intercepts** of the graph of a parabola occur when $y = 0$. [8.6.2, p. 544]

$$x^2 - 5x + 6 = 0$$
$$(x - 3)(x - 2) = 0$$

$$x - 3 = 0 \qquad x - 2 = 0$$
$$x = 3 \qquad\qquad x = 2$$

The x-intercepts are (3, 0) and (2, 0).

The graph of a **quadratic function** $f(x) = ax^2 + bx = c$ is a **parabola** that opens up when $a > 0$ and down when $a < 0$. The **axis of symmetry** is a line that passes through the vertex of the parabola. [8.6.1, pp. 540–541]

The graph of $f(x) = ax^2 + bx + x$ has a **minimum** value if $a > 0$ and a **maximum** value if $a < 0$. [8.7.1, p. 557]

Essential Rules and Procedures

Principle of Zero Products

If $ab = 0$, then $a = 0$ or $b = 0$. [8.1.1, p. 496]

$$(x - 3)(x + 4) = 0$$

$$x - 3 = 0 \qquad x + 4 = 0$$
$$x = 3 \qquad\qquad x = -4$$

A quadratic equation can be solved by **taking the square root of each side of the equation**. [8.1.3, p. 498]

$$(x + 2)^2 - 9 = 0$$
$$(x + 2)^2 = 9$$
$$\sqrt{(x + 2)^2} = \sqrt{9}$$

$$x + 2 = \pm\sqrt{9}$$
$$x + 2 = \pm 3$$

$$x + 2 = 3 \qquad x + 2 = -3$$
$$x = 1 \qquad\qquad x = -5$$

A quadratic equation can be solved by **completing the square**. [8.2.1, p. 507]

$$x^2 + 4x - 1 = 0$$
$$x^2 + 4x = 1$$
$$x^2 + 4x + 4 = 1 + 4$$
$$(x + 2)^2 = 5$$
$$\sqrt{(x + 2)^2} = \sqrt{5}$$
$$x + 2 = \pm\sqrt{5}$$

$$x + 2 = \sqrt{5} \qquad\qquad x + 2 = -\sqrt{5}$$
$$x = -2 + \sqrt{5} \qquad\quad x = -2 - \sqrt{5}$$

Quadratic Formula

$$x = \frac{-b \pm \sqrt{b^2 - 4ac}}{2a}$$ [8.2.2, p. 511]

$$2x^2 - 3x + 4 = 0$$
$$a = 2, b = -3, c = 4$$

$$x = \frac{-(-3) \pm \sqrt{(-3)^2 - 4(2)(4)}}{2(2)}$$

$$= \frac{3 \pm \sqrt{9 - 32}}{4} = \frac{3 \pm \sqrt{-23}}{4}$$

$$= \frac{3 \pm i\sqrt{23}}{4} = \frac{3}{4} \pm \frac{\sqrt{23}}{4}i$$

Vertex of a parabola

The coordinates of the vertex of a parabola are $\left(-\dfrac{b}{2a}, f\left(-\dfrac{b}{2a}\right)\right)$. [8.6.1, p. 542]

$$f(x) = x^2 - 2x - 4 \quad a = 1, b = -2$$

$$-\frac{b}{2a} = -\frac{-2}{2(1)} = 1$$

$$f(1) = 1^2 - 2(1) - 4 = -5$$

The coordinates of the vertex are $(1, -5)$.

Discriminant [8.6.2, p. 548]
If $b^2 - 4ac = 0$, the equation has a double root.

$x^2 + 8x + 16 = 0$ has a double root because

$$b^2 - 4ac = 8^2 - 4(1)(16) = 0$$

If $b^2 - 4ac > 0$, the equation has two real number solutions that are not equal.

$2x^2 + 3x - 5 = 0$ has two unequal real number solutions because

$$b^2 - 4ac = 3^2 - 4(2)(-5) = 49$$

If $b^2 - 4ac < 0$, the equation has two complex number solutions.

$3x^2 + 2x + 4 = 0$ has two complex number solutions because

$$b^2 - 4ac = 2^2 - 4(3)(4) = -44$$

Chapter 8 Review Exercises

1. Solve: $2x^2 - 3x = 0$

2. Solve for x: $6x^2 + 9xc = 6c^2$

3. Solve: $x^2 = 48$

4. Solve: $\left(x + \dfrac{1}{2}\right)^2 + 4 = 0$

5. Find the minimum value of the function $f(x) = x^2 - 7x + 8$.

6. Find the maximum value of the function $f(x) = -2x^2 + 4x + 1$.

7. Write a quadratic equation that has integer coefficients and has solutions $\dfrac{1}{3}$ and -3.

8. Solve: $2x^2 + 9x = 5$

9. Solve: $2(x + 1)^2 - 36 = 0$

10. Solve: $x^2 + 6x + 10 = 0$

11. Solve: $\dfrac{2}{x - 4} + 3 = \dfrac{x}{2x - 3}$

12. Solve: $x^4 - 6x^2 + 8 = 0$

13. Solve: $\sqrt{2x - 1} + \sqrt{2x} = 3$

14. Solve: $2x^{\frac{2}{3}} + 3x^{\frac{1}{3}} - 2 = 0$

15. Solve: $\sqrt{3x - 2} + 4 = 3x$

16. Solve: $x^2 - 6x - 2 = 0$

17. Solve: $\dfrac{2x}{x - 4} + \dfrac{6}{x + 1} = 11$

18. Solve: $2x^2 - 2x = 1$

19. Solve: $2x = 4 - 3\sqrt{x - 1}$

20. Solve: $3x = \dfrac{9}{x - 2}$

21. Solve: $\dfrac{3x + 7}{x + 2} + x = 3$

22. Solve: $\dfrac{x - 2}{2x + 3} - \dfrac{x - 4}{x} = 2$

23. Solve: $1 - \dfrac{x + 4}{2 - x} = \dfrac{x - 3}{x + 2}$

24. Find the axis of symmetry of the parabola whose equation is $y = -x^2 + 6x - 5$.

25. Find the vertex of the parabola whose equation is $y = -x^2 + 3x - 2$.

26. Find two values of x in the domain of $f(x) = x^2 - 8x - 4$ for which $f(x) = 1$.

27. Use the discriminant to determine the number of x-intercepts of the parabola whose equation is $y = 3x^2 - 2x - 4$.

28. Find the x-intercepts of the parabola whose equation is $y = 4x^2 + 12x + 4$.

29. Find the x-intercepts of the parabola whose equation is $y = -2x^2 - 3x + 2$.

30. Find the zeros of $f(x) = 3x^2 + 2x + 2$.

31. Solve: $(x + 3)(2x - 5) < 0$

32. Solve: $(x - 2)(x + 4)(2x + 3) \leq 0$

33. Solve and graph the solution set of $\dfrac{x - 2}{2x - 3} \geq 0$.

34. Solve and graph the solution set of $\dfrac{(2x - 1)(x + 3)}{x - 4} \leq 0$.

35. Graph $f(x) = x^2 + 2x - 4$. State the domain and range.

36. Find the vertex and axis of symmetry of the parabola whose equation is $y = x^2 - 2x + 3$. Then graph the equation.

37. **Integer Problem** The sum of the squares of three consecutive even integers is fifty-six. Find the three integers.

38. **Geometry** The length of a rectangle is 2 cm more than twice the width. The area of the rectangle is 60 cm². Find the length and width of the rectangle.

39. **Work Problem** An older computer requires 12 min longer to print the payroll than does a newer computer. Together the computers can print the payroll in 8 min. Find the time for the newer computer, working alone, to complete the payroll.

40. **Uniform Motion** A car travels 200 mi. A second car, traveling 10 mph faster than the first car, makes the same trip in 1 h less time. Find the speed of each car.

Chapter 8 Test

1. Solve: $2x^2 + x = 6$

2. Solve: $12x^2 + 7x - 12 = 0$

3. Find the maximum value of the function $f(x) = -x^2 + 8x - 7$.

4. Write the quadratic equation that has integer coefficients and has solutions $-\frac{1}{3}$ and 3.

5. Solve: $2(x + 3)^2 - 36 = 0$

6. Solve: $x^2 + 4x - 1 = 0$

7. Find the zeros of $g(x) = x^2 + 3x - 8$.

8. Solve: $3x^2 - x + 8 = 0$

9. Solve: $\dfrac{2x}{x - 1} + \dfrac{3}{x + 2} = 1$

10. Solve: $2x + 7x^{\frac{1}{2}} - 4 = 0$

11. Solve: $x^4 - 11x^2 + 18 = 0$

12. Solve: $\sqrt{2x + 1} + 5 = 2x$

13. Find two values of x in the domain of $f(x) = x^2 - 4x - 2$ for which $f(x) = 4$.

14. Use the discriminant to determine the number of x-intercepts of the parabola $y = 3x^2 + 2x - 4$.

15. Find the x-intercepts of the parabola whose equation is $y = 2x^2 + 5x - 12$.

16. Find the axis of symmetry of the parabola whose equation is $y = 2x^2 + 6x + 3$.

17. Graph $y = \frac{1}{2}x^2 + x - 4$. State the domain and range.

18. Solve and graph the solution set of $\dfrac{2x - 3}{x + 4} \leq 0$.

19. **Geometry** The base of a triangle is 3 ft more than three times the height. The area of the triangle is 30 ft². Find the base and height of the triangle.

20. **Uniform Motion** The rate of a river's current is 2 mph. A canoe was rowed 6 mi down the river and back in 4 h. Find the rowing rate in calm water.

Cumulative Review Exercises

1. Evaluate $2a^2 - b^2 \div c^2$ when $a = 3$, $b = -4$, and $c = -2$.

2. Solve: $\dfrac{2x - 3}{4} - \dfrac{x + 4}{6} = \dfrac{3x - 2}{8}$

3. Find the slope of the line that contains the points $(3, -4)$ and $(-1, 2)$.

4. Find the equation of the line that contains the point $(1, 2)$ and is parallel to the line $x - y = 1$.

5. Factor: $-3x^3y + 6x^2y^2 - 9xy^3$

6. Factor: $6x^2 - 7x - 20$

7. Factor: $a^n x + a^n y - 2x - 2y$

8. Divide: $(3x^3 - 13x^2 + 10) \div (3x - 4)$

9. Multiply: $\dfrac{x^2 + 2x + 1}{8x^2 + 8x} \cdot \dfrac{4x^3 - 4x^2}{x^2 - 1}$

10. Find the distance between the points $(-2, 3)$ and $(2, 5)$.

11. Solve $S = \dfrac{n}{2}(a + b)$ for b.

12. Multiply: $-2i(7 - 4i)$

13. Simplify: $a^{-\frac{1}{2}}\left(a^{\frac{1}{2}} - a^{\frac{3}{2}}\right)$

14. Simplify: $\dfrac{\sqrt[3]{8x^4y^5}}{\sqrt[3]{16xy^6}}$

15. Solve: $\dfrac{x}{x + 2} - \dfrac{4x}{x + 3} = 1$

16. Solve: $\dfrac{x}{2x + 3} - \dfrac{3}{4x^2 - 9} = \dfrac{x}{2x - 3}$

17. Solve: $x^4 - 6x^2 + 8 = 0$

18. Solve: $\sqrt{3x + 1} - 1 = x$

19. Solve: $|3x - 2| < 8$

20. Find the x- and y-intercepts of the graph of $6x - 5y = 15$.

21. Graph the solution set: $\begin{aligned} x + y &\le 3 \\ 2x - y &< 4 \end{aligned}$

22. Solve the system of equations:
$$\begin{aligned} x + y + z &= 2 \\ -x + 2y - 3z &= -9 \\ x - 2y - 2z &= -1 \end{aligned}$$

23. Given $f(x) = \dfrac{2x - 3}{x^2 - 1}$ find $f(-2)$.

24. Find the domain of the function
$$f(x) = \frac{x - 2}{x^2 - 2x - 15}.$$

25. Solve and graph the solution set of $x^3 + x^2 - 6x < 0$.

26. Solve and graph the solution set of $\dfrac{(x - 1)(x - 5)}{x + 3} \geq 0$.

27. **Forestry** The table at the right is based on data from a forestry study that looked at the diameters and heights of trees over a period of time. Between the ages of 2 years and 8 years, what is the average annual rate of change in the height of the trees? Round to the nearest tenth.

Age (in years)	Height (in feet)	Diameter (in inches)
2	7	0.8
3	12	2.0
4	20	3.8
5	22	4.2
6	30	6.9
7	37	7.1
8	42	8.1

28. **Mechanics** A piston rod for an automobile is $9\frac{3}{8}$ in. with a tolerance of $\frac{1}{64}$ in. Find the lower and upper limits of the length of the piston rod.

29. **Geometry** The base of a triangle is $(x + 8)$ ft. The height is $(2x - 4)$ ft. Find the area of the triangle in terms of the variable x.

30. **Depreciation** The graph shows the relationship between the cost of a building and the depreciation allowed for income tax purposes. Find the slope of the line between the two points shown on the graph. Write a sentence that states the meaning of the slope.

CHAPTER

9 Functions and Relations

OBJECTIVES

9.1
1 Graph by using translations

9.2
1 Perform operations on functions
2 Find the composition of two functions

9.3
1 Determine whether a function is one-to-one
2 Find the inverse of a function

DVD SSM **Online Study Center**

Have you ever found yourself wondering why certain products are so expensive? Manufacturing something as complex as a computer requires a lot of high-tech equipment and a lot of money. Usually the price at which a computer is sold can be determined by how much it costs to make the computer plus a certain markup. For a store to calculate the cost of each product, they must use a function such as the one discussed in the **Projects and Group Activities on page 603.**

Prep Test

1. Evaluate $|x + 4|$ for $x = -6$.

2. Given $y = -x^2 + 2x + 1$, find the value of y when $x = -2$.

3. Given $f(x) = x^2 - 3x + 2$, find $f(-4)$.

4. Evaluate $p(r) = r^2 - 5$ when $r = 2 + h$.

5. Solve $x = 2y + 4$ for y.

6. Find the domain and range of the relation $\{(-2, 4), (3, 5), (4, 6), (6, 5)\}$. Is the relation a function?

7. What value is excluded from the domain of $f(x) = \dfrac{3}{x - 8}$?

8. Graph: $f(x) = |x|$ **9.** Graph: $f(x) = x^2 - 2$

9.1 Translations of Graphs

OBJECTIVE 1 Graph by using translations

The graphs of $f(x) = |x|$ and $g(x) = |x| + 2$ are shown in Figure 1. Note that for a given x-coordinate, the y-coordinate on the graph of g is 2 units higher than that on the graph of f. The graph of g is said to be a **vertical translation,** or **vertical shift,** of the graph of f.

Note that because $f(x) = |x|$,

$$g(x) = |x| + 2$$
$$= f(x) + 2$$

Thus $g(x)$ is 2 units more than $f(x)$.

Now consider the graphs of the functions $f(x) = |x|$ and $h(x) = |x| - 3$, shown in Figure 2. Note that for a given x-coordinate, the y-coordinate on the graph of h is 3 units lower than that on the graph of f. The graph of h is a vertical translation of the graph of f.

In Figure 1, the graph of $g(x) = |x| + 2$ is the graph of f shifted *up* 2 units, whereas in Figure 2, the graph of $h(x) = |x| - 3$ is the graph of f shifted *down* 3 units.

Take Note

Remember that $g(x)$ and $f(x)$ are y-coordinates of an ordered pair. The fact that $g(x)$ is 2 units more than $f(x)$ means that, for a given value of x, the y values for g are 2 units higher than the y values for f.

Figure 1

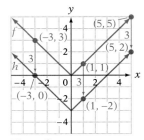

Figure 2

> ### Vertical Translation
>
> If f is a function and c is a positive constant, then
>
> $y = f(x) + c$ is the graph of $y = f(x)$ shifted up c units.
> $y = f(x) - c$ is the graph of $y = f(x)$ shifted down c units.

EXAMPLE 1   Given the graph of the function $f(x) = \sqrt[3]{x}$ shown at the right in blue, graph $g(x) = \sqrt[3]{x} + 3$ by using a vertical translation.

Solution   The graph of $g(x) = \sqrt[3]{x} + 3$ is the graph of $f(x) = \sqrt[3]{x}$ shifted 3 units up. This graph is shown in red at the right.

PROBLEM 1   Given the graph of the function $f(x) = x^2 - 2x$ shown at the right, graph $g(x) = x^2 - 2x - 3$ by using a vertical translation.

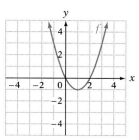

Solution   See page S27.

The graphs of $f(x) = |x|$ and $g(x) = |x - 2|$ are shown in Figure 3. Note that the graph of g is the graph of f shifted 2 units to the right. The graph of g is a **horizontal translation,** or **horizontal shift,** of the graph of f. In this situation, each x-coordinate is moved to the right 2 units, but the y-coordinates are unchanged.

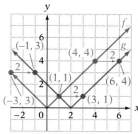

Figure 3

The graphs of $f(x) = |x|$ and $h(x) = |x + 3|$ are shown in Figure 4. In this case, the graph of f is translated 3 units to the left.

For horizontal translations, note that when $f(x) = |x|$,

$$f(x - 2) = |x - 2| = g(x)$$

is a translation to the right and

$$f(x + 3) = |x + 3| = h(x)$$

is a translation to the left.

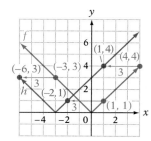

Figure 4

Take Note

Recall that evaluation of a function is accomplished by replacing a variable by another quantity.

$$f(x) = |x|$$
$$f(-3) = |-3|$$
$$f(x - 2) = |x - 2| = g(x)$$
$$f(x + 3) = |x + 3| = h(x)$$

One way to determine the direction of the horizontal shift is to ask, "For what value of x is $y = 0$?" For instance, the horizontal shift of g in Figure 3 is 2 units to the right because $y = 0$ when $x = 2$.

$$g(x) = |x - 2|$$
$$g(2) = |2 - 2| = 0$$

Horizontal Translation

If f is a function and c is a positive constant, then

$y = f(x - c)$ is the graph of $y = f(x)$ shifted to the right c units.

$y = f(x + c)$ is the graph of $y = f(x)$ shifted to the left c units.

Point of Interest

Translations of a figure or pattern may be applied in the design of wallpaper, in the background of a Web page, and in the use of shadows to create an illusion of a letter raised off a page.

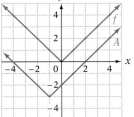

EXAMPLE 2 Given the graph of the function $F(x) = x^3$ shown at the right in blue, graph $G(x) = (x + 2)^3$ by using a horizontal translation.

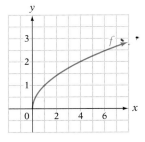

Solution The graph of G (shown in red) is the graph of F shifted horizontally 2 units to the left. Note that if

$$(x + 2)^3 = 0, \text{ then } x = -2.$$

The result, -2, is one confirmation that the graph should be shifted 2 units to the left.

PROBLEM 2 Given the graph of the function $f(x) = \sqrt{x}$ shown at the right, graph $g(x) = \sqrt{x - 3}$ by using a horizontal translation.

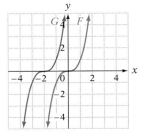

Solution See page S27.

It is possible for a graph to involve both a horizontal and a vertical translation.

EXAMPLE 3 Given the graph of the function $f(x) = |x|$ shown at the left in blue, graph $A(x) = |x + 1| - 3$ by using both a horizontal and a vertical translation.

Solution The graph of A includes a horizontal shift of 1 unit to the left ($|x + 1| = 0$ means that $x = -1$) and a vertical shift of 3 units down. The graph of A is shown in red at the left.

PROBLEM 3 Given the graph of the function $g(x) = x^3$ shown at the right, graph $V(x) = (x - 2)^3 + 1$ by using both a horizontal and a vertical translation.

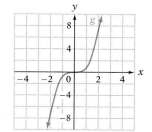

■ **Solution** See page S27.

9.1 Concept Review

Determine whether the following statements are always true, sometimes true, or never true.

1. If c is a positive constant, the graph of $y = f(x) + c$ is the graph of $y = f(x)$ shifted upward c units.

2. If c is a positive constant, the graph of $y = f(x + c)$ is the graph of $y = f(x)$ translated c units to the right.

3. The graph of $y = f(x - 2)$ is the graph of $y = f(x)$ translated 2 units to the right.

4. The graph of $y = |x| + 2$ is the graph of $y = |x|$ translated 2 units to the left.

5. If c_1 and c_2 are positive constants, the graph of $y = f(x + c_1) + c_2$ is the graph of $y = f(x)$ translated c_1 units to the right and shifted up c_2 units.

6. The graph of $y = (x - 2)^3 + 3$ is the graph of $y = x^3$ translated 2 units to the right and shifted 3 units up.

9.1 Exercises

1 **Graph by using translations**

Complete Exercises 1 to 4 by using the word *up*, *down*, *right*, or *left*.

1. The graph of $g(x) = x^2 - 5$ is the graph of $f(x) = x^2$ shifted 5 units
____?____.

2. The graph of $g(x) = (x - 3)^3$ is the graph of $f(x) = x^3$ shifted 3 units
____?____.

3. The graph of $g(x) = |x + 7|$ is the graph of $f(x) = |x|$ shifted 7 units _____?_____ .

4. The graph of $g(x) = (x - 2)^2 + 4$ is the graph of $f(x) = x^2$ shifted 2 units _____?_____ and 4 units _____?_____ .

In Exercises 5 to 30, use translations to draw the graphs. Many of these exercises refer to Figures 1 to 3 below.

Figure 1

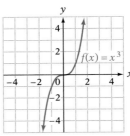

Figure 2

Figure 3

5. Given the graph of $f(x) = |x|$ shown in Figure 1 above, graph $g(x) = |x| + 4$.

6. Given the graph of $f(x) = |x|$ shown in Figure 1 above, graph $g(x) = |x| - 3$.

7. Given the graph of $f(x) = x^2$ shown in Figure 2 above, graph $g(x) = x^2 - 2$.

8. Given the graph of $f(x) = x^2$ shown in Figure 2 above, graph $g(x) = x^2 + 1$.

9. Given the graph of $f(x) = x^3$ shown in Figure 3 above, graph $g(x) = x^3 + 1$.

10. Given the graph of $f(x) = x^3$ shown in Figure 3 above, graph $g(x) = x^3 - 2$.

11. Given the graph of $f(x) = x^2$ shown in Figure 2 above, graph $g(x) = (x - 3)^2$.

12. Given the graph of $f(x) = x^2$ shown in Figure 2 above, graph $g(x) = (x + 2)^2$.

13. Given the graph of $f(x) = |x|$ shown in Figure 1 above, graph $g(x) = |x - 1|$.

14. Given the graph of $f(x) = |x|$ shown in Figure 1 above, graph $g(x) = |x + 4|$.

15. Given the graph of $f(x) = x^3$ shown in Figure 3 on page 580, graph $g(x) = (x - 4)^3$.

16. Given the graph of $f(x) = x^3$ shown in Figure 3 on page 580, graph $g(x) = (x + 3)^3$.

17. Given the graph of $f(x) = -x^2$ shown below, graph $g(x) = -x^2 + 2$.

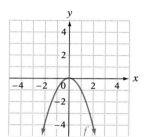

18. Given the graph of $f(x) = -|x|$ shown below, graph $g(x) = -|x| - 2$.

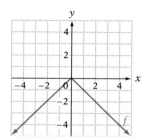

19. Given the graph of $f(x) = x^3$ shown in Figure 3 on page 580, graph $g(x) = (x + 1)^3 - 2$.

20. Given the graph of $f(x) = x^3$ shown in Figure 3 on page 580, graph $g(x) = (x - 2)^3 + 1$.

21. Given the graph of $f(x) = x^2$ shown in Figure 2 on page 580, graph $g(x) = (x - 3)^2 - 4$.

22. Given the graph of $f(x) = x^2$ shown in Figure 2 on page 580, graph $g(x) = (x + 2)^2 + 4$.

23. Given the graph of $f(x) = \sqrt{x}$ shown below, graph $g(x) = \sqrt{x - 1} + 2$.

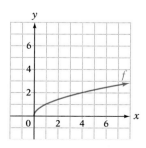

24. Given the graph of $f(x) = -\sqrt{x}$ shown below, graph $g(x) = -\sqrt{x + 1} - 3$.

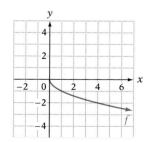

25. Given the graph of
$f(x) = x^2 - 2x$ shown below,
graph $g(x) = x^2 - 2x - 1$.

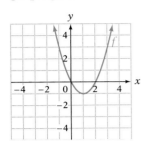

26. Given the graph of
$f(x) = x^3 - 4x$ shown below,
graph $g(x) = x^3 - 4x + 2$.

27. Given the graph of $f(x) = -x^2$
shown in Exercise 17, graph
$g(x) = -(x + 1)^2 - 2$.

28. Given the graph of $f(x) = -x^2$
shown in Exercise 17, graph
$g(x) = -(x - 1)^2 + 1$.

29. Given the graph of $f(x) = -\sqrt{x}$
shown in Exercise 24, graph
$g(x) = -\sqrt{x - 2} + 1$.

30. Given the graph of $f(x) = \sqrt{x}$
shown in Exercise 23, graph
$g(x) = \sqrt{x + 2} - 3$.

31.   **a.** If $(0, 7)$ is the y-intercept of $y = f(x) - 2$, then what point is the
y-intercept of $y = f(x)$?
b. If $(5, 0)$ is an x-intercept of $y = f(x)$, then what point is an x-intercept
of $y = f(x - 3)$?

32.   The graph of $y = f(x)$ is shown at the
right. Is graph **a, b,** or **c** the graph of
$y = f(x + 2) - 3$?

a.

b.

c.

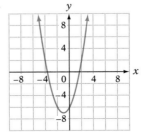

9.1   Applying Concepts

In Exercises 33 to 40, use translations to draw the graph. These exercises refer
to Figures 4 to 6 below. No equations are given for the graphs.

Figure 4

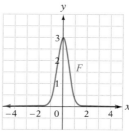

Figure 5

Figure 6

33. Given the graph of $y = f(x)$
shown in Figure 4 above, graph
$y = f(x) + 1$.

34. Given the graph of $y = f(x)$
shown in Figure 4 above, graph
$y = f(x) - 2$.

35. Given the graph of $y = g(x)$
shown in Figure 5 above, graph
$y = g(x) - 3$.

36. Given the graph of $y = g(x)$
shown in Figure 5 above, graph
$y = g(x) + 1$.

37. Given the graph of $y = f(x)$
shown in Figure 4 above, graph
$y = f(x - 2)$.

38. Given the graph of $y = f(x)$
shown in Figure 4 above, graph
$y = f(x + 1)$.

39. Given the graph of $y = F(x)$
shown in Figure 6 above, graph
$y = F(x + 3)$.

40. Given the graph of $y = F(x)$
shown in Figure 6 above, graph
$y = F(x - 1)$.

41. Given the triangle shown below, draw the triangle for which every value of x is translated
3 units to the right and every value of y is translated 2 units up.

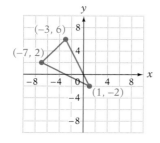

42. Given the rectangle shown below, draw the rectangle for which every value of x is translated
2 units to the right and every value of y is translated 1 unit up.

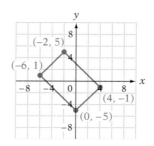

9.2 Algebra of Functions

OBJECTIVE **1** **Perform operations on functions**

The operations of addition, subtraction, multiplication, and division of functions are defined as follows:

Operations on Functions

If f and g are functions and x is an element of the domain of each function, then

$$(f + g)(x) = f(x) + g(x)$$
$$(f - g)(x) = f(x) - g(x)$$
$$(f \cdot g)(x) = f(x) \cdot g(x)$$
$$\left(\frac{f}{g}\right)(x) = \frac{f(x)}{g(x)}, \; g(x) \neq 0$$

Given $f(x) = x^2 + 1$ and $g(x) = 3x - 2$, find $(f + g)(3)$ and $(f \cdot g)(-1)$.

$$
\begin{aligned}
(f + g)(3) &= f(3) + g(3) \\
&= [(3)^2 + 1] + [3(3) - 2] \\
&= 10 + 7 = 17
\end{aligned}
$$

$$
\begin{aligned}
(f \cdot g)(-1) &= f(-1) \cdot g(-1) \\
&= [(-1)^2 + 1] \cdot [3(-1) - 2] \\
&= 2 \cdot (-5) = -10
\end{aligned}
$$

Consider the functions f and g above. Find $S(x)$, the sum of the two functions.

Use the definition of addition.

Substitute $x^2 + 1$ for $f(x)$ and $3x - 2$ for $g(x)$.

$$
\begin{aligned}
S(x) &= (f + g)(x) \\
&= f(x) + g(x) \\
&= (x^2 + 1) + (3x - 2) \\
S(x) &= x^2 + 3x - 1
\end{aligned}
$$

Now evaluate $S(3)$.

$$
\begin{aligned}
S(3) &= (3)^2 + 3(3) - 1 \\
&= 9 + 9 - 1 \\
&= 17 = (f + g)(3)
\end{aligned}
$$

Note that $S(3) = 17$ and $(f + g)(3) = 17$. This shows that adding $f(x) + g(x)$ and then evaluating is the same as evaluating $f(x)$ and $g(x)$ and then adding. The same is true for the other operations on functions. For instance, let $P(x)$ be the product of the functions f and g. Then

$$
\begin{aligned}
P(x) &= (f \cdot g)(x) \\
&= f(x) \cdot g(x) \\
&= (x^2 + 1)(3x - 2) \\
&= 3x^3 - 2x^2 + 3x - 2
\end{aligned}
$$

$$P(-1) = 3(-1)^3 - 2(-1)^2 + 3(-1) - 2$$
$$= -3 - 2 - 3 - 2$$
$$= -10 = (f \cdot g)(-1)$$

Given $f(x) = 2x^2 - 5x + 3$ and $g(x) = x^2 - 1$, find $\left(\dfrac{f}{g}\right)(1)$.

$$\left(\frac{f}{g}\right)(1) = \frac{f(1)}{g(1)}$$
$$= \frac{2(1)^2 - 5(1) + 3}{(1)^2 - 1}$$
$$= \frac{0}{0} \leftarrow \text{This is not a real number.}$$

Because $\dfrac{0}{0}$ is not defined, the expression $\left(\dfrac{f}{g}\right)(1)$ cannot be evaluated.

EXAMPLE 1 Given $f(x) = x^2 - x + 1$ and $g(x) = x^3 - 4$, find $(f - g)(3)$.

Solution $(f - g)(3) = f(3) - g(3)$
$$= (3^2 - 3 + 1) - (3^3 - 4)$$
$$= 7 - 23$$
$$= -16$$

$(f - g)(3) = -16$

PROBLEM 1 Given $f(x) = x^2 + 2x$ and $g(x) = 5x - 2$, find $(f + g)(-2)$.

Solution See page S27.

EXAMPLE 2 Given $f(x) = x^2 + 2$ and $g(x) = 2x + 3$, find $(f \cdot g)(-2)$.

Solution $(f \cdot g)(-2) = f(-2) \cdot g(-2)$
$$= [(-2)^2 + 2] \cdot [2(-2) + 3]$$
$$= 6 \cdot [-1]$$
$$= -6$$

$(f \cdot g)(-2) = -6$

PROBLEM 2 Given $f(x) = 4 - x^2$ and $g(x) = 3x - 4$, find $(f \cdot g)(3)$.

Solution See page S28.

EXAMPLE 3 Given $f(x) = x^2 + 4x + 4$ and $g(x) = x^3 - 2$, find $\left(\dfrac{f}{g}\right)(3)$.

Solution $\left(\dfrac{f}{g}\right)(3) = \dfrac{f(3)}{g(3)}$
$$= \frac{3^2 + 4(3) + 4}{3^3 - 2}$$
$$= \frac{25}{25}$$
$$= 1$$

$\left(\dfrac{f}{g}\right)(3) = 1$

> **PROBLEM 3**   Given $f(x) = x^2 - 4$ and $g(x) = x^2 + 2x + 1$, find $\left(\dfrac{f}{g}\right)(4)$.
>
> ■ **Solution**   See page S28.

OBJECTIVE **2**   ## Find the composition of two functions

Composition of functions is another way in which functions can be combined. This method of combining functions uses the output of one function as the input for a second function.

Suppose that a propane heater is used to heat the air in a hot-air balloon and that the shape of the balloon can be approximated by a sphere. The propane expands the air in the balloon in such a way that the radius of the balloon, in feet, is given by $r(t) = 0.3t$, where t is the time, in minutes, that the propane heater has been running.

The volume of the balloon depends on its radius and is given by $V(r) = \dfrac{4}{3}\pi r^3$. To

find the volume of the balloon 20 min after the heater is turned on, we first find the radius of the balloon and then use that number to find the volume of the balloon.

$$r(t) = 0.3t$$

$$r(20) = 0.3(20) \quad \bullet \ t = 20 \text{ min}$$

$$= 6$$

The radius is 6 ft.

$$V(r) = \dfrac{4}{3}\pi r^3$$

$$V(6) = \dfrac{4}{3}\pi(6^3) \quad \bullet \ r = 6 \text{ ft}$$

$$= 288\pi$$

$$\approx 904.78$$

The volume is approximately 904.78 ft³.

There is an alternative way to solve this problem. Because the volume of the balloon depends on the radius and the radius depends on the time, there is a relationship between the volume and the time. We can determine that relationship by evaluating the formula for the volume using $r(t) = 0.3t$. This will give the volume of the balloon as a function of time.

$$V(r) = \dfrac{4}{3}\pi r^3$$

$$V[r(t)] = \dfrac{4}{3}\pi[r(t)]^3 \quad \bullet \text{ Replace } r \text{ by } r(t).$$

$$= \dfrac{4}{3}\pi[0.3t]^3 \quad \bullet \ r(t) = 0.3t$$

$$= 0.036\pi t^3$$

The volume of the balloon as a function of time is $V(t) = 0.036\pi t^3$. To find the volume of the balloon 20 min after the heater is turned on, evaluate this function at $t = 20$.

$$V(t) = 0.036\pi t^3$$

$$V(20) = 0.036\pi(20)^3 \quad \bullet \ t = 20 \text{ min}$$

$$= 288\pi$$

$$\approx 904.78$$

This is exactly the same result we calculated earlier.

The function $V(t) = 0.036\pi t^3$ is referred to as the *composition* of V with r. The notation $V \circ r$ is used to denote this composition of functions. That is,

$$(V \circ r)(t) = 0.036\pi t^3$$

Definition of the Composition of Two Functions

Let f and g be two functions such that $g(x)$ is in the domain of f for all x in the domain of g. Then the **composition** of the two functions, denoted by $f \circ g$, is the function whose value at x is given by $(f \circ g)(x) = f[g(x)]$.

The function defined by $(f \circ g)(x)$ is called the **composite** of f and g. We read $(f \circ g)(x)$ as "f circle g of x," and we read $f[g(x)]$ as "f of g of x."

Consider the functions $f(x) = 2x$ and $g(x) = x^2$. Then $(f \circ g)(3) = f[g(3)]$ means to evaluate the function f at $g(3)$.

$$g(3) = 3^2 = 9$$

$$f[g(3)] = f(9) = 2(9) = 18$$

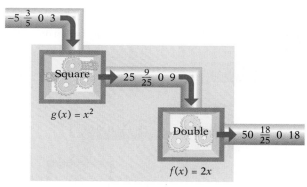

The function machine that is illustrated at the right shows the composition of $g(x) = x^2$ and $f(x) = 2x$. Note that the composite function, $(f \circ g)(x) = f[g(x)]$, uses the output of the square function $g(x) = x^2$ as the input of the double function $f(x) = 2x$.

The requirement in the definition of the composition of two functions that $g(x)$ be in the domain of f for all x in the domain of g is important. For instance, let

$$f(x) = \frac{1}{x - 1} \quad \text{and} \quad g(x) = 3x - 5$$

When $x = 2$,

$$g(2) = 3(2) - 5 = 1$$

$$f[g(2)] = f(1) = \frac{1}{1 - 1} = \frac{1}{0} \leftarrow \text{This is not a real number.}$$

In this case, $g(2)$ is not in the domain of f. Thus the composition is not defined at 2.

Given $f(x) = x^3 - x + 1$ and $g(x) = 2x^2 - 10$, evaluate $(g \circ f)(2)$.

$$f(2) = (2)^3 - (2) + 1$$
$$= 7$$

$$(g \circ f)(2) = g[f(2)]$$
$$= g(7)$$
$$= 2(7)^2 - 10 = 88$$

$$(g \circ f)(2) = 88$$

Given $f(x) = 3x - 2$ and $g(x) = x^2 - 2x$, evaluate $(f \circ g)(x)$.

$$(f \circ g)(x) = f[g(x)] = 3(x^2 - 2x) - 2$$
$$= 3x^2 - 6x - 2$$

When we evaluate compositions of functions, the order in which the functions are applied is important. In the two diagrams that follow, the *square function*, $g(x) = x^2$, and the *double function*, $f(x) = 2x$, are interchanged. Note that the final outputs are different. Therefore, $(f \circ g)(x) \neq (g \circ f)(x)$.

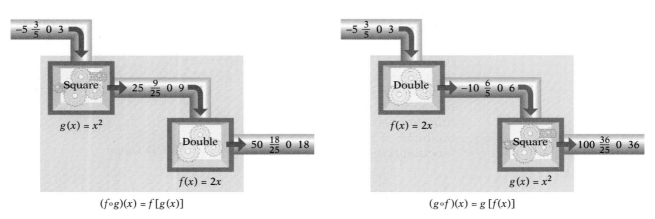

$(f \circ g)(x) = f[g(x)]$ $(g \circ f)(x) = g[f(x)]$

EXAMPLE 4   Given $f(x) = x^2 - 1$ and $g(x) = 3x + 4$, evaluate each composite function.

A. $f[g(0)]$ **B.** $g[f(x)]$

Solution   **A.** $g(x) = 3x + 4$
                          $g(0) = 3(0) + 4 = 4$ • To evaluate $f[g(0)]$, first evaluate $g(0)$.

                          $f(x) = x^2 - 1$
                          $f[g(0)] = f(4) = 4^2 - 1 = 15$ • Substitute the value of $g(0)$ for x in $f(x)$; $g(0) = 4$.

                          $f[g(0)] = 15$

B. $g[f(x)] = g(x^2 - 1)$ • $f(x) = x^2 - 1$
         $= 3(x^2 - 1) + 4$ • Substitute $x^2 - 1$ for x in the function $g(x)$; $g(x) = 3x + 4$.
         $= 3x^2 - 3 + 4$
         $= 3x^2 + 1$

PROBLEM 4   Given $g(x) = 3x - 2$ and $h(x) = x^2 + 1$, evaluate each composite function.

A. $g[h(0)]$ **B.** $h[g(x)]$

■ **Solution**   See page S28.

9.2   Concept Review

Determine whether the following statements are always true, sometimes true, or never true.

1. $(f \circ g)(x) = f[g(x)]$

2. If $f(x) = 2x$ and $g(x) = \frac{1}{2}x$, then $(f \circ g)(x) = (g \circ f)(x)$.

3. If $f(x) = 2x + 1$ and $g(x) = x + 4$, then $(f \circ g)(x) = (2x + 1)(x + 4)$.

4. If $f(x) = x^2 - 4$ and $g(x) = x^3$, then $(f \circ g)(x) = (x^2 - 4)^3$.

9.2   Exercises

1   **Perform operations on functions**

1. Given $f(x) = x^2 + 2x$ and $g(x) = 3x - 1$, find $(f - g)(-2)$.

$(f - g)(-2) = f(-2) - g(-2)$

       $= [(\underline{\quad ? \quad})^2 + 2(\underline{\quad ? \quad})]$
            $- [3(\underline{\quad ? \quad}) - 1]$

       $= [\underline{\quad ? \quad} - \underline{\quad ? \quad}]$
            $- [\underline{\quad ? \quad} - 1]$

       $= \underline{\quad ? \quad} - (\underline{\quad ? \quad})$

       $= \underline{\quad ? \quad}$

- For all x in the domains of f and g, $(f - g)(x) = f(x) - g(x)$.
- In each function, replace x with -2.
- Evaluate the expressions inside the grouping symbols.
- Subtract.

2. Given $f(x) = 2x^3 - x$ and $g(x) = x^2 + 1$, find $(f \cdot g)(-1)$.

$(f \cdot g)(-1) = f(-1) \cdot g(-1)$

       $= [2(\underline{\quad ? \quad})^3 - (\underline{\quad ? \quad})]$
            $\cdot [(\underline{\quad ? \quad})^2 + 1]$

       $= [\underline{\quad ? \quad} + \underline{\quad ? \quad}]$
            $\cdot [\underline{\quad ? \quad} + 1]$

       $= \underline{\quad ? \quad} \cdot \underline{\quad ? \quad}$

       $= \underline{\quad ? \quad}$

- For all x in the domains of f and g, $(f \cdot g)(x) = f(x) \cdot g(x)$.
- In each function, replace x with -1.
- Evaluate the expressions inside the grouping symbols.
- Multiply.

Given $f(x) = 2x^2 - 3$ and $g(x) = -2x + 4$, find:

3. $(f - g)(2)$ **4.** $(f - g)(3)$ **5.** $(f + g)(0)$

6. $(f + g)(1)$ **7.** $(f \cdot g)(2)$ **8.** $(f \cdot g)(-1)$

9. $\left(\dfrac{f}{g}\right)(4)$ **10.** $\left(\dfrac{f}{g}\right)(-1)$ **11.** $\left(\dfrac{g}{f}\right)(-3)$

Given $f(x) = 2x^2 + 3x - 1$ and $g(x) = 2x - 4$, find:

12. $(f + g)(-3)$ **13.** $(f + g)(1)$ **14.** $(f + g)(-2)$

15. $(f - g)(4)$ **16.** $(f \cdot g)(-2)$ **17.** $(f \cdot g)(1)$

18. $\left(\dfrac{f}{g}\right)(2)$ **19.** $\left(\dfrac{f}{g}\right)(-3)$ **20.** $(f \cdot g)\left(\dfrac{1}{2}\right)$

Given $f(x) = x^2 + 3x - 5$ and $g(x) = x^3 - 2x + 3$, find:

21. $(f - g)(2)$ **22.** $(f \cdot g)(-3)$ **23.** $\left(\dfrac{f}{g}\right)(-2)$

For Exercises 24 to 27, use the functions $f(x) = \sqrt{x}$, $g(x) = \sqrt{x^2}$, and $h(x) = \sqrt{a - x}$, where $a > 0$. State whether the given expression is *defined* or *undefined*.

24. $(f \cdot g)(a)$ **25.** $(f \cdot g)(-a)$

26. $\left(\dfrac{f}{h}\right)(a)$ **27.** $\left(\dfrac{h}{g}\right)(a)$

2   Find the composition of two functions

For Exercises 28 and 29, use the functions $f(x) = x^2 - 2x$ and $g(x) = 4x$.

28. Evaluate $g[f(-1)]$.

$f(-1) = (\underline{\ \ ?\ \ })^2 - 2(\underline{\ \ ?\ \ }) = \underline{\ \ ?\ \ }$ • First evaluate $f(-1)$.
$g(f(-1)) = g(\underline{\ \ ?\ \ })$ • Replace $g[f(-1)]$ with its value, 3.
$ = 4(\underline{\ \ ?\ \ })$ • Replace x with 3 in $g(x) = 4x$.
$ = \underline{\ \ ?\ \ }$ • Evaluate.

29. Find $f[g(x)]$.

$f[g(x)] = f(4x)$ • $g(x) = \underline{\ \ ?\ \ }$.
$ = (\underline{\ \ ?\ \ })^2 - 2(\underline{\ \ ?\ \ })$ • Replace x in $f(x) = x^2 - 2x$ with 4x.
$ = \underline{\ \ ?\ \ } - \underline{\ \ ?\ \ }$ • Simplify.

30.   Explain the meaning of the notation $f[g(2)]$.

31.   What is the meaning of the notation $(f \circ g)(x)$?

Given $f(x) = 2x - 3$ and $g(x) = 4x - 1$, evaluate the composite function.

32. $f[g(0)]$ **33.** $g[f(0)]$ **34.** $f[g(2)]$ **35.** $g[f(-2)]$ **36.** $f[g(x)]$ **37.** $g[f(x)]$

Given $g(x) = x^2 + 3$ and $h(x) = x - 2$, evaluate the composite function.

38. $g[h(0)]$ **39.** $h[g(0)]$ **40.** $g[h(4)]$ **41.** $h[g(-2)]$ **42.** $g[h(x)]$ **43.** $h[g(x)]$

Given $f(x) = x^2 + x + 1$ and $h(x) = 3x + 2$, evaluate the composite function.

44. $f[h(0)]$ **45.** $h[f(0)]$ **46.** $f[h(-1)]$ **47.** $h[f(-2)]$ **48.** $f[h(x)]$ **49.** $h[f(x)]$

Given $f(x) = x - 2$ and $g(x) = x^3$, evaluate the composite function.

50. $f[g(2)]$ **51.** $f[g(-1)]$ **52.** $g[f(2)]$ **53.** $g[f(-1)]$ **54.** $f[g(x)]$ **55.** $g[f(x)]$

For Exercises 56 to 59, state whether or not the given pair of functions will produce the composite function $(f \circ g)(x) = 3x^2 - 3$.

56. $f(x) = x^2 - 1$ and $g(x) = 3x$ **57.** $f(x) = x^2$ and $g(x) = 3x - 3$

58. $f(x) = 3x - 3$ and $g(x) = x^2$ **59.** $f(x) = 3x$ and $g(x) = x^2 - 1$

9.2   Applying Concepts

Given $g(x) = x^2 - 1$, find:

60. $g(2 + h)$ **61.** $g(3 + h) - g(3)$ **62.** $g(-1 + h) - g(-1)$

63. $\dfrac{g(1 + h) - g(1)}{h}$ **64.** $\dfrac{g(-2 + h) - g(-2)}{h}$ **65.** $\dfrac{g(a + h) - g(a)}{h}$

Given $f(x) = 2x$, $g(x) = 3x - 1$, and $h(x) = x - 2$, find:

66. $f(g[h(2)])$ **67.** $g(h[f(1)])$ **68.** $h(g[f(-1)])$

69. $f(h[g(0)])$ **70.** $f(g[h(x)])$ **71.** $g(f[h(x)])$

The graphs of the functions f and g are shown at the right. Use these graphs to determine the values of the following composite functions.

72. $f[g(0)]$ **73.** $f[g(2)]$

74. $f[g(4)]$ **75.** $f[g(-2)]$

76. $f[g(-4)]$ **77.** $g[f(0)]$

78. $g[f(4)]$ **79.** $g[f(-4)]$

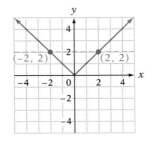

9.3 One-to-One and Inverse Functions

OBJECTIVE 1 ## Determine whether a function is one-to-one

Recall that a function is a set of ordered pairs in which no two ordered pairs that have the same first component have different second components. This means that given any x, there is only one y that can be paired with that x. A **one-to-one function** satisfies the additional condition that given any y, there is only one x that can be paired with the given y. One-to-one functions are commonly expressed by writing 1–1.

The function given by the equation $y = |x|$ is not a 1–1 function since, given $y = 2$, there are two possible values of x, 2 and -2, that can be paired with the given y-value. The graph at the left illustrates that a horizontal line intersects the graph more than once.

Just as the vertical line test can be used to determine whether a graph represents a function, a **horizontal line test** can be used to determine whether the graph of a function represents a 1–1 function.

> ### Horizontal Line Test
>
> A graph of a function is the graph of a 1–1 function if any horizontal line intersects the graph at no more than one point.

Since any vertical line will intersect the graph at the right at no more than one point, the graph is the graph of a function. Since any horizontal line will intersect the graph at no more than one point, the graph is the graph of a 1–1 function.

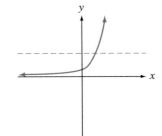

The graph of a quadratic function is shown at the right. Note that a horizontal line can intersect the graph at more than one point. Therefore, this graph is not the graph of a 1–1 function. In general, $f(x) = ax^2 + bx + c$, $a \neq 0$, is not a 1–1 function.

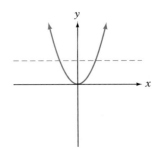

EXAMPLE 1 Determine whether or not the graph represents the graph of a 1–1 function.

A.

B.

Solution A.

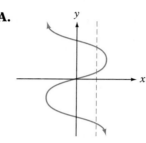

This is not the graph of a 1–1 function.

• A vertical line can intersect the graph at more than one point. The graph does not represent a function.

B.

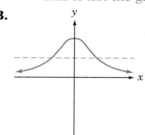

This is not the graph of a 1–1 function.

• A horizontal line can intersect the curve at more than one point.

PROBLEM 1 Determine whether or not the graph represents the graph of a 1–1 function.

A.

B.

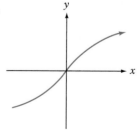

■ Solution See page S28.

OBJECTIVE 2 Find the inverse of a function

The **inverse of a function** is the set of ordered pairs formed by reversing the coordinates of each ordered pair of the function.

For example, the set of ordered pairs of the function defined by $f(x) = 2x$ with domain $\{-2, -1, 0, 1, 2\}$ is $\{(-2, -4), (-1, -2), (0, 0), (1, 2), (2, 4)\}$. The set of ordered pairs of the inverse function is $\{(-4, -2), (-2, -1), (0, 0), (2, 1), (4, 2)\}$.

From the ordered pairs of f, we have

Domain $= \{-2, -1, 0, 1, 2\}$ and   Range $= \{-4, -2, 0, 2, 4\}$

From the ordered pairs of the inverse function, we have

Domain $= \{-4, -2, 0, 2, 4\}$ and   Range $= \{-2, -1, 0, 1, 2\}$

Note that the domain of the inverse function is the range of the function, and the range of the inverse function is the domain of the function.

Now consider the function defined by $g(x) = x^2$ with domain $\{-2, -1, 0, 1, 2\}$. The set of ordered pairs of this function is $\{(-2, 4), (-1, 1), (0, 0), (1, 1), (2, 4)\}$. Reversing the ordered pairs gives $\{(4, -2), (1, -1), (0, 0), (1, 1), (4, 2)\}$. These ordered pairs do not satisfy the condition of a function, because there are ordered pairs with the same first coordinate and different second coordinates. This example illustrates that not all functions have an inverse function.

The graphs of $f(x) = 2x$ and $g(x) = x^2$ with the set of real numbers as the domain are shown below.

$f(x) = 2x$

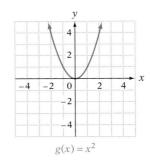
$g(x) = x^2$

By the horizontal line test, f is a 1–1 function but g is not.

Condition for an Inverse Function

A function f has an inverse function if and only if f is a 1–1 function.

The symbol f^{-1} is used to denote the inverse of a 1–1 function f. The symbol $f^{-1}(x)$ is read "f inverse of x."

$f^{-1}(x)$ is *not* the reciprocal of $f(x)$ but is the notation for the inverse of a 1–1 function.

To find the inverse of a function, interchange x and y. Then solve for y.

Find the inverse of the function defined by $f(x) = 3x + 6$.

$$f(x) = 3x + 6$$

Replace $f(x)$ by y. $y = 3x + 6$

Interchange x and y. $x = 3y + 6$

Solve for y. $x - 6 = 3y$

$$\frac{1}{3}x - 2 = y$$

Replace y by $f^{-1}(x)$. $f^{-1}(x) = \frac{1}{3}x - 2$

The inverse of the function is given by $f^{-1}(x) = \frac{1}{3}x - 2$.

Domain of f Range of f
Range of f^{-1} Domain of f^{-1}

The fact that the ordered pairs of the inverse of a function are the reverse of those of the function has a graphical interpretation. The function shown at the left below includes the points $(-2, 0)$, $(-1, 2)$, $(1, 4)$, and $(5, 6)$. In the graph in the middle, the points with these coordinates reversed are plotted. The inverse function is graphed by drawing a smooth curve through those points, as shown in the figure at the right.

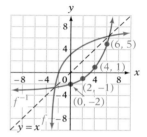

Note that the dashed graph of $y = x$ is shown in the figure at the right. If two functions are inverses of each other, then their graphs are mirror images with respect to the graph of the line $y = x$.

The composition of a function and its inverse have a special property.

Composition of Inverse Functions Property

$$f^{-1}[f(x)] = x \qquad \text{and} \qquad f[f^{-1}(x)] = x$$

This property can be used to determine whether two functions are inverses of each other.

Are $f(x) = 2x - 4$ and $g(x) = \frac{1}{2}x + 2$ inverses of each other?

To determine whether the functions are inverses, use the Composition of Inverse Functions Property.

$$f[g(x)] = 2\left(\frac{1}{2}x + 2\right) - 4 \qquad g[f(x)] = \frac{1}{2}(2x - 4) + 2$$
$$= x + 4 - 4 \qquad\qquad\qquad = x - 2 + 2$$
$$= x \qquad\qquad\qquad\qquad\quad = x$$

Because $f[g(x)] = x$ and $g[f(x)] = x$, the functions are inverses of each other.

EXAMPLE 2 Find the inverse of the function defined by the equation
$f(x) = 2x - 4$.

Solution
$$f(x) = 2x - 4$$
$$y = 2x - 4$$ • Think of the function as the equation $y = 2x - 4$.
$$x = 2y - 4$$ • Interchange x and y.
$$2y = x + 4$$ • Solve for y.
$$y = \frac{1}{2}x + 2$$

$$f^{-1}(x) = \frac{1}{2}x + 2$$

PROBLEM 2 Find the inverse of the function defined by the equation
$f(x) = 4x + 2$.

Solution   See page S28.

EXAMPLE 3 Are the functions defined by the equations $f(x) = -2x + 3$
and $g(x) = -\frac{1}{2}x + \frac{3}{2}$ inverses of each other?

Solution
$$f[g(x)] = f\left(-\frac{1}{2}x + \frac{3}{2}\right)$$ • Use the property that, for inverses,
$$f[f^{-1}(x)] = f^{-1}[f(x)] = x.$$
$$= -2\left(-\frac{1}{2}x + \frac{3}{2}\right) + 3$$
$$= x - 3 + 3$$
$$= x$$ • $f[g(x)] = x$

$$g[f(x)] = g(-2x + 3)$$
$$= -\frac{1}{2}(-2x + 3) + \frac{3}{2}$$
$$= x - \frac{3}{2} + \frac{3}{2}$$
$$= x$$ • $g[f(x)] = x$

The functions are inverses of each other.

PROBLEM 3 Are the functions defined by the equations $h(x) = 4x + 2$
and $g(x) = \frac{1}{4}x - \frac{1}{2}$ inverses of each other?

Solution   See page S28.

The function given by the equation $f(x) = \frac{1}{2}x^2$ does not have an inverse that is a function. Two of the ordered-pair solutions of this function are $(4, 8)$ and $(-4, 8)$.

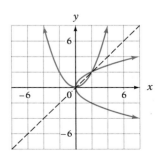

The graph of $f(x) = \frac{1}{2}x^2$ is shown at the left. This graph does not pass the horizontal line test for the graph of a 1–1 function. The mirror image of the graph with respect to the line $y = x$ is also shown. This graph does not pass the vertical line test for the graph of a function.

A quadratic function with domain the real numbers does not have an inverse function.

9.3   Concept Review

Determine whether the following statements are always true, sometimes true, or never true.

1. The graph of a function represents the graph of a 1–1 function if any horizontal line intersects the graph at no more than one point.

2. A function has an inverse if and only if it is a 1–1 function.

3. The inverse of the function $\{(2, 3), (4, 5), (6, 3)\}$ is the function $\{(3, 2), (5, 4), (3, 6)\}$.

4. The inverse of a function is a relation.

5. The inverse of a function is a function.

6. The graph of $y = x^2$ is the graph of a 1–1 function.

9.3   Exercises

1   Determine whether a function is one-to-one

1. What is a 1–1 function?

2. What is the horizontal line test?

3. The function $y = x^2$ is not a 1–1 function because, for example, the x values 2 and ___?___ are both paired with the same y value, ___?___

4. Suppose the horizontal line $y = b$ intersects the graph of the function $y = f(x)$ in two different points (a, b) and (c, b). The function $y = f(x)$ is not a 1–1 function because two different x values, ___?___ and ___?___, are paired with the same y value, ___?___

Determine whether the graph represents the graph of a 1–1 function.

5.

6.

7.

8.

9.

10.

11.

12.

13.

14.

15.

16.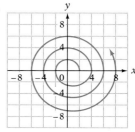

For Exercises 17 to 20, state whether the function is a 1–1 function.

17. $f(x) = x$

18. $f(x) = a$, where a is any real number

19. $f(x) = |x| + a$, where a is any real number

20. $f(x) = x^3$

2   Find the inverse of a function

21. If $(2, -3)$ is a point on the graph of the function $y = f(x)$, then the point (__?__ , __?__) is a point on the graph of the inverse of $y = f(x)$.

22. a. The only functions whose inverses are also functions are __?__ functions.
   b. The notation used to denote the inverse function of the 1–1 function f is __?__ .

Find the inverse of the function. If the function does not have an inverse, write "No inverse."

23. $\{(1, 0), (2, 3), (3, 8), (4, 15)\}$

24. $\{(1, 0), (2, 1), (-1, 0), (-2, 1)\}$

25. $\{(3, 5), (-3, -5), (2, 5), (-2, -5)\}$

26. $\{(-5, -5), (-3, -1), (-1, 3), (1, 7)\}$

27. $f(x) = 4x - 8$

28. $f(x) = 3x + 15$

29. $f(x) = x^2 - 1$

30. $f(x) = 2x + 4$

31. $f(x) = x - 5$

32. $f(x) = \dfrac{1}{2}x - 1$

33. $f(x) = \dfrac{1}{3}x + 2$

34. $f(x) = -2x + 2$

35. $f(x) = -3x - 9$

36. $f(x) = 2x^2 + 2$

37. $f(x) = \dfrac{2}{3}x + 4$

38. $f(x) = \dfrac{3}{4}x - 4$

39. $f(x) = -\dfrac{1}{3}x + 1$

40. $f(x) = -\dfrac{1}{2}x + 2$

41. $f(x) = 2x - 5$

42. $f(x) = 3x + 4$

43. $f(x) = x^2 + 3$

44. $f(x) = 5x - 2$

Given $f(x) = 3x - 5$, find:

45. $f^{-1}(0)$

46. $f^{-1}(2)$

47. $f^{-1}(4)$

State whether the graph is the graph of a function. If it is the graph of a function, does it have an inverse?

48.

49.

50.
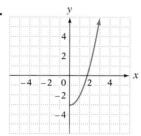

Use the Composition of Inverse Functions Property to determine whether the functions are inverses of each other.

51. $f(x) = 4x;\ g(x) = \dfrac{x}{4}$

52. $g(x) = x + 5;\ h(x) = x - 5$

53. $f(x) = 3x;\ h(x) = \dfrac{1}{3x}$

54. $h(x) = x + 2;\ g(x) = 2 - x$

55. $g(x) = 3x + 2;\ f(x) = \dfrac{1}{3}x - \dfrac{2}{3}$

56. $h(x) = 4x - 1;\ f(x) = \dfrac{1}{4}x + \dfrac{1}{4}$

57. $f(x) = \dfrac{1}{2}x - \dfrac{3}{2};\ g(x) = 2x + 3$

58. $g(x) = -\dfrac{1}{2}x - \dfrac{1}{2};\ h(x) = -2x + 1$

Complete.

59. The domain of the inverse function f^{-1} is the _____ of f.

60. The range of the inverse function f^{-1} is the _____ of f.

61. For any function f and its inverse f^{-1}, $f[f^{-1}(3)] =$ _____.

62. For any function f and its inverse f^{-1}, $f^{-1}[f(-4)] =$ _____.

If f is a 1–1 function and $f(0) = 5$, $f(1) = 7$, $f(2) = 9$, and $f(3) = 11$, find:

63. $f^{-1}(5)$ **64.** $f^{-1}(11)$ **65.** $f^{-1}(9)$ **66.** $f^{-1}(7)$

For Exercises 67 to 70, f is a 1–1 function such that $f(a) = b$, $f(b) = c$, and $f(c) = a$.

67. Find $f^{-1}(a)$.

68. Find $f^{-1}(f^{-1}(a))$.

69. Find $f(f^{-1}(a))$.

70. 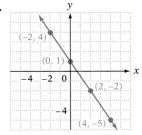 Find $f^{-1}(f^{-1}(b))$.

71. Given $f(x) = 3x + 2$ and $g(x) = 5x + 4$, show that $f[g(x)] = g[f(x)]$. Are f and g inverse functions?

72. Given $f(x) = 7x - 4$ and $g(x) = -2x + 2$, show that $f[g(x)] = g[f(x)]$. Are f and g inverse functions?

9.3 Applying Concepts

Given the graph of the 1–1 function, draw the graph of the inverse of the function by using the technique shown in this section.

73.

74.

75.

76.

77.

78.

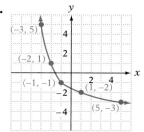

Each of the following tables defines a function. Is the inverse of the function a function? Explain your answer.

79.

Grading Scale Table

Score	Grade
90 – 100	A
80 – 89	B
70 – 79	C
60 – 69	D
0 – 59	F

80.

First-Class Postage

Weight (in oz)	Cost
$0 < w \leq 1$	$.39
$1 < w \leq 2$	$.63
$2 < w \leq 3$	$.87
$3 < w \leq 4$	$1.11

Exercises 81 and 82 demonstrate the essence of secure communication over the Internet. In practice, the coding functions are very complicated so that it is extremely unlikely that anyone will find the inverse and break the code.

81. Internet Commerce Inverse functions are used to secure business transactions over the Internet. Here is a very simple example of how it can be done. Let A = 10, B = 11, C = 12, ..., Z = 35. For instance, NAME would be coded as 23102214. Now choose a function that has an inverse function, say $f(x) = 2x - 4$. The function f is used to code NAME by evaluating the function at 23102214:

$$f(23102214) = 2(23102214) - 4 = 46204428 - 4 = 46204424$$

The number 46204424 would be sent over the Internet. The computer receiving the code would use the inverse of f to find the original word.

a. Find f^{-1} and show that $f^{-1}(46204424) = 23102214$.

b. Suppose that 44205830 is received by a computer. What word was sent?

82. Cryptography Friends send each other coded messages by using the scheme in Exercise 81. They decide to use the coding function $f(x) = 2x + 1$. If one person receives the message 58285659, what word was sent?

83. **Unit Conversion** The function given by $f(x) = 3x$ converts yards into feet. Find f^{-1} and explain what it does.

84. **Unit Conversion** The function given by $f(x) = 16x$ converts pounds into ounces. Find f^{-1} and explain what it does.

85. **Geometry** The formula for the perimeter of a square is $P(x) = 4x$. Find $P^{-1}(x)$ and explain what it does.

Focus on Problem Solving

Proof in Mathematics

Mathematics is based on the concept of proof, which in turn is based on principles of logic. It was Aristotle (384 B.C.–322 B.C.) who took the logical principles that had developed over time and set them in a structured form. From this structured form, several methods of proof were developed.

A **deductive proof** is one that proceeds in a carefully ordered sequence of steps. It is the type of proof you may have seen in a geometry class. Deductive proofs have a model as shown at the left.

$$\text{A true} \xrightarrow{\text{implies}} \text{B true} \xrightarrow{\text{implies}} \text{C true}$$
$$\text{A true} \xrightarrow{\text{implies}} \text{C true}$$

Here is an example of a deductive proof. It proves that the product of a negative and a positive number is a negative number. The proof is based on the fact that every real number has exactly one additive inverse. For instance, the additive inverse of 4 is -4 and the additive inverse of $-\frac{2}{3}$ is $\frac{2}{3}$.

Theorem: If a and b are positive real numbers, then $(-a)b = -(ab)$.

Proof:
$$\begin{aligned}(-a)b + ab &= (-a + a)b & &\bullet \textbf{ Distributive Property}\\ &= 0 \cdot b & &\bullet \textbf{ Inverse Property of Addition}\\ &= 0 & &\bullet \textbf{ Multiplication Property of Zero}\end{aligned}$$

Since $(-a)b + ab = 0$, $(-a)b$ is the additive inverse of ab. But $-(ab)$ is also the additive inverse of ab, and because every number has exactly one additive inverse, $(-a)b = -(ab)$.

Here is another example of a deductive proof. It is a proof of the Pythagorean Theorem.

Theorem: If a and b are the lengths of the legs of a right triangle and c is the length of the hypotenuse, then $a^2 + b^2 = c^2$.

Proof: Let $\triangle DBA$ be a right triangle and let BC be the altitude to the hypotenuse of $\triangle DBA$, as shown at the left. Then $\triangle BCD$ and $\triangle BCA$ are right triangles.

1. $\triangle DBA$ is a right triangle with height BC.

   Given.

2. $\triangle DBC$ is similar to $\triangle BCA$ and $\triangle DBA$ is similar to $\triangle BCA$.

   Theorem from geometry: the altitude to the hypotenuse of a right triangle forms triangles that are similar to each other.

3. $\dfrac{a}{b} = \dfrac{x}{a}$

   The ratios of corresponding sides of similar triangles are equal.

4. $a^2 = bx$

   Multiply each side by ab.

5. $\dfrac{x + b}{c} = \dfrac{c}{b}$

   The ratios of corresponding sides of similar triangles are equal.

6. $bx + b^2 = c^2$

   Multiply each side by cb.

7. $a^2 + b^2 = c^2$

   Substitution Property from (4).

Because the first statement of the proof is true and each subsequent statement of the proof is true, the first statement means the last statement is true. Therefore we have proved: If a and b are the lengths of the legs of a right triangle and c is the length of the hypotenuse, then $a^2 + b^2 = c^2$.

Projects & Group Activities

Applications of the Composition of Functions

Suppose a company's manufacturing cost, in dollars, per computer monitor is given by

$$M(x) = \frac{180x + 2600}{x}$$

where x is the number of computer monitors to be manufactured. An electronics outlet agrees to sell the computer monitors by marking up the manufacturing cost per monitor, $M(x)$, by 30%. Note that the selling price S will be a function of $M(x)$. We can write this as

$$S[M(x)] = 1.30(M(x))$$

Simplifying $S[M(x)]$ yields

$$S[M(x)] = 1.30\left(\frac{180x + 2600}{x}\right)$$

$$= 1.30(180) + 1.30\left(\frac{2600}{x}\right)$$

$$= 234 + \left(\frac{3380}{x}\right)$$

The function produced in this manner is referred to as the composition of M by S. The notation $S \circ M$ is used to denote this composition of functions. That is,

$$(S \circ M)(x) = 234 + \left(\frac{3380}{x}\right)$$

Suppose 10,000 computer monitors are manufactured. Then

$$(S \circ M)(10,000) = 234 + \frac{3380}{10,000}$$

$$= 234.338$$

If 10,000 computer monitors are manufactured, the selling price per computer monitor is \$234.34.

Solve.

1. Let x be the number of compact disk players to be manufactured. The manufacturing cost, in dollars, per compact disk player is given by the function

$$M(x) = \frac{60x + 34,000}{x}$$

A computer store will sell the disk players by marking up the manufacturing cost per disk player, $M(x)$, by 45%. Thus the selling price S is a function of $M(x)$ given by the equation $S[M(x)] = 1.45[M(x)]$.

a. Express the selling price as a function of the number of disk players to be manufactured. That is, find $S \circ M$.

b. Find $(S \circ M)(24{,}650)$. What does this represent?

2. The number of bookcases b that a factory can produce per day is a function of the number of hours h it operates.

$$b(h) = 40\,h \quad \text{for } 0 \le h \le 12$$

The daily cost c to manufacture b bookcases is given by the function

$$c(b) = 0.1b^2 + 90b + 800$$

Evaluate each of the following and interpret your answers.

a. $b(5)$ **b.** $c(5)$ **c.** $(c \circ b)(h)$ **d.** $(c \circ b)(10)$

3. A car dealership offers a $1500 rebate and a 10% discount off the price of a new car. Let p be the sticker price of a new car on the dealer's lot, let r be the rebate, and let d be the discount. Then $r(p) = p - 1500$ and $d(p) = 0.90p$.

a. Write a composite function for the dealer taking the rebate first and then the discount.

b. Write a composite function for the dealer taking the discount first and then the rebate.

c. Which composite function would you prefer the dealer use if you were buying a new car?

4. **a.** Write the area of a circle as a function of r.

b. Write the radius of a circle as a function of the circumference.

c. Write the area of a circle as a function of the circumference.

Chapter 9 Summary

Key Words

The **inverse of a function** is the set of ordered pairs formed by reversing the coordinates of each ordered pair of the function. [9.3.2, p. 593]

Examples

Function: {(2, 4), (3, 5), (6, 7), (8, 9)}
Inverse: {(4, 2), (5, 3), (7, 6), (9, 8)}

Essential Rules and Procedures

Vertical Translation [9.1.1, p. 577]
The graph of $y = f(x) + c$, $c > 0$, is the graph of $y = f(x)$ shifted up c units.

The graph $g(x) = x^2 + 1$ is the graph of $f(x) = x^2$ shifted up 1 unit.

The graph of $y = f(x) - c$, $c > 0$, is the graph of $y = f(x)$ shifted down c units.

The graph of $G(x) = x^3 - 3$ is the graph of $F(x) = x^3$ shifted down 3 units.

Horizontal Translation [9.1.1, p. 578]

The graph of $y = f(x - c)$, $c > 0$, is the graph of $y = f(x)$ shifted horizontally c units to the right.

The graph of $y = f(x + c)$, $c > 0$, is the graph of $y = f(x)$ shifted horizontally c units to the left.

The graph $g(x) = (x - 2)^2$ is the graph of $f(x) = x^2$ shifted 2 units to the right.

The graph of $G(x) = (x + 4)^3$ is the graph of $F(x) = x^3$ shifted 4 units to the left.

Operations on Functions [9.2.1, p. 584]

If f and g are functions and x is an element of the domain of each function, then

$$(f + g)(x) = f(x) + g(x)$$

$$(f - g)(x) = f(x) - g(x)$$

$$(f \cdot g)(x) = f(x) \cdot g(x)$$

$$\left(\frac{f}{g}\right)(x) = \frac{f(x)}{g(x)}, g(x) \neq 0$$

Given $f(x) = x + 2$ and $g(x) = 2x$, then

$$\begin{aligned}(f + g)(4) &= f(4) + g(4) \\ &= (4 + 2) + 2(4) = 6 + 8 \\ &= 14\end{aligned}$$

$$\begin{aligned}(f - g)(4) &= f(4) - g(4) \\ &= (4 + 2) - 2(4) = 6 - 8 \\ &= -2\end{aligned}$$

$$\begin{aligned}(f \cdot g)(4) &= f(4) \cdot g(4) \\ &= (4 + 2) \cdot (2)(4) = 6 \cdot 8 \\ &= 48\end{aligned}$$

$$\left(\frac{f}{g}\right)(4) = \frac{f(4)}{g(4)} = \frac{4 + 2}{2(4)} = \frac{6}{8} = \frac{3}{4}$$

Composition of Two Functions

$(f \circ g)(x) = f[g(x)]$ [9.2.2, p. 587]

Given $f(x) = x - 4$ and $g(x) = 4x$, then

$$\begin{aligned}(f \circ g)(2) &= f[g(2)] \\ &= f(8) \qquad \text{because } g(2) = 8 \\ &= 8 - 4 = 4\end{aligned}$$

Horizontal Line Test

A function f is a 1–1 function if any horizontal line intersects the graph at no more than one point. [9.3.1, p. 592]

A 1–1 function

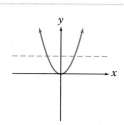

Not a 1–1 function

Condition for an Inverse Function

A function f has an inverse if and only if f is a 1–1 function. [9.3.2, p. 594]

The function $f(x) = x^2$ does not have an inverse function. When $y = 4$, $x = 2$ or -2; therefore, the function $f(x)$ is not a 1–1 function.

Composition of Inverse Functions Property

$f^{-1}[f(x)] = x$ and $f[f^{-1}(x)] = x$ [9.3.2, p. 595]

$$f(x) = 2x - 3 \qquad f^{-1}(x) = \frac{1}{2}x + \frac{3}{2}$$

$$f^{-1}[f(x)] = \frac{1}{2}(2x - 3) + \frac{3}{2} = x$$

$$f[f^{-1}(x)] = 2\left(\frac{1}{2}x + \frac{3}{2}\right) - 3 = x$$

Chapter 9 Review Exercises

1. Use the graph of $f(x) = x^2$ shown below to graph $g(x) = (x - 1)^2$.

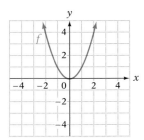

2. Use the graph of $f(x) = x^3$ shown below to graph $g(x) = x^3 + 3$.

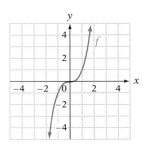

3. Use the graph of $f(x) = |x|$ shown below to graph $g(x) = |x - 1| + 2$.

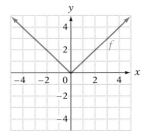

4. Use the graph of $f(x) = \sqrt{x}$ shown below to graph $g(x) = \sqrt{x + 1} - 2$.

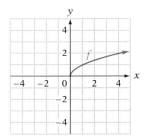

In Exercises 5 to 8, given $f(x) = x^2 + 2x - 3$ and $g(x) = x^2 - 2$, find:

5. $(f + g)(2)$

6. $(f - g)(-4)$

7. $(f \cdot g)(-4)$

8. $\left(\dfrac{f}{g}\right)(3)$

9. Given $f(x) = 3x^2 - 4$ and $g(x) = 2x + 1$, find $f[g(x)]$.

10. Given $f(x) = x^2 + 4$ and $g(x) = 4x - 1$, find $f[g(0)]$.

11. Given $f(x) = 6x + 8$ and $g(x) = 4x + 2$, find $g[f(-1)]$.

12. Given $f(x) = 2x^2 + x - 5$ and $g(x) = 3x - 1$, find $g[f(x)]$.

13. Is the set of ordered pairs a 1–1 function?
$\{(-3, 0), (-2, 0), (-1, 1), (0, 1)\}$

14. Find the inverse of the function
$\{(-2, 1), (2, 3), (5, -4), (7, 9)\}$.

15. Determine whether the graph is the graph of a 1–1 function.

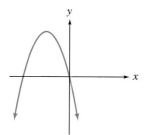

16. Determine whether the graph is the graph of a 1–1 function.

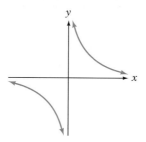

17. Find the inverse of the function $f(x) = \frac{1}{2}x + 8$.

18. Find the inverse of the function $f(x) = -6x + 4$.

19. Find the inverse of the function $f(x) = \frac{2}{3}x - 12$.

20. Are the functions $f(x) = -\frac{1}{4}x + \frac{5}{4}$ and $g(x) = -4x + 5$ inverses of each other?

Chapter 9 Test

1. Determine whether the graph represents the graph of a 1–1 function.

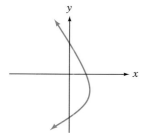

2. Given $f(x) = x^2 + 2x - 3$ and $g(x) = x^3 - 1$, find $(f - g)(2)$.

3. Given $f(x) = x^3 + 1$ and $g(x) = 2x - 3$ find $(f \cdot g)(-3)$.

4. Given $f(x) = 4x - 5$ and $g(x) = x^2 + 3x + 4$, find $\left(\frac{f}{g}\right)(-2)$.

5. Given $f(x) = x^2 + 4$ and $g(x) = 2x^2 + 2x + 1$, find $(f - g)(-4)$.

6. Given $f(x) = 4x + 2$ and $g(x) = \frac{x}{x + 1}$, find $f[g(3)]$.

7. Use the graph of $f(x) = -x^3$ shown below to graph $g(x) = -x^3 - 2$.

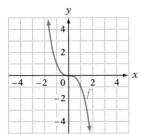

8. Use the graph of $f(x) = -|x|$ shown below to graph $g(x) = -|x| + 3$.

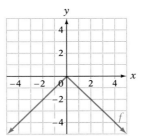

9. If $f(3) = 7$ and $g(x) = x^2 - 2$, find $g[f(3)]$.

10. Use the graph of $f(x) = |x|$ shown below to graph $g(x) = |x + 2| - 3$.

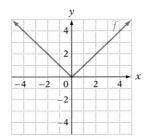

11. Use the graph of $f(x) = -x^2$ shown below to graph $g(x) = -(x - 2)^2 + 2$.

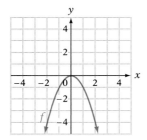

12. Find the inverse of the function $f(x) = \frac{1}{4}x - 4$.

13. Find the inverse of the function $\{(2, 6), (3, 5), (4, 4), (5, 3)\}$.

14. Are the functions $f(x) = \frac{1}{2}x + 2$ and $g(x) = 2x - 4$ inverses of each other?

15. Given $f(x) = 2x^2 - 7$ and $g(x) = x - 1$, find $f[g(x)]$.

16. Find the inverse of the function $f(x) = \frac{1}{2}x - 3$.

17. Are the functions $f(x) = \frac{2}{3}x + 3$ and $g(x) = \frac{3}{2}x - 3$ inverses of each other?

18. Determine whether the graph is the graph of a 1–1 function.

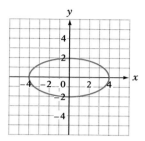

Cumulative Review Exercises

1. Evaluate $-3a + \left|\dfrac{3b - ab}{3b - c}\right|$ when $a = 2$, $b = 2$, and $c = -2$.

2. Graph: $\{x \,|\, x < -3\} \cap \{x \,|\, x > -4\}$

3. Solve: $\dfrac{3x - 1}{6} - \dfrac{5 - x}{4} = \dfrac{5}{6}$

4. Solve: $4x - 2 < -10$ or $3x - 1 > 8$

5. Graph $f(x) = \frac{1}{4}x^2$. Find the vertex and axis of symmetry.

6. Graph the solution set of $3x - 4y \geq 8$.

7. Solve: $|8 - 2x| \geq 0$

8. Simplify: $\left(\dfrac{3a^3b}{2a}\right)^2 \left(\dfrac{a^2}{-3b^2}\right)^3$

9. Multiply: $(x - 4)(2x^2 + 4x - 1)$

10. Factor: $a^4 - 2a^2 - 8$

11. Factor: $x^3y + x^2y^2 - 6xy^3$

12. Solve: $(b + 2)(b - 5) = 2b + 14$

13. Solve: $x^2 - 2x > 15$

14. Subtract: $\dfrac{x^2 + 4x - 5}{2x^2 - 3x + 1} - \dfrac{x}{2x - 1}$

15. Solve: $\dfrac{5}{x^2 + 7x + 12} = \dfrac{9}{x + 4} - \dfrac{2}{x + 3}$

16. Simplify: $\dfrac{4 - 6i}{2i}$

17. Find the equation of the line that contains the points $(-3, 4)$ and $(2, -6)$.

18. Find the equation of the line that contains the point $(-3, 1)$ and is perpendicular to the line $2x - 3y = 6$.

19. Solve: $3x^2 = 3x - 1$

20. Solve: $\sqrt{8x + 1} = 2x - 1$

21. Find the minimum value of the function $f(x) = 2x^2 - 3$.

22. Find the range of $f(x) = |3x - 4|$ if the domain is $\{0, 1, 2, 3\}$.

23. Is this set of ordered pairs a function?

$\{(-3, 0), (-2, 0), (-1, 1), (0, 1)\}$

24. Solve: $\sqrt[3]{5x - 2} = 2$

25. Given $g(x) = 3x - 5$ and $h(x) = \frac{1}{2}x + 4$, find $g[h(2)]$.

26. Find the inverse of the function given by $f(x) = -3x + 9$.

27. **Food Mixtures** Find the cost per pound of a tea mixture made from 30 lb of tea costing \$4.50 per pound and 45 lb of tea costing \$3.60 per pound.

28. **Metallurgy** How many pounds of an 80% copper alloy must be mixed with 50 lb of a 20% copper alloy to make an alloy that is 40% copper?

29. **Mixture Problem** Six ounces of an insecticide are mixed with 16 gal of water to make a spray for spraying an orange grove. How much additional insecticide is required if it is to be mixed with 28 gal of water?

30. **Work Problem** A large pipe can fill a tank in 8 min less time than it takes a smaller pipe to fill the same tank. Working together, both pipes can fill the tank in 3 min. How long would it take the larger pipe, working alone, to fill the tank?

31. **Physics** The distance (d) that a spring stretches varies directly as the force (f) used to stretch the spring. If a force of 50 lb can stretch the spring 30 in., how far can a force of 40 lb stretch the spring?

32. **Wind Power** The table at the right shows actual and projected gigawatts (billions of watts) of energy generated in the United States by wind power plants. If the projections are accurate, what will be the average rate of change in the production of energy, in gigawatts per year, from wind power plants between 2003 and 2009? Round to the nearest hundredth.

33. **Music** The frequency of vibration (f) in an open pipe organ varies inversely as the length (L) of the pipe. If the air in a pipe 2 m long vibrates 60 times per minute, find the frequency in a pipe that is 1.5 m long.

Year	Energy Generated (in gigawatts)
2003	11.19
2004	14.15
2005	23.22
2006	35.25
2007	48.62
2008	49.50
2009	50.20

Source: Energy Information Administration

10 Exponential and Logarithmic Functions

Having a credit card can be very helpful when making big purchases, but forgetting to pay your bills can cause major problems later on. When applying for things such as student loans, the lender generally wants to know your past credit history. Usually, they will turn to a credit-reporting agency for a full credit report and a credit score, which helps them determine the likelihood that you will repay the loan in a timely manner. One of the most widely used credit scores is the FICO® score. To learn more about credit reports and FICO scores, see the **Projects and Group Activities on page 666.**

DVD

SSM

Online Study Center

Need help? For online student resources, such as section quizzes, visit the Online Study Center at college.hmco.com/info/aufmanndevmathhb.

Prep Test

1. Simplify: 3^{-2}

2. Simplify: $\left(\dfrac{1}{2}\right)^{-4}$

3. Complete: $\dfrac{1}{8} = 2^{?}$

4. Evaluate $f(x) = x^4 + x^3$ for $x = -1$ and $x = 3$.

5. Solve: $3x + 7 = x - 5$

6. Solve: $16 = x^2 - 6x$

7. Evaluate $A(1 + i)^n$ for $A = 5000$, $i = 0.04$, and $n = 6$. Round to the nearest hundredth.

8. Graph: $f(x) = x^2 - 1$

10.1 Exponential Functions

OBJECTIVE 1 **Evaluate exponential functions**

Deoxyribonucleic acid (DNA) is the basic material of all living organisms. DNA resembles a twisted rope ladder with the ropes made up of sugar and phosphate molecules. The rungs of the ladder are base pairs, adenine–thymine and cytosine–guanine. The order of these base pairs determines whether an organism is, for example, a flower, a frog, or a human. Molecular biologists are trying to determine the sequences for various organisms. The growth in the number of sequences that have been identified is shown in the graph at the right. This graph is an example of exponential growth.

Nuclear medicine physicians use radioisotopes for the diagnosis and treatment of certain diseases. One of the most widely used isotopes is technetium-99m. One use of this isotope is in the diagnosis of cardiovascular disease. The graph at the right shows the amount of technetium-99m in a patient after its injection into the patient. This graph is an example of exponential decay.

> ### Definition of an Exponential Function
>
> The **exponential function** with base b is defined by
> $$f(x) = b^x$$
> where $b > 0$, $b \neq 1$, and x is any real number.

In the definition of an exponential function, b, the base, is required to be positive. If the base were a negative number, the value of the function would be a complex number for some values of x. For instance, the value of $f(x) = (-4)^x$ when $x = \frac{1}{2}$ is $f\left(\frac{1}{2}\right) = (-4)^{\frac{1}{2}} = \sqrt{-4} = 2i$. To avoid complex number values of a function, the base of the exponential function is a positive number.

Evaluate $f(x) = 2^x$ at $x = 3$ and $x = -2$.

Substitute 3 for x and simplify. $f(3) = 2^3 = 8$

Substitute -2 for x and simplify. $f(-2) = 2^{-2} = \dfrac{1}{2^2} = \dfrac{1}{4}$

To evaluate an exponential expression for an irrational number such as $\sqrt{2}$, we obtain an approximation to the value of the function by approximating the irrational number. For instance, the value of $f(x) = 4^x$ when $x = \sqrt{2}$ can be approximated by using an approximation of $\sqrt{2}$.

$$f\left(\sqrt{2}\right) = 4^{\sqrt{2}} \approx 4^{1.4142} \approx 7.1029$$

Because $f(x) = b^x$ ($b > 0$, $b \neq 1$) can be evaluated at both rational and irrational numbers, the domain of f is all real numbers. And because $b^x > 0$ for all values of x, the range of f is the positive real numbers.

EXAMPLE 1   Evaluate $f(x) = \left(\frac{1}{2}\right)^x$ at $x = 2$ and $x = -3$.

Solution $f(x) = \left(\frac{1}{2}\right)^x$

$f(2) = \left(\frac{1}{2}\right)^2 = \dfrac{1}{4}$ $f(-3) = \left(\frac{1}{2}\right)^{-3} = 2^3 = 8$

PROBLEM 1   Evaluate $f(x) = \left(\frac{2}{3}\right)^x$ at $x = 3$ and $x = -2$.

Solution   See page S28.

EXAMPLE 2 Evaluate $f(x) = 2^{3x-1}$ at $x = 1$ and $x = -1$.

Solution $f(x) = 2^{3x-1}$

$$f(1) = 2^{3(1)-1} = 2^2 = 4 \qquad f(-1) = 2^{3(-1)-1} = 2^{-4} = \frac{1}{2^4} = \frac{1}{16}$$

PROBLEM 2 Evaluate $f(x) = 2^{2x+1}$ at $x = 0$ and $x = -2$.

Solution See page S28.

EXAMPLE 3 Evaluate $f(x) = \left(\sqrt{5}\right)^x$ at $x = 4$, $x = -2.1$, and $x = \pi$. Round to the nearest ten-thousandth.

Solution $f(x) = \left(\sqrt{5}\right)^x$

$$f(4) = \left(\sqrt{5}\right)^4 \qquad f(-2.1) = \left(\sqrt{5}\right)^{-2.1} \qquad f(\pi) = \left(\sqrt{5}\right)^{\pi}$$
$$= 25 \qquad\qquad \approx 0.1845 \qquad\qquad \approx 12.5297$$

PROBLEM 3 Evaluate $f(x) = \pi^x$ at $x = 3$, $x = -2$, and $x = \pi$. Round to the nearest ten-thousandth.

Solution See page S28.

A frequently used base in applications of exponential functions is an irrational number designated by e. The number e is approximately 2.71828183. It is an irrational number, so it has a nonterminating, nonrepeating decimal representation.

> ### Natural Exponential Function
>
> The function defined by $f(x) = e^x$ is called the **natural exponential function.**

The $\boxed{e^x}$ key on a calculator can be used to evaluate the natural exponential function. The graph of $y = e^x$ is shown at the left.

EXAMPLE 4 Evaluate $f(x) = e^x$ at $x = 2$, $x = -3$, and $x = \pi$. Round to the nearest ten-thousandth.

Solution $f(x) = e^x$
$$f(2) = e^2 \qquad\qquad f(-3) = e^{-3} \qquad\qquad f(\pi) = e^{\pi}$$
$$\approx 7.3891 \qquad\qquad \approx 0.0498 \qquad\qquad \approx 23.1407$$

PROBLEM 4 Evaluate $f(x) = e^x$ at $x = 1.2$, $x = -2.5$, and $x = e$. Round to the nearest ten-thousandth.

Solution See page S28.

OBJECTIVE **2**   ## Graph exponential functions

Some of the properties of an exponential function can be seen by considering its graph.

Point of Interest

The natural exponential function is an extremely important function. It is used extensively in applied problems in virtually all disciplines from archeology to zoology. Leonhard Euler (1707–1783) was the first to use the letter e as the base of the natural exponential function.

To graph $f(x) = 2^x$, think of the function as the equation $y = 2^x$.

Choose values of x, and find the corresponding values of y. The results can be recorded in a table.

Graph the ordered pairs on a rectangular coordinate system.

Connect the points with a smooth curve.

x	$f(x) = y$
-2	$2^{-2} = \dfrac{1}{4}$
-1	$2^{-1} = \dfrac{1}{2}$
0	$2^0 = 1$
1	$2^1 = 2$
2	$2^2 = 4$
3	$2^3 = 8$

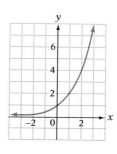

Note that a vertical line would intersect the graph at only one point. Therefore, by the vertical line test, $f(x) = 2^x$ is the graph of a function. Also note that a horizontal line would intersect the graph at only one point. Therefore, $f(x) = 2^x$ is the graph of a 1–1 function.

Graph: $f(x) = \left(\dfrac{1}{2}\right)^x$

Think of the function as the equation $y = \left(\dfrac{1}{2}\right)^x$.

Choose values of x, and find the corresponding values of y.

Graph the ordered pairs on a rectangular coordinate system.

Connect the points with a smooth curve.

x	$f(x) = y$
-3	$\left(\dfrac{1}{2}\right)^{-3} = 8$
-2	$\left(\dfrac{1}{2}\right)^{-2} = 4$
-1	$\left(\dfrac{1}{2}\right)^{-1} = 2$
0	$\left(\dfrac{1}{2}\right)^{0} = 1$
1	$\left(\dfrac{1}{2}\right)^{1} = \dfrac{1}{2}$
2	$\left(\dfrac{1}{2}\right)^{2} = \dfrac{1}{4}$

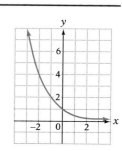

Applying the vertical and horizontal line tests reveals that $f(x) = \left(\dfrac{1}{2}\right)^x$ is also the graph of a 1–1 function.

Exponential Functions Are 1–1

The exponential function defined by $f(x) = b^x$, $b > 0$, $b \neq 1$, is a 1–1 function.

<table>
<tr><td></td></tr>
</table>

Graph $f(x) = 2^{-x}$.

Think of this as the equation $y = 2^{-x}$.

Choose values of x and find the corresponding values of y.

Graph the ordered pairs on a rectangular coordinate system.

Connect the points with a smooth curve.

x	y
-3	8
-2	4
-1	2
0	1
1	$\frac{1}{2}$
2	$\frac{1}{4}$

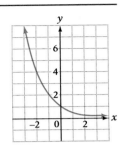

Take Note

Note that because

$2^{-x} = (2^{-1})^x = \left(\frac{1}{2}\right)^x$, the graphs

of $f(x) = 2^{-x}$ and $f(x) = \left(\frac{1}{2}\right)^x$ are

the same.

EXAMPLE 5 Graph.   **A.** $f(x) = 3^{\frac{1}{2}x - 1}$ **B.** $f(x) = 2^x - 1$

Solution **A.**

x	y
-2	$\frac{1}{9}$
0	$\frac{1}{3}$
2	1
4	3

B.

x	y
-2	$-\frac{3}{4}$
-1	$-\frac{1}{2}$
0	0
1	1
2	3
3	7

PROBLEM 5 Graph.   **A.** $f(x) = 2^{-\frac{1}{2}x}$ **B.** $f(x) = 2^x + 1$

Solution See page S28.

EXAMPLE 6 Graph. **A.** $f(x) = 3^{x+1}$ **B.** $f(x) = e^x - 1$

Solution **A.**

x	y
-3	$\dfrac{1}{9}$
-2	$\dfrac{1}{3}$
-1	1
0	3
1	9

B.

x	y
-2	-0.86
-1	-0.63
0	0
1	1.72
2	6.39

PROBLEM 6 Graph. **A.** $f(x) = 2^{-x} + 2$ **B.** $f(x) = e^{-2x} - 4$

Solution ■ See page S29.

EXAMPLE 7 Graph $f(x) = -\dfrac{1}{3}e^{2x} + 2$ and approximate the zero of f to the nearest tenth.

Solution

• Recall that a zero of f is a value of x for which $f(x) = 0$. Use the features of a graphing utility to determine the x-intercept of the graph, which is the zero of f.

To the nearest tenth, the zero of f is 0.9.

PROBLEM 7 Graph $f(x) = 2\left(\dfrac{3}{4}\right)^x - 3$ and approximate, to the nearest tenth, the value of x for which $f(x) = 1$.

Solution ■ See page S29.

10.1   Concept Review

Determine whether the following statements are always true, sometimes true, or never true.

1. The domain of an exponential function $f(x) = b^x$, $b > 0$, $b \neq 1$, is the set of positive numbers.

2. An exponential function $f(x) = b^x$, $b > 0$, $b \neq 1$, is a 1–1 function.

3. The graph of the exponential function $f(x) = b^x$, $b > 0$, $b \neq 1$, passes through the point $(0, 0)$.

4. For the function $f(x) = b^x$, $b > 0$, $b \neq 1$, the base b is a positive integer.

5. An exponential function $f(x) = b^x$, $b > 0$, $b \neq 1$, has two x-intercepts.

10.1   Exercises

1   Evaluate exponential functions

1. What is an exponential function?

2. What is the natural exponential function?

3. Which of the following cannot be the base of an exponential function?

    a. 7   **b.** $\dfrac{1}{4}$ **c.** -5 **d.** 0.01

4. Which of the following cannot be the base of an exponential function?

    a. 0.9   **b.** 476   **c.** 8   **d.** $-\dfrac{1}{2}$

5. Given $f(x) = 4^{x-1}$, evaluate $f(1)$.

$$f(1) = 4^{\underline{\;\;?\;\;}-1} = 4^{\underline{\;\;?\;\;}} = \underline{\;\;\;?\;\;\;}$$

6. Given $g(x) = e^{3x}$, evaluate $g\left(\dfrac{1}{6}\right)$. Round to the nearest ten-thousandth.

$$g\left(\frac{1}{6}\right) = e^{3(\underline{\;\;?\;\;})} \qquad \text{• Replace } x \text{ with } \frac{1}{6}.$$

$$= e^{\underline{\;\;?\;\;}} \qquad \text{• Simplify the exponent.}$$

$$\approx \underline{\;\;\;?\;\;\;} \qquad \text{• Use the } e^x \text{ key on a calculator.}$$

7. Given $f(x) = 3^x$, evaluate:
   a. $f(2)$ **b.** $f(0)$ **c.** $f(-2)$

8. Given $H(x) = 2^x$, evaluate:
   a. $H(-3)$ **b.** $H(0)$ **c.** $H(2)$

9. Given $g(x) = 2^{x+1}$, evaluate:
   a. $g(3)$ **b.** $g(1)$ **c.** $g(-3)$

10. Given $F(x) = 3^{x-2}$, evaluate:
   a. $F(-4)$ **b.** $F(-1)$ **c.** $F(0)$

11. Given $P(x) = \left(\dfrac{1}{2}\right)^{2x}$, evaluate:
   a. $P(0)$ **b.** $P\left(\dfrac{3}{2}\right)$ **c.** $P(-2)$

12. Given $R(t) = \left(\dfrac{1}{3}\right)^{3t}$, evaluate:
   a. $R\left(-\dfrac{1}{3}\right)$ **b.** $R(1)$ **c.** $R(-2)$

13. Given $G(x) = e^{\frac{x}{2}}$, evaluate the following. Round to the nearest ten-thousandth.
   a. $G(4)$ **b.** $G(-2)$ **c.** $G\left(\dfrac{1}{2}\right)$

14. Given $f(x) = e^{2x}$, evaluate the following. Round to the nearest ten-thousandth.
   a. $f(-2)$ **b.** $f\left(-\dfrac{2}{3}\right)$ **c.** $f(2)$

15. Given $H(r) = e^{-r+3}$, evaluate the following. Round to the nearest ten-thousandth.
   a. $H(-1)$ **b.** $H(3)$ **c.** $H(5)$

16. Given $P(t) = e^{-\frac{1}{2}t}$, evaluate the following. Round to the nearest ten-thousandth.
   a. $P(-3)$ **b.** $P(4)$ **c.** $P\left(\dfrac{1}{2}\right)$

17. Given $F(x) = 2^{x^2}$, evaluate:
   a. $F(2)$ **b.** $F(-2)$ **c.** $F\left(\dfrac{3}{4}\right)$

18. Given $Q(x) = 2^{-x^2}$, evaluate:
   a. $Q(3)$ **b.** $Q(-1)$ **c.** $Q(-2)$

19. Given $f(x) = e^{-\frac{x^2}{2}}$, evaluate the following. Round to the nearest ten-thousandth.
   a. $f(-2)$ **b.** $f(2)$ **c.** $f(-3)$

20. Given $f(x) = e^{-2x} + 1$, evaluate the following. Round to the nearest ten-thousandth.
   a. $f(-1)$ **b.** $f(3)$ **c.** $f(-2)$

Complete Exercises 21 to 24 without using a calculator.

21. Which number is a rational number, $(-3)^{1/2}$ or $\left(\dfrac{1}{2}\right)^{-3}$?

22. For which number can you give only an approximate decimal value, $(\sqrt{7})^4$ or $\sqrt[4]{7}$?

23. Is e^3 greater than or less than 27?

24. Is e^{-1} greater than or less than $\dfrac{1}{2}$?

2   Graph exponential functions

25. To find the y-coordinate of the point on the graph of $f(x) = 3^x$ that has an x-coordinate of -3, evaluate $f(-3) = 3^{\underline{\ ?\ }} = \dfrac{1}{\underline{\ ?\ }} = \underline{\ ?\ }$. The point on the graph of $f(x) = 3^x$ with an x-coordinate of -3 is ($\underline{\ ?\ }$, $\underline{\ ?\ }$).

26. To find the y-coordinate of the point on the graph of $g(x) = 2^{x+1}$ that has an x-coordinate of -1, evaluate $g(-1) = 2^{\underline{?}+1} = 2^{\underline{?}} = \underline{\quad?\quad}$. The point on the graph of $g(x) = 2^{x+1}$ with an x-coordinate of -1 is $(\underline{\quad?\quad}, \underline{\quad?\quad})$.

Graph.

27. $f(x) = 3^x$

28. $f(x) = 3^{-x}$

29. $f(x) = 2^{x+1}$

30. $f(x) = 2^{x-1}$

31. $f(x) = \left(\dfrac{1}{3}\right)^x$

32. $f(x) = \left(\dfrac{2}{3}\right)^x$

33. $f(x) = 2^{-x} + 1$

34. $f(x) = 2^x - 3$

35. $f(x) = \left(\dfrac{1}{3}\right)^{-x}$

36. $f(x) = \left(\dfrac{3}{2}\right)^{-x}$

37. $f(x) = \left(\dfrac{1}{2}\right)^{-x} + 2$

38. $f(x) = \left(\dfrac{1}{2}\right)^x - 1$

39. Which of the following functions have the same graph?

    a. $f(x) = 3^x$ **b.** $f(x) = \left(\dfrac{1}{3}\right)^x$ **c.** $f(x) = x^3$ **d.** $f(x) = 3^{-x}$

40. Which of the following functions have the same graph?

    a. $f(x) = x^4$ **b.** $f(x) = 4^{-x}$ **c.** $f(x) = 4^x$ **d.** $f(x) = \left(\dfrac{1}{4}\right)^x$

41. Graph $f(x) = 3^x$ and $f(x) = 3^{-x}$ and find the point of intersection of the two graphs.

42. Graph $f(x) = 2^{x+1}$ and $f(x) = 2^{-x+1}$ and find the point of intersection of the two graphs.

43. Graph $f(x) = \left(\dfrac{1}{3}\right)^x$. What are the x- and y-intercepts of the graph of the function?

44. Graph $f(x) = \left(\dfrac{1}{3}\right)^{-x}$. What are the x- and y-intercepts of the graph of the function?

45. If the graph of $f(x) = b^x$ rises from left to right, is b greater than 1 or less than 1?

46. Which function has a graph that falls from left to right, $f(x) = 10^x$ or $g(x) = 10^{-x}$?

47. Both a and b are positive and $b \neq 1$. Which function has an x-intercept, $f(x) = b^{x-a}$ or $g(x) = b^x - a$?

48. Is the y-intercept of $f(x) = 5^x$ greater than, equal to, or less than the y-intercept of $f(x) = 5^{-x}$?

Use a graphing calculator to solve Exercises 49 to 55.

49. Graph $f(x) = 2^x - 3$ and approximate the zero of f to the nearest tenth.

50. Graph $f(x) = 5 - 3^x$ and approximate the zero of f to the nearest tenth.

51. Graph $f(x) = e^x$ and approximate, to the nearest tenth, the value of x for which $f(x) = 3$.

52. Graph $f(x) = e^{-2x-3}$ and approximate, to the nearest tenth, the value of x for which $f(x) = 2$.

53. Investments The exponential function given by $F(n) = 500(1.00021918)^{365n}$ gives the value in n years of a \$500 investment in a certificate of deposit that earns 8% annual interest compounded daily. Graph F and determine in how many years the investment will be worth \$1000.

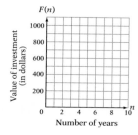

54. Chemistry The number of grams of radioactive cesium that remain after t years from an original sample of 30 g is given by $N(t) = 30(2^{-0.0322t})$. Graph N and determine in how many years there will be 20 g of cesium remaining.

55. Oceanography The percent of light that reaches m meters below the surface of the ocean is given by the equation $P(m) = 100e^{-1.38m}$. Graph P and determine the depth to which 50% of the light will reach.

10.1 Applying Concepts

56. Evaluate $\left(1 + \dfrac{1}{n}\right)^n$ for $n = 100, 1000, 10{,}000$, and $100{,}000$ and compare the results with the value of e, the base of the natural exponential function. On the basis of your evaluation, complete the following sentence:

As n increases, $\left(1 + \dfrac{1}{n}\right)^n$ becomes closer to _____ .

57. **Physics** If air resistance is ignored, the speed v, in feet per second, of an object t seconds after it has been dropped is given by the equation $v = 32t$. This is true regardless of the mass of the object. However, if air resistance is considered, then the speed depends on the mass (and on other things). For a certain mass, the speed t seconds after it has been dropped is given by $v = 64\left(1 - e^{-\frac{t}{2}}\right)$.

    a. Graph this equation. *Suggestion:* Use Xmin $= -0.5$, Xmax $= 10$, Xscl $= 1$, Ymin $= -0.5$, Ymax $= 70$, and Yscl $= 10$.

    b. The point whose approximate coordinates are $(4, 55.3)$ is on the graph. Write a sentence that explains the meaning of these coordinates.

58. Graph $f(x) = e^x$, $g(x) = e^{x-2}$, and $h(x) = e^{x+2}$ on the same rectangular coordinate system. Explain how the graphs are similar and how they are different.

59. Graph $f(x) = 2^x$, $g(x) = 2^x - 2$, and $h(x) = 2^x + 2$ on the same rectangular coordinate system. Explain how the graphs are similar and how they are different.

10.2   Introduction to Logarithms

OBJECTIVE **1**   **Write equivalent exponential and logarithmic equations**

In Michael Crichton's novel *The Andromeda Strain*, we read, "A single cell of the bacterium *E. coli* would, under ideal circumstances, divide every twenty minutes." If a colony of *E. coli* originally contained 1000 bacteria, then a modified version of Crichton's statement, where the bacteria divide once per hour, can be modeled by the exponential growth equation $A = 1000(2^t)$, where A is the number of *E. coli* present after t hours. The table below shows the number of *E. coli* for selected times.

Time, t (in hours)	$1000(2^t) = A$
3 h	$1000(2^3) = 8000$
6 h	$1000(2^6) = 64{,}000$
8 h	$1000(2^8) = 256{,}000$
12 h	$1000(2^{12}) = 4{,}096{,}000$

Take Note

Crichton goes on to say, in the same paragraph, "In this way it can be shown that in a single day, one cell of *E. coli* could produce a super-colony equal in size and weight to the entire planet Earth." In the model we are using, where the bacteria divide once an hour (instead of three times an hour, as in *The Andromeda Strain*), it would take the colony 3 days to become the size of Earth.

This model would be true if uncontrolled biological growth were possible, but it is not. Other factors, such as food to sustain growth, would not be sufficient to support continued exponential growth.

To determine when there would be 32,000 bacteria in the culture, we would solve the exponential equation $32{,}000 = 1000(2^t)$ for t. Because $A = 1000(2^t)$ is a growth equation and 32,000 is between 8000 and 64,000, t must be between 3 h and 6 h. By trial and error, we find that $t = 5$ h.

$$A = 1000(2^t)$$
$$A = 1000(2^5)$$ • **Replace *t* by 5.**
$$A = 1000(32) = 32{,}000$$

Now suppose we want to find how long it would take for the colony to reach 1,000,000 bacteria. From the table, 1,000,000 is between 256,000 and 4,096,000, so this will happen sometime between 8 h and 12 h. If we try 10 h, halfway between 8 and 12, we have

$$A = 1000(2^t)$$
$$A = 1000(2^{10})$$ • **Replace *t* by 10.**
$$A = 1000(1024) = 1{,}024{,}000$$

Because 1,000,000 is less than 1,024,000, the actual value of t is less than 10 h.

We could continue to use trial and error to find t, but it would be more efficient if we could just solve the equation $1{,}000{,}000 = 1000(2^t)$ for t. Using methods described earlier in the text, we have

$$1{,}000{,}000 = 1000(2^t)$$
$$1000 = 2^t$$ • **Divide each side of the equation by 1000.**

To solve this equation, it would be helpful to have a function that would give the power of 2 that produces 1000. Around the mid-16th century, mathematicians created such a function, which we now call a *logarithmic function*. We write the solution of $1000 = 2^t$ as $t = \log_2 1000$. This is read "t equals the logarithm base 2 of 1000," and it means "t equals the power of 2 that produces 1000."

When logarithms were first introduced, tables were used to find the numerical value of t. Today, a calculator is used. Using a calculator, we can approximate the value of t as 9.97. Thus $9.97 \approx \log_2 1000$ and $1000 \approx 2^{9.97}$.

The ideas presented above are related to the concept of inverse function discussed in the last chapter. Because the exponential function given by $y = b^x$ is a 1–1 function, it has an inverse function. To find that function, we follow the same procedure we used to find the inverse of other functions.

$$y = b^x$$
$$x = b^y$$ • **Interchange *x* and *y*.**

The equation $x = b^y$ says that y equals the power of b that produces x. That is, y is the logarithm base b of x. The inverse of the exponential function $y = b^x$ is a logarithmic function.

Here is a general definition of logarithm.

Take Note

Recall that for the equation $2^t = 1000$, we said that "t equals the power of 2 that produces 1000" means that "t is the logarithm base 2 of 1000." We are doing the same with $x = b^y$.

Definition of Logarithm

If $x > 0$ and b is a positive constant not equal to 1, then $y = \log_b x$ is equivalent to $b^y = x$.

Read $\log_b x$ as "the logarithm base b of x" or "the log base b of x."

The following table shows equivalent statements written in both exponential and logarithmic form.

Exponential Form		Logarithmic Form
$2^4 = 16$	$\longleftrightarrow$	$\log_2 16 = 4$
$\left(\dfrac{2}{3}\right)^2 = \dfrac{4}{9}$	$\longleftrightarrow$	$\log_{\frac{2}{3}}\left(\dfrac{4}{9}\right) = 2$
$10^{-1} = 0.1$	$\longleftrightarrow$	$\log_{10}(0.1) = -1$
$b^a = x$	$\longleftrightarrow$	$\log_b x = a$

EXAMPLE 1   Write $4^5 = 1024$ in logarithmic form.

Solution $4^5 = 1024$ is equivalent to $\log_4 1024 = 5$.

PROBLEM 1   Write $3^{-4} = \dfrac{1}{81}$ in logarithmic form.

Solution   See page S29.

EXAMPLE 2   Write $\log_7 343 = 3$ in exponential form.

Solution $\log_7 343 = 3$ is equivalent to $7^3 = 343$.

PROBLEM 2   Write $\log_{10} 0.0001 = -4$ in exponential form.

Solution   See page S29.

Recalling the equations $y = \log_b x$ and $x = b^y$ from the definition of a logarithm, note that because $b^y > 0$ for all values of y, x is always a positive number. Therefore, in the equation $y = \log_b x$, x is a positive number. The logarithm of a negative number is not a real number.

The 1–1 property of exponential functions can be used to evaluate some logarithms.

Equality of Exponents Property

For $b > 0$, $b \neq 1$, if $b^u = b^v$, then $u = v$.

Evaluate: $\log_2 8$

Write an equation.	$\log_2 8 = x$
Write the equation in its equivalent exponential form.	$8 = 2^x$
Write 8 in exponential form using 2 as the base.	$2^3 = 2^x$
Use the Equality of Exponents Property.	$3 = x$
	$\log_2 8 = 3$

EXAMPLE 3   Evaluate: $\log_3\left(\dfrac{1}{9}\right)$

Solution $\log_3\left(\dfrac{1}{9}\right) = x$ • Write an equation.

$\dfrac{1}{9} = 3^x$ • Write the equation in its equivalent exponential form.

$3^{-2} = 3^x$ • Write $\dfrac{1}{9}$ in exponential form using 3 as the base.

$-2 = x$ • Solve for x using the Equality of Exponents Property.

$\log_3\left(\dfrac{1}{9}\right) = -2$

PROBLEM 3   Evaluate: $\log_4 64$

Solution   See page S29.

Solve $\log_4 x = -2$ for x. $\log_4 x = -2$

Write the equation in its equivalent $4^{-2} = x$
exponential form.

Solve for x. $\dfrac{1}{16} = x$

The solution is $\dfrac{1}{16}$.

In this example, $\dfrac{1}{16}$ is called the antilogarithm base 4 of negative 2. In general, if $\log_b M = N$, then M is the antilogarithm base b of N. The antilogarithm of a number can be determined by rewriting the logarithmic expression in exponential form. For instance, the exponential form of $\log_5 x = 3$ is $5^3 = x$; x is the antilogarithm base 5 of 3.

Definition of Antilogarithm

If $\log_b M = N$, the **antilogarithm** base b of N is M. In exponential form,

$$M = b^N$$

EXAMPLE 4   Solve $\log_6 x = 2$ for x.

Solution $\log_6 x = 2$
$6^2 = x$ • Write $\log_6 x = 2$ in its equivalent exponential form.
$36 = x$
The solution is 36.

PROBLEM 4   Solve $\log_2 x = -4$ for x.

Solution   See page S29.

Logarithms base 10 are called **common logarithms.** We usually omit the base, 10, when writing the common logarithm of a number. Therefore, $\log_{10} x$ is written $\log x$. To find the common logarithm of most numbers, a calculator is necessary. A calculator was used to find the value of log 384, shown below.

$$\log 384 \approx 2.584331224$$

When e (the base of the natural exponential function) is used as a base of a logarithm, the logarithm is referred to as the **natural logarithm** and is abbreviated $\ln x$. This is read "el en x." Using a calculator, we find that

$$\ln 23 \approx 3.135494216$$

EXAMPLE 5   Solve $\ln x = -1$ for x. Round to the nearest ten-thousandth.

Solution $\ln x = -1$ • $\ln x$ is the abbreviation for $\log_e x$.
$e^{-1} = x$ • Write the equation in its equivalent
$0.3679 \approx x$ exponential form. Evaluate.

The solution is 0.3679.

PROBLEM 5   Solve $\log x = 1.5$ for x. Round to the nearest ten-thousandth.

Solution   See page S29.

OBJECTIVE **2**   **The properties of logarithms**

Because a logarithm is an exponent, the properties of logarithms are similar to the properties of exponents.

The table at the right shows some powers of 2 and the equivalent logarithmic form of each.

The table can be used to show that $\log_2 4 + \log_2 8$ equals $\log_2 32$.

$2^0 = 1$	$\log_2 1 = 0$
$2^1 = 2$	$\log_2 2 = 1$
$2^2 = 4$	$\log_2 4 = 2$
$2^3 = 8$	$\log_2 8 = 3$
$2^4 = 16$	$\log_2 16 = 4$
$2^5 = 32$	$\log_2 32 = 5$

$$\log_2 4 + \log_2 8 = 2 + 3 = 5$$
$$\log_2 32 = 5$$
$$\log_2 4 + \log_2 8 = \log_2 32$$

Note that $\log_2 32 = \log_2(4 \times 8) = \log_2 4 + \log_2 8$.

The property of logarithms that states that the logarithm of the product of two numbers equals the sum of the logarithms of the two numbers is similar to the property of exponents that states that to multiply two exponential expressions with the same base, we add the exponents.

Product Property of Logarithms

For any positive real numbers x, y, and b, $b \neq 1$,

$$\log_b(xy) = \log_b x + \log_b y$$

Proof:
Let $\log_b x = m$ and $\log_b y = n$.

Write each equation in its equivalent exponential form.	$x = b^m \qquad y = b^n$
Use substitution and the properties of exponents.	$xy = b^m b^n$ $xy = b^{m+n}$
Write the equation in its equivalent logarithmic form.	$\log_b xy = m + n$
Substitute $\log_b x$ for m and $\log_b y$ for n.	$\log_b xy = \log_b x + \log_b y$

The Product Property of Logarithms is used to rewrite logarithmic expressions.

The $\log_b 6z$ is written in **expanded form** as $\log_b 6 + \log_b z$.

$$\log_b 6z = \log_b 6 + \log_b z$$

The $\log_b 12 + \log_b r$ is written as a single logarithm as $\log_b 12r$.

$$\log_b 12 + \log_b r = \log_b 12r$$

The Product Property of Logarithms can be extended to include the logarithm of the product of more than two factors. For example,

$$\log_b xyz = \log_b(xy)z = \log_b xy + \log_b z = \log_b x + \log_b y + \log_b z$$

To write $\log_b 5st$ in expanded form, use the Product Property of Logarithms.

$$\log_b 5st = \log_b 5 + \log_b s + \log_b t$$

A second property of logarithms involves the logarithm of the quotient of two numbers. This property of logarithms is also based on the fact that a logarithm is an exponent and that to divide two exponential expressions with the same base, we subtract the exponents.

> ### Take Note
>
> This theorem is used to rewrite expressions such as
>
> $$\log_5\left(\frac{m}{8}\right) = \log_5 m - \log_5 8$$
>
> It does *not* state any relationship that involves $\dfrac{\log_b x}{\log_b y}$.
>
> **This expression cannot be simplified.**

Quotient Property of Logarithms

For any positive real numbers x, y, and b, $b \neq 1$, $\log_b \dfrac{x}{y} = \log_b x - \log_b y$.

Proof:
Let $\log_b x = m$ and $\log_b y = n$.

Write each equation in its equivalent exponential form.	$x = b^m \qquad y = b^n$
Use substitution and the properties of exponents.	$\dfrac{x}{y} = \dfrac{b^m}{b^n}$ $\dfrac{x}{y} = b^{m-n}$
Write the equation in its equivalent logarithmic form.	$\log_b \dfrac{x}{y} = m - n$
Substitute $\log_b x$ for m and $\log_b y$ for n.	$\log_b \dfrac{x}{y} = \log_b x - \log_b y$

The Quotient Property of Logarithms is used to rewrite logarithmic expressions.

The $\log_b \frac{p}{8}$ is written in expanded form as $\log_b p - \log_b 8$.

$$\log_b \frac{p}{8} = \log_b p - \log_b 8$$

The $\log_b y - \log_b v$ is written as a single logarithm as $\log_b \frac{y}{v}$.

$$\log_b y - \log_b v = \log_b \frac{y}{v}$$

A third property of logarithms, useful especially in the computation of a power of a number, is based on the fact that a logarithm is an exponent and that the power of an exponential expression is found by multiplying the exponents.

The table of the powers of 2 shown earlier can be used to show that $\log_2 2^3$ equals $3 \log_2 2$.

$$\log_2 2^3 = \log_2 8 = 3$$
$$3 \log_2 2 = 3 \cdot 1 = 3$$
$$\log_2 2^3 = 3 \log_2 2$$

Power Property of Logarithms

For any positive real numbers x and b, $b \neq 1$, and for any real number r, $\log_b x^r = r \log_b x$.

Proof:
Let $\log_b x = m$.

Write the equation in its equivalent exponential form. $x = b^m$

Raise each side to the r power. $x^r = (b^m)^r$
$x^r = b^{mr}$

Write the equation in its equivalent logarithmic form. $\log_b x^r = mr$

Substitute $\log_b x$ for m. $\log_b x^r = r \log_b x$

The Power Property of Logarithms is used to rewrite logarithmic expressions.

The $\log_b x^3$ is written in terms of $\log_b x$ as $3 \log_b x$.

$$\log_b x^3 = 3 \log_b x$$

$\frac{2}{3} \log_4 z$ is written with a coefficient of 1 as $\log_4 z^{\frac{2}{3}}$.

$$\frac{2}{3} \log_4 z = \log_4 z^{\frac{2}{3}}$$

The properties of logarithms can be used in combination to simplify expressions that contain logarithms.

EXAMPLE 6   Write the logarithm in expanded form.

A. $\log_b \dfrac{xy}{z}$ **B.** $\ln \dfrac{x^2}{y^3}$ **C.** $\log_8 \sqrt{x^3 y}$

Solution

A. $\log_b \dfrac{xy}{z} = \log_b(xy) - \log_b z$ • Use the Quotient Property of Logarithms.

$= \log_b x + \log_b y - \log_b z$ • Use the Product Property of Logarithms.

B. $\ln \dfrac{x^2}{y^3} = \ln x^2 - \ln y^3$ • Use the Quotient Property of Logarithms.

$= 2 \ln x - 3 \ln y$ • Use the Power Property of Logarithms.

C. $\log_8 \sqrt{x^3 y} = \log_8 (x^3 y)^{\frac{1}{2}}$ • Write the radical expression as an exponential expression.

$= \dfrac{1}{2} \log_8 x^3 y$ • Use the Power Property of Logarithms.

$= \dfrac{1}{2}(\log_8 x^3 + \log_8 y)$ • Use the Product Property of Logarithms.

$= \dfrac{1}{2}(3 \log_8 x + \log_8 y)$ • Use the Power Property of Logarithms.

$= \dfrac{3}{2} \log_8 x + \dfrac{1}{2} \log_8 y$ • Use the Distributive Property.

PROBLEM 6   Write the logarithm in expanded form.

A. $\log_b \dfrac{x^2}{y}$ **B.** $\ln y^{\frac{1}{3}} z^3$ **C.** $\log_8 \sqrt[3]{xy^2}$

Solution   See page S29.

EXAMPLE 7   Express as a single logarithm with a coefficient of 1.

A. $3 \log_5 x + \log_5 y - 2 \log_5 z$

B. $\dfrac{1}{2}(\log_3 x - 3 \log_3 y + \log_3 z)$

C. $\dfrac{1}{3}(2 \ln x - 4 \ln y)$

Solution

A. $3 \log_5 x + \log_5 y - 2 \log_5 z$

$= \log_5 x^3 + \log_5 y - \log_5 z^2$ • Use the Power Property of Logarithms.

$= \log_5 x^3 y - \log_5 z^2$ • Use the Product Property of Logarithms.

$= \log_5 \dfrac{x^3 y}{z^2}$ • Use the Quotient Property of Logarithms.

B. $\frac{1}{2}(\log_3 x - 3 \log_3 y + \log_3 z)$

$= \frac{1}{2}(\log_3 x - \log_3 y^3 + \log_3 z)$ • Use the Power Property of Logarithms.

$= \frac{1}{2}\left(\log_3 \frac{x}{y^3} + \log_3 z\right)$ • Use the Quotient Property of Logarithms.

$= \frac{1}{2}\left(\log_3 \frac{xz}{y^3}\right)$ • Use the Product Property of Logarithms.

$= \log_3\left(\frac{xz}{y^3}\right)^{\frac{1}{2}} = \log_3 \sqrt{\frac{xz}{y^3}}$ • Use the Power Property of Logarithms. Write the exponential expression as a radical expression.

C. $\frac{1}{3}(2 \ln x - 4 \ln y)$

$= \frac{1}{3}(\ln x^2 - \ln y^4)$ • Use the Power Property of Logarithms.

$= \frac{1}{3}\left(\ln \frac{x^2}{y^4}\right)$ • Use the Quotient Property of Logarithms.

$= \ln\left(\frac{x^2}{y^4}\right)^{\frac{1}{3}} = \ln\sqrt[3]{\frac{x^2}{y^4}}$ • Use the Power Property of Logarithms. Write the exponential expression as a radical expression.

PROBLEM 7   Express as a single logarithm with a coefficient of 1.

A. $2 \log_b x - 3 \log_b y - \log_b z$

B. $\frac{1}{3}(\log_4 x - 2 \log_4 y + \log_4 z)$

C. $\frac{1}{2}(2 \ln x - 5 \ln y)$

Solution   See page S29.

There are three other properties of logarithms that are useful in simplifying logarithmic expressions.

Properties of Logarithms

Logarithmic Property of One
For any positive real number b, $b \neq 1$, $\log_b 1 = 0$.

Inverse Property of Logarithms
For any positive real numbers x and b, $b \neq 1$, $\log_b b^x = x$.

1–1 Property of Logarithms
For any positive real numbers x, y, and b, $b \neq 1$, if $\log_b x = \log_b y$, then $x = y$.

EXAMPLE 8   Simplify.   **A.** $8 \log_4 4$ **B.** $\log_8 1$

Solution   **A.** $8 \log_4 4 = \log_4 4^8$ • Use the Power Property of Logarithms.
$= 8$ • Use the Inverse Property of Logarithms.

B. $\log_8 1 = 0$ • Use the Logarithmic Property of One.

PROBLEM 8   Simplify.   **A.** $\log_{16} 1$ **B.** $12 \log_3 3$

Solution   See page S29.

Although only common logarithms and natural logarithms are programmed into a calculator, the logarithms for other positive bases can be found.

Evaluate $\log_5 22$. Round to the nearest ten-thousandth.

Write an equation.	$\log_5 22 = x$
Write the equation in its equivalent exponential form.	$5^x = 22$
Apply the common logarithm to each side of the equation.	$\log 5^x = \log 22$
Use the Power Property of Logarithms.	$x \log 5 = \log 22$
This is an exact answer.	$x = \dfrac{\log 22}{\log 5}$
This is an approximate answer.	$x \approx 1.9206$
	$\log_5 22 \approx 1.9206$

In the third step above, the natural logarithm, instead of the common logarithm, could have been applied to each side of the equation. The same result would have been obtained.

Using a procedure similar to the one used to evaluate $\log_5 22$, a formula for changing bases can be derived.

Change-of-Base Formula

$$\log_a N = \frac{\log_b N}{\log_b a}$$

EXAMPLE 9   Evaluate $\log_7 32$. Round to the nearest ten-thousandth.

Solution $\log_7 32 = \dfrac{\ln 32}{\ln 7} \approx 1.7810$ • Use the Change-of-Base Formula.
$N = 32, a = 7, b = e$

PROBLEM 9   Evaluate $\log_4 2.4$. Round to the nearest ten-thousandth.

Solution   See page S29.

EXAMPLE 10   Rewrite $f(x) = -3 \log_7(2x - 5)$ in terms of natural logarithms.

Solution $f(x) = -3 \log_7(2x - 5)$

$$= -3 \cdot \frac{\ln(2x - 5)}{\ln 7}$$

$$= -\frac{3}{\ln 7} \ln(2x - 5)$$

• Use the Change-of-Base Formula to rewrite $\log_7(2x - 5)$ as $\frac{\ln(2x - 5)}{\ln 7}$.

PROBLEM 10   Rewrite $f(x) = 4 \log_8(3x + 4)$ in terms of common logarithms.

Solution   See page S29.

In Example 10, it is important to understand that $-\frac{3}{\ln 7} \ln(2x - 5)$ and $-3 \log_7(2x - 5)$ are *exactly* equal. If common logarithms had been used, the result would have been $f(x) = -\frac{3}{\log 7} \log(2x - 5)$. The expressions $-\frac{3}{\log 7} \log(2x - 5)$ and $-3 \log_7(2x - 5)$ are also *exactly* equal.

If you are working in a base other than base 10 or base e, the Change-of-Base Formula will enable you to calculate the value of the logarithm in that base just as though that base were programmed into the calculator.

10.2   Concept Review

Determine whether the following statements are always true, sometimes true, or never true.

1. For $x > 0$, $b > 0$, $b \neq 1$, $y = \log_b x$ is equivalent to $b^y = x$.

2. $\log_b \dfrac{x}{y} = \dfrac{\log_b x}{\log_b y}$

3. $\dfrac{\log x}{\log y} = \dfrac{x}{y}$

4. $\log(x + y) = \log x + \log y$

5. $\log_b \sqrt{x} = \dfrac{1}{2} \log_b x$

6. $\log(x^{-1}) = \dfrac{1}{\log x}$

7. The inverse of an exponential function is a logarithmic function.

8. If x and y are positive real numbers, $x < y$, and $b > 0$, $b \neq 1$, then $\log_b x < \log_b y$.

10.2   Exercises

1   Write equivalent exponential and logarithmic equations

1.   **a.** What is a common logarithm?
      b. How is the common logarithm of $4z$ written?

2.   **a.** What is a natural logarithm?
      b. How is the natural logarithm of $3x$ written?

3. The notation "$\log_b x$" can be read as "log ____?____ of ____?____."

4. A logarithm is an exponent. For example, $\log_2 8$ is the exponent used on ____?____ to give a result of ____?____, so $\log_2 8$ is ____?____.

Write the exponential equation in logarithmic form.

5. $5^2 = 25$ **6.** $10^3 = 1000$ **7.** $4^{-2} = \dfrac{1}{16}$

8. $3^{-3} = \dfrac{1}{27}$ **9.** $10^y = x$ **10.** $e^y = x$

11. $a^x = w$ **12.** $b^y = c$

Write the logarithmic equation in exponential form.

13. $\log_3 9 = 2$ **14.** $\log_2 32 = 5$ **15.** $\log 0.01 = -2$ **16.** $\log_5 \dfrac{1}{5} = -1$

17. $\ln x = y$ **18.** $\log x = y$ **19.** $\log_b u = v$ **20.** $\log_c x = y$

21. Complete the Equality of Exponents Property: For $b > 0$, $b \neq 1$, if $b^u = b^v$, then ____?____.

22. Evaluate $\log_4 64$.

$\log_4 64 = x$ • **Write an equation.**

$\underline{\quad ? \quad} = 4^{\underline{\quad ? \quad}}$ • **Write the equation in its equivalent exponential form.**

$4^{\underline{\quad ? \quad}} = 4^x$ • **Write 64 as a power of 4.**

$\underline{\quad ? \quad} = x$ • **Solve for x using the Equality of Exponents Property.**

Evaluate.

23. $\log_3 81$ **24.** $\log_7 49$ **25.** $\log_2 128$ **26.** $\log_5 125$

27. $\log 100$ **28.** $\log 0.001$ **29.** $\ln e^3$ **30.** $\ln e^2$

31. $\log_8 1$ **32.** $\log_3 243$ **33.** $\log_5 625$ **34.** $\log_2 64$

Solve for x.

35. $\log_3 x = 2$

36. $\log_5 x = 1$

37. $\log_4 x = 3$

38. $\log_2 x = 6$

39. $\log_7 x = -1$

40. $\log_8 x = -2$

41. $\log_6 x = 0$

42. $\log_4 x = 0$

Solve for x. Round to the nearest hundredth.

43. $\log x = 2.5$

44. $\log x = 3.2$

45. $\log x = -1.75$

46. $\log x = -2.1$

47. $\ln x = 2$

48. $\ln x = 4$

49. $\ln x = -\dfrac{1}{2}$

50. $\ln x = -1.7$

51. $b > 1$ and m and n are positive numbers such that $m > n$. Is $\log_b m$ less than, equal to, or greater than $\log_b n$?

52. $0 < b < 1$ and $m > 1$. Is $\log_b m$ less than, equal to, or greater than zero?

2 The properties of logarithms

53. What is the Product Property of Logarithms?

54. What is the Quotient Property of Logarithms?

55. Complete the Power Property of Logarithms: For any positive real numbers x and b, $b \neq 1$, and any real number r, $\log_b x^r = $ ___?___.

56. Write $\log_4 x^8 y$ in expanded form.

$\log_4 x^8 y = \log_4(\underline{\quad ? \quad}) + \log_4(\underline{\quad ? \quad})$
- By the Product Property of Logarithms, the log of a product expands into the sum of the logs of the factors.

$= (\underline{\quad ? \quad})\log_4 x + \log_4 y$
- Use the Power Property of Logarithms.

Write the logarithm in expanded form.

57. $\log_8(xz)$

58. $\log_7(4y)$

59. $\log_3 x^5$

60. $\log_2 y^7$

61. $\ln\left(\dfrac{r}{s}\right)$

62. $\ln\left(\dfrac{z}{4}\right)$

63. $\log_3(x^2 y^6)$

64. $\log_4(t^4 u^2)$

65. $\log_7\left(\dfrac{u^3}{v^4}\right)$

66. $\log\left(\dfrac{s^5}{t^2}\right)$

67. $\log_2(rs)^2$

68. $\log_3(x^2 y)^3$

69. $\log_9 x^2yz$

70. $\log_6 xy^2z^3$

71. $\ln\left(\dfrac{xy^2}{z^4}\right)$

72. $\ln\left(\dfrac{r^2s}{t^3}\right)$

73. $\log_8\left(\dfrac{x^2}{yz^2}\right)$

74. $\log_9\left(\dfrac{x}{y^2z^3}\right)$

75. $\log_7\sqrt{xy}$

76. $\log_8\sqrt[3]{xz}$

77. $\log_2\sqrt{\dfrac{x}{y}}$

78. $\log_3\sqrt[3]{\dfrac{r}{s}}$

79. $\ln\sqrt{x^3y}$

80. $\ln\sqrt{x^5y^3}$

81. $\log_7\sqrt{\dfrac{x^3}{y}}$

82. $\log_b\sqrt[3]{\dfrac{r^2}{t}}$

Express as a single logarithm with a coefficient of 1.

83. $\log_3 x^3 - \log_3 y$

84. $\log_7 t + \log_7 v^2$

85. $\log_8 x^4 + \log_8 y^2$

86. $\log_2 r^2 + \log_2 s^3$

87. $3 \ln x$

88. $4 \ln y$

89. $3 \log_5 x + 4 \log_5 y$

90. $2 \log_6 x + 5 \log_6 y$

91. $-2 \log_4 x$

92. $-3 \log_2 y$

93. $2 \log_3 x - \log_3 y + 2 \log_3 z$

94. $4 \log_5 r - 3 \log_5 s + \log_5 t$

95. $\log_b x - (2 \log_b y + \log_b z)$

96. $2 \log_2 x - (3 \log_2 y + \log_2 z)$

97. $2(\ln x + \ln y)$

98. $3(\ln r + \ln t)$

99. $\dfrac{1}{2}(\log_6 x - \log_6 y)$

100. $\dfrac{1}{3}(\log_8 x - \log_8 y)$

101. $2(\log_4 s - 2 \log_4 t + \log_4 r)$

102. $3(\log_9 x + 2 \log_9 y - 2 \log_9 z)$

103. $\log_5 x - 2(\log_5 y + \log_5 z)$

104. $\log_4 t - 3(\log_4 u + \log_4 v)$

105. $3 \ln t - 2(\ln r - \ln v)$

106. $2 \ln x - 3(\ln y - \ln z)$

107. $\dfrac{1}{2}(3 \log_4 x - 2 \log_4 y + \log_4 z)$

108. $\dfrac{1}{3}(4 \log_5 t - 3 \log_5 u - 3 \log_5 v)$

Complete Exercises 109 to 112 without using a calculator.

109. True or false? $\log_b 10 + \log_b 5 = \log_b 15$

110. True or false? $\log_b 10 - \log_b 5 = \log_b 2$

111. True or false? $\log_b b^{10} - \log_b 1 = 10$

112. True or false? $\dfrac{\log_b 10}{\log_b 2} = \log_b 8$

Evaluate. Round to the nearest ten-thousandth.

113. $\ln 4$

114. $\ln 6$

115. $\ln\left(\dfrac{17}{6}\right)$

116. $\ln\left(\dfrac{13}{17}\right)$

117. $\log_8 6$

118. $\log_4 8$

119. $\log_5 30$

120. $\log_6 28$

121. $\log_3(0.5)$

122. $\log_5(0.6)$

123. $\log_7(1.7)$

124. $\log_6(3.2)$

125. $\log_5 15$

126. $\log_3 25$

127. $\log_{12} 120$

128. $\log_9 90$

Rewrite each function in terms of common logarithms.

129. $f(x) = \log_3(3x - 2)$

130. $f(x) = \log_5(x^2 + 4)$

131. $f(x) = \log_8(4 - 9x)$

132. $f(x) = \log_7(3x^2)$

133. $f(x) = 5\log_9(6x + 7)$

134. $f(x) = 3\log_2(2x^2 - x)$

Rewrite each function in terms of natural logarithms.

135. $f(x) = \log_2(x + 5)$

136. $f(x) = \log_4(3x + 4)$

137. $f(x) = \log_3(x^2 + 9)$

138. $f(x) = \log_7(9 - x^2)$

139. $f(x) = 7\log_8(10x - 7)$

140. $f(x) = 7\log_3(2x^2 - x)$

10.2 Applying Concepts

Use the properties of logarithms to solve for x.

141. $\log_8 x = 3\log_8 2$

142. $\log_5 x = 2\log_5 3$

143. $\log_4 x = \log_4 2 + \log_4 3$

144. $\log_3 x = \log_3 4 + \log_3 7$

145. $\log_6 x = 3 \log_6 2 - \log_6 4$

146. $\log_9 x = 5 \log_9 2 - \log_9 8$

147. $\log x = \dfrac{1}{3} \log 27$

148. $\log_2 x = \dfrac{3}{2} \log_2 4$

149. Complete the statement using the equation $\log_a b = c$.
$a^c = $ _____

150. Given $f(x) = 3 \log_6(2x - 1)$, determine $f(7)$ to the nearest hundredth.

151. Given $S(t) = 8 \log_5(6t + 2)$, determine $S(2)$ to the nearest hundredth.

152. Given $P(v) = -3 \log_6(4 - 2v)$, determine $P(-4)$ to the nearest hundredth.

153. Given $G(x) = -5 \log_7(2x + 19)$, determine $G(-3)$ to the nearest hundredth.

154. Solve for x: $\log_2(\log_2 x) = 3$

155. Solve for x: $\ln(\ln x) = 1$

156. **Biology** To discuss the variety of species that live in a certain environment, a biologist needs a precise definition of *diversity*. Let $p_1, p_2, \ldots, p_n$ be the proportions of n species that live in an environment. The biological diversity, D, of this system is

$$D = -(p_1 \log_2 p_1 + p_2 \log_2 p_2 + \cdots + p_n \log_2 p_n)$$

The larger the value of D, the greater the diversity of the system. Suppose an ecosystem has exactly five different varieties of grass: rye (R), Bermuda (B), blue (L), fescue (F), and St. Augustine (A).

a. Calculate the diversity of this ecosystem if the proportions are as shown in Table 1.

b. Because Bermuda and St. Augustine are virulent grasses, after a time the proportions are as shown in Table 2. Does this system have more or less diversity than the one given in Table 1?

c. After an even longer period, the Bermuda and St. Augustine completely overrun the environment, and the proportions are as in Table 3. Calculate the diversity of this system. (*Note:* For purposes of the diversity definition, $0 \log_2 0 = 0$.) Does it have more or less diversity than the system given in Table 2?

d. Finally, the St. Augustine overruns the Bermuda, and the proportions are as in Table 4. Calculate the diversity of this system. Write a sentence that describes your answer.

Table 1

R	B	L	F	A
$\dfrac{1}{5}$	$\dfrac{1}{5}$	$\dfrac{1}{5}$	$\dfrac{1}{5}$	$\dfrac{1}{5}$

Table 2

R	B	L	F	A
$\dfrac{1}{8}$	$\dfrac{3}{8}$	$\dfrac{1}{16}$	$\dfrac{1}{8}$	$\dfrac{5}{16}$

Table 3

R	B	L	F	A
0	$\dfrac{1}{4}$	0	0	$\dfrac{3}{4}$

Table 4

R	B	L	F	A
0	0	0	0	1

10.3 | Graphs of Logarithmic Functions

OBJECTIVE 1   ### Graph logarithmic functions

The graph of a logarithmic function can be drawn by using the relationship between the exponential and logarithmic functions.

To graph $f(x) = \log_2 x$, think of the function as the equation $y = \log_2 x$.

$$f(x) = \log_2 x$$
$$y = \log_2 x$$

Write the equivalent exponential equation.

$$x = 2^y$$

Because the equation is solved for x in terms of y, it is easier to choose values of y and find the corresponding values of x. The results can be recorded in a table.

Graph the ordered pairs on a rectangular coordinate system.

Connect the points with a smooth curve.

x	y
$\dfrac{1}{4}$	-2
$\dfrac{1}{2}$	-1
1	0
2	1
4	2

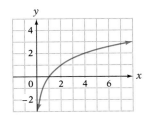

Applying the vertical line and horizontal line tests reveals that $f(x) = \log_2 x$ is the graph of a 1–1 function.

Recall that the graph of the inverse of a function f is the mirror image of the graph of f with respect to the line $y = x$. The graph of $f(x) = 2^x$ was shown earlier. Because $g(x) = \log_2 x$ is the inverse of $f(x) = 2^x$, the graphs of these functions are mirror images of each other with respect to the line $y = x$.

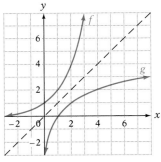

■ Graph: $f(x) = \log_2 x + 1$

Think of the function as the equation $y = \log_2 x + 1$.

$$f(x) = \log_2 x + 1$$
$$y = \log_2 x + 1$$

Solve the equation for $\log_2 x$.

$$y - 1 = \log_2 x$$

Write the equivalent exponential equation.

$$2^{y-1} = x$$

Choose values of y, and find the corresponding values of x.

Graph the ordered pairs on a rectangular coordinate system.

Connect the points with a smooth curve.

x	y
$\dfrac{1}{4}$	-1
$\dfrac{1}{2}$	0
$\dfrac{1}{2}$	2
4	3

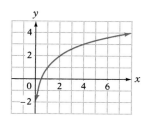

EXAMPLE 1 Graph.   **A.** $f(x) = \log_3 x$ **B.** $f(x) = 2 \log_3 x$

Solution **A.** $f(x) = \log_3 x$
$$y = \log_3 x$$
$$x = 3^y$$

x	y
$\dfrac{1}{9}$	-2
$\dfrac{1}{3}$	-1
1	0
3	1

• Substitute y for $f(x)$.
• Write the equivalent exponential equation.
• Choose values of y, and find the corresponding values of x. Graph the ordered pairs on a rectangular coordinate system. Connect the points with a smooth curve.

B. $f(x) = 2 \log_3 x$
$$y = 2 \log_3 x$$
$$\frac{y}{2} = \log_3 x$$
$$x = 3^{\frac{y}{2}}$$

x	y
$\dfrac{1}{9}$	-4
$\dfrac{1}{3}$	-2
1	0
3	2

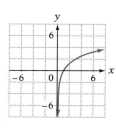

• Substitute y for $f(x)$.
• Solve the equation for $\log_3 x$.
• Write the equivalent exponential equation.
• Choose values of y, and find the corresponding values of x. Graph the ordered pairs on a rectangular coordinate system. Connect the points with a smooth curve.

PROBLEM 1 Graph.   **A.** $f(x) = \log_2(x - 1)$ **B.** $f(x) = \log_3 2x$

Solution See page S30.

EXAMPLE 2 Graph: $f(x) = 2 \ln x + 3$

Solution The graph is shown below. To verify the accuracy of the graph, evaluate $f(x)$ for a few values of x, and compare the results to values found by using the TRACE feature of the graphing utility. For example, $f(1) = 2 \ln(1) + 3 = 3$, so $(1, 3)$ is a point on the graph. When $x = 3$, $f(3) = 2 \ln(3) + 3 \approx 5.2$, so $(3, 5.2)$ is a point on the graph.

PROBLEM 2 Graph: $f(x) = 10 \log(x - 2)$

Solution See page S30.

 The graphs of logarithmic functions to other than base e or base 10 can be drawn with a graphing utility by first using the Change-of-Base Formula $\log_a N = \dfrac{\log_b N}{\log_b a}$ to rewrite the logarithmic function in terms of base e or base 10.

 Graph: $f(x) = \log_3 x$

Use the Change-of-Base Formula to rewrite $\log_3 x$ in terms of $\log x$ or $\ln x$. The natural logarithm function $\ln x$ is used here.

$$\log_3 x = \frac{\ln x}{\ln 3}$$

To graph $f(x) = \log_3 x$ using a graphing utility, use the equivalent form $f(x) = \dfrac{\ln x}{\ln 3}$.

The graph is shown at the right.

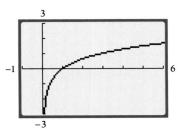

The graph of $f(x) = \log_3 x$ could have been drawn by rewriting $\log_3 x$ in terms of $\log x$, $\log_3 x = \dfrac{\log x}{\log 3}$. The graph of $f(x) = \log_3 x$ is identical to the graph of $f(x) = \dfrac{\log x}{\log 3}$.

The example that follows was graphed by rewriting the logarithmic function in terms of the natural logarithmic function. The common logarithmic function could also have been used.

EXAMPLE 3   Graph: $f(x) = -3 \log_2 x$

Solution $f(x) = -3 \log_2 x$

$$= -3 \cdot \frac{\ln x}{\ln 2} = -\frac{3}{\ln 2} \ln x$$

- Rewrite $\log_2 x$ in terms of $\ln x$.
- The graph of $f(x) = -3 \log_2 x$ is the same as the graph of

$$f(x) = -\frac{3}{\ln 2} \ln x.$$

PROBLEM 3   Graph: $f(x) = 2 \log_4 x$

Solution   See page S30.

10.3   Concept Review

Determine whether the following statements are always true, sometimes true, or never true.

1. The domain of $f(x) = \log_b x$, $b > 0$, $b \neq 1$, is the real numbers.

2. The range of $f(x) = \log_b x$, $b > 0$, $b \neq 1$, is the real numbers.

3. The graphs of $x = 2^y$ and $y = \log_2 x$ are identical graphs.

4. The range of $f(x) = \ln x$ is the real numbers greater than zero.

10.3 Exercises

1 Graph logarithmic functions

1. Is the function $f(x) = \log x$ a 1–1 function? Why or why not?

2. Name two characteristics of the graph of $y = \log_b x$, $b > 1$.

3. What is the relationship between the graph of $x = 3^y$ and that of $y = \log_3 x$?

4. What is the relationship between the graph of $y = 3^x$ and that of $y = \log_3 x$?

5. To find points on the graph of $f(x) = \log_3(x - 1)$, first replace $f(x)$ with ___?___ and write the equation in ___?___ form: $x - 1 = 3^y$. Solve the equation for x: $x =$ ___?___. Choose values for ___?___ and find the corresponding values for ___?___.

6. Use the results of Exercise 5. The x-coordinate of the point on the graph of $f(x) = \log_3(x - 1)$ that has y-coordinate 2 is $3^{\underline{?}} + 1 =$ ___?___. The point on the graph of $f(x) = \log_3(x - 1)$ with a y-coordinate of 2 is (___?___, ___?___).

Graph.

7. $f(x) = \log_4 x$

8. $f(x) = \log_2(x + 1)$

9. $f(x) = \log_3(2x - 1)$

10. $f(x) = \log_2\left(\dfrac{1}{2}x\right)$

11. $f(x) = 3 \log_2 x$

12. $f(x) = \dfrac{1}{2} \log_2 x$

13. $f(x) = -\log_2 x$

14. $f(x) = -\log_3 x$

15. $f(x) = \log_2(x - 1)$

16. $f(x) = \log_3(2 - x)$

17. $f(x) = -\log_2(x - 1)$

18. $f(x) = -\log_2(1 - x)$

Use a graphing utility to graph the following.

19. $f(x) = \log_2 x - 3$

20. $f(x) = \log_3 x + 2$

21. $f(x) = -\log_2 x + 2$

22. $f(x) = -\dfrac{1}{2} \log_2 x - 1$

23. $f(x) = x - \log_2(1 - x)$

24. $f(x) = x + \log_3(2 - x)$

Graph the functions on the same rectangular coordinate system.

25. $f(x) = 4^x$; $g(x) = \log_4 x$

26. $f(x) = 3^x$; $g(x) = \log_3 x$

27. $f(x) = \left(\dfrac{1}{2}\right)^x$; $g(x) = \log_{\frac{1}{2}} x$

28. $f(x) = 10^x$; $g(x) = \log_{10} x$

29. Which function(s) will have the same graph as the graph of the function $f(x) = \log_3 3x$?

a. $g(x) = 3 \log_3 x$ **b.** $h(x) = 1 + \log_3 x$

c. $F(x) = \log_3 x^3$ **d.** $G(x) = \dfrac{\log 3x}{\log 3}$

30. Which function(s) will have the same graph as the graph of the function $f(x) = -\log_b x$?

a. $g(x) = \log_b(-x)$ **b.** $h(x) = \dfrac{1}{\log_b x}$

c. $F(x) = \log_b \dfrac{1}{x}$ **d.** $G(x) = \dfrac{\log b}{\log x}$

10.3 Applying Concepts

31. Employment The proficiency of a typist decreases (without practice) over time. An equation that approximates this decrease is given by $S = 60 - 7 \ln(t + 1)$, where S is the typing speed in words per minute and t is the number of months without typing.

    a. Graph the equation.

    b. The point whose approximate coordinates are (4, 49) is on the graph. Write a sentence that describes the meaning of this ordered pair.

32. Astronomy Astronomers use the *distance modulus* of a star as a method of determining the star's distance from Earth. The formula is $M = 5 \log s - 5$, where M is the distance modulus and s is the star's distance from Earth in parsecs. (One parsec $\approx 2.1 \times 10^{13}$ miles.)

    a. Graph the equation.

    b. The point whose approximate coordinates are (25.1, 2) is on the graph. Write a sentence that describes the meaning of this ordered pair.

33. **Energy** The Energy Information Administration forecasts energy production for the United States. Based on data from that agency, the equation $y = 4.1596 + 1.2296 \ln t$ models the estimated quadrillion BTU, y, of energy that will be produced in the United States by renewable energy sources such as wind energy, solar power, biomass energy, and geothermal energy, during year t, where t is the number of years after 2002.

    a. Graph the equation.

    b. According to this model, in what year will energy production from renewable sources first exceed 6 quadrillion BTU?

    c. According to this model, what will be the energy production from renewable energy sources in 2010? Round to the nearest tenth of a quadrillion.

Determine whether the ordered pairs in the table belong to a linear function, a quadratic function, an exponential function, or a logarithmic function.

34.

x	y
0	5
1	3
2	1
3	−1
4	−3

35.

x	y
−1	6
0	1
1	2
2	9
3	22

36.

x	y
0	1
1	4
2	16
3	64
4	256

37.

x	y
0	−3
2	−2
4	−1
6	0
8	1

38.

x	y
0	-3
1	-7
2	-9
3	-9
4	-7

39.

x	y
0	160
1	80
2	40
3	20
4	10

40.

x	y
$\dfrac{1}{2}$	-1
1	0
2	1
4	2
8	3

41.

x	y
$\dfrac{1}{4}$	-2
1	0
4	2
16	4
256	8

42. Using the Power Property of Logarithms, $\ln x^2 = 2 \ln x$. Graph the equations $f(x) = \ln x^2$ and $g(x) = 2 \ln x$ on the same rectangular coordinate system. Are the graphs the same? Why or why not?

43. Because $f(x) = e^x$ and $g(x) = \ln x$ are inverse functions of each other, $f[g(x)] = x$ and $g[f(x)] = x$. Graph $f[g(x)] = e^{\ln x}$ and $g[f(x)] = \ln e^x$. Explain why the graphs are different even though $f[g(x)] = g[f(x)]$.

10.4 Exponential and Logarithmic Equations

OBJECTIVE 1 Solve exponential equations

An **exponential equation** is one in which a variable occurs in the exponent. The examples at the right are exponential equations.

$$6^{2x+1} = 6^{3x-2}$$
$$4^x = 3$$
$$2^{x+1} = 7$$

An exponential equation in which each side of the equation can be expressed in terms of the same base can be solved by using the Equality of Exponents Property. Recall that the Equality of Exponents Property states that

$$\text{If } b^u = b^v, \text{ then } u = v.$$

In Example 1 below, this property is used to solve an exponential equation.

EXAMPLE 1 Solve and check: $9^{x+1} = 27^{x-1}$

Solution

$$9^{x+1} = 27^{x-1}$$
$$(3^2)^{x+1} = (3^3)^{x-1}$$ • **Rewrite each side of the equation using the same base.**
$$3^{2x+2} = 3^{3x-3}$$
$$2x + 2 = 3x - 3$$ • **Use the Equality of Exponents Property to equate the exponents.**
$$2 = x - 3$$ • **Solve the resulting equation.**
$$5 = x$$

Check: $9^{x+1} = 27^{x-1}$

$$\frac{9^{5+1}}{} \Big| \frac{27^{5-1}}{}$$
$$9^6 \Big| 27^4$$
$$(3^2)^6 \Big| (3^3)^4$$
$$3^{12} = 3^{12}$$

The solution is 5.

PROBLEM 1   Solve and check: $10^{3x+5} = 10^{x-3}$

Solution   See page S30.

When both sides of an exponential equation cannot easily be expressed in terms of the same base, logarithms are used to solve the exponential equation.

EXAMPLE 2   Solve for x. Round to the nearest ten-thousandth.
   A. $4^x = 7$ **B.** $3^{2x} = 4$

Solution   **A.**
$$4^x = 7$$
$$\log 4^x = \log 7$$ • Take the common logarithm of each side of the equation.
$$x \log 4 = \log 7$$ • Rewrite using the properties of logarithms.
$$x = \frac{\log 7}{\log 4}$$ • Solve for x.
$$x \approx 1.4037$$

The solution is 1.4037.

   B.
$$3^{2x} = 4$$
$$\log 3^{2x} = \log 4$$ • Take the common logarithm of each side of the equation.
$$2x \log 3 = \log 4$$ • Rewrite using the properties of logarithms.
$$2x = \frac{\log 4}{\log 3}$$ • Solve for x.
$$x = \frac{\log 4}{2 \log 3}$$
$$x \approx 0.6309$$

The solution is 0.6309.

PROBLEM 2   Solve for x. Round to the nearest ten-thousandth.
   A. $4^{3x} = 25$ **B.** $(1.06)^x = 1.5$

Solution   See page S30.

Take Note

To evaluate $\frac{\log 7}{\log 4}$ on a scientific calculator, use the keystrokes

7 [log] [÷] 4 [log] [=]

The display should read 1.4036775.

The equations in Example 2 can be solved by graphing. For Example 2A, by subtracting 7 from each side of the equation $4^x = 7$, the equation can be written as $4^x - 7 = 0$. The graph of $f(x) = 4^x - 7$ is shown on the next page. The values of x for which $f(x) = 0$ are the solutions of the equation $4^x = 7$. These values of x are the zeros of the function. By using the features of a graphing utility, it is possible to determine a very accurate solution. The solution to the nearest tenth is shown in the graph.

EXAMPLE 3 Solve $e^x = 2x + 1$ for x. Round to the nearest hundredth.

Solution Rewrite the equation by subtracting $2x + 1$ from each side and writing the equation as $e^x - 2x - 1 = 0$. The zeros of $f(x) = e^x - 2x - 1$ are the solutions of $e^x = 2x + 1$. Graph f and use the features of a graphing utility to estimate the solutions to the nearest hundredth.

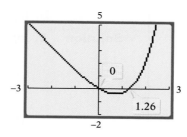

The solutions are 0 and 1.26.

PROBLEM 3 Solve $e^x = x$ for x. Round to the nearest hundredth.

Solution See page S30.

OBJECTIVE **2** **Solve logarithmic equations**

A logarithmic equation can be solved by using the properties of logarithms. Here is an example.

Solve: $\log_9 x + \log_9(x - 8) = 1$

Use the Product Property of Logarithms to rewrite the left side of the equation.

$$\log_9 x + \log_9(x - 8) = 1$$
$$\log_9 x(x - 8) = 1$$

Write the equation in exponential form.

$$9^1 = x(x - 8)$$

Simplify and solve for x.

$$9 = x^2 - 8x$$
$$0 = x^2 - 8x - 9$$
$$0 = (x - 9)(x + 1)$$

$$x - 9 = 0 \qquad x + 1 = 0$$
$$x = 9 \qquad\quad x = -1$$

When x is replaced by 9 in the original equation, 9 checks as a solution. When x is replaced by -1, the original equation contains the expression $\log_9(-1)$. Because the logarithm of a negative number is not a real number, -1 does not check as a solution.

The solution of the equation is 9. ∎

Some logarithmic equations can be solved by using the 1–1 Property of Logarithms, which states that for $x > 0$, $y > 0$, $b > 0$, $b \neq 1$,

$$\text{If } \log_b x = \log_b y, \text{ then } x = y.$$

This property is used in Example 4B.

EXAMPLE 4   Solve for x.

A. $\log_3(2x - 1) = 2$

B. $\log_2 x - \log_2(x - 1) = \log_2 2$

Solution   **A.** $\log_3(2x - 1) = 2$

$$3^2 = 2x - 1 \qquad \bullet \textbf{ Rewrite in exponential form.}$$
$$9 = 2x - 1 \qquad \bullet \textbf{ Solve for } \textit{x.}$$
$$10 = 2x$$
$$5 = x$$

The solution is 5.

B. $\log_2 x - \log_2(x - 1) = \log_2 2$

$$\log_2\left(\frac{x}{x - 1}\right) = \log_2 2 \qquad \begin{array}{l} \bullet \textbf{ Use the Quotient Property} \\ \textbf{ of Logarithms.} \end{array}$$

$$\frac{x}{x - 1} = 2 \qquad \begin{array}{l} \bullet \textbf{ Use the 1–1 Property of} \\ \textbf{ Logarithms.} \end{array}$$

$$(x - 1)\left(\frac{x}{x - 1}\right) = (x - 1)2 \qquad \bullet \textbf{ Solve for } \textit{x.}$$

$$x = 2x - 2$$
$$-x = -2$$
$$x = 2$$

The solution is 2.

PROBLEM 4   Solve for x.

A. $\log_4(x^2 - 3x) = 1$

B. $\log_3 x + \log_3(x + 3) = \log_3 4$

Solution   See page S30. ∎

Some logarithmic equations cannot be solved algebraically. In these cases, a graphical approach may be appropriate.

EXAMPLE 5   Solve $\ln(2x + 4) = x^2$ for x. Round to the nearest hundredth.

Solution Rewrite the equation by subtracting x^2 from each side and writing the equation as $\ln(2x + 4) - x^2 = 0$. The zeros of the function defined by $f(x) = \ln(2x + 4) - x^2$ are the solutions of the equation. Graph f and then use the features of a graphing utility to estimate the solutions to the nearest hundredth.

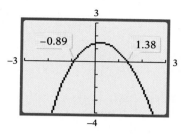

The solutions are -0.89 and 1.38.

PROBLEM 5   Solve $\log(3x - 2) = -2x$ for x. Round to the nearest hundredth.

Solution See page S31.

Recall the equation $\log_9 x + \log_9(x - 8) = 1$ from the beginning of this objective. The algebraic solution showed that although -1 and 9 may be solutions, only 9 satisfies the equation. The extraneous solution was introduced at the second step. The Product Property of Logarithms, $\log_b(xy) = \log_b x + \log_b y$, applies only when both x and y are positive numbers. This occurs when $x > 8$. Therefore, a solution to this equation must be greater than 8. The graphs of $f(x) = \log_9 x + \log_9(x - 8) - 1$ and $g(x) = \log_9 x(x - 8) - 1$ are shown below.

   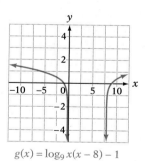

$f(x) = \log_9 x + \log_9(x - 8) - 1$ $g(x) = \log_9 x(x - 8) - 1$

Note that the only zero of f is 9, whereas the zeros of g are -1 and 9.

10.4   Concept Review

Determine whether the following are always true, sometimes true, or never true.

1. Suppose $b > 0$, $b \neq 1$. If $b^x = b^y$, then $x = y$.

2. $\log x + \log(x + 2) = \log(2x + 2)$

3. $\log_2(-4) = -2$

4. $\log(2x - 2) - \log x = 4$ is equivalent to $\log \dfrac{2x - 2}{x} = 4$.

5. $\log(2x) + \log 4 = 6$ is equivalent to $\log(8x) = 6$.

6. $\log_{10} 10^4 = 4$

10.4 Exercises

1 Solve exponential equations

1. What is an exponential equation?

2. **a.** What does the Equality of Exponents Property state?
      b. Describe when you would use this property.

3. Solve: $3^{3x-1} = 9^{2x}$.

$3^{3x-1} = 9^{2x}$ • Both bases are powers of ___?___.

$3^{3x-1} = (3^{\underline{?}})^{2x}$ • Write 9 as a power of 3.

$3^{3x-1} = 3^{\underline{?}}$ • Simplify the exponent.

$\underline{\ ?\ } = \underline{\ ?\ }$ • Use the Equality of Exponents Property to equate the exponents.

$x = \underline{\ ?\ }$ • Solve for x.

4. Solve: $5^x = 18$

$5^x = 18$ • The bases are not powers of the same number.

$\log 5^x = \log 18$ • Take the ___?___ of each side of the equation.

$(\underline{\ ?\ }) \log 5 = \log 18$ • Use the Power Property of Logarithms.

$x = \dfrac{?}{?}$ • Solve for x by dividing each side of the equation by ___?___.

$x \approx \underline{\ ?\ }$ • Use a calculator to evaluate x to the nearest ten-thousandth.

Solve for x. Round to the nearest ten-thousandth.

5. $5^{4x-1} = 5^{x+2}$ **6.** $7^{4x-3} = 7^{2x+1}$ **7.** $8^{x-4} = 8^{5x+8}$

8. $10^{4x-5} = 10^{x+4}$ **9.** $5^x = 6$ **10.** $7^x = 10$

11. $12^x = 6$ **12.** $10^x = 5$ **13.** $\left(\dfrac{1}{2}\right)^x = 3$

14. $\left(\dfrac{1}{3}\right)^x = 2$ **15.** $(1.5)^x = 2$ **16.** $(2.7)^x = 3$

17. $10^x = 21$

18. $10^x = 37$

19. $2^{-x} = 7$

20. $3^{-x} = 14$

21. $2^{x-1} = 6$

22. $4^{x+1} = 9$

23. $3^{2x-1} = 4$

24. $4^{-x+2} = 12$

25. $9^x = 3^{x+1}$

26. $2^{x-1} = 4^x$

27. $8^{x+2} = 16^x$

28. $9^{3x} = 81^{x-4}$

29. $5^{x^2} = 21$

30. $3^{x^2} = 40$

31. $2^{4x-2} = 20$

32. $4^{3x+8} = 12$

33. $3^{-x+2} = 18$

34. $5^{-x+1} = 15$

35. $4^{2x} = 100$

36. $3^{3x} = 1000$

37. $2.5^{-x} = 4$

38. $3.25^{x+1} = 4.2$

39. $0.25^x = 0.125$

40. $0.1^{5x} = 10^{-2}$

41. Given that a is any real number, which equations have the same solution?

    a. $9^{x-a} = 81^x$ **b.** $5^{2x-2a} = 25^{2x}$ **c.** $49^{(x-a)/4} = 7^x$ **d.** $9^x = 81^{x-a}$

42. Use the graphs shown below. Which graph(s) can be used to solve the equation $e^x - 5 = x$? How many positive solutions does the equation $e^x - 5 = x$ have?

    a. $y = e^x + x + 5$ **b.** $y = e^x - x - 5$

 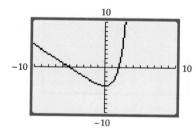

    c. $y = x + 5 - e^x$

Solve for x by graphing. Round to the nearest hundredth.

43. $3^x = 2$

44. $5^x = 9$

45. $2^x = 2x + 4$

46. $3^x = -x - 1$

47. $e^x = -2x - 2$

48. $e^x = 3x + 4$

2   Solve logarithmic equations

49. What is a logarithmic equation?

50. What does the 1–1 Property of Logarithms state?

51. A logarithmic equation in the form $\log_b$ (expression) $= n$, where n is a real number, can be solved by rewriting the equation in ___?___ .

52. A logarithmic equation in the form $\log_b$(expression) $= \log_b$(expression), can be solved by using the ___?___ Property of Logarithms to set the two expressions ___?___ to each other.

53. Look at the equation in each exercise. State whether you will use the method described in Exercise 51 or the method described in Exercises 52 to solve the equation.
   a. Exercise 63   **b.** Exercise 65   **c.** Exercise 67   **d.** Exercise 69

54. Use the graphs shown below. Which equation has no solution, $\log(x - 1) = -2x + 3$ or $\log(x - 1) = 2x - 3$?

$y = \log(x - 1) - 2x + 3$

$y = \log(x - 1) + 2x - 3$

Solve for x.

55. $\log_3(x + 1) = 2$

56. $\log_5(x - 1) = 1$

57. $\log_2(2x - 3) = 3$

58. $\log_4(3x + 1) = 2$

59. $\log_2(x^2 + 2x) = 3$

60. $\log_3(x^2 + 6x) = 3$

61. $\log_5\left(\dfrac{2x}{x - 1}\right) = 1$

62. $\log_6 \dfrac{3x}{x + 1} = 1$

63. $\log_7 x = \log_7(1 - x)$

64. $\dfrac{3}{4} \log x = 3$

65. $\dfrac{2}{3} \log x = 6$

66. $\log(x - 2) - \log x = 3$

67. $\log_2(x - 3) + \log_2(x + 4) = 3$

68. $\log x - 2 = \log(x - 4)$

69. $\log_3 x + \log_3(x - 1) = \log_3 6$

70. $\log_4 x + \log_4(x - 2) = \log_4 15$

71. $\log_2(8x) - \log_2(x^2 - 1) = \log_2 3$

72. $\log_5(3x) - \log_5(x^2 - 1) = \log_5 2$

73. $\log_9 x + \log_9(2x - 3) = \log_9 2$

74. $\log_6 x + \log_6(3x - 5) = \log_6 2$

75. $\log_8(6x) = \log_8 2 + \log_8(x - 4)$

76. $\log_7(5x) = \log_7 3 + \log_7(2x + 1)$

77. $\log_9(7x) = \log_9 2 + \log_9(x^2 - 2)$

78. $\log_3 x = \log_3 2 + \log_3(x^2 - 3)$

79. $\log(x^2 + 3) - \log(x + 1) = \log 5$

80. $\log(x + 3) + \log(2x - 4) = \log 3$

Solve for x by graphing. Round to the nearest hundredth.

81. $\log x = -x + 2$

82. $\log x = -2x$

83. $\log(2x - 1) = -x + 3$

84. $\log(x + 4) = -2x + 1$

85. $\ln(x + 2) = x^2 - 3$

86. $\ln x = -x^2 + 1$

10.4 Applying Concepts

Solve for x. Round to the nearest ten-thousandth.

87. $8^{\frac{x}{2}} = 6$

88. $4^{\frac{x}{3}} = 2$

89. $5^{\frac{3x}{2}} = 7$

90. $9^{\frac{2x}{3}} = 8$

91. $1.2^{\frac{x}{2} - 1} = 1.4$

92. $5.6^{\frac{x}{3} + 1} = 7.8$

Solve.

93. If $4^x = 7$, find the value of $2^{(6x + 3)}$.

94. **Physics** A model for the distance s (in feet) that an object experiencing air resistance will fall in t seconds is given by $s = 78 \ln\left(\dfrac{e^{0.8t} + e^{-0.8t}}{2}\right)$.
   a. Graph this equation. *Suggestion:* Use Xmin = 0, Xmax = 4.5, Xscl = 0.5, Ymin = 0, Ymax = 140, and Yscl = 20.
   b. Determine, to the nearest hundredth of a second, the time it takes the object to travel 125 ft.

95. **Physics** A model for the distance s (in feet) that an object experiencing air resistance will fall in t seconds is given by $s = 312.5 \ln\left(\dfrac{e^{0.32t} + e^{-0.32t}}{2}\right)$.
   a. Graph this equation. *Suggestion:* Use Xmin = 0, Xmax = 4.5, Xscl = 0.5, Ymin = 0, Ymax = 140, and Yscl = 20.
   b. Determine, to the nearest hundredth of a second, the time it takes the object to travel 100 ft.

96. The following "proof" appears to show that $0.04 < 0.008$. Explain the error.

$$2 < 3$$
$$2 \log 0.2 < 3 \log 0.2$$
$$\log(0.2)^2 < \log(0.2)^3$$
$$(0.2)^2 < (0.2)^3$$
$$0.04 < 0.008$$

10.5   Applications of Exponential and Logarithmic Functions

OBJECTIVE 1   **Application problems**

A biologist places one single-celled bacterium in a culture, and each hour that particular species of bacterium divides into two bacteria. After one hour there will be two bacteria. After two hours, each of the two bacteria will divide and there will be four bacteria. After three hours, each of the four bacteria will divide and there will be eight bacteria.

Time, t	Number of Bacteria, N
0	1
1	2
2	4
3	8
4	16

The table at the left shows the number of bacteria in the culture after various intervals of time, t, in hours. Values in this table could also be found by using the exponential equation $N = 2^t$.

The equation $N = 2^t$ is an example of an **exponential growth equation.** In general, any equation that can be written in the form $A = A_0 b^{kt}$, where A is the size at time t, A_0 is the initial size, $b > 1$, and k is a positive real number, is an exponential growth equation. These equations are important not only in population growth studies but also in physics, chemistry, psychology, and economics.

Recall that interest is the amount of money one pays (or receives) when borrowing (or investing) money. **Compound interest** is interest that is computed not only on the original principal but also on the interest already earned. The compound interest formula is an exponential growth equation.

The **compound interest formula** is $P = A(1 + i)^n$, where A is the original value of an investment, i is the interest rate per compounding period, n is the total number of compounding periods, and P is the value of the investment after n periods.

An investment broker deposits $1000 into an account that earns 12% annual interest compounded quarterly. What is the value of the investment after 2 years? Round to the nearest dollar.

Find i, the interest rate per quarter. The quarterly rate is the annual rate divided by 4, the number of quarters in 1 year.

$$i = \frac{12\%}{4} = \frac{0.12}{4} = 0.03$$

Find n, the number of compounding periods. The investment is compounded quarterly, 4 times a year, for 2 years.

$$n = 4 \cdot 2 = 8$$

Use the compound interest formula.	$P = A(1 + i)^n$
Replace A, i, and n by their values.	$P = 1000(1 + 0.03)^8$
Solve for P.	$P \approx 1267$

The value of the investment after 2 years is $1267.

Exponential decay can also be modeled by an exponential equation. One of the most common illustrations of exponential decay is the decay of a radioactive substance.

A radioactive isotope of cobalt has a half-life of approximately 5 years. This means that one-half of any given amount of the cobalt isotope will disintegrate in 5 years. Suppose you begin with 10 mg of a cobalt isotope. The table at the left indicates the amount of the initial 10 mg of the cobalt isotope that remains after various intervals of time, t, in years. Values in this table could also be found by using the exponential equation $A = 10\left(\frac{1}{2}\right)^{\frac{t}{5}}$.

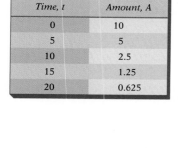

Time, t	Amount, A
0	10
5	5
10	2.5
15	1.25
20	0.625

The equation $A = 10\left(\frac{1}{2}\right)^{\frac{t}{5}}$ is an example of an **exponential decay equation.**

Compare this equation to the exponential growth equation, and note that for exponential growth, the base of the exponential expression is greater than 1, whereas for exponential decay, the base is between 0 and 1.

A method by which an archeologist can measure the age of a bone is called **carbon dating.** Carbon dating is based on a radioactive isotope of carbon called carbon-14, which has a half-life of approximately 5570 years. The exponential decay equation is given by $A = A_0\left(\frac{1}{2}\right)^{\frac{t}{5570}}$, where A_0 is the original amount of carbon-14 present in the bone, t is the age of the bone, and A is the amount of carbon-14 present after t years.

A bone that originally contained 100 mg of carbon-14 now has 70 mg of carbon-14. What is the approximate age of the bone? Round to the nearest year.

Use the exponential decay equation.

$$A = A_0\left(\frac{1}{2}\right)^{\frac{t}{5570}}$$

Replace A_0 and A by their given values, and solve for t.

$$70 = 100\left(\frac{1}{2}\right)^{\frac{t}{5570}}$$

$$70 = 100(0.5)^{\frac{t}{5570}}$$

Divide each side of the equation by 100.

$$0.7 = (0.5)^{\frac{t}{5570}}$$

Take the common logarithm of each side of the equation. Then simplify.

$$\log 0.7 = \log(0.5)^{\frac{t}{5570}}$$

$$\log 0.7 = \frac{t}{5570} \log 0.5$$

$$\frac{5570 \log 0.7}{\log 0.5} = t$$

$$2866 \approx t$$

The age of the bone is approximately 2866 years.

EXAMPLE 1 The number of words per minute a student can type will increase with practice and can be approximated by the equation $N = 100[1 - (0.9)^t]$, where N is the number of words typed per minute after t days of practice. In how many days will the student be able to type 60 words per minute?

Strategy To find the number of days, replace N by 60 and solve for t.

Solution

$$N = 100[1 - (0.9)^t]$$
$$60 = 100[1 - (0.9)^t]$$
$$0.6 = 1 - (0.9)^t$$

$$-0.4 = -(0.9)^t$$
$$0.4 = (0.9)^t$$
$$\log 0.4 = \log(0.9)^t$$
$$\log 0.4 = t \log 0.9$$

$$t = \frac{\log 0.4}{\log 0.9} \approx 8.6967184$$

• Divide each side of the equation by 100.
• Subtract 1 from each side of the equation.

After approximately 9 days the student will type 60 words per minute.

The graph at the left is the graph of $N = 100[1 - (0.9)^t]$. Note that t is approximately 8.7 when $N = 60$.

Words per minute

Number of days

(8.7, 60)

PROBLEM 1 An investment of $3000 is placed into an account that earns 12% annual interest compounded monthly. In approximately how many years will the investment be worth twice the original amount? Round to the nearest whole number.

Solution See page S31.

The first applications of logarithms (and the main reason why they were developed) were to reduce computational drudgery. Today, with the widespread use of calculators and computers, the computational uses of logarithms have diminished. However, a number of other applications of logarithms have emerged.

A chemist measures the acidity or alkalinity of a solution by the formula **pH = −log(H⁺)**, where H^+ is the concentration of hydrogen ions in the solution. A neutral solution such as distilled water has a pH of 7, acids have a pH less than 7, and alkaline solutions (also called basic solutions) have a pH greater than 7.

Søren Sørensen

The pH scale was created by the Danish biochemist Søren Sørensen in 1909 to measure the acidity of water used in the brewing of beer. pH is an abbreviation for pondus hydrogenii, which translates as "potential hydrogen."

Point of Interest

Find the pH of vinegar for which $H^+ = 1.26 \times 10^{-3}$. Round to the nearest tenth.

Use the pH equation.
$H^+ = 1.26 \times 10^{-3}$.

$$pH = -\log(H^+)$$
$$= -\log(1.26 \times 10^{-3})$$
$$= -(\log 1.26 + \log 10^{-3})$$
$$\approx -[0.1004 + (-3)] = 2.8996$$

The pH of vinegar is approximately 2.9.

Logarithmic functions are used to scale very large or very small numbers into numbers that are easier to comprehend. For instance, the *Richter scale* magnitude of an earthquake uses a logarithmic function to convert the intensity of shock waves I into a number M, which for most earthquakes is in the range of 0 to 10. The intensity I of an earthquake is often given in terms of the constant I_0, where I_0 is the intensity of the smallest earthquake, called a **zero-level earthquake,** that can be measured on a seismograph near the earthquake's epicenter. An earthquake with an intensity I_0 has a Richter scale magnitude of

$$M = \log \frac{I}{I_0},$$ where I_0 is the measure of a zero-level earthquake.

The earthquake with the largest intensity ever recorded in the continental United States since 1900 occurred in San Francisco, California, in 1906. The intensity I of the quake was approximately $50{,}118{,}000 I_0$. Find the Richter scale magnitude of the earthquake. Round to the nearest tenth.

$$M = \log \frac{I}{I_0}$$

$I = 50{,}118{,}000 I_0.$

$$M = \log \frac{50{,}118{,}000\, I_0}{I_0}$$

Divide the numerator and denominator by I_0.

$$M = \log 50{,}118{,}000$$

Evaluate $\log 50{,}118{,}000$.

$$M \approx 7.7$$

The San Francisco earthquake had a Richter scale magnitude of 7.7.

> **Take Note**
>
> Note that we do not need to know the value of I_0 in order to determine the Richter scale magnitude of the quake.

If you know the Richter scale magnitude of an earthquake, you can determine the intensity of the earthquake.

In 1964, Prince William Sound, Alaska, experienced what was then the earthquake with the largest magnitude ever to have occurred in the United States. The magnitude of the earthquake was 9.2 on the Richter scale. Find the intensity of this earthquake in terms of I_0. Round to the nearest thousand.

Replace M in $M = \log \dfrac{I}{I_0}$ by 9.2.

$$9.2 = \log \frac{I}{I_0}$$

Write the equation in its equivalent exponential form.

$$10^{9.2} = \frac{I}{I_0}$$

Multiply by I_0.

$$10^{9.2} I_0 = I$$

Evaluate $10^{9.2}$.

$$1{,}584{,}893{,}000 I_0 \approx I$$

The Prince William Sound earthquake had an intensity that was approximately 1,584,893,000 times the intensity of a zero-level earthquake.

The percent of light that will pass through a substance is given by the equation **log $P = -kd$,** where P is the percent of light, as a decimal, passing through the substance, k is a constant that depends on the substance, and d is the thickness of the substance in centimeters.

Find the percent of light that will pass through translucent glass for which $k = 0.4$ and d is 0.5 cm.

Replace k and d in the equation by their given values, and solve for P.

$$\log P = -kd$$
$$\log P = -(0.4)(0.5)$$
$$\log P = -0.2$$

Use the relationship between the logarithmic and exponential functions.

$$P = 10^{-0.2}$$
$$P \approx 0.6310$$

Approximately 63.1% of the light will pass through the glass.

EXAMPLE 2   Find the hydrogen ion concentration, H^+, of orange juice that has a pH of 3.6.

Strategy   To find the hydrogen ion concentration, replace pH by 3.6 in the equation $pH = -\log(H^+)$ and solve for H^+.

Solution
$$pH = -\log(H^+)$$
$$3.6 = -\log(H^+)$$
$$-3.6 = \log(H^+)$$
$$10^{-3.6} = H^+$$
$$0.00025 \approx H^+$$

The hydrogen ion concentration is approximately 0.00025.

PROBLEM 2   On September 3, 2000, an earthquake measuring 5.2 on the Richter scale struck the Napa Valley, 50 mi north of San Francisco. Find the intensity of the quake in terms of I_0.

Solution   See page S31.

10.5 Concept Review

Determine whether the following statements are always true, sometimes true, or never true.

1. In the exponential growth equation $A = A_0 b^{kt}$, A_0 is the initial size of the growth material.

2. An investor deposits $1000 into an account that earns 8% compounded quarterly. The investor receives interest of $20 every quarter.

3. The equation $A = A_0 e^{kt}$ is an exponential growth equation. An equivalent equation to this exponential growth equation is $t = \dfrac{1}{k} \ln \dfrac{A}{A_0}$.

4. The hydrogen ion concentration of a solution is given by the equation pH $= -\log(\text{H}^+)$. Solving this equation for H^+ gives the equivalent equation $\text{H}^+ = 10^{-\text{pH}}$.

10.5 Exercises

1   Application Problems

1. What is meant by the phrase *exponential decay*?

2. Explain how compound interest differs from simple interest. Is compound interest an example of exponential decay or exponential growth?

Finance For Exercises 3 to 8, use the compound interest formula $P = A(1 + i)^n$, where A is the original value of an investment, i is the interest rate per compounding period, n is the total number of compounding periods, and P is the value of the investment after n periods.

Replace the question marks in Exercises 3 and 4 with the correct number from the problem situation or with the word "unknown."

3. Problem Situation: You invest $3000 in an account that earns 3% annual interest compounded monthly. In approximately how many years will your investment be worth $4000?

In the formula $P = A(1 + i)^n$, $P =$ ___?___ , $A =$ ___?___ , $i =$ ___?___ , and $n =$ ___?___ .

4. Problem Situation: A sample of a radioactive isotope with a half-life of 4 h contains 40 mg. How much of the radioactive isotope is present after 24 h?

In the formula $A = A_0\left(\dfrac{1}{2}\right)^{t/k}$, $A =$ ___?___ , $A_0 =$ ___?___ , $t =$ ___?___ , and $k =$ ___?___ .

5. An investment broker deposits $1000 into an account that earns 8% annual interest compounded quarterly. What is the value of the investment after 2 years? Round to the nearest dollar.

6. A financial advisor recommends that a client deposit $2500 into a fund that earns 7.5% annual interest compounded monthly. What will be the value of the investment after 3 years? Round to the nearest cent.

7. To save for college tuition, the parents of a preschooler invest $5000 in a bond fund that earns 6% annual interest compounded monthly. In approximately how many years will the investment be worth $15,000? Round to the nearest whole number.

8. A hospital administrator deposits $10,000 into an account that earns 9% annual interest compounded monthly. In approximately how many years will the investment be worth $15,000? Round to the nearest whole number.

Biology For Exercises 9 to 12, use the exponential decay equation $A = A_0\left(\dfrac{1}{2}\right)^{t/k}$,

where A is the amount of a radioactive material present after time t, k is the half-life of the radioactive material, and A_0 is the original amount of radioactive substance. Round to the nearest tenth.

9. An isotope of technetium is used to prepare images of internal body organs. This isotope has a half-life of approximately 6 h. A patient is injected with 30 mg of this isotope.
   a. What will be the amount of technetium in the patient after 3 h?
   b. How long (in hours) will it take for the amount of technetium in the patient to reach 20 mg?

10. Iodine-131 is an isotope that is used to study the functioning of the thyroid gland. This isotope has a half-life of approximately 8 days. A patient is given an injection that contains 8 micrograms of iodine-131.
   a. What will be the amount of iodine in the patient after 5 days?
   b. How long (in days) will it take for the amount of iodine in the patient to reach 5 micrograms?

11. A sample of promethium-147 (used in some luminous paints) contains 25 mg. One year later, the sample contains 18.95 mg. What is the half-life of promethium-147, in years?

12. Francium-223 is a very rare radioactive isotope discovered in 1939 by Marguerite Percy. A 3-microgram sample of francium-223 decays to 2.54 micrograms in 5 min. What is the half-life of francium-223, in minutes?

13. After 6 years, $\dfrac{1}{8}$ of the original amount of a radioactive isotope is left. What is the half-life of the isotope?

14. After 12 h, $\dfrac{1}{16}$ of the original amount of a radioactive isotope is left. What is the half-life of the isotope?

15. **Atmospheric Pressure** Earth's atmospheric pressure changes as you rise above the surface. At an altitude of h kilometers, where $0 < h < 80$, the pressure P in newtons per square centimeter is approximately modeled by the equation $P(h) = 10.13e^{-0.116h}$.
   a. What is the approximate pressure at 40 km above Earth?
   b. What is the approximate pressure on Earth's surface?
   c. Does atmospheric pressure increase or decrease as you rise above Earth's surface?

16.   Demography The number of centenarians (people aged 100 or older) in the United States has been increasing dramatically. Based on data from the U.S. Census Bureau, and using $x = 0$ to correspond to the year 2000, the equation $y = 66.77(1.0532^x)$ approximates the projected U.S. centenarian population through 2050, where y is in thousands.

   a. According to the model, what is the predicted population of centenarians in 2015? Round to the nearest thousand.
   b. In what year does the model predict that the U.S. centenarian population will first exceed 250,000?

Chemistry For Exercises 17 and 18, use the equation $pH = -\log(H^+)$, where H^+ is the hydrogen ion concentration of a solution. Round to the nearest hundredth.

17. Find the pH of milk, for which the hydrogen ion concentration is 3.97×10^{-7}.

18. Find the pH of a baking soda solution, for which the hydrogen ion concentration is 3.98×10^{-9}.

Optics For Exercises 19 and 20, use the equation $\log P = -kd$, which gives the relationship between the percent P, as a decimal, of light passing through a substance of thickness d.

19. The value of k for a swimming pool is approximately 0.05. At what depth, in meters, will the percent of light be 75% of the light at the surface of the pool?

20. The constant k for a piece of blue stained glass is 20. What percent of light will pass through a piece of this glass that is 0.005 m thick?

Acoustics The number of decibels, D, of a sound can be given by the equation $D = 10(\log I + 16)$, where I is the power of a sound measured in watts. Use this equation for Exercises 21 and 22. Round to the nearest whole number.

21.   Find the number of decibels of normal conversation. The power of the sound of normal conversation is approximately 3.2×10^{-10} watts.

22.   The loudest sound made by any animal is made by the blue whale and can be heard over 500 mi away. The power of the sound is 630 watts. Find the number of decibels of sound emitted by the blue whale.

23. E. coli The actual equation for the population growth of E. coli bacteria mentioned in the novel The Andromeda Strain by Michael Crichton is given by $y = 2^{t/3}$, where y is the size of the population in t hours. The mass of Earth is 5.98×10^{27} g, and the mass of one E. coli bacterium is approximately 6.7×10^{-15} g. Assuming that a colony of E. coli bacteria continues to grow as predicted by the equation, in how many hours would the mass of the colony be equal to the mass of Earth? Round to the nearest hour. Is this more or less time than predicted in the novel? (See the Take Note on page 623.)

24. **Electricity** The current, in amperes, in a electric circuit is given by $I = 6(1 - e^{-2t})$, where t is the time in seconds. Using this model, after how many seconds is the current 4 amperes? Round to the nearest hundredth.

25. **Medicine** The intensity I of an x-ray after it has passed through a material that is x centimeters thick is given by $I = I_0 e^{-kx}$, where I_0 is the initial intensity and k is a number that depends on the material. The constant k for copper is 3.2. Find the thickness of copper that is needed so that the intensity of the x-ray after passing through the copper is 25% of the original intensity. Round to the nearest tenth.

26. **Energy** One model for the time it will take for the world's oil supply to be depleted is given by the equation $T = 14.29 \ln (0.00411r + 1)$, where r is the estimated world oil reserves in billions of barrels and T is the time before that amount of oil is depleted. Use this equation to determine how many barrels of oil are necessary to last 20 years. Round to the nearest tenth.

Geology For Exercises 27 to 30, use the Richter scale equation $M = \log \dfrac{I}{I_0}$, where M is the magnitude of an earthquake, I is the intensity of the shock waves, and I_0 is the measure of a zero-level earthquake.

27. The largest earthquake ever recorded occurred on May 22, 1960, off the coast of Chile. The earthquake had an intensity of approximately $I = 3,162,277,000 I_0$. Find the Richter scale magnitude of the earthquake. Round to the nearest tenth.

28. One of the largest earthquakes ever recorded in the United States occurred on February 3, 1965, in the Rat Islands of Alaska. The earthquake had an intensity of approximately $I = 501,187,000 I_0$. Find the Richter scale magnitude of the earthquake. Round to the nearest tenth.

29. The Kamchatka Peninsula is located off the northeastern coast of Russia. This peninsula has experienced two of the ten largest earthquakes ever recorded. The smaller of the two Kamchatka earthquakes measured 8.5 on the Richter scale. Find the intensity of this earthquake in terms of I_0. Round to the nearest thousand.

30. The magnitude of the Sumatra–Andaman earthquake that occurred on December 26, 2004, off the northern coast of Sumatra was 9.15 on the Richter scale. Find the intensity of the earthquake in terms of I_0.

Geology Shown at the right is a **seismogram,** which is used to measure the magnitude of an earthquake. The magnitude is determined by the amplitude A of the wave and the time t between the occurrence of two types of waves, called primary waves and secondary waves. As you can see on the graph, a primary wave is abbreviated p-wave, and a secondary wave is abbreviated s-wave. The amplitude A of a wave is one-half the difference

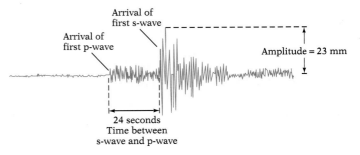

between its highest and lowest points. For this graph, A is 23 millimeters. The equation of the graph is $M = \log A + 3 \log 8t - 2.92$.

31. Determine the magnitude of the earthquake for the seismogram given in the graph. Round to the nearest tenth.

32. Find the magnitude of an earthquake that has a seismogram with an amplitude of 30 mm and for which t is 21 s.

33. Find the magnitude of an earthquake that has a seismogram with an amplitude of 28 mm and for which t is 28 s.

10.5   Applying Concepts

34. Biology At 9 A.M., a culture of bacteria had a population of 1.5×10^6. At noon, the population was 3.0×10^6. If the population is growing exponentially, at what time will the population be 9×10^6? Round to the nearest hour.

35. Inflation If the average annual rate of inflation is 5%, in how many years will prices double? Round to the nearest whole number.

36. Investments The value of an investment in an account that earns an annual interest rate of 10% compounded daily grows according to the equation $A + A_0\left(1 + \dfrac{0.10}{365}\right)^{365t}$. Find the time for the investment to double in value. Round to the nearest whole number.

37. Investments Some banks now use continuous compounding of an amount invested. In this case, the equation that relates the value of an initial investment of A dollars after t years at an annual interest rate of $r\%$ is $P = Ae^{rt}$. Using this equation, find the value after 5 years of an investment of $2500 in an account that earns 5% annual interest.

Rocketry When a rock is tossed into the air, the mass of the rock remains constant and a reasonable model for the height of the rock can be given by a quadratic function. However, when a rocket is launched straight up from Earth's surface, the rocket is burning fuel, so the mass of the rocket is always changing. The height of the rocket above Earth can be approximated by the equation

$$y(t) = At - 16t^2 + \frac{A}{k}(M + m - kt) \ln\left(1 - \frac{k}{M + m}t\right)$$

where M is the mass of the rocket, m is the mass of the fuel, A is the rate at which fuel is ejected from the engines, k is the rate at which fuel is burned, t is the time in seconds, and $y(t)$ is the height in feet after t seconds.

38. During the development of the V-2 rocket program in the United States, approximate values for a V-2 rocket were $M = 8000$ lb, $m = 16{,}000$ lb, $A = 8000$ ft/s, and $k = 250$ lb/s.

a. Use a graphing utility to estimate, to the nearest second, the time required for the rocket to reach a height of 1 mi (5280 ft).

b. Use $v(t) = -32t + A \ln\left(\dfrac{M + m}{M + m - kt}\right)$, and the answer to part (a), to determine the velocity of the rocket. Round to the nearest whole number.

c. Determine the domain of the velocity function.

39. **Mortgages** When you purchase a car or home and make monthly payments on the loan, you are amortizing the loan. Part of each monthly payment is interest on the loan, and the remaining part of the payment is a repayment of the loan amount. The amount remaining to be repaid on the loan after x months is given by $y = A(1 + i)^x + B$, where y is the amount of the loan to be repaid. In this equation, $A = \dfrac{Pi - M}{i}$ and $B = \dfrac{M}{i}$, where P is the original loan amount, i is the monthly interest rate $\left(\dfrac{\text{annual interest rate}}{12}\right)$, and M is the monthly payment. For a 30-year home mortgage of $100,000 with an annual interest rate of 8%, $i = 0.00667$ and $M = 733.76$.

a. How many months are required to reduce the loan amount to $90,000? Round to the nearest month.

b. How many months are required to reduce the loan amount to one-half the original amount? Round to the nearest month.

c. The total amount of interest that is paid after x months is given by $I = Mx + A(1 + i)^x + B - P$. Determine the month in which the total interest paid exceeds $100,000. Round to the nearest month.

40. One scientific study suggested that the *carrying capacity* of Earth is around 10 billion people. What is meant by "carrying capacity"? Find the current world population, and project when Earth's population would reach 10 billion, assuming population growth rates of 1%, 2%, 3%, 4%, and 5%. Find the current rate of world population growth and use that number to determine when, according to your model, the population will reach 10 billion.

41. Radioactive carbon dating can be used only in certain situations. Other methods of radioactive dating, such as the rubidium-strontium method, are appropriate in other situations. Write a report on radioactive dating methods. Include in your report a description of when each form of dating is appropriate.

Focus on Problem Solving

Proof by Contradiction   The four-step plan for solving problems that we have used before is restated here.

1. Understand the problem.

2. Devise a plan.

3. Carry out the plan.

4. Review the solution.

One of the techniques that can be used in the second step is a method called *proof by contradiction*. In this method, you assume that the conditions of the problem you are trying to solve can be met and then show that your assumption leads to a condition you already know is not true.

To illustrate this method, suppose we try to prove that $\sqrt{2}$ is a rational number. We begin by recalling that a rational number is one that can be written as the quotient of integers. Therefore, let a and b be two integers with *no common factors* other than 1. If $\sqrt{2}$ is a rational number, then

$$\sqrt{2} = \frac{a}{b}$$

$$(\sqrt{2})^2 = \left(\frac{a}{b}\right)^2 \qquad \bullet \textbf{ Square each side.}$$

$$2 = \frac{a^2}{b^2}$$

$$2b^2 = a^2 \qquad \bullet \textbf{ Multiply both sides by } b^2.$$

The last equation states that a^2 is an even number. Because a^2 is an even number, a is an even number. Now divide each side of the last equation by 2.

$$2b^2 = a^2$$
$$2b^2 = a \cdot a$$
$$b^2 = a \cdot x \qquad \bullet x = \frac{a}{2}$$

Because a is an even number, $a \cdot x$ is an even number. Because $a \cdot x$ is an even number, b^2 is an even number, and this in turn means that b is an even number. This result, however, contradicts the assumption that a and b are two integers with *no common factors* other than 1. Because this assumption is now known not to be true, we conclude that our original assumption, that $\sqrt{2}$ is a rational number, is false. This proves that $\sqrt{2}$ is an irrational number.

Try a proof by contradiction for the following problem: "Is it possible to write numbers using each of the digits 0, 1, 2, 3, 4, 5, 6, 7, 8, and 9 exactly once so that the sum of the numbers is exactly 100?"[1] Some suggestions for the proof are outlined on the next page.

[1]G. Polya, *How to Solve It: A New Aspect of Mathematical Method,* copyright © 1945 by G. Polya; renewed 1973 Princeton University Press. Reprinted by permission of Princeton University Press.

First note that the sum of the ten digits is 45. This means that some of the digits must be used as tens digits. Let x be the sum of those digits.

a. What is the sum of the remaining units digits?
b. Express "the sum of the units digits and the tens digits equals 100" as an equation. (*Note:* Writing an equation is one of the possible problem-solving strategies.)
c. Solve the equation for x.
d. Explain why this means that it is impossible to satisfy both conditions of the problem.

Projects & Group Activities

Credit Reports and FICO® Scores[2]

When a consumer applies for a loan, the lender generally wants to know the consumer's credit history. For this, the lender turns to a credit reporting agency. These agencies maintain files on millions of borrowers. They provide the lender with a credit report, which lists information such as the types of credit the consumer uses, the length of time the consumer's credit accounts have been open, the amounts owed by the consumer, and whether the consumer has paid his or her bills on time. Along with the credit report, the lender can buy a credit score based on the information in the report. The credit score gives the lender a quick measure of the consumer's credit risk, or how likely the consumer is to repay a debt. It answers the lender's question: "If I lend this person money (or give this person a credit card), what is the probability that I will be paid back in a timely manner?"

One of the most widely used credit bureau scores is the FICO® score, so named because scores are produced from software developed by Fair, Isaac and Company (FICO). FICO scores range from 300 to 850. The higher the score, the lower the predicted credit risk for lenders.

The following graph shows the delinquency rate, or credit risk, associated with ranges of FICO scores. For example, the delinquency rate of consumers in the 550–599 range of scores is 51%. This means that within the next 2 years, for every 100 borrowers in this range, approximately 51 will default on a loan, file for bankruptcy, or fail to pay a credit card bill within 90 days of the due date.

[2]Source: Information provided by Fair, Isaac and Company, Inc. For more information on credit scoring, please visit www.myfico.com. Copyright © 2002 Fair, Isaac and Company, Inc. All Rights Reserved. FAIR, ISAAC, and FICO are registered trademarks of Fair, Isaac and Company, Inc.

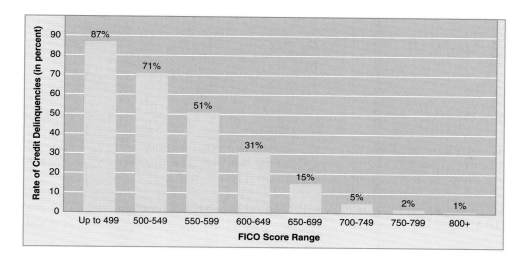

Because the delinquency rate depends on the FICO score, we can let the independent variable x represent the FICO score and the dependent variable y represent the delinquency rate. We will use the middle of each range for the values of x. The resulting ordered pairs are recorded in the table at the right.

x	y
400	87
525	71
575	51
625	31
675	15
725	5
775	2
825	1

1. Use your graphing calculator to find a logarithmic equation that approximates these data. Here are instructions from the TI-83, the TI-83 Plus, and the TI-84 Plus:

Press STAT ENTER. This will bring up a table into which you can enter data. Enter the values of x in L1. Enter the values of y in L2.

Press STAT again, press the right arrow key to highlight CALC, and arrow down to LnReg (ln for the natural logarithm). Press ENTER twice. The values for a and b in the equation $y = a + b \ln x$ will appear on the screen.

2. Use your equation to predict the delinquency rate of a consumer with a score of 500. Round to the nearest whole number.

3. The equation pairs a delinquency rate of 36% with what score?

4. What is the highest FICO score that will result in a delinquency rate of 71% or more?

5. What is the lowest FICO score that will result in a delinquency rate of 5% or lower?

6. Use the Internet to find the name of at least one of the major credit reporting agencies.

Chapter 10 Summary

Key Words	Examples
A function of the form $f(x) = b^x$, where b is a positive real number not equal to 1, is an **exponential function**. The number b is the **base** of the exponential function. [10.1.1, p. 613]	$f(x) = 3^x$; 3 is the base of the function.
The function $f(x) = e^x$ is called the **natural exponential function**. [10.1.1, p. 614]	$f(x) = e^x$; e is an irrational number approximately equal to 2.71828183.
For $x > 0$, $b > 0$, $b \neq 1$, $y = \log_b x$ is equivalent to $x = b^y$. Read $\log_b x$ as "the **logarithm** of x, base b." [10.2.1, p. 623]	$\log_2 8 = 3$ is equivalent to $8 = 2^3$.
Common logarithms are logarithms to the base 10. [10.2.1, p. 626]	$\log_{10} 100 = 2$ is usually written as $\log 100 = 2$.
Natural logarithms are logarithms to the base e. [10.2.1, p. 626]	$\log_e 100 \approx 4.61$ is usually written as $\ln 100 \approx 4.61$.
An **exponential equation** is an equation in which a variable occurs in the exponent. [10.4.1, p. 645]	$2^x = 12$ is an exponential equation.

Essential Rules and Procedures

Equality of Exponents Property For $b > 0$, $b \neq 1$, if $b^u = b^v$, then $u = v$. [10.2.1, p. 624]	If $b^x = b^5$, then $x = 5$.
Definition of Antilogarithm If $\log_b M = N$, the antilogarithm base b of N is M. In exponential form, $M = b^N$. [10.2.1, p. 625]	$\log_4 x = 2$ $\quad 4^2 = x$ $\quad 16 = x$ The antilogarithm base 4 of 2 is 16.
Product Property of Logarithms For any positive real numbers x, y, and b, $b \neq 1$, $\log_b(xy) = \log_b x + \log_b y$. [10.2.2, p. 626]	$\log_b(3x) = \log_b 3 + \log_b x$
Quotient Property of Logarithms For any positive real numbers x, y, and b, $b \neq 1$, $\log_b \dfrac{x}{y} = \log_b x - \log_b y$. [10.2.2, p. 627]	$\log_b \dfrac{x}{20} = \log_b x - \log_b 20$
Power Property of Logarithms For any positive real numbers x and b, $b \neq 1$, and for any real number r, $\log_b x^r = r \log_b x$. [10.2.2, p. 628]	$\log_b x^5 = 5 \log_b x$

Logarithmic Property of One
For any positive real number b, $b \neq 1$, $\log_b 1 = 0$.
[10.2.2, p. 630]

$\log_6 1 = 0$

Inverse Property of Logarithms
For any positive real numbers x and b, $b \neq 1$, $\log_b b^x = x$.
[10.2.2, p. 630]

$\log_3 3^4 = 4$

1–1 Property of Logarithms
For any positive real numbers x, y, and b, $b \neq 1$, if
$\log_b x = \log_b y$, then $x = y$. [10.2.2, p. 630]

If $\log_5(x - 2) = \log_5 3$, then $x - 2 = 3$.

Change-of-Base Formula
$\log_a N = \dfrac{\log_b N}{\log_b a}$ [10.2.2, p. 631]

$\log_3 12 = \dfrac{\log 12}{\log 3}$ $\log_6 16 = \dfrac{\ln 16}{\ln 6}$

Chapter 10 Review Exercises

1. Evaluate: $\log_4 16$

2. Write $\frac{1}{2}(\log_3 x - \log_3 y)$ as a single logarithm with a coefficient of 1.

3. Evaluate the function $f(x) = e^{x-2}$ at $x = 2$.

4. Solve for x: $8^x = 2^{x-6}$

5. Evaluate $f(x) = \left(\dfrac{2}{3}\right)^x$ at $x = 0$.

6. Solve for x: $\log_3 x = -2$

7. Write $2^5 = 32$ in logarithmic form.

8. Solve for x: $\log x + \log(x - 4) = \log 12$

9. Write $\log_6 \sqrt{xy^3}$ in expanded form.

10. Solve for x: $4^{5x-2} = 4^{3x+2}$

11. Solve for x: $3^{7x+1} = 3^{4x-5}$

12. Evaluate $f(x) = 3^{x+1}$ at $x = -2$.

13. Evaluate: $\log_2 16$

14. Solve for x: $\log_6 2x = \log_6 2 + \log_6(3x - 4)$

15. Evaluate $\log_2 5$. Round to the nearest ten-thousandth.

16. Evaluate $\log_6 22$. Round to the nearest ten-thousandth.

17. Solve for x: $4^x = 8^{x-1}$

18. Evaluate $f(x) = \left(\dfrac{1}{4}\right)^x$ at $x = -1$.

19. Write $\log_5 \sqrt{\dfrac{x}{y}}$ in expanded form.

20. Solve for x: $\log_5 \dfrac{7x + 2}{3x} = 1$

21. Solve for x: $\log_5 x = 3$

22. Solve for x: $\log x + \log(2x + 3) = \log 2$

23. Write $3 \log_b x - 5 \log_b y$ as a single logarithm with a coefficient of 1.

24. Evaluate $f(x) = 2^{-x-1}$ at $x = -3$.

25. Evaluate $\log_3 19$. Round to the nearest ten-thousandth.

26. Solve $3^{x+2} = 5$ for x. Round to the nearest ten-thousandth.

27. Graph: $f(x) = 2^x - 3$

28. Graph: $f(x) = \left(\dfrac{1}{2}\right)^x + 1$

29. Graph: $f(x) = \log_2(2x)$

30. Graph: $f(x) = \log_2 x - 1$

31. Graph $f(x) = \dfrac{\log x}{x}$ and approximate the zeros of f to the nearest tenth.

32. **Radioactivity** Use the exponential decay equation $A = A_0 \left(\dfrac{1}{2}\right)^{\frac{t}{k}}$, where A is the amount of a radioactive material present after time t, k is the half-life, and A_0 is the original amount of radioactive material, to find the half-life of a material that decays from 10 mg to 9 mg in 5 h. Round to the nearest whole number.

33. **Optics** The percent of light that will pass through a translucent material is given by the equation $\log P = -0.5d$, where P is the percent of light, as a decimal, that passes through the material, and d is the thickness of the material in centimeters. How thick must this translucent material be so that only 50% of the light that is incident to the material will pass through it? Round to the nearest thousandth.

Chapter 10 Test

1. Evaluate $f(x) = \left(\dfrac{3}{4}\right)^x$ at $x = 0$.

2. Evaluate $f(x) = 4^{x-1}$ at $x = -2$.

3. Evaluate: $\log_4 64$

4. Solve for x: $\log_4 x = -2$

5. Write $\log_6 \sqrt[3]{x^2 y^5}$ in expanded form.

6. Write $\dfrac{1}{2}(\log_5 x - \log_5 y)$ as a single logarithm with a coefficient of 1.

7. Solve for x: $\log_6 x + \log_6(x - 1) = 1$

8. Evaluate $f(x) = 3^{x+1}$ at $x = -2$.

9. Solve for x: $3^x = 17$

10. Solve for x: $\log_2 x + 3 = \log_2(x^2 - 20)$

11. Solve for x: $5^{6x-2} = 5^{3x+7}$

12. Solve for x: $4^x = 2^{3x+4}$

13. Solve for x: $\log(2x + 1) + \log x = \log 6$

14. Graph: $f(x) = 2^x - 1$

15. Graph: $f(x) = 2^x + 2$

16. Graph: $f(x) = \log_2(3x)$

17. Graph: $f(x) = \log_3(x + 1)$

18. Graph $f(x) = 3 - 2^x$ and approximate the zeros of f to the nearest tenth.

19. **Investments** Find the value of $10,000 invested for 6 years at 7.5% compounded monthly. Use the compound interest formula $P = A(1 + i)^n$, where A is the original value of the investment, i is the interest rate per compounding period, and n is the number of compounding periods. Round to the nearest dollar.

20. **Radioactivity** Use the exponential decay equation $A = A_0\left(\dfrac{1}{2}\right)^{\frac{t}{k}}$ where A is the amount of a radioactive material present after time t, k is the half-life, and A_0 is the original amount of radioactive material, to find the half-life of a material that decays from 40 mg to 30 mg in 10 h. Round to the nearest whole number.

Cumulative Review Exercises

1. Solve: $4 - 2[x - 3(2 - 3x) - 4x] = 2x$

2. Solve $S = 2WH + 2WL + 2LH$ for L.

3. Solve: $|2x - 5| \le 3$

4. Factor: $4x^{2n} + 7x^n + 3$

5. Solve: $x^2 + 4x - 5 \le 0$

6. Simplify: $\dfrac{1 - \dfrac{5}{x} + \dfrac{6}{x^2}}{1 + \dfrac{1}{x} - \dfrac{6}{x^2}}$

7. Simplify: $\dfrac{\sqrt{xy}}{\sqrt{x} - \sqrt{y}}$

8. Simplify: $y\sqrt{18x^5y^4} - x\sqrt{98x^3y^6}$

9. Simplify: $\dfrac{i}{2 - i}$

10. Find the equation of the line that contains the point $(2, -2)$ and is parallel to the line $2x - y = 5$.

11. Write a quadratic equation that has integer coefficients and has as solutions $\frac{1}{3}$ and -3.

12. Solve: $x^2 - 4x - 6 = 0$

13. Find the range of $f(x) = x^2 - 3x - 4$ if the domain is $\{-1, 0, 1, 2, 3\}$.

14. Given $f(x) = x^2 + 2x + 1$ and $g(x) = 2x - 3$, find $f[g(0)]$.

15. Solve by the addition method:
$$3x - y + z = 3$$
$$x + y + 4z = 7$$
$$3x - 2y + 3z = 8$$

16. Solve: $y = -2x - 3$
$\quad\quad\quad\; y = 2x - 1$

17. Evaluate $f(x) = 3^{-x+1}$ at $x = -4$.

18. Solve for x: $\log_4 x = 3$

19. Solve for x: $2^{3x+2} = 4^{x+5}$

20. Solve for x: $\log x + \log(3x + 2) = \log 5$

21. Graph: $\{x \,|\, x < 0\} \cap \{x \,|\, x > -4\}$

22. Graph the solution set of $\dfrac{x + 2}{x - 1} \ge 0$.

23. Graph: $y = -x^2 - 2x + 3$

24. Graph: $f(x) = |x| - 2$

25. Graph: $f(x) = \left(\dfrac{1}{2}\right)^x - 1$

26. Graph: $f(x) = \log_2 x + 1$

27. Metallurgy An alloy containing 25% tin is mixed with an alloy containing 50% tin. How much of each were used to make 2000 lb of an alloy containing 40% tin?

28. Compensation An account executive earns $500 per month plus 8% commission on the amount of sales. The executive's goal is to earn a minimum of $3000 per month. What amount of sales will enable the executive to earn $3000 or more per month?

29. Education The table below shows the actual and projected number of high school graduates, in thousands, for selected years. (*Source: Department of Education, Office of Policy Research and Improvement.*) Draw a scatter diagram of these data.

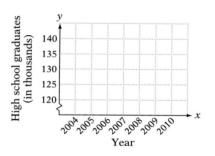

Year, x	High School Graduates (in thousands)
2004	124
2005	132
2006	133
2007	134
2008	135
2009	139
2010	141

30. Work Problem A new printer can print checks three times faster than an older printer. The old printer can print the checks in 30 min. How long would it take to print the checks with both printers operating?

31. Chemistry For a constant temperature, the pressure (P) of a gas varies inversely as the volume (V). If the pressure is 50 lb/in² when the volume is 250 ft³, find the pressure when the volume is 25 ft³.

32. Purchasing A contractor buys 45 yd of nylon carpet and 30 yd of wool carpet for $2340. A second purchase, at the same prices, includes 25 yd of nylon carpet and 80 yd of wool carpet for $2820. Find the cost per yard of the wool carpet.

33. Investments An investor deposits $10,000 into an account that earns 9% interest compounded monthly. What is the value of the investment after 5 years? Use the compound interest formula $P = A(1 + i)^n$, where A is the original value of an investment, i is the interest rate per compounding period, n is the total number of compounding periods, and P is the value of the investment after n periods. Round to the nearest dollar.

11 Sequences and Series

Did you ever wonder how scanners at the grocery store know which items you're buying? Usually the cashier will use a laser to scan a code on each product. The laser reads this code—on groceries a Universal Product Code (UPC), and on books an International Standard Book Number (ISBN)—and interprets the numbers, identifying the product. As we learn in the **Projects and Group Activities on pages 712–713**, these codes are determined by specific patterns and sequences.

Online Study Center

Need help? For online student resources, such as section quizzes, visit the Online Study Center at college.hmco.com/info/aufmanndevmathhb.

DVD   SSM

Prep Test

1. Simplify: $[3(1) - 2] + [3(2) - 2] + [3(3) - 2]$

2. Evaluate $f(n) = \dfrac{n}{n + 2}$ for $n = 6$.

3. Evaluate $a_1 + (n - 1)d$ for $a_1 = 2$, $n = 5$, and $d = 4$.

4. Evaluate $a_1 r^{n-1}$ for $a_1 = -3$, $r = -2$, and $n = 6$.

5. Evaluate $\dfrac{a_1(1 - r^n)}{1 - r}$ for $a_1 = -2$, $r = -4$, and $n = 5$.

6. Simplify: $\dfrac{\dfrac{4}{10}}{1 - \dfrac{1}{10}}$

7. Simplify: $(x + y)^2$

8. Simplify: $(x + y)^3$

Introduction to Sequences and Series

11.1

OBJECTIVE 1   Write the terms of a sequence

An investor deposits $100 in an account that earns 10% interest compounded annually. The amount of interest earned each year can be determined by using the compound interest formula. The amount of interest earned in each of the first four years of the investment is shown below.

Year	1	2	3	4
Interest Earned	$10	$11	$12.10	$13.31

The list of numbers 10, 11, 12.10, 13.31 is called a sequence. A **sequence** is an ordered list of numbers. The list 10, 11, 12.10, 13.31 is ordered because the position of a number in this list indicates the year in which the amount of interest was earned. Each of the numbers of a sequence is called a **term of the sequence.**

Examples of other sequences are shown at the right. These sequences are separated into two groups. A **finite sequence** contains a finite number of terms. An **infinite sequence** contains an infinite number of terms.

$$\left.\begin{array}{l} 1, 1, 2, 3, 5, 8 \\ 1, 2, 3, 4, 5, 6, 7, 8 \\ 1, -1, 1, -1 \end{array}\right\} \begin{array}{l}\text{Finite}\\\text{sequences}\end{array}$$

$$\left.\begin{array}{l} 1, 3, 5, 7, \ldots \\ 1, \frac{1}{2}, \frac{1}{4}, \frac{1}{8}, \ldots \\ 1, 1, 2, 3, 5, 8, \ldots \end{array}\right\} \begin{array}{l}\text{Infinite}\\\text{sequences}\end{array}$$

For the sequence at the right, the first term is 2, the second term is 4, the third term is 6, and the fourth term is 8.

$2, 4, 6, 8, \ldots$

A general sequence is shown at the right. The first term is a_1, the second term is a_2, the third term is a_3, and the nth term, also called the **general term** of the sequence, is a_n. Note that each term of the sequence is paired with a natural number.

$a_1, a_2, a_3, \ldots, a_n, \ldots$

Frequently, a sequence has a definite pattern that can be expressed by a formula.

Each term of the sequence shown at the right is paired with a natural number by the formula $a_n = 3n$. The first term, a_1, is 3. The second term, a_2, is 6. The third term, a_3, is 9. The nth term, a_n, is $3n$.

$a_n = 3n$

$$\begin{array}{ccccc} a_1, & a_2, & a_3, & \ldots, & a_n, \ldots \\ 3(1), & 3(2), & 3(3), & \ldots, & 3(n), \ldots \\ 3, & 6, & 9, & \ldots, & 3n, \ldots \end{array}$$

EXAMPLE 1 Write the first three terms of the sequence whose nth term is given by the formula $a_n = 2n - 1$.

Solution $a_n = 2n - 1$
$a_1 = 2(1) - 1 = 1$ • **Replace _n_ by 1.**
$a_2 = 2(2) - 1 = 3$ • **Replace _n_ by 2.**
$a_3 = 2(3) - 1 = 5$ • **Replace _n_ by 3.**

The first term is 1, the second term is 3, and the third term is 5.

PROBLEM 1 Write the first four terms of the sequence whose nth term is given by the formula $a_n = n(n + 1)$.

Solution See page S31.

EXAMPLE 2 Find the eighth and tenth terms of the sequence whose nth term is given by the formula $a_n = \frac{n}{n + 1}$.

Solution $a_n = \frac{n}{n + 1}$

$a_8 = \frac{8}{8 + 1} = \frac{8}{9}$ • **Replace _n_ by 8.**

$a_{10} = \frac{10}{10 + 1} = \frac{10}{11}$ • **Replace _n_ by 10.**

The eighth term is $\frac{8}{9}$, and the tenth term is $\frac{10}{11}$.

> **PROBLEM 2** Find the sixth and ninth terms of the sequence whose nth term is given by the formula $a_n = \dfrac{1}{n(n+2)}$.
>
> **Solution** See page S31.

OBJECTIVE 2 Evaluate a series

At the beginning of this section, the sequence 10, 11, 12.10, 13.31 was shown to represent the amount of interest earned in each of 4 years of an investment.

10, 11, 12.10, 13.31

The sum of the terms of this sequence represents the total interest earned by the investment over the 4-year period.

$10 + 11 + 12.10 + 13.31 = 46.41$
The total interest earned over the 4-year period is $46.41.

The indicated sum of the terms of a sequence is called a **series.** Given the sequence 10, 11, 12.10, 13.31, the series $10 + 11 + 12.10 + 13.31$ can be written.

S_n is used to indicate the sum of the first n terms of a sequence.

For the preceding example, the sums of the series S_1, S_2, S_3, and S_4 represent the total interest earned for 1, 2, 3, and 4 years, respectively.

$S_1 = 10 \qquad\qquad\qquad = 10$
$S_2 = 10 + 11 \qquad\qquad = 21$
$S_3 = 10 + 11 + 12.10 \qquad = 33.10$
$S_4 = 10 + 11 + 12.10 + 13.31 = 46.41$

For the general sequence a_1, a_2, a_3, ..., a_n, the series S_1, S_2, S_3, and S_n are shown at the right.

$S_1 = a_1$
$S_2 = a_1 + a_2$
$S_3 = a_1 + a_2 + a_3$
$S_n = a_1 + a_2 + a_3 + \cdots + a_n$

It is convenient to represent a series in a compact form called **summation notation,** or **sigma notation.** The Greek letter sigma, Σ, is used to indicate a sum.

The first four terms of the sequence whose nth term is given by the formula $a_n = 2n$ are 2, 4, 6, 8. The corresponding series is shown at the right written in summation notation and is read "the summation from 1 to 4 of $2n$." The letter n is called the **index of the summation.**

$\displaystyle\sum_{n=1}^{4} 2n$

To write the terms of the series, replace n by the consecutive integers from 1 to 4.

$\displaystyle\sum_{n=1}^{4} 2n = 2(1) + 2(2) + 2(3) + 2(4)$

The series is $2 + 4 + 6 + 8$.

$= 2 + 4 + 6 + 8$

The sum of the series is 20.

$= 20$

EXAMPLE 3 Evaluate the series.   **A.** $\displaystyle\sum_{i=1}^{3}(2i-1)$ **B.** $\displaystyle\sum_{n=3}^{6}\frac{1}{2}n$

Solution **A.** $\displaystyle\sum_{i=1}^{3}(2i-1)$

$= [2(1)-1] + [2(2)-1] + [2(3)-1]$ • Replace i by 1, 2, and 3.

$= 1 + 3 + 5$ • Write the series.

$= 9$ • Find the sum of the series.

B. $\displaystyle\sum_{n=3}^{6}\frac{1}{2}n$

$= \dfrac{1}{2}(3) + \dfrac{1}{2}(4) + \dfrac{1}{2}(5) + \dfrac{1}{2}(6)$ • Replace n by 3, 4, 5, and 6.

$= \dfrac{3}{2} + 2 + \dfrac{5}{2} + 3$ • Write the series.

$= 9$ • Find the sum of the series.

Take Note

The placement of the parentheses in this example is important. For instance,

$\displaystyle\sum_{i=1}^{3}2i - 1$
$= 2(1) + 2(2) + 2(3) - 1$
$= 2 + 4 + 6 - 1 = 11$

This is *not* the same result as for $\displaystyle\sum_{i=1}^{3}(2i-1)$.

PROBLEM 3 Evaluate the series.   **A.** $\displaystyle\sum_{n=1}^{4}(7-n)$ **B.** $\displaystyle\sum_{i=3}^{6}(i^2-2)$

Solution See page S31.

EXAMPLE 4 Write $\displaystyle\sum_{i=1}^{5}x^i$ in expanded form.

Solution $\displaystyle\sum_{i=1}^{5}x^i = x + x^2 + x^3 + x^4 + x^5$ • This is a variable series. Replace i by 1, 2, 3, 4, and 5.

PROBLEM 4 Write $\displaystyle\sum_{n=1}^{5}nx$ in expanded form.

Solution See page S31.

11.1 Concept Review

State whether the following statements are always true, sometimes true, or never true.

1. A sequence is an ordered list of numbers.

2. The indicated sum of the terms of a sequence is called a series.

3. The first term of the sequence $a_n = \dfrac{n}{n+3}$ is $\dfrac{1}{4}$.

4. The sum of the series $\displaystyle\sum_{i=1}^{3}2i + 2$ is 18.

11.1 Exercises

1 Write the terms of a sequence

1. What is a sequence?

2. What is the difference between a finite sequence and an infinite sequence?

3. The third term of the sequence 2, 5, 8, 11, 14, . . . is ___?___.

4. The fourth term of the sequence 1, 2, 4, 8, 16, 32, . . . is ___?___.

5. The notation a_1 is used to represent the ___?___ term of a sequence. The notation a_2 is used to represent the ___?___ term of a sequence. The notation a_n is used to represent the ___?___ term of a sequence.

6. To find the first term of the sequence given by the formula $a_n = 2n - 5$, replace n in the formula by 1: $a_1 = 2(\underline{}) - 5 = \underline{}$. To find the second term, replace n by ___?___: $a_{\underline{?}} = 2(\underline{}) - 5 = \underline{}$.

Write the first four terms of the sequence whose nth term is given by the formula.

7. $a_n = n + 1$

8. $a_n = n - 1$

9. $a_n = 2n + 1$

10. $a_n = 3n - 1$

11. $a_n = 2 - 2n$

12. $a_n = 1 - 2n$

13. $a_n = 2^n$

14. $a_n = 3^n$

15. $a_n = n^2 + 1$

16. $a_n = n^2 - 1$

17. $a_n = \dfrac{n}{n^2 + 1}$

18. $a_n = \dfrac{n^2 - 1}{n}$

19. $a_n = n - \dfrac{1}{n}$

20. $a_n = n^2 - \dfrac{1}{n}$

21. $a_n = (-1)^{n+1}n$

22. $a_n = \dfrac{(-1)^{n+1}}{n + 1}$

23. $a_n = \dfrac{(-1)^{n+1}}{n^2 + 1}$

24. $a_n = (-1)^n(n^2 + 2n + 1)$

25. $a_n = (-1)^n 2^n$

26. $a_n = \dfrac{1}{3}n^3 + 1$

27. $a_n = 2\left(\dfrac{1}{3}\right)^{n+1}$

Find the indicated term of the sequence whose nth term is given by the formula.

28. $a_n = 3n + 4;\ a_{12}$

29. $a_n = 2n - 5;\ a_{10}$

30. $a_n = n(n - 1);\ a_{11}$

31. $a_n = \dfrac{n}{n + 1};\ a_{12}$

32. $a_n = (-1)^{n-1}n^2;\ a_{15}$

33. $a_n = (-1)^{n-1}(n - 1);\ a_{25}$

34. $a_n = \left(\dfrac{1}{2}\right)^n$; a_8

35. $a_n = \left(\dfrac{2}{3}\right)^n$; a_5

36. $a_n = (n + 2)(n + 3)$; a_{17}

37. $a_n = (n + 4)(n + 1)$; a_7

38. $a_n = \dfrac{(-1)^{2n-1}}{n^2}$; a_6

39. $a_n = \dfrac{(-1)^{2n}}{n + 4}$; a_{16}

40. $a_n = \dfrac{3}{2}n^2 - 2$; a_8

41. $a_n = \dfrac{1}{3}n + n^2$; a_6

42. $a_n = \dfrac{3}{4}n^2 - \dfrac{1}{4}n$; a_4

43. True or false? For any real number b, all terms of the sequence given by the formula $a_n = bn$ are greater than b.

44. True or false? The 99th term of the sequence given by the formula $a_n = (-1)^{n+1}n$ is positive.

2   Evaluate a series

45. What is a series?

46. The sigma notation $\displaystyle\sum_{n=1}^{4}(3n + 1)$ represents the indicated sum of the first ___?___ terms of the sequence given by the formula $a_n =$ ___?___ .

47. To evaluate the series from Exercise 46, first write the series in expanded form by replacing n by 1, 2, 3, and 4:

$$\sum_{n=1}^{4}(3n + 1)$$
$$= [3(\underline{\;?\;}) + 1] + [3(\underline{\;?\;}) + 1] + [3(\underline{\;?\;}) + 1] + [3(\underline{\;?\;}) + 1]$$
$$= \underline{\;?\;} + \underline{\;?\;} + \underline{\;?\;} + \underline{\;?\;}$$
$$= \underline{\;?\;}$$

• Simplify each term of the series.
• Find the sum of the terms.

Evaluate the series.

48. $\displaystyle\sum_{n=1}^{5}(2n + 3)$

49. $\displaystyle\sum_{i=1}^{7}(i + 2)$

50. $\displaystyle\sum_{i=1}^{4}2i$

51. $\displaystyle\sum_{n=1}^{7}n$

52. $\displaystyle\sum_{i=1}^{6}i^2$

53. $\displaystyle\sum_{i=1}^{5}(i^2 + 1)$

54. $\displaystyle\sum_{n=1}^{6}(-1)^n$

55. $\displaystyle\sum_{n=1}^{4}\dfrac{1}{2n}$

56. $\displaystyle\sum_{i=3}^{6}i^3$

57. $\displaystyle\sum_{n=2}^{4}2^n$

58. $\displaystyle\sum_{n=3}^{7}\dfrac{n}{n - 1}$

59. $\displaystyle\sum_{i=3}^{6}\dfrac{i + 1}{i}$

60. $\displaystyle\sum_{i=1}^{4} \frac{1}{2^i}$

61. $\displaystyle\sum_{i=1}^{5} \frac{1}{2i}$

62. $\displaystyle\sum_{n=1}^{4} (-1)^{n-1} n^2$

63. $\displaystyle\sum_{i=1}^{4} (-1)^{i-1}(i + 1)$

64. $\displaystyle\sum_{n=3}^{5} \frac{(-1)^{n-1}}{n - 2}$

65. $\displaystyle\sum_{n=4}^{7} \frac{(-1)^{n-1}}{n - 3}$

Write the series in expanded form.

66. $\displaystyle\sum_{n=1}^{5} 2x^n$

67. $\displaystyle\sum_{n=1}^{4} \frac{2n}{x}$

68. $\displaystyle\sum_{i=1}^{5} \frac{x^i}{i}$

69. $\displaystyle\sum_{i=1}^{4} \frac{x^i}{i + 1}$

70. $\displaystyle\sum_{i=3}^{5} \frac{x^i}{2i}$

71. $\displaystyle\sum_{i=2}^{4} \frac{x^i}{2i - 1}$

72. $\displaystyle\sum_{n=1}^{5} x^{2n}$

73. $\displaystyle\sum_{n=1}^{4} x^{2n-1}$

74. Which of the following series are equivalent to the series $\displaystyle\sum_{n=1}^{4} n^2$?

  a. $\displaystyle\sum_{n=3}^{6} (n^2 + 2)$ **b.** $\displaystyle\sum_{n=3}^{6} (n^2 + 2)^2$ **c.** $\displaystyle\sum_{n=3}^{6} (n - 2)^2$ **d.** $\displaystyle\sum_{n=10}^{13} (n - 9)^2$

75. Which of the following series is equivalent to the series $\displaystyle\sum_{n=1}^{m} a_n$?

  a. $\displaystyle\sum_{n=1+b}^{m+b} (a_n + b)$ **b.** $\displaystyle\sum_{n=1+b}^{m+b} a_{n+b}$ **c.** $\displaystyle\sum_{n=1+b}^{m+b} a_{n-b}$ **d.** $\displaystyle\sum_{n=1+b}^{m+b} (a_n - b)$

11.1 Applying Concepts

Write a formula for the nth term of the sequence.

76. The sequence of the natural numbers

77. The sequence of the odd natural numbers

78. The sequence of the negative even integers

79. The sequence of the negative odd integers

80. The sequence of the positive multiples of 7

81. The sequence of the positive integers that are divisible by 4

Evaluate the series. Write your answer as a single logarithm.

82. $\displaystyle\sum_{n=1}^{5} \log n$

83. $\displaystyle\sum_{i=1}^{4} \log 2i$

Solve.

84. **Number Problem** The first 22 numbers in the sequence 4, 44, 444, 4444, ... are added together. What digit is in the thousands place of the sum?

85. **Number Problem** The first 31 numbers in the sequence 6, 66, 666, 6666, ... are added together. What digit is in the hundreds place of the sum?

A recursive sequence is one for which each term of the sequence is defined by using preceding terms. Find the first four terms of each recursively defined sequence.

86. $a_1 = 1, a_n = na_{n-1}, n \geq 2$ **87.** $a_1 = 1, a_2 = 1, a_n = a_{n-1} + a_{n-2}, n \geq 3$

88. In the first box below, $\frac{1}{2}$ of the box is shaded.

In successive boxes the sums $\frac{1}{2} + \frac{1}{4}$ and $\frac{1}{2} + \frac{1}{4} + \frac{1}{8}$ are shown.

Can you identify the sum $\frac{1}{2} + \frac{1}{4} + \frac{1}{8} + \frac{1}{16} + \cdots$? Explain your answer.

89. Rewrite $1 + \frac{1}{2} + \frac{1}{3} + \cdots + \frac{1}{n}$ using sigma notation.

11.2 Arithmetic Sequences and Series

OBJECTIVE 1   **Find the *n*th term of an arithmetic sequence**

A company's expenses for training a new employee are quite high. To encourage employees to continue their employment with the company, a company that has a 6-month training program offers a starting salary of $1600 a month and then a $200-per-month pay increase each month during the training period.

The sequence below shows the employee's monthly salaries during the training period. Each term of the sequence is found by adding $200 to the previous term.

Month	1	2	3	4	5	6
Salary	1600	1800	2000	2200	2400	2600

The sequence 1600, 1800, 2000, 2200, 2400, 2600 is called an arithmetic sequence. An **arithmetic sequence,** or **arithmetic progression,** is one in which the difference between any two consecutive terms is constant. The difference between consecutive terms is called the **common difference** of the sequence.

Take Note

Arithmetic sequences are a special type of sequence, one for which the difference between *any* two successive terms is the same constant. For instance, 5, 10, 15, 20, 25, ... is an arithmetic sequence. The difference between any two successive terms is 5. The sequence 1, 4, 9, 16, ... is not an arithmetic sequence because $4 - 1 \neq 9 - 4$.

Each sequence shown below is an arithmetic sequence. To find the common difference of an arithmetic sequence, subtract the first term from the second term.

$2, 7, 12, 17, 22, \ldots$ Common difference: 5
$3, 1, -1, -3, -5, \ldots$ Common difference -2
$1, \frac{3}{2}, 2, \frac{5}{2}, 3, \frac{7}{2}$ Common difference: $\frac{1}{2}$

Consider an arithmetic sequence in which the first term is a_1 and the common difference is d. Adding the common difference to each successive term of the arithmetic sequence yields a formula for the nth term.

The first term is a_1. $a_1 = a_1$

To find the second term, add the common difference d to the first term. $a_2 = a_1 + d$

To find the third term, add the common difference d to the second term. $a_3 = a_2 + d = (a_1 + d) + d$
$a_3 = a_1 + 2d$

To find the fourth term, add the common difference d to the third term. $a_4 = a_3 + d = (a_1 + 2d) + d$
$a_4 = a_1 + 3d$

Note the relationship between the term number and the number that multiplies d. The multiplier of d is 1 less than the term number. $a_n = a_1 + (n - 1)d$

Formula for the *n*th Term of an Arithmetic Sequence

The nth term of an arithmetic sequence with a common difference of d is given by $a_n = a_1 + (n - 1)d$.

EXAMPLE 1 Find the 27th term of the arithmetic sequence $-4, -1, 2, 5, 8, \ldots$.

Solution $d = a_2 - a_1 = -1 - (-4) = 3$ • Find the common difference.

$a_n = a_1 + (n - 1)d$ • Use the Formula for the *n*th Term
$a_{27} = -4 + (27 - 1)3$ of an Arithmetic Sequence to find
$= -4 + (26)3$ the 27th term. $n = 27$, $a_1 = -4$,
$= -4 + 78$ $d = 3$
$= 74$

PROBLEM 1 Find the 15th term of the arithmetic sequence $9, 3, -3, -9, \ldots$.

Solution See page S31.

EXAMPLE 2   Find the formula for the nth term of the arithmetic sequence $-5, -1, 3, 7, \ldots$.

Solution $d = a_2 - a_1 = -1 - (-5) = 4$ • Find the common difference.

$a_n = a_1 + (n - 1)d$ • Use the Formula for the nth Term
$a_n = -5 + (n - 1)4$ of an Arithmetic Sequence.
$a_n = -5 + 4n - 4$ $a_1 = -5, d = 4$
$a_n = 4n - 9$

PROBLEM 2   Find the formula for the nth term of the arithmetic sequence $-3, 1, 5, 9, \ldots$.

Solution   See page S31.

EXAMPLE 3   Find the number of terms in the finite arithmetic sequence $7, 10, 13, \ldots, 55$.

Solution $d = a_2 - a_1 = 10 - 7 = 3$ • Find the common difference.

$a_n = a_1 + (n - 1)d$ • Use the Formula for the nth Term
$55 = 7 + (n - 1)3$ of an Arithmetic Sequence.
$55 = 7 + 3n - 3$ $a_n = 55, a_1 = 7, d = 3$
$55 = 3n + 4$ • Solve for n.
$51 = 3n$
$17 = n$

There are 17 terms in the sequence.

PROBLEM 3   Find the number of terms in the finite arithmetic sequence $7, 9, 11, \ldots, 59$.

Solution   See page S32.

OBJECTIVE   **2**   **Evaluate an arithmetic series**

The indicated sum of the terms of an arithmetic sequence is called an **arithmetic series**. The sum of an arithmetic series can be found by using a formula.

Formula for the Sum of n Terms of an Arithmetic Series

Let a_1 be the first term of a finite arithmetic sequence, let n be the number of terms, and let a_n be the last term of the sequence. Then the sum of the series S_n is given by $S_n = \dfrac{n}{2}(a_1 + a_n)$.

Each term of the arithmetic sequence shown at the right was found by adding 3 to the previous term. $2, 5, 8, \ldots, 17, 20$

Each term of the reverse arithmetic sequence can be found by subtracting 3 from the previous term. $20, 17, 14, \ldots, 5, 2$

This idea is used in the following proof of the Formula for the Sum of n Terms of an Arithmetic Series.

Let S_n represent the sum of the series.

$$S_n = a_1 + (a_1 + d) + (a_1 + 2d) + \cdots + a_n$$

Write the terms of the sum of the series in reverse order. The sum is the same.

$$S_n = a_n + (a_n - d) + (a_n - 2d) + \cdots + a_1$$

Add the two equations.

$$2S_n = (a_1 + a_n) + (a_1 + a_n) + (a_1 + a_n) + \cdots + (a_1 + a_n)$$

Simplify the right side of the equation by using the fact that there are n terms in the sequence.

$$2S_n = n(a_1 + a_n)$$

Solve for S_n.

$$S_n = \frac{n}{2}(a_1 + a_n)$$

EXAMPLE 4   Find the sum of the first 10 terms of the arithmetic sequence 2, 4, 6, 8, ...

Solution $d = a_2 - a_1 = 4 - 2 = 2$ • **Find the common difference.**

$a_n = a_1 + (n - 1)d$ • **Use the Formula for the**
$a_{10} = 2 + (10 - 1)2$ **nth Term of an Arithmetic**
$\quad = 2 + (9)2$ **Sequence to find the**
$\quad = 2 + 18 = 20$ **10th term.**

$S_n = \frac{n}{2}(a_1 + a_n)$

• **Use the Formula for the Sum**
  of n Terms of an Arithmetic
$S_{10} = \frac{10}{2}(2 + 20) = 5(22) = 110$ **Series. $n = 10$, $a_1 = 2$,**
  $a_n = 20$

PROBLEM 4   Find the sum of the first 25 terms of the arithmetic sequence $-4, -2, 0, 2, 4, \ldots$.

Solution   See page S32.

EXAMPLE 5   Evaluate the arithmetic series $\sum\limits_{n=1}^{25}(3n + 1)$.

Solution $a_n = 3n + 1$
$a_1 = 3(1) + 1 = 4$ • **Find the first term.**
$a_{25} = 3(25) + 1 = 76$ • **Find the 25th term.**

$S_n = \frac{n}{2}(a_1 + a_n)$

• **Use the Formula for the Sum of n Terms of**
  an Arithmetic Series. $n = 25$, $a_1 = 4$,
  $a_n = 76$

$S_{25} = \frac{25}{2}(4 + 76)$

$\quad = \frac{25}{2}(80)$

$\quad = 1000$

PROBLEM 5 Evaluate the arithmetic series $\sum_{n=1}^{18}(3n-2)$.

Solution See page S32.

OBJECTIVE 3 **Application problems**

EXAMPLE 6 The distance a ball rolls down a ramp each second is given by an arithmetic sequence. The distance in feet traveled by the ball during the nth second is given by $2n-1$. Find the distance the ball will travel during the first 10 s.

Strategy To find the distance:

▶ Find the first and tenth terms of the sequence.

▶ Use the Formula for the Sum of n Terms of an Arithmetic Series to find the sum of the first ten terms.

Solution
$a_n = 2n - 1$
$a_1 = 2(1) - 1 = 1$
$a_{10} = 2(10) - 1 = 19$

$$S_n = \frac{n}{2}(a_1 + a_n)$$

$$S_{10} = \frac{10}{2}(1 + 19) = 5(20) = 100$$

The ball will roll 100 ft during the first 10 s.

PROBLEM 6 A contest offers 20 prizes. The first prize is $10,000, and each successive prize is $300 less than the preceding prize. What is the value of the 20th-place prize? What is the total amount of prize money that is being awarded?

Solution See page S32.

11.2 Concept Review

State whether the following statements are always true, sometimes true, or never true.

1. The sum of the successive terms of an arithmetic series increases in value.

2. Each successive term in an arithmetic sequence is found by adding a fixed number to the previous term.

3. The first term of an arithmetic sequence is a positive number.

4. The nth term of an arithmetic sequence is found by using the formula $a_n = a_1 + (n - 1)d$.

11.2   Exercises

1   Find the *n*th term of an arithmetic sequence

1.   How does an arithmetic sequence differ from any other type of sequence?

2.   Explain how to find the common difference for an arithmetic sequence.

3. a. The sequence 3, 7, 11, 15, 19, ... is an arithmetic sequence because the difference between each pair of consecutive terms is ___?___. This number is called the ___?___ difference of the sequence.

b. Find the 50th term of the arithmetic sequence given in part a.

$a_n = a_1 + (n - 1)d$ • Use the Formula for the ___?___ **Term of an Arithmetic Sequence.**

$a_{50} = 3 + (50 - 1)(4)$ • Replace *n* by ___?___, a_1 by ___?___, and *d* by ___?___.

$= $ ___?___   • Simplify.

4. Find the formula for the *n*th term of the arithmetic sequence 10, 8, 6, 4, ...

$d = a_2 - a_1 = $ ___?___ $-$ ___?___   • To find the common difference, subtract the first term from the second term.

$= $ ___?___

$a_n = a_1 + (n - 1)d$ • Use the Formula for the *n*th Term of an Arithmetic Sequence.

$a_n = $ ___?___ $+ (n - 1)($___?___$)$ • Replace a_1 by 10 and *d* by −2.

$a_n = 10 - $ ___?___ $+ $ ___?___   • Use the Distributive Property.

$a_n = $ ___?___   • Simplify.

Find the indicated term of the arithmetic sequence.

5. 1, 11, 21, ... ; a_{15}

6. 3, 8, 13, ... ; a_{20}

7. −6, −2, 2, ... ; a_{15}

8. −7, −2, 3, ... ; a_{14}

9. 3, 7, 11, ... ; a_{18}

10. −13, −6, 1, ... ; a_{31}

11. $-\dfrac{3}{4}, 0, \dfrac{3}{4}, \dots$; a_{11}

12. $\dfrac{3}{8}, 1, \dfrac{13}{8}, \dots$; a_{17}

13. $2, \dfrac{5}{2}, 3, \dots$; a_{31}

14. $1, \dfrac{5}{4}, \dfrac{3}{2}, \dots$; a_{17}

15. 6, 5.75, 5.50, ... ; a_{10}

16. 4, 3.7, 3.4, ... ; a_{12}

Find the formula for the *n*th term of the arithmetic sequence.

17. 1, 2, 3, ...

18. 1, 4, 7, ...

19. 6, 2, −2, ...

20. 3, 0, −3, ...

21. $2, \dfrac{7}{2}, 5, \dots$

22. 7, 4.5, 2, ...

23. −8, −13, −18, ...

24. 17, 30, 43, ...

25. 26, 16, 6, ...

Find the number of terms in the finite arithmetic sequence.

26. $-2, 1, 4, \ldots, 73$

27. $7, 11, 15, \ldots, 171$

28. $-\dfrac{1}{2}, \dfrac{3}{2}, \dfrac{7}{2}, \ldots, \dfrac{71}{2}$

29. $\dfrac{1}{3}, \dfrac{5}{3}, 3, \ldots, \dfrac{61}{3}$

30. $1, 5, 9, \ldots, 81$

31. $3, 8, 13, \ldots, 98$

32. $2, 0, -2, \ldots, -56$

33. $1, -3, -7, \ldots, -75$

34. $\dfrac{5}{2}, 3, \dfrac{7}{2}, \ldots, 13$

35. $\dfrac{7}{3}, \dfrac{13}{3}, \dfrac{19}{3}, \ldots, \dfrac{79}{3}$

36. $1, 0.75, 0.50, \ldots, -4$

37. $3.5, 2, 0.5, \ldots, -25$

 For Exercises 38 to 41, $a_1, a_2, a_3, a_4, \ldots$ is an arithmetic sequence with common difference d. Determine whether the statement is true or false.

38. If $a_1 < 0$ and $d < 0$, then all terms of the sequence are negative.

39. $a_7 - a_3 = 4d$

40. If $d < 0$, then $a_n < a_{n+1}$.

41. If $a_1 < 0$ and $d > 0$, then the sequence has a finite number of negative terms and an infinite number of positive terms.

2   Evaluate an arithmetic series

42. Give the meaning of each part of the Formula for the Sum of n Terms of an Arithmetic Series, $S_n = \dfrac{n}{2}(a_1 + a_n)$.

S_n is the ___?___ of n terms of the series.
n is the ___?___ of terms.
a_1 is the ___?___ term.
a_n is the ___?___ term.

43. Find the sum of the arithmetic series $\displaystyle\sum_{n=1}^{10}(n-3)$.

This series is the sum of the first ___?___ terms of the sequence given by the formula $a_n = $ ___?___.

$a_1 = $ ___?___ $-3 = $ ___?___   • To find the first term, replace n by 1 and simplify.
$a_{10} = $ ___?___ $-3 = $ ___?___   • To find the last term, replace n by 10 and simplify.

$S_n = \dfrac{n}{2}(a_1 + a_n)$ • Use the Formula for the Sum of n Terms of an ___?___

$S_{\underline{?}} = \dfrac{\underline{\;?\;}}{2} \cdot (\underline{\;?\;} + \underline{\;?\;})$ • Replace n by 10, a_1 by -2, and a_{10} by 7.
$= (\underline{\;?\;})(\underline{\;?\;})$ • Simplify.
$= \underline{\;?\;}$ • Simplify.

Find the sum of the indicated number of terms of the arithmetic sequence.

44. $1, 3, 5, \ldots ; n = 50$

45. $2, 4, 6, \ldots ; n = 25$

46. $20, 18, 16, \ldots ; n = 40$

47. $25, 20, 15, \ldots ; n = 22$

48. $\frac{1}{2}, 1, \frac{3}{2}, \ldots ; n = 27$

49. $2, \frac{11}{4}, \frac{7}{2}, \ldots ; n = 10$

Evaluate the arithmetic series.

50. $\sum_{i=1}^{15} (3i - 1)$

51. $\sum_{i=1}^{15} (3i + 4)$

52. $\sum_{n=1}^{17} \left(\frac{1}{2} n + 1 \right)$

53. $\sum_{n=1}^{10} (1 - 4n)$

54. $\sum_{i=1}^{15} (4 - 2i)$

55. $\sum_{n=1}^{10} (5 - n)$

56. State whether the series can be evaluated using the formula $S_n = \frac{n}{2}(a_1 + a_n)$.

    a. $12 + 7 + 2 - 3 - 8$

    b. $2 + 4 + 8 + \cdots + 64$

57. Will the sum of the series $\sum_{n=1}^{100} (5 - n)$ be positive or negative?

3   Application problems

For Exercises 58 and 59, use this problem situation: A theater section has 8 rows of seats. The first row has 3 seats, the second row has 5 seats, the third row has 7 seats, and so on in an arithmetic sequence.

58. a. Give the value of each of the following for the sequence of numbers of seats per row.

$a_1 = \underline{\quad ? \quad}$

$d = \underline{\quad ? \quad}$

$n = \underline{\quad ? \quad}$

    b. Find the number of seats in the last row.

$a_n = a_1 + (n - 1)d$

$a_{\underline{?}} = \underline{\quad ? \quad} + (\underline{\quad ? \quad} - 1)(\underline{\quad ? \quad})$

        $= \underline{\quad ? \quad}$

• Write the Formula for the *n*th Terms of an Arithmetic Sequence.
• Replace *n*, a_1, and *d* by the values listed in part a.
• Simplify.

59. Use the results of Exercise 58 to find the total number of seats in the theater section.

$S_n = \frac{n}{2} (a_1 + a_n).$ • Write the Formula for the Sum of *n* Terms of an Arithmetic Series.

$S_{\underline{?}} = \frac{\underline{\quad ? \quad}}{2} \cdot (\underline{\quad ? \quad} + \underline{\quad ? \quad})$

        $= \underline{\quad ? \quad}$

• Replace *n*, a_1, and a_n by the values you found in Exercise 58.
• Simplify.

Solve.

60. **Physics** The distance that an object dropped from a cliff will fall is 16 ft the first second, 48 ft the next second, 80 ft the third second, and so on in an arithmetic sequence. What is the total distance the object will fall in 6 s?

61. **Health Science** An exercise program calls for walking 12 min each day for a week. Each week thereafter, the amount of time spent walking increases by 6 min per day. In how many weeks will a person be walking 60 min each day?

62. **Business** A display of cans in a grocery store consists of 20 cans in the bottom row, 18 cans in the next row, and so on in an arithmetic sequence. The top row has 4 cans. Find the total number of cans in the display.

63. **Construction** A theater in the round has 52 seats in the first row, 58 seats in the second row, 64 seats in the third row, and so on in an arithmetic sequence. Find the total number of seats in the theater if there are 20 rows of seats.

64. **Construction** The loge seating section in a concert hall consists of 26 rows of chairs. There are 65 seats in the first row, 71 seats in the second row, 77 seats in the third row, and so on in an arithmetic sequence. How many seats are in the loge seating section?

65. **Human Resources** The salary schedule for an engineering assistant is $2200 for the first month and a $150-per-month salary increase for the next 9 months. Find the monthly salary during the tenth month. Find the total salary for the 10-month period.

For Exercises 66 and 67, refer to the problem situations in Exercises 60 to 65. State the exercise number of the problem situation that is modeled by the given series.

66. $\sum_{n=1}^{9} (22 - 2n)$

67. $\sum_{n=1}^{6} (32n - 16)$

11.2 Applying Concepts

Solve.

68. Find the sum of the first 50 positive integers.

69. How many terms of the arithmetic sequence $-3, 2, 7, \ldots$ must be added together for the sum of the series to be 116?

70. Given an arithmetic sequence for which $a_1 = -9$, $a_n = 21$, and $S_n = 36$, find d and n.

71. The fourth term of an arithmetic sequence is 9, and the ninth term is 29. Find the first term.

72. Write $\sum\limits_{i=1}^{2}\log 2i$ as a single logarithm with a coefficient of 1.

73. **Geometry** The sum of the interior angles of a triangle is 180°. The sum is 360° for a quadrilateral and 540° for a pentagon. Assuming that this pattern continues, find the sum of the angles of a dodecagon (12-sided figure). Find a formula for the sum of the angles of an n-sided polygon.

$$a + b + c = 180°$$

74. **Sports** The International Amateur Athletic Federation (IAAF) specifies the design of tracks on which world records can be set. A typical design is shaped like a rectangle with semicircles on either end, as shown at the right. There are eight lanes, and each lane is 1.22 m wide. The distance around the track for each lane is measured from the center of that lane. Find a formula for the sequence of radii of the circular portion of the track (the two ends). Round to the nearest hundredth.

finish line

83.4 m

36.5 m

75. **Sports** Using the information in the preceding exercise, write a formula for the sequence of distances around the track for each lane. Round to the nearest hundredth and use 3.14 as an approximation for π. Remember that the distance around the circular portion of the track is measured from the center of the lane. Explain why the IAAF staggers the starting position for runners in a 400-meter race.

76. **Business** Straight-line depreciation is used by some companies to determine the value of an asset. A model for this depreciation method is $a_n = V - dn$, where a_n is the value of the asset after n years, V is the original value of the asset, d is the annual decrease in the asset's value, and n is the number of years. Suppose that an asset has an original value of $20,000 and that the annual decrease in value is $3000.
   a. Substitute the values of V and d into the equation, and write an expression for a_n.
   b. Show that a_n is an arithmetic sequence.

77. Write an essay on the Fibonacci sequence and its relationship to natural phenomena.

11.3   Geometric Sequences and Series

OBJECTIVE **1**   **Find the nth term of a geometric sequence**

An ore sample contains 20 mg of a radioactive material with a half-life of 1 week. The amount of the radioactive material that the sample contains at the beginning of each week can be determined by using an exponential decay equation.

The following sequence represents the amount in the sample at the beginning of each week. Each term of the sequence is found by multiplying the preceding term by $\frac{1}{2}$.

Week	1	2	3	4	5
Amount	20	10	5	2.5	1.25

The sequence 20, 10, 5, 2.5, 1.25 is called a geometric sequence. A **geometric sequence,** or **geometric progression,** is one in which each successive term of the sequence is the same nonzero constant multiple of the preceding term. The common multiple is called the **common ratio** of the sequence.

Take Note

Geometric sequences are different from arithmetic sequences. For a geometric sequence, every two successive terms have the same *ratio*. For an arithmetic sequence, every two successive terms have the same *difference*.

Each of the sequences shown below is a geometric sequence. To find the common ratio of a geometric sequence, divide the second term of the sequence by the first term.

$$3, 6, 12, 24, 48, \ldots \qquad \text{Common ratio: } 2$$
$$4, -12, 36, -108, 324, \ldots \qquad \text{Common ratio: } -3$$
$$6, 4, \frac{8}{3}, \frac{16}{9}, \frac{32}{27}, \ldots \qquad \text{Common ratio: } \frac{2}{3}$$

Consider a geometric sequence in which the first term is a_1 and the common ratio is r. Multiplying each successive term of the geometric sequence by the common ratio yields a formula for the nth term.

The first term is a_1. $\qquad\qquad a_1 = a_1$

To find the second term, multiply the first term by the common ratio r. $\qquad a_2 = a_1 r$

To find the third term, multiply the second term by the common ratio r.
$$a_3 = (a_2)r = (a_1 r)r$$
$$a_3 = a_1 r^2$$

To find the fourth term, multiply the third term by the common ratio r.
$$a_4 = (a_3)r = (a_1 r^2)r$$
$$a_4 = a_1 r^3$$

Note the relationship between the term number and the number that is the exponent on r. The exponent on r is 1 less than the term number.

$$a_n = a_1 r^{n-1}$$

Formula for the nth Term of a Geometric Sequence

The nth term of a geometric sequence with first term a_1 and common ratio r is given by $a_n = a_1 r^{n-1}$.

EXAMPLE 1 Find the 6th term of the geometric sequence 3, 6, 12, ...

Solution $r = \dfrac{a_2}{a_1} = \dfrac{6}{3} = 2$ • **Find the common ratio.**

$a_n = a_1 r^{n-1}$ • **Use the Formula for the nth Term of a Geometric**
$a_6 = 3(2)^{6-1}$ **Sequence to find the 6th term. $n = 6, a_1 = 3, r = 2$**
$\quad = 3(2)^5$
$\quad = 3(32)$
$\quad = 96$

PROBLEM 1 Find the 5th term of the geometric sequence 5, 2, $\frac{4}{5}$, ...

Solution See page S32.

EXAMPLE 2 Find a_3 for the geometric sequence 8, a_2, a_3, 27, ...

Solution

$a_n = a_1 r^{n-1}$

$a_4 = a_1 r^{4-1}$

- Use the Formula for the *n*th Term of a Geometric Sequence to find the common ratio. The 1st and 4th terms are known. Substitute 4 for *n*.

$27 = 8r^{4-1}$

- $a_4 = 27, a_1 = 8$

$\dfrac{27}{8} = r^3$

$\dfrac{3}{2} = r$

- Take the cube root of each side of the equation.

$a_3 = 8\left(\dfrac{3}{2}\right)^{3-1}$

- Use the Formula for *n*th Term of a Geometric Sequence to find a_3. $n = 3, a_1 = 8, r = \dfrac{3}{2}$

$= 8\left(\dfrac{3}{2}\right)^2$

$= 8\left(\dfrac{9}{4}\right) = 18$

PROBLEM 2 Find a_3 for the geometric sequence 3, a_2, a_3, -192, ...

Solution See page S32.

OBJECTIVE 2

Finite geometric series

The indicated sum of the terms of a geometric sequence is called a **geometric series.** The sum of a geometric series can be found by a formula.

Formula for the Sum of *n* Terms of a Finite Geometric Series

Let a_1 be the first term of a finite geometric sequence, let n be the number of terms, and let r be the common ratio, $r \neq 1$. Then the sum of the series S_n is given by $S_n = \dfrac{a_1(1 - r^n)}{1 - r}$.

Proof of the Formula for the Sum of *n* Terms of a Finite Geometric Series:

Let S_n represent the sum of n terms of the sequence.

$$S_n = a_1 + a_1 r + a_1 r^2 + \cdots + a_1 r^{n-2} + a_1 r^{n-1}$$

Multiply each side of the equation by r.

$$rS_n = a_1 r + a_1 r^2 + a_1 r^3 + \cdots + a_1 r^{n-1} + a_1 r^n$$

Subtract the two equations.

$$S_n - rS_n = a_1 - a_1 r^n$$

Assuming that $r \neq 1$, solve for S_n.

$$(1 - r)S_n = a_1(1 - r^n)$$

$$S_n = \dfrac{a_1(1 - r^n)}{1 - r}$$

EXAMPLE 3 Find the sum of the terms of the geometric sequence 2, 8, 32, 128, 512.

Solution $r = \dfrac{a_2}{a_1} = \dfrac{8}{2} = 4$ • Find the common ratio.

$$S_n = \frac{a_1(1 - r^n)}{1 - r}$$ • Use the Formula for the Sum of n Terms of a Finite Geometric Series. $n = 5$, $a_1 = 2$, $r = 4$.

$$S_5 = \frac{2(1 - 4^5)}{1 - 4}$$

$$= \frac{2(1 - 1024)}{-3}$$

$$= \frac{2(-1023)}{-3}$$

$$= \frac{-2046}{-3}$$

$$= 682$$

PROBLEM 3 Find the sum of the terms of the geometric sequence 1, $-\dfrac{1}{3}$, $\dfrac{1}{9}$, $-\dfrac{1}{27}$.

Solution See page S32.

EXAMPLE 4 Evaluate the geometric series $\displaystyle\sum_{n=1}^{10}(-20)(-2)^{n-1}$.

Solution $a_n = (-20)(-2)^{n-1}$
$a_1 = (-20)(-2)^{1-1}$ • Find the first term.
$= (-20)(-2)^0$
$= (-20)(1) = -20$

$a_2 = (-20)(-2)^{2-1}$ • Find the second term.
$= (-20)(-2)^1$
$= (-20)(-2) = 40$

$r = \dfrac{a_2}{a_1} = \dfrac{40}{-20} = -2$ • Find the common ratio.

$$S_n = \frac{a_1(1 - r^n)}{1 - r}$$ • Use the Formula for the Sum of n Terms of a Finite Geometric Series. $n = 10$, $a_1 = -20$, $r = -2$

$$S_{10} = \frac{-20[1 - (-2)^{10}]}{1 - (-2)}$$

$$= \frac{-20(1 - 1024)}{3}$$

$$= \frac{-20(-1023)}{3}$$

$$= \frac{20,460}{3}$$

$$= 6820$$

> **PROBLEM 4**   Evaluate the geometric series $\sum_{n=1}^{5}\left(\frac{1}{2}\right)^{n}$.
>
> ■ **Solution**   See page S33.

OBJECTIVE 3   Infinite geometric series

When the absolute value of the common ratio of a geometric sequence is less than 1, $|r| < 1$, then as n becomes larger, r^n becomes closer to zero.

Examples of geometric sequences for which $|r| < 1$ are shown at the right. As the number of terms increases, the absolute value of the last term listed gets closer to zero.

$$1, \frac{1}{3}, \frac{1}{9}, \frac{1}{27}, \frac{1}{81}, \frac{1}{243}, \cdots$$

$$1, -\frac{1}{2}, \frac{1}{4}, -\frac{1}{8}, \frac{1}{16}, -\frac{1}{32}, \cdots$$

The indicated sum of the terms of an infinite geometric sequence is called an **infinite geometric series.**

An example of an infinite geometric series is shown at the right. The first term is 1. The common ratio is $\frac{1}{3}$.

$$1 + \frac{1}{3} + \frac{1}{9} + \frac{1}{27} + \frac{1}{81} + \frac{1}{243} + \cdots$$

The sum of the first 5, 7, 12, and 15 terms, along with the values of r^n, are shown at the right. Note that as n increases, the sum of the terms gets closer to 1.5, and the value of r^n gets closer to zero.

n	S_n	r^n
5	1.4938272	0.0041152
7	1.4993141	0.0004572
12	1.4999972	0.0000019
15	1.4999999	0.0000001

Using the Formula for the Sum of n Terms of a Geometric Series and the fact that r^n approaches zero when $|r| < 1$ and n increases, a formula for the sum of an infinite geometric series can be found.

The sum of the first n terms of a geometric series is shown at the right. If $|r| < 1$, then r^n can be made very close to zero by using larger and larger values of n. Therefore, the sum of the first n terms is approximately $\frac{a_1}{1 - r}$.

$$\text{Approximately zero} \downarrow$$

$$S_n = \frac{a_1(1 - r^n)}{1 - r}$$

$$S_n \approx \frac{a_1(1 - 0)}{1 - r} = \frac{a_1}{1 - r}$$

> **Formula for the Sum of an Infinite Geometric Series**
>
> The sum of an infinite geometric series in which $|r| < 1$ and a_1 is the first term is given by $S = \dfrac{a_1}{1 - r}$.

When $|r| \geq 1$, the infinite geometric series does not have a finite sum. For example, the sum of the infinite geometric series $1 + 2 + 4 + 8 + \cdots$ increases without limit.

EXAMPLE 5   Find the sum of the terms of the infinite geometric sequence
$1, -\frac{1}{2}, \frac{1}{4}, -\frac{1}{8}, \ldots$.

Solution $S = \dfrac{a_1}{1-r} = \dfrac{1}{1-\left(-\dfrac{1}{2}\right)}$ • The common ratio is $-\dfrac{1}{2}$. $\left|-\dfrac{1}{2}\right| < 1$. Use
the Formula for the Sum of an Infinite
Geometric Series.

$= \dfrac{1}{\dfrac{3}{2}} = \dfrac{2}{3}$

PROBLEM 5   Find the sum of the terms of the infinite geometric sequence
$3, -2, \frac{4}{3}, -\frac{8}{9}, \ldots$.

Solution   See page S33.

The sum of an infinite geometric series can be used to find a fraction that is equivalent to a nonterminating, repeating decimal.

The repeating decimal shown at the right has been rewritten as an infinite geometric series, with first term $\frac{3}{10}$ and common ratio $\frac{1}{10}$.

$0.\overline{3} = 0.3 + 0.03 + 0.003 + \cdots$
$= \dfrac{3}{10} + \dfrac{3}{100} + \dfrac{3}{1000} + \cdots$

Use the Formula for the Sum of an Infinite Geometric Series.

$S = \dfrac{a_1}{1-r} = \dfrac{\dfrac{3}{10}}{1 - \dfrac{1}{10}} = \dfrac{\dfrac{3}{10}}{\dfrac{9}{10}} = \dfrac{3}{9} = \dfrac{1}{3}$

$\frac{1}{3}$ is equivalent to the nonterminating, repeating decimal $0.\overline{3}$.

EXAMPLE 6   Find an equivalent fraction for $0.1\overline{2}$.

Solution   Write the decimal as an infinite geometric series. The geometric series does not begin with the first term. The series begins with $\frac{2}{100}$. The common ratio is $\frac{1}{10}$.

$0.1\overline{2} = 0.1 + 0.02 + 0.002 + 0.0002 + \cdots$
$= \dfrac{1}{10} + \dfrac{2}{100} + \dfrac{2}{1000} + \dfrac{2}{10,000} + \cdots$

$S = \dfrac{a_1}{1-r} = \dfrac{\dfrac{2}{100}}{1 - \dfrac{1}{10}} = \dfrac{\dfrac{2}{100}}{\dfrac{9}{10}} = \dfrac{2}{90}$ • Use the Formula for the
Sum of an Infinite
Geometric Series.

$0.1\overline{2} = \dfrac{1}{10} + \dfrac{2}{90} = \dfrac{11}{90}$ • Add $\dfrac{1}{10}$ to the sum of
the series.

An equivalent fraction is $\frac{11}{90}$.

PROBLEM 6   Find an equivalent fraction for $0.\overline{36}$.

Solution   See page S33.

OBJECTIVE **4**   **Application problems**

Point of Interest

Galileo used pendulums extensively in his experiments. His investigations into their behavior early in his career led him to use them as measurement devices in later experiments.

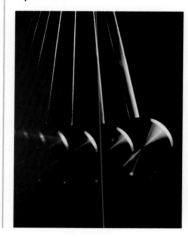

EXAMPLE 7   On the first swing, the length of the arc through which a pendulum swings is 16 in. The length of each successive swing is $\frac{7}{8}$ of the preceding swing. Find the length of the arc on the fifth swing. Round to the nearest tenth.

Strategy   To find the length of the arc on the fifth swing, use the Formula for the nth Term of a Geometric Sequence. $n = 5$, $a_1 = 16$, $r = \frac{7}{8}$

Solution $a_n = a_1 r^{n-1}$

$$a_5 = 16\left(\frac{7}{8}\right)^{5-1} = 16\left(\frac{7}{8}\right)^4 = 16\left(\frac{2401}{4096}\right) = \frac{38{,}416}{4096} \approx 9.4$$

The length of the arc on the fifth swing is 9.4 in.

PROBLEM 7   You start a chain letter and send it to three friends. Each of the three friends sends the letter to three other friends, and the sequence is repeated. If no one breaks the chain, how many letters will have been mailed from the first through the sixth mailings?

Solution   See page S33.

11.3   Concept Review

Determine whether the following statements are always true, sometimes true, or never true.

1. Each successive term of a geometric sequence is found by multiplying the preceding term by a nonzero constant.

2. The sum of an infinite geometric series is infinity.

3. The sum of a geometric series increases in value as more terms are added.

4. $1, 8, 27, \ldots, k^3, \ldots$ is a geometric sequence.

5. $\sqrt{1}, \sqrt{2}, \sqrt{3}, \ldots, \sqrt{n}, \ldots$ is a geometric sequence.

11.3 Exercises

1 **Find the *n*th term of a geometric sequence**

1. Explain the difference between an arithmetic sequence and a geometric sequence.

2. Explain how to find the common ratio for a geometric sequence.

3. **a.** The sequence $2, 6, 18, 54, \ldots$ is a geometric sequence because each term can be found by multiplying the preceding term by ___?___. This number is called the ___?___ of the sequence.
   b. Find the seventh term of the geometric sequence given in part a.

   $a_n = a_1 r^{n-1}$ • Use the Formula for the ___?___ Term of a Geometric Sequence.

   $a_7 = 2(3)^{7-1}$ • Replace *n* by ___?___, a_1 by ___?___, and *r* by ___?___.

   $= 2(3^{\underline{\ ?\ }})$ • Simplify.

   $= 2(\underline{\ \ ?\ \ })$ • Evaluate 3^6.

   $= \underline{\ \ ?\ \ }$ • Multiply.

4. Find the common ratio of the geometric sequence $18, a_2, a_3, \dfrac{16}{3}, \ldots$.

   $a_n = a_1 r^{n-1}$ • Use the Formula for the *n*th Term of a Geometric Sequence.

   $\dfrac{16}{3} = 18r^{4-1}$ • Replace a_n by ___?___, a_1 by ___?___, and *n* by ___?___.

   $\dfrac{1}{\underline{\ ?\ }} \cdot \dfrac{16}{3} = r^{\underline{\ ?\ }}$ • Simplify the exponent. Divide each side of the equation by 18.

   $\dfrac{\underline{\ ?\ }}{\underline{\ ?\ }} = r^3$ • Simplify the left side of the equation.

   $\underline{\ ?\ } = r$ • Take the cube root of each side of the equation.

Find the indicated term of the geometric sequence.

5. $2, 8, 32, \ldots ; a_9$

6. $4, 3, \dfrac{9}{4}, \ldots ; a_8$

7. $6, -4, \dfrac{8}{3}, \ldots ; a_7$

8. $-5, 15, -45, \ldots ; a_7$

9. $1, \sqrt{2}, 2, \ldots ; a_9$

10. $3, 3\sqrt{3}, 9, \ldots ; a_8$

Find a_2 and a_3 for the geometric sequence.

11. $9, a_2, a_3, \dfrac{8}{3}, \ldots$

12. $8, a_2, a_3, \dfrac{27}{8}, \ldots$

13. $3, a_2, a_3, -\dfrac{8}{9}, \ldots$

14. $6, a_2, a_3, -48, \ldots$

15. $-3, a_2, a_3, 192, \ldots$

16. $5, a_2, a_3, 625, \ldots$

For Exercises 17 and 18, $a_1, a_2, a_3, a_4, \ldots$ is a geometric sequence with common ratio r.

17. True or false? If $r < 0$, then all terms of the sequence are negative.

18. True or false? If $0 < r < 1$, then $a_n < a_{n+1}$.

2 **Finite geometric series**

19. Give the meaning of each part of the Formula for the Sum of n Terms of a Finite Geometric Series, $S_n \dfrac{a_1(1 - r^n)}{1 - r}$.

S_n is the ___?___ of n terms of the series.

n is the ___?___ of terms.

a_1 is the ___?___ term.

r is the ___?___.

20. Evaluate the geometric series $\displaystyle\sum_{n=1}^{4} 10^n$.

This series is the sum of the first ___?___ terms of the sequence given by the formula $a_n = $ ___?___.

$a_1 = 10^{\underline{?}} = $ ___?___
- To find the first term, replace n by 1 and simplify.

$a_2 = 10^{\underline{?}} = $ ___?___
- To find the second term, replace n by 2 and simplify.

$r = \dfrac{a_2}{a_1} = \dfrac{\underline{?}}{\underline{?}} = $ ___?___
- Use the first two terms to find the common ratio.

$S_n = \dfrac{a_1(1 - r^n)}{1 - r}$
- Use the Formula for the Sum of n Terms of a ___?___.

$S_4 = \dfrac{\underline{?}\,(1 - \underline{?}^{\,4})}{1 - \underline{?}}$

$= \dfrac{10(\underline{\quad?\quad})}{\underline{?}}$
- Simplify.

$= $ ___?___

Find the sum of the indicated number of terms of the geometric sequence.

21. $2, 6, 18, \ldots ; n = 7$

22. $-4, 12, -36, \ldots ; n = 7$

23. $12, 9, \dfrac{27}{4}, \ldots ; n = 5$

24. $3, 3\sqrt{2}, 6, \ldots ; n = 12$

Find the sum of the geometric series.

25. $\displaystyle\sum_{i=1}^{5} (2)^i$

26. $\displaystyle\sum_{n=1}^{6} \left(\dfrac{3}{2}\right)^n$

27. $\displaystyle\sum_{i=1}^{5} \left(\dfrac{1}{3}\right)^i$

28. $\displaystyle\sum_{n=1}^{6} \left(\dfrac{2}{3}\right)^n$

29. $\displaystyle\sum_{i=1}^{5} (4)^i$

30. $\displaystyle\sum_{n=1}^{8} (3)^n$

31. $\displaystyle\sum_{i=1}^{4} (7)^i$

32. $\displaystyle\sum_{n=1}^{5} (5)^n$

33. $\sum_{i=1}^{5}\left(\dfrac{3}{4}\right)^{i}$ **34.** $\sum_{n=1}^{3}\left(\dfrac{7}{4}\right)^{n}$ **35.** $\sum_{i=1}^{4}\left(\dfrac{5}{3}\right)^{i}$ **36.** $\sum_{n=1}^{6}\left(\dfrac{1}{2}\right)^{n}$

37. State whether the series can be evaluated using the formula $S_n = \dfrac{a_1(1-r^n)}{1-r}$.

a. $1 + 4 + 9 + \cdots + 81$ **b.** $\sqrt{3} - 3 + 3\sqrt{3} - 9 + 9\sqrt{3}$

38. If $b > 1$, will the sum of the series $\sum_{n=1}^{100}(-b)^n$ be positive or negative?

3   Infinite geometric series

39. The formula $S = \dfrac{a_1}{1-r}$ can be used to find the sum of an infinite geometric series as long as the common ratio r is a number between ____?____ and ____?____; that is as long as $|r| < $ ____?____.

40. Find the sum of the infinite geometric series $8 + 4 + 2 + \cdots$.

$r = \dfrac{a_2}{a_1} = \dfrac{?}{?} = $ ____?____   • Use the first two terms to find the common ratio.

$S = \dfrac{a_1}{1-r}$ • $|r| < 1$. Use the Formula for the Sum of an ____?____.

$S = \dfrac{?}{1 - ?}$ • Replace a_1 by 8 and r by $\dfrac{1}{2}$.

$= \dfrac{8}{?}$ • Simplify.

$= $ ____?____

Find the sum of the infinite geometric series.

41. $3 + 2 + \dfrac{4}{3} + \cdots$ **42.** $2 - \dfrac{1}{4} + \dfrac{1}{32} + \cdots$ **43.** $6 - 4 + \dfrac{8}{3} + \cdots$

44. $\dfrac{1}{10} + \dfrac{1}{100} + \dfrac{1}{1000} + \cdots$ **45.** $\dfrac{7}{10} + \dfrac{7}{100} + \dfrac{7}{1000} + \cdots$ **46.** $\dfrac{5}{100} + \dfrac{5}{10,000} + \dfrac{5}{1,000,000} + \cdots$

47. State whether the series can be evaluated using the formula $S = \dfrac{a_1(1-r^n)}{1-r}$.

a. $1 + \dfrac{\sqrt{2}}{2} + \dfrac{1}{2} + \cdots$ **b.** $\dfrac{4}{3} - \dfrac{16}{9} + \dfrac{64}{27} - \cdots$

48. $a_1 + a_2 + a_3 + \cdots$ is an infinite geometric series with $a_1 < 0$ and common ratio r such that $-1 < r < 0$. Is the sum of the series greater than or less than a_1?

Find an equivalent fraction for the repeating decimal.

49. $0.88\overline{8}$ **50.** $0.55\overline{5}$ **51.** $0.22\overline{2}$ **52.** $0.99\overline{9}$

53. $0.45\overline{45}$ **54.** $0.18\overline{18}$ **55.** $0.166\overline{6}$ **56.** $0.833\overline{3}$

4 Application problems

For Exercises 57 and 58, use this problem situation: A population of bacteria doubles every hour. The population starts at 350 bacteria.

57. After 1 h, the original population of 350 bacteria has doubled to ___?___ bacteria. After 2 h, the population has doubled again, to ___?___ bacteria. The sequence 350, 700, 1400, ... is a ___?___ sequence with $a_1 =$ ___?___ and $r =$ ___?___ .

58. Use the results of Exercise 57 to find a formula for the population of bacteria after n hours.

$a_n = a_1 r^{n-1}$ • Write the Formula for the nth Term of a Geometric Sequence.

$a_n = ($ ___?___ $)($ ___?___ $)^{n-1}$ • Replace a_1 by ___?___ and r by ___?___ .

59. Art The fabric designer Jhane Barnes created a fabric pattern based on the *Sierpinski triangle*. This triangle is a *fractal*, which is a geometric pattern that is repeated at ever smaller scales to produce irregular shapes. The first four stages in the construction of a Sierpinski triangle are shown at the right. The initial triangle is an equilateral triangle with sides 1 unit long. The cut-out triangles are formed by connecting the midpoints of the sides of the unshaded triangles. This pattern is repeated indefinitely. Find a formula for the nth term of the number of unshaded triangles.

60. Art A *Sierpinski carpet* is similar to a Sierpinski triangle (see Exercise 59) except that all of the unshaded squares must be divided into nine congruent smaller squares with the one in the center shaded. The first three stages of the pattern are shown at the right. Find a formula for the nth term of the number of unshaded squares.

61. Physics A laboratory ore sample contains 500 mg of a radioactive material with a half-life of 1 day. Find the amount of radioactive material in the sample at the beginning of the seventh day.

62. Recreation On the first swing, the length of the arc through which a pendulum swings is 18 in. The length of each successive swing is $\frac{3}{4}$ of the preceding swing. What is the total distance the pendulum has traveled during the first five swings? Round to the nearest tenth.

63. Sports To test the bounce of a tennis ball, the ball is dropped from a height of 8 ft. The ball bounces to 80% of its previous height with each bounce. How high does the ball bounce on the fifth bounce? Round to the nearest tenth.

64. Physics The temperature of a hot-water spa is 75°F. Each hour, the temperature is 10% higher than during the previous hour. Find the temperature of the spa after 3 h. Round to the nearest tenth.

65. Real Estate A real estate broker estimates that a piece of land will increase in value at a rate of 12% each year. If the original value of the land is $15,000, what will be its value in 15 years?

66. Business Suppose an employee receives a wage of 1¢ the first day of work, 2¢ the second day, 4¢ the third day, and so on in a geometric sequence. Find the total amount of money earned for working 30 days.

Day 1   Day 2   Day 3

67. Real Estate Assume the average value of a home increases 5% per year. How much would a house costing $100,000 be worth in 30 years?

68. Biology A culture of bacteria doubles every 2 h. If there are 500 bacteria at the beginning, how many bacteria will there be after 24 h?

State whether the sequence is arithmetic (A), geometric (G), or neither (N), and write the next term in the sequence.

69. 4, −2, 1, . . .

70. −8, 0, 8, . . .

71. 5, 6.5, 8, . . .

72. −7, 14, −28, . . .

73. 1, 4, 9, 16, . . .

74. $\sqrt{1}, \sqrt{2}, \sqrt{3}, \sqrt{4}$

75. $x^8, x^6, x^4, \ldots$

76. $5a^2, 3a^2, a^2, \ldots$

77. $\log x, 2 \log x, 3 \log x, \ldots$

78. $\log x, 3 \log x, 9 \log x, \ldots$

11.3 Applying Concepts

Solve.

79. The third term of a geometric sequence is 3, and the sixth term is $\frac{1}{9}$. Find the first term.

80. Given $a_n = 162$, $r = -3$, and $S_n = 122$ for a geometric sequence, find a_1 and n.

81. For the geometric sequence given by $a_n = 2^n$, show that the sequence $b_n = \log a_n$ is an arithmetic sequence.

82. For the geometric sequence given by $a_n = e^n$, show that the sequence $b_n = \ln a_n$ is an arithmetic sequence.

83. For the arithmetic sequence given by $a_n = 3n - 2$, show that the sequence $b_n = 2^{a_n}$ is a geometric sequence.

84. For $f(n) = ab^n$, n a natural number, show that $f(n)$ is a geometric sequence.

85. Finance A car loan is normally structured so that each month, part of the payment reduces the loan amount and the remainder of the payment pays interest on the loan. You pay interest only on the loan amount that remains to be paid (the unpaid balance). If you have a car loan of $5000 at an annual interest rate of 9%, your monthly payment for a 5-year loan is $103.79. The amount of the loan repaid, R_n, in the nth payment of the loan is a geometric sequence given by $R_n = R_1(1.0075)^{n-1}$. For the situation described above, $R_1 = 66.29$.

  a. How much of the loan is repaid in the 27th payment?
  b. The total amount, T, of the loan repaid after n payments is the sum of a geometric sequence, $T = \sum_{k=1}^{n} R_1(1.0075)^{k-1}$. Find the total amount repaid after 20 payments.
  c. Determine the unpaid balance on the loan after 20 payments.

11.4 Binomial Expansions

OBJECTIVE **1** **Expand $(a + b)^n$**

By carefully observing the expansion of the binomial $(a + b)^n$ shown below, it is possible to identify some interesting patterns.

$$(a + b)^1 = a + b$$
$$(a + b)^2 = a^2 + 2ab + b^2$$
$$(a + b)^3 = a^3 + 3a^2b + 3ab^2 + b^3$$
$$(a + b)^4 = a^4 + 4a^3b + 6a^2b^2 + 4ab^3 + b^4$$
$$(a + b)^5 = a^5 + 5a^4b + 10a^3b^2 + 10a^2b^3 + 5ab^4 + b^5$$

PATTERNS FOR THE VARIABLE PART

1. The first term is a^n. The exponent on a decreases by 1 for each successive term.

2. The exponent on b increases by 1 for each successive term. The last term is b^n.

3. The degree of each term is n.

Point of Interest

Blaise Pascal (1623–1662) is given credit for this triangle, which he first published in 1654. In that publication, the triangle looked like

```
  1  2   3   4   5...
1 1  1   1   1   1...
2 1  2   3   4...
3 1  3   6...
4 1  4...
5 1
```

Thus the triangle was rotated 45° from the way it is shown today. The first European publication of the triangle is attributed to Peter Apianus in 1527. However, there are versions of it in a Chinese text by Yang Hui that dates from 1250. In that text, Hui demonstrated how to find the third, fourth, fifth, and sixth roots of a number by using the triangle.

Write the variable parts of the terms of the expansion of $(a + b)^6$.

The first term is a^6. For each successive term, the exponent on a decreases by 1, and the exponent on b increases by 1. The last term is b^6.

$a^6, a^5b, a^4b^2, a^3b^3, a^2b^4, ab^5, b^6$

The variable parts of the general expansion of $(a + b)^n$ are

$$a^n, a^{n-1}b, a^{n-2}b^2, \ldots, a^{n-r}b^r, \ldots, ab^{n-1}, b^n$$

A pattern for the coefficients of the terms of the expanded binomial can be found by writing the coefficients in a triangular array known as **Pascal's Triangle.**

Each row begins and ends with the number 1. Any other number in a row is the sum of the two closest numbers above it. For example, $4 + 6 = 10$.

For $(a + b)^1$:   1   1

For $(a + b)^2$:   1   2   1

For $(a + b)^3$:   1   3   3   1

For $(a + b)^4$:   1   4   6   4   1

For $(a + b)^5$: 1   5   10   10   5   1

Write the sixth row of Pascal's Triangle.

To write the sixth row, first write the numbers of the fifth row. The first and last numbers of the sixth row are 1. Each of the other numbers of the sixth row can be obtained by finding the sum of the two closest numbers above it in the fifth row.

1   5   10   10   5   1
1   6   15   20   15   6   1

The numbers in the sixth row of Pascal's Triangle will be the coefficients of the terms of the expansion of $(a + b)^6$.

Using these numbers for the coefficients, and using the pattern for the variable part of each term, we can write the expanded form of $(a + b)^6$ as follows:

$$(a + b)^6 = a^6 + 6a^5b + 15a^4b^2 + 20a^3b^3 + 15a^2b^4 + 6ab^5 + b^6$$

Although Pascal's Triangle can be used to find the coefficients for the expanded form of the power of any binomial, this method is inconvenient when the power of the binomial is large. An alternative method for determining these coefficients is based on the concept of **factorial.**

Point of Interest

The exclamation point was first used as a notation for factorial in 1808 in the book Eléments d'Arithmétique Universelle *for the convenience of the printer of the book. Some English textbooks suggested using the phrase "n-admiration" for* n!

n Factorial

$n!$ (which is read "*n* factorial") is the product of the first n consecutive natural numbers. $0!$ is defined to be 1.

$$n! = n(n - 1)(n - 2) \cdot \cdots \cdot 3 \cdot 2 \cdot 1$$

$1!, 5!,$ and $7!$ are shown at the right.

$$1! = 1$$
$$5! = 5 \cdot 4 \cdot 3 \cdot 2 \cdot 1 = 120$$
$$7! = 7 \cdot 6 \cdot 5 \cdot 4 \cdot 3 \cdot 2 \cdot 1 = 5040$$

EXAMPLE 1   Evaluate: $\dfrac{7!}{4!\,3!}$

Solution $\dfrac{7!}{4!\,3!} = \dfrac{7 \cdot 6 \cdot 5 \cdot 4 \cdot 3 \cdot 2 \cdot 1}{(4 \cdot 3 \cdot 2 \cdot 1)(3 \cdot 2 \cdot 1)}$ • **Write each factorial as a product.**

$= 35$ • **Simplify.**

PROBLEM 1   Evaluate: $\dfrac{12!}{7!\,5!}$

Solution   See page S33.

Point of Interest

Leonhard Euler (1707–1783) used the notation $\left(\dfrac{n}{r}\right)$ *and* $\left[\dfrac{n}{r}\right]$ *for binomial coefficients around 1784. The notation* $\dbinom{n}{r}$ *appeared in the late 1820s.*

The coefficients in a binomial expansion can be given in terms of factorials. Note that in the expansion of $(a + b)^5$ shown below, the coefficient of a^2b^3 can be given by $\dfrac{5!}{2!\,3!}$. The numerator is the factorial of the power of the binomial. The denominator is the product of the factorials of the exponents on a and b.

$$(a + b)^5 = a^5 + 5a^4b + 10a^3b^2 + 10a^2b^3 + 5ab^4 + b^5$$

$$\frac{5!}{2!\,3!} = \frac{5 \cdot 4 \cdot 3 \cdot 2 \cdot 1}{(2 \cdot 1)(3 \cdot 2 \cdot 1)} = 10$$

In general, the coefficients of $(a + b)^n$ are given as the quotients of factorials.

The coefficient of $a^{n-r}b^r$ is $\dfrac{n!}{(n - r)!\,r!}$. The symbol $\dbinom{n}{r}$ is used to express this quotient of factorials.

$$\binom{n}{r} = \frac{n!}{(n - r)!\,r!}$$

EXAMPLE 2   Evaluate: $\dbinom{8}{5}$

Solution $\dbinom{8}{5} = \dfrac{8!}{(8-5)!\,5!}$ • Write the quotient of the factorials.

$= \dfrac{8!}{3!5!} = \dfrac{8 \cdot 7 \cdot 6 \cdot 5 \cdot 4 \cdot 3 \cdot 2 \cdot 1}{(3 \cdot 2 \cdot 1)(5 \cdot 4 \cdot 3 \cdot 2 \cdot 1)} = 56$ • Simplify.

PROBLEM 2   Evaluate: $\dbinom{7}{0}$

Solution   See page S33.

Using factorials and the pattern for the variable part of each term, we can write a formula for any natural-number power of a binomial.

Binomial Expansion Formula

$$(a + b)^n = \binom{n}{0}a^n + \binom{n}{1}a^{n-1}b + \binom{n}{2}a^{n-2}b^2 + \cdots + \binom{n}{r}a^{n-r}b^r + \cdots + \binom{n}{n}b^n$$

The Binomial Expansion Formula is used below to expand $(a + b)^7$.

$$(a + b)^7 = \binom{7}{0}a^7 + \binom{7}{1}a^6b + \binom{7}{2}a^5b^2 + \binom{7}{3}a^4b^3 + \binom{7}{4}a^3b^4 + \binom{7}{5}a^2b^5 + \binom{7}{6}ab^6 + \binom{7}{7}b^7$$

$$= a^7 + 7a^6b + 21a^5b^2 + 35a^4b^3 + 35a^3b^4 + 21a^2b^5 + 7ab^6 + b^7$$

EXAMPLE 3   Write $(4x + 3y)^3$ in expanded form.

Solution $(4x + 3y)^3$

$$= \binom{3}{0}(4x)^3 + \binom{3}{1}(4x)^2(3y) + \binom{3}{2}(4x)(3y)^2 + \binom{3}{3}(3y)^3$$

$$= 1(64x^3) + 3(16x^2)(3y) + 3(4x)(9y^2) + 1(27y^3)$$

$$= 64x^3 + 144x^2y + 108xy^2 + 27y^3$$

PROBLEM 3   Write $(3m - n)^4$ in expanded form.

Solution   See page S33.

EXAMPLE 4   Find the first three terms in the expansion of $(x + 3)^{15}$.

Solution $(x + 3)^{15} = \binom{15}{0}x^{15} + \binom{15}{1}x^{14}(3) + \binom{15}{2}x^{13}(3)^2 + \cdots$

$$= 1x^{15} + 15x^{14}(3) + 105x^{13}(9) + \cdots$$

$$= x^{15} + 45x^{14} + 945x^{13} + \cdots$$

> **PROBLEM 4** Find the first three terms in the expansion of $(y - 2)^{10}$.
>
> ■ **Solution** See page S33.

The Binomial Theorem can also be used to write any term of a binomial expansion.

Note below that in the expansion of $(a + b)^5$, the exponent on b is 1 less than the term number.

$$(a + b)^5 = a^5 + 5a^4b + 10a^3b^2 + 10a^2b^3 + 5ab^4 + b^5$$

Formula for the rth Term in a Binomial Expansion

The rth term of $(a + b)^n$ is $\binom{n}{r - 1}a^{n-r+1}b^{r-1}$.

EXAMPLE 5 Find the fourth term in the expansion of $(x + 3)^7$.

Solution $\binom{n}{r - 1}a^{n-r+1}b^{r-1}$

$\binom{7}{4 - 1}x^{7-4+1}(3)^{4-1} = \binom{7}{3}x^4(3)^3$

• Use the Formula for the rth Term in a Binomial Expansion. $r = 4$, $n = 7$, $a = x$, $b = 3$

$= 35x^4(27)$

$= 945x^4$

PROBLEM 5 Find the third term in the expansion of $(t - 2s)^7$.

■ **Solution** See page S33.

11.4 Concept Review

Determine whether the following statements are always true, sometimes true, or never true.

1. $0! \cdot 4! = 0$

2. $\frac{4!}{0!}$ is undefined.

3. In the expansion $(a + b)^8$, the exponent on a for the fifth term is 5.

4. By definition, $n!$ is the sum of the first n positive numbers.

5. There are n terms in the expansion of $(a + b)^n$.

6. The sum of the exponents in each term of the expansion of $(a + b)^n$ is n.

11.4 Exercises

1 Expand $(a + b)^n$

1. ✎ What is the factorial of a number?

2. ✎ What is a purpose of the Binomial Expansion Formula?

3. The notation $n!$ is read "n __?__."

4. $6! = \underline{\quad ? \quad} \cdot \underline{\quad ? \quad} \cdot \underline{\quad ? \quad} \cdot \underline{\quad ? \quad} \cdot \underline{\quad ? \quad} \cdot \underline{\quad ? \quad}$
$= \underline{\quad ? \quad}$

5. The notation $\binom{n}{r}$ means $\dfrac{\underline{\quad ? \quad}}{\underline{\quad ? \quad} r!}$.

6. $\binom{5}{4} = \dfrac{\underline{\quad ? \quad}}{(\underline{\ ? \ })(\underline{\ ? \ })} = \dfrac{\underline{\ ? \ } \cdot \underline{\ ? \ } \cdot \underline{\ ? \ } \cdot \underline{\ ? \ } \cdot \underline{\ ? \ }}{(\underline{\ ? \ })(\underline{\ ? \ } \cdot \underline{\ ? \ } \cdot \underline{\ ? \ } \cdot \underline{\ ? \ })}$
$= \underline{\quad ? \quad}$

Evaluate.

7. $3!$ 8. $4!$ 9. $8!$ 10. $9!$ 11. $0!$ 12. $1!$

13. $\dfrac{5!}{2!\,3!}$ 14. $\dfrac{8!}{5!\,3!}$ 15. $\dfrac{6!}{6!\,0!}$ 16. $\dfrac{10!}{10!\,0!}$ 17. $\dfrac{9!}{6!\,3!}$ 18. $\dfrac{10!}{2!\,8!}$

Evaluate.

19. $\binom{7}{2}$ 20. $\binom{8}{6}$ 21. $\binom{10}{2}$ 22. $\binom{9}{6}$ 23. $\binom{9}{0}$ 24. $\binom{10}{10}$

25. $\binom{6}{3}$ 26. $\binom{7}{6}$ 27. $\binom{11}{1}$ 28. $\binom{13}{1}$ 29. $\binom{4}{2}$ 30. $\binom{8}{4}$

31. ✎ True or false? $\dfrac{(2n)!}{n!} = 2$

32. ✎ True or false? $\dfrac{n!}{n} = (n - 1)!$

33. The first term in the expanded form of $(x + 2)^5$ is __?__, and the last term is __?__.

34. The third term in the expanded form of $(x + 2)^5$ is
$\left(\dfrac{\underline{\ ? \ }}{\underline{\ ? \ }}\right)(x^{\underline{\ ? \ }})(2^{\underline{\ ? \ }}) = (\underline{\ ? \ })x^3(\underline{\ ? \ }) = \underline{\ ? \ }$.

Write in expanded form.

35. $(x + y)^4$

36. $(r - s)^3$

37. $(x - y)^5$

38. $(y - 3)^4$

39. $(2m + 1)^4$

40. $(2x + 3y)^3$

41. $(2r - 3)^5$

42. $(x + 3y)^4$

Find the first three terms in the expansion.

43. $(a + b)^{10}$

44. $(a + b)^9$

45. $(a - b)^{11}$

46. $(a - b)^{12}$

47. $(2x + y)^8$

48. $(x + 3y)^9$

49. $(4x - 3y)^8$

50. $(2x - 5)^7$

51. $\left(x + \dfrac{1}{x}\right)^7$

52. $\left(x - \dfrac{1}{x}\right)^8$

53. $(x^2 + 3)^5$

54. $(x^2 - 2)^6$

Find the indicated term in the expansion.

55. $(2x - 1)^7$; 4th term

56. $(x + 4)^5$; 3rd term

57. $(x^2 - y^2)^6$; 2nd term

58. $(x^2 + y^2)^7$; 6th term

59. $(y - 1)^9$; 5th term

60. $(x - 2)^8$; 8th term

61. $\left(n + \dfrac{1}{n}\right)^5$; 2nd term

62. $\left(x + \dfrac{1}{2}\right)^6$; 3rd term

63. $\left(\dfrac{x}{2} + 2\right)^5$; 1st term

64. $\left(y - \dfrac{2}{3}\right)^6$; 3rd term

65. Suppose n is odd, and a and b are constants such that $a > 0$ and $b < 0$. Is the constant term in the expanded form of $(ax + b)^n$ positive or negative?

66. Suppose $n > 7$, and a and b are constants such that $a > 0$ and $b < 0$. Is the coefficient of the seventh term of the expanded form of $(ax + b)^n$ positive or negative?

11.4 Applying Concepts

Solve.

67. Write the seventh row of Pascal's Triangle.

68. Evaluate $\dfrac{n!}{(n-2)!}$ for $n = 50$.

69. Simplify: $\dfrac{n!}{(n-1)!}$

70. Write the term that contains an x^3 in the expansion of $(x + a)^7$.

Expand the binomial.

71. $\left(x^{\frac{1}{2}} + 2\right)^4$

72. $(x^{-1} + y^{-1})^3$

73. $(1 + i)^6$

74. For $0 \le r \le n$, show that $\dbinom{n}{r} = \dbinom{n}{n-r}$.

75. For $n \ge 1$, evaluate $\dfrac{2 \cdot 4 \cdot 6 \cdot 8 \cdot \ldots \cdot (2n)}{2^n n!}$.

A mathematical theorem is used to expand $(a + b + c)^n$. According to this theorem, the coefficient of $a^r b^k c^{n-r-k}$ in the expansion of $(a + b + c)^n$ is $\dfrac{n!}{r!\,k!\,(n - r - k)!}$.

76. Use the mathematical theorem to find the coefficient of $a^2 b^3 c$ in the expansion of $(a + b + c)^6$.

77. Use the mathematical theorem to find the coefficient of $a^4 b^2 c^3$ in the expansion of $(a + b + c)^9$.

78. Write a summary of the history of the development of Pascal's Triangle. Include some of the properties of the triangle.

Focus on Problem Solving

Forming Negations   A **statement** is a declarative sentence that is either true or false but not both true and false. Here are a few examples of statements.

> Denver is the capital of Colorado.
> The word *dog* has four letters.
> Florida is a state in the United States.
> In the year 2020, the president of the United States will be a woman.

Problem solving sometimes requires that you be able to form the **negation** of a statement. If a statement is true, its negation must be false. If a statement is false, its negation must be true. For instance,

"Mark McGwire broke Babe Ruth's single-season home run record" is a true sentence. Accordingly, the sentence "Mark McGwire did not break Babe Ruth's home run record" is false.

"Dogs have twelve paws" is a false sentence, so the sentence "Dogs do not have twelve paws" is a true sentence.

To form the negation of a statement requires a precise understanding of the statement being negated. Here are some phrases that demand special attention.

Statement	Meaning
At least seven	Greater than or equal to seven
More than seven	More than seven (does not include 7)
At most seven	Less than or equal to seven
Less than (or *fewer than*) seven	Less than seven (does not include 7)

Consider the sentence "At least 3 people scored over 90 on the last test." The negation of that sentence is "Fewer than 3 people scored over 90 on the last test."

For each of the following, write the negation of the given sentence.

1. There was at least one error on the test.

2. The temperature was less than 30 degrees.

3. The mountain is more than 5000 feet tall.

4. There are at most 5 vacancies for a field trip to New York.

When the word *all*, *no* (or *none*), or *some* occurs in a sentence, forming the negation requires careful thought. Consider the sentence "All roads are paved with cement." This sentence is not true because there are some roads—dirt roads, for example—that are not paved with cement. Because the sentence is false, its negation must be true. You might be tempted to write "All roads are not paved with cement" as the negation, but that sentence is not true because some roads are paved with cement. The correct negation is "Some roads are *not* paved with cement."

Now consider the sentence "Some fish live in aquariums." Because this sentence is true, the negation must be false. Writing "Some fish do not live in aquariums" as the negation is not correct because that sentence is true. The correct negation is "*All* fish do *not* live in aquariums."

The sentence "No houses have basements" is false because there is at least one house with a basement. Because this sentence is false, its negation must be true. The negation is "Some houses do have basements."

Statement	Negation
All *A* are *B*.	Some *A* are not *B*.
No *A* are *B*.	Some *A* are *B*.
Some *A* are *B*.	All *A* are not *B*.
Some *A* are not *B*.	All *A* are *B*.

Write the negation of each sentence.

5. All trees are tall.

   6. All cats chase mice.

   7. Some flowers have red blooms.

   8. No golfers like tennis.

   9. Some students do not like math.

   10. No honest people are politicians.

   11. All cars have power steering.

   12. Some televisions are black and white.

Projects & Group Activities

ISBN and UPC Numbers

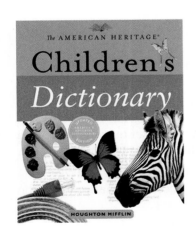

Every book that is cataloged for the Library of Congress must have an ISBN (International Standard Book Number). An ISBN is a 10-digit number of the form a_1-$a_2 a_3 a_4$-$a_5 a_6 a_7 a_8 a_9$-c. (In 2007, ISBN numbers will be 13 digits. We will discuss this modification later in this project.) For instance, the ISBN for the Windows version of the CD-ROM containing the *American Heritage Children's Dictionary* is 0-395-73580-7. The first number, 0, indicates that the book is written in English. The next three numbers, 395, indicate the publisher (Houghton Mifflin Company). The next five numbers, 73580, identify the book (*American Heritage Children's Dictionary*), and the last digit, c, is called a *check digit*. This digit is chosen such that the following sum is divisible by 11.

$$a_1(10) + a_2(9) + a_3(8) + a_4(7) + a_5(6) + a_6(5) + a_7(4) + a_8(3) + a_9(2) + c$$

For the *American Heritage Children's Dictionary*,

$$0(10) + 3(9) + 9(8) + 5(7) + 7(6) + 3(5) + 5(4) + 8(3) + 0(2) + c$$
$$= 235 + c$$

The last digit of the ISBN is chosen as 7 because $235 + 7 = 242$ and $242 \div 11 = 22$. The value of c could be any number from 0 to 10. The number 10 is coded as an X.

One purpose of the ISBN method of coding books is to ensure that orders placed for books are accurately filled. For instance, suppose a clerk sends an order for the *American Heritage Children's Dictionary* and inadvertently enters the number 0-395-75380-7 (the 3 and 5 have been transposed). Now

$$0(10) + 3(9) + 9(8) + 5(7) + 7(6) + 5(5) + 3(4) + 8(3) + 0(2) + 7 = 244$$

and 244 is not divisible by 11. Thus an error in the ISBN has been made.

1. Determine the check digit for the book *Reader's Digest Book of Facts*. The first nine digits of the ISBN are 0-895-77692-?

2. Is 0-395-12370-4 a possible ISBN?

3. Check the ISBN of this intermediate algebra textbook.

Another coding scheme that is closely related to ISBN is the UPC (universal product code). This number is particularly useful in grocery stores.

A checkout clerk passes the number by a scanner that reads the number and records the product and its price.

There are two major UPC codes: Type A consists of 12 digits and type E consists of 8 digits. For type A UPC symbols, the first 6 digits identify the manufacturer. The next 5 digits constitute a product identification number given by the manufacturer to identify the product. The final digit is a check digit. The check digit is chosen so that the following sum is divisible by 10.

$$a_1(13) + a_2 + a_3(13) + a_4 + a_5(13) + a_6 + a_7(13) + a_8 + a_9(13) + a_{10} + a_{11}(13) + c$$

The UPC for the TI-83 Plus is 0-33317-19865-8. Using the expression above,

$$0(13) + 3 + 3(13) + 3 + 1(13) + 7 + 1(13) + 9 + 8(13) + 6 + 5(13) + c$$
$$= 262 + c$$

ISBN 0-395-75524-7

0 46442 77018 7

/
7 is the
check digit

Because $262 + 8$ is a multiple of 10, the check digit is 8.

4. What numbers can the check digit of a type A UPC be?

5. Check the UPC shown at the left.

6. Check the UPC of a product in your home.

In 2007, all publishers must convert to a 13-digit ISBN number. This is accomplished by adding the digits 978 to the beginning of an existing ISBN and recalculating the check digit. For example, the first 12 digits of the new ISBN for the *American Heritage Children's Dictionary* will be 978-0-395-73580. The check digit is chosen so that the following sum is divisible by 10.

$$9(1) + 7(3) + 8(1) + 0(3) + 3(1) + 9(3) + 5(1) + 7(3) + 3(1) + 5(3) + 8(1) + 0(3) + c$$

7. Calculate the check digit for the new ISBN for the *American Heritage Children's Dictionary*.

Chapter 11 Summary

Key Words

A **sequence** is an ordered list of numbers. Each of the numbers of a sequence is called a **term** of the sequence. [11.1.1, p. 675]

A **finite sequence** contains a finite number of terms. [11.1.1, p. 676]

An **infinite sequence** contains an infinite number of terms. [11.1.1, p. 676]

The indicated sum of the terms of a sequence is a **series**. [11.1.2, p. 677]

Examples

$1, \frac{1}{3}, \frac{1}{9}, \frac{1}{27}$, is a sequence.
The terms are $1, \frac{1}{3}, \frac{1}{9}$, and $\frac{1}{27}$.

2, 4, 6, 8 is a finite sequence.

1, 3, 5, 7, ... is an infinite sequence.

1, 5, 9, 13 is a sequence.

The series is $1 + 5 + 9 + 13$.

Summation notation is used to represent a series in compact form. The Greek letter sigma, Σ, is used to indicate the sum. [11.1.2, p. 677]

$$\sum_{n=1}^{4} 2n = 2(1) + 2(2) + 2(3) + 2(4)$$
$$= 20$$

An **arithmetic sequence**, or **arithmetic progression**, is one in which the difference between any two consecutive terms is constant. The difference between consecutive terms is called the **common difference** of the sequence. [11.2.1, p. 683]

3, 9, 15, 21, ... is an arithmetic sequence.

$9 - 3 = 6$; 6 is the common difference.

A **geometric sequence**, or **geometric progression**, is one in which each successive term of the sequence is the same nonzero constant multiple of the preceding term. The common multiple is called the **common ratio** of the sequence. [11.3.1, p. 692]

$9, 3, 1, \frac{1}{3}, \ldots$ is a geometric sequence.

$\frac{3}{9} = \frac{1}{3}; \frac{1}{3}$ is the common ratio.

An **arithmetic series** is the indicated sum of the terms of an arithmetic sequence. [11.2.2, p. 684]

1, 2, 3, 4, 5 is an arithmetic sequence.

The indicated sum is
$1 + 2 + 3 + 4 + 5$.

A **geometric series** is the indicated sum of the terms of a geometric sequence. [11.3.2, p. 693]

5, 10, 20, 40 is a geometric sequence.

The indicated sum is
$5 + 10 + 20 + 40$.

n factorial, written $n!$, is the product of the first n natural numbers. $0!$ is defined to be 1. [11.4.1, p. 705]

$5! = 5 \cdot 4 \cdot 3 \cdot 2 \cdot 1 = 120$

Essential Rules and Procedures

Formula for the nth Term of an Arithmetic Sequence
The nth term of an arithmetic sequence with a common difference of d is given by $a_n = a_1 + (n - 1)d$. [11.2.1, p. 683]

4, 7, 10, 13, ... $d = 7 - 4 = 3, a_1 = 4$

$a_{10} = 4 + (10 - 1)3 = 4 + 27 = 31$

Formula for the Sum of n Terms of an Arithmetic Series
Let a_1 be the first term of a finite arithmetic sequence, let n be the number of terms, and let a_n be the last term of the sequence. Then the sum of the series is given by
$S_n = \frac{n}{2}(a_1 + a_n)$. [11.2.2, p. 684]

5, 8, 11, 14, ... $d = 3, a_{12} = 38$

$S_{12} = \frac{12}{2}(5 + 38) = 258$

Formula for the nth Term of a Geometric Sequence
The nth term of a geometric sequence with first term a_1 and common ratio r is given by $a_n = a_1 r^{n-1}$. [11.3.1, p. 692]

2, 6, 18, 54, ... $a_1 = 2, r = 3$

$a_{10} = 2(3)^{10-1} = 2(3)^9 = 39{,}366$

Formula for the Sum of n Terms of a Finite Geometric Series
Let a_1 be the first term of a finite geometric sequence, let n be the number of terms, and let r be the common ratio. Then the sum of the series S_n is given by $S_n = \frac{a_1(1 - r^n)}{1 - r}$. [11.3.2, p. 693]

1, 4, 16, 64, ... $a_1 = 1, r = 4$

$S_8 = \frac{1(1 - 4^8)}{1 - 4} = \frac{1 - 65{,}536}{-3}$
$= 21{,}845$

Formula for the Sum of an Infinite Geometric Series
The sum of an infinite geometric series in which $|r| < 1$ and a_1
is the first term is given by $S = \dfrac{a_1}{1 - r}$. [11.3.3, p. 695]

$$2, 1, \frac{1}{2}, \frac{1}{4}, \ldots \qquad a_1 = 2, r = \frac{1}{2}$$

$$S = \frac{2}{1 - \dfrac{1}{2}} = \frac{2}{\dfrac{1}{2}} = 4$$

Binomial Coefficients
The coefficients of $a^{n-r}b^r$ in the expansion of $(a + b)^n$ are given
by $\binom{n}{r}$, where $\binom{n}{r} = \dfrac{n!}{(n - r)!r!}$. [11.4.1, p. 705]

$$\binom{6}{2} = \frac{6!}{(6-2)!\,2!} = \frac{6!}{4!\,2!} = 15$$

Binomial Expansion Formula
$(a + b)^n =$
$$\binom{n}{0}a^n + \binom{n}{1}a^{n-1}b + \binom{n}{2}a^{n-2}b^2 + \cdots + \binom{n}{r}a^{n-r}b^r + \cdots + \binom{n}{n}b^n$$
[11.4.1, p. 706]

$$(x + y)^4$$
$$= \binom{4}{0}x^4 + \binom{4}{1}x^3y + \binom{4}{2}x^2y^2 +$$
$$\binom{4}{3}xy^3 + \binom{4}{4}y^4$$
$$= x^4 + 4x^3y + 6x^2y^2 + 4xy^3 + y^4$$

Formula for the rth Term in a Binomial Expansion
The rth term of $(a + b)^n$ is $\binom{n}{r-1}a^{n-r+1}b^{r-1}$. [11.4.1, p. 707]

The sixth term of $(2x - y)^9$ is
$$\binom{9}{5}(2x)^{9-6+1}(-y)^{6-1} = -2016x^4y^5$$

Chapter 11 Review Exercises

1. Write $\displaystyle\sum_{i=1}^{4} 3x^i$ in expanded form.

2. Find the number of terms in the finite arithmetic sequence $-5, -8, -11, \ldots, -50$.

3. Find the 7th term of the geometric sequence $4, 4\sqrt{2}, 8, \ldots$.

4. Find the sum of the terms of the infinite geometric sequence $4, 3, \dfrac{9}{4}, \ldots$.

5. Evaluate: $\binom{9}{3}$

6. Write the 14th term of the sequence whose nth term is given by the formula $a_n = \dfrac{8}{n + 2}$.

7. Find the 10th term of the arithmetic sequence $-10, -4, 2, \ldots$.

8. Find the sum of the first 18 terms of the arithmetic sequence $-25, -19, -13, \ldots$.

9. Find the sum of the first five terms of the geometric sequence $-6, 12, -24, \ldots$.

10. Evaluate: $\dfrac{8!}{4!\,4!}$

11. Find the 7th term in the expansion of $(3x + y)^9$.

12. Find the sum of the series $\displaystyle\sum_{n=1}^{4}(3n + 1)$.

13. Write the 6th term of the sequence whose nth term is given by the formula $a_n = \dfrac{n+1}{n}$.

14. Find the formula for the nth term of the arithmetic sequence 12, 9, 6, ...

15. Find the 5th term of the geometric sequence $6, 2, \dfrac{2}{3}, \ldots$.

16. Find an equivalent fraction for $0.2\overline{3}$.

17. Find the 35th term of the arithmetic sequence $-13, -16, -19, \ldots$.

18. Find the sum of the first six terms of the geometric sequence $1, \dfrac{3}{2}, \dfrac{9}{4}, \ldots$.

19. Find the sum of the first 21 terms of the arithmetic sequence 5, 12, 19, ...

20. Find the 4th term in the expansion of $(x - 2y)^7$.

21. Find the number of terms in the finite arithmetic sequence $1, 7, 13, \ldots, 121$.

22. Find the 8th term of the geometric sequence $\dfrac{3}{8}, \dfrac{3}{4}, \dfrac{3}{2}, \ldots$.

23. Evaluate the series $\displaystyle\sum_{i=1}^{5} 2i$.

24. Find the sum of the first five terms of the geometric sequence 1, 4, 16, ...

25. Evaluate: 5!

26. Find the 3rd term in the expansion of $(x - 4)^6$.

27. Find the 30th term of the arithmetic sequence $-2, 3, 8, \ldots$.

28. Find the sum of the first 25 terms of the arithmetic sequence 25, 21, 17, ...

29. Write the 5th term of the sequence whose nth term is given by the formula $a_n = \dfrac{(-1)^{2n-1}n}{n^2 + 2}$.

30. Write $\displaystyle\sum_{i=1}^{4} 2x^{i-1}$ in expanded form.

31. Find an equivalent fraction for $0.\overline{23}$.

32. Find the sum of the infinite geometric series $4 - 1 + \dfrac{1}{4} - \cdots$.

33. Evaluate the geometric series $\displaystyle\sum_{n=1}^{5} 2(3)^n$.

34. Find the 8th term in the expansion of $(x - 2y)^{11}$.

35. Evaluate the geometric series $\displaystyle\sum_{n=1}^{8} \left(\dfrac{1}{2}\right)^n$. Round to the nearest thousandth.

36. Find the sum of the infinite geometric series $2 + \dfrac{4}{3} + \dfrac{8}{9} + \cdots$.

37. Find an equivalent fraction for $0.6\overline{3}$.

38. Write $(x - 3y^2)^5$ in expanded form.

39. Find the number of terms in the finite arithmetic sequence $8, 2, -4, \ldots, -118$.

40. Evaluate: $\dfrac{12!}{5!\,8!}$

41. Write $\displaystyle\sum_{i=1}^{5} \frac{(2x)^i}{i}$ in expanded form.

42. Evaluate the series $\displaystyle\sum_{n=1}^{4} \frac{(-1)^{n-1}n}{n+1}$.

43. **Compensation** The salary schedule for an apprentice electrician is \$2400 for the first month and an \$80-per-month salary increase for the next 9 months. Find the total salary for the first 9 months.

44. **Temperature** The temperature of a hot-water spa is 102°F. Each hour, the temperature is 5% lower than during the previous hour. Find the temperature of the spa after 8 h. Round to the nearest tenth.

Chapter 11 Test

1. Write the 14th term of the sequence whose nth term is given by the formula $a_n = \dfrac{6}{n+4}$.

2. Write the 9th and 10th terms of the sequence whose nth term is given by the formula $a_n = \dfrac{n-1}{n}$.

3. Evaluate the series $\displaystyle\sum_{n=1}^{4} (2n+3)$.

4. Write $\displaystyle\sum_{i=1}^{4} 2x^{2i}$ in expanded form.

5. Find the 28th term of the arithmetic sequence $-12, -16, -20, \ldots$.

6. Find the formula for the nth term of the arithmetic sequence $-3, -1, 1, \ldots$.

7. Find the number of terms in the finite arithmetic sequence $7, 3, -1, \ldots, -77$.

8. Find the sum of the first 15 terms of the arithmetic sequence $-42, -33, -24, \ldots$.

9. Find the sum of the first 24 terms of the arithmetic sequence $-4, 2, 8, \ldots$.

10. Evaluate: $\dfrac{10!}{5!\,5!}$

11. Find the 10th term of the geometric sequence $4, -4\sqrt{2}, 8, \ldots$.

12. Find the 5th term of the geometric sequence $5, 3, \dfrac{9}{5}, \ldots$.

13. Find the sum of the first five terms of the geometric sequence $1, \dfrac{3}{4}, \dfrac{9}{16}, \ldots$.

14. Find the sum of the first five terms of the geometric sequence $-5, 10, -20, \ldots$.

15. Find the sum of the terms of the infinite geometric sequence $2, 1, \dfrac{1}{2}, \ldots$.

16. Find an equivalent fraction for $0.2\overline{3}$.

17. Evaluate: $\dbinom{11}{4}$

18. Find the 5th term in the expansion of $(3x - y)^8$.

19. **Inventory** An inventory of supplies for a fabric manufacturer indicated that 7500 yd of material were in stock on January 1. On February 1, and on the first of the month for each successive month, the manufacturer sent 550 yd of material to retail outlets. How much material was in stock after the shipment on October 1?

20. **Radioactivity** An ore sample contains 320 mg of a radioactive substance with a half-life of 1 day. Find the amount of radioactive material in the sample at the beginning of the fifth day.

Cumulative Review Exercises

1. Subtract: $\dfrac{4x^2}{x^2 + x - 2} - \dfrac{3x - 2}{x + 2}$

2. Factor: $2x^6 + 16$

3. Multiply: $\sqrt{2y}\left(\sqrt{8xy} - \sqrt{y}\right)$

4. Simplify: $\left(\dfrac{x^{-\frac{3}{4}} \cdot x^{\frac{3}{2}}}{x^{-\frac{5}{2}}}\right)^{-8}$

5. Solve: $5 - \sqrt{x} = \sqrt{x + 5}$

6. Solve: $2x^2 - x + 7 = 0$

7. Solve by the addition method: $3x - 3y = 2$
   $\qquad\qquad\qquad\qquad\quad 6x - 4y = 5$

8. Solve: $2x - 1 > 3$ or $1 - 3x > 7$

9. Evaluate the determinant: $\begin{vmatrix} -3 & 1 \\ 4 & 2 \end{vmatrix}$

10. Write $\log_5 \sqrt{\dfrac{x}{y}}$ in expanded form.

11. Solve for x: $4^x = 8^{x-1}$

12. Write the 5th and 6th terms of the sequence whose nth term is given by the formula $a_n = n(n - 1)$.

13. Evaluate the series $\displaystyle\sum_{n=1}^{7}(-1)^{n-1}(n + 2)$.

14. Solve by the addition method:
    $x + 2y + z = 3$
    $2x - y + 2z = 6$
    $3x + y - z = 5$

15. Solve for x: $\log_6 x = 3$

16. Divide: $(4x^3 - 3x + 5) \div (2x + 1)$

17. For $g(x) = -3x + 4$, find $g(1 + h)$.

18. Find the range of $f(a) = \dfrac{a^3 - 1}{2a + 1}$ if the domain is $\{0, 1, 2\}$.

19. Graph: $3x - 2y = -4$

20. Graph the solution set of $2x - 3y < 9$.

21. Work Problem A new computer can complete a payroll in 16 min less time than it takes an older computer to complete the same payroll. Working together, both computers can complete the payroll in 15 min. How long would it take each computer, working alone, to complete the payroll?

22. Uniform Motion A boat traveling with the current went 15 mi in 2 h. Against the current, it took 3 h to travel the same distance. Find the rate of the boat in calm water and the rate of the current.

23. Radioactivity An 80-milligram sample of a radioactive material decays to 55 mg in 30 days. Use the exponential decay equation $A = A_0\left(\frac{1}{2}\right)^{\frac{t}{k}}$, where A is the amount of radioactive material present after time t, k is the half-life, and A_0 is the original amount of radioactive material, to find the half-life of the 80-milligram sample. Round to the nearest whole number.

24. Theaters A "theater in the round" has 62 seats in the first row, 74 seats in the second row, 86 seats in the third row, and so on in an arithmetic sequence. Find the total number of seats in the theater if there are 12 rows of seats.

25. Sports To test the "bounce" of a ball, the ball is dropped from a height of 10 ft. The ball bounces to 80% of its previous height with each bounce. How high does the ball bounce on the fifth bounce? Round to the nearest tenth.

12 Conic Sections

OBJECTIVES

12.1 1 Graph parabolas

12.2 1 Find the equation of a circle and then graph the circle
 2 Write the equation of a circle in standard form and then graph the circle

12.3 1 Graph an ellipse with center at the origin
 2 Graph a hyperbola with center at the origin

12.4 1 Solve nonlinear systems of equations

12.5 1 Graph the solution set of a quadratic inequality in two variables
 2 Graph the solution set of a nonlinear system of inequalities

You would be amazed at the precision necessary to create a parabolic-shaped mirror for use in high-tech spacecraft. The multimillion dollar Hubble Telescope, pictured above, made international headlines when it was discovered that the outer edge of its primary mirror was ground too flat by one-fiftieth the thickness of a human hair! This mistake (which was later corrected) caused the Hubble to transmit fuzzy images because the light from viewed objects was scattering instead of reflecting to a single focus. You are asked to demonstrate how to calculate the placement of this focus in **Exercises 37 and 38 on page 727.**

 Online Study Center DVD SSM

Need help? For online student resources, such as section quizzes, visit the Online Study Center at college.hmco.com/info/aufmanndevmathhb.

Prep Test

1. Find the distance between the points whose coordinates are $(-2, 3)$ and $(4, -1)$. Round to the nearest hundredth.

2. Complete the square on $x^2 - 8x$. Write the resulting perfect-square trinomial as the square of a binomial.

3. Solve $\dfrac{x^2}{16} + \dfrac{y^2}{9} = 1$ for x when $y = 3$ and when $y = 0$.

4. Solve by the substitution method: $7x + 4y = 3$
$$y = x - 2$$

5. Solve by the addition method: $4x - y = 9$
$$2x + 3y = -13$$

6. Find the axis of symmetry and the vertex of the graph of $y = x^2 - 4x + 2$.

7. Graph: $f(x) = -2x^2 + 4x$ 8. Graph the solution set of $5x - 2y > 10$.

9. Graph the solution set: $x + 2y \le 4$
$$x - y \le 2$$

12.1 The Parabola

OBJECTIVE 1   Graph parabolas

The **conic sections** are curves that can be constructed from the intersection of a plane and a right circular cone. The four conic sections are the parabola, circle, ellipse, and hyperbola. The **parabola** was introduced earlier. Here we will review some of that previous discussion and look at equations of parabolas that were not discussed before.

A parabola is a conic section formed by the intersection of a right circular cone and a plane parallel to the side of the cone. Every parabola has an **axis of symmetry** and a **vertex** that is on the axis of symmetry. To understand the axis of symmetry, think of folding the paper along that axis. The two halves of the curve will match up.

The graph of the equation $y = ax^2 + bx + c$, $a \neq 0$, is a parabola with the axis of symmetry parallel to the y-axis. The parabola opens up when $a > 0$ and opens down when $a < 0$. When the parabola opens up, the vertex is the lowest point on the parabola. When the parabola opens down, the vertex is the highest point on the parabola.

The coordinates of the vertex can be found by completing the square.

Find the vertex of the parabola whose equation is $y = x^2 - 4x + 5$.

$$y = x^2 - 4x + 5$$

Group the terms involving x.
$$y = (x^2 - 4x) + 5$$

Complete the square on $x^2 - 4x$. Note that 4 is added and subtracted. Because $4 - 4 = 0$, the equation is not changed.
$$y = (x^2 - 4x + 4) - 4 + 5$$

Factor the trinomial and combine like terms.
$$y = (x - 2)^2 + 1$$

The coefficient of x^2 is positive, so the parabola opens up. The vertex is the lowest point on the parabola, or the point that has the least y-coordinate.

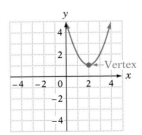

Because $(x - 2)^2 \geq 0$ for all x, the least y-coordinate occurs when $(x - 2)^2 = 0$, which occurs when $x = 2$. This means the x-coordinate of the vertex is 2.

To find the y-coordinate of the vertex, replace x in $y = (x - 2)^2 + 1$ by 2 and solve for y.
$$y = (x - 2)^2 + 1$$
$$= (2 - 2)^2 + 1 = 1$$

The vertex is $(2, 1)$.

By following the procedure of the last example and completing the square on the equation $y = ax^2 + bx + c$, we find that the **x-coordinate of the vertex** is

Golden Gate Bridge

The suspension cables for some bridges, such as the Golden Gate bridge, hang in the shape of a parabola. Parabolic shapes are also used for mirrors in telescopes and in certain antenna designs.

$-\dfrac{b}{2a}$. The y-coordinate of the vertex can then be determined by substituting this value of x into $y = ax^2 + bx + c$ and solving for y.

Because the axis of symmetry is parallel to the y-axis and passes through the vertex, the equation of the **axis of symmetry** is $x = -\dfrac{b}{2a}$.

EXAMPLE 1   Find the vertex and the axis of symmetry of the parabola given by the equation $y = x^2 + 2x - 3$. Then sketch the graph of the parabola.

Solution $-\dfrac{b}{2a} = -\dfrac{2}{2(1)} = -1$ • The x-coordinate of the vertex is $-\dfrac{b}{2a}$.

$y = x^2 + 2x - 3$
$y = (-1)^2 + 2(-1) - 3$ • Find the y-coordinate of the vertex by replacing x by -1 and solving for y.
$y = -4$

The vertex is $(-1, -4)$.

The axis of symmetry is the line $x = -1$.   • The axis of symmetry is the line $x = -\dfrac{b}{2a}$.

• Because a is positive, the parabola opens up. Use the vertex and axis of symmetry to sketch the graph.

PROBLEM 1   Find the vertex and the axis of symmetry of the parabola given by the equation $y = -x^2 + x + 3$. Then sketch the graph of the parabola.

Solution   See page S34.

The graph of an equation of the form $x = ay^2 + by + c$, $a \neq 0$, is also a parabola. In this case, the parabola opens to the right when a is positive and opens to the left when a is negative.

For a parabola of this form, the **y-coordinate of the vertex is** $-\dfrac{b}{2a}$. The **axis of symmetry** is the line $y = -\dfrac{b}{2a}$.

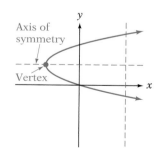

Using the vertical line test reveals that the graph of a parabola of this form is not the graph of a function. The graph of $x = ay^2 + by + c$ is the graph of a relation.

EXAMPLE 2 Find the vertex and the axis of symmetry of the parabola whose equation is $x = 2y^2 - 8y + 5$. Then sketch its graph.

Solution

$-\dfrac{b}{2a} = -\dfrac{-8}{2(2)} = 2$

• Find the *y*-coordinate of the vertex.
  $a = 2, b = -8$

$x = 2y^2 - 8y + 5$
$x = 2(2)^2 - 8(2) + 5$
$x = -3$

• Find the *x*-coordinate of the vertex by replacing *y* by 2 and solving for *x*.

The vertex is $(-3, 2)$.

The axis of symmetry is the line $y = 2$.

• The axis of symmetry is the line $y = -\dfrac{b}{2a}$.

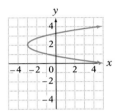

• Because *a* is positive, the parabola opens to the right. Use the vertex and axis of symmetry to sketch the graph.

PROBLEM 2 Find the vertex and the axis of symmetry of the parabola whose equation is $x = -2y^2 - 4y - 3$. Then sketch its graph.

Solution See page S34.

12.1 Concept Review

Determine whether the following statements are always true, sometimes true, or never true.

1. The graph of a parabola is the graph of a function.

2. The axis of symmetry of a parabola passes through the vertex.

3. The graph of a parabola has two *x*-intercepts.

4. The graph of a parabola has a minimum value.

5. The axis of symmetry of a parabola is the *x*-axis or the *y*-axis.

6. The equation of the axis of symmetry of a parabola is $x = -\dfrac{b}{2a}$.

12.1   Exercises

1   Graph parabolas

State **a** whether the axis of symmetry is a vertical or a horizontal line and **b** the direction in which the parabola opens.

1. $y = 3x^2 - 4x + 7$

2. $y = -x^2 + 5x - 2$

3. $x = y^2 + 2y - 8$

4. $x = -3y^2 - y + 9$

5. $x = -\dfrac{1}{2}y^2 - 4y - 7$

6. $y = \dfrac{1}{4}x^2 + 6x - 1$

7. For a parabola with an equation in the form $x = ay^2 + by + c$, $-\dfrac{b}{2a}$ is the _____?_____-coordinate of the vertex. The parabola opens to the right when a is _____?_____. The parabola opens to the left when a is _____?_____.

8. a. For the equation $y = 3x^2 - 4y + 6$, the value of $-\dfrac{b}{2a}$ is $-\dfrac{\stackrel{?}{}}{2(\underline{?})} = \underline{?}$.

   b. The axis of symmetry of the parabola with equation $y = 3x^2 - 4y + 6$ is _____?_____ $= \dfrac{2}{3}$.

Find the vertex and the axis of symmetry of the parabola given by the equation. Then sketch its graph.

9. $y = x^2 - 2x - 4$

10. $y = x^2 + 4x - 4$

11. $y = -x^2 + 2x - 3$

12. $y = -x^2 + 4x - 5$

13. $x = y^2 + 6y + 5$

14. $x = y^2 - y - 6$

15. $y = 2x^2 - 4x + 1$

16. $y = 2x^2 + 4x - 5$

17. $y = x^2 - 5x + 4$

18. $y = x^2 + 5x + 6$

19. $x = y^2 - 2y - 5$

20. $x = y^2 - 3y - 4$

21. $y = -3x^2 - 9x$

22. $y = -2x^2 + 6x$

23. $x = -\dfrac{1}{2}y^2 + 4$

24. $x = -\dfrac{1}{4}y^2 - 1$

25. $x = \dfrac{1}{2}y^2 - y + 1$

26. $x = -\dfrac{1}{2}y^2 + 2y - 3$

27. $y = \dfrac{1}{2}x^2 + 2x - 6$

28. $y = -\dfrac{1}{2}x^2 + x - 3$

For Exercises 29 to 32, state whether the equation of the parabola shown in the graph is in the form $y = ax^2 + bx + c$ or in the form $x = ay^2 + by + c$. Then state whether a is positive or negative and whether c is positive, zero, or negative.

29.

30.

31.

32.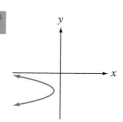

12.1 Applying Concepts

Use the vertex and the direction in which the parabola opens to determine the domain and range of the relation.

33. $y = x^2 - 4x - 2$

34. $y = -x^2 + 2x - 3$

35. $x = y^2 + 6y - 5$

36. $x = -y^2 - 2y + 6$

Parabolas have a unique property that is important in the design of telescopes and antennas. If a parabola has a mirrored surface, then all light rays parallel to the axis of symmetry of the parabola are reflected to a single point called the **focus** of the parabola. The location of this point is p units from the vertex on the axis of symmetry. The value of p is given by $p = \frac{1}{4a}$, where $y = ax^2$ is the equation of a parabola with vertex at the origin. For the graph of $y = \frac{1}{4}x^2$ shown at the right, the coordinates of the focus are $(0, 1)$. For Exercises 37 and 38, find the coordinates of the focus of the parabola given by the equation.

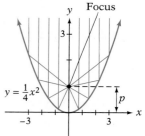

Parallel rays of light are reflected to the focus

$a = \frac{1}{4}$

$p = \frac{1}{4a} = \frac{1}{4(1/4)} = 1$

37. $y = 2x^2$

38. $y = \frac{1}{10}x^2$

39. **Astronomy**   Mirrors used in reflecting telescopes have a cross section that is a parabola. The 200-inch mirror at the Palomar Observatory in California is made from Pyrex, is 2 ft thick at the ends, and weighs 14.75 tons. The cross section of the mirror has been ground to a true parabola within 0.0000015 in. No matter where light strikes the parabolic surface, the light is reflected to a point called the focus of the parabola, as shown in the figure at the right.

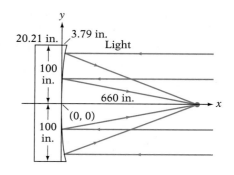

a. Determine an equation of the mirror. Round to the nearest whole number.

b. Over what interval for x is the equation valid?

40. 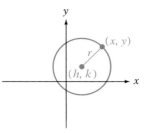 **Meteorology**   A radar dish used in the Cassegrain radar system has a cross section that is a parabola. The radar dish, used in weather forecasting, has a diameter of 84 ft. It is made of structural steel and has a depth of 17.7 ft. Signals from the radar system are reflected off clouds, collected by the radar system, and then analyzed.

  a. Determine an equation of the radar dish. Round the value of a to the nearest hundredth.

  b. Over what interval for x is the equation valid?

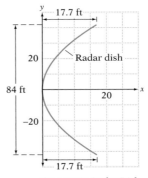

Cassegrain Radar Dish

41. Explain how the graph of $f(x) = ax^2$ changes, depending on the value of a.

42. Explain why $x = y^2 + 4$ isn't an equation that defines y as a function of x.

43. When $y = 0$, the x values of the equation $y = x^2 + 2x + 3$ are imaginary numbers. What does this mean for the graph of the equation?

12.2   The Circle

OBJECTIVE 1   Find the equation of a circle and then graph the circle

A **circle** is a conic section formed by the intersection of a cone and a plane that is parallel to the base of the cone.

Take Note

As the angle of the plane that intersects the cone changes, different conic sections are formed. For a parabola, the plane is *parallel to the side* of the cone. For a circle, the plane is *parallel to the base* of the cone.

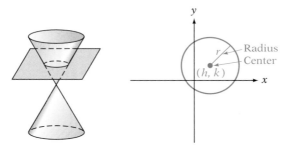

A **circle** can be defined as all the points (x, y) in the plane that are a fixed distance from a given point (h, k) called the **center.** The fixed distance is the **radius** of the circle.

The equation of a circle can be determined by using the distance formula.

Let (h, k) be the coordinates of the center of the circle, let r be the radius, and let (x, y) be any point on the circle. Then, by the distance formula,

$$r = \sqrt{(x - h)^2 + (y - k)^2}$$

Squaring each side of the equation gives the equation of a circle.

$$r^2 = \left[\sqrt{(x - h)^2 + (y - k)^2}\right]^2$$
$$r^2 = (x - h)^2 + (y - k)^2$$

Standard Form of the Equation of a Circle

Let r be the radius of a circle and let (h, k) be the coordinates of the center of the circle. Then the equation of the circle is given by

$$(x - h)^2 + (y - k)^2 = r^2$$

Find the equation of the circle with radius 4 and center $C(-1, 2)$.

Use the standard form of the equation of a circle.

$$(x - h)^2 + (y - k)^2 = r^2$$

Replace r by **4**, h by -1, and k by 2.

$$[x - (-1)]^2 + (y - 2)^2 = \mathbf{4}^2$$
$$(x + 1)^2 + (y - 2)^2 = 16$$

To sketch the graph of this circle, draw a circle with center $C(-1, 2)$ and radius 4.

> **Take Note**
>
> Applying the vertical line test reveals that the graph of a circle is not the graph of a function. The graph of a circle is the graph of a relation.

Find the coordinates of the center and the radius of a circle whose equation is $(x + 3)^2 + (y - 5)^2 = 16$.

Note that in the standard form of the equation of a circle, $(x - h)^2$ and $(y - k)^2$ are written using subtraction. Because $(x + 3)^2$ in the given equation is written as addition, we must rewrite this term using subtraction. $(x + 3)^2 = [x - (-3)]^2$.

$$(x + 3)^2 + (y - 5)^2 = 16$$
$$[x - (-3)]^2 + (y - 5)^2 = (4)^2$$
$$(x - h)^2 + (y - k)^2 = r^2$$

The coordinates of the center are $(-3, 5)$. The radius is 4.

Also, $r^2 = 16$, so $r = \sqrt{16} = 4$.

> **Take Note**
>
> For the equation at the right, because $(y - 5)^2$ is already written as subtraction, we do not rewrite this expression.

EXAMPLE 1   Find the equation of the circle with radius 5 and center $C(-1, 3)$. Then sketch its graph.

Solution
$$(x - h)^2 + (y - k)^2 = r^2$$
$$[x - (-1)]^2 + (y - 3)^2 = 5^2$$
$$(x + 1)^2 + (y - 3)^2 = 25$$

Center: $(-1, 3)$

Radius: $\sqrt{25} = 5$

PROBLEM 1   Find the equation of the circle with radius 4 and center $C(2, -3)$. Then sketch its graph.

Solution   See page S34.

Find the radius of a circle that passes through the point $P(2, 1)$ and has as its center the point $C(3, -4)$.

Because the center of the circle and a point on the circle are known, use the distance formula to find the radius of the circle.

$$\sqrt{(x_2 - x_1)^2 + (y_2 - y_1)^2} = r$$
$$\sqrt{(3 - 2)^2 + (-4 - 1)^2} = r$$
$$\sqrt{1^2 + (-5)^2} = r$$
$$\sqrt{1 + 25} = r$$
$$\sqrt{26} = r$$

The equation of the circle is $(x - 3)^2 + (y + 4)^2 = 26$.
The radius is $\sqrt{26}$.

EXAMPLE 2   Find the equation of the circle for which a diameter has endpoints $P_1(-4, -1)$ and $P_2(2, 3)$.

Solution

$$x_m = \frac{x_1 + x_2}{2} \qquad y_m = \frac{y_1 + y_2}{2}$$

$$x_m = \frac{-4 + 2}{2} \qquad y_m = \frac{-1 + 3}{2}$$

$$x_m = -1 \qquad y_m = 1$$

Center: $(x_m, y_m) = (-1, 1)$

- **Let $(x_1, y_1) = (-4, -1)$ and $(x_2, y_2) = (2, 3)$. Find the center of the circle by finding the midpoint of the diameter.**

$$r = \sqrt{(x_1 - x_m)^2 + (y_1 - y_m)^2}$$
$$r = \sqrt{[-4 - (-1)]^2 + (-1 - 1)^2}$$
$$r = \sqrt{9 + 4}$$
$$r = \sqrt{13}$$

- **Find the radius of the circle. Use either point on the circle and the coordinates of the center of the circle. P_1 is used here.**

$$(x + 1)^2 + (y - 1)^2 = 13$$

- **Write the equation of the circle with center $C(-1, 1)$ and radius $\sqrt{13}$.**

PROBLEM 2   Find the equation of the circle for which a diameter has endpoints $P_1(-2, 1)$ and $P_2(4, -1)$.

Solution   See page S34.

OBJECTIVE **2**   **Write the equation of a circle in standard form and then graph the circle**

The equation of a circle can also be expressed in **general form** as

$$x^2 + y^2 + ax + by + c = 0$$

To rewrite this equation in standard form, it is necessary to complete the square on the x and y terms.

Write the equation of the circle $x^2 + y^2 + 4x + 2y + 1 = 0$ in standard form.

Subtract the constant term from each side of the equation.

$$x^2 + y^2 + 4x + 2y + 1 = 0$$
$$x^2 + y^2 + 4x + 2y = -1$$

Rewrite the equation by grouping terms involving x and terms involving y.

$$(x^2 + 4x) + (y^2 + 2y) = -1$$

Complete the square on $x^2 + 4x$ and $y^2 + 2y$.

$$(x^2 + 4x + 4) + (y^2 + 2y + 1) = -1 + 4 + 1$$
$$(x^2 + 4x + 4) + (y^2 + 2y + 1) = 4$$

Factor each trinomial.

$$(x + 2)^2 + (y + 1)^2 = 4$$

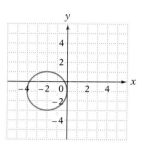

The graph of the equation $(x + 2)^2 + (y + 1)^2 = 4$ is shown at the left.

EXAMPLE 3   Write the equation of the circle $x^2 + y^2 + 3x - 2y = 1$ in standard form. Then sketch its graph.

Solution

$$x^2 + y^2 + 3x - 2y = 1$$
$$(x^2 + 3x) + (y^2 - 2y) = 1$$

- Group terms involving x and terms involving y.

$$\left(x^2 + 3x + \frac{9}{4}\right) + (y^2 - 2y + 1) = 1 + \frac{9}{4} + 1$$

- Complete the square on $x^2 + 3x$ and $y^2 - 2y$.

$$\left(x + \frac{3}{2}\right)^2 + (y - 1)^2 = \frac{17}{4}$$

- Factor each trinomial.

- Draw a circle with center $\left(-\dfrac{3}{2}, 1\right)$ and radius $\sqrt{\dfrac{17}{4}} = \dfrac{\sqrt{17}}{2}$.
$\left(\dfrac{\sqrt{17}}{2} \approx 2.1\right)$

PROBLEM 3   Write the equation of the circle $x^2 + y^2 - 4x + 8y + 15 = 0$ in standard form. Then sketch its graph.

Solution   See page S34.

12.2   Concept Review

Determine whether the following statements are always true, sometimes true, or never true.

1. The center of a circle is at the origin of the coordinate axes.

2. The center of the circle given by the equation $(x + 2)^2 + (y + 1)^2 = 16$ is (2, 1).

3. The equation $x^2 + y^2 - 2x + 3y = 12$ is the equation of a circle.

4. The graph of a circle is the graph of a function.

5. $(x - 2)^2 + (y + 4)^2 = -4$ is the equation of a circle.

12.2   Exercises

1   Find the equation of a circle and then graph the circle

1. Describe how the points on the circumference of a circle are related to the center of the circle.

2. What do the values of h, k, and r represent in the equation of a circle in standard form?

3. The equation $(x - 1)^2 + (y + 4)^2 = 36$ is in the form

$$(x - h)^2 + (y - k)^2 = r^2$$

where $h = \underline{\quad ? \quad}$, $k = \underline{\quad ? \quad}$, and $r = \underline{\quad ? \quad}$. This means that $(x - 1)^2 + (y + 4)^2 = 36$ is the equation of the circle with center $(\underline{\quad ? \quad}, \underline{\quad ? \quad})$ and radius $\underline{\quad ? \quad}$.

4. One way to sketch the graph of the circle in Exercise 3 is to locate four points on the circle:
   a. The point that is 6 units above the center $(1, -4)$ is the point $(1, -4 + 6)$, or $(1, \underline{\quad ? \quad})$.
   b. The point that is 6 units below the center $(1, -4)$ is the point $(1, -4 - \underline{\quad ? \quad})$, or $(1, \underline{\quad ? \quad})$.
   c. The point that is 6 units to the right of the center $(1, -4)$ is the point $(1 + 6, \underline{\quad ? \quad})$, or $(\underline{\quad ? \quad}, \underline{\quad ? \quad})$.
   d. The point that is 6 units to the left of the center $(1, -4)$ is the point $(\underline{\quad ? \quad}, \underline{\quad ? \quad})$, or $(\underline{\quad ? \quad}, \underline{\quad ? \quad})$.

Sketch a graph of the circle given by the equation.

5. $(x - 2)^2 + (y + 2)^2 = 9$ **6.** $(x + 2)^2 + (y - 3)^2 = 16$

7. $(x + 3)^2 + (y - 1)^2 = 25$ **8.** $(x - 2)^2 + (y + 3)^2 = 4$

9. $(x - 4)^2 + (y + 2)^2 = 1$

10. $(x - 3)^2 + (y - 2)^2 = 16$

11. $(x + 5)^2 + (y + 2)^2 = 4$

12. $(x + 1)^2 + (y - 1)^2 = 9$

13. If $h > 0$ and $k < 0$, in which quadrant does the center of the circle with equation $(x - h)^2 + (y - k)^2 = r^2$ lie?

14. Does the circle with equation $(x + 2)^2 + (y - 3)^2 = 4$ pass through quadrant III?

15. Find the equation of the circle with radius 2 and center $C(2, -1)$. Then sketch its graph.

16. Find the equation of the circle with radius 3 and center $C(-1, -2)$. Then sketch its graph.

17. Find the equation of the circle that passes through the point $P(1, 2)$ and whose center is the point $C(-1, 1)$. Then sketch its graph.

18. Find the equation of the circle that passes through the point $P(-1, 3)$ and whose center is the point $C(-2, 1)$. Then sketch its graph.

19. Find the equation of the circle for which a diameter has endpoints $P_1(-1, 4)$ and $P_2(-5, 8)$.

20. Find the equation of the circle for which a diameter has endpoints $P_1(2, 3)$ and $P_2(5, -2)$.

21. Find the equation of the circle for which a diameter has endpoints $P_1(-4, 2)$ and $P_2(0, 0)$.

22. Find the equation of the circle for which a diameter has endpoints $P_1(-8, -3)$ and $P_2(0, -4)$.

2   **Write the equation of a circle in standard form and then graph the circle**

23. a. The first two steps in writing the equation of the circle $x^2 + y^2 + 8x - 4y - 5 = 0$ in standard form are (1) to add 5 to each side of the equation and (2) to group the terms involving x and group the terms involving y. The result is $(x^2 + \underline{\quad ? \quad}) + (y^2 - \underline{\quad ? \quad}) = \underline{\quad ? \quad}$.

   b. The next step is to complete the square on the $x^2 + 8x$ by adding $\underline{\quad ? \quad}$ to each side of the equation, and to complete the square on the $y^2 - 4y$ by adding $\underline{\quad ? \quad}$ to each side of the equation. The result is $(x^2 + 8x + \underline{\quad ? \quad}) + (y^2 - 4y + \underline{\quad ? \quad}) = 5 + \underline{\quad ? \quad} + \underline{\quad ? \quad}$.

   c. Write the equation from part b in standard form by factoring each perfect-square trinomial on the left side of the equation and simplifying the right side of the equation: $(\underline{\quad ? \quad})^2 + (\underline{\quad ? \quad})^2 = \underline{\quad ? \quad}$.

24. Use the result of part c of Exercise 23 to find the center and radius of the circle with equation $x^2 + y^2 + 8x - 4y - 5 = 0$. The center is $\underline{\quad ? \quad}$ and the radius is $\underline{\quad ? \quad}$.

Write the equation of the circle in standard form. Then sketch its graph.

25. $x^2 + y^2 - 2x + 4y - 20 = 0$

26. $x^2 + y^2 - 4x + 8y + 4 = 0$

27. $x^2 + y^2 + 6x + 8y + 9 = 0$

28. $x^2 + y^2 - 6x + 10y + 25 = 0$

29. $x^2 + y^2 - x + 4y + \dfrac{13}{4} = 0$

30. $x^2 + y^2 + 4x + y + \dfrac{1}{4} = 0$

31. $x^2 + y^2 - 6x + 4y + 4 = 0$

32. $x^2 + y^2 - 10x + 8y + 40 = 0$

For Exercises 33 to 36, use the general form of the equation of a circle, $x^2 + y^2 + ax + by + c = 0$. Match the conditions given for a and b with circle A, B, C, or D on the graph.

33. $a = 0$ and $b = 0$

34. $a < 0$ and $b < 0$

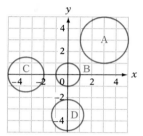

35. $a = 0$ and $b > 0$

36. $a < 0$ and $b = 0$

12.2   Applying Concepts

In Exercises 37 to 39, write the equation of the circle in standard form.

37. The circle has its center at the point $C(3, 0)$ and passes through the origin.

38. The circle has radius 5 and center $(6, -3)$.

39. The circle has radius 1, is tangent to both the x- and y-axes, and lies in quadrant II.

40. **Geometry** The radius of a sphere is 12 in. What is the radius of the circle that is formed by the intersection of a sphere and a plane that is 6 in. from the center of the sphere?

41. Is $x^2 + y^2 + 4x + 8y + 24 = 0$ the equation of a circle? If not, explain why not. If so, find the radius and the coordinates of the center.

42. Explain why the graph of the equation $\dfrac{x^2}{9} + \dfrac{y^2}{9} = 1$ is or is not a circle.

43. Explain the relationship between the distance formula and the standard form of the equation of a circle.

The Ellipse and the Hyperbola

OBJECTIVE **1** **Graph an ellipse with center at the origin**

The orbits of the planets around the sun are "oval" shaped. This oval shape can be described as an **ellipse,** which is another of the conic sections.

There are two **axes of symmetry** for an ellipse. The intersection of these two axes is the **center** of the ellipse.

An ellipse with center at the origin is shown at the right. Note that there are two x-intercepts and two y-intercepts.

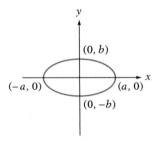

Point of Interest

The word ellipse *comes from the Greek word* ellipsis, *which means "deficient." The method by which the early Greeks analyzed the conics caused a certain area in the construction of the ellipse to be less than another area (deficient). The word* ellipsis *in English, which means "omission," has the same Greek root as the word* ellipse.

> **Standard Form of the Equation of an Ellipse with Center at the Origin**
>
> The equation of an ellipse with center at the origin is $\dfrac{x^2}{a^2} + \dfrac{y^2}{b^2} = 1$. The x-intercepts are $(a, 0)$ and $(-a, 0)$. The y-intercepts are $(0, b)$ and $(0, -b)$.

By finding the x- and y-intercepts for an ellipse and using the fact that the ellipse is "oval" shaped, we can sketch a graph of an ellipse.

EXAMPLE 1 Sketch a graph of the ellipse given by the equation.

A. $\dfrac{x^2}{9} + \dfrac{y^2}{4} = 1$ **B.** $\dfrac{x^2}{16} + \dfrac{y^2}{12} = 1$

Solution   **A.** $\dfrac{x^2}{9} + \dfrac{y^2}{4} = 1$ • $a^2 = 9, b^2 = 4$

x-intercepts: • **The x-intercepts are $(a, 0)$ and $(-a, 0)$.**
(3, 0) and (−3, 0)

y-intercepts:
(0, 2) and (0, −2)

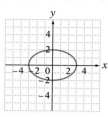

- The *y*-intercepts are (0, *b*) and (0, −*b*).

- Use the intercepts and symmetry to sketch the graph of the ellipse.

B. $\dfrac{x^2}{16} + \dfrac{y^2}{12} = 1$

- $a^2 = 16, b^2 = 12$

x-intercepts:
(4, 0) and (−4, 0)

- The *x*-intercepts are (*a*, 0) and (−*a*, 0).

y-intercepts:
$\left(0, 2\sqrt{3}\right)$ and $\left(0, -2\sqrt{3}\right)$

- The *y*-intercepts are (0, *b*) and (0, −*b*).

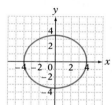

- Use the intercepts and symmetry to sketch the graph of the ellipse. $2\sqrt{3} \approx 3.5$

PROBLEM 1   Sketch a graph of the ellipse given by the equation.

A. $\dfrac{x^2}{4} + \dfrac{y^2}{25} = 1$ **B.** $\dfrac{x^2}{18} + \dfrac{y^2}{9} = 1$

■   **Solution**   See page S34.

OBJECTIVE **2**   **Graph a hyperbola with center at the origin**

A **hyperbola** is a conic section that is formed by the intersection of a right circular cone and a plane perpendicular to the base of the cone.

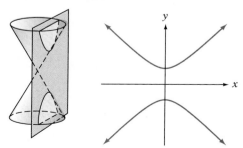

The hyperbola has two **vertices** and an **axis of symmetry** that passes through the vertices. The **center** of a hyperbola is the point halfway between the vertices.

The graphs below show two graphs of a hyperbola with center at the origin.

In the first graph, the axis of symmetry that contains the vertices is the *x*-axis.

 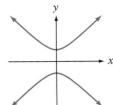

In the second graph, the axis of symmetry that contains the vertices is the *y*-axis.

Note that in either case, the graph of a hyperbola is not the graph of a function. The graph of a hyperbola is the graph of a relation.

Standard Form of the Equation of a Hyperbola with Center at the Origin

The equation of a hyperbola for which the axis of symmetry that contains the vertices is the *x*-axis is $\dfrac{x^2}{a^2} - \dfrac{y^2}{b^2} = 1$. The vertices are $(a, 0)$ and $(-a, 0)$.

The equation of a hyperbola for which the axis of symmetry that contains the vertices is the *y*-axis is $\dfrac{y^2}{b^2} - \dfrac{x^2}{a^2} = 1$. The vertices are $(0, b)$ and $(0, -b)$.

Point of Interest

The word hyperbola *comes from the Greek word* yperboli, *which means "exceeding." The method by which the early Greeks analyzed the conics caused a certain area in the construction of the hyperbola to be greater than (to exceed) another area. The word* hyperbole *in English, which means "exaggeration," has the same Greek root as the word* hyperbola.

The word asymptote *comes from the Greek word* asymptotos, *which means "not capable of meeting."*

To sketch a hyperbola, it is helpful to draw two lines that are "approached" by the hyperbola. These two lines are called **asymptotes.** As a point on the hyperbola gets farther from the origin, the hyperbola "gets closer to" the asymptotes.

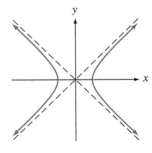

Because the asymptotes are straight lines, their equations are linear equations. The equations of the asymptotes for a hyperbola with center at the origin are $y = \dfrac{b}{a}x$ and $y = -\dfrac{b}{a}x$.

EXAMPLE 2   Sketch a graph of the hyperbola given by the equation.

A. $\dfrac{x^2}{16} - \dfrac{y^2}{4} = 1$ **B.** $\dfrac{y^2}{16} - \dfrac{x^2}{25} = 1$

Solution   **A.** $\dfrac{x^2}{16} - \dfrac{y^2}{4} = 1$ • $a^2 = 16, b^2 = 4$

Axis of symmetry: *x*-axis

Vertices: (4, 0) and (−4, 0)   • The vertices are $(a, 0)$ and $(-a, 0)$.

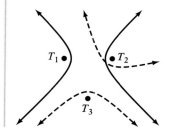

Asymptotes:

$$y = \frac{1}{2}x \text{ and } y = -\frac{1}{2}x$$

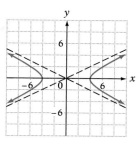

• The asymptotes are $y = \frac{b}{a}x$ and $y = -\frac{b}{a}x.$

• Sketch the asymptotes. Use symmetry and the fact that the hyperbola will approach the asymptotes to sketch its graph.

B. $\dfrac{y^2}{16} - \dfrac{x^2}{25} = 1$

• $a^2 = 25, b^2 = 16$

Axis of symmetry:
y-axis

Vertices:
$(0, 4)$ and $(0, -4)$

• The vertices are $(0, b)$ and $(0, -b)$.

Asymptotes:

$$y = \frac{4}{5}x \text{ and } y = -\frac{4}{5}x$$

• The asymptotes are $y = \frac{b}{a}x$ and $y = -\frac{b}{a}x.$

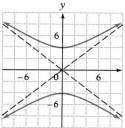

• Sketch the asymptotes. Use symmetry and the fact that the hyperbola will approach the asymptotes to sketch its graph.

PROBLEM 2   Sketch a graph of the hyperbola given by the equation.

A. $\dfrac{x^2}{9} - \dfrac{y^2}{25} = 1$ **B.** $\dfrac{y^2}{9} - \dfrac{x^2}{9} = 1$

Solution   See page S34.

12.3   Concept Review

Determine whether the following statements are always true, sometimes true, or never true.

1. The graph of an ellipse is the graph of a function.

2. The graph of a hyperbola is the graph of a function.

3. An ellipse has two axes of symmetry.

4. An ellipse with center at the origin has two x-intercepts.

5. A hyperbola with center at the origin has two x-intercepts.

6. $4x^2 - y^2 = 16$ is the equation of a hyperbola.

12.3 Exercises

1   Graph an ellipse with center at the origin

1. The equation $\dfrac{x^2}{a^2} + \dfrac{y^2}{b^2} = 1$ is the equation of an ___?___ with center at ___?___. The x-intercepts are ___?___ and ___?___, and the y-intercepts are ___?___ and ___?___.

2. The equation $\dfrac{x^2}{36} + \dfrac{y^2}{49} = 1$ is in the form $\dfrac{x^2}{a^2} + \dfrac{y^2}{b^2} = 1$, with $a^2 = $ ___?___ and $b^2 = $ ___?___. The x-intercepts of the ellipse are ___?___ and ___?___. The y-intercepts of the ellipse are ___?___ and ___?___.

Sketch the graph of the ellipse given by the equation.

3. $\dfrac{x^2}{4} + \dfrac{y^2}{9} = 1$

4. $\dfrac{x^2}{25} + \dfrac{y^2}{16} = 1$

5. $\dfrac{x^2}{25} + \dfrac{y^2}{9} = 1$

6. $\dfrac{x^2}{16} + \dfrac{y^2}{9} = 1$

7. $\dfrac{x^2}{36} + \dfrac{y^2}{16} = 1$

8. $\dfrac{x^2}{49} + \dfrac{y^2}{64} = 1$

9. $\dfrac{x^2}{9} + \dfrac{y^2}{25} = 1$

10. $\dfrac{x^2}{16} + \dfrac{y^2}{36} = 1$

11. $\dfrac{x^2}{36} + \dfrac{y^2}{9} = 1$

12. $\dfrac{x^2}{4} + \dfrac{y^2}{16} = 1$

13. $\dfrac{x^2}{12} + \dfrac{y^2}{4} = 1$

14. $\dfrac{x^2}{8} + \dfrac{y^2}{25} = 1$

15. An ellipse has the equation $\dfrac{x^2}{a^2} + \dfrac{y^2}{b^2} = 1$, where $a > b$. Is the distance between the y-intercepts of the ellipse less than, equal to, or greater than the distance between the x-intercepts of the ellipse?

16. An ellipse has the equation $\dfrac{x^2}{a^2} + \dfrac{y^2}{b^2} = 1$, where $a = b$. Is the distance between the y-intercepts of the ellipse less than, equal to, or greater than the distance between the x-intercepts of the ellipse?

2   Graph a hyperbola with center at the origin

17. How can you tell from an equation whether the graph will be that of an ellipse or a hyperbola?

18. What are the asymptotes of a hyperbola?

For Exercises 19 to 22, use the hyperbola with equation $\dfrac{y^2}{49} - \dfrac{x^2}{25} = 1$.

19. For this hyperbola, $a^2 =$ ___?___ and $b^2 =$ ___?___ .

20. The axis of symmetry of the hyperbola is the ___?___ -axis.

21. The vertices of the hyperbola are on the ___?___ -axis. Their coordinates are ___?___ and ___?___ .

22. The asymptotes of the hyperbola are the lines with equations ___?___ and ___?___ .

Sketch a graph of the hyperbola given by the equation.

23. $\dfrac{x^2}{9} - \dfrac{y^2}{16} = 1$

24. $\dfrac{x^2}{25} - \dfrac{y^2}{4} = 1$

25. $\dfrac{y^2}{16} - \dfrac{x^2}{9} = 1$

26. $\dfrac{y^2}{4} - \dfrac{x^2}{9} = 1$

27. $\dfrac{x^2}{4} - \dfrac{y^2}{25} = 1$

28. $\dfrac{x^2}{9} - \dfrac{y^2}{49} = 1$

29. $\dfrac{y^2}{25} - \dfrac{x^2}{9} = 1$

30. $\dfrac{y^2}{4} - \dfrac{x^2}{16} = 1$

31. $\dfrac{x^2}{25} - \dfrac{y^2}{16} = 1$

32. $\dfrac{x^2}{9} - \dfrac{y^2}{9} = 1$

33. $\dfrac{y^2}{16} - \dfrac{x^2}{4} = 1$

34. $\dfrac{y^2}{9} - \dfrac{x^2}{36} = 1$

35. $\dfrac{x^2}{25} - \dfrac{y^2}{9} = 1$

36. $\dfrac{x^2}{16} - \dfrac{y^2}{25} = 1$

37. $\dfrac{y^2}{16} - \dfrac{x^2}{16} = 1$

38. The equation $25x^2 - 4y^2 = 100$ is the equation of a hyperbola. What step would you take to rewrite the equation in the standard form $\dfrac{x^2}{a^2} - \dfrac{y^2}{b^2} = 1$?

12.3 Applying Concepts

Sketch a graph of the conic section given by the equation. (*Hint:* Divide each term by the number on the right side of the equation.)

39. $4x^2 + y^2 = 16$

40. $x^2 - y^2 = 9$

41. $y^2 - 4x^2 = 16$

42. $9x^2 + 4y^2 = 144$

43. $9x^2 - 25y^2 = 225$

44. $4y^2 - x^2 = 36$

45. **Astronomy** The orbit of comet Halley is an ellipse with a major axis of approximately 36 AU and a minor axis of approximately 9 AU. (1 AU is 1 astronomical unit and is approximately 92,960,000 mi, the average distance of Earth from the sun.)

a. Determine an equation for the orbit of comet Halley in terms of astronomical units. See the diagram at the right.

b. The distance of the sun from the center of comet Halley's elliptical orbit is $\sqrt{a^2 - b^2}$. The aphelion of the orbit (the point at which the comet is farthest from the sun) is a vertex on the major axis. Determine the distance, to the nearest hundred-thousand miles, from the sun to the point at the aphelion of comet Halley.

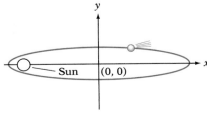

c. The perihelion of the orbit (the point at which the comet is closest
to the sun) is a vertex on the major axis. Determine the distance, to
the nearest hundred-thousand miles, from the sun to the point at the
perihelion of comet Halley.

46. 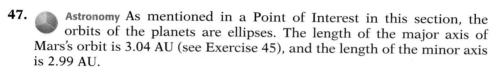 **Astronomy** The orbit of comet Hale–Bopp is an ellipse as shown
at the right. The units are astronomical units (abbreviated AU).
1 AU ≈ 92,960,000 mi.
a. Find the equation of the orbit of the comet.
b. The distance from the center, C, of the orbit to the sun is approximately 182.085 AU. Find the aphelion (the point at which the
comet is farthest from the sun) in miles. Round to the nearest
million miles.
c. Find the perihelion (the point at which the comet is closest to the
sun) in miles. Round to the nearest hundred-thousand miles.

47. 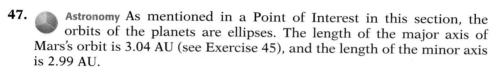 **Astronomy** As mentioned in a Point of Interest in this section, the
orbits of the planets are ellipses. The length of the major axis of
Mars's orbit is 3.04 AU (see Exercise 45), and the length of the minor axis
is 2.99 AU.
a. Determine an equation for the orbit of Mars.
b. Determine the aphelion to the nearest hundred-thousand miles.
c. Determine the perihelion to the nearest hundred-thousand miles.

48. Prepare a report on the system of navigation called loran (long-
range navigation).

12.4   Solving Nonlinear Systems of Equations

OBJECTIVE   1   Solve nonlinear systems of equations

A **nonlinear system of equations** is one in which one or more equations of
the system are not linear equations. Some examples of nonlinear systems and
their graphs are shown here.

$$x^2 + y^2 = 4$$
$$y = x^2 + 2$$

The graphs intersect at one point.
The system of equations has one solution.

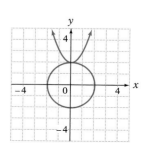

$y = x^2$
$y = -x + 2$

The graphs intersect at two points.
The system of equations has two solutions.

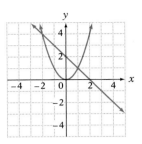

$(x + 2)^2 + (y - 2)^2 = 4$
$x = y^2$

The graphs do not intersect.
The system of equations has no solutions.

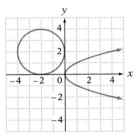

Nonlinear systems of equations can be solved by using either a substitution method or an addition method.

Solve: $2x - y = 4$ (1)
$\quad\quad\quad y^2 = 4x$ (2)

When a system contains both a linear and a quadratic equation, the substitution method is used.

Solve equation (1) for y.	$2x - y = 4$ $-y = -2x + 4$ $y = 2x - 4$
Substitute $2x - 4$ for y into equation (2).	$y^2 = 4x$ $(2x - 4)^2 = 4x$
Write the quadratic equation in standard form.	$4x^2 - 16x + 16 = 4x$ $4x^2 - 20x + 16 = 0$
Solve for x by factoring.	$4(x^2 - 5x + 4) = 0$ $4(x - 4)(x - 1) = 0$ $x - 4 = 0 \quad\quad x - 1 = 0$ $\quad\quad x = 4 \quad\quad\quad\quad x = 1$
Substitute the values of x into the equation $y = 2x - 4$, and solve for y.	$y = 2x - 4 \quad\quad y = 2x - 4$ $y = 2(4) - 4 \quad y = 2(1) - 4$ $y = 4 \quad\quad\quad\quad y = -2$

The solutions are $(4, 4)$ and $(1, -2)$.

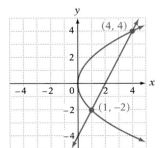

The graph of the system that was solved above is shown at the left. Note that the line intersects the parabola at two points. These points correspond to the solutions.

Solve: $x^2 + y^2 = 4$ (1)

$\quad\quad\quad y = x + 4$ (2)

The system of equations contains a linear equation. The substitution method is used to solve the system.

Substitute the expression for y into equation (1).	$x^2 + y^2 = 4$ $x^2 + (x + 4)^2 = 4$
Write the equation in standard form.	$x^2 + x^2 + 8x + 16 = 4$ $2x^2 + 8x + 16 = 4$ $2x^2 + 8x + 12 = 0$
Because the discriminant of the quadratic equation is less than zero, the equation has no real number solutions. Therefore, the system of equations has no real number solutions.	$b^2 - 4ac = 8^2 - 4(2)(12)$ $= 64 - 96$ $= -32$

The graph of the system of equations that was solved above is shown at the right. Note that the two graphs do not intersect.

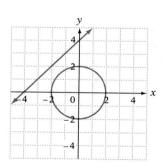

Solve: $4x^2 + y^2 = 16$ (1)

$\quad\quad\quad x^2 + y^2 = 4$ (2)

Use the addition method to solve this system of equations.

Multiply equation (2) by -1 and add it to equation (1).	$4x^2 + y^2 = 16$ $-x^2 - y^2 = -4$ $\quad 3x^2 = 12$
Solve for x.	$x^2 = 4$ $x = \pm 2$

Substitute the values of x into equation (2), and solve for y.

$x^2 + y^2 = 4 \qquad\qquad x^2 + y^2 = 4$

$2^2 + y^2 = 4 \qquad\qquad (-2)^2 + y^2 = 4$

$\quad\quad y^2 = 0 \qquad\qquad\quad\quad y^2 = 0$

$\quad\quad\; y = 0 \qquad\qquad\quad\quad\; y = 0$

The solutions are $(2, 0)$ and $(-2, 0)$.

The graph of the system that was solved on the previous page is shown at the right. Note that the graphs intersect at two points.

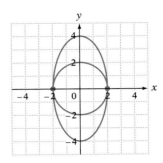

EXAMPLE 1   Solve: **A.** $y = 2x^2 - 3x - 1$ **B.** $3x^2 - 2y^2 = 26$
                                   $y = x^2 - 2x + 5$ $x^2 - y^2 = 5$

Solution   **A.** (1) $y = 2x^2 - 3x - 1$
                     (2) $y = x^2 - 2x + 5$

$2x^2 - 3x - 1 = x^2 - 2x + 5$ • **Use the substitution method.**
$x^2 - x - 6 = 0$
$(x - 3)(x + 2) = 0$

$x - 3 = 0 \qquad x + 2 = 0$
$\quad x = 3 \qquad\quad x = -2$

$y = 2x^2 - 3x - 1$ • **Substitute the values of x into**
$y = 2(3)^2 - 3(3) - 1$ **equation (1).**
$y = 18 - 9 - 1$
$y = 8$

$y = 2x^2 - 3x - 1$
$y = 2(-2)^2 - 3(-2) - 1$
$y = 8 + 6 - 1$
$y = 13$

The solutions are $(3, 8)$ and $(-2, 13)$.

B. (1) $3x^2 - 2y^2 = 26$
       (2) $x^2 - y^2 = 5$

$3x^2 - 2y^2 = 26$ • **Use the addition**
$-2x^2 + 2y^2 = -10$ **method. Multiply**
$x^2 = 16$ **equation (2) by -2.**
$x = \pm 4$

$x^2 - y^2 = 5 \qquad\qquad x^2 - y^2 = 5$ • **Substitute the values**
$4^2 - y^2 = 5 \qquad\quad (-4)^2 - y^2 = 5$ **of x into equation (2).**
$16 - y^2 = 5 \qquad\quad 16 - y^2 = 5$
$\quad -y^2 = -11 \qquad\qquad -y^2 = -11$
$\quady^2 = 11 \qquad\qquady^2 = 11$
$\quady = \pm\sqrt{11} \qquad\qquady = \pm\sqrt{11}$

The solutions are $\left(4, \sqrt{11}\right)$, $\left(4, -\sqrt{11}\right)$, $\left(-4, \sqrt{11}\right)$, and $\left(-4, -\sqrt{11}\right)$.

PROBLEM 1   Solve.   **A.** $y = 2x^2 + x - 3$ **B.** $x^2 - y^2 = 10$
                                   $y = 2x^2 - 2x + 9$ $x^2 + y^2 = 8$

Solution   See pages S34–S35.

12.4   Concept Review

Determine whether the following statements are always true, sometimes true, or never true.

1. It is possible for two ellipses with centers at the origin to intersect in three points.

2. Two circles will intersect in two points.

3. A straight line will intersect a parabola in two points.

4. An ellipse and a circle will intersect in four points.

5. When the graphs of the equations of a system of equations do not intersect, the system has no real number solution.

6. Two circles will intersect in four points.

12.4   Exercises

1   Solve nonlinear systems of equations

1. How do nonlinear systems of equations differ from linear systems of equations?

2. Solve this nonlinear system of equations: $y = x^2 - 5x + 6$
$$y = x - 2$$

$y = x^2 - 5x + 6$
$y = x - 2$

$\underline{\quad ? \quad} = x^2 - 5x + 6$

$0 = x^2 - \underline{\quad ? \quad} x + \underline{\quad ? \quad}$

$0 = (x - 4)(x - \underline{\quad ? \quad})$

$0 = \underline{\quad ? \quad} \qquad 0 = \underline{\quad ? \quad}$

$\underline{\quad ? \quad} = x \qquad \underline{\quad ? \quad} = x$

$y = 4 - 2 \qquad y = 2 - 2$

$\qquad = 2 \qquad \qquad = 0$

- The second equation has variables raised to the first power. Use the substitution method.
- Substitute $x - 2$ from the second equation for y in the first equation.
- Write the quadratic equation in standard form by subtracting x from each side and adding 2 to each side.
- Factor the trinomial.
- Use the Zero Product Property.
- Solve for x. These are the x-coordinates of the solutions of the system.
- Substitute the x-values into the equation $y = \underline{\quad ? \quad}$.
- Simplify. These are the $\underline{\quad ? \quad}$-coordinates of the solutions of the system.

The solutions of the system are $(\underline{\quad ? \quad}, \underline{\quad ? \quad})$ and $(\underline{\quad ? \quad}, \underline{\quad ? \quad})$.

Solve.

3. $y = x^2 - x - 1$
$y = 2x + 9$

4. $y = x^2 - 3x + 1$
$y = x + 6$

5. $y^2 = -x + 3$
$x - y = 1$

6. $y^2 = 4x$
$x - y = -1$

7. $y^2 = 2x$
$x + 2y = -2$

8. $y^2 = 2x$
$x - y = 4$

9. $x^2 + 2y^2 = 12$
$2x - y = 2$

10. $x^2 + 4y^2 = 37$
$x - y = -4$

11. $x^2 + y^2 = 13$
$x + y = 5$

12. $x^2 + y^2 = 16$
$x - 2y = -4$

13. $4x^2 + y^2 = 12$
$y = 4x^2$

14. $2x^2 + y^2 = 6$
$y = 2x^2$

15. $y = x^2 - 2x - 3$
$y = x - 6$

16. $y = x^2 + 4x + 5$
$y = -x - 3$

17. $3x^2 - y^2 = -1$
$x^2 + 4y^2 = 17$

18. $x^2 + y^2 = 10$
$x^2 + 9y^2 = 18$

19. $2x^2 + 3y^2 = 30$
$x^2 + y^2 = 13$

20. $x^2 + y^2 = 61$
$x^2 - y^2 = 11$

21. $y = 2x^2 - x + 1$
$y = x^2 - x + 5$

22. $y = -x^2 + x - 1$
$y = x^2 + 2x - 2$

23. $2x^2 + 3y^2 = 24$
$x^2 - y^2 = 7$

24. $2x^2 + 3y^2 = 21$
$x^2 + 2y^2 = 12$

25. $x^2 + y^2 = 36$
$4x^2 + 9y^2 = 36$

26. $2x^2 + 3y^2 = 12$
$x^2 - y^2 = 25$

27. $11x^2 - 2y^2 = 4$
$3x^2 + y^2 = 15$

28. $x^2 + 4y^2 = 25$
$x^2 - y^2 = 5$

29. $2x^2 - y^2 = 7$
$2x - y = 5$

30. $3x^2 + 4y^2 = 7$
$x - 2y = -3$

31. $y = 3x^2 + x - 4$
$y = 3x^2 - 8x + 5$

32. $y = 2x^2 + 3x + 1$
$y = 2x^2 + 9x + 7$

For Exercises 33 to 36, a nonlinear system of equations is given, along with its solutions. Describe the graph of the system by stating the names of the two figures and the number of points of intersection of the two figures.

33. $x^2 + 4y^2 = 16$
$x^2 + y^2 = 4$
Solutions: $(0, 2), (0, -2)$

34. $2x^2 + y^2 = 4$
$x^2 - 2y^2 = 12$
No solutions

35. $y = x^2 - 3x - 4$
$6x - 2y = 22$
Solution: $(3, -4)$

36. $x^2 - y^2 = 8$
$x = y^2 - 4$
Solutions: $(4, 2\sqrt{2}), (4, -2\sqrt{2}),$
$(-3, 1), (-3, -1)$

12.4 Applying Concepts

 Solve by graphing. Approximate the solutions of the systems to the nearest thousandth.

37. $y = 2^x$
$x + y = 3$

38. $y = 3^{-x}$
$x^2 + y^2 = 9$

39. $y = \log_2 x$
$\dfrac{x^2}{9} + \dfrac{y^2}{1} = 1$

40. $y = \log_3 x$
$x^2 + y^2 = 4$

41. $y = -\log_3 x$
$x + y = 4$

42. $y = \left(\dfrac{1}{2}\right)^x$
$\dfrac{x^2}{9} + \dfrac{y^2}{4} = 1$

43. Is it possible for two circles with centers at the origin to intersect at exactly two points?

12.5 Quadratic Inequalities and Systems of Inequalities

OBJECTIVE **1**   **Graph the solution set of a quadratic inequality in two variables**

The **graph of a quadratic inequality in two variables** is a region of the plane that is bounded by one of the conic sections (parabola, circle, ellipse, or hyperbola). When graphing an inequality of this type, first replace the inequality symbol with an equals sign. Graph the resulting conic using a dashed curve when the original inequality is less than ($<$) or greater than ($>$). Use a solid curve when the original inequality is $\leq$ or $\geq$. Use the point $(0, 0)$ to determine which region of the plane to shade. If $(0, 0)$ is a solution of the inequality, then shade the region of the plane containing $(0, 0)$. If not, shade the other portion of the plane.

Graph the solution set of $x^2 + y^2 > 9$.

Change the inequality to an equality. $x^2 + y^2 > 9$

This is the equation of a circle with center $x^2 + y^2 = 9$
$(0, 0)$ and radius 3.

Because the inequality is $>$, the graph of $x^2 + y^2 = 9$ is drawn as a dashed circle.

Substitute the point $(0, 0)$ into the inequality. Because $0^2 + 0^2 > 9$ is not true, the point $(0, 0)$ should not be in the shaded region.

EXAMPLE 1   Graph the solution set.

A. $y \le x^2 + 2x + 2$ **B.** $\dfrac{y^2}{9} - \dfrac{x^2}{4} \ge 1$

Solution   **A.** $y \le x^2 + 2x + 2$
$y = x^2 + 2x + 2$

• Change the inequality to an equality. This is the equation of a parabola that opens up. The vertex is $(-1, 1)$. The axis of symmetry is the line $x = -1$.
• Because the inequality is $\le$, the graph is drawn as a solid curve.
• Substitute the point $(0, 0)$ into the inequality. Because $0 < 0^2 + 2(0) + 2$ is true, the point $(0, 0)$ should be in the shaded region.

B. $\dfrac{y^2}{9} - \dfrac{x^2}{4} \ge 1$

$\dfrac{y^2}{9} - \dfrac{x^2}{4} = 1$

• Change the inequality to an equality. This is the equation of a hyperbola. The vertices are $(0, -3)$ and $(0, 3)$. The equations of the asymptotes are $y = \dfrac{3}{2}x$ and $y = -\dfrac{3}{2}x$.
• Because the inequality is $\ge$, the graph is drawn as a solid curve.
• Substitute the point $(0, 0)$ into the inequality. Because $\dfrac{0^2}{9} - \dfrac{0^2}{4} \ge 1$ is not true, the point $(0, 0)$ should not be in the shaded region.

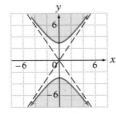

PROBLEM 1   Graph the solution set.

A. $\dfrac{x^2}{9} + \dfrac{y^2}{16} \le 1$ **B.** $\dfrac{x^2}{9} - \dfrac{y^2}{4} \le 1$

Solution   See page S35.

OBJECTIVE **2**   **Graph the solution set of a nonlinear system of inequalities**

Recall that the solution set of a system of inequalities is the intersection of the solution sets of the individual inequalities. To graph the solution set of a system of inequalities, first graph the solution set for each inequality. The graph of the solution set of the system of inequalities is the region of the plane represented by the intersection of the two shaded regions.

Graph the solution set: $x^2 + y^2 \leq 16$
$$y \geq x^2$$

Graph the solution set of each inequality.

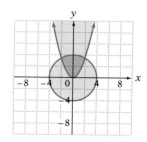

$x^2 + y^2 = 16$ is the equation of a circle with center at the origin and a radius of 4. Because the inequality is $\leq$, use a solid curve.

$y = x^2$ is the equation of a parabola that opens up. The vertex is (0, 0). Because the inequality is $\geq$, use a solid curve.

Substitute the point (0, 0) into the inequality $x^2 + y^2 \leq 16$. $0^2 + 0^2 \leq 16$ is a true statement. Shade inside the circle.

Substitute (2, 0) into the inequality $y \geq x^2$. (We cannot use (0, 0), because it is a point on the parabola.) $0 \geq 4$ is a false statement. Shade inside the parabola.

The solution is the intersection of the two shaded regions.

EXAMPLE 2   Graph the solution set.   **A.** $y > x^2$ **B.** $\dfrac{x^2}{9} - \dfrac{y^2}{16} \geq 1$
$$y < x + 2 \qquad\qquad x^2 + y^2 \leq 4$$

Solution   **A.**

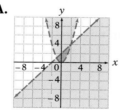

- Graph the solution set of each inequality.
- $y = x^2$ is the equation of a parabola. Use a dashed curve. Shade inside the parabola.
- $y = x + 2$ is the equation of a line. Use a dashed line. Shade below the line.

The solution set is the region of the plane represented by the intersection of the solution sets of each inequality.

B.

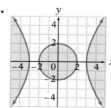

- Graph the solution set of each inequality.
- $\dfrac{x^2}{9} - \dfrac{y^2}{16} = 1$ is the equation of a hyperbola. Use a solid curve. The point (0, 0) should not be in the shaded region.
- $x^2 + y^2 = 4$ is the equation of a circle. Use a solid curve. Shade inside the circle.

The solution sets of the two inequalities do not intersect. This system of inequalities has no real number solution.

PROBLEM 2 Graph the solution set.

A. $\dfrac{x^2}{4} + \dfrac{y^2}{9} \le 1$ **B.** $\dfrac{x^2}{16} + \dfrac{y^2}{25} \ge 1$

$x > y^2 - 2$ $x^2 + y^2 < 9$

Solution See page S35.

12.5 Concept Review

Determine whether the following statements are always true, sometimes true, or never true.

1. The graph of a quadratic inequality in two variables is a region of the plane that is bounded by one of the conic sections.

2. The solution set of a nonlinear system of inequalities is the union of the solution sets of the individual inequalities.

3. The point $(0, 0)$ is a solution of the inequality $x^2 + y^2 > 4$.

4. The graph of the solution set of a quadratic inequality in two variables that is bounded by a hyperbola includes the asymptotes of the hyperbola.

5. The graph of the solution set of a quadratic inequality in two variables that is bounded by a conic section includes the boundary.

6. The solution set of a nonlinear system of inequalities is the empty set.

12.5 Exercises

1 Graph the solution set of a quadratic inequality in two variables

1. Complete the following statements about the graph of the inequality $y < x^2 - 8x + 16$.
   a. The boundary curve is a ___?___.
   b. Because the inequality is $<$, the boundary will be shown as a ___?___ curve.
   c. $(0, 0)$ is a solution of the inequality, so the point $(0, 0)$ ___?___ (is or is not) in the shaded region of the graph.

2. Complete the following statements about the graph of the inequality $\dfrac{x^2}{4} - \dfrac{y^2}{25} \geq 1$.

  a. The boundary curve is a ___?___.

  b. Because the inequality is $\geq$, the boundary will be shown as a ___?___ curve.

  c. $(0, 0)$ is not a solution of the inequality, so the point $(0, 0)$ ___?___ (is or is not) in the shaded region of the graph.

Graph the solution set.

3. $y \leq x^2 - 4x + 3$

4. $y < x^2 - 2x - 3$

5. $(x - 1)^2 + (y + 2)^2 \leq 9$

6. $(x + 2)^2 + (y - 3)^2 > 4$

7. $(x + 3)^2 + (y - 2)^2 \geq 9$

8. $(x - 2)^2 + (y + 1)^2 \leq 16$

9. $\dfrac{x^2}{16} + \dfrac{y^2}{25} < 1$

10. $\dfrac{x^2}{9} + \dfrac{y^2}{4} \geq 1$

11. $\dfrac{x^2}{25} - \dfrac{y^2}{9} \leq 1$

12. $\dfrac{y^2}{25} - \dfrac{x^2}{36} > 1$

13. $\dfrac{x^2}{4} + \dfrac{y^2}{16} \geq 1$

14. $\dfrac{x^2}{4} - \dfrac{y^2}{16} \leq 1$

15. $y \leq x^2 - 2x + 3$

16. $x \leq y^2 + 2y + 1$

17. $\dfrac{y^2}{9} - \dfrac{x^2}{16} \leq 1$

18. $\dfrac{x^2}{16} - \dfrac{y^2}{4} < 1$

19. $\dfrac{x^2}{9} + \dfrac{y^2}{1} \leq 1$

20. $\dfrac{x^2}{16} + \dfrac{y^2}{4} > 1$

21. $(x - 1)^2 + (y + 3)^2 \leq 25$

22. $(x + 1)^2 + (y - 2)^2 \geq 16$

23. $\dfrac{y^2}{25} - \dfrac{x^2}{4} \leq 1$

24. $\dfrac{x^2}{9} - \dfrac{y^2}{25} \geq 1$

25. $\dfrac{x^2}{25} + \dfrac{y^2}{9} \leq 1$

26. $\dfrac{x^2}{36} + \dfrac{y^2}{4} \leq 1$

27. True or false? For all real numbers h, k, and r, the graph of the inequality $(x - h)^2 + (y - k)^2 < r^2$ will be the region inside the circle with equation $(x - h)^2 + (y - k)^2 = r^2$.

28. True or false? For all real numbers a, b, and c, $a \neq 0$, the graph of the inequality $y > ax^2 + bx + c$ will be the region inside the parabola with equation $y = ax^2 + bx + c$.

2 Graph the solution set of a nonlinear system of inequalities

29. To graph the solution set of a system of inequalities, find the _____?_____ of the graphs of the individual inequalities.

30. If there is no overlap between the graphs of the individual inequalities of a system of inequalities, then the system of inequalities has _____?_____ solutions.

Graph the solution set.

31. $y \le x^2 - 4x + 4$
       $y + x > 4$

32. $x^2 + y^2 < 1$
       $x + y \ge 4$

33. $x^2 + y^2 < 16$
       $y > x + 1$

34. $y > x^2 - 4$
       $y < x - 2$

35. $\dfrac{x^2}{4} + \dfrac{y^2}{16} \le 1$

       $y \le -\dfrac{1}{2}x + 2$

36. $\dfrac{y^2}{4} - \dfrac{x^2}{25} \ge 1$

       $y \le \dfrac{2}{3}x + 4$

37. $x \ge y^2 - 3y + 2$
       $y \ge 2x - 2$

38. $x^2 + y^2 \le 25$

       $y \le -\dfrac{1}{3}x + 2$

39. $x^2 + y^2 < 25$
       $\dfrac{x^2}{9} + \dfrac{y^2}{36} < 1$

40. $\dfrac{x^2}{9} - \dfrac{y^2}{4} < 1$

       $\dfrac{x^2}{25} + \dfrac{y^2}{9} < 1$

41. $x^2 + y^2 > 4$
       $x^2 + y^2 < 25$

42. $\dfrac{x^2}{25} + \dfrac{y^2}{16} \le 1$

       $\dfrac{x^2}{4} + \dfrac{y^2}{4} \ge 1$

For Exercises 43 to 46, a and b are positive numbers such that $a < b$.
Describe the solution set of each system of inequalities.

43. $x^2 + y^2 < a$
       $x^2 + y^2 < b$

44. $x^2 + y^2 < a$
       $x^2 + y^2 > b$

45. $x^2 + y^2 > a$
$x^2 + y^2 < b$

46. $x^2 + y^2 > a$
$x^2 + y^2 > b$

12.5 **Applying Concepts**

Graph the solution set.

47. $y > x^2 - 3$
$y < x + 3$
$x \leq 0$

48. $x^2 + y^2 \leq 25$
$y > x + 1$
$x \geq 0$

49. $x^2 + y^2 < 3$
$x > y^2 - 1$
$y \geq 0$

50. $\dfrac{x^2}{4} - \dfrac{y^2}{25} \leq 1$
$\dfrac{x^2}{4} + \dfrac{y^2}{4} \leq 1$
$y \geq 0$

51. $\dfrac{x^2}{4} + \dfrac{y^2}{1} \leq 4$
$x^2 + y^2 \leq 4$
$x \geq 0$
$y \leq 0$

52. $\dfrac{x^2}{4} + \dfrac{y^2}{25} \leq 1$
$x > y^2 - 4$
$x \leq 0$
$y \geq 0$

53. $y > 2^x$
$x + y < 4$

54. $y < \left(\dfrac{1}{2}\right)^x$
$2x - y \geq 2$

55. $y \geq \log_2 x$
$x^2 + y^2 < 9$

56. $y \leq -\log_3 x$
$\dfrac{x^2}{9} + \dfrac{y^2}{4} < 1$

57. $y < 3^{-x}$
$\dfrac{x^2}{4} - \dfrac{y^2}{1} \geq 1$

58. $y \geq 2^{x-1}$
$2x + 3y > 6$

Focus on Problem Solving

Use a Variety of Problem-Solving Strategies

We have examined several problem-solving strategies throughout the text. See if you can apply those techniques to the following problems.

1. Eight coins look exactly alike, but one is lighter than the others. Explain how the different coin can be found in two weighings on a balance scale.

2. For the sequence of numbers 1, 1, 2, 3, 5, 8, 13, ..., identify a possible pattern and then use that pattern to determine the next number in the sequence.

3. Arrange the numbers 1, 2, 3, 4, 5, 6, 7, 8, and 9 in the squares at the right so that the sum of any row or diagonal is 15. (*Suggestion:* Note that 1, 5, 9; 2, 5, 8; 3, 5, 7; and 4, 5, 6 all add to 15. Because 5 is part of each sum, this suggests that 5 be placed in the center of the squares.)

4. A restaurant charges $10.00 for a pizza that has a diameter of 9 in. Determine the selling price of a pizza with a diameter of 18 in. so that the selling price per square inch is the same as for the 9-inch pizza.

5. Can the checkerboard at the right be covered with dominos (which look like 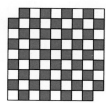) so that every square on the board is covered by a domino? Why or why not? (*Note:* The dominos cannot overlap.)

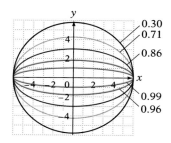

Projects & Group Activities

The Eccentricity and Foci of an Ellipse

The graph of an ellipse can be long and thin, or it can have a shape that is very close to a circle. The **eccentricity,** *e,* of an ellipse is a measure of its "roundness."

The shapes of ellipses with various eccentricities are shown below.

1. On the basis of the eccentricities of the ellipses shown above, complete the following sentence. "As the eccentricity of an ellipse gets closer to 1, the ellipse gets *flatter/rounder.*"

Planet	Eccentricity
Mercury	0.206
Venus	0.007
Earth	0.017
Mars	0.093
Jupiter	0.049
Saturn	0.051
Uranus	0.046
Neptune	0.005
Pluto	0.250

2. The planets travel around the sun in elliptical orbits. The eccentricities of the orbits of the planets are shown in the table at the left. Which planet has the most nearly circular orbit?

For an ellipse given by the equation $\frac{x^2}{a^2} + \frac{y^2}{b^2} = 1$, $a > b$, a formula for eccentricity is $e = \frac{\sqrt{a^2 - b^2}}{a}$. Use this formula to find the eccentricity of the ellipses in Exercises 3 and 4. If necessary, round to the nearest hundredth.

3. $\frac{x^2}{25} + \frac{y^2}{16} = 1$

4. $\frac{x^2}{9} + \frac{y^2}{4} = 1$

The **foci** of an ellipse are two points on the longer axis, called the **major axis,** of the ellipse. F_1 and F_2 are the foci of the ellipse shown below.

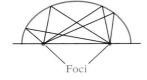

Foci

Ellipses have a reflective property that has been used in the design of some buildings. If light or sound emanates from one focus, it is reflected to the other focus. This phenomenon results in what are called "whispering galleries." The rotunda of the Capitol Building in Washington, D.C., is a whispering gallery. A whisper spoken by a person at one focus can be heard clearly by a person at the other focus.

The foci are c units from the center of an ellipse, where $c = \sqrt{a^2 - b^2}$ for an ellipse whose equation is $\frac{x^2}{a^2} + \frac{y^2}{b^2} = 1$, $a > b$.

5. Find the foci for an ellipse whose equation is $\frac{x^2}{169} + \frac{y^2}{144} = 1$.

Chapter 12 Summary

Key Words

Conic sections are curves that can be constructed from the intersection of a plane and a cone. The four conic sections are the **parabola, circle, ellipse**, and **hyperbola**. [12.1.1, p. 721]

Examples

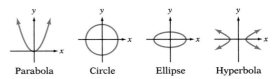

Parabola   Circle   Ellipse   Hyperbola

The **asymptotes** of a hyperbola are the two lines that are "approached" by the hyperbola. As the graph of the hyperbola gets farther from the origin, the hyperbola gets "closer to" the asymptotes. [12.3.2, p. 738]

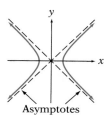

A **nonlinear system of equations** is a system in which one or more of the equations are not linear equations. [12.4.1, p. 743]

$$x^2 + y^2 = 16$$
$$y = x^2 - 2$$

The **graph of a quadratic inequality in two variables** is a region of the plane that is bounded by one of the conic sections. [12.5.1, p. 749]

$$y \geq x^2 - 2x - 4$$

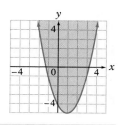

Essential Rules and Procedures

Equation of a parabola [12.1.1, pp. 722–723]
$$y = ax^2 + bx + c$$
When $a > 0$, the parabola opens up.
When $a < 0$, the parabola opens down.

The x-coordinate of the vertex is $-\dfrac{b}{2a}$.

The axis of symmetry is the line $x = -\dfrac{b}{2a}$.

$$y = x^2 + 2x + 2 \qquad y = -\frac{1}{2}x^2 + 2x - 3$$

$$x = ay^2 + by + c$$
When $a > 0$, the parabola opens to the right.
When $a < 0$, the parabola opens to the left.

The y-coordinate of the vertex is $-\dfrac{b}{2a}$.

The axis of symmetry is the line $y = -\dfrac{b}{2a}$.

$$x = 2y^2 - 4y + 1 \qquad x = -y^2 + 4y - 3$$

Equation of a circle [12.2.1, p. 729]
$$(x - h)^2 + (y - k)^2 = r^2$$
The center of the circle is (h, k), and the radius is r.

$$(x - 2)^2 + (y + 1)^2 = 9$$
$$(h, k) = (2, -1)$$
$$r = 3$$

Equation of an ellipse [12.3.1, p. 736]

$$\frac{x^2}{a^2} + \frac{y^2}{b^2} = 1$$

The x-intercepts are $(a, 0)$ and $(-a, 0)$.
The y-intercepts are $(0, b)$ and $(0, -b)$.

$$\frac{x^2}{9} + \frac{y^2}{1} = 1$$

x-intercepts:
$(3, 0)$ and $(-3, 0)$

y-intercepts:
$(0, 1)$ and $(0, -1)$

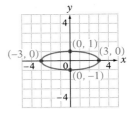

Equation of a hyperbola [12.3.2, p. 738]

$$\frac{x^2}{a^2} - \frac{y^2}{b^2} = 1$$

The axis of symmetry that contains the vertices is the x-axis.
The vertices are $(a, 0)$ and $(-a, 0)$.

The equations of the asymptotes are $y = \frac{b}{a}x$ and $y = -\frac{b}{a}x$.

$$\frac{x^2}{9} - \frac{y^2}{4} = 1$$

Vertices:
$(3, 0)$ and $(-3, 0)$

Asymptotes:
$y = \frac{2}{3}x$ and $y = -\frac{2}{3}x$

$$\frac{y^2}{b^2} - \frac{x^2}{a^2} = 1$$

The axis of symmetry that contains the vertices is the y-axis.
The vertices are $(0, b)$ and $(0, -b)$.

The equations of the asymptotes are $y = \frac{b}{a}x$ and $y = -\frac{b}{a}x$.

$$\frac{y^2}{1} - \frac{x^2}{4} = 1$$

Vertices:
$(0, 1)$ and $(0, -1)$

Asymptotes:
$y = \frac{1}{2}x$ and

$y = -\frac{1}{2}x$

Chapter 12 Review Exercises

1. Find the vertex and axis of symmetry of the parabola $y = x^2 - 4x + 8$.

2. Find the vertex and axis of symmetry of the parabola $y = -x^2 + 7x - 8$.

3. Sketch a graph of $y = -2x^2 + x - 2$.

4. Sketch a graph of $x = 2y^2 - 6y + 5$.

5. Find the equation of the circle that passes through the point $P(2, -1)$ and whose center is the point $C(-1, 2)$.

6. Find the equation of the circle with radius 6 and center $C(-1, 5)$.

7. Sketch a graph of $(x + 3)^2 + (y + 1)^2 = 1$.

8. Sketch a graph of $x^2 + (y - 2)^2 = 9$.

9. Find the equation of the circle that passes through the point $P(4, 6)$ and whose center is the point $C(0, -3)$.

10. Write the equation $x^2 + y^2 + 4x - 2y = 4$ in standard form.

11. Sketch a graph of $\dfrac{x^2}{1} + \dfrac{y^2}{9} = 1$.

12. Sketch a graph of $\dfrac{x^2}{25} + \dfrac{y^2}{9} = 1$.

13. Sketch a graph of $\dfrac{x^2}{25} - \dfrac{y^2}{1} = 1$.

14. Sketch a graph of $\dfrac{y^2}{16} - \dfrac{x^2}{9} = 1$.

15. Solve: $y = x^2 + 5x - 6$
$\qquad\quad y = x - 10$

16. Solve: $2x^2 + y^2 = 19$
$\qquad\quad 3x^2 - y^2 = 6$

17. Solve: $\qquad x = 2y^2 - 3y + 1$
$\qquad\quad 3x - 2y = 0$

18. Solve: $y^2 = 2x^2 - 3x + 6$
$\qquad\quad y^2 = 2x^2 + 5x - 2$

19. Graph the solution set: $(x - 2)^2 + (y + 1)^2 \le 16$

20. Graph the solution set: $\dfrac{x^2}{9} - \dfrac{y^2}{16} < 1$

21. Graph the solution set: $y \geq -x^2 - 2x + 3$

22. Graph the solution set: $\dfrac{x^2}{16} + \dfrac{y^2}{4} > 1$

23. Graph the solution set: $y \geq x^2 - 4x + 2$
$$y \leq \frac{1}{3}x - 1$$

24. Graph the solution set: $\dfrac{x^2}{25} + \dfrac{y^2}{16} \leq 1$
$$\frac{y^2}{4} - \frac{x^2}{4} \geq 1$$

25. Graph the solution set: $\dfrac{x^2}{9} + \dfrac{y^2}{1} \geq 1$
$$\frac{x^2}{4} - \frac{y^2}{1} \leq 1$$

26. Graph the solution set: $\dfrac{x^2}{16} + \dfrac{y^2}{4} < 1$
$$x^2 + y^2 > 9$$

Chapter 12 Test

1. Find the axis of symmetry of the parabola $y = -x^2 + 6x - 5$.

2. Find the vertex of the parabola $y = -x^2 + 3x - 2$.

3. Sketch a graph of $y = \dfrac{1}{2}x^2 + x - 4$.

4. Sketch a graph of $x = y^2 - y - 2$.

5. Find the equation of the circle with radius 4 and center $C(-3, -3)$.

6. Solve: $x^2 + 2y^2 = 4$
$\phantom{\text{Solve: }} x + y = 2$

7. Solve: $x = 3y^2 + 2y - 4$
$\qquad\quad x = y^2 - 5y$

8. Solve: $x^2 - y^2 = 24$
$\qquad\quad 2x^2 + 5y^2 = 55$

9. Find the equation of the circle that passes through the point $P(2, 4)$ and whose center is the point $C(-1, -3)$.

10. Sketch a graph of $(x - 2)^2 + (y + 1)^2 = 9$.

11. Find the equation of the circle with radius 3 and center $C(-2, 4)$.

12. Find the equation of the circle that passes through the point $P(2, 5)$ and whose center is the point $C(-2, 1)$.

13. Write the equation $x^2 + y^2 - 4x + 2y + 1 = 0$ in standard form, and then sketch its graph.

14. Sketch a graph of $\dfrac{y^2}{25} - \dfrac{x^2}{16} = 1$.

15. Sketch a graph of $\dfrac{x^2}{9} - \dfrac{y^2}{4} = 1$.

16. Sketch a graph of $\dfrac{x^2}{16} + \dfrac{y^2}{4} = 1$.

17. Graph the solution set: $\dfrac{x^2}{16} - \dfrac{y^2}{25} < 1$

18. Graph the solution set: $x^2 + y^2 < 36$
$\qquad\qquad\qquad\qquad\qquad\quad x + y > 4$

19. Graph the solution set: $\dfrac{x^2}{25} + \dfrac{y^2}{4} \leq 1$

20. Graph the solution set: $\dfrac{x^2}{25} - \dfrac{y^2}{16} \geq 1$
$\qquad\qquad\qquad\qquad\qquad\quad x^2 + y^2 \leq 9$

Final Exam

1. Simplify: $12 - 8[3 - (-2)]^2 \div 5 - 3$

2. Evaluate $\dfrac{a^2 - b^2}{a - b}$ when $a = 3$ and $b = -4$.

3. Simplify: $5 - 2[3x - 7(2 - x) - 5x]$

4. Solve: $\dfrac{3}{4}x - 2 = 4$

5. Solve: $\dfrac{2 - 4x}{3} - \dfrac{x - 6}{12} = \dfrac{5x - 2}{6}$

6. Solve: $8 - |5 - 3x| = 1$

7. Solve: $|2x + 5| < 3$

8. Solve: $2 - 3x < 6$ and $2x + 1 > 4$

9. Find the equation of the line that contains the point $(-2, 1)$ and is perpendicular to the line $3x - 2y = 6$.

10. Simplify: $2a[5 - a(2 - 3a) - 2a] + 3a^2$

11. Simplify: $\dfrac{3}{2 + i}$

12. Write a quadratic equation that has integer coefficients and has solutions $-\dfrac{1}{2}$ and 2.

13. Factor: $8 - x^3y^3$

14. Factor: $x - y - x^3 + x^2y$

15. Divide: $(2x^3 - 7x^2 + 4) \div (2x - 3)$

16. Divide: $\dfrac{x^2 - 3x}{2x^2 - 3x - 5} \div \dfrac{4x - 12}{4x^2 - 4}$

17. Subtract: $\dfrac{x - 2}{x + 2} - \dfrac{x + 3}{x - 3}$

18. Simplify: $\dfrac{\dfrac{3}{x} + \dfrac{1}{x + 4}}{\dfrac{1}{x} + \dfrac{3}{x + 4}}$

19. Solve: $\dfrac{5}{x - 2} - \dfrac{5}{x^2 - 4} = \dfrac{1}{x + 2}$

20. Solve $a_n = a_1 + (n - 1)d$ for d.

21. Simplify: $\left(\dfrac{4x^2y^{-1}}{3x^{-1}y}\right)^{-2}\left(\dfrac{2x^{-1}y^2}{9x^{-2}y^2}\right)^3$

22. Simplify: $\left(\dfrac{3x^{\frac{2}{3}}y^{\frac{1}{2}}}{6x^2y^{\frac{4}{3}}}\right)^6$

23. Subtract: $x\sqrt{18x^2y^3} - y\sqrt{50x^4y}$

24. Simplify: $\dfrac{\sqrt{16x^5y^4}}{\sqrt{32xy^7}}$

25. Solve by using the quadratic formula: $2x^2 - 3x - 1 = 0$

26. Solve: $x^{\frac{2}{3}} - x^{\frac{1}{3}} - 6 = 0$

27. Find the equation of the line containing the points $(3, -2)$ and $(1, 4)$.

28. Solve: $\dfrac{2}{x} - \dfrac{2}{2x + 3} = 1$

29. Solve by the addition method: $3x - 2y = 1$
$5x - 3y = 3$

30. Evaluate the determinant: $\begin{vmatrix} 3 & 4 \\ -1 & 2 \end{vmatrix}$

31. Solve for x: $\log_3 x - \log_3(x - 3) = \log_3 2$

32. Write $\displaystyle\sum_{i=1}^{5} 2y^i$ in expanded form.

33. Find an equivalent fraction for $0.5\overline{1}$.

34. Find the 3rd term in the expansion of $(x - 2y)^9$.

35. Solve: $x^2 - y^2 = 4$
$x + y = 1$

36. Find the inverse function of $f(x) = \dfrac{2}{3}x - 4$.

37. Write $2(\log_2 a - \log_2 b)$ as a single logarithm with a coefficient of 1.

38. Graph $2x - 3y = 9$ by using the x- and y-intercepts.

39. Graph the solution set of $3x + 2y > 6$.

40. Graph: $f(x) = -x^2 + 4$

41. Graph: $\dfrac{x^2}{16} + \dfrac{y^2}{4} = 1$

42. Graph: $f(x) = \log_2(x + 1)$

43. Graph $f(x) = x + 2^{-x}$ and approximate to the nearest tenth the values of x for which $f(x) = 2$.

44. Given the graph of $f(x) = \ln x$ shown below, graph $g(x) = \ln(x + 3)$.

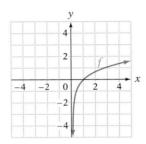

45. **Test Scores** An average score of 70–79 in a history class receives a C grade. A student has grades of 64, 58, 82, and 77 on four history tests. Find the range of scores on the fifth test that will give the student a C grade for the course.

46. **Uniform Motion** A jogger and a cyclist set out at 8 A.M. from the same point headed in the same direction. The average speed of the cyclist is two and a half times the average speed of the jogger. In 2 h, the cyclist is 24 mi ahead of the jogger. How far did the cyclist ride?

47. **Investments** You have a total of $12,000 invested in two simple interest accounts. On one account, a money market fund, the annual simple interest rate is 8.5%. On the other account, a tax-free bond fund, the annual simple interest rate is 6.4%. The total annual interest earned by the two accounts is $936. How much do you have invested in each account?

48. **Geometry** The length of a rectangle is 1 ft less than three times the width. The area of the rectangle is 140 ft². Find the length and width of the rectangle.

49. **Investments** Three hundred shares of a utility stock earn a yearly dividend of $486. How many additional shares of the utility stock would give a total dividend income of $810?

50. **Uniform Motion** An account executive traveled 45 mi by car and then an additional 1050 mi by plane. The rate of the plane was seven times the rate of the car. The total time of the trip was $3\frac{1}{4}$ h. Find the rate of the plane.

51. Physics An object is dropped from the top of a building. Find the distance the object has fallen when the speed reaches 75 ft/s. Use the equation $v = \sqrt{64d}$, where v is the speed of the object and d is the distance. Round to the nearest whole number.

52. Uniform Motion A small plane made a trip of 660 mi in 5 h. The plane traveled the first 360 mi at a constant rate before increasing its speed by 30 mph. Another 300 mi was traveled at the increased speed. Find the rate of the plane for the first 360 mi.

53. Light The intensity (L) of a light source is inversely proportional to the square of the distance (d) from the source. If the intensity is 8 lumens at a distance of 20 ft, what is the intensity when the distance is 4 ft?

54. Uniform Motion A motorboat traveling with the current can go 30 mi in 2 h. Against the current, it takes 3 h to go the same distance. Find the rate of the motorboat in calm water and the rate of the current.

55. Investments An investor deposits $4000 into an account that earns 9% annual interest compounded monthly. Use the compound interest formula $P = A(1 + i)^n$, where A is the original value of the investment, i is the interest rate per compounding period, n is the total number of compounding periods, and P is the value of the investment after n periods, to find the value of the investment after 2 years. Round to the nearest cent.

56. Appreciation Assume the average value of a home increases 6% per year. How much would a house costing $180,000 be worth in 20 years? Round to the nearest dollar.

Appendix

Table of Properties

Properties of Real Numbers

The Associative Property of Addition

If a, b, and c are real numbers, then
$(a + b) + c = a + (b + c)$.

The Commutative Property of Addition

If a and b are real numbers, then $a + b = b + a$.

The Addition Property of Zero

If a is a real number, then $a + 0 = 0 + a = a$.

The Multiplication Property of Zero

If a is a real number, then $a \cdot 0 = 0 \cdot a = 0$.

The Inverse Property of Addition

If a is a real number, then
$a + (-a) = (-a) + a = 0$.

The Associative Property of Multiplication

If a, b, and c are real numbers, then
$(a \cdot b) \cdot c = a \cdot (b \cdot c)$.

The Commutative Property of Multiplication

If a and b are real numbers, then $a \cdot b = b \cdot a$.

The Multiplication Property of One

If a is a real number, then $a \cdot 1 = 1 \cdot a = a$.

The Inverse Property of Multiplication

If a is a real number and $a \neq 0$, then
$$a \cdot \frac{1}{a} = \frac{1}{a} \cdot a = 1.$$

Distributive Property

If a, b, and c are real numbers, then
$a(b + c) = ab + ac$ or $(b + c)a = ba + ca$.

Properties of Equations

Addition Property of Equations

The same number or variable term can be added to each side of an equation without changing the solution of the equation.

Multiplication Property of Equations

Each side of an equation can be multiplied by the same nonzero number without changing the solution of the equation.

Properties of Inequalities

Addition Property of Inequalities

If $a > b$, then $a + c > b + c$.

If $a < b$, then $a + c < b + c$.

Multiplication Property of Inequalities

If $a > b$ and $c > 0$, then $ac > bc$.

If $a < b$ and $c > 0$, then $ac < bc$.

If $a > b$ and $c < 0$, then $ac < bc$.

If $a < b$ and $c < 0$, then $ac > bc$.

Properties of Exponents

If m and n are integers, then $x^m \cdot x^n = x^{m+n}$.

If m and n are integers, then $(x^m)^n = x^{mn}$.

If $x \neq 0$, then $x^0 = 1$.

If m and n are integers and $x \neq 0$, then
$$\frac{x^m}{x^n} = x^{m-n}.$$

If m, n, and p are integers, then
$(x^m \cdot y^n)^p = x^{mp} y^{np}$.

If n is a positive integer and $x \neq 0$, then
$$x^{-n} = \frac{1}{x^n} \text{ and } \frac{1}{x^{-n}} = x^n.$$

If m, n, and p are integers and $y \neq 0$, then
$$\left(\frac{x^m}{y^n} \right)^p = \frac{x^{mp}}{y^{np}}.$$

Table of Properties (*continued*)

Principle of Zero Products

If $a \cdot b = 0$, then $a = 0$ or $b = 0$.

Properties of Radical Expressions

If a and b are positive real numbers, then
$\sqrt[n]{ab} = \sqrt[n]{a}\,\sqrt[n]{b}$.

If a and b are positive real numbers, then

$$\sqrt[n]{\frac{a}{b}} = \frac{\sqrt[n]{a}}{\sqrt[n]{b}}.$$

Property of Squaring Both Sides of an Equation

If a and b are real numbers and $a = b$, then $a^2 = b^2$.

Properties of Logarithms

If x, y, and b are positive real numbers and $b \neq 1$, then $\log_b(xy) = \log_b x + \log_b y$.

If x, y, and b are positive real numbers and $b \neq 1$, then $\log_b \frac{x}{y} = \log_b x - \log_b y$.

If x and b are positive real numbers, $b \neq 1$, and r is any real number, then $\log_b x^r = r \log_b x$.

If x and b are positive real numbers and $b \neq 1$, then $\log_b b^x = x$.

Keystroke Guide for the TI-83, TI-83 Plus, and TI-84 Plus

Basic Operations

Numerical calculations are performed on the **home screen.** You can always return to the home screen by pressing [2nd] QUIT. Pressing [CLEAR] erases the home screen.

To evaluate the expression $-2(3 + 5) - 8 \div 4$, use the following keystrokes.

[(-)] 2 [( ] 3 [+] 5 [ )] [−] 8 [÷] 4 [ENTER]

Note: There is a difference between the key to enter a negative number, [(-)], and the key for subtraction, [−]. You cannot use these keys interchangeably.

The [2nd] key is used to access the commands in gold writing above a key. For instance, to evaluate the $\sqrt{49}$, press [2nd] √ 49 [ )] [ENTER] .

The [ALPHA] key is used to place a letter on the screen. One reason to do this is to store a value of a variable. The following keystrokes give A the value of 5.

5 [STO▶] [ALPHA] A [ENTER]

This value is now available in calculations. For instance, we can find the value of $3a^2$ by using the following keystrokes: 3 [ALPHA] A [x^2] . To display the value of the variable on the screen, press [2nd] RCL [ALPHA] A.

Note: When you use the [ALPHA] key, only capital letters are available on the TI-83 calculator.

Complex Numbers

To perform operations on complex numbers, first press [MODE] and then use the arrow keys to select a+bi. Then press [ENTER] [2nd] QUIT.

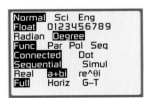

Addition of complex numbers To add $(3 + 4i) + (2 - 7i)$, use the keystrokes

[( ] 3 [+] 4 [2nd] i [ )] [+]

[( ] 2 [−] 7 [2nd] i [ )] [ENTER] .

Division of complex numbers To divide $\frac{26 + 2i}{2 + 4i}$, use the keystrokes [( ] 26 [+] 2 [2nd] i [ )] [÷]

[( ] 2 [+] 4 [2nd] i [ )] [ENTER] .

Note: Operations for subtraction and multiplication are similar.

Additional operations on complex numbers can be found by selecting CPX under the MATH key.

To find the absolute value of $2 - 5i$, press MATH (scroll to CPX) (scroll to abs) ENTER (2 − 5 2nd i) ENTER .

Evaluating Functions

There are various methods of evaluating a function, but all methods require that the expression be entered as one of the ten functions Y₁ to Y₀. To evaluate $f(x) = \frac{x^2}{x - 1}$ when $x = -3$, enter the expression into, for instance, Y₁, and then press VARS ▸ 11 ((−) 3) ENTER .

Take Note

Use the down arrow key to scroll past Y₇ to see Y₈, Y₉, and Y₀.

Note: If you try to evaluate a function at a number that is not in the domain of the function, you will get an error message. For instance, 1 is not in the domain of $f(x) = \frac{x^2}{x - 1}$. If we try to evaluate the function at 1, the error screen at the right appears.

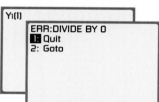

Evaluating Variable Expressions

To evaluate a variable expression, first store the values of each variable. Then enter the variable expression. For instance, to evaluate $s^2 + 2sl$ when $s = 4$ and $l = 5$, use the following keystrokes.

4 STO▸ ALPHA S ENTER 5 STO▸ ALPHA L ENTER ALPHA S
x^2 + 2 ALPHA S ALPHA L ENTER

Graph

To graph a function, use the Y= key to enter the expression for the function, select a suitable viewing window, and then press GRAPH . For instance, to graph $f(x) = 0.1x^3 - 2x - 1$ in the standard viewing window, use the following keystrokes.

Y= 0.1 X,T,θ,n ^ 3 − 2 X,T,θ,n − 1 ZOOM (scroll to 6) ENTER

Note: For the keystrokes above, you do not have to scroll to 6. Alternatively, use ZOOM 6. This will select the standard viewing window and automatically start the graph. Use the WINDOW key to create a custom window for a graph.

Graphing Inequalities

To illustrate this feature, we will graph $y \le 2x - 1$. Enter $2x - 1$ into Y_1. Because $y \le 2x - 1$, we want to shade below the graph. Move the cursor to the left of Y_1 and press ⟨ENTER⟩ three times. Press ⟨GRAPH⟩.

Note: To shade above the graph, move the cursor to the left of Y_1 and press ⟨ENTER⟩ two times. An inequality with the symbol $\le$ or $\ge$ should be graphed with a solid line, and an inequality with the symbol $<$ or $>$ should be graphed with a dashed line. However, the graph of a linear inequality on a graphing calculator does not distinguish between a solid line and a dashed line.

To graph the solution set of a system of inequalities, solve each inequality for y and graph each inequality. The solution set is the intersection of the two inequalities. The solution set of $\begin{array}{l} 3x + 2y > 10 \\ 4x - 3y \le 5 \end{array}$ is shown at the right.

Intersect

The INTERSECT feature is used to solve a system of equations. To illustrate this feature, we will use the system of equations $\begin{array}{l} 2x - 3y = 13 \\ 3x + 4y = -6 \end{array}$.

Note: Some equations can be solved by this method. See the section "Solve an equation" below. Also, this method is used to find a number in the domain of a function for a given number in the range. See the section "Find a domain element."

Solve each of the equations in the system of equations for y. In this case, we have $y = \frac{2}{3}x - \frac{13}{3}$ and $y = -\frac{3}{4}x - \frac{3}{2}$.

Use the Y-editor to enter $\frac{2}{3}x - \frac{13}{3}$ into Y_1 and $-\frac{3}{4}x - \frac{3}{2}$ into Y_2. Graph the two functions in the standard viewing window. (If the window does not show the point of intersection of the two graphs, adjust the window until you can see the point of intersection.)

Press ⟨2nd⟩ CALC (scroll to 5, intersect) ⟨ENTER⟩.

Alternatively, you can just press ⟨2nd⟩ CALC 5.

First curve? is shown at the bottom of the screen and identifies one of the two graphs on the screen. Press [ENTER].

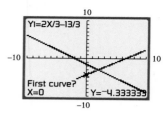

Second curve? is shown at the bottom of the screen and identifies the second of the two graphs on the screen. Press [ENTER].

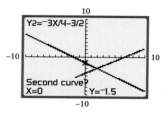

Guess? shown at the bottom of the screen asks you to use the left or right arrow key to move the cursor to the *approximate* location of the point of intersection. (If there are two or more points of intersection, it does not matter which one you choose first.) Press [ENTER].

The solution of the system of equations is $(2, -3)$.

Solve an equation   To illustrate the steps involved, we will solve the equation $2x + 4 = -3x - 1$. The idea is to write the equation as the system of equations $\begin{aligned} y &= 2x + 4 \\ y &= -3x - 1 \end{aligned}$ and then use the steps for solving a system of equations.

Use the Y-editor to enter the left and right sides of the equation into Y₁ and Y₂. Graph the two functions and then follow the steps for **Intersect**.

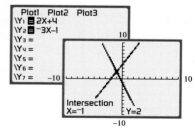

The solution is -1, the x-coordinate of the point of intersection.

Find a domain element   For this example, we will find a number in the domain of $f(x) = -\frac{2}{3}x + 2$ that corresponds to 4 in the range of the function. This is like solving the system of equations $y = -\frac{2}{3}x + 2$ and $y = 4$.

Use the Y-editor to enter the expression for the function in Y₁ and the desired output, 4, in Y₂. Graph the two functions and then follow the steps for **Intersect**.

The point of intersection is $(-3, 4)$. The number -3 in the domain of f produces an output of 4 in the range of f.

Math   Pressing [MATH] gives you access to many built-in functions. The following keystrokes will convert 0.125 into a fraction: .125 [MATH] 1 [ENTER].

Additional built-in functions under **MATH** can be found by pressing **MATH** . For instance, to evaluate $-|-25|$, press (-) **MATH** 1 (-) 25 **)** **ENTER** .

See your owner's manual for assistance with other functions under the **MATH** key.

Min and Max   The local minimum and the local maximum values of a function are calculated by accessing the CALC menu. For this demonstration, we will find the minimum value and the maximum value of $f(x) = 0.2x^3 + 0.3x^2 - 3.6x + 2$.

Enter the function into Y₁. Press **2nd** CALC (scroll to 3 for minimum of the function) **ENTER** .

Alternatively, you can just press **2nd** CALC 3.

Left Bound? shown at the bottom of the screen asks you to use the left or right arrow key to move the cursor to the *left* of the minimum. Press **ENTER** .

Right Bound? shown at the bottom of the screen asks you to use the left or right arrow key to move the cursor to the *right* of the minimum. Press **ENTER** .

Guess? shown at the bottom of the screen asks you to use the left or right arrow key to move the cursor to the *approximate* location of the minimum. Press **ENTER** .

The minimum value of the function is the *y*-coordinate. For this example, the minimum value of the function is -2.4.

The *x*-coordinate for the minimum is 2. However, because of rounding errors in the calculation, it is shown as a number close to 2.

To find the maximum value of the function, follow the same steps as above except select **maximum** under the CALC menu. The screens for this calculation are shown on the next page.

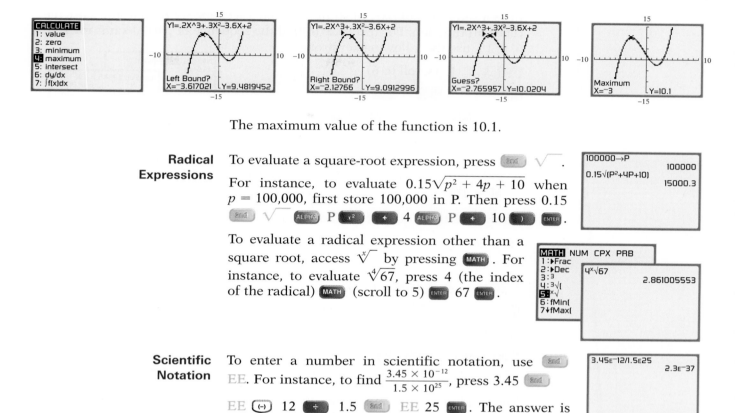

The maximum value of the function is 10.1.

Radical Expressions

To evaluate a square-root expression, press ⌜2nd⌝ √ .
For instance, to evaluate $0.15\sqrt{p^2 + 4p + 10}$ when $p = 100,000$, first store 100,000 in P. Then press 0.15
⌜2nd⌝ √ ⌜ALPHA⌝ P ⌜x^2⌝ ⌜+⌝ 4 ⌜ALPHA⌝ P ⌜+⌝ 10 ⌜)⌝ ⌜ENTER⌝.

To evaluate a radical expression other than a square root, access $\sqrt[x]{}$ by pressing ⌜MATH⌝. For instance, to evaluate $\sqrt[4]{67}$, press 4 (the index of the radical) ⌜MATH⌝ (scroll to 5) ⌜ENTER⌝ 67 ⌜ENTER⌝.

Scientific Notation

To enter a number in scientific notation, use ⌜2nd⌝ EE. For instance, to find $\dfrac{3.45 \times 10^{-12}}{1.5 \times 10^{25}}$, press 3.45 ⌜2nd⌝
EE ⌜(-)⌝ 12 ⌜÷⌝ 1.5 ⌜2nd⌝ EE 25 ⌜ENTER⌝. The answer is 2.3×10^{-37}.

Sequences and Series

The terms of a sequence and the sum of a series can be calculated by using the ⌜2nd⌝ LIST feature.

Store a sequence A sequence is stored in one of the lists L₁ through L₆. For instance, to store the sequence 1, 3, 5, 7, 9 in L₁, use the following keystrokes.

⌜2nd⌝ { 1 ⌜,⌝ 3 ⌜,⌝ 5 ⌜,⌝ 7 ⌜,⌝
9 ⌜2nd⌝ } ⌜STO ▸⌝ ⌜2nd⌝ L1 ⌜ENTER⌝

Display the terms of a sequence The terms of a sequence are displayed by using the function seq(expression, variable, begin, end, increment). For instance, to display the third through eighth terms of the sequence given by $a_n = n^2 + 6$, enter the following keystrokes.

⌜2nd⌝ LIST ⌜▸⌝ (scroll to 5)

⌜ENTER⌝ ⌜X,T,θ,n⌝ ⌜x^2⌝ ⌜+⌝ 6

⌜,⌝ ⌜X,T,θ,n⌝ ⌜,⌝ 3 ⌜,⌝ 8

⌜,⌝ 1 ⌜ENTER⌝ ⌜STO ▸⌝ ⌜2nd⌝ L1 ⌜ENTER⌝

The keystrokes ⌜STO ▸⌝ ⌜2nd⌝ L1 ⌜ENTER⌝ store the terms of the sequence in L₁. This is not necessary but is sometimes helpful if additional work will be done with that sequence.

Find a sequence of partial sums   To find a sequence of partial sums, use the cumSum(function. For instance, to find the sequence of partial sums for 2, 4, 6, 8, 10, use the following keystrokes.

 LIST ○ (scroll to 6)

ENTER 2nd [2 ● , 4 ● , 6

● , 8 ● , 10 2nd] ●) ENTER

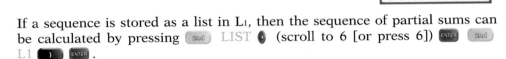

If a sequence is stored as a list in L₁, then the sequence of partial sums can be calculated by pressing 2nd LIST ○ (scroll to 6 [or press 6]) ENTER 2nd L1 ●) ENTER .

Find the sum of a series   The sum of a series is calculated using sum<list, start, end>. For instance, to find $\sum_{n=3}^{6} (n^2 + 2)$, enter the following keystrokes.

2nd LIST ○ ○ (scroll to 5)

ENTER 2nd LIST ○ (scroll to 5 [or press 5])

ENTER X,T,θ,n x² + 2 ● , X,T,θ,n ● , 3

● , 6 ● , 1 ●) ENTER

Table   There are three steps in creating an input/output table for a function. First use the (Y=) editor to input the function. The second step is setting up the table, and the third step is displaying the table.

To set up the table, press 2nd TBLSET. TblStart is the first value of the independent variable in the input/output table. △Tbl is the difference between successive values. Setting this to 1 means that, for this table, the input values are −2, −1, 0, 1, 2. . . . If △Tbl = 0.5, then the input values are −2, −1.5, −1, −0.5, 0, 0.5, . . .

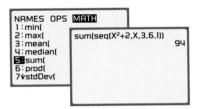

Indpnt is the independent variable. When this is set to Auto, values of the independent variable are automatically entered into the table. Depend is the dependent variable. When this is set to Auto, values of the dependent variable are automatically entered into the table.

To display the table, press 2nd TABLE. An input/output table for $f(x) = x^2 - 1$ is shown at the right.

Once the table is on the screen, the up and down arrow keys can be used to display more values in the table. For the table at the right, we used the up arrow key to move to $x = -7$.

An input/output table for any given input can be created by selecting Ask for the independent variable. The table at the right shows an input/output table for $f(x) = \dfrac{4x}{x-2}$ for selected values of x. Note the word **ERROR** when 2 was entered. This occurred because f is not defined when $x = 2$.

Note: Using the table feature in **Ask** mode is the same as evaluating a function for given values of the independent variable. For instance, from the table at the right, we have $f(4) = 8$.

Test   The TEST feature has many uses, one of which is to graph the solution set of a linear inequality in one variable. To illustrate this feature, we will graph the solution set of $x - 1 < 4$. Press (Y=) (X,T,θ,n) (−) 1 (2nd) TEST (scroll to 5) (ENTER) 4 (GRAPH) .

Trace   Once a graph is drawn, pressing (TRACE) will place a cursor on the screen, and the coordinates of the point below the cursor are shown at the bottom of the screen. Use the left and right arrow keys to move the cursor along the graph. For the graph at the right, we have $f(4.8) = 3.4592$, where $f(x) = 0.1x^3 - 2x + 2$ is shown at the top left of the screen.

In TRACE mode, you can evaluate a function at any value of the independent variable that is within Xmin and Xmax. To do this, first graph the function. Now press (TRACE) (the value of x) (ENTER) . For the graph at the left below, we used $x = -3.5$. If a value of x is chosen outside the window, an error message is displayed.

   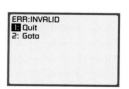

In the example above where we entered -3.5 for x, the value of the function was calculated as 4.7125. This means that $f(-3.5) = 4.7125$. The keystrokes (2nd) QUIT (VARS) (▸) 11 (MATH) 1 (ENTER) will convert the decimal value into a fraction.

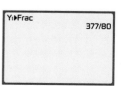

When the TRACE feature is used with two or more graphs, the up and down arrow keys are used to move between the graphs. The graphs below are for the functions $f(x) = 0.1x^3 - 2x + 2$ and $g(x) = 2x - 3$. By using the up and down arrows, we can place the cursor on either graph. The right and left arrows are used to move along the graph.

Window   The viewing window for a graph is controlled by pressing **WINDOW**. Xmin and Xmax are the minimum value and maximum value, respectively, of the independent variable shown on the graph. Xscl is the distance between tic marks on the x-axis. Ymin and Ymax are the minimum value and maximum value, respectively, of the dependent variable shown on the graph. Yscl is the distance between tic marks on the y-axis. Leave Xres as 1.

Note: In the standard viewing window, the distance between tic marks on the x-axis is different from the distance between tic marks on the y-axis. This will distort a graph. A more accurate picture of a graph can be created by using a square viewing window. See **ZOOM**.

    The **Y=** editor is used to enter the expression for a function. There are ten possible functions, labeled Y_1 to Y_0, that can be active at any one time. For instance, to enter $f(x) = x^2 + 3x - 2$ as Y_1, use the following keystrokes.

Y= **X,T,θ,n** **x²** **+** 3 **X,T,θ,n** **−** 2

Note: If an expression is already entered for Y_1, place the cursor anywhere on that expression and press **CLEAR**.

To enter $s = \dfrac{2v - 1}{v^3 - 3}$ into Y_2, place the cursor to the right of the equals sign for Y_2. Then press **(** 2 **X,T,θ,n** **−**

1 **)** **÷** **(** **X,T,θ,n** **^** 3 **−** 3 **)** .

Note: When we enter an equation, the independent variable, v in the expression above, is entered using **X,T,θ,n**. The dependent variable, s in the expression above, is one of Y_1 to Y_0. Also note the use of parentheses to ensure the correct order of operations.

Observe the black rectangle that covers the equals sign for the two examples we have shown. This rectangle means that the function is "active." If we were to press **GRAPH**, then the graph of both functions would appear. You can make a function inactive by using the arrow keys to move the cursor over the

equals sign of that function and then pressing **ENTER**. This will remove the black rectangle. We have done that for Y_2, as shown at the right. Now if **GRAPH** is pressed, only Y_1 will be graphed.

It is also possible to control the appearance of the graph by moving the cursor on the **Y=** screen to the left of any Y. With the cursor in this position, pressing **ENTER** will change the appearance of the graph. The options are shown at the right.

Zero   The ZERO feature of a graphing calculator is used for various calculations: to find the x-intercepts of a function, to solve some equations, and to find the zero of a function.

x-intercepts   To illustrate the procedure for finding x-intercepts, we will use $f(x) = x^2 + x - 2$.

First, use the Y-editor to enter the expression for the function and then graph the function in the standard viewing window. (It may be necessary to adjust this window so that the intercepts are visible.) Once the graph is displayed, use the following keystrokes to find the x-intercepts of the graph of the function.

Press **2nd** CALC (scroll to 2 for **zero** of the function) **ENTER**.

Alternatively, you can just press **2nd** CALC 2.

Left Bound? shown at the bottom of the screen asks you to use the left or right arrow key to move the cursor to the *left* of the desired x-intercept. Press **ENTER**.

Right Bound? shown at the bottom of the screen asks you to use the left or right arrow key to move the cursor to the *right* of the desired x-intercept. Press **ENTER**.

Guess? shown at the bottom of the screen asks you to use the left or right arrow key to move the cursor to the *approximate* location of the desired x-intercept. Press **ENTER**.

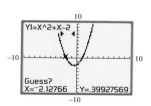

The x-coordinate of an x-intercept is -2. Therefore, an x-intercept is $(-2, 0)$.

To find the other x-intercept, follow the same steps as above. The screens for this calculation are shown below.

A second x-intercept is $(1, 0)$.

Solve an equation To use the ZERO feature to solve an equation, first rewrite the equation with all terms on one side. For instance, one way to solve the equation $x^3 - x + 1 = -2x + 3$ is first to rewrite it as $x^3 + x - 2 = 0$. Enter $x^3 + x - 2$ into Y₁ and then follow the steps for finding x-intercepts.

Find the real zeros of a function To find the real zeros of a function, follow the steps for finding x-intercepts.

Zoom Pressing **ZOOM** enables you to select some preset viewing windows. This key also gives you access to ZBox, Zoom In, and Zoom Out. These functions enable you to redraw a selected portion of a graph in a new window. Some windows used frequently in this text are shown below.

Solutions to Chapter Problems

Solutions to Chapter 1 Problems

SECTION 1.1

Problem 1

Replace z by each of the elements of the set and determine whether the inequality is true.

$z > -5$

$-10 > -5$ False

$-5 > -5$ False

$6 > -5$ True

The inequality is true for 6.

Problem 2

Replace z by each element of the set and determine the value of the expression.

$|z|$

$|-11| = 11$

$|0| = 0$

$|8| = 8$

Problem 3

$\{1, 3, 5, 7, 9, 11\}$

Problem 4

$\{x \,|\, x < 7, x \in \text{real numbers}\}$

Problem 5

$A \cup C = \{-5, -2, -1, 0, 1, 2, 5\}$

Problem 6

$E \cap F = \varnothing$

Problem 7

Problem 8

Problem 9

$[-8, -1)$

Problem 10

$\{x \,|\, x > -12\}$

Problem 11

SECTION 1.2

Problem 1

$6 - (-8) - 10 = 6 + 8 + (-10)$
$$= 14 + (-10)$$
$$= 4$$

Problem 2

A. $2|-7|(-8) = 2(7)(-8)$
$$= 14(-8) = -112$$

B. $-\dfrac{-36}{-3} = -\left(\dfrac{-36}{-3}\right) = -12$

Problem 3

$-\dfrac{5}{8} \div \left(-\dfrac{15}{16}\right) = \dfrac{5}{8} \cdot \dfrac{16}{15} = \dfrac{5 \cdot 16}{8 \cdot 15} = \dfrac{2}{3}$

Problem 4

A. $-\dfrac{5}{12} \div \dfrac{10}{27} = -\dfrac{5}{12} \cdot \dfrac{27}{10}$
$$= -\dfrac{5 \cdot 27}{12 \cdot 10}$$
$$= -\dfrac{9}{8}$$

B. $\begin{array}{r} 12.094 \\ -\ 8.729 \\ \hline 3.365 \end{array}$

$-8.729 + 12.094 = 3.365$

C. $-8 - |5 - 12| = -8 - |-7|$
$$= -8 - 7$$
$$= -15$$

Problem 5

$\begin{array}{r} 4.027 \\ \times\ \ 0.49 \\ \hline 36243 \\ 16108\ \ \\ \hline 1.97323 \end{array} \approx 1.97$

$-4.027(0.49) \approx -1.97$

Problem 6

$(-4)^2 = (-4)(-4) = 16$

$-4^2 = -(4)(4) = -16$

Problem 7

$-\left(\dfrac{2}{5}\right)^3 \cdot 5^2 = -\left(\dfrac{2}{5}\right)\left(\dfrac{2}{5}\right)\left(\dfrac{2}{5}\right) \cdot (5)(5)$
$$= -\dfrac{8}{5}$$

Problem 8

$(3.81 - 1.41)^2 \div 0.036 - 1.89$
$$= (2.40)^2 \div 0.036 - 1.89$$
$$= 5.76 \div 0.036 - 1.89$$
$$= 160 - 1.89$$
$$= 158.11$$

Problem 9

$\dfrac{1}{3} + \dfrac{5}{8} \div \dfrac{15}{16} - \dfrac{7}{12}$

$= \dfrac{1}{3} + \dfrac{5}{8} \cdot \dfrac{16}{15} - \dfrac{7}{12}$

$$= \frac{1}{3} + \frac{2}{3} - \frac{7}{12}$$

$$= 1 - \frac{7}{12}$$

$$= \frac{5}{12}$$

Problem 10

$$\frac{11}{12} - \frac{\dfrac{5}{4}}{2 - \dfrac{7}{2}} \cdot \frac{3}{4}$$

$$= \frac{11}{12} - \frac{\dfrac{5}{4}}{-\dfrac{3}{2}} \cdot \frac{3}{4}$$

$$= \frac{11}{12} - \left[\frac{5}{4} \cdot \left(-\frac{2}{3} \right) \right] \cdot \frac{3}{4}$$

$$= \frac{11}{12} - \left(-\frac{5}{6} \right) \cdot \frac{3}{4}$$

$$= \frac{11}{12} - \left(-\frac{5}{8} \right)$$

$$= \frac{37}{24}$$

SECTION 1.3

Problem 1

$$(x)\left(\frac{1}{4} \right) = \left(\frac{1}{4} \right)(x)$$

Problem 2
The Associative Property of Addition

Problem 3
$(b - c)^2 \div ab$
$[2 - (-4)]^2 \div (-3)(2)$
$= [6]^2 \div (-3)(2)$
$= 36 \div (-3)(2)$
$= -12(2)$
$= -24$

Problem 4
$SA = \pi r^2 + \pi r l$
$SA = \pi(5)^2 + \pi(5)(12)$
$SA = 25\pi + 60\pi$
$SA = 85\pi$
$SA \approx 267.04$

The exact area is 85π cm².
The approximate area is 267.04 cm².

Problem 5
$(2x + xy - y) - (5x - 7xy + y)$
$= 2x + xy - y - 5x + 7xy - y$
$= -3x + 8xy - 2y$

Problem 6
$2x - 3[y - 3(x - 2y + 4)]$
$= 2x - 3[y - 3x + 6y - 12]$
$= 2x - 3[7y - 3x - 12]$
$= 2x - 21y + 9x + 36$
$= 11x - 21y + 36$

SECTION 1.4

Problem 1
the unknown number: n
the difference between 8 and twice the unknown
   number: $8 - 2n$

$n - (8 - 2n)$
$= n - 8 + 2n$
$= 3n - 8$

Problem 2
the unknown number: n

three-eighths of the number: $\dfrac{3}{8}n$

five-twelfths of the number: $\dfrac{5}{12}n$

$\dfrac{3}{8}n + \dfrac{5}{12}n = \dfrac{9}{24}n + \dfrac{10}{24}n = \dfrac{19}{24}n$

Problem 3
the pounds of caramel: c
the pounds of milk chocolate: $c + 3$

Problem 4
the depth of the shallow end: D
the depth of the deep end: $2D + 2$

Solutions to Chapter 2 Problems

SECTION 2.1

Problem 1
$-3x = -18$
$\dfrac{-3x}{-3} = \dfrac{-18}{-3}$
$x = 6$

The solution is 6.

Problem 2
$6x - 5 - 3x = 14 - 5x$
$3x - 5 = 14 - 5x$
$3x + 5x - 5 = 14 - 5x + 5x$
$8x - 5 = 14$
$8x - 5 + 5 = 14 + 5$
$8x = 19$
$\dfrac{8x}{8} = \dfrac{19}{8}$
$x = \dfrac{19}{8}$

The solution is $\dfrac{19}{8}$.

Problem 3

$6(5 - x) - 12 = 2x - 3(4 + x)$
$30 - 6x - 12 = 2x - 12 - 3x$
$18 - 6x = -x - 12$
$18 - 5x = -12$
$-5x = -30$
$x = 6$

The solution is 6.

Problem 4

The LCM of 3, 5, and 30 is 30.

$$\frac{2x - 7}{3} - \frac{5x + 4}{5} = \frac{-x - 4}{30}$$

$$30\left(\frac{2x - 7}{3} - \frac{5x + 4}{5}\right) = 30\left(\frac{-x - 4}{30}\right)$$

$$\frac{30(2x - 7)}{3} - \frac{30(5x + 4)}{5} = \frac{30(-x - 4)}{30}$$

$10(2x - 7) - 6(5x + 4) = -x - 4$
$20x - 70 - 30x - 24 = -x - 4$
$-10x - 94 = -x - 4$
$-9x - 94 = -4$
$-9x = 90$
$x = -10$

The solution is −10.

Problem 5

Strategy Next year's salary: s
Next year's salary is the sum of this year's salary and the raise.

Solution $s = 34{,}500 + 0.08(34{,}500)$
$= 34{,}500 + 2760$
$= 37{,}260$

Next year's salary is $37,260.

SECTION 2.2

Problem 1

Strategy ▶ Number of 3¢ stamps: x
Number of 10¢ stamps: $2x + 2$
Number of 15¢ stamps: $3x$

	Number	Value	Total value
3¢ stamp	x	3	$3x$
10¢ stamp	$2x + 2$	10	$10(2x + 2)$
15¢ stamp	$3x$	15	$45x$

▶ The sum of the total values of the individual types of stamps equals the total value of all the stamps (156 cents).

Solution $3x + 10(2x + 2) + 45x = 156$
$3x + 20x + 20 + 45x = 156$
$68x + 20 = 156$
$68x = 136$
$x = 2$

$3x = 3(2) = 6$

There are six 15¢ stamps in the collection.

Problem 2

Strategy ▶ The first number: n
The second number: $2n$
The third number: $4n - 3$

▶ The sum of the numbers is 81.

Solution $n + 2n + (4n - 3) = 81$
$7n - 3 = 81$
$7n = 84$
$n = 12$

$2n = 2(12) = 24$
$4n - 3 = 4(12) - 3 = 48 - 3 = 45$

The numbers are 12, 24, and 45.

SECTION 2.3

Problem 1

Strategy ▶ Pounds of $4.00 hamburger: x
Pounds of $2.80 hamburger: $75 - x$

	Amount	Cost	Value
$4.00 hamburger	x	4.00	$4.00x$
$2.80 hamburger	$75 - x$	2.80	$2.80(75 - x)$
Mixture	75	3.20	$75(3.20)$

▶ The sum of the values before mixing equals the value after mixing.

Solution $4.00x + 2.80(75 - x) = 75(3.20)$
$4x + 210 - 2.80x = 240$
$1.2x + 210 = 240$
$1.2x = 30$
$x = 25$
$75 - x = 75 - 25 = 50$

The mixture must contain 25 lb of the $4.00 hamburger and 50 lb of the $2.80 hamburger.

Problem 2

Strategy The distance is 350 mi. Therefore, $d = 350$. The plane is flying into a headwind, so the rate of the plane is the difference between its rate in calm air (175 mph) and the rate of the wind (35 mph): 175 mph − 35 mph = 140 mph. Therefore, $r = 140$. To find the time, solve the equation $d = rt$ for t.

Solution $d = rt$

$$350 = 140t$$

$$\frac{350}{140} = \frac{140t}{140}$$

$$2.5 = t$$

It takes the plane 2.5 h to travel 350 mi.

Problem 3

Strategy ▶ Rate of the second plane: r
Rate of the first plane: $r + 30$

	Rate	Time	Distance
First plane	$r + 30$	4	$4(r + 30)$
Second plane	r	4	$4r$

▶ The total distance traveled by the two planes is 1160 mi.

Solution
$$4(r + 30) + 4r = 1160$$
$$4r + 120 + 4r = 1160$$
$$8r + 120 = 1160$$
$$8r = 1040$$
$$r = 130$$
$$r + 30 = 130 + 30 = 160$$

The first plane is traveling 160 mph.
The second plane is traveling 130 mph.

SECTION 2.4

Problem 1

Strategy ▶ Amount invested at 7.5%: x

	Principal	Rate	Interest
Amount at 5.2%	3500	0.052	0.052(3500)
Amount at 7.5%	x	0.075	0.075x

▶ The sum of the amounts of interest earned by the two investments equals the total annual interest earned ($575).

Solution
$$0.052(3500) + 0.075x = 575$$
$$182 + 0.075x = 575$$
$$0.075x = 393$$
$$x = 5240$$

The amount invested at 7.5% is $5240.

Problem 2

Strategy ▶ Pounds of 22% fat hamburger: x
Pounds of 12% fat hamburger: $80 - x$

	Amount	Percent	Quantity
22%	x	0.22	0.22x
12%	$80 - x$	0.12	0.12(80 − x)
18%	80	0.18	0.18(80)

▶ The sum of the quantities before mixing is equal to the quantity after mixing.

Solution
$$0.22x + 0.12(80 - x) = 0.18(80)$$
$$0.22x + 9.6 - 0.12x = 14.4$$
$$0.10x + 9.6 = 14.4$$
$$0.10x = 4.8$$
$$x = 48$$
$$80 - x = 80 - 48 = 32$$

The butcher needs 48 lb of the hamburger that is 22% fat and 32 lb of the hamburger that is 12% fat.

SECTION 2.5

Problem 1

$$2x - 1 < 6x + 7$$
$$-4x - 1 < 7$$
$$-4x < 8$$
$$\frac{-4x}{-4} > \frac{8}{-4}$$
$$x > -2$$
$$\{x \mid x > -2\}$$

Problem 2

$$5x - 2 \le 4 - 3(x - 2)$$
$$5x - 2 \le 4 - 3x + 6$$
$$5x - 2 \le 10 - 3x$$
$$8x - 2 \le 10$$
$$8x \le 12$$
$$\frac{8x}{8} \le \frac{12}{8}$$
$$x \le \frac{3}{2}$$
$$\left(-\infty, \frac{3}{2}\right]$$

Problem 3

$$-2 \le 5x + 3 \le 13$$
$$-2 - 3 \le 5x + 3 - 3 \le 13 - 3$$
$$-5 \le 5x \le 10$$
$$\frac{-5}{5} \le \frac{5x}{5} \le \frac{10}{5}$$
$$-1 \le x \le 2$$
$$[-1, 2]$$

Problem 4

$$5 - 4x > 1 \quad \text{and} \quad 6 - 5x < 11$$
$$-4x > -4 \qquad\qquad -5x < 5$$
$$x < 1 \qquad\qquad\quad x > -1$$
$$\{x \mid x < 1\} \qquad\quad \{x \mid x > -1\}$$
$$\{x \mid x < 1\} \cap \{x \mid x > -1\} = (-1, 1)$$

Problem 5

$2 - 3x > 11$ or $5 + 2x > 7$
$\quad -3x > 9 \qquad\qquad 2x > 2$
$\qquad x < -3 \qquad\qquad x > 1$
$\{x\,|\,x < -3\} \qquad\quad \{x\,|\,x > 1\}$
$\{x\,|\,x < -3\} \cup \{x\,|\,x > 1\}$
$\quad = \{x\,|\,x < -3 \text{ or } x > 1\}$

Problem 6

Strategy To find the maximum height, substitute the given values in the inequality $\frac{1}{2}bh < A$ and solve for x.

Solution $\qquad \dfrac{1}{2}bh < A$

$$\frac{1}{2}(12)(x + 2) < 50$$
$$6(x + 2) < 50$$
$$6x + 12 < 50$$
$$6x < 38$$
$$x < \frac{19}{3}$$

The largest integer less than $\frac{19}{3}$ is 6.

$$x + 2 = 6 + 2 = 8$$

The maximum height of the triangle is 8 in.

Problem 7

Strategy To find the range of scores, write and solve an inequality using N to represent the score on the fifth exam.

Solution $\qquad 80 \le \dfrac{72 + 94 + 83 + 70 + N}{5} \le 89$

$$80 \le \frac{319 + N}{5} \le 89$$
$$5(80) \le 5\left(\frac{319 + N}{5}\right) \le 5(89)$$
$$400 \le 319 + N \le 445$$
$$400 - 319 \le 319 - 319 + N \le 445 - 319$$
$$81 \le N \le 126$$

Because 100 is a maximum score, the range of scores that will give the student a B for the course is $81 \le N \le 100$.

SECTION 2.6

Problem 1

A. $|x| = 25$
$\quad x = 25 \qquad x = -25$

The solutions are 25 and −25.

B. $|2x - 3| = 5$
$\quad 2x - 3 = 5 \qquad 2x - 3 = -5$

$\quad 2x = 8 \qquad\qquad 2x = -2$
$\quad\; x = 4 \qquad\qquad\; x = -1$

The solutions are 4 and −1.

C. $|x - 3| = -2$

The absolute value of a number must be nonnegative.

There is no solution to this equation.

D. $5 - |3x + 5| = 3$
$\quad\; -|3x + 5| = -2$
$\quad\;\;\; |3x + 5| = 2$
$\quad\quad 3x + 5 = 2 \qquad 3x + 5 = -2$
$\quad\quad\quad\; 3x = -3 \qquad\quad 3x = -7$
$\quad\quad\quad\;\; x = -1 \qquad\quad\;\; x = -\dfrac{7}{3}$

The solutions are -1 and $-\dfrac{7}{3}$.

Problem 2

$|3x + 2| < 8$
$\quad -8 < 3x + 2 < 8$
$-8 - 2 < 3x + 2 - 2 < 8 - 2$
$\quad -10 < 3x < 6$
$\quad \dfrac{-10}{3} < \dfrac{3x}{3} < \dfrac{6}{3}$
$\quad -\dfrac{10}{3} < x < 2$
$\left\{x\,\middle|\,-\dfrac{10}{3} < x < 2\right\}$

Problem 3

$|3x - 7| < 0$

The absolute value of a number must be nonnegative. The solution set is the empty set.

$\varnothing$

Problem 4

$|5x + 3| > 8$
$5x + 3 < -8 \qquad$ or $\quad 5x + 3 > 8$
$\quad 5x < -11 \qquad\qquad\qquad 5x > 5$
$\quad\; x < -\dfrac{11}{5} \qquad\qquad\qquad\; x > 1$
$\left\{x\,\middle|\,x < -\dfrac{11}{5}\right\} \qquad \{x\,|\,x > 1\}$
$\left\{x\,\middle|\,x < -\dfrac{11}{5}\right\} \cup \{x\,|\,x > 1\}$
$= \left\{x\,\middle|\,x < -\dfrac{11}{5} \text{ or } x > 1\right\}$

Problem 5

Strategy Let b represent the desired diameter of the bushing, T the tolerance, and d the actual diameter of the bushing. Solve the absolute value inequality $|d - b| \le T$ for d.

Solution
$$|d - b| \leq T$$
$$|d - 2.55| \leq 0.003$$
$$-0.003 \leq d - 2.55 \leq 0.003$$
$$-0.003 + 2.55 \leq d - 2.55 + 2.55 \leq 0.003 + 2.55$$
$$2.547 \leq d \leq 2.553$$

The lower and upper limits of the diameter of the bushing are 2.547 in. and 2.553 in.

Solutions to Chapter 3 Problems

SECTION 3.1

Problem 1
Replace x by -2 and solve for y.
$$y = \frac{3x}{x + 1} = \frac{3(-2)}{-2 + 1} = \frac{-6}{-1} = 6$$

The ordered-pair solution is $(-2, 6)$.

Problem 2
$y = |x + 1|$

x	y
-3	2
-2	1
-1	0
0	1
1	2

Problem 3
$(x_1, y_1) = (5, -2)$ $(x_2, y_2) = (-4, 3)$
$$d = \sqrt{(x_2 - x_1)^2 + (y_2 - y_1)^2}$$
$$= \sqrt{(-4 - 5)^2 + (3 - (-2))^2}$$
$$= \sqrt{(-9)^2 + (5)^2}$$
$$= \sqrt{81 + 25}$$
$$= \sqrt{106}$$

Problem 4
$(x_1, y_1) = (-3, -5)$ $(x_2, y_2) = (-2, 3)$
$$x_m = \frac{x_1 + x_2}{2} \qquad y_m = \frac{y_1 + y_2}{2}$$
$$= \frac{-3 + (-2)}{2} \qquad = \frac{-5 + 3}{2}$$
$$= -\frac{5}{2} \qquad = -1$$

The midpoint is $\left(-\frac{5}{2}, -1\right)$.

Problem 5

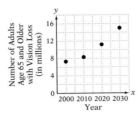

Problem 6
In 1900, the population was 1.5 million: (1900, 1.5)
In 2000, the population was 33.9 million: (2000, 33.9)

Average rate of change
$$= \frac{\text{change in } y}{\text{change in } x}$$
$$= \frac{\text{population in 2000} - \text{population in 1900}}{2000 - 1900}$$
$$= \frac{33.9 - 1.5}{2000 - 1900}$$
$$= \frac{32.4}{100} = 0.324$$

The average rate of change in the population was 324,000 people per year.

Problem 7

Solution A. In 1990, the median salary was 437,500:
(1990, 437,500)
In 2005, the median salary was 5,833,334:
(2005, 5,833,334)

The average rate of change
$$= \frac{\text{change in } y}{\text{change in } x}$$
$$= \frac{\text{median salary in 2005} - \text{median salary in 1990}}{2005 - 1990}$$
$$= \frac{5,833,334 - 437,500}{2005 - 1990}$$
$$= \frac{5,395,834}{15} \approx 360,000$$

The average rate of change was $360,000 per year.

B. $360,000 > $173,000

The average annual rate of change in the median salary of New York Yankees players between 1990 and 2005 is greater than the average annual rate of change in the median salary of Boston Red Sox players between 1990 and 2005.

SECTION 3.2

Problem 1

$\{(-2, 6), (-1, 3), (0, 0), (1, -3), (2, -6), (3, -9)\}$

Domain $= \{-2, -1, 0, 1, 2, 3\}$ • The domain of the relation is the set of first coordinates of the ordered pairs.

Range $= \{-9, -6, -3, 0, 3, 6\}$ • The range of the relation is the set of second coordinates of the ordered pairs.

Because there are no two ordered pairs with the same first coordinate and different second coordinates, the relation is a function.

Problem 2

A. $f(z) = z + |z|$ • Replace z by −4.
$f(-4) = -4 + |-4| = -4 + 4$ Then simplify.
$f(-4) = 0$

B. To find the value of f when $z = 3$ means to evaluate the function when $z = 3$.

$f(z) = z + |z|$
$f(3) = 3 + |3| = 3 + 3$ • Replace z by 3.
$f(3) = 6$ Then simplify.

The value of the function when $z = 3$ is 6.

Problem 3

$r(s) = 3s - 6$
$r(2a + 3) = 3(2a + 3) - 6$ • Replace s by 2a + 3.
$= 6a + 9 - 6$ • Simplify.
$= 6a + 3$

Problem 4

Evaluate the function for each element of the domain. The range includes the values of $f(-3), f(-2), f(-1), f(0), f(1),$ and $f(2)$.

$f(x) = x^3 + x$
$f(-3) = (-3)^3 + (-3) = -30$
$f(-2) = (-2)^3 + (-2) = -10$
$f(-1) = (-1)^3 + (-1) = -2$
$f(0) = (0)^3 + 0 = 0$
$f(1) = (1)^3 + 1 = 2$
$f(2) = (2)^3 + 2 = 10$

The range is $\{-30, -10, -2, 0, 2, 10\}$.

Problem 5

$f(x) = 2x - 5$
$f(c) = 2c - 5$ • Replace x by c.
$-3 = 2c - 5$ • f(c) = −3.
$2 = 2c$ • Solve for c.
$1 = c$

The value of c is 1. The corresponding ordered pair is $(1, -3)$.

Problem 6

x	$y = f(x) = -x^2 - 4x + 2$	(x, y)
−5	$f(-5) = -(-5)^2 - 4(-5) + 2$	$(-5, -3)$
−4	$f(-4) = -(-4)^2 - 4(-4) + 2$	$(-4, 2)$
−3	$f(-3) = -(-3)^2 - 4(-3) + 2$	$(-3, 5)$
−2	$f(-2) = -(-2)^2 - 4(-2) + 2$	$(-2, 6)$
−1	$f(-1) = -(-1)^2 - 4(-1) + 2$	$(-1, 5)$
0	$f(0) = -(0)^2 - 4(0) + 2$	$(0, 2)$
1	$f(1) = -(1)^2 - 4(1) + 2$	$(1, -5)$

Problem 7

x	$y = f(x) = |x - 2|$	(x, y)
−1	$f(-1) = |-1 - 2| = 3$	$(-1, 3)$
0	$f(0) = |0 - 2| = 2$	$(0, 2)$
1	$f(1) = |1 - 2| = 1$	$(1, 1)$
2	$f(2) = |2 - 2| = 0$	$(2, 0)$
3	$f(3) = |3 - 2| = 1$	$(3, 1)$
4	$f(4) = |4 - 2| = 2$	$(4, 2)$

Problem 8

A. Any vertical line intersects the graph at most once. The graph is the graph of a function.

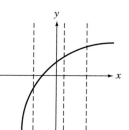

B. There are vertical lines that intersect the graph at more than one point. The graph is not the graph of a function.

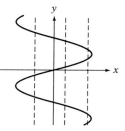

SECTION 3.3

Problem 1

x	y
−5	−7
0	−4
5	−1

Problem 2

$$-3x + 2y = 4$$
$$2y = 3x + 4$$
$$y = \frac{3}{2}x + 2$$

x	y
-2	-1
0	2
2	5

Problem 3

$$y - 3 = 0$$
$$y = 3$$

Problem 4

x-intercept: y-intercept:

$$3x - y = 2 \qquad 3x - y = 2$$
$$3x - 0 = 2 \qquad 3(0) - y = 2$$
$$3x = 2 \qquad\qquad -y = 2$$
$$x = \frac{2}{3} \qquad\qquad\quad y = -2$$

$$\left(\frac{2}{3}, 0\right) \qquad\qquad (0, -2)$$

Problem 5

$$f(x) = \frac{2}{3}x + 4$$
$$0 = \frac{2}{3}x + 4$$
$$-4 = \frac{2}{3}x$$
$$-6 = x$$

The zero is -6.

Problem 6

The ordered pair (32, 74) means that a person with a stride of 32 in. is 74 in. tall.

SECTION 3.4

Problem 1

Let $P_1 = (4, -3)$ and $P_2 = (2, 7)$.

$$m = \frac{y_2 - y_1}{x_2 - x_1} = \frac{7 - (-3)}{2 - 4} = \frac{10}{-2} = -5$$

The slope is -5.

Problem 2

$$m = \frac{55,000 - 25,000}{2 - 5} = \frac{30,000}{-3} = -10,000$$

A slope of $-10,000$ means that the value of the printing press is decreasing by $10,000 per year.

Problem 3

$$2x + 3y = 6$$
$$3y = -2x + 6$$
$$y = -\frac{2}{3}x + 2$$

$$m = -\frac{2}{3} = \frac{-2}{3}$$

y-intercept $= (0, 2)$

Problem 4

$$(x_1, y_1) = (-3, -2)$$

$$m = 3 = \frac{3}{1} = \frac{\text{change in } y}{\text{change in } x}$$

SECTION 3.5

Problem 1

$$m = -3 \qquad (x_1, y_1) = (4, -3)$$

$$y - y_1 = m(x - x_1)$$
$$y - (-3) = -3(x - 4)$$
$$y + 3 = -3x + 12$$
$$y = -3x + 9$$

The equation of the line is $y = -3x + 9$.

Problem 2

Let $(x_1, y_1) = (2, 0)$ and $(x_2, y_2) = (5, 3)$.

$$m = \frac{y_2 - y_1}{x_2 - x_1} = \frac{3 - 0}{5 - 2} = \frac{3}{3} = 1$$

$$y - y_1 = m(x - x_1)$$
$$y - 0 = 1(x - 2)$$
$$y = x - 2$$

The equation of the line is $y = x - 2$.

Problem 3

Strategy ▶ Select the independent and dependent variables. Because the function will predict the Celsius temperature, that quantity is the dependent variable, y. The Fahrenheit temperature is the independent variable.

▶ From the given data, two ordered pairs are (212, 100) and (32, 0). Use these ordered pairs to determine the linear function.

Solution Let $(x_1, y_1) = (32, 0)$ and $(x_2, y_2) = (212, 100)$.

$$m = \frac{y_2 - y_1}{x_2 - x_1} = \frac{100 - 0}{212 - 32} = \frac{100}{180} = \frac{5}{9}$$

$$y - y_1 = m(x - x_1)$$

$$y - 0 = \frac{5}{9}(x - 32)$$

$$y = \frac{5}{9}(x - 32), \text{ or } C = \frac{5}{9}(F - 32).$$

The linear function is $f(F) = \frac{5}{9}(F - 32)$.

SECTION 3.6

Problem 1

$$5x + 2y = 2$$
$$2y = -5x + 2$$
$$y = -\frac{5}{2}x + 1$$
$$m_1 = -\frac{5}{2}$$
$$5x + 2y = -6$$
$$2y = -5x - 6$$
$$y = -\frac{5}{2}x - 3$$
$$m_2 = -\frac{5}{2}$$
$$m_1 = m_2 = -\frac{5}{2}$$

Yes, the lines are parallel.

Problem 2

$y - y_1 = m(x - x_1)$ • **Use the point-slope formula.**

$y - 1 = \frac{3}{4}(x - 4)$ • $m = \frac{3}{4}$**, the slope of the line**

$y = \frac{3}{4}x - 1$**.** $(x_1, y_1) = (4, 1)$**, the given point.**

$y - 1 = \frac{3}{4}x - 3$ • **Use the Distributive Property.**

$y = \frac{3}{4}x - 2$ • **Add 1 to each side of the equation.**

The equation of the line is $y = \frac{3}{4}x - 2$.

Problem 3

$$x - 4y = 3$$
$$-4y = -x + 3$$
$$y = \frac{1}{4}x - \frac{3}{4}$$
$$m_1 = \frac{1}{4}$$
$$m_1 \cdot m_2 = -1$$
$$\frac{1}{4} \cdot m_2 = -1$$
$$m_2 = -4$$

$$y - y_1 = m(x - x_1)$$
$$y - 3 = -4[x - (-2)]$$
$$y - 3 = -4(x + 2)$$
$$y - 3 = -4x - 8$$
$$y = -4x - 5$$

The equation of the line is $y = -4x - 5$.

SECTION 3.7

Problem 1

$$x + 3y > 6$$
$$3y > -x + 6$$
$$y > -\frac{1}{3}x + 2$$

Problem 2

$y < 2$

Solutions to Chapter 4 Problems

SECTION 4.1

Problem 1

The solution is $(-1, 2)$.

Problem 2

A.

The lines are parallel and therefore do not intersect. The system of equations has no solution. The system of equations is inconsistent.

B.

The two equations represent the same line. The system of equations is dependent. The solutions are the ordered pairs $\left(x, \frac{3}{4}x - 3\right)$.

Problem 3

A. (1) $3x - y = 3$
  (2) $6x + 3y = -4$

Solve equation (1) for y.

$$3x - y = 3$$
$$-y = -3x + 3$$
$$y = 3x - 3$$

Substitute into equation (2).

$$6x + 3y = -4$$
$$6x + 3(3x - 3) = -4$$
$$6x + 9x - 9 = -4$$
$$15x - 9 = -4$$
$$15x = 5$$
$$x = \frac{5}{15} = \frac{1}{3}$$

Substitute into equation (1).
$$3x - y = 3$$
$$3\left(\frac{1}{3}\right) - y = 3$$
$$1 - y = 3$$
$$-y = 2$$
$$y = -2$$

The solution is $\left(\frac{1}{3}, -2\right)$.

B. (1) $6x - 3y = 6$
(2) $2x - y = 2$

Solve equation (2) for y.
$$2x - y = 2$$
$$-y = -2x + 2$$
$$y = 2x - 2$$

Substitute into equation (1).
$$6x - 3y = 6$$
$$6x - 3(2x - 2) = 6$$
$$6x - 6x + 6 = 6$$
$$6 = 6$$

$6 = 6$ is a true equation. The system of equations is dependent. The solutions are the ordered pairs $(x, 2x - 2)$.

SECTION 4.2

Problem 1

A. (1) $2x + 5y = 6$
(2) $3x - 2y = 6x + 2$

Write equation (2) in the form $Ax + By = C$.
$$3x - 2y = 6x + 2$$
$$-3x - 2y = 2$$

Solve the system: $2x + 5y = 6$
$$-3x - 2y = 2$$

Eliminate y.
$$2(2x + 5y) = 2(6)$$
$$5(-3x - 2y) = 5(2)$$

$$4x + 10y = 12$$
$$-15x - 10y = 10$$

Add the equations.
$$-11x = 22$$
$$x = -2$$

Replace x in equation (1).
$$2x + 5y = 6$$
$$2(-2) + 5y = 6$$
$$-4 + 5y = 6$$
$$5y = 10$$
$$y = 2$$

The solution is $(-2, 2)$.

B. $2x + y = 5$
$$4x + 2y = 6$$

Eliminate y.
$$-2(2x + y) = -2(5)$$
$$4x + 2y = 6$$

$$-4x - 2y = -10$$
$$4x + 2y = 6$$

Add the equations.
$$0x + 0y = -4$$
$$0 = -4$$

$0 = -4$ is not a true equation. The system is inconsistent and therefore has no solution.

Problem 2

(1) $x - y + z = 6$
(2) $2x + 3y - z = 1$
(3) $x + 2y + 2z = 5$

Eliminate z. Add equations (1) and (2).
$$x - y + z = 6$$
$$2x + 3y - z = 1$$
(4) $3x + 2y = 7$

Eliminate z. Multiply equation (2) by 2 and add to equation (3).
$$4x + 6y - 2z = 2$$
$$x + 2y + 2z = 5$$
(5) $5x + 8y = 7$

Solve the system of two equations.
(4) $3x + 2y = 7$
(5) $5x + 8y = 7$

Multiply equation (4) by -4 and add to equation (5).
$$-12x - 8y = -28$$
$$5x + 8y = 7$$
$$-7x = -21$$
$$x = 3$$

Replace x by 3 in equation (4).
$$3x + 2y = 7$$
$$3(3) + 2y = 7$$
$$9 + 2y = 7$$
$$2y = -2$$
$$y = -1$$

Replace x by 3 and y by -1 in equation (1).
$$x - y + z = 6$$
$$3 - (-1) + z = 6$$
$$4 + z = 6$$
$$z = 2$$

The solution is $(3, -1, 2)$.

SECTION 4.3

Problem 1

A. $\begin{vmatrix} -1 & -4 \\ 3 & -5 \end{vmatrix} = -1(-5) - 3(-4)$

$= 5 + 12 = 17$

The value of the determinant is 17.

B. Expand by cofactors of the first column.

$\begin{vmatrix} 1 & 4 & -2 \\ 3 & 1 & 1 \\ 0 & -2 & 2 \end{vmatrix} = 1\begin{vmatrix} 1 & 1 \\ -2 & 2 \end{vmatrix} - 3\begin{vmatrix} 4 & -2 \\ -2 & 2 \end{vmatrix} + 0$

$= 1(2 + 2) - 3(8 - 4)$

$= 4 - 12$

$= -8$

The value of the determinant is -8.

Problem 2

$D = \begin{vmatrix} 6 & -6 \\ 2 & -10 \end{vmatrix} = -48$

$D_x = \begin{vmatrix} 5 & -6 \\ -1 & -10 \end{vmatrix} = -56$

$D_y = \begin{vmatrix} 6 & 5 \\ 2 & -1 \end{vmatrix} = -16$

$x = \dfrac{D_x}{D} = \dfrac{-56}{-48} = \dfrac{7}{6} \qquad y = \dfrac{D_y}{D} = \dfrac{-16}{-48} = \dfrac{1}{3}$

The solution is $\left(\dfrac{7}{6}, \dfrac{1}{3}\right)$.

Problem 3

$D = \begin{vmatrix} 2 & -1 & 1 \\ 3 & 2 & -1 \\ 1 & 3 & 1 \end{vmatrix} = 21$

$D_x = \begin{vmatrix} -1 & -1 & 1 \\ 3 & 2 & -1 \\ -2 & 3 & 1 \end{vmatrix} = 9$

$D_y = \begin{vmatrix} 2 & -1 & 1 \\ 3 & 3 & -1 \\ 1 & -2 & 1 \end{vmatrix} = -3$

$D_z = \begin{vmatrix} 2 & -1 & -1 \\ 3 & 2 & 3 \\ 1 & 3 & -2 \end{vmatrix} = -42$

$x = \dfrac{D_x}{D} = \dfrac{9}{21} = \dfrac{3}{7} \qquad y = \dfrac{D_y}{D} = \dfrac{-3}{21} = -\dfrac{1}{7}$

$z = \dfrac{D_z}{D} = \dfrac{-42}{21} = -2$

The solution is $\left(\dfrac{3}{7}, -\dfrac{1}{7}, -2\right)$.

Problem 4

$\left[\begin{array}{ccc|c} 2 & -3 & 1 & 4 \\ 1 & 0 & -2 & 3 \\ 0 & 1 & 2 & -3 \end{array}\right]$

$2x - 3y + z = 4$

$x - 2z = 3$

$y + 2z = -3$

Problem 5

A. $\left[\begin{array}{ccc|c} 1 & 8 & -2 & 3 \\ 2 & -3 & 4 & 1 \\ 3 & 5 & -7 & 3 \end{array}\right] \quad R_2 \leftrightarrow R_3 \quad \left[\begin{array}{ccc|c} 1 & 8 & -2 & 3 \\ 3 & 5 & -7 & 3 \\ 2 & -3 & 4 & 1 \end{array}\right]$

B. $\left[\begin{array}{ccc|c} 1 & 8 & -2 & 3 \\ 2 & -3 & 4 & 1 \\ 3 & 5 & -7 & 3 \end{array}\right] \quad 3R_2 \to \quad \left[\begin{array}{ccc|c} 1 & 8 & -2 & 3 \\ 6 & -9 & 12 & 3 \\ 3 & 5 & -7 & 3 \end{array}\right]$

C. $\left[\begin{array}{ccc|c} 1 & 8 & -2 & 3 \\ 2 & -3 & 4 & 1 \\ 3 & 5 & -7 & 3 \end{array}\right] \quad -3R_1 + R_3 \to \quad \left[\begin{array}{ccc|c} 1 & 8 & -2 & 3 \\ 2 & -3 & 4 & 1 \\ 0 & -19 & -1 & -6 \end{array}\right]$

Problem 6

$\left[\begin{array}{ccc|c} 1 & -3 & 2 & 1 \\ -4 & 14 & 0 & -2 \\ 2 & -5 & -3 & 16 \end{array}\right] \quad 4R_1 + R_2 \to \quad \left[\begin{array}{ccc|c} 1 & -3 & 2 & 1 \\ 0 & 2 & 8 & 2 \\ 2 & -5 & -3 & 16 \end{array}\right]$

$\left[\begin{array}{ccc|c} 1 & -3 & 2 & 1 \\ 0 & 2 & 8 & 2 \\ 2 & -5 & -3 & 16 \end{array}\right] \quad -2R_1 + R_3 \to \quad \left[\begin{array}{ccc|c} 1 & -3 & 2 & 1 \\ 0 & 2 & 8 & 2 \\ 0 & 1 & -7 & 14 \end{array}\right]$

$\left[\begin{array}{ccc|c} 1 & -3 & 2 & 1 \\ 0 & 2 & 8 & 2 \\ 0 & 1 & -7 & 14 \end{array}\right] \quad \dfrac{1}{2}R_2 \to \quad \left[\begin{array}{ccc|c} 1 & -3 & 2 & 1 \\ 0 & 1 & 4 & 1 \\ 0 & 1 & -7 & 14 \end{array}\right]$

$\left[\begin{array}{ccc|c} 1 & -3 & 2 & 1 \\ 0 & 1 & 4 & 1 \\ 0 & 1 & -7 & 14 \end{array}\right] \quad -1R_2 + R_3 \to \quad \left[\begin{array}{ccc|c} 1 & -3 & 2 & 1 \\ 0 & 1 & 4 & 1 \\ 0 & 0 & -11 & 13 \end{array}\right]$

$\left[\begin{array}{ccc|c} 1 & -3 & 2 & 1 \\ 0 & 1 & 4 & 1 \\ 0 & 0 & -11 & 13 \end{array}\right] \quad -\dfrac{1}{11}R_3 \to \quad \left[\begin{array}{ccc|c} 1 & -3 & 2 & 1 \\ 0 & 1 & 4 & 1 \\ 0 & 0 & 1 & -\dfrac{13}{11} \end{array}\right]$

A row echelon form of the matrix is $\left[\begin{array}{ccc|c} 1 & -3 & 2 & 1 \\ 0 & 1 & 4 & 1 \\ 0 & 0 & 1 & -\dfrac{13}{11} \end{array}\right]$.

Problem 7

$4x - 5y = 17$

$3x + 2y = 7$

$\left[\begin{array}{cc|c} 4 & -5 & 17 \\ 3 & 2 & 7 \end{array}\right] \quad \xrightarrow[\frac{1}{4}R_1]{\text{Change } a_{11} \text{ to 1.}} \quad \left[\begin{array}{cc|c} 1 & -\dfrac{5}{4} & \dfrac{17}{4} \\ 3 & 2 & 7 \end{array}\right]$

• We multiplied R_1 by the reciprocal of a_{11}.

$$\begin{bmatrix} 1 & -\dfrac{5}{4} & \bigg| & \dfrac{17}{4} \\ 3 & 2 & \bigg| & 7 \end{bmatrix} \xrightarrow[\substack{-3R_1 + R_2}]{\text{Change } a_{21} \text{ to } 0.} \begin{bmatrix} 1 & -\dfrac{5}{4} & \bigg| & \dfrac{17}{4} \\ 0 & \dfrac{23}{4} & \bigg| & -\dfrac{23}{4} \end{bmatrix}$$

- **We multiplied R_1 by the opposite of a_{21}.**

$$\begin{bmatrix} 1 & -\dfrac{5}{4} & \bigg| & \dfrac{17}{4} \\ 0 & \dfrac{23}{4} & \bigg| & -\dfrac{23}{4} \end{bmatrix} \xrightarrow[\substack{\frac{4}{23}R_2}]{\text{Change } a_{22} \text{ to } 1.} \begin{bmatrix} 1 & -\dfrac{5}{4} & \bigg| & \dfrac{17}{4} \\ 0 & 1 & \bigg| & -1 \end{bmatrix}$$

- **This is row echelon form.**

$$x - \frac{5}{4}y = \frac{17}{4}$$
$$y = -1$$

$$x - \frac{5}{4}(-1) = \frac{17}{4}$$
$$x + \frac{5}{4} = \frac{17}{4}$$
$$x = 3$$

The solution is $(3, -1)$.

Problem 8

$$2x + 3y + 3z = -2$$
$$x + 2y - 3z = 9$$
$$3x - 2y - 4z = 1$$

$$\begin{bmatrix} 2 & 3 & 3 & | & -2 \\ 1 & 2 & -3 & | & 9 \\ 3 & -2 & -4 & | & 1 \end{bmatrix} \xrightarrow{R_1 \leftrightarrow R_2} \begin{bmatrix} 1 & 2 & -3 & | & 9 \\ 2 & 3 & 3 & | & -2 \\ 3 & -2 & -4 & | & 1 \end{bmatrix}$$

$$\begin{bmatrix} 1 & 2 & -3 & | & 9 \\ 2 & 3 & 3 & | & -2 \\ 3 & -2 & -4 & | & 1 \end{bmatrix} \xrightarrow{-2R_1 + R_2} \begin{bmatrix} 1 & 2 & -3 & | & 9 \\ 0 & -1 & 9 & | & -20 \\ 3 & -2 & -4 & | & 1 \end{bmatrix}$$

$$\begin{bmatrix} 1 & 2 & -3 & | & 9 \\ 0 & -1 & 9 & | & -20 \\ 3 & -2 & -4 & | & 1 \end{bmatrix} \xrightarrow{-3R_1 + R_3} \begin{bmatrix} 1 & 2 & -3 & | & 9 \\ 0 & -1 & 9 & | & -20 \\ 0 & -8 & 5 & | & -26 \end{bmatrix}$$

$$\begin{bmatrix} 1 & 2 & -3 & | & 9 \\ 0 & -1 & 9 & | & -20 \\ 0 & -8 & 5 & | & -26 \end{bmatrix} \xrightarrow{-1R_2} \begin{bmatrix} 1 & 2 & -3 & | & 9 \\ 0 & 1 & -9 & | & 20 \\ 0 & -8 & 5 & | & -26 \end{bmatrix}$$

$$\begin{bmatrix} 1 & 2 & -3 & | & 9 \\ 0 & 1 & -9 & | & 20 \\ 0 & -8 & 5 & | & -26 \end{bmatrix} \xrightarrow{8R_2 + R_3} \begin{bmatrix} 1 & 2 & -3 & | & 9 \\ 0 & 1 & -9 & | & 20 \\ 0 & 0 & -67 & | & 134 \end{bmatrix}$$

$$\begin{bmatrix} 1 & 2 & -3 & | & 9 \\ 0 & 1 & -9 & | & 20 \\ 0 & 0 & -67 & | & 134 \end{bmatrix} \xrightarrow{-\frac{1}{67}R_2} \begin{bmatrix} 1 & 2 & -3 & | & 9 \\ 0 & 1 & -9 & | & 20 \\ 0 & 0 & 1 & | & -2 \end{bmatrix}$$

$$x + 2y - 3z = 9$$
$$y - 9z = 20$$
$$z = -2$$

$$y - 9(-2) = 20$$
$$y + 18 = 20$$
$$y = 2$$

$$x + 2(2) - 3(-2) = 9$$
$$x + 10 = 9$$
$$x = -1$$

The solution is $(-1, 2, -2)$.

SECTION 4.4

Problem 1

Strategy ▶ Rate of the rowing team in calm water: t
Rate of the current: c

	Rate	Time	Distance
With current	$t + c$	2	$2(t + c)$
Against current	$t - c$	2	$2(t - c)$

▶ The distance traveled with the current is 18 mi.
The distance traveled against the current is 10 mi.

Solution
$$2(t + c) = 18 \rightarrow t + c = 9$$
$$2(t - c) = 10 \rightarrow t - c = 5$$
$$2t = 14$$
$$t = 7$$

$$t + c = 9$$
$$7 + c = 9$$
$$c = 2$$

The rate of the rowing team in calm water is 7 mph.
The rate of the current is 2 mph.

Problem 2

Strategy ▶ Cost of an orange tree: x
Cost of a grapefruit tree: y

First purchase:

	Amount	Unit cost	Value
Orange trees	25	x	$25x$
Grapefruit trees	20	y	$20y$

Second purchase:

	Amount	Unit cost	Value
Orange trees	20	x	$20x$
Grapefruit trees	30	y	$30y$

▶ The total of the first purchase was $290.
The total of the second purchase was $330.

Solution

$$25x + 20y = 290$$
$$20x + 30y = 330$$

$$4(25x + 20y) = 4 \cdot 290$$
$$-5(20x + 30y) = -5 \cdot 330$$

$$100x + 80y = 1160$$
$$-100x - 150y = -1650$$
$$-70y = -490$$
$$y = 7$$

$$25x + 20y = 290$$
$$25x + 20(7) = 290$$
$$25x + 140 = 290$$
$$25x = 150$$
$$x = 6$$

The cost of an orange tree is $6.
The cost of a grapefruit tree is $7.

Problem 3

Strategy Number of full-price tickets sold: x
Number of member admission tickets sold: y
Number of student tickets sold: z

There were 750 tickets sold: $x + y + z = 750$
The income was $5400: $10x + 7y + 5z = 5400$
20 more student tickets were sold than full-price tickets: $z = x + 20$

Solution
(1) $\qquad\qquad x + y + z = 750$
(2) $\qquad 10x + 7y + 5z = 5400$
(3) $\qquad\qquad\qquad z = x + 20$

Solve the system of equations by substitution. Replace z in equation (1) and equation (2) by $x + 20$.

$$x + y + (x + 20) = 750$$
$$10x + 7y + 5(x + 20) = 5400$$

(4) $\qquad\qquad 2x + y = 730$
(5) $\qquad\qquad 15x + 7y = 5300$

Multiply equation (4) by -7 and add to equation (5).

$$-14x - 7y = -5110$$
$$15x + 7y = 5300$$
$$x = 190$$

Substitute the value of x into equation (4) and solve for y.

$$2x + y = 730$$
$$2(190) + y = 730$$
$$380 + y = 730$$
$$y = 350$$

Substitute the values of x and y into equation (1) and solve for z.

$$x + y + z = 750$$
$$190 + 350 + z = 750$$
$$540 + z = 750$$
$$z = 210$$

The museum sold 190 full-priced tickets, 350 member tickets, and 210 student tickets.

SECTION 4.5

Problem 1

A. Shade above the solid line $y = 2x - 3$.
Shade above the dashed line $y = -3x$.

The solution set of the system is the intersection of the solution sets of the individual inequalities.

B. $3x + 4y > 12$
$$4y > -3x + 12$$
$$y > -\frac{3}{4}x + 3$$

Shade above the dashed line $y = -\frac{3}{4}x + 3$.

Shade below the dashed line $y = \frac{3}{4}x - 1$.

The solution set of the system is the intersection of the solution sets of the individual inequalities.

Solutions to Chapter 5 Problems

SECTION 5.1

Problem 1

$(7xy^3)(-5x^2y^2)(-xy^2) = 35x^4y^7$

Problem 2

A. $(y^3)^6 = y^{18}$

B. $(x^n)^3 = x^{3n}$

C. $(-2ab^3)^4 = (-2)^4 a^{1 \cdot 4} b^{3 \cdot 4} = 16a^4b^{12}$

D. $6a(2a)^2 + 3a(2a^2) = 6a(2^2a^2) + 6a^3$
$\qquad\qquad\qquad\qquad = 6a(4a^2) + 6a^3$
$\qquad\qquad\qquad\qquad = 24a^3 + 6a^3 = 30a^3$

Problem 3

A. $(2x^{-5}y)(5x^4y^{-3}) = 10x^{-5+4}y^{1+(-3)}$
$$= 10x^{-1}y^{-2} = \frac{10}{xy^2}$$

B. $\dfrac{a^{-1}b^4}{a^{-2}b^{-2}} = a^{-1-(-2)}b^{4-(-2)} = ab^6$

C. $\left(\dfrac{2^{-1}x^2y^{-3}}{4x^{-2}y^{-5}}\right)^{-2} = \left(\dfrac{x^4y^2}{8}\right)^{-2} = \dfrac{x^{-8}y^{-4}}{8^{-2}} = \dfrac{8^2}{x^8y^4}$

$$= \dfrac{64}{x^8y^4}$$

Problem 4

$942{,}000{,}000 = 9.42 \times 10^8$

Problem 5

$2.7 \times 10^{-5} = 0.000027$

Problem 6

$\dfrac{5{,}600{,}000 \times 0.000000081}{900 \times 0.000000028}$

$= \dfrac{5.6 \times 10^6 \times 8.1 \times 10^{-8}}{9 \times 10^2 \times 2.8 \times 10^{-8}}$

$= \dfrac{(5.6)(8.1) \times 10^{6+(-8)-2-(-8)}}{(9)(2.8)} = 1.8 \times 10^4$

Problem 7

Strategy To find the number of arithmetic operations:
- ▶ Find the reciprocal of 1×10^{-7}, which is the number of operations performed in 1 s.
- ▶ Write the number of seconds in 1 min (60) in scientific notation.
- ▶ Multiply the number of arithmetic operations per second by the number of seconds in 1 min.

Solution $\dfrac{1}{1 \times 10^{-7}} = 10^7$

$60 = 6 \times 10$

$6 \times 10 \times 10^7 = 6 \times 10^8$

The computer can perform 6×10^8 operations in 1 min.

SECTION 5.2

Problem 1

Strategy Evaluate the function when $r = 0.4$.

Solution $v(r) = 600r^2 - 1000r^3$
$= 600(0.4)^2 - 1000(0.4)^3$
$= 32$

The velocity will be 32 cm/s.

Problem 2

The leading coefficient is -3, the constant term is -12, and the degree is 4.

Problem 3

A. This is a polynomial function.

B. This is not a polynomial function. A polynomial function does not have a variable expression raised to a negative power.

C. This is not a polynomial function. A polynomial function does not have a variable expression within a radical.

Problem 4

x	y
-1	3
0	0
1	-1
2	0
3	3

$f(x) = x^2 - 2x$

Problem 5

x	y
-3	28
-2	9
-1	2
0	1
1	0
2	-7
3	-26

$F(x) = -x^3 + 1$

Problem 6

$\begin{aligned} &5x^2 + 3x - 1 \\ &2x^2 + 4x - 6 \\ &\underline{x^2 - 7x + 8} \\ &8x^2 \qquad\quad + 1 \end{aligned}$

Problem 7

Rewrite the subtraction as the addition of the opposite.

$(-5x^2 + 2x - 3) + (-6x^2 - 3x + 7)$

$\begin{aligned} &-5x^2 + 2x - 3 \\ &\underline{-6x^2 - 3x + 7} \\ &-11x^2 - \ x + 4 \end{aligned}$

Problem 8

$D(x) = P(x) - R(x)$
$= (4x^3 - 3x^2 + 2) - (-2x^2 + 2x - 3)$
$= (4x^3 - 3x^2 + 2) + (2x^2 - 2x + 3)$
$= 4x^3 - x^2 - 2x + 5$

SECTION 5.3

Problem 1

A. $-4y(y^2 - 3y + 2)$
$= -4y(y^2) - (-4y)(3y) + (-4y)(2)$
$= -4y^3 + 12y^2 - 8y$

B. $x^2 - 2x[x - x(4x - 5) + x^2]$
$= x^2 - 2x[x - 4x^2 + 5x + x^2]$
$= x^2 - 2x[6x - 3x^2]$
$= x^2 - 12x^2 + 6x^3$
$= 6x^3 - 11x^2$

C. $y^{n+3}(y^{n-2} - 3y^2 + 2)$
$$= y^{n+3}(y^{n-2}) - (y^{n+3})(3y^2) + (y^{n+3})(2)$$
$$= y^{n+3+(n-2)} - 3y^{n+3+2} + 2y^{n+3}$$
$$= y^{2n+1} - 3y^{n+5} + 2y^{n+3}$$

Problem 2

$$\begin{array}{r} -2b^2 + 5b - 4 \\ -3b + 2 \\ \hline -4b^2 + 10b - 8 \\ 6b^3 - 15b^2 + 12b \\ \hline 6b^3 - 19b^2 + 22b - 8 \end{array}$$

Problem 3

A. $(5a - 3b)(2a + 7b)$
$$= 10a^2 + 35ab - 6ab - 21b^2$$
$$= 10a^2 + 29ab - 21b^2$$

B. $(2x^n + y^n)(x^n - 4y^n)$
$$= 2x^{2n} - 8x^n y^n + x^n y^n - 4y^{2n}$$
$$= 2x^{2n} - 7x^n y^n - 4y^{2n}$$

Problem 4

A. $(3x - 7)(3x + 7) = 9x^2 - 49$

B. $(3x - 4y)^2 = 9x^2 - 24xy + 16y^2$

C. $(2x^n + 3)(2x^n - 3) = 4x^{2n} - 9$

D. $(2x^n - 8)^2 = 4x^{2n} - 32x^n + 64$

Problem 5

Strategy To find the area, replace the variables b and h in the equation $A = \frac{1}{2}bh$ with the given values and solve for A.

Solution $A = \frac{1}{2}bh$

$$A = \frac{1}{2}(2x + 6)(x - 4)$$
$$A = (x + 3)(x - 4)$$
$$A = x^2 - 4x + 3x - 12$$
$$A = x^2 - x - 12$$

The area is $(x^2 - x - 12)$ ft².

Problem 6

Strategy To find the volume, subtract the volume of the small rectangular solid from the volume of the large rectangular solid.

Large rectangular solid: Length $= L_1 = 12x$
Width $= W_1 = 7x + 2$
Height $= H_1 = 5x - 4$

Small rectangular solid: Length $= L_2 = 12x$
Width $= W_2 = x$
Height $= H_2 = 2x$

Solution
$V =$ Volume of large rectangular solid $-$ volume of small rectangular solid
$$V = (L_1 \cdot W_1 \cdot H_1) - (L_2 \cdot W_2 \cdot H_2)$$
$$V = (12x)(7x + 2)(5x - 4) - (12x)(x)(2x)$$
$$V = (84x^2 + 24x)(5x - 4) - (12x^2)(2x)$$
$$V = (420x^3 - 336x^2 + 120x^2 - 96x) - (24x^3)$$
$$V = 396x^3 - 216x^2 - 96x$$

The volume is $(396x^3 - 216x^2 - 96x)$ ft³.

SECTION 5.4

Problem 1

$$\frac{15y^3 + 10y^2 - 25y}{-5y} = \frac{15y^3}{-5y} + \frac{10y^2}{-5y} - \frac{25y}{-5y}$$
$$= -3y^2 - 2y + 5$$

Problem 2

$$\frac{12x^2y^2 - 16xy^2 - 8x}{4x^2y} = \frac{12x^2y^2}{4x^2y} - \frac{16xy^2}{4x^2y} - \frac{8x}{4x^2y}$$
$$= 3y - \frac{4y}{x} - \frac{2}{xy}$$

Problem 3

A.
$$\begin{array}{r} 5x - 1 \\ 3x + 4 \overline{)15x^2 + 17x - 20} \\ \underline{15x^2 + 20x} \\ -3x - 20 \\ \underline{-3x - 4} \\ -16 \end{array}$$

$$\frac{15x^2 + 17x - 20}{3x + 4} = 5x - 1 - \frac{16}{3x + 4}$$

B.
$$\begin{array}{r} x^2 + 3x - 1 \\ 3x - 1 \overline{)3x^3 + 8x^2 - 6x + 2} \\ \underline{3x^3 - x^2} \\ 9x^2 - 6x \\ \underline{9x^2 - 3x} \\ -3x + 2 \\ \underline{-3x + 1} \\ 1 \end{array}$$

$$\frac{3x^3 + 8x^2 - 6x + 2}{3x - 1} = x^2 + 3x - 1 + \frac{1}{3x - 1}$$

Problem 4

A.

$$\begin{array}{r|rrr} -2 & 6 & 8 & -5 \\ & & -12 & 8 \\ \hline & 6 & -4 & 3 \end{array}$$

$$(6x^2 + 8x - 5) \div (x + 2) = 6x - 4 + \frac{3}{x + 2}$$

B.

3	2	−3	−8	0	−2
		6	9	3	9
	2	3	1	3	7

$(2x^4 - 3x^3 - 8x^2 - 2) \div (x - 3)$

$= 2x^3 + 3x^2 + x + 3 + \dfrac{7}{x - 3}$

Problem 5

3	2	0	−4	−5
		6	18	42
	2	6	14	37

By the Remainder Theorem, $P(3) = 37$.

SECTION 5.5

Problem 1

A. The GCF of $3x^3y$, $6x^2y^2$, and $3xy^3$ is $3xy$.

$3x^3y - 6x^2y^2 - 3xy^3 = 3xy(x^2 - 2xy - y^2)$

B. The GCF of $6t^{2n}$ and $9t^n$ is $3t^n$.

$6t^{2n} - 9t^n = 3t^n(2t^n - 3)$

Problem 2

A. $6a(2b - 5) + 7(5 - 2b)$

$= 6a(2b - 5) - 7(2b - 5)$

$= (2b - 5)(6a - 7)$

B. $3rs - 2r - 3s + 2$

$= (3rs - 2r) - (3s - 2)$

$= r(3s - 2) - (3s - 2)$

$= (3s - 2)(r - 1)$

Problem 3

A. $x^2 + 13x + 42 = (x + 6)(x + 7)$

B. $x^2 - x - 20 = (x + 4)(x - 5)$

C. $x^2 + 5xy + 6y^2 = (x + 2y)(x + 3y)$

Problem 4

$x^2 + 5x - 1$

There are no factors of −1 whose sum is 5.

The trinomial is nonfactorable over the integers.

Problem 5

A. $4x^2 + 15x - 4$

Factors of 4	Factors of −4
1, 4	1, −4
2, 2	−1, 4
	2, −2

Trial Factors	Middle Term
$(4x + 1)(x - 4)$	$-16x + x = -15x$
$(4x - 1)(x + 4)$	$16x - x = 15x$

$4x^2 + 15x - 4 = (4x - 1)(x + 4)$

B. $10x^2 + 39x + 14$

Factors of 10	Factors of 14
1, 10	1, 14
2, 5	2, 7

Trial Factors	Middle Term
$(x + 2)(10x + 7)$	$7x + 20x = 27x$
$(2x + 1)(5x + 14)$	$28x + 5x = 33x$
$(10x + 1)(x + 14)$	$140x + x = 141x$
$(5x + 2)(2x + 7)$	$35x + 4x = 39x$

$10x^2 + 39x + 14 = (5x + 2)(2x + 7)$

Problem 6

A. $6x^2 + 7x - 20$

$a \cdot c = -120$

Factors of −120	Sum
−1, 120	119
−2, 60	58
−3, 40	37
−4, 30	26
−5, 24	19
−6, 20	14
−8, 15	7

$6x^2 + 7x - 20$

$= 6x^2 + 15x - 8x - 20$

$= (6x^2 + 15x) - (8x + 20)$

$= 3x(2x + 5) - 4(2x + 5)$

$= (2x + 5)(3x - 4)$

B. $2 - x - 6x^2$

$a \cdot c = -12$

Factors of −12	Sum
1, −12	−11
2, −6	−4
3, −4	−1

$2 - x - 6x^2 = 2 - 4x + 3x - 6x^2$

$= (2 - 4x) + (3x - 6x^2)$

$= 2(1 - 2x) + 3x(1 - 2x)$

$= (1 - 2x)(2 + 3x)$

Problem 7

A. $3a^3b^3 + 3a^2b^2 - 60ab$

$= 3ab(a^2b^2 + ab - 20)$

$= 3ab(ab + 5)(ab - 4)$

B. $40a - 10a^2 - 15a^3 = 5a(8 - 2a - 3a^2)$

$= 5a(2 + a)(4 - 3a)$

SECTION 5.6

Problem 1

$$x^2 - 36y^4 = x^2 - (6y^2)^2$$
$$= (x + 6y^2)(x - 6y^2)$$

Problem 2

$$9x^2 + 12x + 4 = (3x + 2)^2$$

Problem 3

A. $8x^3 + y^3z^3 = (2x)^3 + (yz)^3$
$\qquad\qquad = (2x + yz)(4x^2 - 2xyz + y^2z^2)$

B. $(x - y)^3 + (x + y)^3$
$\qquad = [(x - y) + (x + y)]$
$\qquad\quad \times [(x - y)^2 - (x - y)(x + y) + (x + y)^2]$
$\qquad = 2x[x^2 - 2xy + y^2 - (x^2 - y^2) + x^2 + 2xy + y^2]$
$\qquad = 2x[x^2 - 2xy + y^2 - x^2 + y^2 + x^2 + 2xy + y^2]$
$\qquad = 2x(x^2 + 3y^2)$

Problem 4

A. $6x^2y^2 - 19xy + 10$
$\quad = (3xy - 2)(2xy - 5)$

B. $3x^4 + 4x^2 - 4 = (x^2 + 2)(3x^2 - 2)$

Problem 5

A. $4x - 4y - x^3 + x^2y$
$\quad = (4x - 4y) - (x^3 - x^2y)$
$\quad = 4(x - y) - x^2(x - y)$
$\quad = (x - y)(4 - x^2)$
$\quad = (x - y)(2 + x)(2 - x)$

B. $x^{4n} - x^{2n}y^{2n} = x^{2n+2n} - x^{2n}y^{2n}$
$\quad = x^{2n}(x^{2n} - y^{2n})$
$\quad = x^{2n}[(x^n)^2 - (y^n)^2]$
$\quad = x^{2n}(x^n + y^n)(x^n - y^n)$

SECTION 5.7

Problem 1

A. $\qquad 4x^2 + 11x = 3$
$\quad 4x^2 + 11x - 3 = 0$
$\quad (4x - 1)(x + 3) = 0$

$4x - 1 = 0 \quad x + 3 = 0$
$\quad\; 4x = 1 \qquad\quad x = -3$
$\qquad\; x = \dfrac{1}{4}$

The solutions are $\dfrac{1}{4}$ and -3.

B. $(x - 2)(x + 5) = 8$
$\quad\; x^2 + 3x - 10 = 8$
$\quad\; x^2 + 3x - 18 = 0$
$\quad (x + 6)(x - 3) = 0$

$x + 6 = 0 \quad x - 3 = 0$
$\quad\; x = -6 \qquad x = 3$

The solutions are -6 and 3.

C. $\qquad x^3 + 4x^2 - 9x - 36 = 0$
$\quad (x^3 + 4x^2) - (9x + 36) = 0$
$\qquad x^2(x + 4) - 9(x + 4) = 0$
$\qquad\qquad (x + 4)(x^2 - 9) = 0$
$\quad (x + 4)(x + 3)(x - 3) = 0$

$x + 4 = 0 \qquad x + 3 = 0 \qquad x - 3 = 0$
$\quad x = -4 \qquad\quad x = -3 \qquad\quad x = 3$

The solutions are -4, -3, and 3.

Problem 2

$$s(c) = 4$$
$$c^2 - c - 2 = 4$$
$$c^2 - c - 6 = 0$$
$$(c + 2)(c - 3) = 0$$

$c + 2 = 0 \quad c - 3 = 0$
$\quad c = -2 \qquad c = 3$

The values of c are -2 and 3.

Problem 3

We must find the values of c for which $f(c) = 0$.

$$f(c) = 0$$
$$c^2 + 5c - 14 = 0$$
$$(c + 7)(c - 2) = 0$$

$c + 7 = 0 \quad c - 2 = 0$
$\quad c = -7 \qquad c = 2$

- $f(t) = t^2 + 5t - 14$, thus $f(c) = c^2 + 5c - 14$.
- **Factor and use the Principle of Zero Products.**

The zeros of f are -7 and 2.

Problem 4

Strategy Replace D by 20 in the equation
$$D = \frac{n(n - 3)}{2}$$
and then solve for n.

Solution $D = \dfrac{n(n - 3)}{2}$

$20 = \dfrac{n(n - 3)}{2}$

$40 = n^2 - 3n$

$0 = n^2 - 3n - 40$

$0 = (n - 8)(n + 5)$

$n - 8 = 0 \quad n + 5 = 0$
$\quad n = 8 \qquad\quad n = -5$

The answer -5 does not make sense in the context of this problem.

The polygon has 8 sides.

Solutions to Chapter 6 Problems

SECTION 6.1

Problem 1

$$f(x) = \frac{3 - 5x}{x^2 + 5x + 6}$$

$$f(2) = \frac{3 - 5(2)}{2^2 + 5(2) + 6}$$

$$f(2) = \frac{3 - 10}{4 + 10 + 6}$$

$$f(2) = \frac{-7}{20}$$

$$f(2) = -\frac{7}{20}$$

Problem 2

$$x^2 - 4 = 0$$
$$(x - 2)(x + 2) = 0$$

$$x - 2 = 0 \qquad x + 2 = 0$$
$$x = 2 \qquad x = -2$$

The domain is $\{x \mid x \neq -2, 2\}$.

Problem 3

$x^2 + 4$ is a positive number.

The domain is $\{x \mid x \in \text{real numbers}\}$.

Problem 4

A. $\dfrac{6x^4 - 24x^3}{12x^3 - 48x^2} = \dfrac{6x^3(x - 4)}{12x^2(x - 4)}$

$$= \frac{6x^3 \overset{1}{\cancel{(x - 4)}}}{12x^2 \underset{1}{\cancel{(x - 4)}}} = \frac{x}{2}$$

B. $\dfrac{20x - 15x^2}{15x^3 - 5x^2 - 20x} = \dfrac{5x(4 - 3x)}{5x(3x^2 - x - 4)}$

$$= \frac{5x(4 - 3x)}{5x(3x - 4)(x + 1)}$$

$$= \frac{\overset{-1}{5x\cancel{(4 - 3x)}}}{5x\underset{1}{\cancel{(3x - 4)}}(x + 1)}$$

$$= -\frac{1}{x + 1}$$

C. $\dfrac{x^{2n} + x^n - 12}{x^{2n} - 3x^n} = \dfrac{(x^n + 4)(x^n - 3)}{x^n(x^n - 3)}$

$$= \frac{(x^n + 4)\overset{1}{\cancel{(x^n - 3)}}}{x^n\underset{1}{\cancel{(x^n - 3)}}} = \frac{x^n + 4}{x^n}$$

SECTION 6.2

Problem 1

A. $\dfrac{12 + 5x - 3x^2}{x^2 + 2x - 15} \cdot \dfrac{2x^2 + x - 45}{3x^2 + 4x}$

$$= \frac{(4 + 3x)(3 - x)}{(x + 5)(x - 3)} \cdot \frac{(2x - 9)(x + 5)}{x(3x + 4)}$$

$$= \frac{(4 + 3x)(3 - x)(2x - 9)(x + 5)}{(x + 5)(x - 3) \cdot x(3x + 4)}$$

$$= \frac{(4 + 3x)\overset{-1}{\cancel{(3 - x)}}(2x - 9)\overset{1}{\cancel{(x + 5)}}}{\underset{1}{\cancel{(x + 5)}}\underset{1}{\cancel{(x - 3)}} \cdot x\underset{1}{\cancel{(3x + 4)}}}$$

$$= -\frac{2x - 9}{x}$$

B. $\dfrac{2x^2 - 13x + 20}{x^2 - 16} \cdot \dfrac{2x^2 + 9x + 4}{6x^2 - 7x - 5}$

$$= \frac{(2x - 5)(x - 4)}{(x - 4)(x + 4)} \cdot \frac{(2x + 1)(x + 4)}{(3x - 5)(2x + 1)}$$

$$= \frac{(2x - 5)(x - 4)(2x + 1)(x + 4)}{(x - 4)(x + 4)(3x - 5)(2x + 1)}$$

$$= \frac{(2x - 5)\overset{1}{\cancel{(x - 4)}}\overset{1}{\cancel{(2x + 1)}}\overset{1}{\cancel{(x + 4)}}}{\underset{1}{\cancel{(x - 4)}}\underset{1}{\cancel{(x + 4)}}(3x - 5)\underset{1}{\cancel{(2x + 1)}}}$$

$$= \frac{2x - 5}{3x - 5}$$

Problem 2

A. $\dfrac{6x^2 - 3xy}{10ab^4} \div \dfrac{16x^2y^2 - 8xy^3}{15a^2b^2}$

$$= \frac{6x^2 - 3xy}{10ab^4} \cdot \frac{15a^2b^2}{16x^2y^2 - 8xy^3}$$

$$= \frac{3x(2x - y)}{10ab^4} \cdot \frac{15a^2b^2}{8xy^2(2x - y)}$$

$$= \frac{45a^2b^2x(2x - y)}{80ab^4xy^2(2x - y)} = \frac{45a^2b^2x\overset{1}{\cancel{(2x - y)}}}{80ab^4xy^2\underset{1}{\cancel{(2x - y)}}}$$

$$= \frac{9a}{16b^2y^2}$$

B. $\dfrac{6x^2 - 7x + 2}{3x^2 + x - 2} \div \dfrac{4x^2 - 8x + 3}{5x^2 + x - 4}$

$$= \frac{6x^2 - 7x + 2}{3x^2 + x - 2} \cdot \frac{5x^2 + x - 4}{4x^2 - 8x + 3}$$

$$= \frac{(2x - 1)(3x - 2)}{(x + 1)(3x - 2)} \cdot \frac{(x + 1)(5x - 4)}{(2x - 1)(2x - 3)}$$

$$= \frac{(2x - 1)(3x - 2)(x + 1)(5x - 4)}{(x + 1)(3x - 2)(2x - 1)(2x - 3)}$$

$$= \frac{\overset{1}{\cancel{(2x - 1)}}\overset{1}{\cancel{(3x - 2)}}\overset{1}{\cancel{(x + 1)}}(5x - 4)}{\underset{1}{\cancel{(x + 1)}}\underset{1}{\cancel{(3x - 2)}}\underset{1}{\cancel{(2x - 1)}}(2x - 3)}$$

$$= \frac{5x - 4}{2x - 3}$$

Problem 3

The LCM is $a(a - 5)(a + 5)$.

$$\frac{a - 3}{a^2 - 5a} + \frac{a - 9}{a^2 - 25}$$

$$= \frac{a - 3}{a(a - 5)} \cdot \frac{a + 5}{a + 5} + \frac{a - 9}{(a - 5)(a + 5)} \cdot \frac{a}{a}$$

$$= \frac{a^2 + 2a - 15}{a(a - 5)(a + 5)} + \frac{a^2 - 9a}{a(a - 5)(a + 5)}$$

$$= \frac{(a^2 + 2a - 15) + (a^2 - 9a)}{a(a - 5)(a + 5)}$$

$$= \frac{a^2 + 2a - 15 + a^2 - 9a}{a(a - 5)(a + 5)}$$

$$= \frac{2a^2 - 7a - 15}{a(a - 5)(a + 5)} = \frac{(2a + 3)(a - 5)}{a(a - 5)(a + 5)}$$

$$= \frac{(2a + 3)(a - 5)}{a(a - 5)(a + 5)} = \frac{2a + 3}{a(a + 5)}$$

Problem 4

The LCM is $(x - 2)(2x - 3)$.

$$\frac{x - 1}{x - 2} - \frac{7 - 6x}{2x^2 - 7x + 6} + \frac{4}{2x - 3}$$

$$= \frac{x - 1}{x - 2} \cdot \frac{2x - 3}{2x - 3} - \frac{7 - 6x}{(x - 2)(2x - 3)}$$

$$+ \frac{4}{2x - 3} \cdot \frac{x - 2}{x - 2}$$

$$= \frac{2x^2 - 5x + 3}{(x - 2)(2x - 3)} - \frac{7 - 6x}{(x - 2)(2x - 3)}$$

$$+ \frac{4x - 8}{(x - 2)(2x - 3)}$$

$$= \frac{(2x^2 - 5x + 3) - (7 - 6x) + (4x - 8)}{(x - 2)(2x - 3)}$$

$$= \frac{2x^2 - 5x + 3 - 7 + 6x + 4x - 8}{(x - 2)(2x - 3)}$$

$$= \frac{2x^2 + 5x - 12}{(x - 2)(2x - 3)} = \frac{(x + 4)(2x - 3)}{(x - 2)(2x - 3)}$$

$$= \frac{(x + 4)(2x - 3)}{(x - 2)(2x - 3)} = \frac{x + 4}{x - 2}$$

SECTION 6.3

Problem 1

A. The LCM of x and x^2 is x^2.

$$\frac{3 + \frac{16}{x} + \frac{16}{x^2}}{6 + \frac{5}{x} - \frac{4}{x^2}} = \frac{3 + \frac{16}{x} + \frac{16}{x^2}}{6 + \frac{5}{x} - \frac{4}{x^2}} \cdot \frac{x^2}{x^2}$$

$$= \frac{3 \cdot x^2 + \frac{16}{x} \cdot x^2 + \frac{16}{x^2} \cdot x^2}{6 \cdot x^2 + \frac{5}{x} \cdot x^2 - \frac{4}{x^2} \cdot x^2}$$

$$= \frac{3x^2 + 16x + 16}{6x^2 + 5x - 4}$$

$$= \frac{(3x + 4)(x + 4)}{(2x - 1)(3x + 4)}$$

$$= \frac{(3x + 4)(x + 4)}{(2x - 1)(3x + 4)} = \frac{x + 4}{2x - 1}$$

B. The LCM is $x - 3$.

$$\frac{2x + 5 + \frac{14}{x - 3}}{4x + 16 + \frac{49}{x - 3}}$$

$$= \frac{2x + 5 + \frac{14}{x - 3}}{4x + 16 + \frac{49}{x - 3}} \cdot \frac{x - 3}{x - 3}$$

$$= \frac{(2x + 5)(x - 3) + \frac{14}{x - 3}(x - 3)}{(4x + 16)(x - 3) + \frac{49}{x - 3}(x - 3)}$$

$$= \frac{2x^2 - x - 15 + 14}{4x^2 + 4x - 48 + 49} = \frac{2x^2 - x - 1}{4x^2 + 4x + 1}$$

$$= \frac{(2x + 1)(x - 1)}{(2x + 1)(2x + 1)} = \frac{(2x + 1)(x - 1)}{(2x + 1)(2x + 1)}$$

$$= \frac{x - 1}{2x + 1}$$

SECTION 6.4

Problem 1

A.
$$\frac{5}{2x - 3} = \frac{-2}{x + 1}$$

$$(x + 1)(2x - 3)\frac{5}{2x - 3} = (x + 1)(2x - 3)\frac{-2}{x + 1}$$

$$5(x + 1) = -2(2x - 3)$$
$$5x + 5 = -4x + 6$$
$$9x + 5 = 6$$
$$9x = 1$$
$$x = \frac{1}{9}$$

The solution is $\frac{1}{9}$.

B.
$$\frac{4x + 1}{2x - 1} = 2 + \frac{3}{x - 3}$$

$$(2x - 1)(x - 3)\frac{4x + 1}{2x - 1} = (2x - 1)(x - 3)\left(2 + \frac{3}{x - 3}\right)$$

$$(x - 3)(4x + 1) = (2x - 1)(x - 3)2 + (2x - 1)3$$
$$4x^2 - 11x - 3 = 4x^2 - 14x + 6 + 6x - 3$$
$$-11x - 3 = -8x + 3$$
$$-3x = 6$$
$$x = -2$$

The solution is -2.

Problem 2

Strategy ▶ Time required for the small pipe to fill the tank: x

	Rate	Time	Part
Large pipe	$\dfrac{1}{9}$	6	$\dfrac{6}{9}$
Small pipe	$\dfrac{1}{x}$	6	$\dfrac{6}{x}$

▶ The sum of the part of the task completed by the large pipe and the part of the task completed by the small pipe is 1.

Solution
$$\frac{6}{9} + \frac{6}{x} = 1$$
$$\frac{2}{3} + \frac{6}{x} = 1$$
$$3x\left(\frac{2}{3} + \frac{6}{x}\right) = 3x \cdot 1$$
$$2x + 18 = 3x$$
$$18 = x$$

The small pipe working alone will fill the tank in 18 h.

Problem 3

Strategy ▶ Rate of the wind: r

	Distance	Rate	Time
With wind	700	$150 + r$	$\dfrac{700}{150 + r}$
Against wind	500	$150 - r$	$\dfrac{500}{150 - r}$

▶ The time flying with the wind equals the time flying against the wind.

Solution

$$\frac{700}{150 + r} = \frac{500}{150 - r}$$
$$(150 + r)(150 - r)\left(\frac{700}{150 + r}\right) =$$
$$(150 + r)(150 - r)\left(\frac{500}{150 - r}\right)$$
$$(150 - r)700 = (150 + r)500$$
$$105{,}000 - 700r = 75{,}000 + 500r$$
$$30{,}000 = 1200r$$
$$25 = r$$

The rate of the wind is 25 mph.

SECTION 6.5

Problem 1

Strategy To find the cost, write and solve a proportion using x to represent the cost.

Solution
$$\frac{2}{5.80} = \frac{15}{x}$$
$$x(5.80)\frac{2}{5.80} = x(5.80)\frac{15}{x}$$
$$2x = 15(5.80)$$
$$2x = 87$$
$$x = 43.5$$

The cost of 15 lb of cashews is $43.50.

Problem 2

Strategy To find the distance:

▶ Write the basic direct variation equation, replace the variables by the given values, and solve for k.

▶ Write the direct variation equation, replacing k by its value. Substitute 5 for t, and solve for s.

Solution
$$s = kt^2$$
$$64 = k(2)^2$$
$$64 = k \cdot 4$$
$$16 = k$$

$$s = 16t^2$$
$$s = 16(5)^2 = 400$$

The object will fall 400 ft in 5 s.

Problem 3

Strategy To find the resistance:

▶ Write the basic inverse variation equation, replace the variables by the given values, and solve for k.

▶ Write the inverse variation equation, replacing k by its value. Substitute 0.02 for d, and solve for R.

Solution
$$R = \frac{k}{d^2}$$
$$0.5 = \frac{k}{(0.01)^2}$$
$$0.5 = \frac{k}{0.0001}$$
$$0.00005 = k$$
$$R = \frac{0.00005}{d^2}$$
$$R = \frac{0.00005}{(0.02)^2} = 0.125$$

The resistance is 0.125 ohm.

Problem 4

Strategy To find the strength of the beam:

▶ Write the basic combined variation equation, replace the variables by the given values, and solve for k.

▶ Write the basic combined variation equation, replacing k by its value and substituting 4 for W, 8 for d, and 16 for L. Solve for s.

Solution

$$s = \frac{kWd^2}{L} \qquad s = \frac{50Wd^2}{L}$$

$$1200 = \frac{k(2)(12)^2}{12} \qquad s = \frac{50(4)8^2}{16}$$

$$1200 = \frac{k(288)}{12} \qquad s = \frac{12{,}800}{16}$$

$$14{,}400 = 288k \qquad s = 800$$

$$50 = k$$

The strength of the beam is 800 lb.

SECTION 6.6

Problem 1

A.
$$\frac{1}{R_1} + \frac{1}{R_2} = \frac{1}{R}$$

$$RR_1R_2\left(\frac{1}{R_1} + \frac{1}{R_2}\right) = RR_1R_2\left(\frac{1}{R}\right)$$

$$RR_1R_2\left(\frac{1}{R_1}\right) + RR_1R_2\left(\frac{1}{R_2}\right) = R_1R_2$$

$$RR_2 + RR_1 = R_1R_2$$

$$R(R_2 + R_1) = R_1R_2$$

$$R = \frac{R_1R_2}{R_2 + R_1}$$

B.
$$t = \frac{r}{r+1}$$

$$(r+1)t = (r+1)\left(\frac{r}{r+1}\right)$$

$$tr + t = r$$

$$t = r - tr$$

$$t = r(1 - t)$$

$$\frac{t}{1-t} = r$$

Solutions to Chapter 7 Problems

SECTION 7.1

Problem 1

A. $64^{\frac{2}{3}} = (2^6)^{\frac{2}{3}} = 2^4 = 16$

B. $16^{-\frac{3}{4}} = (2^4)^{-\frac{3}{4}} = 2^{-3} = \frac{1}{2^3} = \frac{1}{8}$

C. $(-81)^{\frac{3}{4}}$

The base of the exponential expression is negative, and the denominator of the exponent is a positive even number.

Therefore, $(-81)^{\frac{3}{4}}$ is not a real number.

Problem 2

A. $\dfrac{x^{\frac{1}{2}}y^{-\frac{5}{4}}}{x^{-\frac{4}{3}}y^{3}} = \dfrac{x^{\frac{1}{2}+\frac{4}{3}}}{y^{\frac{1}{3}+\frac{5}{4}}} = \dfrac{x^{\frac{11}{6}}}{y^{\frac{19}{12}}}$

B. $\left(x^{\frac{3}{4}}y^{\frac{1}{2}}z^{-\frac{2}{3}}\right)^{-\frac{4}{3}} = x^{-1}y^{-\frac{2}{3}}z^{\frac{8}{9}} = \dfrac{z^{\frac{8}{9}}}{xy^{\frac{2}{3}}}$

C. $\left(\dfrac{16a^{-2}b^{\frac{4}{3}}}{9a^4b^{-\frac{2}{3}}}\right)^{-\frac{1}{2}} = \left(\dfrac{2^4a^{-6}b^2}{3^2}\right)^{-\frac{1}{2}} = \dfrac{2^{-2}a^3b^{-1}}{3^{-1}}$

$$= \frac{3a^3}{2^2b} = \frac{3a^3}{4b}$$

Problem 3

A. $(2x^3)^{\frac{3}{4}} = \sqrt[4]{(2x^3)^3} = \sqrt[4]{8x^9}$

B. $-5a^{\frac{5}{6}} = -5(a^5)^{\frac{1}{6}} = -5\sqrt[6]{a^5}$

Problem 4

A. $\sqrt[3]{3ab} = (3ab)^{\frac{1}{3}}$

B. $\sqrt[4]{x^4 + y^4} = (x^4 + y^4)^{\frac{1}{4}}$

Problem 5

A. $\sqrt{121x^{10}y^4} = 11x^5y^2$

B. $\sqrt[3]{-8x^{12}y^3} = -2x^4y$

C. $-\sqrt[4]{81x^{12}y^8} = -3x^3y^2$

SECTION 7.2

Problem 1

$$\sqrt[5]{128x^7} = \sqrt[5]{32x^5(4x^2)}$$
$$= \sqrt[5]{32x^5}\sqrt[5]{4x^2}$$
$$= 2x\sqrt[5]{4x^2}$$

Problem 2

A. $3xy\sqrt[3]{81x^5y} - \sqrt[3]{192x^8y^4}$
$$= 3xy\sqrt[3]{27x^3}\sqrt[3]{3x^2y} - \sqrt[3]{64x^6y^3}\sqrt[3]{3x^2y}$$
$$= 3xy \cdot 3x\sqrt[3]{3x^2y} - 4x^2y\sqrt[3]{3x^2y}$$
$$= 9x^2y\sqrt[3]{3x^2y} - 4x^2y\sqrt[3]{3x^2y}$$
$$= 5x^2y\sqrt[3]{3x^2y}$$

B. $4a\sqrt[3]{54a^7b^9} + a^2b\sqrt[3]{128a^4b^6}$
$$= 4a\sqrt[3]{27a^6b^9}\sqrt[3]{2a} + a^2b\sqrt[3]{64a^3b^6}\sqrt[3]{2a}$$
$$= 4a \cdot 3a^2b^3\sqrt[3]{2a} + a^2b \cdot 4ab^2\sqrt[3]{2a}$$
$$= 12a^3b^3\sqrt[3]{2a} + 4a^3b^3\sqrt[3]{2a}$$
$$= 16a^3b^3\sqrt[3]{2a}$$

Problem 3

$\sqrt{5b}\left(\sqrt{3b} - \sqrt{10}\right)$
$= \sqrt{15b^2} - \sqrt{50b}$
$= \sqrt{b^2}\sqrt{15} - \sqrt{25}\sqrt{2b}$
$= b\sqrt{15} - 5\sqrt{2b}$

Problem 4

A. $\left(2\sqrt[3]{2x} - 3\right)\left(\sqrt[3]{2x} - 5\right)$
$= 2\sqrt[3]{4x^2} - 10\sqrt[3]{2x} - 3\sqrt[3]{2x} + 15$
$= 2\sqrt[3]{4x^2} - 13\sqrt[3]{2x} + 15$

B. $\left(2\sqrt{x} - 3\right)\left(2\sqrt{x} + 3\right)$
$= \left(2\sqrt{x}\right)^2 - 9 = 4x - 9$

Problem 5

A. $\dfrac{y}{\sqrt{3y}} = \dfrac{y}{\sqrt{3y}} \cdot \dfrac{\sqrt{3y}}{\sqrt{3y}} = \dfrac{y\sqrt{3y}}{\sqrt{9y^2}} = \dfrac{y\sqrt{3y}}{3y}$
$= \dfrac{\sqrt{3y}}{3}$

B. $\dfrac{3}{\sqrt[3]{3x^2}} = \dfrac{3}{\sqrt[3]{3x^2}} \cdot \dfrac{\sqrt[3]{9x}}{\sqrt[3]{9x}} = \dfrac{3\sqrt[3]{9x}}{\sqrt[3]{27x^3}} = \dfrac{3\sqrt[3]{9x}}{3x}$
$= \dfrac{\sqrt[3]{9x}}{x}$

Problem 6

A. $\dfrac{4 + \sqrt{2}}{3 - \sqrt{3}} = \dfrac{4 + \sqrt{2}}{3 - \sqrt{3}} \cdot \dfrac{3 + \sqrt{3}}{3 + \sqrt{3}}$
$= \dfrac{12 + 4\sqrt{3} + 3\sqrt{2} + \sqrt{6}}{9 - \left(\sqrt{3}\right)^2}$
$= \dfrac{12 + 4\sqrt{3} + 3\sqrt{2} + \sqrt{6}}{6}$

B. $\dfrac{\sqrt{2} + \sqrt{x}}{\sqrt{2} - \sqrt{x}} = \dfrac{\sqrt{2} + \sqrt{x}}{\sqrt{2} - \sqrt{x}} \cdot \dfrac{\sqrt{2} + \sqrt{x}}{\sqrt{2} + \sqrt{x}}$
$= \dfrac{\sqrt{4} + \sqrt{2x} + \sqrt{2x} + \sqrt{x^2}}{\left(\sqrt{2}\right)^2 - \left(\sqrt{x}\right)^2}$
$= \dfrac{2 + 2\sqrt{2x} + x}{2 - x}$

SECTION 7.3

Problem 1

A. Because Q contains an odd root, there are no restrictions on the radicand.

The domain is $(-\infty, \infty)$.

B. $3x + 9 \geq 0$
$3x \geq -9$
$x \geq -3$

The domain is $[-3, \infty)$.

Problem 2

Problem 3

SECTION 7.4

Problem 1

A. $\sqrt{4x + 5} - 12 = -5$
$\sqrt{4x + 5} = 7$
$\left(\sqrt{4x + 5}\right)^2 = 7^2$
$4x + 5 = 49$
$4x = 44$
$x = 11$

Check: $\dfrac{\sqrt{4x + 5} - 12 = -5}{}$

$\begin{array}{c|c} \sqrt{4 \cdot 11 + 5} - 12 & -5 \\ \sqrt{44 + 5} - 12 & \\ \sqrt{49} - 12 & \\ 7 - 12 & \\ & -5 = -5 \end{array}$

The solution is 11.

B. $\sqrt[4]{x - 8} = 3$
$\left(\sqrt[4]{x - 8}\right)^4 = 3^4$
$x - 8 = 81$
$x = 89$

Check: $\dfrac{\sqrt[4]{x - 8} = 3}{}$

$\begin{array}{c|c} \sqrt[4]{89 - 8} & 3 \\ \sqrt[4]{81} & \\ & 3 = 3 \end{array}$

The solution is 89.

Problem 2

A. $x + 3\sqrt{x + 2} = 8$
$3\sqrt{x + 2} = 8 - x$
$\left(3\sqrt{x + 2}\right)^2 = (8 - x)^2$
$9(x + 2) = 64 - 16x + x^2$
$9x + 18 = 64 - 16x + x^2$
$0 = x^2 - 25x + 46$
$0 = (x - 2)(x - 23)$

$\begin{array}{ll} x - 2 = 0 & x - 23 = 0 \\ \quad x = 2 & \quad x = 23 \end{array}$

Check:
$$\begin{array}{c|c} x + 3\sqrt{x+2} = 8 \\ 2 + 3\sqrt{2+2} & 8 \\ 2 + 3\sqrt{4} \\ 2 + 3 \cdot 2 \\ 2 + 6 \\ 8 = 8 \end{array}$$

$$\begin{array}{c|c} x + 3\sqrt{x+2} = 8 \\ 23 + 3\sqrt{23+2} & 8 \\ 23 + 3\sqrt{25} \\ 23 + 3 \cdot 5 \\ 23 + 15 \\ 38 \neq 8 \end{array}$$

23 does not check as a solution. The solution is 2.

B.
$$\sqrt{x+5} = 5 - \sqrt{x}$$
$$(\sqrt{x+5})^2 = (5 - \sqrt{x})^2$$
$$x + 5 = 25 - 10\sqrt{x} + x$$
$$-20 = -10\sqrt{x}$$
$$2 = \sqrt{x}$$
$$2^2 = (\sqrt{x})^2$$
$$4 = x$$

Check:
$$\begin{array}{c|c} \sqrt{x+5} = 5 - \sqrt{x} \\ \sqrt{4+5} & 5 - \sqrt{4} \\ \sqrt{9} & 5 - 2 \\ 3 = 3 \end{array}$$

The solution is 4.

Problem 3

Strategy To find the diagonal, use the Pythagorean Theorem. One leg is the length of the rectangle. The second leg is the width of the rectangle. The hypotenuse is the diagonal of the rectangle.

Solution
$$c^2 = a^2 + b^2$$
$$c^2 = (6)^2 + (3)^2$$
$$c^2 = 36 + 9$$
$$c^2 = 45$$
$$(c^2)^{\frac{1}{2}} = (45)^{\frac{1}{2}}$$
$$c = \sqrt{45}$$
$$c \approx 6.7$$

The diagonal is 6.7 cm.

SECTION 7.5

Problem 1

$$\sqrt{-45} = i\sqrt{45} = i\sqrt{9 \cdot 5} = 3i\sqrt{5}$$

Problem 2

$$\sqrt{98} - \sqrt{-60} = \sqrt{98} - i\sqrt{60}$$
$$= \sqrt{49 \cdot 2} - i\sqrt{4 \cdot 15}$$
$$= 7\sqrt{2} - 2i\sqrt{15}$$

Problem 3

$$(-4 + 2i) - (6 - 8i) = -10 + 10i$$

Problem 4

$$(16 - \sqrt{-45}) - (3 + \sqrt{-20})$$
$$= (16 - i\sqrt{45}) - (3 + i\sqrt{20})$$
$$= (16 - i\sqrt{9 \cdot 5}) - (3 + i\sqrt{4 \cdot 5})$$
$$= (16 - 3i\sqrt{5}) - (3 + 2i\sqrt{5})$$
$$= 13 - 5i\sqrt{5}$$

Problem 5

$$\sqrt{-3}(\sqrt{27} - \sqrt{-6})$$
$$= i\sqrt{3}(\sqrt{27} - i\sqrt{6})$$
$$= i\sqrt{81} - i^2\sqrt{18}$$
$$= i\sqrt{81} - (-1)\sqrt{9 \cdot 2}$$
$$= 9i + 3\sqrt{2}$$
$$= 3\sqrt{2} + 9i$$

Problem 6

A. $(4 - 3i)(2 - i) = 8 - 4i - 6i + 3i^2$
$$= 8 - 10i + 3i^2 = 8 - 10i + 3(-1)$$
$$= 5 - 10i$$

B. $(3 - i)\left(\dfrac{3}{10} + \dfrac{1}{10}i\right)$
$$= \frac{9}{10} + \frac{3}{10}i - \frac{3}{10}i - \frac{1}{10}i^2 = \frac{9}{10} - \frac{1}{10}i^2$$
$$= \frac{9}{10} - \frac{1}{10}(-1) = \frac{9}{10} + \frac{1}{10} = 1$$

C. $(3 + 6i)(3 - 6i) = 3^2 + 6^2 = 9 + 36$
$$= 45$$

D. $(1 + 5i)^2 = 1 + 10i + 25i^2$
$$= 1 + 10i + 25(-1)$$
$$= 1 + 10i - 25$$
$$= -24 + 10i$$

Problem 7

$$\frac{2 - 3i}{4i} = \frac{2 - 3i}{4i} \cdot \frac{i}{i} = \frac{2i - 3i^2}{4i^2} = \frac{2i - 3(-1)}{4(-1)}$$
$$= \frac{3 + 2i}{-4} = -\frac{3}{4} - \frac{1}{2}i$$

Problem 8

$$\frac{2 + 5i}{3 - 2i} = \frac{(2 + 5i)}{(3 - 2i)} \cdot \frac{(3 + 2i)}{(3 + 2i)}$$
$$= \frac{6 + 4i + 15i + 10i^2}{3^2 + 2^2} = \frac{6 + 19i + 10(-1)}{13}$$
$$= \frac{-4 + 19i}{13} = -\frac{4}{13} + \frac{19}{13}i$$

Solutions to Chapter 8 Problems

SECTION 8.1

Problem 1

$$x^2 - 3ax - 4a^2 = 0$$
$$(x + a)(x - 4a) = 0$$

$$x + a = 0 \qquad x - 4a = 0$$
$$x = -a \qquad x = 4a$$

The solutions are $-a$ and $4a$.

Problem 2

$$(x - r_1)(x - r_2) = 0$$

$$\left[x - \left(-\frac{2}{3}\right)\right]\left(x - \frac{1}{6}\right) = 0$$

$$\left(x + \frac{2}{3}\right)\left(x - \frac{1}{6}\right) = 0$$

$$x^2 + \frac{3}{6}x - \frac{2}{18} = 0$$

$$18\left(x^2 + \frac{3}{6}x - \frac{2}{18}\right) = 0$$

$$18x^2 + 9x - 2 = 0$$

Problem 3

$$2(x + 1)^2 + 24 = 0$$
$$2(x + 1)^2 = -24$$
$$(x + 1)^2 = -12$$
$$\sqrt{(x + 1)^2} = \sqrt{-12}$$
$$|x + 1| = 2i\sqrt{3}$$
$$x + 1 = \pm 2i\sqrt{3}$$

$$x + 1 = 2i\sqrt{3} \qquad x + 1 = -2i\sqrt{3}$$
$$x = -1 + 2i\sqrt{3} \qquad x = -1 - 2i\sqrt{3}$$

The solutions are $-1 + 2i\sqrt{3}$ and $-1 - 2i\sqrt{3}$.

SECTION 8.2

Problem 1

A. $4x^2 - 4x - 1 = 0$
$$4x^2 - 4x = 1$$
$$\frac{4x^2 - 4x}{4} = \frac{1}{4}$$
$$x^2 - x = \frac{1}{4}$$

Complete the square.

$$x^2 - x + \frac{1}{4} = \frac{1}{4} + \frac{1}{4}$$

$$\left(x - \frac{1}{2}\right)^2 = \frac{2}{4}$$

$$\sqrt{\left(x - \frac{1}{2}\right)^2} = \sqrt{\frac{2}{4}}$$

$$\left|x - \frac{1}{2}\right| = \frac{\sqrt{2}}{2}$$

$$x - \frac{1}{2} = \pm\frac{\sqrt{2}}{2}$$

$$x - \frac{1}{2} = \frac{\sqrt{2}}{2} \qquad x - \frac{1}{2} = -\frac{\sqrt{2}}{2}$$

$$x = \frac{1}{2} + \frac{\sqrt{2}}{2} \qquad x = \frac{1}{2} - \frac{\sqrt{2}}{2}$$

The solutions are $\dfrac{1 + \sqrt{2}}{2}$ and $\dfrac{1 - \sqrt{2}}{2}$.

B. $2x^2 + x - 5 = 0$
$$2x^2 + x = 5$$
$$\frac{2x^2 + x}{2} = \frac{5}{2}$$
$$x^2 + \frac{1}{2}x = \frac{5}{2}$$

Complete the square.

$$x^2 + \frac{1}{2}x + \frac{1}{16} = \frac{5}{2} + \frac{1}{16}$$

$$\left(x + \frac{1}{4}\right)^2 = \frac{41}{16}$$

$$\sqrt{\left(x + \frac{1}{4}\right)^2} = \sqrt{\frac{41}{16}}$$

$$\left|x + \frac{1}{4}\right| = \frac{\sqrt{41}}{4}$$

$$x + \frac{1}{4} = \pm\frac{\sqrt{41}}{4}$$

$$x + \frac{1}{4} = \frac{\sqrt{41}}{4} \qquad x + \frac{1}{4} = -\frac{\sqrt{41}}{4}$$

$$x = -\frac{1}{4} + \frac{\sqrt{41}}{4} \qquad x = -\frac{1}{4} - \frac{\sqrt{41}}{4}$$

The solutions are $\dfrac{-1 + \sqrt{41}}{4}$ and $\dfrac{-1 - \sqrt{41}}{4}$.

Problem 2

A. $x^2 + 6x - 9 = 0$

$$a = 1, b = 6, c = -9$$

$$x = \frac{-b \pm \sqrt{b^2 - 4ac}}{2a}$$

$$= \frac{-6 \pm \sqrt{6^2 - 4(1)(-9)}}{2 \cdot 1}$$

$$= \frac{-6 \pm \sqrt{36 + 36}}{2}$$

$$= \frac{-6 \pm \sqrt{72}}{2}$$

$$= \frac{-6 \pm 6\sqrt{2}}{2} = -3 \pm 3\sqrt{2}$$

The solutions are $-3 + 3\sqrt{2}$ and $-3 - 3\sqrt{2}$.

B.
$$4x^2 = 4x - 1$$
$$4x^2 - 4x + 1 = 0$$

$$a = 4, b = -4, c = 1$$

$$x = \frac{-b \pm \sqrt{b^2 - 4ac}}{2a}$$

$$= \frac{-(-4) \pm \sqrt{(-4)^2 - 4(4)(1)}}{2 \cdot 4}$$

$$= \frac{4 \pm \sqrt{16 - 16}}{8}$$

$$= \frac{4 \pm \sqrt{0}}{8} = \frac{4}{8} = \frac{1}{2}$$

The solution is $\frac{1}{2}$.

Problem 3

$3x^2 - x - 1 = 0$

$a = 3, b = -1, c = -1$

$b^2 - 4ac = (-1)^2 - 4(3)(-1)$

$\qquad = 1 + 12 = 13$

$13 > 0$

Because the discriminant is greater than zero, the equation has two real number solutions.

SECTION 8.3

Problem 1

A. $\qquad x - 5x^{\frac{1}{2}} + 6 = 0$

$\qquad \left(x^{\frac{1}{2}}\right)^2 - 5\left(x^{\frac{1}{2}}\right) + 6 = 0$

$\qquad\qquad u^2 - 5u + 6 = 0$

$\qquad\qquad (u - 2)(u - 3) = 0$

$u - 2 = 0$	$u - 3 = 0$
$u = 2$	$u = 3$

Replace u with $x^{\frac{1}{2}}$.

$x^{\frac{1}{2}} = 2$	$x^{\frac{1}{2}} = 3$
$\left(x^{\frac{1}{2}}\right)^2 = 2^2$	$\left(x^{\frac{1}{2}}\right)^2 = 3^2$
$x = 4$	$x = 9$

4 and 9 check as solutions.

The solutions are 4 and 9.

B. $\qquad 4x^4 + 35x^2 - 9 = 0$

$\qquad 4(x^2)^2 + 35(x^2) - 9 = 0$

$\qquad\qquad 4u^2 + 35u - 9 = 0$

$\qquad\qquad (4u - 1)(u + 9) = 0$

$4u - 1 = 0$	$u + 9 = 0$
$4u = 1$	$u = -9$
$u = \dfrac{1}{4}$	

Replace u with x^2.

$x^2 = \dfrac{1}{4}$	$x^2 = -9$
$\sqrt{x^2} = \sqrt{\dfrac{1}{4}}$	$\sqrt{x^2} = \sqrt{-9}$
$|x| = \dfrac{1}{2}$	$|x| = 3i$

$x = \pm\dfrac{1}{2}$	$x = \pm 3i$

The solutions are $\dfrac{1}{2}$, $-\dfrac{1}{2}$, $3i$, and $-3i$.

Problem 2

$\sqrt{2x + 1} + x = 7$

$\qquad \sqrt{2x + 1} = 7 - x$

$\qquad \left(\sqrt{2x + 1}\right)^2 = (7 - x)^2$

$\qquad 2x + 1 = 49 - 14x + x^2$

$\qquad 0 = x^2 - 16x + 48$

$\qquad 0 = (x - 4)(x - 12)$

$x - 4 = 0$	$x - 12 = 0$
$x = 4$	$x = 12$

4 checks as a solution, but 12 does not check as a solution.

The solution is 4.

Problem 3

$\sqrt{2x - 1} + \sqrt{x} = 2$

Solve for one of the radical expressions.

$\qquad \sqrt{2x - 1} = 2 - \sqrt{x}$

$\qquad \left(\sqrt{2x - 1}\right)^2 = \left(2 - \sqrt{x}\right)^2$

$\qquad 2x - 1 = 4 - 4\sqrt{x} + x$

$\qquad x - 5 = -4\sqrt{x}$

Square each side of the equation.

$\qquad (x - 5)^2 = \left(-4\sqrt{x}\right)^2$

$\qquad x^2 - 10x + 25 = 16x$

$\qquad x^2 - 26x + 25 = 0$

$\qquad (x - 1)(x - 25) = 0$

$x - 1 = 0$	$x - 25 = 0$
$x = 1$	$x = 25$

1 checks as a solution, but 25 does not check as a solution.

The solution is 1.

Problem 4

$$3y + \frac{25}{3y - 2} = -8$$

$$(3y - 2)\left(3y + \frac{25}{3y - 2}\right) = (3y - 2)(-8)$$

$$(3y - 2)(3y) + (3y - 2)\left(\frac{25}{3y - 2}\right) = (3y - 2)(-8)$$

$$9y^2 - 6y + 25 = -24y + 16$$

$$9y^2 + 18y + 9 = 0$$

$$9(y^2 + 2y + 1) = 0$$

$$9(y + 1)(y + 1) = 0$$

$y + 1 = 0$	$y + 1 = 0$
$y = -1$	$y = -1$

The solution is -1.

SECTION 8.4

Problem 1

Strategy ▶ This is a geometry problem.
▶ Width of the rectangle: W
   Length of the rectangle: $W + 3$
▶ Use the equation $A = L \cdot W$.

Solution
$$A = L \cdot W$$
$$54 = (W + 3)(W)$$
$$54 = W^2 + 3W$$
$$0 = W^2 + 3W - 54$$
$$0 = (W + 9)(W - 6)$$

$$W + 9 = 0 \qquad W - 6 = 0$$
$$W = -9 \qquad W = 6$$

The solution -9 is not possible.

Length $= W + 3 = 6 + 3 = 9$

The length is 9 m.

SECTION 8.5

Problem 1

$$2x^2 - x - 10 \le 0$$
$$(2x - 5)(x + 2) \le 0$$

```
2x - 5  --- | -------- | +++
x + 2   --- | ++++++++  | +++
       +--+--+--+--+--+--+--+
       -3 -2 -1  0  1  2  3
```

$$\left\{ x \,\middle|\, -2 \le x \le \frac{5}{2} \right\}$$

```
+--+--+--[--+--+--]+--+--+
-5 -4 -3 -2 -1  0  1  2  3  4  5
```

Problem 2

$$\frac{x}{x - 2} \le 0$$

```
x      ---- | +++ | ++++++
x - 2  ---- | --- | ++++++
       +--+--+--+--+--+
      -1  0  1  2  3  4
```

$$\{ x \,|\, 0 \le x < 2 \}$$

```
+--+--+--+--+--+[--+--)--+--+
-5 -4 -3 -2 -1  0  1  2  3  4  5
```

SECTION 8.6

Problem 1

x-coordinate: $-\dfrac{b}{2a} = -\dfrac{0}{2(1)} = 0$

$$y = x^2 - 2$$
$$ = 0^2 - 2$$
$$ = -2$$

The vertex is $(0, -2)$.

The axis of symmetry is the line $x = 0$.

Problem 2

The domain is $\{x \,|\, x \in \text{real numbers}\}$. The range is $\{y \,|\, y \ge -6\}$.

Problem 3

A. $y = 2x^2 - 5x + 2$
$$0 = 2x^2 - 5x + 2$$
$$0 = (2x - 1)(x - 2)$$

$$2x - 1 = 0 \qquad x - 2 = 0$$
$$2x = 1 \qquad x = 2$$
$$x = \frac{1}{2}$$

The x-intercepts are $\left(\dfrac{1}{2}, 0 \right)$ and $(2, 0)$.

B. $y = x^2 + 4x + 4$
$$0 = x^2 + 4x + 4$$
$$0 = (x + 2)(x + 2)$$

$$x + 2 = 0 \qquad x + 2 = 0$$
$$x = -2 \qquad x = -2$$

The x-intercept is $(-2, 0)$.

Problem 4

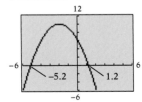

The approximate values of the zeros are -5.2 and 1.2.

Problem 5

$$f(x) = -x^2 - 4x + 2$$
$$-4 = -x^2 - 4x + 2$$
$$0 = -x^2 - 4x + 6$$

$$x = \frac{-b \pm \sqrt{b^2 - 4ac}}{2a}$$
$$= \frac{4 \pm \sqrt{-(-4)^2 - 4(-1)(6)}}{2(-1)}$$
$$= \frac{4 \pm \sqrt{16 + 24}}{-2}$$

$$= \frac{4 \pm \sqrt{40}}{-2}$$

$$= \frac{4 \pm 2\sqrt{10}}{-2}$$

$$= -2 \pm \sqrt{10}$$

The values of x for which $f(x) = -4$ are $-2 + \sqrt{10}$ and $-2 - \sqrt{10}$.

Problem 6

$$y = x^2 - x - 6$$

$$a = 1, b = -1, c = -6$$

$$b^2 - 4ac = (-1)^2 - 4(1)(-6)$$
$$= 1 + 24 = 25$$

Because the discriminant is greater than zero, the parabola has two x-intercepts.

SECTION 8.7

Problem 1

$$x = -\frac{b}{2a} = -\frac{-3}{2(2)} = \frac{3}{4}$$

$$f(x) = 2x^2 - 3x + 1$$

$$f\left(\frac{3}{4}\right) = 2\left(\frac{3}{4}\right)^2 - 3\left(\frac{3}{4}\right) + 1 = \frac{9}{8} - \frac{9}{4} + 1$$
$$= -\frac{1}{8}$$

Because a is positive, the function has a minimum value. The minimum value of the function is $-\frac{1}{8}$.

Problem 2

Strategy ▶ To find the time it takes the ball to reach its maximum height, find the t-coordinate of the vertex.
▶ To find the maximum height, evaluate the function at the t-coordinate of the vertex.

Solution $t = -\dfrac{b}{2a} = -\dfrac{64}{2(-16)} = 2$

The ball reaches its maximum height in 2 s.

$$s(t) = -16t^2 + 64t$$
$$s(2) = -16(2)^2 + 64(2) = -64 + 128 = 64$$

The maximum height is 64 ft.

Problem 3

Strategy $P = 2x + y$
      $100 = 2x + y$ • $P = 100$
      $100 - 2x = y$ • **Solve for y.**

Express the area of the rectangle in terms of x.

$$A = xy$$
$$A = x(100 - 2x)$$ • **y = 100 − 2x**
$$A = -2x^2 + 100x$$

▶ To find the width, find the x-coordinate of the vertex of $f(x) = -2x^2 + 100x$.
▶ To find the length, replace x in $y = 100 - 2x$ by the x-coordinate of the vertex.

Solution $x = -\dfrac{b}{2a} = -\dfrac{100}{2(-2)} = 25$

The width is 25 ft.

$$100 - 2x = 100 - 2(25)$$
$$= 100 - 50 = 50$$

The length is 50 ft.

Solutions to Chapter 9 Problems

SECTION 9.1

Problem 1

The graph of $g(x) = x^2 - 2x - 3$ is the graph of $f(x) = x^2 - 2x$ shifted 3 units down.

Problem 2

The graph of $g(x) = \sqrt{x - 3}$ is the graph of $f(x) = \sqrt{x}$ shifted 3 units to the right.

Problem 3

The graph of $V(x) = (x - 2)^3 + 1$ is the graph of $g(x) = x^3$ shifted up 1 unit and shifted 2 units to the right.

SECTION 9.2

Problem 1

$$(f + g)(-2) = f(-2) + g(-2)$$
$$= [(-2)^2 + 2(-2)] + [5(-2) - 2]$$
$$= (4 - 4) + (-10 - 2)$$
$$= -12$$

$$(f + g)(-2) = -12$$

Problem 2

$(f \cdot g)(3) = f(3) \cdot g(3)$
$= (4 - 3^2) \cdot [3(3) - 4]$
$= (4 - 9) \cdot (9 - 4)$
$= (-5)(5)$
$= -25$

$(f \cdot g)(3) = -25$

Problem 3

$\left(\dfrac{f}{g}\right)(4) = \dfrac{f(4)}{g(4)}$

$= \dfrac{4^2 - 4}{4^2 + 2 \cdot 4 + 1}$

$= \dfrac{16 - 4}{16 + 8 + 1}$

$= \dfrac{12}{25}$

$\left(\dfrac{f}{g}\right)(4) = \dfrac{12}{25}$

Problem 4

A. $h(x) = x^2 + 1$
$h(0) = 0 + 1 = 1$

$g(x) = 3x - 2$
$g(1) = 3(1) - 2 = 1$

$g[h(0)] = 1$

B. $h[g(x)] = h(3x - 2)$
$= (3x - 2)^2 + 1$
$= 9x^2 - 12x + 4 + 1$
$= 9x^2 - 12x + 5$

SECTION 9.3

Problem 1

A. Because any vertical line will intersect the graph at no more than one point, and any horizontal line will intersect the graph at no more than one point, the graph is the graph of a 1–1 function.

B. Because any vertical line will intersect the graph at no more than one point, and any horizontal line will intersect the graph at no more than one point, the graph is the graph of a 1–1 function.

Problem 2

$f(x) = 4x + 2$
$y = 4x + 2$
$x = 4y + 2$
$4y = x - 2$
$y = \dfrac{1}{4}x - \dfrac{1}{2}$
$f^{-1}(x) = \dfrac{1}{4}x - \dfrac{1}{2}$

Problem 3

$h[g(x)] = 4\left(\dfrac{1}{4}x - \dfrac{1}{2}\right) + 2$
$= x - 2 + 2 = x$

$g[h(x)] = \dfrac{1}{4}(4x + 2) - \dfrac{1}{2}$

$= x + \dfrac{1}{2} - \dfrac{1}{2} = x$

The functions are inverses of each other.

Solutions to Chapter 10 Problems

SECTION 10.1

Problem 1

$f(x) = \left(\dfrac{2}{3}\right)^x$

$f(3) = \left(\dfrac{2}{3}\right)^3 = \dfrac{8}{27}$

$f(-2) = \left(\dfrac{2}{3}\right)^{-2} = \left(\dfrac{3}{2}\right)^2 = \dfrac{9}{4}$

Problem 2

$f(x) = 2^{2x+1}$
$f(0) = 2^{2(0)+1} = 2^1 = 2$

$f(-2) = 2^{2(-2)+1} = 2^{-3} = \dfrac{1}{2^3} = \dfrac{1}{8}$

Problem 3

$f(x) = \pi^x$
$f(3) = \pi^3$
≈ 31.0063
$f(-2) = \pi^{-2}$
≈ 0.1013
$f(\pi) = \pi^\pi$
≈ 36.4622

Problem 4

$f(x) = e^x$
$f(1.2) = e^{1.2}$
≈ 3.3201
$f(-2.5) = e^{-2.5}$
≈ 0.0821
$f(e) = e^e$
≈ 15.1543

Problem 5

A.   **B.**

Problem 6

A.

B.

Problem 7

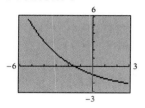

−2.4

SECTION 10.2

Problem 1

$3^{-4} = \dfrac{1}{81}$ is equivalent to $\log_3 \dfrac{1}{81} = -4$.

Problem 2

$\log_{10} 0.0001 = -4$ is equivalent to $10^{-4} = 0.0001$.

Problem 3

$\log_4 64 = x$
$64 = 4^x$
$4^3 = 4^x$
$3 = x$
$\log_4 64 = 3$

Problem 4

$\log_2 x = -4$
$2^{-4} = x$
$\dfrac{1}{2^4} = x$
$\dfrac{1}{16} = x$

The solution is $\dfrac{1}{16}$.

Problem 5

$\log x = 1.5$
$10^{1.5} = x$
$31.6228 \approx x$

The solution is 31.6228.

Problem 6

A. $\log_b \dfrac{x^2}{y} = \log_b x^2 - \log_b y$
$= 2\log_b x - \log_b y$

B. $\ln y^{\frac{1}{3}} z^3 = \ln y^{\frac{1}{3}} + \ln z^3$
$= \dfrac{1}{3}\ln y + 3\ln z$

C. $\log_8 \sqrt[3]{xy^2} = \log_8 (xy^2)^{\frac{1}{3}}$
$= \dfrac{1}{3}\log_8 xy^2$
$= \dfrac{1}{3}(\log_8 x + \log_8 y^2)$
$= \dfrac{1}{3}(\log_8 x + 2\log_8 y)$
$= \dfrac{1}{3}\log_8 x + \dfrac{2}{3}\log_8 y$

Problem 7

A. $2\log_b x - 3\log_b y - \log_b z = \log_b x^2 - \log_b y^3 - \log_b z$
$= \log_b \dfrac{x^2}{y^3} - \log_b z$
$= \log_b \dfrac{x^2}{y^3 z}$

B. $\dfrac{1}{3}(\log_4 x - 2\log_4 y + \log_4 z)$
$= \dfrac{1}{3}(\log_4 x - \log_4 y^2 + \log_4 z)$
$= \dfrac{1}{3}\left(\log_4 \dfrac{x}{y^2} + \log_4 z\right)$
$= \dfrac{1}{3}\left(\log_4 \dfrac{xz}{y^2}\right)$
$= \log_4 \left(\dfrac{xz}{y^2}\right)^{\frac{1}{3}} = \log_4 \sqrt[3]{\dfrac{xz}{y^2}}$

C. $\dfrac{1}{2}(2\ln x - 5\ln y) = \dfrac{1}{2}(\ln x^2 - \ln y^5)$
$= \dfrac{1}{2}\left(\ln \dfrac{x^2}{y^5}\right)$
$= \ln \left(\dfrac{x^2}{y^5}\right)^{\frac{1}{2}}$
$= \ln \sqrt{\dfrac{x^2}{y^5}}$

Problem 8

A. $\log_{16} 1 = 0$

B. $12\log_3 3 = \log_3 3^{12} = 12$

Problem 9

$\log_4 2.4 = \dfrac{\ln 2.4}{\ln 4} \approx 0.6315$

Problem 10

$f(x) = 4\log_8(3x + 4) = 4 \cdot \dfrac{\log(3x + 4)}{\log 8}$
$= \dfrac{4}{\log 8}\log(3x + 4)$

SECTION 10.3

Problem 1

A. $f(x) = \log_2(x - 1)$
$\quad y = \log_2(x - 1)$

$\quad y = \log_2(x - 1)$ is equivalent to $2^y = x - 1$.

$\quad 2^y + 1 = x$

B. $f(x) = \log_3 2x$
$\quad y = \log_3 2x$

$\quad y = \log_3 2x$ is equivalent to $3^y = 2x$.

$\quad \dfrac{3^y}{2} = x$

Problem 2

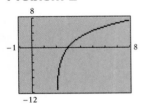

Problem 3

$f(x) = 2 \log_4 x$

$\quad = 2 \cdot \dfrac{\ln x}{\ln 4}$

$\quad = \dfrac{2}{\ln 4} \ln x$

SECTION 10.4

Problem 1

$10^{3x+5} = 10^{x-3}$

$3x + 5 = x - 3$
$2x + 5 = -3$
$\quad 2x = -8$
$\quad\quad x = -4$

Check: $\dfrac{10^{3x+5} = 10^{x-3}}{}$

$\quad\dfrac{10^{3(-4)+5} \;\big|\; 10^{-4-3}}{10^{-12+5} \;\big|\; 10^{-7}}$

$\quad\quad\quad 10^{-7} = 10^{-7}$

The solution is -4.

Problem 2

A. $\quad 4^{3x} = 25$
$\quad \log 4^{3x} = \log 25$
$\quad 3x \log 4 = \log 25$
$\quad\quad 3x = \dfrac{\log 25}{\log 4}$
$\quad\quad\quad x = \dfrac{\log 25}{3 \log 4}$
$\quad\quad\quad x \approx 0.7740$

The solution is 0.7740.

B. $\quad (1.06)^x = 1.5$
$\quad \log(1.06)^x = \log 1.5$
$\quad x \log 1.06 = \log 1.5$
$\quad\quad\quad x = \dfrac{\log 1.5}{\log 1.06}$
$\quad\quad\quad x \approx 6.9585$

The solution is 6.9585.

Problem 3

$\quad e^x = x$
$e^x - x = 0$

Graph $f(x) = e^x - x$.

The equation has no real number solutions.

Problem 4

A. $\log_4(x^2 - 3x) = 1$

Rewrite in exponential form.

$4^1 = x^2 - 3x$
$\quad 4 = x^2 - 3x$
$\quad 0 = x^2 - 3x - 4$
$\quad 0 = (x + 1)(x - 4)$

$x + 1 = 0 \qquad x - 4 = 0$
$\quad\quad x = -1 \qquad\quad x = 4$

The solutions are -1 and 4.

B. $\log_3 x + \log_3(x + 3) = \log_3 4$
$\quad\quad\quad \log_3[x(x + 3)] = \log_3 4$

Use the One-to-One Property of Logarithms.

$\quad\quad x(x + 3) = 4$
$\quad\quad x^2 + 3x = 4$
$\quad x^2 + 3x - 4 = 0$
$\quad (x + 4)(x - 1) = 0$

$x + 4 = 0 \qquad x - 1 = 0$
$\quad\quad x = -4 \qquad\quad x = 1$

-4 does not check as a solution. The solution is 1.

Problem 5

$$\log(3x - 2) = -2x$$
$$\log(3x - 2) + 2x = 0$$

Graph $f(x) = \log(3x - 2) + 2x$.

The solution is 0.68.

SECTION 10.5

Problem 1

Strategy ▶ To find the time, solve the compound interest formula for n. Use $P = 6000$, $A = 3000$, and $i = \frac{12\%}{12} = \frac{0.12}{12} = 0.01$.

Solution
$$P = A(1 + i)^n$$
$$6000 = 3000(1 + 0.01)^n$$
$$6000 = 3000(1.01)^n$$
$$2 = (1.01)^n$$
$$\log 2 = \log(1.01)^n$$
$$\log 2 = n \log 1.01$$
$$\frac{\log 2}{\log 1.01} = n$$
$$70 \approx n$$

70 months ÷ 12 ≈ 5.8 years

In approximately 6 years, the investment will be worth $6000.

Problem 2

Strategy ▶ To find the intensity, use the equation for the Richter scale magnitude of an earthquake, $M = \log \dfrac{I}{I_0}$. Replace M by 5.2 and solve for I.

Solution
$$M = \log \frac{I}{I_0}$$
$$5.2 = \log \frac{I}{I_0} \qquad \text{• Replace } M \text{ by 5.2.}$$
$$10^{5.2} = \frac{I}{I_0} \qquad \text{• Write in exponential form.}$$
$$10^{5.2}I_0 = I$$
$$158,489I_0 \approx I$$

The earthquake had an intensity that was approximately 158,489 times the intensity of a zero-level earthquake.

Solutions to Chapter 11 Problems

SECTION 11.1

Problem 1

$$a_n = n(n + 1)$$
$$a_1 = 1(1 + 1) = 2 \qquad \text{The first term is 2.}$$
$$a_2 = 2(2 + 1) = 6 \qquad \text{The second term is 6.}$$
$$a_3 = 3(3 + 1) = 12 \qquad \text{The third term is 12.}$$
$$a_4 = 4(4 + 1) = 20 \qquad \text{The fourth term is 20.}$$

Problem 2

$$a_n = \frac{1}{n(n + 2)}$$
$$a_6 = \frac{1}{6(6 + 2)} = \frac{1}{48} \qquad \text{The sixth term is } \frac{1}{48}.$$
$$a_9 = \frac{1}{9(9 + 2)} = \frac{1}{99} \qquad \text{The ninth term is } \frac{1}{99}.$$

Problem 3

A. $\displaystyle\sum_{n=1}^{4}(7 - n)$

$$= (7 - 1) + (7 - 2) + (7 - 3) + (7 - 4)$$
$$= 6 + 5 + 4 + 3 = 18$$

B. $\displaystyle\sum_{i=3}^{6}(i^2 - 2)$

$$= (3^2 - 2) + (4^2 - 2) + (5^2 - 2) + (6^2 - 2)$$
$$= 7 + 14 + 23 + 34 = 78$$

Problem 4

$$\sum_{n=1}^{5}nx = x + 2x + 3x + 4x + 5x$$

SECTION 11.2

Problem 1

$9, 3, -3, -9, \ldots$

$$d = a_2 - a_1 = 3 - 9 = -6$$
$$a_n = a_1 + (n - 1)d$$
$$a_{15} = 9 + (15 - 1)(-6) = 9 + (14)(-6)$$
$$= 9 - 84 = -75$$

Problem 2

$-3, 1, 5, 9, \ldots$

$$d = a_2 - a_1 = 1 - (-3) = 4$$
$$a_n = a_1 + (n - 1)d$$
$$a_n = -3 + (n - 1)4$$
$$a_n = -3 + 4n - 4$$
$$a_n = 4n - 7$$

Problem 3

$7, 9, 11, \ldots, 59$

$d = a_2 - a_1 = 9 - 7 = 2$

$a_n = a_1 + (n - 1)d$
$59 = 7 + (n - 1)2$
$59 = 7 + 2n - 2$
$59 = 5 + 2n$
$54 = 2n$
$27 = n$

There are 27 terms in the sequence.

Problem 4

$-4, -2, 0, 2, 4, \ldots$

$d = a_2 - a_1 = -2 - (-4) = 2$

$a_n = a_1 + (n - 1)d$
$a_{25} = -4 + (25 - 1)2$
$\quad = -4 + (24)2 = -4 + 48 = 44$

$S_n = \dfrac{n}{2}(a_1 + a_n)$

$S_{25} = \dfrac{25}{2}(-4 + 44)$

$\quad = \dfrac{25}{2}(40) = 25(20) = 500$

Problem 5

$\displaystyle\sum_{n=1}^{18}(3n - 2)$

$a_n = 3n - 2$
$a_1 = 3(1) - 2 = 1$
$a_{18} = 3(18) - 2 = 52$

$S_n = \dfrac{n}{2}(a_1 + a_n)$

$S_{18} = \dfrac{18}{2}(1 + 52) = 9(53) = 477$

Problem 6

Strategy To find the value of the 20th-place prize:

▶ Write the equation for the nth-place prize.

▶ Find the 20th term of the sequence.

To find the total amount of prize money being awarded, use the Formula for the Sum of n Terms of an Arithmetic Series.

Solution $10,000, 9700, \ldots$

$d = a_2 - a_1 = 9700 - 10,000 = -300$

$a_n = a_1 + (n - 1)d$
$\quad = 10,000 + (n - 1)(-300)$
$\quad = 10,000 - 300n + 300$
$\quad = -300n + 10,300$
$a_{20} = -300(20) + 10,300$
$\quad = -6000 + 10,300 = 4300$

$S_n = \dfrac{n}{2}(a_1 + a_n)$

$S_{20} = \dfrac{20}{2}(10,000 + 4300)$

$\quad = 10(14,300) = 143,000$

The value of the 20th-place prize is \$4300.

The total amount of prize money being awarded is \$143,000.

SECTION 11.3

Problem 1

$5, 2, \dfrac{4}{5}, \ldots$

$r = \dfrac{a_2}{a_1} = \dfrac{2}{5}$

$a_n = a_1 r^{n-1}$

$a_5 = 5\left(\dfrac{2}{5}\right)^{5-1} = 5\left(\dfrac{2}{5}\right)^4 = 5\left(\dfrac{16}{625}\right) = \dfrac{16}{125}$

Problem 2

$3, a_2, a_3, -192, \ldots$

$a_n = a_1 r^{n-1}$
$a_4 = 3r^{4-1}$
$-192 = 3r^{4-1}$
$-192 = 3r^3$
$-64 = r^3$
$-4 = r$

$a_n = a_1 r^{n-1}$
$a_3 = 3(-4)^{3-1} = 3(-4)^2 = 3(16)$
$\quad = 48$

Problem 3

$1, -\dfrac{1}{3}, \dfrac{1}{9}, -\dfrac{1}{27}$

$r = \dfrac{a_2}{a_1} = \dfrac{-\dfrac{1}{3}}{1} = -\dfrac{1}{3}$

$S_n = \dfrac{a_1(1 - r^n)}{1 - r}$

$S_4 = \dfrac{1\left[1 - \left(-\dfrac{1}{3}\right)^4\right]}{1 - \left(-\dfrac{1}{3}\right)}$

$\quad = \dfrac{1 - \dfrac{1}{81}}{\dfrac{4}{3}} = \dfrac{\dfrac{80}{81}}{\dfrac{4}{3}} = \dfrac{80}{81} \cdot \dfrac{3}{4} = \dfrac{20}{27}$

Problem 4

$$\sum_{n=1}^{5}\left(\frac{1}{2}\right)^n$$

$$a_n = \left(\frac{1}{2}\right)^n$$

$$a_1 = \left(\frac{1}{2}\right)^1 = \frac{1}{2}$$

$$a_2 = \left(\frac{1}{2}\right)^2 = \frac{1}{4}$$

$$r = \frac{a_2}{a_1} = \frac{\dfrac{1}{4}}{\dfrac{1}{2}} = \frac{1}{4} \cdot \frac{2}{1} = \frac{1}{2}$$

$$S_n = \frac{a_1(1 - r^n)}{1 - r}$$

$$S_5 = \frac{\dfrac{1}{2}\left[1 - \left(\dfrac{1}{2}\right)^5\right]}{1 - \dfrac{1}{2}}$$

$$= \frac{\dfrac{1}{2}\left(1 - \dfrac{1}{32}\right)}{\dfrac{1}{2}} = \frac{\dfrac{1}{2}\left(\dfrac{31}{32}\right)}{\dfrac{1}{2}} = \frac{\dfrac{31}{64}}{\dfrac{1}{2}}$$

$$= \frac{31}{64} \cdot \frac{2}{1} = \frac{31}{32}$$

Problem 5

$$3, -2, \frac{4}{3}, -\frac{8}{9}, \ldots$$

$$r = \frac{a_2}{a_1} = \frac{-2}{3} = -\frac{2}{3}$$

$$S = \frac{a_1}{1 - r} = \frac{3}{1 - \left(-\dfrac{2}{3}\right)}$$

$$= \frac{3}{1 + \dfrac{2}{3}} = \frac{3}{\dfrac{5}{3}} = \frac{9}{5}$$

Problem 6

$$0.\overline{36} = 0.36 + 0.0036 + 0.000036 + \cdots$$

$$S = \frac{a_1}{1 - r} = \frac{\dfrac{36}{100}}{1 - \dfrac{1}{100}} = \frac{\dfrac{36}{100}}{\dfrac{99}{100}} = \frac{36}{99} = \frac{4}{11}$$

An equivalent fraction is $\dfrac{4}{11}$.

Problem 7

Strategy To find the total number of letters mailed, use the Formula for the Sum of n Terms of a Finite Geometric Series.

Solution $n = 6, a_1 = 3, r = 3$

$$S_n = \frac{a_1(1 - r^n)}{1 - r}$$

$$S_6 = \frac{3(1 - 3^6)}{1 - 3} = \frac{3(1 - 729)}{1 - 3} = \frac{3(-728)}{-2}$$

$$= \frac{-2184}{-2} = 1092$$

From the first through the sixth mailings, 1092 letters will have been mailed.

SECTION 11.4

Problem 1

$$\frac{12!}{7!\,5!} = \frac{12 \cdot 11 \cdot 10 \cdot 9 \cdot 8 \cdot 7 \cdot 6 \cdot 5 \cdot 4 \cdot 3 \cdot 2 \cdot 1}{(7 \cdot 6 \cdot 5 \cdot 4 \cdot 3 \cdot 2 \cdot 1)(5 \cdot 4 \cdot 3 \cdot 2 \cdot 1)}$$

$$= 792$$

Problem 2

$$\binom{7}{0} = \frac{7!}{(7 - 0)!\,0!} = \frac{7!}{7!\,0!}$$

$$= \frac{7 \cdot 6 \cdot 5 \cdot 4 \cdot 3 \cdot 2 \cdot 1}{(7 \cdot 6 \cdot 5 \cdot 4 \cdot 3 \cdot 2 \cdot 1)(1)} = 1$$

Problem 3

$$(3m - n)^4$$

$$= \binom{4}{0}(3m)^4 + \binom{4}{1}(3m)^3(-n) + \binom{4}{2}(3m)^2(-n)^2 +$$

$$\binom{4}{3}(3m)(-n)^3 + \binom{4}{4}(-n)^4$$

$$= 1(81m^4) + 4(27m^3)(-n) + 6(9m^2)(n^2) +$$

$$4(3m)(-n^3) + 1(n^4)$$

$$= 81m^4 - 108m^3n + 54m^2n^2 - 12mn^3 + n^4$$

Problem 4

$$(y - 2)^{10} = \binom{10}{0}y^{10} + \binom{10}{1}y^9(-2) + \binom{10}{2}y^8(-2)^2 + \cdots$$

$$= 1(y^{10}) + 10y^9(-2) + 45y^8(4) + \cdots$$

$$= y^{10} - 20y^9 + 180y^8 + \cdots$$

Problem 5

$$(t - 2s)^7$$

$$n = 7, a = t, b = -2s, r = 3$$

$$\binom{7}{3 - 1}(t)^{7-3+1}(-2s)^{3-1} = \binom{7}{2}(t)^5(-2s)^2$$

$$= 21t^5(4s^2) = 84t^5s^2$$

Solutions to Chapter 12 Problems

SECTION 12.1

Problem 1

$$-\frac{b}{2a} = -\frac{1}{2(-1)} = \frac{1}{2}$$

$$y = -x^2 + x + 3$$

$$y = -\left(\frac{1}{2}\right)^2 + \frac{1}{2} + 3 = \frac{13}{4}$$

The vertex is $\left(\frac{1}{2}, \frac{13}{4}\right)$.

The axis of symmetry is the line $x = \frac{1}{2}$.

Problem 2

y-coordinate: $-\dfrac{b}{2a} = -\dfrac{-4}{2(-2)} = -1$

$$x = -2y^2 - 4y - 3$$
$$x = -2(-1)^2 - 4(-1) - 3$$
$$x = -1$$

The vertex is $(-1, -1)$.
The axis of symmetry is the line $y = -1$.

SECTION 12.2

Problem 1

$$(x - h)^2 + (y - k)^2 = r^2$$
$$(x - 2)^2 + [y - (-3)]^2 = 4^2$$
$$(x - 2)^2 + (y + 3)^2 = 16$$

Problem 2

$$x_m = \frac{x_1 + x_2}{2} \qquad y_m = \frac{y_1 + y_2}{2}$$

$$x_m = \frac{-2 + 4}{2} = 1 \qquad y_m = \frac{1 + (-1)}{2} = 0$$

Center: $(1, 0)$

$$r = \sqrt{(x_1 - x_m)^2 + (y_1 - y_m)^2}$$
$$r = \sqrt{(-2 - 1)^2 + (1 - 0)^2} = \sqrt{9 + 1}$$
$$= \sqrt{10}$$

Radius: $\sqrt{10}$

$$(x - h)^2 + (y - k)^2 = r^2$$
$$(x - 1)^2 + (y - 0)^2 = (\sqrt{10})^2$$
$$(x - 1)^2 + y^2 = 10$$

Problem 3

$$x^2 + y^2 - 4x + 8y + 15 = 0$$
$$(x^2 - 4x) + (y^2 + 8y) = -15$$
$$(x^2 - 4x + 4) + (y^2 + 8y + 16) = -15 + 4 + 16$$
$$(x - 2)^2 + (y + 4)^2 = 5$$

Center: $(2, -4)$

Radius: $\sqrt{5}$

SECTION 12.3

Problem 1

A. x-intercepts:
  $(2, 0)$ and $(-2, 0)$

  y-intercepts:
  $(0, 5)$ and $(0, -5)$

B. x-intercepts:
  $\left(3\sqrt{2}, 0\right)$ and $\left(-3\sqrt{2}, 0\right)$

  y-intercepts:
  $(0, 3)$ and $(0, -3)$

$$\left(3\sqrt{2} \approx 4\frac{1}{4}\right)$$

Problem 2

A. Axis of symmetry:
  x-axis

  Vertices:
  $(3, 0)$ and $(-3, 0)$

  Asymptotes:

$$y = \frac{5}{3}x \text{ and } y = -\frac{5}{3}x$$

B. Axis of symmetry:
  y-axis

  Vertices:
  $(0, 3)$ and $(0, -3)$

  Asymptotes:
  $y = x$ and $y = -x$

SECTION 12.4

Problem 1

A. (1) $y = 2x^2 + x - 3$
  (2) $y = 2x^2 - 2x + 9$

  Use the substitution method.
$$2x^2 - 2x + 9 = 2x^2 + x - 3$$
$$-3x + 9 = -3$$
$$-3x = -12$$
$$x = 4$$

Substitute the value of x into equation (1).

$y = 2x^2 + x - 3$
$y = 2(4)^2 + 4 - 3$
$y = 32 + 4 - 3$
$y = 33$

The solution is (4, 33).

B. (1) $x^2 - y^2 = 10$
(2) $x^2 + y^2 = 8$

Use the addition method.
$2x^2 = 18$
$x^2 = 9$
$x = \pm\sqrt{9} = \pm 3$

Substitute the values of x into equation (2).

$x^2 + y^2 = 8$	$x^2 + y^2 = 8$
$3^2 + y^2 = 8$	$(-3)^2 + y^2 = 8$
$9 + y^2 = 8$	$9 + y^2 = 8$
$y^2 = -1$	$y^2 = -1$
$y = \pm\sqrt{-1}$	$y = \pm\sqrt{-1}$

y is not a real number. Therefore, the system of equations has no real number solution.

SECTION 12.5

Problem 1

A. Graph the ellipse $\dfrac{x^2}{9} + \dfrac{y^2}{16} = 1$ as a solid curve.

Shade the region of the plane that includes (0, 0).

B. Graph the hyperbola $\dfrac{x^2}{9} - \dfrac{y^2}{4} = 1$ as a solid curve.

Shade the region that includes (0, 0).

Problem 2

A. Graph the ellipse $\dfrac{x^2}{4} + \dfrac{y^2}{9} = 1$ as a solid curve.

Shade inside the ellipse.

Graph the parabola $x = y^2 - 2$ as a dashed curve.

Shade inside the parabola.

The solution set is the region of the plane represented by the intersection of the solution sets of the two inequalities.

B. Graph the ellipse $\dfrac{x^2}{16} + \dfrac{y^2}{25} = 1$ as a solid curve.

Shade outside the ellipse.

Graph the circle $x^2 + y^2 = 9$ as a dashed curve.

Shade inside the circle.

The solution sets of the two inequalities do not intersect. This system of inequalities has no real number solution.

Answers to Selected Exercises

Answers to Chapter 1 Selected Exercises

PREP TEST

1. $\frac{13}{20}$ **2.** $\frac{11}{60}$ **3.** $\frac{2}{9}$ **4.** $\frac{2}{3}$ **5.** 44.405   **6.** 73.63   **7.** 7.446   **8.** 54.06
9. a, c, d   **10.** a and C; b and D; c and A; d and B

CONCEPT REVIEW 1.1

1. Sometimes true   **3.** Sometimes true   **5.** Never true   **7.** Always true

SECTION 1.1

1. a. Natural numbers: 9, 53   **b.** Whole numbers: 0, 9, 53   **c.** Integers: -14, 9, 0, 53, -626
d. Positive integers: 9, 53   **e.** Negative integers: -14, -626 **3. a.** Integers: 0, -3
b. Rational: $-\frac{15}{2}$, 0, -3, $2.\overline{33}$ **c.** Irrational: π, 4.232232223..., $\frac{\sqrt{5}}{4}$, $\sqrt{7}$ **d.** Real: all   **9.** irrational

11. is an element of   **13.** -27 **15.** $-\frac{3}{4}$ **17.** 0   **19.** $\sqrt{33}$ **21.** 91   **23.** $-3, 0$

25. 7   **27.** $-2, -1$ **29.** 9, 0, -9 **31.** 4, 0, 4   **33.** $-6, -2, 0, -1, -4$
35. Yes; negative real numbers   **39.** roster; set-builder   **41.** infinity   **43.** $\{-2, -1, 0, 1, 2, 3, 4\}$
45. $\{2, 4, 6, 8, 10, 12\}$ **47.** $\{3, 6, 9, 12, 15, 18, 21, 24, 27, 30\}$ **49.** $\{-35, -30, -25, -20, -15, -10, -5\}$
51. $\{x \mid x > 4, x \in \text{integers}\}$ **53.** $\{x \mid x \geq -2\}$ **55.** $\{x \mid 0 < x < 1\}$ **57.** $\{x \mid 1 \leq x \leq 4\}$
59. $\{1, 2, 4, 6, 9\}$ **61.** $\{2, 3, 5, 8, 9, 10\}$ **63.** $\{-4, -2, 0, 2, 4, 8\}$ **65.** $\{1, 2, 3, 4, 5\}$ **67.** $\{6\}$
69. $\{5, 10, 20\}$ **71.** $\varnothing$ **73.** $\{4, 6\}$ **75.** [number line]

77. [number line]   **79.** [number line]   **81.** [number line]
83. [number line]   **85.** [number line]   **87.** [number line]
89. [number line]   **91.** $\{x \mid 0 < x < 8\}$ **93.** $\{x \mid -5 \leq x \leq 7\}$ **95.** $\{x \mid -3 \leq x < 6\}$
97. $\{x \mid x \leq 4\}$ **99.** $\{x \mid x > 5\}$ **101.** $(-2, 4)$ **103.** $[-1, 5]$ **105.** $(-\infty, 1)$ **107.** $[-2, 6)$
109. $(-\infty, \infty)$ **111.** [number line]   **113.** [number line]
115. [number line]   **117.** [number line]   **119.** [number line]
121. [number line]   **123.** [number line]   **125.** c   **127.** A   **129.** B
131. A   **133.** R   **135.** R   **137.** 0   **139.** [number line]
141. [number line]   **143.** [number line]   **145.** [number line]
147. $\{x \mid x > 0, x \in \text{integers}\}$ **149.** $\{x \mid x \geq 15, x \in \text{odd integers}\}$ **151.** b and c

CONCEPT REVIEW 1.2

1. Sometimes true   **3.** Never true   **5.** Always true   **7.** Never true   **9.** Always true

SECTION 1.2

5. 3; -5; 5   **7.** -30 **9.** -17 **11.** -96 **13.** -6 **15.** 5   **17.** 11,200
19. 98,915   **21.** 96   **23.** 23   **25.** 7   **27.** 17   **29.** -4 **31.** -62 **33.** -25

35. 7   **37.** 587   **39.** 26   **41.** -83 **43. a.** Negative   **b.** Positive   **c.** Negative
d. Positive   **47.** 56; 35; 2; 16   **49.** 3   **51.** $\dfrac{43}{48}$ **53.** $-\dfrac{67}{45}$ **55.** $-\dfrac{13}{36}$ **57.** $\dfrac{11}{24}$

59. $\dfrac{13}{24}$ **61.** $-\dfrac{3}{56}$ **63.** $-\dfrac{2}{3}$ **65.** $-\dfrac{11}{14}$ **67.** $-\dfrac{1}{24}$ **69.** -12.974 **71.** -6.008

73. 1.9215   **75.** -6.02 **77.** -6.7 **79.** -1.11 **81.** -2030.44 **83. a.** Negative
b. Negative   **c.** Positive   **d.** Negative   **85.** base; exponent; -6; -6; -6; -216 **87.** 125
89. -8 **91.** -125 **93.** 324   **95.** -36 **97.** -72 **99.** 864   **101.** -160

103. -5 **105.** 24,576   **107.** Negative   **111.** 5; 25; 125; 25; 0   **113.** -7 **115.** $\dfrac{177}{11}$

117. $\dfrac{16}{3}$ **119.** -40 **121.** 32   **123.** 24   **125.** $\dfrac{2}{15}$ **127.** $\dfrac{1}{2}$ **129.** $-\dfrac{97}{72}$

131. 6.284   **133.** 5.4375   **135.** 6.44   **137.** b   **139.** 0   **141.** No, zero does not have a
multiplicative inverse.   **143.** 9   **145.** 625   **147.** Find b^c; then find $a^{(b^c)}$.

CONCEPT REVIEW 1.3
1. Sometimes true   **3.** Sometimes true   **5.** Always true

SECTION 1.3
1. Commutative   **3.** zero   **5.** 3   **7.** 3   **9.** 0   **11.** 6   **13.** 0   **15.** 1
17. $(2 \cdot 3)$ **19.** Division Property of Zero   **21.** Inverse Property of Multiplication   **23.** Addition
Property of Zero   **25.** Division Property of Zero   **27.** Distributive Property   **29.** Associative Property
of Multiplication   **31.** Zero   **35.** -5; -3; -2; 2; 25; 50   **37.** 10   **39.** -8 **41.** 0
43. $-\dfrac{1}{7}$ **45.** $\dfrac{9}{2}$ **47.** $\dfrac{1}{2}$ **49.** 2   **51.** 3   **53.** -12 **55.** 2   **57.** 6   **59.** -2
61. -14 **63.** 56   **65.** 256   **67.** The volume of the rectangular solid is 840 in³.   **69.** The
volume of the pyramid is 15 ft³.   **71.** The volume of the sphere is exactly 4.5π cm³. The volume of the sphere is
approximately 14.14 cm³.   **73.** The surface area of the rectangular solid is 94 m².   **75.** The surface area of
the pyramid is 56 m².   **77.** The surface area of the cylinder is exactly 96π in². The surface area of the cylinder is
approximately 301.59 in².   **79.** Negative   **83.** -5; 25; Commutative; Associative; $4y$ **85.** $13x$
87. $-4x$ **89.** $7a + 7b$ **91.** x **93.** $-3x + 6$ **95.** $5x + 10$ **97.** $x + y$
99. $3x - 6y - 5$ **101.** $-11a + 21$ **103.** $-x + 6y$ **105.** $140 - 30a$ **107.** $-10y + 30x$
109. $-10a + 2b$ **111.** $-12a + b$ **113.** $-2x - 144y - 96$ **115.** $5x - 32 + 3y$ **117.** $x + 6$
119. a. No   **b.** Yes   **121.** Distributive Property   **123.** Incorrect use of the Distributive Property;
$2 + 3x = 2 + 3x$ **125.** Incorrect use of the Associative Property of Multiplication; $2(3y) = (2 \cdot 3)y = 6y$
127. Commutative Property of Addition   **129. a.** The Distributive Property   **b.** The Commutative
Property of Addition   **c.** The Associative Property of Addition   **d.** The Distributive Property
131. a. The Distributive Property   **b.** The Associative Property of Multiplication   **c.** The Multiplication
Property of One

CONCEPT REVIEW 1.4
1. Never true   **3.** Never true   **5.** Sometimes true

SECTION 1.4
1. more than; product   **3.** difference between; times; times   **5.** $n - (n + 2)$; -2 **7.** $\dfrac{1}{3}n + \dfrac{4}{5}n$; $\dfrac{17}{15}n$

9. $5(8n)$; $40n$ **11.** $17n - 2n$; $15n$ **13.** $n^2 - (12 + n^2)$; -12 **15.** $15n + (5n + 12)$; $20n + 12$

17. $2x + (15 - x + 2); x + 17$ **19.** $(34 - x + 2) - 2x; -3x + 36$ **21.** c **23.** width; $W + 8$
25. The population of Houston: P; the population of New York City: $4P$ **27.** The distance from Earth to the
moon: d; the distance from Earth to the sun: $390d$ **29.** $10,000 - x$ **31.** The flying time between San Diego
and New York: t; the flying time between New York and San Diego: $13 - t$ **33.** The measure of angle B: x; the
measure of angle A: $2x$; the measure of angle C: $4x$ **35.** The sum of twice a number and three **37.** Twice

the sum of a number and three **39.** $\frac{1}{2}gt^2$ **41.** Av^2

CHAPTER 1 REVIEW EXERCISES[1]

1. $\frac{3}{4}$ [1.3.1] **2.** 0, 2 [1.1.1] **3.** $-4, 0, -7$ [1.1.1] **4.** $\{-2, -1, 0, 1, 2, 3\}$ [1.1.2]

5. $\{x \mid x < -3\}$ [1.1.2] **6.** $\{x \mid -2 \le x \le 3\}$ [1.1.2] **7.** $\{1, 2, 3, 4, 5, 6, 7, 8\}$ [1.1.2] **8.** $\{2, 3\}$ [1.1.2]
9. [1.1.2] **10.** [1.1.2]
11. [1.1.2] **12.** [1.1.2] **13.** -15 [1.2.1]

14. 12 [1.2.1] **15.** 14 [1.2.1] **16.** -288 [1.2.1] **17.** $\frac{7}{120}$ [1.2.2] **18.** $\frac{2}{15}$ [1.2.2]

19. $-\frac{5}{8}$ [1.2.2] **20.** -2.84 [1.2.2] **21.** 3.1 [1.2.2] **22.** 52 [1.2.4] **23.** 20 [1.3.2]

24. $\frac{7}{6}$ [1.3.2] **25.** 3 [1.3.1] **26.** y [1.3.1] **27.** (ab) [1.3.1] **28.** 4 [1.3.1] **29.** The

Inverse Property of Addition [1.3.1] **30.** The Associative Property of Multiplication [1.3.1]
31. $-6x + 14$ [1.3.3] **32.** $16y - 15x + 18$ [1.3.3] **33.** $4(x + 4); 4x + 16$ [1.4.1]
34. $2(x - 2) + 8; 2x + 4$ [1.4.1] **35.** $2x + (40 - x) + 5; x + 45$ [1.4.1] **36.** $[2(9 - x) + 3] - (x + 1)$;
$-3x + 20$ [1.4.1] **37.** The width of the rectangle: W; the length of the rectangle: $3W - 3$ [1.4.2]
38. The first integer: x; the second integer: $4x + 5$ [1.4.2]

CHAPTER 1 TEST

1. 12 [1.1.1] **2.** -5 [1.1.1] **3.** 12 [1.2.1] **4.** -30 [1.2.1] **5.** -15 [1.2.1]

6. 2 [1.2.1] **7.** -100 [1.2.3] **8.** -72 [1.2.3] **9.** $\frac{25}{36}$ [1.2.2] **10.** $-\frac{4}{27}$ [1.2.2]

11. -1.41 [1.2.2] **12.** -4.9 [1.2.2] **13.** 10 [1.2.4] **14.** 6 [1.2.4] **15.** -5 [1.3.2]
16. 2 [1.3.2] **17.** 4 [1.3.1] **18.** The Distributive Property [1.3.1] **19.** $13x - y$ [1.3.3]

20. $14x + 48y$ [1.3.3] **21.** $13 - (n - 3)(9); 40 - 9n$ [1.4.1] **22.** $\frac{1}{3}(12n + 27); 4n + 9$ [1.4.1]

23. $\{1, 2, 3, 4, 5, 7\}$ [1.1.2] **24.** $\{-2, -1, 0, 1, 2, 3\}$ [1.1.2] **25.** $\{5, 7\}$ [1.1.2]
26. $\{-1, 0, 1\}$ [1.1.2] **27.** [1.1.2] **28.** [1.1.2]
29. [1.1.2] **30.** [1.1.2]

[1]The numbers in brackets following the answers in the Chapter Review Exercises are a
reference to the objective that corresponds to that problem. For example, the reference
[1.2.1] stands for Section 1.2, Objective 1. This notation will be used for all Prep Tests,
Chapter Reviews, Chapter Tests, and Cumulative Reviews throughout the text.

Answers to Chapter 2 Selected Exercises

PREP TEST

1. -4 [1.2.1] **2.** -6 [1.2.1] **3.** 3 [1.2.1] **4.** 1 [1.2.2] **5.** $-\dfrac{1}{2}$ [1.2.2]
6. $10x - 5$ [1.3.3] **7.** $6x - 9$ [1.3.3] **8.** $3n + 6$ [1.3.3] **9.** $0.03x + 20$ [1.3.3]
10. $20 - n$ [1.4.2]

CONCEPT REVIEW 2.1

1. Never true **3.** Sometimes true **5.** Never true **7.** Always true

SECTION 2.1

5. Yes **7.** Yes **9.** 42; 55 **11.** $-\dfrac{5}{2}$; -20 **13.** 9 **15.** -10 **17.** 4 **19.** $\dfrac{11}{21}$

21. $-\dfrac{1}{8}$ **23.** 20 **25.** -49 **27.** $-\dfrac{21}{20}$ **29.** -3.73 **31.** $\dfrac{3}{2}$ **33.** 8 **35.** No

solution **37.** -3 **39.** 1 **41.** $\dfrac{7}{4}$ **43.** 24 **45.** $\dfrac{5}{3}$ **47.** $-\dfrac{3}{2}$ **49.** No solution

51. $\dfrac{11}{2}$ **53.** -1.25 **55.** Greater than **57.** 42 **59.** 6 **61.** $\dfrac{1}{2}$ **63.** -6

65. $-\dfrac{4}{3}$ **67.** $\dfrac{6}{7}$ **69.** $\dfrac{35}{12}$ **71.** -1 **73.** -33 **75.** 6 **77.** 1 **79.** $\dfrac{25}{14}$

81. $\dfrac{3}{4}$ **83.** $-\dfrac{4}{29}$ **85.** 3 **87.** -10 **89.** 11 **91.** 9.4 **93.** 0.5 **95.** a

97. $8; 3; 10 - n$ **99.** The customer bought 8 bags of feed. **101.** The charge per hour for labor was $42.
103. Her regular hourly rate is $12. **105.** There were 7 grandstand tickets and 5 right field box tickets

purchased. **107.** There were 2 mezzanine tickets purchased. **109.** -9 **111.** $-\dfrac{15}{2}$ **113.** No

solution **115.** -1 **117.** All real numbers

CONCEPT REVIEW 2.2

1. Always true **3.** Always true **5.** Sometimes true

SECTION 2.2

1. Row 1: 5; $5n$; Row 2: $35 - n$; 25; $25(35 - n)$ **7. a.** $20d$ **b.** $10d$ **c.** $4d$ **5.** There are 24 dimes
in the collection. **7.** The cashier has 26 twenty-dollar bills. **9.** There are eight 20¢ stamps and sixteen 15¢
stamps in the collection. **11.** There are 8 dimes in the bank. **13.** There are five 3¢ stamps in the
collection. **15.** There are seven 18¢ stamps in the collection. **17.** consecutive **21.** The integers are
3 and 7. **23.** The integers are 21 and 29. **25.** The three numbers are 21, 44, and 58. **27.** The three
integers are -20, -19, and -18. **29.** There is no solution. **31.** The three integers are 5, 7, and 9.
33. d **35.** There is $4.30 in the bank. **37.** There are fourteen 3¢ stamps in the collection. **39.** The
sum of the smallest and largest integers is -32. **41.** The number is 312.

CONCEPT REVIEW 2.3

1. Sometimes true **3.** Never true **5.** Never true

SECTION 2.3

1. a. $8.40 **b.** $.70 **3.** The vegetable medley costs $1.66 per pound. **5.** There were 320 adult tickets sold.   **7.** The mixture must contain 225 L of imitation maple syrup.   **9.** The instructor used 8 lb of peanuts.   **11.** The cost of the mixture is $4.04 per pound.   **13.** The mixture must contain 37.5 gal of cranberry juice.   **15.** d and f   **17. a.** 12t; 15t **b.** 400; 360   **19. a.** Less than   **b.** Equal to   **c.** 3 mi   **21.** The student drives at an average rate of 40 mph.   **23.** It would take a Boeing 737-800 jet 3.2 h to make the same trip.   **25.** The two cyclists will meet at 2:30 P.M.   **27.** The bicyclist overtakes the in-line skater 11.25 mi from the starting point.   **29.** The speed of the first plane is 420 mph. The speed of the second plane is 500 mph.   **31.** The rate of the first plane is 255 mph. The rate of the second plane is 305 mph.   **33.** The distance to the island is 43.2 mi.   **35.** The distance between the student's home and the bicycle shop is 2.8 mi.   **37.** The two trains will pass each other in 2 h.   **39.** It would take a spacecraft 1600 years to reach this star.   **41.** The cars are $3\frac{1}{3}$ mi apart 2 min before impact.   **43.** No

CONCEPT REVIEW 2.4

1. Never true   **3.** Never true

SECTION 2.4

3. 0.0625x; 0.06(x − 500); 115   **5.** Joseph will earn $327.50 on the two accounts.   **7.** Deon must invest $1600 in the account that earns 8% interest.   **9.** The amount invested in the CD is $15,000.   **11.** An additional $2000 must be invested at an annual simple interest rate of 10.5%.   **13.** The amount invested at 8.5% is $3000. The amount invested at 6.4% is $5000.   **15.** She must invest an additional $3000 at an annual interest rate of 10%.   **17.** The amount that should be invested at 4.2% is $8000. The amount that should be invested at 6% is $5600.   **19. a.** 5.5% and 7.2%   **b.** $6000   **21.** 0.10; 3.2   **23.** A 40-ounce bottle of Orange Ade contains 10 oz of orange juice.   **25.** The 850-milliliter solution contains 12.5 more milliliters of hydrogen peroxide.   **27.** The resulting alloy is 30% silver.   **29.** The resulting alloy is $33\frac{1}{3}$% silver.   **31.** 500 lb of the 12% aluminum alloy is needed.   **33.** 25 L of the 65% solution and 25 L of the 15% solution were used.   **35.** 3 qt of water must be added.   **37.** 30 oz of pure water must be added.   **39.** The result is 6% real fruit juice.   **41.** The resulting alloy is 31.1% copper.   **43.** b   **45.** The amount invested at 9% was $5000. The amount invested at 8% was $6000. The amount invested at 9.5% was $9000.   **47.** The cost per pound of the tea mixture is $4.84.   **49.** 60 g of pure water were in the beaker before the acid was added.   **51. a.** 2000   **b.** 2005

CONCEPT REVIEW 2.5

1. Always true   **3.** Sometimes true   **5.** Sometimes true

SECTION 2.5

3. a, c   **5.** remains the same   **7.** is reversed   **9.** $\{x \mid x < 5\}$ **11.** $\{x \mid x \leq 2\}$ **13.** $\{x \mid x < -4\}$ **15.** $\{x \mid x > 3\}$ **17.** $\{x \mid x > 4\}$ **19.** $\{x \mid x > -2\}$ **21.** $\{x \mid x \geq 2\}$ **23.** $\{x \mid x \leq 3\}$ **25.** $\{x \mid x < -3\}$ **27.** $(-\infty, 5]$ **29.** $[1, \infty)$ **31.** $(-\infty, -5)$ **33.** $\left(-\infty, \frac{23}{16}\right)$ **35.** $\left[\frac{8}{3}, \infty\right)$ **37.** $(-\infty, 1)$ **39.** $(-\infty, 3)$ **41.** Only positive numbers   **43.** Only negative numbers   **47.** 4; 2; 1; 6   **49.** Only interval of real numbers   **51.** Empty set   **53.** $(-1, 2)$ **55.** $(-\infty, 1] \cup [3, \infty)$ **57.** $(-2, 4)$ **59.** $(-\infty, -3) \cup (0, \infty)$ **61.** $[3, \infty)$ **63.** $\emptyset$ **65.** $\emptyset$ **67.** $(-\infty, 1) \cup (3, \infty)$ **69.** $\{x \mid -3 < x < 4\}$ **71.** $\{x \mid 3 < x < 5\}$ **73.** $\left\{x \mid x > 3 \text{ or } x \leq -\frac{5}{2}\right\}$

75. $\{x \mid x > 4\}$ **77.** $\varnothing$ **79.** $\{x \mid x \in \text{real numbers}\}$ **81.** $\{x \mid -4 < x < -2\}$
83. $\{x \mid x < -4 \text{ or } x > 3\}$ **85.** $\{x \mid -4 \le x < 1\}$ **87.** $\left\{x \mid x > \dfrac{27}{2} \text{ or } x < \dfrac{5}{2}\right\}$ **89.** $\left\{x \mid -10 \le x \le \dfrac{11}{2}\right\}$
91. $n \ge 40$ **93.** The smallest integer is 3.   **95.** The maximum width of the rectangle is 2 ft.
97. The four integers are 15, 16, 17, 18; or 16, 17, 18, 19; or 17, 18, 19, 20.   **99.** The length of the second side
could be 5 in., 6 in., or 7 in.   **101.** A customer can use a cellular phone 60 min before the charges exceed the
first option.   **103.** The AirTouch Plan is less expensive for more than 460 messages.   **105.** A call must be
7 min or less if it is to be cheaper to pay with coins.   **107.** If a business chooses the Glendale Federal Bank, then
the business writes more than 200 checks per month.   **109.** The car can travel between 429 mi and 536.25 mi on
a full tank of gasoline.   **111.** $\{1, 2\}$ **113.** $\{1, 2, 3, 4, 5, 6\}$ **115.** $\{1, 2, 3, 4\}$ **117.** $\{1, 2\}$
119. The temperature is between 25°C and 30°C.   **121.** The largest whole number of minutes the call would last
is 10 min.

CONCEPT REVIEW 2.6

1. Always true   **3.** Never true   **5.** Never true

SECTION 2.6

1. Yes   **3.** Yes   **5.** 8, −8   **7.** −7 and 7   **9.** −3 and 3   **11.** No solution   **13.** −5 and
1   **15.** 8 and 2   **17.** 2   **19.** No solution   **21.** $\dfrac{1}{2}$ and $\dfrac{9}{2}$ **23.** 0 and $\dfrac{4}{5}$ **25.** −1
27. No solution   **29.** 4 and 14   **31.** 4 and 12   **33.** $\dfrac{7}{4}$ **35.** No solution   **37.** −3 and $\dfrac{3}{2}$
39. $\dfrac{4}{5}$ and 0   **41.** No solution   **43.** No solution   **45.** −2 and 1   **47.** $-\dfrac{3}{5}$ **49.** Two
positive solutions   **51.** Two negative solutions   **53.** <; >   **55.** $\{x \mid x > 3 \text{ or } x < -3\}$
57. $\{x \mid x > 1 \text{ or } x < -3\}$ **59.** $\{x \mid 4 \le x \le 6\}$ **61.** $\{x \mid x \le -1 \text{ or } x \ge 5\}$ **63.** $\{x \mid -3 < x < 2\}$
65. $\left\{x \mid x > 2 \text{ or } x < -\dfrac{14}{5}\right\}$ **67.** $\varnothing$ **69.** $\{x \mid x \in \text{real numbers}\}$ **71.** $\left\{x \mid x \le -\dfrac{1}{3} \text{ or } x \ge 3\right\}$
73. $\left\{x \mid -2 \le x \le \dfrac{9}{2}\right\}$ **75.** $\{x \mid x = 2\}$ **77.** $\left\{x \mid x < -2 \text{ or } x > \dfrac{22}{9}\right\}$ **79.** All negative solutions
81. tolerance; 5.5; upper; 49.5; lower   **83.** The lower and upper limits of the diameter of the bushing are 1.742
in. and 1.758 in.   **85.** The lower and upper limits of the amount of medicine to be given to the patient are 2.3 cc
and 2.7 cc.   **87.** The lower and upper limits of voltage to the computer are 93.5 volts and 126.5 volts.
89. The lower and upper limits of the length of the piston rod are $10\dfrac{11}{32}$ in. and $10\dfrac{13}{32}$ in.   **91.** 5 in.; 0.01 in.
93. The lower and upper limits of the resistor are 13,500 ohms and 16,500 ohms.   **95.** The lower and upper
limits of the resistor are 53.2 ohms and 58.8 ohms.   **97.** $2, -\dfrac{2}{3}$ **99.** $\{x \mid -7 \le x \le 8\}$ **101.** $\{y \mid y \ge -6\}$
103. $\{b \mid b \le 7\}$ **105.** $|x - 2| < 5$ **107.** **a.** $\le$ **b.** $\ge$ **c.** $\ge$ **d.** $=$ **e.** $=$

CHAPTER 2 REVIEW EXERCISES

1. −9 [2.1.1]   **2.** $-\dfrac{1}{12}$ [2.1.1]   **3.** 7 [2.1.1]   **4.** $\dfrac{2}{3}$ [2.1.1]   **5.** $\dfrac{8}{5}$ [2.1.1]   **6.** 6 [2.1.1]
7. $\dfrac{26}{17}$ [2.1.2]   **8.** $\dfrac{5}{2}$ [2.1.2]   **9.** $-\dfrac{17}{2}$ [2.1.2]   **10.** $-\dfrac{9}{19}$ [2.1.2]   **11.** $\left(\dfrac{5}{3}, \infty\right)$ [2.5.1]
12. $(-4, \infty)$ [2.5.1]   **13.** $\left\{x \mid x \le -\dfrac{87}{14}\right\}$ [2.5.1]   **14.** $\left\{x \mid x \ge \dfrac{16}{13}\right\}$ [2.5.1]   **15.** $(-1, 2)$ [2.5.2]

16. $(-\infty, -2) \cup (2, \infty)$ [2.5.2] **17.** $\left\{x \mid -3 < x < \dfrac{4}{3}\right\}$ [2.5.2] **18.** $\{x \mid x \in \text{real numbers}\}$ [2.5.2]

19. $-\dfrac{5}{2}$ and $\dfrac{11}{2}$ [2.6.1] **20.** $-\dfrac{8}{5}$ [2.6.1] **21.** No solution [2.6.1] **22.** $\{x \mid 1 \le x \le 4\}$ [2.6.2]

23. $\left\{x \mid x \le \dfrac{1}{2} \text{ or } x \ge 2\right\}$ [2.6.2] **24.** $\varnothing$ [2.6.2] **25.** The lower and upper limits of the diameter of the bushing are 2.747 in. and 2.753 in. [2.6.3] **26.** The lower and upper limits of the amount of medicine to be given are 1.75 cc and 2.25 cc. [2.6.3] **27.** The integers are 6 and 14. [2.2.2] **28.** The integers are -1, 0, and 1. [2.2.2] **29.** There are 7 quarters in the collection. [2.2.1] **30.** The mixture costs $4.25 per ounce. [2.3.1] **31.** The mixture must contain 52 gal of apple juice. [2.3.1] **32.** The speed of the first plane is 440 mph. The speed of the second plane is 520 mph. [2.3.2] **33.** The amount invested at 10.5% was $3000. The amount invested at 6.4% was $5000. [2.4.1] **34.** 375 lb of the 30% tin alloy and 125 lb of the 70% tin alloy were used. [2.4.2] **35.** The executive's amount of sales must be $55,000 or more. [2.5.3] **36.** The range of scores to receive a B grade is $82 \le N \le 100$. [2.5.3]

CHAPTER 2 TEST

1. -2 [2.1.1] **2.** $-\dfrac{1}{8}$ [2.1.1] **3.** $\dfrac{5}{6}$ [2.1.1] **4.** 4 [2.1.1] **5.** $\dfrac{32}{3}$ [2.1.1]

6. $-\dfrac{1}{5}$ [2.1.1] **7.** 1 [2.1.2] **8.** -24 [2.1.2] **9.** $\dfrac{12}{7}$ [2.1.2] **10.** $(-\infty, -3]$ [2.5.1]

11. $(-1, \infty)$ [2.5.1] **12.** $\{x \mid x > -2\}$ [2.5.2] **13.** $\varnothing$ [2.5.2] **14.** 3 and $-\dfrac{9}{5}$ [2.6.1]

15. 7 and -2 [2.6.1] **16.** $\left\{x \mid -\dfrac{1}{3} \le x \le 1\right\}$ [2.6.2] **17.** $\{x \mid x > 2 \text{ or } x < -1\}$ [2.6.2]

18. No solution [2.6.1] **19.** It costs less to rent from agency A if the car is driven less than 120 mi. [2.5.3] **20.** The lower and upper limits of the amount of medication to be given are 2.9 cc and 3.1 cc. [2.6.3] **21.** There are six 21¢ stamps. [2.2.1] **22.** The price of the hamburger mixture is $3.20/lb. [2.3.1] **23.** The jogger ran a total distance of 12 mi. [2.3.2] **24.** The amount invested at 7.8% was $5000. The amount invested at 9% was $7000. [2.4.1] **25.** 100 oz of pure water must be added. [2.4.2]

CUMULATIVE REVIEW EXERCISES

1. -108 [1.2.3] **2.** 3 [1.2.4] **3.** -64 [1.2.4] **4.** -8 [1.3.2] **5.** The Commutative Property of Addition [1.3.1] **6.** $\{3, 9\}$ [1.1.2] **7.** $-17x + 2$ [1.3.3] **8.** $25y$ [1.3.3]

9. 2 [2.1.1] **10.** $\dfrac{1}{2}$ [2.1.1] **11.** 1 [2.1.1] **12.** 24 [2.1.1] **13.** 2 [2.1.2]

14. 2 [2.1.2] **15.** $-\dfrac{13}{5}$ [2.1.2] **16.** $\{x \mid x \le -3\}$ [2.5.1] **17.** $\varnothing$ [2.5.2]

18. $\{x \mid x > -2\}$ [2.5.2] **19.** -1 and 4 [2.6.1] **20.** -4 and 7 [2.6.1] **21.** $\left\{x \mid \dfrac{1}{3} \le x \le 3\right\}$ [2.6.2]

22. $\left\{x \mid x > 2 \text{ or } x < -\dfrac{1}{2}\right\}$ [2.6.2] **23.** [1.1.2]

24. [1.1.2] **25.** $3n + (3n + 6)$; $6n + 6$ [1.4.1] **26.** The first integer is 1. [2.2.2] **27.** There are eleven 19¢ stamps. [2.2.1] **28.** 48 adult tickets were sold. [2.3.1] **29.** The speed of the faster plane is 340 mph. [2.3.2] **30.** 3 L of 12% acid solution must be in the mixture. [2.4.2] **31.** $6500 was invested at 9.8%. [2.4.1]

Answers to Chapter 3 Selected Exercises

PREP TEST

1. $-4x + 12$ [1.3.3]   **2.** 10 [1.2.4]   **3.** -2 [1.2.4]   **4.** 11 [1.3.2]   **5.** 2.5 [1.3.2]
6. 5 [1.3.2]   **7.** 1 [1.3.2]   **8.** 4 [2.1.1]

CONCEPT REVIEW 3.1

1. Always true   **3.** Never true   **5.** Never true

SECTION 3.1

1. right; down   **3.**   **5.** A is $(0, 3)$; B is $(1, 1)$; C is $(3, -4)$; D is $(-4, 4)$.   **7.**

9.   **11.**   **13.**   **15.**   **17.**

19. a. I   **b.** II   **c.** IV   **d.** III   **21.** $3; -1; -3; 4$ **23.** Length: $\sqrt{17}$; midpoint: $\left(\dfrac{7}{2}, 3\right)$

25. Length: $\sqrt{5}$; midpoint: $\left(-1, \dfrac{7}{2}\right)$ **27.** Length: $\sqrt{26}$; midpoint: $\left(-\dfrac{1}{2}, -\dfrac{9}{2}\right)$ **29.** Length: $\sqrt{85}$;

midpoint: $\left(2, \dfrac{3}{2}\right)$ **31.** Length: 3; midpoint: $\left(\dfrac{7}{2}, -5\right)$ **33.** I   **35. a.** There are 275 calories in a

hamburger.   **b.** There are 1100 mg of sodium in a Big Mac.   **37. a.** $1.8 trillion   **b.** 2003

c. Greater than   **39.** 1920; 2000; 35; 97; 1920; 2000; 35; 97   **41.**

43. a. The average rate of change in the population was 179,000 people per year.   **b.** The average annual rate of change in the population from 1900 to 1950 was less than the average annual rate of change from 1950 to 2000. **c.** The average annual rate of change in the population of Texas from 1980 to 1990 was less than the average annual rate of change in the population of California from 1980 to 1990.   **45.** 1970s   **47. a.** The average annual rate of change in the number of pedestrian fatalities from 1990 to 2000 was -175.5 pedestrians per year.   **b.** The answer to part a can be considered encouraging because it reflects the fact that the number of fatalities is decreasing. **49. a.** The average rate of change in the number of applications from 1990 to 2000 was 25,500 applications per year. **b.** The average annual rate of change in the number of applications from 1995 to 2000 was 29,000 applications per year greater than that from 1990 to 1995.   **51.**   **53.**

CONCEPT REVIEW 3.2

1. Sometimes true   **3.** Sometimes true   **5.** Always true

SECTION 3.2

3. exactly one   **5.** Function; D = {−3, −2, 1, 4}; R = {−7, 1, 2, 5}   **7.** Function; D = {1, 2, 3, 4, 5}; R = {5}

9. Function; D = {−2, −1, 1, 2, 3}; R = $\left\{-1, -\frac{1}{2}, \frac{1}{3}, \frac{1}{2}, 1\right\}$ **11.** Not a function; D = {2, 4, 6, 8}; R = {3, 5, 7, 8, 9}

13. Yes, each element of the domain is paired with exactly one element of the range.   **15.** No, 1 and 4 in the domain are paired with more than one element in range.   **17.** Yes, each element of the domain is paired with exactly one element of the range.   **19. a.** Yes   **b.** $29.25   **23.** True   **25.** 3; 3; 8   **27. a.** 13   **b.** −3   **c.** 13   **29. a.** −3   **b.** 12   **c.** 8   **31. a.** −8   **b.** 1   **c.** −4   **33. a.** 1   **b.** −1   **c.** $-\frac{1}{2}$ **35. a.** 4a + 11   **b.** 8a − 1   **37. a.** 17   **b.** 7   **c.** −1   **39. a.** 15   **b.** 2   **c.** $3w^2 − 4w − 5$ **41. a.** 2   **b.** 2   **c.** $a^2 + 2a − 1$ **43. a.** 35   **b.** 0   **c.** $4a^2 + 8a + 3$ **45. a.** 4   **b.** 2   **c.** 0   **47. a.** 7   **b.** 10   **c.** −2   **49. a.** 5   **b.** −10   **c.** −10   **51.** 0   **53.** 13

55. 1   **57.** {−14, −11, −8, −5, −2, 1}   **59.** $\left\{-\frac{3}{2}, -1, -\frac{1}{2}, 0, \frac{1}{2}, 1\right\}$ **61.** {3, 4, 7, 12}

63. {−26, −8, −2, 4}   **65.** 4; (4, 5)   **67.** 4; (4, −7)   **69.** 3; (3, 0)   **71.** A, C   **73.** No

75. Yes   **77.**   **79.**   **81.**   **83.**

85.   **87.**   **89.**   **91.**   **93.**

95. Function   **97.** Function   **99.** Function   **101.** Not a function   **103.** Function
105. a. Yes   **b.** Yes   **c.** Yes   **d.** Yes   **107.** −2, 6   **109.** 4h   **111. a.** Yes
b. Yes   **c.** {(−6, −3), (−4, −2), (−2, −1), (0, 0), (2, 1), (4, 2), (6, 3)}, Yes
d. {(9, −3), (4, −2), (1, −1), (0, 0), (1, 1), (4, 2), (9, 3)}, No   **e.** No   **113.** 61.2 ft   **117. a.** 20 ft/s
b. 28 ft/s   **119. a.** 60°F   **b.** 52°F

CONCEPT REVIEW 3.3

1. Never true   **3.** Always true   **5.** Sometimes true

SECTION 3.3

3. a. −7; −1; −7   **b.** −5; 0; −5   **c.** −3; 1; −3   **5.**   **7.**

9.   **11.**   **13.**   **15.**   **17.**

19.   **21.**   **23.**   **25.**

27. x-intercept: $(-4, 0)$
y-intercept: $(0, 2)$

29. x-intercept: $\left(\dfrac{9}{2}, 0\right)$
y-intercept: $(0, -3)$

31. x-intercept: $(2, 0)$
y-intercept: $(0, -4)$

33. x-intercept: $\left(\dfrac{5}{3}, 0\right)$
y-intercept: $\left(0, \dfrac{5}{2}\right)$

35. x-intercept: $\left(\dfrac{4}{3}, 0\right)$
y-intercept: $(0, 2)$

37. x-intercept: $(3, 0)$
y-intercept: $\left(0, -\dfrac{9}{5}\right)$

39. Below   **41.** -3 **43.** -1 **45.** 3 **47.** 3 **49.** $\dfrac{5}{2}$ **51.** 8 **53.** 6 **55.** $-\dfrac{8}{3}$

57. $\dfrac{8}{3}$ **59. a.** 0; 1500; 1500 **b.** 8; 2340; 8; 2340 **c.** 1500; 2340

61. The roller coaster travels 940 ft in 5 s.

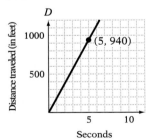

63. The realtor will earn a monthly income of \$4000 for \$60,000 worth of property.

65. The caterer will charge \$614 for 120 hot appetizers.

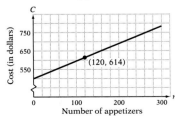

67. The sale price is $160.   **69.**   **71.**   **73.**

CONCEPT REVIEW 3.4

1. Always true   **3.** Never true

SECTION 3.4

1. $-5; -4; 3; 2$ **3.** -1 **5.** $\dfrac{1}{3}$ **7.** $-\dfrac{2}{3}$ **9.** $-\dfrac{3}{4}$ **11.** Undefined   **13.** $\dfrac{7}{5}$ **15.** 0

17. $-\dfrac{1}{2}$ **19.** Undefined   **21.** The slope is 40. The slope is the average speed of the motorist in miles

per hour.   **23.** The slope is -0.05. For each mile the car is driven, approximately 0.05 gal of fuel is used.

25. Line A represents Lois's distance; line B, Tanya's distance; and line C, the distance between Lois and Tanya.

27. a. The ramp does not meet the ANSI requirements.   **b.** The ramp does meet the ANSI requirements.

29. $5; (0, -3)$ **31.**   **33.**   **35.**   **37.**

39.   **41.** Below; upward   **43.**   **45.**   **47.** increases by 2

49. increases by $\dfrac{1}{2}$ **51.** 10   **53.** i and D; ii and C; iii and B; iv and F; v and E; vi and A

CONCEPT REVIEW 3.5

1. Always true   **3.** Never true   **5.** Never true   **7.** Never true

SECTION 3.5

1. $-\dfrac{6}{5}; 2; -\dfrac{6}{5}x + 2$ **3.** $y = 2x + 5$ **5.** $y = \dfrac{1}{2}x + 2$ **7.** $y = -\dfrac{5}{3}x + 5$ **9.** $y = -3x + 4$

11. $y = \dfrac{1}{2}x$ **13.** $y = 3x - 9$ **15.** $y = -\dfrac{2}{3}x + 7$ **17.** $y = -x - 3$ **19.** $x = 3$ **21.** $y = -3$

23. $y = -2x + 3$ **25.** $x = -5$ **27.** The line slants downward to the right, so the value of m must be

negative. The line appears to cross the y-axis at $(0, 2)$, so the value of b cannot be 6.   **29.** $y = x + 2$

31. $y = -2x - 3$ **33.** $y = \dfrac{1}{3}x + \dfrac{10}{3}$ **35.** $y = -\dfrac{3}{2}x + 3$ **37.** $y = x - 1$ **39.** $y = \dfrac{2}{3}x + \dfrac{5}{3}$

41. $y = \dfrac{1}{2}x - 1$ **43.** $y = -4$ **45.** $y = \dfrac{3}{4}x$ **47.** $x = -2$ **49.** $y = x - 1$ **51.** $y = -x + 3$

53. 1000; 500   **55.** $y = 1200x$; the model predicts the plane will be 13,200 ft above sea level in 11 min.

57. $y = 0.59x + 4.95$; the model predicts that using a cell phone for 13 min in one month will cost $12.62.

59. $y = 63x$; the model predicts that there are 315 calories in a 5-ounce serving of lean hamburger.

61. $y = -0.431x + 864$; the model predicts that in 1967 a plane could travel from New York to Paris in 16.2 h.

63. $y = -0.032x + 16$; the model predicts that this car would contain 11.2 gal of gas after driving 150 mi.

65. $\left(-\dfrac{b}{m}, 0\right)$ **67.** 0   **69.** Changing b moves the graph of the line up or down.

CONCEPT REVIEW 3.6

1. Sometimes true   **3.** Never true   **5.** Always true   **7.** Always true

SECTION 3.6

3. -5 **5.** $-\dfrac{1}{4}$ **7.** $-\dfrac{1}{3}$ **9.** Yes   **11.** No   **13.** No   **15.** Yes   **17.** Yes

19. Yes   **21.** No   **23.** Yes   **25.** Yes   **27.** $y = \dfrac{2}{3}x - \dfrac{8}{3}$ **29.** $y = \dfrac{1}{3}x - \dfrac{1}{3}$

31. $y = -\dfrac{5}{3}x - \dfrac{14}{3}$ **33.** Downward to the right   **35.** $\dfrac{A_1}{B_1} = \dfrac{A_2}{B_2}$ **37.** $y = -2x + 15$

39. Any equation of the form $y = 2x + b$, where $b \neq -13$, or of the form $y = -\dfrac{3}{2}x + c$, where $c \neq 8$

CONCEPT REVIEW 3.7

1. Never true   **3.** Always true   **5.** Always true

SECTION 3.7

3. Yes   **5.** No   **7.**   **9.**   **11.**   **13.**

15.   **17.**   **19.**   **21.**   **23.**

25. Negative

CHAPTER 3 REVIEW EXERCISES

1. $(4, 2)$ [3.2.1]   **2.** Midpoint: $\left(\dfrac{1}{2}, \dfrac{9}{2}\right)$; length: $\sqrt{26}$ [3.1.2]   **3.** [3.2.2]

4.   [3.3.2]   **5.** $P(-2) = -2$; $P(a) = 3a + 4$ [3.2.1]   **6.** Domain: $\{-1, 0, 1, 2, 5\}$; range: $\{0, 2, 3\}$; Yes [3.2.1]

7. Range: $\{-2, -1, 2\}$ [3.2.1]   **8.** 2; $(2, 5)$ [3.2.1]   **9.** x-intercept: $(3, 0)$ y-intercept: $(0, -2)$ [3.3.2]

10. [3.3.1]   **11.** [3.3.2]   **12.** −1 [3.4.1]

13. x-intercept: $\left(-\dfrac{4}{3}, 0\right)$ [3.3.2]   **14.** [3.4.2]   **15.** $y = \dfrac{5}{2}x + \dfrac{23}{2}$ [3.5.1]

y-intercept: $(0, -2)$

16. $y = -\dfrac{7}{6}x + \dfrac{5}{3}$ [3.5.2]   **17.** $y = -3x + 7$ [3.6.1]   **18.** $y = \dfrac{2}{3}x - \dfrac{8}{3}$ [3.6.1]

19. $y = \dfrac{3}{2}x + 2$ [3.6.1]   **20.** $y = -\dfrac{1}{2}x - \dfrac{5}{2}$ [3.6.1]   **21.** 4 [3.3.2]   **22.** Yes [3.2.3]

23. [3.7.1]   **24.** [3.7.1]   **25.** [3.1.3]

26. a. The average rate of change in the number of foreign-born people living in the United States from 1980 to 2000 was 715,000 people per year.   **b.** The average rate of change in the number of foreign-born people living in the United States from 1970 to 1980 was 450,000 people per year. This was less than the average annual rate of change from 1980 to 1990. [3.1.4]   **27.** After 4 h, the car has traveled 220 mi. [3.3.3]

28. The slope is 20. The cost of manufacturing one calculator is $20. [3.4.1]   **29.** $y = 80x + 25{,}000$; this model predicts that the cost to build a house that contains 2000 ft² will be $185,000. [3.5.3]

CHAPTER 3 TEST

1. [3.2.2]   **2.** $(-3, 0)$ [3.1.1]   **3.** [3.3.1]   **4.** [3.3.2]

5. $x = -2$ [3.5.1]   **6.** Midpoint: $\left(-\dfrac{1}{2}, 5\right)$; length: $\sqrt{117}$ [3.1.2]   **7.** $-\dfrac{1}{6}$ [3.4.1]   **8.** 9 [3.2.1]

9. [3.3.2]   **10.** [3.4.2]   **11.** $y = \dfrac{2}{5}x + 4$ [3.5.1]   **12.** 1; $(1, 3)$ [3.2.1]

13. $y = -\dfrac{7}{5}x + \dfrac{1}{5}$ [3.5.2]   **14.** 6 [3.3.2]   **15.** Domain: $\{-4, -2, 0, 3\}$; range: $\{0, 2, 5\}$; Yes [3.2.1]

16. $y = -\dfrac{3}{2}x + \dfrac{7}{2}$ [3.6.1]   **17.** $y = 2x + 1$ [3.6.1]   **18.**   [3.7.1]   **19.** No

20. $y = -\dfrac{3}{10}x + 175$; this model predicts that 85 students will enroll when the tuition is $300.   [3.5.3]

21. The slope is $-\dfrac{10{,}000}{3}$. The value of the house decreases by $3333.33 each year.   [3.4.1]

22.

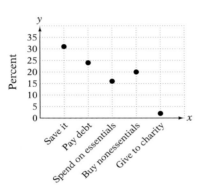

CUMULATIVE REVIEW EXERCISES

1. Commutative Property of Multiplication   [1.3.1]   **2.** $\dfrac{9}{2}$ [2.1.2]   **3.** $\dfrac{8}{9}$ [2.1.2]   **4.** $-\dfrac{1}{14}$ [2.1.2]

5. $\left\{ x \mid x < -1 \text{ or } x > \dfrac{1}{2} \right\}$ [2.5.2]   **6.** $\dfrac{5}{2}$ and $-\dfrac{3}{2}$ [2.6.1]   **7.** $\left\{ x \mid 0 < x < \dfrac{10}{3} \right\}$ [2.6.2]   **8.** 8   [1.2.4]

9. -18 [1.3.2]   **10.**   [1.1.2]   **11.** $\varnothing$ [2.5.2]   **12.** 14   [3.2.1]

13. $(-8, 13)$ [3.1.1]   **14.** $-\dfrac{7}{4}$ [3.4.1]   **15.** $y = \dfrac{3}{2}x + \dfrac{13}{2}$ [3.5.1]   **16.** $y = -\dfrac{5}{4}x + 3$ [3.5.2]

17. $y = -\dfrac{3}{2}x + 7$ [3.6.1]   **18.** $y = -\dfrac{2}{3}x + \dfrac{8}{3}$ [3.6.1]   **19.**   [3.3.2]

20. [3.4.2]   **21.** [3.7.1]

22. There are 12 nickels in the coin purse.   [2.2.1]   **23.** The rate of the first plane is 200 mph, and the rate of the second plane is 400 mph.   [2.3.2]   **24.** The mixture consists of 32 lb of $8 coffee and 48 lb of $3 coffee.   [2.3.1]
25. $y = -2500x + 15{,}000$; the value of the truck decreases by $2500 each year.   [3.4.1, 3.5.2]

Answers to Chapter 4 Selected Exercises

PREP TEST

1. $6x + 5y$ [1.3.3]   **2.** 7 [1.3.2]   **3.** 0 [2.1.1]   **4.** −3 [2.1.2]   **5.** 1000 [2.1.2]
6. [3.3.1]   **7.** [3.3.2]   **8.** [3.7.1]

CONCEPT REVIEW 4.1

1. Always true   **3.** Sometimes true   **5.** Always true

SECTION 4.1

1. No   **3.** Yes   **5.** Independent   **7.** Inconsistent   **9.** (−2, 3)

11.   **13.**   **15.**   **17.**   **19.**

(3, −1)   (2, 4)   (4, 3)   (4, −1)   (3, −2)

21.   **23.**   **25.**   **27.** Inconsistent   **31.** 3; −2; 3; −2

Inconsistent $\left(x, \dfrac{2}{5}x - 2\right)$ (0, −3)

33. (2, 1)   **35.** (1, 1)   **37.** (2, 1)   **39.** (−2, −3)   **41.** (3, −4)   **43.** (0, −1)   **45.** $\left(\dfrac{1}{2}, 3\right)$

47. (1, 2)   **49.** (−1, 2)   **51.** (−2, 5)   **53.** (0, 0)   **55.** (−4, −6)   **57.** Inconsistent

59. $\left(x, \dfrac{1}{2}x - 4\right)$ **61.** Inconsistent   **63.** (1, 5)   **65.** (5, 2)   **67.** (1, 4)   **69.** Dependent

71. 2   **73.** $\dfrac{1}{2}$ **75.** The two numbers are 26 and 18.   **77.** The two numbers are 8 and 11.

79. (2, 1)   **81.** $\left(\dfrac{13}{11}, \dfrac{13}{5}\right)$ **83.** (1.20, 1.40)   **85.** (0.64, −0.10)   **87. a.** No   **b.** 2016
c. The population is decreasing at a rate of 3600 people per year.   **d.** The population is increasing at a rate of 41,900 people per year.

CONCEPT REVIEW 4.2

1. Always true   **3.** Sometimes true   **5.** Never true

SECTION 4.2

3. (6, 1)   **5.** (1, 1)   **7.** (2, 1)   **9.** (x, 3x − 4)   **11.** $\left(-\dfrac{1}{2}, 2\right)$ **13.** Inconsistent

15. (−1, −2)   **17.** (2, 5)   **19.** $\left(\dfrac{1}{2}, \dfrac{3}{4}\right)$ **21.** (0, 0)   **23.** $\left(\dfrac{2}{3}, -\dfrac{2}{3}\right)$ **25.** (1, −1)

27. $\left(x, \frac{4}{3}x - 6\right)$ **29.** (5, 3)   **31.** $\left(\frac{1}{3}, -1\right)$ **33.** $\left(\frac{5}{3}, \frac{1}{3}\right)$ **35.** Inconsistent

39. Dependent   **41.** The first and second equations, the second and third equations   **43.** (−1, 2, 1)
45. (6, 2, 4)   **47.** (4, 1, 5)   **49.** (3, 1, 0)   **51.** (−1, −2, 2)   **53.** Inconsistent   **55.** (2, 1, −3)
57. (2, −1, 3)   **59.** (6, −2, 2)   **61.** (0, −2, 0)   **63.** (2, 3, 1)   **65.** (1, 1, 3)   **67.** (2, 1)
69. (2, −1)   **71.** (2, 0, −1)   **73.** $A = 2, B = 3, C = -3$ **75.** The number of nickels is $3z - 5$, the
number of dimes is $-4z + 35$, and the number of quarters is z, when $z = 2, 3, 4, 5, 6, 7,$ or 8.   **77.** (1, 1)
79. (3, 2)

CONCEPT REVIEW 4.3

1. Always true   **3.** Sometimes true   **5.** Always true

SECTION 4.3

1. 5   **3.** square   **5.** 8; −1; 13   **7.** 11   **9.** 18   **11.** 0   **13.** 15   **15.** −30
17. 0   **19. a.** 2; −3; −5; 4   **b.** −7   **21. a.** 2; 5; −5; −2   **b.** 21   **23.** (3, −4)
25. (4, −1)   **27.** $\left(\frac{11}{14}, \frac{17}{21}\right)$ **29.** $\left(\frac{1}{2}, 1\right)$ **31.** Not possible by Cramer's Rule   **33.** (−1, 0)
35. (1, −1, 2)   **37.** (2, −2, 3)   **39.** Not possible by Cramer's Rule   **41.** $\left(\frac{68}{25}, \frac{56}{25}, -\frac{8}{25}\right)$
43. 1; −3; 2   **45.** 9   **47.** −3; 6; −9; −6   **49.** $x - 2y + 3z = 2; y - 5z = -3; z = 1$
51. $\begin{bmatrix} 1 & -2 & \Big| & \frac{1}{2} \\ 0 & 1 & \Big| & -\frac{5}{2} \end{bmatrix}$ **53.** $\begin{bmatrix} 1 & -\frac{2}{5} & \Big| & \frac{3}{5} \\ 0 & 1 & \Big| & 26 \end{bmatrix}$ **55.** $\begin{bmatrix} 1 & 4 & 1 & \Big| & -2 \\ 0 & 1 & 4 & \Big| & -8 \\ 0 & 0 & 1 & \Big| & -\frac{32}{19} \end{bmatrix}$ **57.** $\begin{bmatrix} 1 & -3 & \frac{1}{2} & \Big| & -\frac{3}{2} \\ 0 & 1 & \frac{3}{2} & \Big| & \frac{5}{2} \\ 0 & 0 & 1 & \Big| & 3 \end{bmatrix}$
59. (−7, 4, 3)   **61.** (1, 3)   **63.** (−1, −3)   **65.** (3, 2)   **67.** Inconsistent   **69.** (−2, 2)
71. (0, 0, −3)   **73.** (1, −1, −1)   **75.** Inconsistent   **77.** $\left(\frac{1}{3}, \frac{1}{2}, 0\right)$ **79.** $\left(\frac{1}{5}, \frac{2}{5}, -\frac{3}{5}\right)$
81. $\left(\frac{1}{4}, 0, -\frac{2}{3}\right)$ **83.** −14   **85.** 0   **87. a.** 0   **b.** 0   **89.** The area of the polygon is 239 ft².

CONCEPT REVIEW 4.4

1. Never true   **3.** Always true

SECTION 4.4

1. Row 1: $b + c$; 3; $3(b + c)$; Row 2: $b - c$; 5; $5(b - c)$ **3.** Less than   **5.** The rate of the plane in calm air
is 150 mph. The rate of the wind is 10 mph.   **7.** The rate of the cabin cruiser in calm water is 14 mph. The rate
of the current is 2 mph.   **9.** The rate of the plane in calm air is 165 mph. The rate of the wind is 15 mph.
11. The rate of the boat in calm water is 19 km/h. The rate of the current is 3 km/h.   **13.** The rate of the plane
in calm air is 105 mph. The rate of the wind is 15 mph.   **15.** The rate of the boat in calm water is 16.5 mph. The
rate of the current is 1.5 mph.   **17.** Table 1, Row 1: 200; h; $200h$; Row 2: 300; w; $300w$; Table 2, Row 1: 350; h;
$350h$; Row 2: 100; w; $100w$ **19.** Greater than   **21.** The cost of the pine is $.18 per foot. The cost of the
redwood is $.30 per foot.   **23.** The cost per unit of gas is $.16.   **25.** There are 18 quarters in the bank.
27. The company plans to manufacture 25 mountain bikes during the week.   **29.** The pharmacist should use
200 mg of the first powder and 450 mg of the second powder.   **31.** The model IV costs $4000.   **33.** $8000
was invested at 9%, $6000 at 7%, and $4000 at 5%.   **35.** The distances are $d_1 = 6$ in., $d_2 = 3$ in., and $d_3 = 9$ in.
37. There were 10 nickels, 5 dimes, and 4 quarters.   **39.** There was $14,000 invested at 12%, $10,000 invested

at 8%, and $9000 invested at 9%.   **41.** The measures of the two angles are 9° and 81°.   **43.** There are 25 nickels, 10 dimes, and 5 quarters in the coin bank.

CONCEPT REVIEW 4.5

1. Sometimes true   **3.** Always true

SECTION 4.5

1. b   **3. a.** A; D   **b.** A; B   **c.** A   **5.**   **7.**

9.   **11.**   **13.**   **15.**   **17.**

19.   **21.**   **23.** Points below the line $x + y = b$ **25.** Region between the parallel lines $x + y = a$ and $x + y = b$

27.   **29.**   **31.**

CHAPTER 4 REVIEW EXERCISES

1. Inconsistent [4.1.2]   **2.** $\left(x, -\dfrac{1}{4}x + \dfrac{3}{2}\right)$ [4.1.2]   **3.** $(-4, 7)$ [4.2.1]   **4.** $\left(x, \dfrac{1}{3}x - 2\right)$ [4.2.1]

5. $(5, -2, 3)$ [4.2.2]   **6.** $(3, -1, -2)$ [4.2.2]   **7.** 28 [4.3.1]   **8.** 0 [4.3.1]   **9.** $(3, -1)$ [4.3.2]

10. $\left(\dfrac{110}{23}, \dfrac{25}{23}\right)$ [4.3.2]   **11.** $(-1, -3, 4)$ [4.3.2]   **12.** $(2, 3, -5)$ [4.3.2]   **13.** $(1, -1, 4)$ [4.2.2]

14. $\left(\dfrac{8}{5}, \dfrac{7}{5}\right)$ [4.3.2]   **15.** $\left(\dfrac{1}{2}, -1, \dfrac{1}{3}\right)$ [4.3.3]   **16.** 12 [4.3.1]   **17.** $(2, -3)$ [4.3.2]

18. $(2, -3, 1)$ [4.3.3]   **19.**   [4.1.1]   **20.**   [4.1.1]

$(0, 3)$ $(x, 2x - 4)$

21.   [4.5.1]   **22.**   [4.5.1]   **23.** The rate of the cabin cruiser in calm water is 16 mph. The rate of the current is 4 mph. [4.4.1]

24. The rate of the plane in calm air is 175 mph. The rate of the wind is 25 mph. [4.4.1]   **25.** The number of children attending on Friday was 100. [4.4.2]   **26.** There is $10,400 invested at 8%, $5200 invested at 6%, and $9400 invested at 4%. [4.2.2]

CHAPTER 4 TEST

1. $\left(\dfrac{3}{4}, \dfrac{7}{8}\right)$ [4.1.2]   **2.** $(-3, -4)$ [4.1.2]   **3.** $(2, -1)$ [4.1.2]   **4.** $(-2, 1)$ [4.3.3]

5. Inconsistent [4.2.1]   **6.** $(1, 1)$ [4.2.1]   **7.** Inconsistent [4.2.2]   **8.** $(2, -1, -2)$ [4.3.3]

9. 10 [4.3.1]   **10.** -32 [4.3.1]   **11.** $\left(-\dfrac{1}{3}, -\dfrac{10}{3}\right)$ [4.3.2]   **12.** $\left(\dfrac{1}{5}, -\dfrac{6}{5}, \dfrac{3}{5}\right)$ [4.3.2]

13. $(0, -2, 3)$ [4.3.2]   **14.**   [4.1.1]   **15.**   [4.1.1]

$(3, 4)$ $(-5, 0)$

16.   [4.5.1]   **17.**   [4.5.1]   **18.** $(-0.14, 2.43)$ [4.1.1]

19. The rate of the plane in calm air is 150 mph. The rate of the wind is 25 mph. [4.4.1]   **20.** The cost per yard of cotton is $9. The cost per yard of wool is $14. [4.4.2]

CUMULATIVE REVIEW EXERCISES

1. $-\dfrac{11}{28}$ [2.1.1]   **2.** $y = 5x - 11$ [3.5.2]   **3.** $3x - 24$ [1.3.3]   **4.** -4 [1.3.2]

5. $\{x \mid x < 6\}$ [2.5.2]   **6.** $\{x \mid -4 < x < 8\}$ [2.6.2]   **7.** $\{x \mid x > 4 \text{ or } x < -1\}$ [2.6.2]   **8.** -98 [3.2.1]

9. $\{0, 1, 5, 8, 16\}$ [3.2.1]   **10.** 1 [3.2.1]   **11.** $3h$ [3.2.1]   **12.**   [1.1.2]

13. $y = -\dfrac{2}{3}x + \dfrac{5}{3}$ [3.5.1]   **14.** $y = -\dfrac{3}{2}x + \dfrac{1}{2}$ [3.6.1]   **15.** $2\sqrt{10}$ [3.1.2]   **16.** $\left(-\dfrac{1}{2}, 4\right)$ [3.1.2]

17.   [3.4.2]   **18.**   [3.7.1]   **19.** $(-5, -11)$ [4.1.2]   **20.** $(1, 0, -1)$ [4.2.2]

21. 3 [4.3.1]   **22.**   [4.1.1]   **23.** $(2, -3)$ [4.3.2]   **24.**   [4.5.1]

25. There are 16 nickels in the purse. [2.2.1]   **26.** The amount of water that should be added is 60 ml. [2.4.2]
27. The rate of the wind is 12.5 mph. [4.4.1]   **28.** The cost per pound of steak is $5. [4.4.2]   **29.** The lower and upper limits of the resistor are 10,200 ohms and 13,800 ohms. [2.6.3]   **30.** The slope is 40. The account executive earns $40 for each $1000 of sales. [3.4.1]

Answers to Chapter 5 Selected Exercises

PREP TEST

1. $-12y$ [1.3.3]   **2.** -8 [1.2.3]   **3.** $3a - 8b$ [1.3.3]   **4.** $11x - 2y - 2$ [1.3.3]

5. $-x + y$ [1.3.3]   **6.** $2 \cdot 2 \cdot 2 \cdot 5$ [1.2.2]   **7.** 4 [1.2.2]   **8.** -13 [1.3.2]   **9.** $-\dfrac{1}{3}$ [2.1.1]

CONCEPT REVIEW 5.1

1. Never true   **3.** Never true   **5.** Never true

SECTION 5.1

1. x^4y^5; 9   **3. a.** Yes   **b.** No   **c.** No   **d.** Yes   **5.** a^4b^4 **7.** $-18x^3y^4$ **9.** x^8y^{16}
11. $81x^8y^{12}$ **13.** $729a^{10}b^6$ **15.** x^5y^{11} **17.** $729x^6$ **19.** $a^{18}b^{18}$ **21.** $4096x^{12}y^{12}$
23. $64a^{24}b^{18}$ **25.** x^{2n+1} **27.** y^{6n-2} **29.** a^{3n^2} **31.** x^{15n} **33.** $-6x^5y^5z^4$ **35.** $-12a^2b^9c^2$
37. $-6x^4y^4z^5$ **39.** $-432a^7b^{11}$ **41.** $54a^{13}b^{17}$ **45.** a^{-8}; a^{-16}; $1/a^{16}$ **47.** a^3 **49.** $\dfrac{a^5}{b^3}$
51. 243   **53.** y^3 **55.** $\dfrac{a^3b^2}{4}$ **57.** $\dfrac{1}{x^8}$ **59.** $\dfrac{1}{125x^6}$ **61.** x^9 **63.** a^2 **65.** $\dfrac{1}{x^6y^{10}}$
67. $\dfrac{1}{2187a}$ **69.** $\dfrac{y^6}{x^3}$ **71.** $\dfrac{y^8}{x^4}$ **73.** $\dfrac{b^2c^2}{a^4}$ **75.** $-\dfrac{9a}{8b^6}$ **77.** $\dfrac{b^{10}}{a^{10}}$ **79.** $-\dfrac{1}{y^{6n}}$
81. $\dfrac{x^{n-5}}{y^6}$ **83.** $\dfrac{4x^5}{9y^4}$ **85.** $\dfrac{8b^{15}}{3a^{18}}$ **87.** $x^{12}y^6$ **89.** $\dfrac{b^2}{a^4}$ **91. a.** False   **b.** True
93. 7; right; -7 **95.** 5×10^{-8} **97.** 4.3×10^6 **99.** 9.8×10^9 **101.** 0.0000000000062
103. 634,000   **105.** 4,350,000,000   **107.** 2.848×10^{-10} **109.** 4.608×10^{-3} **111.** 9×10^9
113. 2×10^{10} **115.** 6.92×10^{-1} **117.** 1.38   **119.** 6×10^{-15} **121.** Less than   **123.** 5.4; 9
125. The computer can perform 3×10^{10} operations in 1 min.   **127.** Light travels 2.592×10^{13} m in 1 day.
129. The proton is 1.83664508×10^3 times heavier than the electron.   **131.** The signals traveled
$1.08\overline{1} \times 10^7$ mi/min.   **133.** The weight of one orchid seed is 3.2258065×10^{-8} oz.   **135.** It will take the
satellite 8.86×10^3 h to reach Saturn.   **137.** The volume of the cell is $1.41371669 \times 10^{-11}$ mm³.   **139.** The
space ship travels across the galaxy in 2.24×10^{15} h.   **141.** No   **143.** Yes   **145.** Yes   **147.** -4
149. The perimeter is $10x^n$.   **151.** The area is $20x^2y^2$.   **153.** $6x^3y^6$ **155.** $\dfrac{4}{m^4}$ **157.** No. Let
$a = -1$ and $b = 1$.

CONCEPT REVIEW 5.2

1. Always true   **3.** Always true   **5.** Sometimes true

SECTION 5.2

3. 2; leading; constant   **5. a.** The leading coefficient is -1.   **b.** The constant term is 8.   **c.** The
degree is 2.   **7.** The expression is not a polynomial.   **9.** The expression is not a polynomial.
11. a. The leading coefficient is 3.   **b.** The constant term is π.   **c.** The degree is 5.   **13. a.** The
leading coefficient is -5.   **b.** The constant term is 2.   **c.** The degree is 3.   **15. a.** The leading
coefficient is 14.   **b.** The constant term is 14.   **c.** The degree is 0.   **17.** 13   **19.** 10
21. -11 **23.**   **25.**   **27.**

29. The length of the wave is 23.1 m.   **31.** There must be 56 games scheduled.   **33.** The baked Alaska
needs 260 in³ of meringue.   **35.** A   **37.** $-8x^2 - 3x + 5$ **39.** $6x^2 - 6x + 5$ **41.** $-x^2 + 1$
43. $5y^2 - 15y + 2$ **45.** $7a^2 - a + 2$ **47.** $5x^3 - 4x^2 + 4x - 7$ **49.** $9x^n + 5$ **51.** $3x^4 - 8x^2 + 2x$
53. $-2x^3 + 4x^2 + 8$ **55. a.** Positive   **b.** Positive   **c.** Negative   **57.** -2 **59.** $P(x) + Q(x)$
is a fourth-degree polynomial.   **61.** The maximum deflection of the beam is 3.125 in.   **63.** 2

65.   The graph of k is the graph of f moved 2 units down.

CONCEPT REVIEW 5.3

1. Always true   **3.** Always true   **5.** Always true

SECTION 5.3

3. $-3y^3$; $-3y^3$; Distributive; $-3y^5$; $30y^3$ **5.** $2x^2 - 6x$ **7.** $6x^4 - 3x^3$ **9.** $6x^2y - 9xy^2$
11. $x^{n+1} + x^n$ **13.** $x^{2n} + x^ny^n$ **15.** $-4b^2 + 10b$ **17.** $-6a^4 + 4a^3 - 6a^2$ **19.** $9b^5 - 9b^3 + 24b$
21. $-20x^5 - 15x^4 + 15x^3 - 20x^2$ **23.** $-2x^4y + 6x^3y^2 - 4x^2y^3$ **25.** $x^{3n} + x^{2n} + x^{n+1}$
27. $a^{2n+1} - 3a^{n+2} + 2a^{n+1}$ **29.** $5y^2 - 11y$ **31.** $6y^2 - 31y$ **33.** c and e **35.** $3x$; x; $3x$; 5; -2; x;
-2; 5 **37.** $15x^2 - 61x + 56$ **39.** $14x^2 - 69xy + 27y^2$ **41.** $3a^2 + 16ab - 35b^2$
43. $15x^2 + 37xy + 18y^2$ **45.** $30x^2 - 79xy + 45y^2$ **47.** $2x^2y^2 - 3xy - 35$ **49.** $x^4 - 10x^2 + 24$
51. $x^4 + 2x^2y^2 - 8y^4$ **53.** $x^{2n} - 9x^n + 20$ **55.** $10b^{2n} + 18b^n - 4$ **57.** $3x^{2n} + 7x^nb^n + 2b^{2n}$
59. $x^3 + 8x^2 + 7x - 24$ **61.** $a^4 - a^3 - 6a^2 + 7a + 14$ **63.** $6a^3 - 13a^2b - 14ab^2 - 3b^3$
65. $6b^4 - 6b^3 + 3b^2 + 9b - 18$ **67.** $6a^5 - 15a^4 - 6a^3 + 19a^2 - 20a + 25$ **69.** $x^4 - 5x^3 + 14x^2 - 23x + 7$
71. $3b^3 - 14b^2 + 17b - 6$ **73.** $x^{3n} - 4x^{2n}y^n + 2x^ny^{2n} + y^{3n}$ **75.** No   **77.** $4x$; $4x$; 1; 1; $16x^2$; $8x$; 1
79. $b^2 - 49$ **81.** $b^2 - 121$ **83.** $25x^2 - 40xy + 16y^2$ **85.** $x^4 + 2x^2y^2 + y^4$ **87.** $4a^2 - 9b^2$
89. $x^4 - 1$ **91.** $4x^{2n} + 4x^ny^n + y^{2n}$ **93.** $25a^2 - 81b^2$ **95.** $4x^{2n} - 25$ **97.** $36 - x^2$
99. $9a^2 - 24ab + 16b^2$ **101.** $9x^{2n} + 12x^n + 4$ **103.** $x^{2n} - 9$ **105.** $x^{2n} - 2x^n + 1$
107. $4x^{2n} + 20x^ny^n + 25y^{2n}$ **109.** Zero   **111.** Positive   **113.** **a.** $3x$; 3 **b.** 3; $9x$; x; $x^2 + 3x$;
$9x$; $x^2 + 3x$; $x^2 + 12x$ **115.** The area is $\left(x^2 + \dfrac{x}{2} - 3\right)$ ft^2.   **117.** The area is $(x^2 + 12x + 16)$ ft^2.
119. The volume is $(4x^3 - 72x^2 + 324x)$ in^3.   **121.** The volume is $(2x^3 - 7x^2 - 15x)$ cm^3.   **123.** The
volume is $(4x^3 + 32x^2 + 48x)$ cm^3.   **125.** $9x^2 - 30x + 25$ **127.** $2x^2 + 4xy$ **129.** $6x^5 - 5x^4 + 8x^3 + 13x^2$
131. $5x^2 - 5y^2$ **133.** $4x^4y^2 - 4x^4y + x^4$ **135.** -1 **137.** a^2 **139.** $2x^2 + 11x - 21$
141. $x^2 - 2xy + y^2$ **143.** 256

CONCEPT REVIEW 5.4

1. Sometimes true   **3.** Always true

SECTION 5.4

1. $3y$; $3y$; $3y$; 2 **3.** $a - 2$ **5.** $3w + 2$ **7.** $t^2 - 3t + 4$ **9.** $-2x + 3 - \dfrac{6}{x}$ **11.** $2v^2 - \dfrac{3}{x}v + 3$

13. $-y + 2x$ **15.** $3y - 4 + \dfrac{5y}{x}$ **17.** $-6xy - 4 + \dfrac{3}{xy}$ **19.** $-\dfrac{2}{m} + \dfrac{4}{n} + \dfrac{3}{mn}$

21. $12x^2 + 6x = 3x(4x + 2)$ **25.** $x + 8$ **27.** $x^2 + \dfrac{2}{x - 3}$ **29.** $3x + 5 + \dfrac{3}{2x + 1}$

31. $5x + 7 + \dfrac{2}{2x - 1}$ **33.** $4x^2 + 6x + 9 + \dfrac{18}{2x - 3}$ **35.** $3x^2 + 1 + \dfrac{1}{2x^2 - 5}$ **37.** $x^2 - 3x - 10$

39. $-x^2 + 2x - 1 + \dfrac{1}{x - 3}$ **41.** $2x^3 - 3x^2 + x - 4$ **43.** $x - 4 + \dfrac{x + 3}{x^2 + 1}$ **45.** $2x - 3 + \dfrac{1}{x - 1}$

47. $3x + 1 + \dfrac{10x + 7}{2x^2 - 3}$ **49.** False   **51.** binomial; $x - a$ **53.** $2x - 8$ **55.** $3x + 3 - \dfrac{1}{x - 1}$

57. $x - 4 + \dfrac{7}{x + 4}$ **59.** $x - 2 + \dfrac{16}{x + 2}$ **61.** $2x^2 - 3x + 9$ **63.** $x^2 - 3x + 2$

65. $x^2 - 5x + 16 - \dfrac{41}{x + 2}$ **67.** $x^2 - x + 2 - \dfrac{4}{x + 1}$ **69.** $4x^2 + 8x + 15 + \dfrac{12}{x - 2}$

71. $2x^3 - 3x^2 + x - 4$ **73.** $3x^3 + 2x^2 + 12x + 19 + \dfrac{33}{x - 2}$ **75.** $3x^3 - x + 4 - \dfrac{2}{x + 1}$

77. $2x^3 + 6x^2 + 17x + 51 + \dfrac{155}{x - 3}$ **79.** $x^2 - 5x + 25$ **81.** Yes   **83.** 8; 9; 18; 9; 9   **85.** $P(3) = 8$

87. $R(4) = 43$ **89.** $P(-2) = -39$ **91.** $Q(2) = 31$ **93.** $F(-3) = 190$ **95.** $P(5) = 122$

97. $R(-3) = 302$ **99.** $Q(2) = 0$ **101.** $x - y$ **103.** $a^2 + ab + b^2$ **105.** $x^4 - x^3y + x^2y^2 - xy^3 + y^4$

107. 3   **109.** -1 **111.** $x - 3$

CONCEPT REVIEW 5.5

1. Always true   **3.** Sometimes true

SECTION 5.5

3. $5x(3x - 2)$ **5.** $3a(2a - 5)$ **7.** $x^2(4x - 3)$ **9.** Nonfactorable   **11.** $x(x^4 - x^2 - 1)$

13. $4(4x^2 - 3x + 6)$ **15.** $5b^2(1 - 2b + 5b^2)$ **17.** $x^n(x^n - 1)$ **19.** $x^{2n}(x^n - 1)$ **21.** $a^2(a^{2n} + 1)$

23. $6x^2y(2y - 3x + 4)$ **25.** $4a^2b^2(-4b^2 - 1 + 6a)$ **27.** $y^2(y^{2n} + y^n - 1)$ **29.** No

31. $x^a(1 + x^a + x^{2a} + x^{3a})$ **33.** $(a + 2)(x - 2)$ **35.** $(x - 2)(a + b)$ **37.** $(x + 3)(x + 2)$

39. $(x + 4)(y - 2)$ **41.** $(a + b)(x - y)$ **43.** $(y - 3)(x^2 - 2)$ **45.** $(3 + y)(2 + x^2)$

47. $(2a + b)(x^2 - 2y)$ **49.** $(y - 5)(x^n + 1)$ **51.** $(x + 1)(x^2 + 2)$ **53.** $(2x - 1)(x^2 + 2)$

55. III   **59.** **a.** -3 and 7   **b.** -4 and -5 **61.** $(x - 5)(x - 3)$ **63.** $(a + 11)(a + 1)$

65. $(b + 7)(b - 5)$ **67.** $(y - 3)(y - 13)$ **69.** $(b + 8)(b - 4)$ **71.** $(a - 7)(a - 8)$

73. $(y + 12)(y + 1)$ **75.** $(x + 5)(x - 1)$ **77.** $(a + 6b)(a + 5b)$ **79.** $(x - 12y)(x - 2y)$

81. $(y + 9x)(y - 7x)$ **83.** $(x - 36)(x + 1)$ **85.** $(a + 9)(a + 4)$ **87.** Nonfactorable

89. **a.** Positive   **b.** Negative   **c.** Less than   **91.** Two negative   **93.** Two positive

95. $(2x + 5)(x - 8)$ **97.** $(4y - 3)(y - 3)$ **99.** $(2a + 1)(a + 6)$ **101.** Nonfactorable

103. $(5x + 1)(x + 5)$ **105.** $(11x - 1)(x - 11)$ **107.** $(12x - 5)(x - 1)$ **109.** $(4y - 3)(2y - 3)$

111. Nonfactorable   **113.** Nonfactorable   **115.** $(2x - 3y)(3x + 7y)$ **117.** $(4a + 7b)(a + 9b)$

119. $(5x - 4y)(2x - 3y)$ **121.** $(8 - x)(3 + 2x)$ **123.** Nonfactorable   **125.** $(3 - 4a)(5 + 2a)$

127. $y^2(5y - 4)(y - 5)$ **129.** $2x(2x - 3y)(x + 4y)$ **131.** $5(5 + x)(4 - x)$ **133.** $4x(10 + x)(8 - x)$

135. $2x^2(5 + 3x)(2 - 5x)$ **137.** $a^2b^2(ab - 5)(ab + 2)$ **139.** $5(18a^2b^2 + 9ab + 2)$ **141.** Nonfactorable

143. $2a(a^2 + 5)(a^2 + 2)$ **145.** $3y^2(x^2 - 5)(x^2 - 8)$ **147.** $3b^2(3a + 4)(5a - 6)$

149. $3xy(6x - 5y)(2x + 3y)$ **151.** $6b^2(2a - 3b)(4a + 3b)$ **153.** $xy(3x + y)(x - y)$

155. $3b(b^2 + 5)(b^2 - 2)$ **157.** 5, -5, 1, -1 **159.** 3, -3, 9, -9 **161.** 1, -1, 5, -5

CONCEPT REVIEW 5.6

1. Never true   **3.** Never true   **5.** Never true

SECTION 5.6

1. 4; $25x^6$; $100x^4y^4$ **3.** $4z^4$ **5.** $9a^2b^3$ **7.** **a.** $4x$; 1   **b.** $4x + 1$; $4x - 1$ **11.** $(x + 4)(x - 4)$

13. $(2x + 1)(2x - 1)$ **15.** $(b - 1)^2$ **17.** $(4x - 5)^2$ **19.** $(xy + 10)(xy - 10)$ **21.** Nonfactorable

23. $(x + 3y)^2$ **25.** $(2x + y)(2x - y)$ **27.** $(a^n + 1)(a^n - 1)$ **29.** $(a + 2)^2$ **31.** $(x - 6)^2$

33. $(4x + 11)(4x - 11)$ **35.** $(1 + 3a)(1 - 3a)$ **37.** Nonfactorable   **39.** Nonfactorable

41. $(5 + ab)(5 - ab)$ **43.** $(5a - 4b)^2$ **45.** $(x^n + 3)^2$ **47.** **b** and **d**   **49.** 8; x^9; $27c^{15}d^{18}$

51. $2x^3$ **53.** $4a^2b^6$ **55.** **a.** $5x$; 2   **b.** $5x + 2$; $25x^2 - 10x + 4$ **57.** $(x - 3)(x^2 + 3x + 9)$

59. $(2x - 1)(4x^2 + 2x + 1)$ **61.** $(x - y)(x^2 + xy + y^2)$ **63.** $(m + n)(m^2 - mn + n^2)$
65. $(4x + 1)(16x^2 - 4x + 1)$ **67.** $(3x - 2y)(9x^2 + 6xy + 4y^2)$ **69.** $(xy + 4)(x^2y^2 - 4xy + 16)$
71. Nonfactorable   **73.** Nonfactorable   **75.** $(a - 2b)(a^2 - ab + b^2)$ **77.** $(x^{2n} + y^n)(x^{4n} - x^{2n}y^n + y^{2n})$
79. x^2y **83.** $(xy - 3)(xy - 5)$ **85.** $(xy - 5)(xy - 12)$ **87.** $(x^2 - 6)(x^2 - 3)$
89. $(b^2 - 18)(b^2 + 5)$ **91.** $(x^2y^2 - 6)(x^2y^2 - 2)$ **93.** $(x^n + 2)(x^n + 1)$ **95.** $(3xy - 5)(xy - 3)$
97. $(2ab - 3)(3ab - 7)$ **99.** $(2x^2 - 15)(x^2 + 1)$ **101.** $(2x^n - 1)(x^n - 3)$ **103.** $(2a^n + 5)(3a^n + 2)$
105. grouping   **107.** $3(2x - 3)^2$ **109.** $a(3a - 1)(9a^2 + 3a + 1)$ **111.** $5(2x + 1)(2x - 1)$
113. $y^3(y + 11)(y - 5)$ **115.** $(4x^2 + 9)(2x + 3)(2x - 3)$ **117.** $2a(2 - a)(4 + 2a + a^2)$
119. $(x + 2)(x + 1)(x - 1)$ **121.** $(x + 2)(2x^2 - 3)$ **123.** $(x + 1)(x + 4)(x - 4)$
125. $b^3(ab - 1)(a^2b^2 + ab + 1)$ **127.** $x^2(x - 7)(x + 5)$ **129.** Nonfactorable
131. $2x^3(3x + 1)(x + 12)$ **133.** $(4a^2 + b^2)(2a + b)(2a - b)$ **135.** Nonfactorable
137. $3b^2(b - 2)(b^2 + 2b + 4)$ **139.** $x^2y^2(x - 3y)(x - 2y)$ **141.** $2xy(4x + 7y)(2x - 3y)$
143. $(x - 2)(x + 1)(x - 1)$ **145.** $4(b - 1)(2x - 1)$ **147.** $(y + 1)(y - 1)(2x + 3)(2x - 3)$
149. $(x + 2)(x - 2)^2(x^2 + 2x + 4)$ **151.** $a^2(a^n - 3)^2$ **153.** $x^n(2x - 1)(x - 3)$ **155.** $n + 2$
157. $20, -20$ **159.** $8, -8$ **161.** $(x - 1)(x^2 + x + 1)(a - b)$ **163.** $(y^{2n} + 1)^2(y^n - 1)^2(y^n + 1)^2$
165. The sum of the numbers is 16.   **167.** The palindromic perfect squares less than 500 are 1, 4, 9, 121, and 484.   **169.** $(x^2 - 4x + 8)(x^2 + 4x + 8)$

CONCEPT CHECK 5.7

1. Always true   **3.** Sometimes true   **5.** Sometimes true

SECTION 5.7

3. $0 = 5x^2 + 2x - 3$ **5.** 5   **7.** -4 and -6 **9.** 0 and 7   **11.** 0 and $-\dfrac{5}{2}$ **13.** $-\dfrac{3}{2}$ and 7
15. 7 and -7 **17.** $\dfrac{4}{3}$ and $-\dfrac{4}{3}$ **19.** -5 and 1   **21.** $-\dfrac{3}{2}$ and 4   **23.** 0 and 9   **25.** 0 and 4
27. 7 and -4 **29.** $\dfrac{2}{3}$ and -5 **31.** $\dfrac{2}{5}$ and 3   **33.** $\dfrac{3}{2}$ and $-\dfrac{1}{4}$ **35.** 7 and -5 **37.** 9 and 3
39. $-\dfrac{4}{3}$ and 2   **41.** $\dfrac{4}{3}$ and -5 **43.** 5 and -3 **45.** -11 and -4 **47.** 4 and 2   **49.** 2 and 1
51. 2 and 3   **53.** $-4, -1$, and 1   **55.** 1 and 2   **57.** $-\dfrac{1}{2}$ and 1   **59.** $\dfrac{1}{2}$ **61.** $-4, 1$
63. $-2, 6$ **65.** $1, \dfrac{3}{2}$ **67.** -3 **69.** $x + 1; x^2 + (x + 1)^2$ **71.** The number is -10 or 9.
73. The integers are 8 and 9.   **75.** The number is 0, 3, or 4.   **77.** The width is 8 in. The length is 21 in.
79. The value of x is 2 m or 3 m.   **81.** The velocity of the rocket is 100 m/s.   **83.** The height is 4 cm. The base is 12 cm.   **85.** The object will hit the ground in 5 s.   **87.** The length of the larger rectangle is 11 cm. The width is 8 cm.   **89.** 175 or 15   **91.** -16 or 4   **93.** $-3, -2, 2$ **95.** The length is 18 in. The width is 8 in.   **97.** For example, $x^3 - 4x^2 + x + 6 = 0$

CHAPTER 5 REVIEW EXERCISES

1. $2x^2 - 5x - 2$ [5.2.2]   **2.** $4x^2 - 8xy + 5y^2$ [5.2.2]   **3.** $70xy^2z^6$ [5.1.2]   **4.** $-\dfrac{48y^9z^{17}}{x}$ [5.1.2]
5. $-\dfrac{x^3}{4y^2z^3}$ [5.1.2]   **6.** $\dfrac{c^{10}}{2b^{17}}$ [5.1.2]   **7.** 9.3×10^7 [5.1.3]   **8.** 0.00254 [5.1.3]

9. 2×10^{-6} [5.1.3]   **10.** -7 [5.2.1]   **11.**   [5.2.1]   **12. a.** 3   **b.** 8

c. 5 [5.2.1]   **13.** 68 [5.4.3]   **14.** $2y^2 - 6xy + 4x^2$ [5.4.1]   **15.** $5x + 4 + \dfrac{6}{3x - 2}$ [5.4.1]

16. $2x - 3 - \dfrac{4}{6x + 1}$ [5.4.1]   **17.** $4x^2 + 3x - 8 + \dfrac{50}{x + 6}$ [5.4.1/5.4.2]   **18.** $x^3 + 4x^2 + 16x + 64 + \dfrac{252}{x - 4}$ [5.4.1/5.4.2]   **19.** $12x^5y^3 + 8x^3y^2 - 28x^2y^4$ [5.3.1]   **20.** $a^{3n+3} - 5a^{2n+4} + 2a^{2n+3}$ [5.3.1]

21. $9x^2 + 8x$ [5.3.1]   **22.** $x^{3n+1} - 3x^{2n} - x^{n+2} + 3x$ [5.3.2]   **23.** $x^4 + 3x^3 - 23x^2 - 29x + 6$ [5.3.2]
24. $6x^3 - 29x^2 + 14x + 24$ [5.3.2]   **25.** $25a^2 - 4b^2$ [5.3.3]   **26.** $16x^2 - 24xy + 9y^2$ [5.3.3]
27. $6a^2b(3a^3b - 2ab^2 + 5)$ [5.5.1]   **28.** $x^2(5x^{n+3} + x^{n+1} + 4)$ [5.5.1]   **29.** $(y - 3)(x - 4)$ [5.5.2]
30. $(a + 2b)(2x - 3y)$ [5.5.2]   **31.** $(x + 5)(x + 7)$ [5.5.3]   **32.** $(3 + x)(4 - x)$ [5.5.3]
33. $(x - 7)(x - 9)$ [5.5.3]   **34.** $(3x - 2)(2x - 9)$ [5.5.4]   **35.** $(8x - 1)(3x + 8)$ [5.5.4]
36. $(xy + 3)(xy - 3)$ [5.6.1]   **37.** $(2x + 3y)^2$ [5.6.1]   **38.** $(x^n - 6)^2$ [5.6.1]
39. $(6 + a^n)(6 - a^n)$ [5.6.1]   **40.** $(4a - 3b)(16a^2 + 12ab + 9b^2)$ [5.6.2]
41. $(2 - y^n)(4 + 2y^n + y^{2n})$ [5.6.2]   **42.** $(3x^2 + 2)(5x^2 - 3)$ [5.6.3]   **43.** $(6x^4 - 5)(6x^4 - 1)$ [5.6.3]
44. $(3x^2y^2 + 2)(7x^2y^2 + 3)$ [5.6.3]   **45.** $3a^2(a^2 - 6)(a^2 + 1)$ [5.6.4]   **46.** $(x^n + 2)^2(x^n - 2)^2$ [5.6.4]

47. $3ab(a - b)(a^2 + ab + b^2)$ [5.6.4]   **48.** $-2, 0,$ and 3 [5.7.1]   **49.** $\dfrac{5}{2}$ and 4 [5.7.1]   **50.** $-4, 0,$
and 4 [5.7.1]   **51.** $-1, -6,$ and 6 [5.7.1]   **52.** $-1, 6$ [5.7.1]   **53.** The distance from Earth to the
Great Galaxy of Andromeda is 1.137048×10^{23} mi. [5.1.4]   **54.** The sun generates 1.09×10^{21} horsepower.
[5.1.4]   **55.** The area is $(10x^2 - 29x - 21)$ cm². [5.3.4]   **56.** The volume is $(27x^3 - 27x^2 + 9x - 1)$ ft³.
[5.3.4]   **57.** The area is $(5x^2 + 8x - 8)$ in². [5.3.4]   **58.** The two integers are -6 and -4, or 4 and 6.
[5.7.2]   **59.** The number is -8 or 7. [5.7.2]   **60.** The length of the rectangle is 12 m. [5.7.2]

CHAPTER 5 TEST

1. $2x^3 - 4x^2 + 6x - 14$ [5.2.2]   **2.** $64a^7b^7$ [5.1.1]   **3.** $\dfrac{2b^7}{a^{10}}$ [5.1.2]   **4.** 5.01×10^{-7} [5.1.3]

5. 6.048×10^5 s [5.1.3]   **6.** $\dfrac{x^{12}}{16y^4}$ [5.1.2]   **7.** $35x^2 - 55x$ [5.3.1]   **8.** $6a^2 - 13ab - 28b^2$ [5.3.2]

9. $6t^5 - 8t^4 - 15t^3 + 22t^2 - 5$ [5.3.2]   **10.** $9z^2 - 30z + 25$ [5.3.3]   **11.** $5y - 3 + \dfrac{4y}{x}$ [5.4.1]

12. $2x^2 + 3x + 5$ [5.4.1]   **13.** $x^2 - 2x - 1 + \dfrac{2}{x - 3}$ [5.4.1/5.4.2]   **14.** -3 [5.2.1/5.4.3]

15. -8 [5.4.3]   **16.** $(2a^2 - 5)(3a^2 + 1)$ [5.6.3]   **17.** $3x(2x - 3)(2x + 5)$ [5.6.4]
18. $(4x - 5)(4x + 5)$ [5.6.1]   **19.** $(4t + 3)^2$ [5.6.1]   **20.** $(3x - 2)(9x^2 + 6x + 4)$ [5.6.2]

21. $(3x - 2)(2x - a)$ [5.5.2]   **22.** $-\dfrac{3}{2}, 4$ [5.7.1]   **23.** $-\dfrac{1}{3}$ and $\dfrac{1}{2}$ [5.7.1]   **24.** $-1, -\dfrac{1}{6},$ and 1 [5.7.1]

25. The area of the rectangle is $(10x^2 - 3x - 1)$ ft². [5.3.4]   **26.** It takes 12 h for the space vehicle to reach the
moon. [5.1.4]

CUMULATIVE REVIEW EXERCISES

1. 4 [1.2.4]   **2.** $-\dfrac{5}{4}$ [1.3.2]   **3.** Inverse Property of Addition [1.3.1]   **4.** $-18x + 8$ [1.3.3]

5. $-\dfrac{1}{6}$ [2.1.1]   **6.** $-\dfrac{11}{4}$ [2.1.1]   **7.** $x^2 + 3x + 9 + \dfrac{24}{x-3}$ [5.4.1/5.4.2]   **8.** -1 and $\dfrac{7}{3}$ [2.6.1]

9. 18 [3.2.1]   **10.** -2 [3.2.1]   **11.** $\{-4, -1, 8\}$ [3.2.1]   **12.** $-\dfrac{1}{6}$ [3.4.1]

13. $y = -\dfrac{3}{2}x + \dfrac{1}{2}$ [3.5.1]   **14.** $y = \dfrac{2}{3}x + \dfrac{16}{3}$ [3.6.1]   **15.** $\left(-\dfrac{7}{5}, -\dfrac{8}{5}\right)$ [4.3.2]

16. $\left(-\dfrac{9}{7}, \dfrac{2}{7}, \dfrac{11}{7}\right)$ [4.2.2]   **17.**   [3.3.2]   **18.**   [3.7.1]

19. $(1, -1)$ [4.1.1]   **20.**   [4.5.1]   **21.** $\dfrac{b^5}{a^8}$ [5.1.2]   **22.** $\dfrac{y^2}{25x^6}$ [5.1.2]

23. $\dfrac{21}{8}$ [5.1.2]   **24.** $4x^3 - 7x + 3$ [5.3.2]   **25.** $-2x(2x - 3)(x - 2)$ [5.5.4]

26. $(x - y)(a + b)$ [5.5.2]   **27.** $(x - 2)(x + 2)(x^2 + 4)$ [5.6.4]   **28.** $2(x - 2)(x^2 + 2x + 4)$ [5.6.4]

29. The integers are 9 and 15. [2.2.2]   **30.** 40 oz of pure gold must be mixed with the alloy. [2.3.1]

31. The slower cyclist travels at 5 mph and the faster cyclist travels at 7.5 mph. [2.3.2]   **32.** The additional investment is \$4500. [2.4.1]   **33.** $m = 50$; a slope of 50 means the average speed was 50 mph. [3.4.1]

Answers to Chapter 6 Selected Exercises

PREP TEST

1. 50 [1.2.2]   **2.** $-\dfrac{1}{6}$ [1.2.2]   **3.** $-\dfrac{3}{2}$ [1.2.2]   **4.** $\dfrac{1}{24}$ [1.2.2]   **5.** $\dfrac{5}{24}$ [1.2.2]

6. $-\dfrac{2}{9}$ [1.2.4]   **7.** $\dfrac{1}{3}$ [1.3.2]   **8.** -2 [2.1.2]   **9.** $\dfrac{10}{7}$ [2.1.2]   **10.** 110 mph, 130 mph [2.3.2]

CONCEPT REVIEW 6.1

1. Never true   **3.** Always true   **5.** Never true

SECTION 6.1

3. $-3; -3; -1; 6; -\dfrac{1}{7}$ **5.** $f(4) = 2$ **7.** $f(-2) = -2$ **9.** $f(-2) = \dfrac{1}{9}$ **11.** $f(3) = \dfrac{1}{35}$

13. $f(-1) = \dfrac{3}{4}$ **15.** $\{x \mid x \neq 3\}$ **17.** $\{x \mid x \neq -4\}$ **19.** $\{x \mid x \neq -3\}$ **21.** $\{x \mid x \neq -2, 4\}$

23. $\left\{x \mid x \neq -\dfrac{5}{2}, 2\right\}$ **25.** $\{x \mid x \neq 0\}$ **27.** $\{x \mid x \in \text{real numbers}\}$ **29.** $\{x \mid x \neq -3, 2\}$

31. $\{x \mid x \neq -6, 4\}$ **33.** $\{x \mid x \in \text{real numbers}\}$ **35.** $\left\{x \mid x \neq \dfrac{2}{3}, \dfrac{3}{2}\right\}$ **37.** $\left\{x \mid x \neq 0, \dfrac{1}{2}, -5\right\}$

39. Below   **43.** factored; common   **45.** $1 - 2x$ **47.** $3x - 1$ **49.** $2x$ **51.** $-\dfrac{2}{x}$

53. $\dfrac{x}{2}$ **55.** The expression is in simplest form.   **57.** $4x^2 - 2x + 3$ **59.** $a^2 + 2a - 3$

61. $\dfrac{x^n - 3}{4}$ **63.** $\dfrac{x - 3}{x - 5}$ **65.** $\dfrac{x + y}{x - y}$ **67.** $-\dfrac{x + 3}{3x - 4}$ **69.** $-\dfrac{x + 7}{x - 7}$ **71.** The expression is in

simplest form.   **73.** $\dfrac{a - b}{a^2 - ab + b^2}$ **75.** $\dfrac{x + y}{3x}$ **77.** $\dfrac{x + 2y}{3x + 4y}$ **79.** $-\dfrac{2x - 3}{2(2x + 3)}$ **81.** $\dfrac{x - 2}{a - b}$

83. $\dfrac{x^2 + 2}{(x + 1)(x - 1)}$ **85.** $\dfrac{xy + 7}{xy - 7}$ **87.** $\dfrac{a^n - 2}{a^n + 2}$ **89.** False   **91.** decrease

93. a.

b. The ordered pair (2000, 51) means that when the distance between the object and the lens is 2000 m, the distance

between the lens and the film is 51 mm.   **c.** For $x = 50$, the expression $\dfrac{50x}{x - 50}$ is undefined. For $0 < x < 50$, $f(x)$

is negative, and distance cannot be negative. Therefore, the domain is $x > 50$.   **d.** For $x > 1000$, $f(x)$ changes
very little for large changes in x.

CONCEPT REVIEW 6.2

1. Always true   **3.** Never true

SECTION 6.2

3. $\dfrac{15b^4xy}{4}$ **5.** 1   **7.** $\dfrac{2x - 3}{x^2(x + 1)}$ **9.** $-\dfrac{x - 1}{x - 5}$ **11.** $\dfrac{2(x + 2)}{x - 1}$ **13.** $-\dfrac{x - 3}{2x + 3}$ **15.** $\dfrac{x^n - 6}{x^n - 1}$

17. $x + y$ **19.** $\dfrac{a^2y}{10x}$ **21.** $\dfrac{3}{2}$ **23.** $\dfrac{5(x - y)}{xy(x + y)}$ **25.** $\dfrac{(x - 3)^2}{(x + 3)(x - 4)}$ **27.** $-\dfrac{x + 2}{x + 5}$

29. $\dfrac{x^{2n}}{8}$ **31.** $\dfrac{(x - 3)(3x - 5)}{(2x + 5)(x + 4)}$ **33.** -1 **35.** 1   **37.** $-\dfrac{2(x^2 + x + 1)}{(x + 1)^2}$ **39.** c

41. $(x - 3)^2$; $(x + 3)(x - 3)$; two; one; $(x - 3)^2(x + 3)$ **43. a.** Two   **b.** Zero   **c.** One

45. $\dfrac{9y^3}{12x^2y^4}, \dfrac{17x}{12x^2y^4}$ **47.** $\dfrac{6x^2 + 9x}{(2x - 3)(2x + 3)}, \dfrac{10x^2 - 15x}{(2x - 3)(2x + 3)}$ **49.** $\dfrac{2x}{(x + 3)(x - 3)}, \dfrac{x^2 + 4x + 3}{(x + 3)(x - 3)}$

51. $\dfrac{3x^2 - 3x}{(x + 1)(x - 1)^2}, \dfrac{5x^2 + 5x}{(x + 1)(x - 1)^2}$ **53.** $(x - 4)(x + 3)$; $5x + 15$; $2x - 8$; $5x + 15$; $2x - 8$; $2x$; 8; $3x$; 23

55. $-\dfrac{13}{2xy}$ **57.** $\dfrac{1}{x - 1}$ **59.** $\dfrac{15 - 16xy - 9x}{10x^2y}$ **61.** $-\dfrac{5y + 21}{30xy}$ **63.** $-\dfrac{6x + 19}{36x}$

65. $\dfrac{10x + 6y + 7xy}{12x^2y^2}$ **67.** $-\dfrac{x^2 + x}{(x - 3)(x - 5)}$ **69.** -1 **71.** $\dfrac{5x - 8}{(x + 5)(x - 5)}$ **73.** $-\dfrac{3x^2 - 4x + 8}{x(x - 4)}$

75. $\dfrac{4x^2 - 14x + 15}{2x(2x - 3)}$ **77.** $\dfrac{2x^2 + x + 3}{(x + 1)^2(x - 1)}$ **79.** $\dfrac{x + 1}{x + 3}$ **81.** $\dfrac{x + 2}{x + 3}$ **83.** $-\dfrac{x^n - 2}{(x^n + 1)(x^n - 1)}$

85. $\dfrac{12x + 13}{(2x + 3)(2x - 3)}$ **87.** $\dfrac{2x + 3}{2x - 3}$ **89.** $\dfrac{2x + 5}{(x + 3)(x - 2)(x + 1)}$ **91.** $\dfrac{3x^2 + 4x + 3}{(2x + 3)(x + 4)(x - 3)}$

93. $\dfrac{x - 2}{x - 3}$ **95.** $-\dfrac{2x^2 - 9x - 9}{(x + 6)(x - 3)}$ **97.** $\dfrac{3x^2 - 14x + 24}{(3x - 2)(2x + 5)}$ **99.** $\dfrac{2}{x^2 + 1}$ **101.** $-x - 1$

103. $\dfrac{y - 2}{x^4}$ **105.** $\dfrac{4y}{(y - 1)^2}$ **107.** $\dfrac{5(x + 4)(x - 4)}{2(x + 2)(x - 2)(x - 3)}$ **109.** $-\dfrac{(a + 3)(a - 2)(5a - 2)}{(3a + 1)(a + 2)(2a - 3)}$

111. $\dfrac{6(x - 1)}{x(2x + 1)}$ **113.** $\dfrac{8}{15} \neq \dfrac{1}{8}$ **115.** $\dfrac{3}{y} + \dfrac{6}{x}$ **117.** $\dfrac{4}{b^2} + \dfrac{3}{ab}$ **119 a.** $f(x) = \dfrac{2x^3 + 528}{x}$

b.

c. When the height of the box is 4 in., 164 in^2 of cardboard is needed.

d. The height of the box is 5.1 in.

e. The minimum amount of cardboard is 155.5 in^2.

CONCEPT REVIEW 6.3

1. Sometimes true   **3.** Always true

SECTION 6.3

3. $\dfrac{2}{a}; \dfrac{1}{a^2}; a^2$ **5.** $a^2 + 1$ **7.** $\dfrac{5}{23}$ **9.** $\dfrac{2}{5}$ **11.** $\dfrac{1-y}{y}$ **13.** $\dfrac{5-a}{a}$ **15.** $\dfrac{b}{2(2-b)}$

17. $\dfrac{4}{5}$ **19.** $-\dfrac{1}{2}$ **21.** $\dfrac{2a^2 - 3a + 3}{3a - 2}$ **23.** $3x + 2$ **25.** $\dfrac{x+2}{x-1}$ **27.** $-\dfrac{(x-3)(x+5)}{4x^2 - 5x + 4}$

29. $\dfrac{1}{x+4}$ **31.** $\dfrac{x-7}{x+5}$ **33.** $-\dfrac{2(a+1)}{7a-4}$ **35.** $\dfrac{x+y}{x-y}$ **37.** $-\dfrac{2x}{x^2+1}$ **39.** $\dfrac{6(x-2)}{2x-3}$

41. c   **43.** $\dfrac{2y}{x}$ **45.** $x - 1$ **47.** $\dfrac{c-3}{c-2}$ **49.** $\dfrac{2a(2a-3)}{3a-4}$ **51.** $-\dfrac{1}{x(x+h)}$

53. $\dfrac{3n^2 + 12n + 8}{n(n+2)(n+4)}$ **55. a.** $P(x) = \dfrac{Cx(x+1)^{60}}{(x+1)^{60} - 1}$

b.

c. The interval of annual interest rates is 0% to 30%.

d. The ordered pair (0.005, 386.66) means that when the monthly interest rate on a car loan is 0.5%, the monthly payment on the loan is $386.66.

e. The monthly payment with a loan amount of $20,000 and an annual interest rate of 8% is $406.

CONCEPT REVIEW 6.4

1. Never true   **3.** Always true   **5.** Always true

SECTION 6.4

1. $x; x + 3; x(x + 3)$ **3.** $8(x + 3); 5x; -8$ **5.** -5 **7.** -1 **9.** $\dfrac{5}{2}$ **11.** 0 **13.** -3 and 3

15. 8 **17.** 5 **19.** -3 **21.** No solution   **23.** 4 and 10   **25.** -1 **27.** -3 and 4

29. 2 **31.** $\dfrac{7}{2}$ **33.** No solution   **35.** $3; -4$ **39.** Row 1: $\dfrac{1}{6}; t; \dfrac{t}{6}$; Row 2: $\dfrac{1}{4}; t; \dfrac{t}{4}$

41. It would take 1.2 h to process the data with both computers working.   **43.** With both panels working, it would take 18 min to raise the temperature 1 degree.   **45.** With both members working together, it would take 3 h to wire the telephone lines.   **47.** Working alone, the new machine would take 10 h to package the transistors.   **49.** Working alone, the smaller printer would take 80 min to print the payroll.   **51.** It would take the apprentice 20 h to shingle the roof working alone.   **53.** It will take them 40 min to address 140 envelopes.   **55.** In 30 min, the bathtub will start to overflow.   **57.** With all three pipes open, it would take 30 h to fill the tank.   **59.** Less than n **61. a.** Row 1: 1320; $470 - w$; $\dfrac{1320}{470 - w}$; Row 2: 1500; $470 + w$; $\dfrac{1500}{470 + w}$

b. $\dfrac{1320}{470 - w}$; $\dfrac{1500}{470 + w}$ **63.** The rate of the first skater is 15 mph; the rate of the second skater is 12 mph.

65. The rate of the freight train is 45 mph. The rate of the passenger train is 59 mph.   **67.** The cyclist was riding at the rate of 12 mph.   **69.** The motorist walks at the rate of 4 mph.   **71.** The business executive can walk at the rate of 6 ft/s.   **73.** The rate of the single-engine plane is 180 mph. The rate of the jet is 720 mph.
75. The rate of the Gulf Stream is 6 mph.   **77.** The rate of the current is 3 mph.   **79.** The original fraction is $\dfrac{17}{21}$.   **81.** With all three printers operating, it would take $5\dfrac{1}{3}$ min to print the checks.

83. The bus usually travels at 60 mph.   **85.** The total time is $\dfrac{5}{8}$ h.

CONCEPT REVIEW 6.5

1. Never true   **3.** Never true   **5.** Never true

SECTION 6.5

3. 5 mi; 2 cm; 2 cm; 5 mi   **5.** 3   **7.** -2 **9.** -4 **11.** $-\dfrac{6}{5}$ **13.** True   **15.** There are 4000 ducks in the preserve.   **17.** The caterer will need an additional 3 gal of punch.   **19.** The dimensions of the room are 17 ft by 22 ft.   **21.** To lose 1 pound, a person would need to walk 21.54 mi.
23. An additional 0.5 oz of medication is required.   **25.** An additional 34 oz of insecticide is required.
27. It would take 75 s to download a 5-megabyte file.   **29.** The length of the whale is 96 ft.
33. Direct variation   **35.** The pressure is 13.5 lb/in^2.   **37.** When the company sells 300 products, the profit is $37,500.   **39.** The length of the person's face is 10.2 in.   **41.** The horizon is 24.03 mi from a point that is 800 ft high.   **43.** The ball will roll 80 ft in 4 s.   **45.** When the volume is 150 ft^3, the pressure is $66\dfrac{2}{3}$ lb/in^2.   **47.** A gear that has 30 teeth will make 32 revolutions per minute.   **49.** The repulsive force is 112.5 lb when the distance is 1.2 in.   **51.** The resistance is 56.25 ohms.   **53.** The wind force is 180 lb.
55. a.   **b.** A linear function   **57. a.**   **b.** Yes   **59.** x is halved.

61. directly; inversely   **63.** directly   **65. a.** $\dfrac{2ab}{a + b}$ **b.** 12

CONCEPT REVIEW 6.6

1. Always true   **3.** Never true

SECTION 6.6

1. $n; n; n; R - C; R; R - nP$ **3.** $W = \dfrac{P - 2L}{2}$ **5.** $C = \dfrac{S}{1 - r}$ **7.** $R = \dfrac{PV}{nT}$ **9.** $m_2 = \dfrac{Fr^2}{Gm_1}$

11. $R = \dfrac{E - Ir}{I}$ **13.** $b_2 = \dfrac{2A - hb_1}{h}$ **15.** $R_2 = \dfrac{RR_1}{R_1 - R}$ **17.** $d = \dfrac{a_n - a_1}{n - 1}$ **19.** $H = \dfrac{S - 2WL}{2W + 2L}$

21. $x = \dfrac{-by - c}{a}$ **23.** $x = \dfrac{d - b}{a - c}$ **25.** $x = \dfrac{ac}{b}$ **27.** $x = \dfrac{ab}{a + b}$ **29.** Yes   **31.** $5 + 2y$

33. $0, y$ **35.** $\dfrac{y}{2}, 5y$ **37.** $f = \dfrac{w_2 f_2 + w_1 f_1}{w_1 + w_2}$

CHAPTER 6 REVIEW EXERCISES

1. 4   [6.1.1]   **2.** $\dfrac{2}{21}$ [6.1.1]   **3.** $\{x \mid x \neq 3\}$ [6.1.1]   **4.** $\{x \mid x \neq -3, 2\}$ [6.1.1]

5. $\{x \mid x \in \text{real numbers}\}$ [6.1.1]   **6.** $3a^{2n} + 2a^n - 1$ [6.1.2]   **7.** $-\dfrac{x+4}{x(x+2)}$ [6.1.2]

8. $\dfrac{x^2 + 3x + 9}{x+3}$ [6.1.2]   **9.** $\dfrac{1}{a-1}$ [6.2.1]   **10.** x [6.2.1]   **11.** $-\dfrac{(x+4)(x+3)(x+2)}{6(x-1)(x-4)}$ [6.2.1]

12. $\dfrac{x^n+6}{x^n-3}$ [6.2.1]   **13.** $\dfrac{3x+2}{x}$ [6.2.1]   **14.** $-\dfrac{x-3}{x+3}$ [6.2.1]   **15.** $\dfrac{21a+40b}{24a^2b^4}$ [6.2.2]

16. $\dfrac{4x-1}{x+2}$ [6.2.2]   **17.** $\dfrac{3x+26}{(3x-2)(3x+2)}$ [6.2.2]   **18.** $\dfrac{9x^2+x+4}{(3x-1)(x-2)}$ [6.2.2]

19. $-\dfrac{5x^2-17x-9}{(x-3)(x+2)}$ [6.2.2]   **20.** $\dfrac{x-4}{x+5}$ [6.3.1]   **21.** $\dfrac{x-1}{4}$ [6.3.1]   **22.** $\dfrac{15}{13}$ [6.4.1]

23. -3 and 5   [6.4.1]   **24.** 6   [6.4.1]   **25.** No solution   [6.4.1]   **26.** $R = \dfrac{V}{I}$ [6.6.1]

27. $N = \dfrac{S}{1-Q}$ [6.6.1]   **28.** $r = \dfrac{S-a}{S}$ [6.6.1]   **29.** The number of tanks of fuel is $6\dfrac{2}{3}$.   [6.5.1]

30. The number of miles is 48.   [6.5.1]   **31.** Working alone, the apprentice would take 104 min to install the ceiling fan.   [6.4.2]   **32.** With both pipes open, it would take 40 min to empty the tub.   [6.4.2]   **33.** It would take 4 h for the three painters to paint the dormitory together.   [6.4.2]   **34.** The rate of the current is 2 mph.   [6.4.3]   **35.** The rate of the bus is 45 mph.   [6.4.3]   **36.** The rate of the tractor is 30 mph.   [6.4.3]   **37.** The pressure is 40 lb.   [6.5.2]   **38.** The illumination is 300 lumens 2 ft from the light.   [6.5.2]   **39.** The resistance of the cable is 0.4 ohm.   [6.5.2]

CHAPTER 6 TEST

1. $\dfrac{v(v+2)}{2v-1}$ [6.1.2]   **2.** $-\dfrac{2(a-2)}{3a+2}$ [6.1.2]   **3.** $\dfrac{6(x-2)}{5}$ [6.2.1]   **4.** 2   [6.1.1]

5. $\dfrac{x+1}{3x-4}$ [6.2.1]   **6.** $\dfrac{x^n-1}{x^n+2}$ [6.2.1]   **7.** $\dfrac{4y^2+6x^2-5xy}{2x^2y^2}$ [6.2.2]   **8.** $\dfrac{2(5x+2)}{(x-2)(x+2)}$ [6.2.2]

9. $\{x \mid x \neq -3, 3\}$ [6.1.1]   **10.** $-\dfrac{x^2+5x-2}{(x+1)(x+4)(x-1)}$ [6.2.2]   **11.** $\dfrac{x-4}{x+3}$ [6.3.1]

12. $\dfrac{x+4}{x+2}$ [6.3.1]   **13.** 2   [6.4.1]   **14.** No solution   [6.4.1]   **15.** $x = \dfrac{c}{a-b}$ [6.6.1]

16. It would take 80 min to empty the full tank with both pipes open.   [6.4.2]   **17.** The office requires 14 rolls of wallpaper.   [6.5.1]   **18.** Working together, the landscapers would complete the task in 10 min.   [6.4.2]   **19.** The rate of the cyclist is 10 mph.   [6.4.3]   **20.** The stopping distance of the car is 61.2 ft.   [6.5.2]

CUMULATIVE REVIEW EXERCISES

1. $\dfrac{36}{5}$ [1.2.4]   **2.** $\dfrac{15}{2}$ [2.1.2]   **3.** 7 and 1   [2.6.1]   **4.** $\{x \mid x \neq 3\}$ [6.1.1]   **5.** $\dfrac{3}{7}$ [6.1.1]

6. 3.5×10^{-8} [5.1.3]   **7.** No solution   [6.4.1]   **8.** $\dfrac{1}{9}$ and 4   [5.7.1]   **9.** $\dfrac{8b^3}{a}$ [5.1.2]

10. $\{x \mid x \leq 4\}$ [2.5.1]   **11.** $-4a^4 + 6a^3 - 2a^2$ [5.3.1]   **12.** $(2x^n - 1)(x^n + 2)$ [5.6.3]

13. $(xy - 3)(x^2y^2 + 3xy + 9)$ [5.6.2]   **14.** $x + 3y$ [6.1.2]   **15.** $y = \dfrac{3}{2}x + 2$ [3.6.1]

16. $\dfrac{x}{x^2 - 1}$ [5.1.2] **17.** [3.3.2] **18.** [4.5.1]

19. $4x^2 + 10x + 10 + \dfrac{21}{x - 2}$ [5.4.2] **20.** $\dfrac{3xy}{x - y}$ [6.2.1] **21.** $\{x \mid x \in \text{real numbers}\}$ [6.1.1]

22. $-\dfrac{x}{(3x + 2)(x + 1)}$ [6.2.2] **23.** -28 [4.3.1] **24.** $\dfrac{x - 3}{x + 3}$ [6.3.1] **25.** $(1, 1, 1)$ [4.2.2 or 4.3.2]

26. $1, 2$ [5.7.1] **27.** 9 [6.5.1] **28.** 13 [6.4.1] **29.** $a^4 + 5a^3 - 3a^2 - 11a + 20$ [5.3.2]

30. $r = \dfrac{E - IR}{I}$ [6.6.1] **31.** No [3.6.1] **32.** [5.2.1]

33. The smaller integer is 5 and the larger integer is 10. [2.2.2] **34.** The number of pounds of almonds is 50. [2.3.1] **35.** The number of people expected to vote is 75,000. [6.5.1] **36.** It would take the new computer 14 min to do the job working alone. [6.4.2] **37.** The rate of the wind is 60 mph. [6.4.3] **38.** The frequency of vibration of the open pipe organ is 80 vibrations/min. [6.5.2]

Answers to Chapter 7 Selected Exercises

PREP TEST

1. 16 [1.2.1] **2.** 32 [1.2.3] **3.** 9 [1.2.2] **4.** $\dfrac{1}{12}$ [1.2.2] **5.** $-5x - 1$ [1.3.3]

6. $\dfrac{xy^5}{4}$ [5.1.2] **7.** $9x^2 - 12x + 4$ [5.3.3] **8.** $-12x^2 + 14x + 10$ [5.3.2] **9.** $36x^2 - 1$ [5.3.3]

10. $-1, 15$ [5.7.1]

CONCEPT REVIEW 7.1

1. Sometimes true **3.** Always true **5.** Always true

SECTION 7.1

1. third; 125; 5 **3.** $8; 8; -3; 8^3; \dfrac{1}{512}$ **5.** d **7.** 2 **9.** 27 **11.** $\dfrac{1}{9}$ **13.** 4

15. Not a real number **17.** $\dfrac{343}{125}$ **19.** x **21.** $y^{\frac{1}{2}}$ **23.** $x^{\frac{1}{12}}$ **25.** $a^{\frac{7}{12}}$ **27.** $\dfrac{1}{a}$

29. $\dfrac{1}{y}$ **31.** $y^{\frac{3}{2}}$ **33.** $\dfrac{1}{x}$ **35.** $\dfrac{1}{x^4}$ **37.** a **39.** $x^{\frac{3}{10}}$ **41.** a^3 **43.** $\dfrac{1}{x^{\frac{1}{2}}}$ **45.** $y^{\frac{2}{3}}$

47. x^4y **49.** $x^6y^3z^9$ **51.** $\dfrac{x}{y^2}$ **53.** $\dfrac{x^{\frac{3}{2}}}{y^{\frac{1}{4}}}$ **55.** x^2y^8 **57.** $\dfrac{1}{x^{\frac{11}{12}}}$ **59.** $\dfrac{1}{y^{\frac{5}{2}}}$ **61.** $\dfrac{1}{b^{\frac{7}{8}}}$

63. a^5b^{13} **65.** $\dfrac{m^2}{4n^{\frac{3}{2}}}$ **67.** $\dfrac{y^{\frac{17}{2}}}{x^3}$ **69.** $\dfrac{16b^2}{a^{\frac{1}{3}}}$ **71.** $\dfrac{y^2}{x^3}$ **73.** $a - a^2$ **75.** $y + 1$

77. $a - \dfrac{1}{a}$ **79.** $\dfrac{1}{a^{10}}$ **81.** $a^{\frac{n}{6}}$ **83.** $\dfrac{1}{b^{\frac{2m}{3}}}$ **85.** x^{10n^2} **87.** $x^{3n}y^{2n}$ **89.** $4; 5; \dfrac{4}{5}$

91. True **93.** $\sqrt{5}$ **95.** $\sqrt[3]{b^4}$ **97.** $\sqrt[3]{9x^2}$ **99.** $-3\sqrt[5]{a^2}$ **101.** $\sqrt[4]{x^6 y^9}$ **103.** $\sqrt{a^9 b^{21}}$

105. $\sqrt[3]{3x-2}$ **107.** $14^{\frac{1}{2}}$ **109.** $x^{\frac{1}{3}}$ **111.** $x^{\frac{4}{3}}$ **113.** $b^{\frac{3}{5}}$ **115.** $(2x^2)^{\frac{1}{3}}$ **117.** $-(3x^5)^{\frac{1}{2}}$

119. $3xy^{\frac{2}{3}}$ **121.** $(a^2+2)^{\frac{1}{2}}$ **123.** $2;\ a^2;\ b^3$ **125.** Negative **127.** Positive **129.** y^7

131. $-a^3$ **133.** $a^7 b^3$ **135.** $11y^6$ **137.** $a^2 b^4$ **139.** $-a^3 b^3$ **141.** $5b^5$ **143.** $-a^2 b^3$

145. $5x^4 y$ **147.** Not a real number **149.** $2a^7 b^2$ **151.** $-3ab^5$ **153.** y^3 **155.** $3a^5$

157. $-a^4 b$ **159.** ab^5 **161.** $2a^2 b^5$ **163.** $-2x^3 y^4$ **165.** $\dfrac{4x}{y^7}$ **167.** $\dfrac{3b}{a^3}$ **169.** $2x+3$

171. $x+1$ **173.** x **175.** b **177.** ab^2 **179.** $\dfrac{3}{5}$ **181.** $\dfrac{3}{4}$

CONCEPT REVIEW 7.2

1. Sometimes true **3.** Never true **5.** Always true

SECTION 7.2

1. 25; 25; 2; 5 **3. a.** Irrational **b.** Rational **c.** Irrational **d.** Rational **7.** $3\sqrt{2}$

9. $7\sqrt{2}$ **11.** $2\sqrt[3]{9}$ **13.** $2\sqrt[4]{2}$ **15.** $x^2 yz^2\sqrt{yz}$ **17.** $2ab^4\sqrt{2a}$ **19.** $3xyz^2\sqrt{5yz}$

21. $-5y\sqrt[3]{x^2 y}$ **23.** $-6xy^3\sqrt[3]{x^2}$ **25.** $ab^2\sqrt[3]{a^2 b^2}$ **27.** radicand; index **29. a.** No **b.** No

c. Yes **d.** Yes **31.** $2\sqrt{2}$ **33.** $3\sqrt[3]{7}$ **35.** $-6\sqrt{x}$ **37.** $-2\sqrt{2}$ **39.** $\sqrt{2x}$

41. $3\sqrt{3a}-2\sqrt{2a}$ **43.** $10x\sqrt{2x}$ **45.** $2x\sqrt{3xy}$ **47.** $xy\sqrt{2y}$ **49.** $5a^2 b^2\sqrt{ab}$ **51.** $9\sqrt[3]{2}$

53. $-7a\sqrt[3]{3a}$ **55.** $-5xy^2\sqrt[3]{x^2 y}$ **57.** $16ab\sqrt[4]{ab}$ **59.** $6\sqrt{3}-6\sqrt{2}$ **61.** $6x^3 y^2\sqrt{xy}$

63. $-9a^2\sqrt{3ab}$ **65.** 18; 3x; 3 **67.** 16 **69.** $2\sqrt[3]{4}$ **71.** $xy^3\sqrt{x}$ **73.** $8xy\sqrt{x}$

75. $2x^2 y\sqrt[3]{2}$ **77.** $2ab\sqrt[4]{3a^2 b}$ **79.** 6 **81.** $x-\sqrt{2x}$ **83.** $4x-8\sqrt{x}$ **85.** $x-6\sqrt{x}+9$

87. $84+16\sqrt{5}$ **89.** $672x^2 y^2$ **91.** $4a^3 b^3\sqrt[3]{a}$ **93.** $-8\sqrt{5}$ **95.** $x-y^2$ **97.** $12x-y$

99. $x-3\sqrt{x}-28$ **101.** $\sqrt[3]{x^2}+\sqrt[3]{x}-20$ **103.** False **105.** Quotient; 9; 8; $2x^2$

107. a. Yes **b.** No **c.** No **d.** No **109.** $4\sqrt{x}$ **111.** $b^2\sqrt{3a}$ **113.** $\dfrac{\sqrt{5}}{5}$

115. $\dfrac{\sqrt{2x}}{2x}$ **117.** $\dfrac{\sqrt{5x}}{x}$ **119.** $\dfrac{\sqrt{5x}}{5}$ **121.** $\dfrac{3\sqrt[3]{4}}{2}$ **123.** $\dfrac{3\sqrt[3]{2x}}{2x}$ **125.** $\dfrac{\sqrt{2xy}}{2y}$

127. $\dfrac{2\sqrt{3ab}}{3b^2}$ **129.** $2\sqrt{5}-4$ **131.** $\dfrac{3\sqrt{y}+6}{y-4}$ **133.** $-5+2\sqrt{6}$ **135.** $8+4\sqrt{3}-2\sqrt{2}-\sqrt{6}$

137. $\dfrac{\sqrt{15}+\sqrt{10}-\sqrt{6}-5}{3}$ **139.** $\dfrac{3\sqrt[4]{2x}}{2x}$ **141.** $\dfrac{2\sqrt[5]{2a^3}}{a}$ **143.** $\dfrac{\sqrt[5]{16x^2}}{2}$ **145.** $\dfrac{1+2\sqrt{ab}+ab}{1-ab}$

147. $\dfrac{5x\sqrt{y}+5y\sqrt{x}}{x-y}$ **149.** $2\sqrt{2}$ **151.** $29\sqrt{2}-45$ **153.** $\dfrac{3\sqrt{y+1}-3}{y}$ **155.** $\sqrt[6]{x+y}$

157. $\sqrt[4]{2y(x+3)^2}$ **159.** $\sqrt[6]{a^3(a+3)^2}$ **161.** $16^{\frac{1}{4}},\ 2$ **163.** $32^{-\frac{1}{5}},\ \dfrac{1}{2}$ **165. a.** $D(x)=3.06\sqrt[10]{x^3}$

b. The model predicts a national debt of \$4.96 trillion. **c.** The model predicts a national debt of \$6.61 trillion.

CONCEPT REVIEW 7.3

1. Always true **3.** Never true

SECTION 7.3

3. a. ≥ 0 **b.** $\in$ real numbers **5. a.** $(-\infty, 0]$ **b.** Empty set **c.** $[0, \infty)$ **d.** All real

numbers **7.** $\{x \mid x \in \text{real numbers}\}$ **9.** $\{x \mid x \geq -1\}$ **11.** $\{x \mid x \geq 0\}$ **13.** $\{x \mid x \geq 0\}$

15. $\{x \mid x \geq 2\}$ **17.** $(-\infty, \infty)$ **19.** $(-\infty, 3]$ **21.** $[2, \infty)$ **23.** $\left(-\infty, \dfrac{2}{3}\right]$ **25.** ≥ 5

27. 14; 9; −3   **29.**   **31.**   **33.**   **35.**

37.   **39.**   **41.**   **43.**   **45.**

47.   **49.**   **51. a.** Both   **b.** Below   **c.** Above   **d.** Above

CONCEPT REVIEW 7.4

1. Sometimes true   **3.** Sometimes true

SECTION 7.4

1. $\sqrt{2x + 1} = 7$ **5.** 25   **7.** 27   **9.** 48   **11.** −2   **13.** No solution   **15.** 9

17. −23   **19.** −16   **21.** $\frac{9}{4}$ **23.** 14   **25.** 7   **27.** 7   **29.** −122   **31.** 35

33. 45   **35.** 23   **37.** −4   **39.** 10   **41.** 1   **43.** 3   **45.** 21   **47.** $\frac{25}{72}$ **49.** 5

51. −2, 4   **53.** 6   **55.** 0, 1   **57.** −2, 1   **59.** 2, 11   **61.** 3   **63. a.** One
b. Two   **65. d**   **67.** The air pressure is 909.8 mb. The wind speed increases.   **69.** The mean
distance is 295,000 km.   **71.** The elephant weighs 3700 lb.   **73.** The distance is 10 ft.   **75.** The
distance between the joggers after 3 min is 829.76 m.   **77.** The length of the diagonal is 8.9 cm.   **79.** The
periscope must be 8.17 ft above the water.   **81.** The distance is 225 ft.   **83.** The distance is 96 ft.

85. The satellite is 711,000 m above Earth's surface.   **87.** 27   **89.** $d = \frac{v^2}{64}$ **91.** $r = \frac{\sqrt{V\pi h}}{\pi h}$

93. 2   **95.** The distance between the corners is 7.81 in.   **97.** $\sqrt{6}$

CONCEPT REVIEW 7.5

1. Always true   **3.** Always true

SECTION 7.5

3. −1   **5.** i; 9; 6; $3i$ **7.** $10 - \sqrt{-9}$ **9.** $2i$ **11.** $7i\sqrt{2}$ **13.** $3i\sqrt{3}$ **15.** $4 + 2i$
17. $2\sqrt{3} - 3i\sqrt{2}$ **19.** $4\sqrt{10} - 7i\sqrt{3}$ **21.** $2ai$ **23.** $7x^6i$ **25.** $12ab^2i\sqrt{ab}$
27. $2\sqrt{a} + 2ai\sqrt{3}$ **29.** $3b^2\sqrt{2b} - 3bi\sqrt{3b}$ **31.** $5x^3y\sqrt{y} + 5xyi\sqrt{2xy}$ **33.** $2a^2bi\sqrt{a}$
35. $2a\sqrt{3a} + 3bi\sqrt{3b}$ **37.** 8; 6; −8i; 6; 8i   **39.** $10 - 7i$ **41.** $11 - 7i$ **43.** $-6 + i$
45. $-4 - 8i\sqrt{3}$ **47.** $-\sqrt{10} - 11i\sqrt{2}$ **49.** $6 - 4i$ **51.** 0   **53.** $11 + 6i$ **55.** True
57. Negative   **59.** −24   **61.** −15   **63.** $-5\sqrt{2}$ **65.** $-15 - 12i$ **67.** 1; 9; 1; 81; 82
69. $3\sqrt{2} + 6i$ **71.** $-10i$ **73.** $29 - 2i$ **75.** 1   **77.** 1   **79.** 89   **81.** 50

83. $7 - 24i$ **85.** $-2i$ **87.** False   **89.** $2 + 3i$ **91.** $-\frac{4}{5}i$ **93.** $-\frac{5}{3} + \frac{16}{3}i$

95. $\frac{30}{29} - \frac{12}{29}i$ **97.** $\frac{20}{17} + \frac{5}{17}i$ **99.** $\frac{11}{13} + \frac{29}{13}i$ **101.** $-\frac{1}{5} + \frac{\sqrt{6}}{10}i$ **103.** $-1 + 4i$

105. True   **107.** -1 **109.** i **111.** -1 **113.** -1 **115. a.** Yes   **b.** Yes

117. a. $2, -2$; integer, rational number, real number   **b.** $i, -i$; imaginary

c. $\dfrac{16}{15}$; rational number, real number   **d.** $2\sqrt{2}, -2\sqrt{2}$; irrational number, real number   **e.** 16; integer, rational number, real number   **f.** $-19{,}683$; integer, rational number, real number

CHAPTER 7 REVIEW EXERCISES

1. $\dfrac{1}{3}$ [7.1.1]   **2.** $\dfrac{1}{x^5}$ [7.1.1]   **3.** $\dfrac{1}{a^{10}}$ [7.1.1]   **4.** $\dfrac{160y^{11}}{x}$ [7.1.1]   **5.** $3\sqrt[4]{x^3}$ [7.1.2]

6. $7x^{\frac{2}{3}}y$ [7.1.2]   **7.** $3a^2b^3$ [7.1.3]   **8.** $-7x^3y^8$ [7.1.3]   **9.** $-2a^2b^4$ [7.1.3]

10. $3ab^3\sqrt{2a}$ [7.2.1]   **11.** $-2ab^2\sqrt[5]{2a^3b^2}$ [7.2.1]   **12.** $xy^2z^2\sqrt[4]{x^2z^2}$ [7.2.1]   **13.** $5\sqrt{6}$ [7.2.2]

14. $4x^2\sqrt{3xy} - 4x^2\sqrt{5xy}$ [7.2.2]   **15.** $2a^2b\sqrt{2b}$ [7.2.2]   **16.** $6x^2\sqrt{3y}$ [7.2.2]   **17.** 40 [7.2.3]

18. $4xy^2\sqrt[3]{x^2}$ [7.2.3]   **19.** $3x + 3\sqrt{3x}$ [7.2.3]   **20.** $31 - 10\sqrt{6}$ [7.2.3]   **21.** $-13 + 6\sqrt{3}$ [7.2.3]

22. $5x\sqrt{x}$ [7.2.4]   **23.** $\dfrac{8\sqrt{3y}}{3y}$ [7.2.4]   **24.** $\dfrac{x\sqrt{x} - x\sqrt{2} + 2\sqrt{x} - 2\sqrt{2}}{x - 2}$ [7.2.4]

25. $\dfrac{x + 2\sqrt{xy} + y}{x - y}$ [7.2.4]   **26.** $6i$ [7.5.1]   **27.** $5i\sqrt{2}$ [7.5.1]   **28.** $7 - 4i$ [7.5.1]

29. $10\sqrt{2} + 2i\sqrt{3}$ [7.5.1]   **30.** $9 - i$ [7.5.2]   **31.** $-12 + 10i$ [7.5.2]   **32.** $14 + 2i$ [7.5.2]

33. $-4\sqrt{2} + 8i\sqrt{2}$ [7.5.2]   **34.** $10 - 9i$ [7.5.2]   **35.** -16 [7.5.3]   **36.** $7 + 3i$ [7.5.3]

37. $-6\sqrt{2}$ [7.5.3]   **38.** $39 - 2i$ [7.5.3]   **39.** $6i$ [7.5.4]   **40.** $\dfrac{2}{3} - \dfrac{5}{3}i$ [7.5.4]

41. $\dfrac{14}{5} + \dfrac{7}{5}i$ [7.5.4]   **42.** $1 + i$ [7.5.4]   **43.** $-2 + 7i$ [7.5.4]   **44.** -24 [7.4.1]

45. $\left\{x \mid x \ge \dfrac{2}{3}\right\}$ [7.3.1]   **46.** $\{x \mid x \in \text{real numbers}\}$ [7.3.1]   **47.** [7.3.2]

48. [7.3.2]   **49.** $\dfrac{13}{3}$ [7.4.1]   **50.** -2 [7.4.1]   **51.** The width is 5 in.   [7.4.2]

52. The amount of power is 120 watts.   [7.4.2]   **53.** The distance required is 242 ft.   [7.4.2]

54. The distance is 6.63 ft.   [7.4.2]

CHAPTER 7 TEST

1. $r^{\frac{1}{6}}$ [7.1.1]   **2.** $\dfrac{64x^3}{y^6}$ [7.1.1]   **3.** $\dfrac{b^3}{8a^6}$ [7.1.1]   **4.** $3\sqrt[5]{y^2}$ [7.1.2]   **5.** $\dfrac{1}{2}x^{\frac{3}{4}}$ [7.1.2]

6. $\{x \mid x \le 4\}$ [7.3.1]   **7.** $(-\infty, \infty)$ [7.3.1]   **8.** $3abc^2\sqrt[3]{ac}$ [7.2.1]   **9.** $8a\sqrt{2a}$ [7.2.2]

10. $-2x^2y\sqrt[3]{2x}$ [7.2.2]   **11.** $-4x\sqrt{3}$ [7.2.3]   **12.** $14 + 10\sqrt{3}$ [7.2.3]

13. $2a - \sqrt{ab} - 15b$ [7.2.3]   **14.** $4x + 4\sqrt{xy} + y$ [7.2.3]   **15.** $\dfrac{4x^2}{y}$ [7.2.4]   **16.** 2 [7.2.4]

17. $\dfrac{x + \sqrt{xy}}{x - y}$ [7.2.4]   **18.** -4 [7.5.3]   **19.** $-3 + 2i$ [7.5.2]   **20.** $18 + 16i$ [7.5.3]

21. $-\dfrac{4}{5} + \dfrac{7}{5}i$ [7.5.4]   **22.** 4 [7.5.2]   **23.** 4 [7.4.1]   **24.** -3 [7.4.1]   **25.** The length of the guy wire is 30.6 ft.   [7.4.2]

CUMULATIVE REVIEW EXERCISES

1. The Distributive Property [1.3.1] **2.** $-x - 24$ [1.3.3] **3.** $\varnothing$ [1.1.2] **4.** 16 [7.4.1]

5. $\dfrac{3}{2}$ [2.1.1] **6.** $\dfrac{2}{3}$ [2.1.2] **7.** $\{x \mid x \geq -1\}$ [2.5.1] **8.** $\{x \mid 4 < x < 5\}$ [2.5.2]

9. $\left\{x \mid x < 2 \text{ or } x > \dfrac{8}{3}\right\}$ [2.6.2] **10.** $(8a + b)(8a - b)$ [5.6.1] **11.** $x(x^2 + 3)(x + 1)(x - 1)$ [5.6.4]

12. $\dfrac{2}{3}$ and -5 [5.7.1] **13.**   [7.3.2] **14.** Yes [3.6.1] **15.** $\dfrac{3x^3}{y}$ [5.1.2]

16. $\dfrac{y^8}{x^2}$ [7.1.1] **17.** $-x\sqrt{5x}$ [7.2.2] **18.** $11 - 5\sqrt{5}$ [7.2.3] **19.** $\dfrac{x\sqrt[3]{4y^2}}{2y}$ [7.2.4]

20. $-\dfrac{3}{5} + \dfrac{6}{5}i$ [7.5.4] **21.**   [1.1.2] **22.** $\{x \mid x \in \text{real numbers}\}$ [7.3.1]

23. 34 [3.2.1] **24.** $y = \dfrac{1}{3}x + \dfrac{7}{3}$ [3.5.2] **25.** 3 [4.3.1] **26.** $\left(\dfrac{17}{4}, \dfrac{9}{2}\right)$ [4.3.2]

27. $m = \dfrac{3}{2}, b = 3$ [3.3.2] **28.** [3.7.1]

29. There are nineteen 18¢ stamps. [2.2.1] **30.** The additional investment must be $4000. [2.4.1]
31. The length is 12 ft. The width is 6 ft. [5.7.2] **32.** The rate of the plane is 250 mph. [6.4.3]
33. The time is 1.25 s. [5.1.4] **34.** The height of the periscope is 32.7 ft. [7.4.2] **35.** The slope is 0.08.
A slope of 0.08 means that the annual interest income is 8% of the investment. [3.4.1]

Answers to Chapter 8 Selected Exercises

PREP TEST

1. $3\sqrt{2}$ [7.2.1] **2.** $3i$ [7.5.1] **3.** $\dfrac{2x - 1}{x - 1}$ [6.2.2] **4.** 8 [1.3.2] **5.** Yes [5.6.1]

6. $(2x - 1)^2$ [5.6.1] **7.** $(3x + 2)(3x - 2)$ [5.6.1] **8.** [1.1.2]
9. $-3, 5$ [5.7.1] **10.** 4 [6.4.1]

CONCEPT REVIEW 8.1

1. Sometimes true **3.** Never true

SECTION 8.1

3. $2x^2 - 4x - 5 = 0; a = 2, b = -4, c = -5$ **5.** $4x^2 - 5x - 6 = 0; a = 4, b = -5, c = -6$ **7.** standard;
$x + 7; x - 7; 0; 0;$ Zero Products; $-7; 7$ **9.** 0 and 4 **11.** -5 and 5 **13.** -2 and 3 **15.** 3

17. 0 and 2 **19.** -2 and 5 **21.** 2 and 5 **23.** 6 and $-\dfrac{3}{2}$ **25.** $\dfrac{1}{4}$ and 2 **27.** -4 and $\dfrac{1}{3}$

29. $-\dfrac{2}{3}$ and $\dfrac{9}{2}$ **31.** -4 and $\dfrac{1}{4}$ **33.** -2 and 9 **35.** -2 and $-\dfrac{3}{4}$ **37.** 2 and -5 **39.** $-\dfrac{3}{2}$

and -4 **41.** $2b$ and $7b$ **43.** $-c$ and $7c$ **45.** $-\dfrac{b}{2}$ and $-b$ **47.** $\dfrac{2a}{3}$ and $4a$ **49. a.** One

positive and one negative   **b.** Two negative   **c.** Two positive   **51.** $x - r$ **53.** $x^2 - 7x + 10 = 0$
55. $x^2 + 6x + 8 = 0$ **57.** $x^2 - 5x - 6 = 0$ **59.** $x^2 - 9 = 0$ **61.** $x^2 - 8x + 16 = 0$
63. $x^2 - 5x = 0$ **65.** $x^2 - 3x = 0$ **67.** $2x^2 - 7x + 3 = 0$ **69.** $4x^2 - 5x - 6 = 0$
71. $3x^2 + 11x + 10 = 0$ **73.** $9x^2 - 4 = 0$ **75.** $6x^2 - 5x + 1 = 0$ **77.** $10x^2 - 7x - 6 = 0$
79. $8x^2 + 6x + 1 = 0$ **81.** $50x^2 - 25x - 3 = 0$ **83.** b is positive and c is positive.   **85.** b is positive

and c is negative.   **87.** 6; -6 **89.** 7 and -7 **91.** $2i$ and $-2i$ **93.** 2 and -2 **95.** $\dfrac{9}{2}$ and

$-\dfrac{9}{2}$ **97.** $7i$ and $-7i$ **99.** $4\sqrt{3}$ and $-4\sqrt{3}$ **101.** $5\sqrt{3}$ and $-5\sqrt{3}$ **103.** $3i\sqrt{2}$ and $-3i\sqrt{2}$

105. 7 and -5 **107.** 0 and -6 **109.** -7 and 3   **111.** $-5 + 5i$ and $-5 - 5i$ **113.** $4 + 2i$ and

$4 - 2i$ **115.** $9 + 3i$ and $9 - 3i$ **117.** 0 and 1   **119.** $-\dfrac{1}{5}$ and 1   **121.** $-\dfrac{3}{2}$ and 0   **123.** $\dfrac{7}{3}$

and 1   **125.** $-5 + \sqrt{6}$ and $-5 - \sqrt{6}$ **127.** $2 + 2\sqrt{6}$ and $2 - 2\sqrt{6}$ **129.** $-1 + 2i\sqrt{3}$ and $-1 - 2i\sqrt{3}$

131. $3 + 3i\sqrt{5}$ and $3 - 3i\sqrt{5}$ **133.** $\dfrac{-2 + 9\sqrt{2}}{3}$ and $\dfrac{-2 - 9\sqrt{2}}{3}$ **135.** $-\dfrac{1}{2} + 2i\sqrt{10}$ and $-\dfrac{1}{2} - 2i\sqrt{10}$

137. Two complex solutions   **139.** One real solution   **141.** $x^2 - 2 = 0$ **143.** $x^2 + 1 = 0$

145. $x^2 - 8 = 0$ **147.** $x^2 - 12 = 0$ **149.** $x^2 + 12 = 0$ **151.** $-\dfrac{5z}{y}$ and $\dfrac{5z}{y}$ **153.** $y + 2$ and

$y - 2$ **155.** 1

CONCEPT REVIEW 8.2

1. Always true   **3.** Never true   **5.** Never true

SECTION 8.2

1. a. perfect-square; x; 14; 49   **b.** 49; $x + 7$ **5.** 5 and -1 **7.** -9 and 1   **9.** 3

11. $-2 + \sqrt{11}$ and $-2 - \sqrt{11}$ **13.** $3 + \sqrt{2}$ and $3 - \sqrt{2}$ **15.** $1 + i$ and $1 - i$ **17.** $\dfrac{1 + \sqrt{5}}{2}$ and

$\dfrac{1 - \sqrt{5}}{2}$ **19.** $3 + \sqrt{13}$ and $3 - \sqrt{13}$ **21.** 3 and 5   **23.** $2 + 3i$ and $2 - 3i$

25. $-3 + 2i$ and $-3 - 2i$ **27.** $1 + 3\sqrt{2}$ and $1 - 3\sqrt{2}$ **29.** $\dfrac{1 + \sqrt{17}}{2}$ and $\dfrac{1 - \sqrt{17}}{2}$

31. $1 + 2i\sqrt{3}$ and $1 - 2i\sqrt{3}$ **33.** $-\dfrac{1}{2}$ and -1 **35.** $\dfrac{1}{2}$ and $\dfrac{3}{2}$ **37.** $-\dfrac{1}{2}$ and $\dfrac{4}{3}$ **39.** $\dfrac{1}{2} + i$ and

$\dfrac{1}{2} - i$ **41.** $\dfrac{1}{3} + \dfrac{1}{3}i$ and $\dfrac{1}{3} - \dfrac{1}{3}i$ **43.** $\dfrac{2 + \sqrt{14}}{2}$ and $\dfrac{2 - \sqrt{14}}{2}$ **45.** $-\dfrac{3}{2}$ and 1   **47.** $1 + \sqrt{5}$ and

$1 - \sqrt{5}$ **49.** $\dfrac{1}{2}$ and 5   **51.** $2 + \sqrt{5}$ and $2 - \sqrt{5}$ **53.** -3.236 and 1.236   **55.** 1.707 and 0.293

57. 0.309 and -0.809 **59.** False   **65.** $6x$; 10; $x^2 - 6x + 10$; 1; -6; 10   **67.** complex

69. 5 and -2 **71.** 4 and -9 **73.** $4 + 2\sqrt{22}$ and $4 - 2\sqrt{22}$ **75.** 3 and -8 **77.** $\dfrac{1}{2}$ and -3

79. $-\dfrac{1}{4}$ and $\dfrac{3}{2}$ **81.** $1 + 2\sqrt{2}$ and $1 - 2\sqrt{2}$ **83.** 10 and -2 **85.** $6 + 2\sqrt{3}$ and $6 - 2\sqrt{3}$

87. $\dfrac{1 + 2\sqrt{2}}{2}$ and $\dfrac{1 - 2\sqrt{2}}{2}$ **89.** $\dfrac{1}{2}$ and 1   **91.** $\dfrac{-5 + \sqrt{7}}{3}$ and $\dfrac{-5 - \sqrt{7}}{3}$ **93.** $\dfrac{2}{3}$ and $\dfrac{5}{2}$

95. $2 + i$ and $2 - i$ **97.** $-3 + 2i$ and $-3 - 2i$ **99.** $3 + i$ and $3 - i$ **101.** $-\dfrac{3}{2}$ and $-\dfrac{1}{2}$

103. $-\frac{1}{2} + \frac{5}{2}i$ and $-\frac{1}{2} - \frac{5}{2}i$ **105.** $\frac{-3 + \sqrt{6}}{3}$ and $\frac{-3 - \sqrt{6}}{3}$ **107.** $1 + \frac{\sqrt{6}}{3}i$ and $1 - \frac{\sqrt{6}}{3}i$ **109.** $-\frac{3}{2}$ and -1 **111.** $-\frac{3}{2}$ and 4 **113.** 7.606 and 0.394   **115.** 0.236 and -4.236 **117.** 1.851 and -1.351 **119.** Two complex   **121.** One real   **123.** Two real   **125.** Two real   **127.** True   **129.** Quadratic   **131.** Linear   **133.** Quadratic   **135.** $\frac{\sqrt{2}}{2}$ and $-2\sqrt{2}$ **137.** $-3\sqrt{2}$ and $\frac{\sqrt{2}}{2}$ **139.** $\frac{\sqrt{3}}{2} + \frac{1}{2}i$ and $\frac{\sqrt{3}}{2} - \frac{1}{2}i$ **141.** $2a$ and $-a$ **143.** $\frac{a}{2}$ and $-2a$ **145.** $1 + \sqrt{y + 1}$ and $1 - \sqrt{y + 1}$ **147.** $\{p|p < 9, p \in \text{real numbers}\}$ **149.** $\{p|p > 1, p \in \text{real numbers}\}$ **151.** $i, -2i$ **153.** The ball takes 4.43 s to hit the ground.   **155.** **a.** 1.05; The model predicts that the population will increase. **b.** 0.96; The model predicts that the population will decrease.

CONCEPT REVIEW 8.3

1. Always true   **3.** Always true

SECTION 8.3

1. x^4 **5.** $3, -3, 2, -2$ **7.** $2, -2, \sqrt{2}, -\sqrt{2}$ **9.** 1 and 4   **11.** 16   **13.** $2i, -2i, 1, -1$ **15.** $4i, -4i, 2, -2$ **17.** 16   **19.** 512 and 1   **21.** $2, 1, -1 + i\sqrt{3}, -1 - i\sqrt{3}, -\frac{1}{2} + \frac{\sqrt{3}}{2}i, -\frac{1}{2} - \frac{\sqrt{3}}{2}i$ **23.** $1, -1, 2, -2, i, -i, 2i, -2i$ **25.** -64 and 8   **27.** $\frac{1}{4}$ and 1   **29.** a and d   **31.** $\sqrt{a + 1}$; 7; square   **33.** 38, 39, 40, 44, 45, 46, 48, 49, 52   **35.** 3   **37.** 9   **39.** 2 and -1 **41.** 0 and 2   **43.** $-\frac{1}{2}$ and 2   **45.** -2 **47.** 1   **49.** 1   **51.** -3 **53.** **a.** $y; y - 4; y(y - 4)$ **b.** $4y - 16$ **c.** $y^2 - 6y$ **d.** $4y - 16; y^2 - 6y$ **55.** 10 and -1 **57.** $-\frac{1}{2} + \frac{\sqrt{7}}{2}i$ and $-\frac{1}{2} - \frac{\sqrt{7}}{2}i$ **59.** 1 and -3 **61.** 0 and -1 **63.** $\frac{1}{2}$ and $-\frac{1}{3}$ **65.** 6 and $-\frac{2}{3}$ **67.** $\frac{4}{3}$ and 3   **69.** $-\frac{1}{4}$ and 3   **71.** $\frac{-5 + \sqrt{33}}{2}$ and $\frac{-5 - \sqrt{33}}{2}$ **73.** 4 and -6 **75.** 5 and 4   **77.** $3, -3, i, -i$ **79.** $i\sqrt{6}, -i\sqrt{6}, 2, -2$ **81.** $\sqrt{2}$ **83.** 4

CONCEPT REVIEW 8.4

1. Sometimes true   **3.** Always true

SECTION 8.4

1. **a.** $2w - 4$ **b.** $w(2w - 4)$ **c.** $w(2w - 4); 96$ **3.** False   **5.** The length is 40 ft. The width is 16 ft.   **7.** The length is 13 ft. The width is 5 ft.   **9.** The cardboard needs to be 90 cm by 90 cm.   **11.** The rate returning was 55 mph.   **13.** The projectile takes 12.5 s to return to Earth.   **15.** The maximum speed is 72.5 km/h.   **17.** The rocket will be 300 ft above the ground after 1.74 s and after 10.76 s.   **19.** Working alone, it would take the smaller pipe 12 min to fill the tank. It would take the larger pipe 6 min.   **21.** The rate of the cruise ship for the first 40 mi was 10 mph.   **23.** The rate of the wind is 20 mph.   **25.** The rate of the crew in calm water is 6 mph.   **27.** The fraction is $\frac{3}{6}$.   **29.** The width is 8 cm. The length is 16 cm. The height is 2 cm.   **31.** The depth will be 10 cm after 22.2 s.   **33.** The bottom of the scoop of ice cream is 2.3 in. from the bottom of the cone.

CONCEPT REVIEW 8.5

1. Sometimes true   **3.** Sometimes true

SECTION 8.5

3. positive; negative; negative   **5.** $\{x \mid x < -2 \text{ or } x > 4\}$ **7.** $\{x \mid x \le 1 \text{ or } x \ge 2\}$

    9. $\{x \mid -3 < x < 4\}$ **11.** $\{x \mid x < -2 \text{ or } 1 < x < 3\}$

    13. $\{x \mid x < -2 \text{ or } x > 4\}$ **15.** $\{x \mid -1 < x \le 3\}$

17. $\{x \mid x \le -2 \text{ or } 1 \le x < 3\}$

19. a and d   **21.** $\{x \mid x < -4 \text{ or } x > 4\}$ **23.** $\{x \mid x < 2 \text{ or } x > 2\}$ **25.** $\{x \mid -3 \le x \le 12\}$

27. $\left\{x \mid x \le \dfrac{1}{2} \text{ or } x \ge 2\right\}$ **29.** $\left\{x \mid \dfrac{1}{2} < x < \dfrac{3}{2}\right\}$ **31.** $\{x \mid x \le -3 \text{ or } 2 \le x \le 6\}$

33. $\left\{x \mid -\dfrac{3}{2} < x < \dfrac{1}{2} \text{ or } x > 4\right\}$ **35.** $\{x \mid x \le -3 \text{ or } -1 \le x \le 1\}$ **37.** $\{x \mid -2 \le x \le 1 \text{ or } x \ge 2\}$

39. $\{x \mid x < -1 \text{ or } x > 2\}$ **41.** $\{x \mid -1 < x \le 0\}$ **43.** $\{x \mid -2 < x \le 0 \text{ or } x > 1\}$ **45.** $\left\{x \mid x < 0 \text{ or } x > \dfrac{1}{2}\right\}$

47.   **49.**   **51.**

53.   **55.**

CONCEPT REVIEW 8.6

1. Sometimes true   **3.** Sometimes true   **5.** Always true

SECTION 8.6

3. -5 **5.** $x = 7$ **7. a.** 3; 0; -1 **b.** parabola; up   **c.** 0; 3; 0   **d.** 0; -1; 0; -1

9. Vertex: (0, 0)
Axis of symmetry: $x = 0$

11. Vertex: (0, -2)
Axis of symmetry: $x = 0$

13. Vertex: (0, 3)
Axis of symmetry: $x = 0$

15. Vertex: (0, 0)
Axis of symmetry: $x = 0$

17. Vertex: (0, -1)
Axis of symmetry: $x = 0$

19. Vertex: (1, -1)
Axis of symmetry: $x = 1$

21. Vertex: (1, 2)
Axis of symmetry: $x = 1$

23. Vertex: $\left(\dfrac{1}{2}, -\dfrac{9}{4}\right)$
Axis of symmetry: $x = \dfrac{1}{2}$

25. Vertex: $\left(\dfrac{1}{4}, -\dfrac{41}{8}\right)$

Axis of symmetry: $x = \dfrac{1}{4}$

27.

Domain: $\{x \mid x \in \text{real numbers}\}$
Range: $\{y \mid y \geq -7\}$

29.

Domain: $\{x \mid x \in \text{real numbers}\}$

Range: $\left\{y \mid y \leq \dfrac{25}{8}\right\}$

31.

Domain: $\{x \mid x \in \text{real numbers}\}$
Range: $\{y \mid y \geq 0\}$

33.

Domain: $\{x \mid x \in \text{real numbers}\}$
Range: $\{y \mid y \geq -7\}$

35.

Domain: $\{x \mid x \in \text{real numbers}\}$
Range: $\{y \mid y \leq -1\}$

37. False   **39.** Right   **41.** 3; 0; 3; 0; x **45.** (2, 0) and (−2, 0)   **47.** (0, 0) and (2, 0)

49. (2, 0) and (−1, 0)   **51.** (3, 0) and $\left(-\dfrac{1}{2}, 0\right)$ **53.** $\left(-\dfrac{2}{3}, 0\right)$ and (7, 0)   **55.** (5, 0) and $\left(\dfrac{4}{3}, 0\right)$

57. $\left(\dfrac{2}{3}, 0\right)$ **59.** $\left(\dfrac{\sqrt{2}}{3}, 0\right)$ and $\left(-\dfrac{\sqrt{2}}{3}, 0\right)$ **61.** $\left(-\dfrac{3}{2}, 0\right), \left(\dfrac{5}{2}, 0\right)$ **63.** $\left(-2 + \sqrt{7}, 0\right)$ and

$\left(-2 - \sqrt{7}, 0\right)$ **65.** No x-intercepts   **67.** $\left(-1 + \sqrt{2}, 0\right)$ and $\left(-1 - \sqrt{2}, 0\right)$ **69.** −2 and −1

71. $2 + i$ and $2 - i$ **73.** 0 and $\dfrac{3}{2}$ **75.** $\sqrt{2}$ and $-\sqrt{2}$ **77.** $-\dfrac{3}{4} + \dfrac{\sqrt{7}}{4}i$ and $-\dfrac{3}{4} - \dfrac{\sqrt{7}}{4}i$ **79.** $\dfrac{1}{3}$

and 1   **81.** (−1, 0), (3, 0)   **83.**

85.

87.

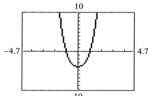

−3.3 and 0.3   −1.3 and 2.8   No real zeros

89. $5 + 4\sqrt{2}$ and $5 - 4\sqrt{2}$ **91.** $1 + 3\sqrt{2}$ and $1 - 3\sqrt{2}$ **93.** The solutions of $x^2 - 2x + 9 = 0$ are complex
numbers.   **95.** No x-intercepts   **97.** Two   **99.** One   **101.** No x-intercepts   **103.** Two
105. No x-intercepts   **107.** One   **109.** Two   **111.** True   **113.** True   **115.** −2
117. 1   **119.** $-2i, 2i, -1$ **121.** $-2i, 2i, -1, 1$

123. 16   **125.** $\dfrac{1 + \sqrt{19}}{3}$ **127.** i and E; ii and F, iii and C; iv and A; v and B; vi and D   **129.** When
the bicyclist is traveling at 15 mph, the drag force on the bicyclist is 33.975 lb.   **131.** $y = (x - 2)^2 + 3$;

vertex: (2, 3)   **133.** $y = \left(x + \dfrac{1}{2}\right)^2 + \dfrac{7}{4}$; vertex: $\left(-\dfrac{1}{2}, \dfrac{7}{4}\right)$ **135.** $y = 3x^2 - 6x + 5$

CONCEPT REVIEW 8.7

1. Sometimes true   **3.** Always true   **5.** Sometimes true

SECTION 8.7

3. -8; down; y **5. a.** Maximum value   **b.** Minimum value   **c.** Maximum value

7. Minimum value at 2   **9.** Maximum value at -1 **11.** Maximum value at $\dfrac{41}{8}$ **13.** Minimum value

at $-\dfrac{73}{8}$ **15.** Maximum value at $-\dfrac{71}{12}$ **17.** Minimum value at $-\dfrac{13}{4}$ **19.** a   **21.** The function

has a minimum value at 7.   **23.** True   **25.** t; 30; -5; 3; 3   **27.** The rock will attain a maximum height

above the beach of 114 ft.   **29.** The maximum profit the tour operator can expect is \$1600.   **31.** The pool

will have the least amount of algae 5 days after treatment.   **33.** The minimum thickness of the mirror is 20.21

in.   **35.** The water will land $31\frac{2}{3}$ ft up on the building.   **37.** The two numbers are 10 and 10.

39. The dimensions that will maximize the enclosed area are 100 ft by 50 ft.   **41.** 3.0   **43.** 0.5

CHAPTER 8 REVIEW EXERCISES

1. 0 and $\dfrac{3}{2}$ [8.1.1]   **2.** $-2c$ and $\dfrac{c}{2}$ [8.1.1]   **3.** $-4\sqrt{3}$ and $4\sqrt{3}$ [8.1.3]   **4.** $-\dfrac{1}{2} - 2i$ and

$-\dfrac{1}{2} + 2i$ [8.1.3]   **5.** $-\dfrac{17}{4}$ [8.7.1]   **6.** 3 [8.7.1]   **7.** $3x^2 + 8x - 3 = 0$ [8.1.2]   **8.** -5 and

$\dfrac{1}{2}$ [8.1.1]   **9.** $-1 - 3\sqrt{2}$ and $-1 + 3\sqrt{2}$ [8.1.3]   **10.** $-3 - i$ and $-3 + i$ [8.2.1]

11. 2 and 3 [8.3.3]   **12.** $-\sqrt{2}, \sqrt{2}, -2, 2$ [8.3.1]   **13.** $\dfrac{25}{18}$ [8.3.2]   **14.** -8 and $\dfrac{1}{8}$ [8.3.1]

15. 2 [8.3.2]   **16.** $3 - \sqrt{11}$ and $3 + \sqrt{11}$ [8.2.2]   **17.** 5 and $-\dfrac{4}{9}$ [8.3.3]   **18.** $\dfrac{1 + \sqrt{3}}{2}$ and

$\dfrac{1 - \sqrt{3}}{2}$ [8.2.2]   **19.** $\dfrac{5}{4}$ [8.3.2]   **20.** 3 and -1 [8.3.3]   **21.** -1 [8.3.3]   **22.** $\dfrac{-3 + \sqrt{249}}{10}$ and

$\dfrac{-3 - \sqrt{249}}{10}$ [8.3.3]   **23.** $\dfrac{-11 - \sqrt{129}}{2}$ and $\dfrac{-11 + \sqrt{129}}{2}$ [8.3.3]   **24.** $x = 3$ [8.6.1]

25. $\left(\dfrac{3}{2}, \dfrac{1}{4}\right)$ [8.6.1]   **26.** $4 + \sqrt{21}$ and $4 - \sqrt{21}$ [8.6.2]   **27.** Two [8.6.2]   **28.** $\left(\dfrac{-3 - \sqrt{5}}{2}, 0\right)$ and

$\left(\dfrac{-3 + \sqrt{5}}{2}, 0\right)$ [8.6.2]   **29.** $(-2, 0)$ and $\left(\dfrac{1}{2}, 0\right)$ [8.6.2]   **30.** $-\dfrac{1}{3} + \dfrac{\sqrt{5}}{3}i$ and $-\dfrac{1}{3} - \dfrac{\sqrt{5}}{3}i$ [8.6.2]

31. $\left\{x \mid -3 < x < \dfrac{5}{2}\right\}$ [8.5.1]   **32.** $\left\{x \mid x \le -4 \text{ or } -\dfrac{3}{2} \le x \le 2\right\}$ [8.5.1]   **33.** $\left\{x \mid x < \dfrac{3}{2} \text{ or } x \ge 2\right\}$

[8.5.1]   **34.** $\left\{x \mid x \le -3 \text{ or } \dfrac{1}{2} \le x < 4\right\}$ [8.5.1]

35. [8.6.1]   **36.** [8.6.1]

Domain: $\{x \mid x \in \text{real numbers}\}$ Vertex: (1, 2)

Range: $\{y \mid y \ge -5\}$ Axis of symmetry: $x = 1$

37. The integers are 2, 4, and 6 or $-6, -4,$ and -2. [8.4.1]   **38.** The width of the rectangle is 5 cm. The length

of the rectangle is 12 cm. [8.4.1]   **39.** Working alone, the new computer can print the payroll in 12 min. [8.4.1]

40. The rate of the first car is 40 mph. The rate of the second car is 50 mph. [8.4.1]

CHAPTER 8 TEST

1. $\frac{3}{2}$ and -2 [8.1.1] **2.** $\frac{3}{4}$ and $-\frac{4}{3}$ [8.1.1] **3.** 9 [8.7.1] **4.** $3x^2 - 8x - 3 = 0$ [8.1.2]

5. $-3 + 3\sqrt{2}$ and $-3 - 3\sqrt{2}$ [8.1.3] **6.** $-2 + \sqrt{5}$ and $-2 - \sqrt{5}$ [8.2.2] **7.** $\dfrac{-3 + \sqrt{41}}{2}$ and

$\dfrac{-3 - \sqrt{41}}{2}$ [8.6.2] **8.** $\dfrac{1}{6} - \dfrac{\sqrt{95}}{6}i$ and $\dfrac{1}{6} + \dfrac{\sqrt{95}}{6}i$ [8.2.2] **9.** $-3 - \sqrt{10}$ and $-3 + \sqrt{10}$ [8.3.3]

10. $\dfrac{1}{4}$ [8.3.1] **11.** $-3, 3, -\sqrt{2}, \sqrt{2}$ [8.3.1] **12.** 4 [8.3.2] **13.** $2 + \sqrt{10}$ and $2 - \sqrt{10}$ [8.6.2]

14. Two [8.6.2] **15.** $(-4, 0)$ and $\left(\dfrac{3}{2}, 0\right)$ [8.6.2] **16.** $x = -\dfrac{3}{2}$ [8.6.1]

17. [8.6.1] **18.** $\left\{x \,\middle|\, -4 < x \le \dfrac{3}{2}\right\}$ [8.5.1]

Domain: $\{x \,|\, x \in \text{real numbers}\}$
Range: $\{y \,|\, y \ge -4.5\}$

19. The height of the triangle is 4 ft. The base of the triangle is 15 ft. [8.4.1] **20.** The rate of the canoe in calm water is 4 mph. [8.4.1]

CUMULATIVE REVIEW EXERCISES

1. 14 [1.3.2] **2.** -28 [2.1.2] **3.** $-\dfrac{3}{2}$ [3.4.1] **4.** $y = x + 1$ [3.6.1]

5. $-3xy(x^2 - 2xy + 3y^2)$ [5.5.1] **6.** $(2x - 5)(3x + 4)$ [5.5.4] **7.** $(x + y)(a^n - 2)$ [5.5.2]

8. $x^2 - 3x - 4 - \dfrac{6}{3x - 4}$ [5.4.1] **9.** $\dfrac{x}{2}$ [6.2.1] **10.** $2\sqrt{5}$ [3.1.2] **11.** $b = \dfrac{2S - an}{n}$ [6.6.1]

12. $-8 - 14i$ [7.5.3] **13.** $1 - a$ [7.1.1] **14.** $\dfrac{x\sqrt[3]{4y^2}}{2y}$ [7.2.4] **15.** $-\dfrac{3}{2}$ and -1 [8.3.3]

16. $-\dfrac{1}{2}$ [8.3.3] **17.** $2, -2, \sqrt{2}$, and $-\sqrt{2}$ [8.3.1] **18.** 0 and 1 [8.3.2]

19. $\left\{x \,\middle|\, -2 < x < \dfrac{10}{3}\right\}$ [2.6.2] **20.** $\left(\dfrac{5}{2}, 0\right)$ and $(0, -3)$ [3.3.2] **21.** [4.5.1]

22. $(1, -1, 2)$ [4.2.2] **23.** $-\dfrac{7}{3}$ [6.1.1] **24.** $\{x \,|\, x \ne 5, -3\}$ [6.1.1]

25. $\{x \,|\, x < -3 \text{ or } 0 < x < 2\}$ [8.5.1]

26. $\{x \,|\, -3 < x \le 1 \text{ or } x \ge 5\}$ [8.5.1] **27.** The average annual rate of change is 5.8 ft. [3.1.4] **28.** The lower and upper limits of the length of the piston rod are $9\frac{23}{64}$ in. and

$9\frac{25}{64}$ in. [2.6.3] **29.** The area of the triangle is $(x^2 + 6x - 16)$ ft^2. [5.3.4] **30.** $m = -\dfrac{25,000}{3}$; a slope of

$-\dfrac{25,000}{3}$ means that the value of the building decreases \$8333.33 each year. [3.4.1]

Answers to Chapter 9 Selected Exercises

PREP TEST

1. 2 [1.3.2] **2.** −7 [1.3.2] **3.** 30 [3.2.1] **4.** $h^2 + 4h − 1$ [3.2.1] **5.** $y = \frac{1}{2}x − 2$ [3.3.2]

6. D: {−2, 3, 4, 6}; R: {4, 5, 6}; Yes [3.2.1] **7.** 8 [6.1.1]

8. [3.2.2] **9.** [8.6.1]

CONCEPT REVIEW 9.1

1. Always true **3.** Always true **5.** Never true

SECTION 9.1

1. down **3.** left

5. **7.** **9.** **11.** **13.**

15. **17.** **19.** **21.** **23.**

25. **27.** **29.** **31. a.** (0, 9) **b.** (8, 0)

33. **35.** **37.** **39.** **41.**

CONCEPT REVIEW 9.2

1. Always true **3.** Never true

SECTION 9.2

1. −2; −2; −2; 4; 4; −6; 0; −7; 7 **3.** 5 **5.** 1 **7.** 0 **9.** $-\frac{29}{4}$ **11.** $\frac{2}{3}$ **13.** 2

15. 39 **17.** −8 **19.** $-\frac{4}{5}$ **21.** −2 **23.** 7 **25.** Undefined **27.** Defined

29. $4x$; $4x$; $4x$; $16x^2$; $8x$ **33.** −13 **35.** −29 **37.** $8x − 13$ **39.** 1 **41.** 5 **43.** $x^2 + 1$

45. 5 **47.** 11 **49.** $3x^2 + 3x + 5$ **51.** −3 **53.** −27 **55.** $x^3 − 6x^2 + 12x − 8$

57. No **59.** Yes **61.** $6h + h^2$ **63.** $2 + h$ **65.** $h + 2a$ **67.** −1 **69.** −6

71. $6x − 13$ **73.** −2 **75.** −2 **77.** 0 **79.** 6

CONCEPT REVIEW 9.3

1. Always true   **3.** Never true   **5.** Sometimes true

SECTION 9.3

3. $-2; 4$ **5.** Yes   **7.** No   **9.** Yes   **11.** No   **13.** No   **15.** No   **17.** Yes
19. No   **21.** $-3; 2$ **23.** $\{(0, 1), (3, 2), (8, 3), (15, 4)\}$ **25.** No inverse

27. $f^{-1}(x) = \dfrac{1}{4}x + 2$ **29.** No inverse   **31.** $f^{-1}(x) = x + 5$ **33.** $f^{-1}(x) = 3x - 6$

35. $f^{-1}(x) = -\dfrac{1}{3}x - 3$ **37.** $f^{-1}(x) = \dfrac{3}{2}x - 6$ **39.** $f^{-1}(x) = -3x + 3$ **41.** $f^{-1}(x) = \dfrac{1}{2}x + \dfrac{5}{2}$

43. No inverse   **45.** $\dfrac{5}{3}$ **47.** 3   **49.** Yes; yes   **51.** Yes   **53.** No   **55.** Yes

57. Yes   **59.** Range   **61.** 3   **63.** 0   **65.** 2   **67.** c   **69.** a
71. $f[g(x)] = f(5x + 4) = 3(5x + 4) + 2 = 15x + 14; g[f(x)] = g(3x + 2) = 5(3x + 2) + 4 = 15x + 14;$ No

73.   **75.**   The function and its inverse have the same graph.

77.   **81. a.** $f^{-1} = \dfrac{1}{2}x + 2$ **b.** MATH   **83.** $f^{-1}(x) = \dfrac{1}{3}x.$ The inverse function

converts feet into yards.

85. $P^{-1}(x) = \dfrac{1}{4}x.$ The inverse function gives the length of a side of a square given its perimeter.

CHAPTER 9 REVIEW EXERCISES

1. 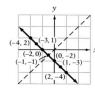   [9.1.1]   **2.**   [9.1.1]   **3.**   [9.1.1]   **4.**   [9.1.1]

5. 7 [9.2.1]   **6.** -9 [9.2.1]   **7.** 70 [9.2.1]   **8.** $\dfrac{12}{7}$ [9.2.1]   **9.** $12x^2 + 12x - 1$ [9.2.2]

10. 5 [9.2.2]   **11.** 10 [9.2.2]   **12.** $6x^2 + 3x - 16$ [9.2.2]   **13.** No [9.3.1]
14. $\{(1, -2), (3, 2), (-4, 5), (9, 7)\}$ [9.3.2]   **15.** No [9.3.1]   **16.** Yes [9.3.1]

17. $f^{-1}(x) = 2x - 16$ [9.3.2]   **18.** $f^{-1}(x) = -\dfrac{1}{6}x + \dfrac{2}{3}$ [9.3.2]   **19.** $f^{-1}(x) = \dfrac{3}{2}x + 18$ [9.3.2]

20. Yes [9.3.2]

CHAPTER 9 TEST

1. No [9.2.1]   **2.** -2 [9.2.1]   **3.** 234 [9.2.1]   **4.** $-\dfrac{13}{2}$ [9.2.1]   **5.** -5 [9.2.1]

6. 5 [9.2.2]   **7.**   [9.1.1]   **8.**   [9.1.1]   **9.** 47 [9.1.1]

10.   [9.1.1]   **11.**   [9.1.1]   **12.** $f^{-1}(x) = 4x + 16$ [9.3.2]

13. $\{(6, 2), (5, 3), (4, 4), (3, 5)\}$ [9.3.2]   **14.** Yes   [9.3.2]   **15.** $2x^2 - 4x - 5$ [9.2.2]

16. $f^{-1}(x) = 2x + 6$ [9.3.2]   **17.** No   [9.3.2]   **18.** No   [9.3.1]

CUMULATIVE REVIEW EXERCISES

1. $-\dfrac{23}{4}$ [1.3.2]   **2.**   [1.1.2]   **3.** 3   [2.1.2]

4. $\{x \mid x < -2 \text{ or } x > 3\}$ [2.5.2]   **5.**   [8.6.1]   **6.**   [3.7.1]

Vertex: $(0, 0)$
Axis of symmetry: $x = 0$

7. $\{x \mid x \in \text{real numbers}\}$ [2.6.2]   **8.** $-\dfrac{a^{10}}{12b^4}$ [5.1.2]   **9.** $2x^3 - 4x^2 - 17x + 4$ [5.3.2]

10. $(a + 2)(a - 2)(a^2 + 2)$ [5.6.4]   **11.** $xy(x - 2y)(x + 3y)$ [5.6.4]   **12.** -3 and 8 [5.7.1]

13. $\{x \mid x < -3 \text{ or } x > 5\}$ [8.5.1]   **14.** $\dfrac{5}{2x - 1}$ [6.2.2]   **15.** -2 [6.4.1]   **16.** $-3 - 2i$ [7.5.4]

17. $y = -2x - 2$ [3.5.2]   **18.** $y = -\dfrac{3}{2}x - \dfrac{7}{2}$ [3.6.1]   **19.** $\dfrac{1}{2} + \dfrac{\sqrt{3}}{6}i$ and $\dfrac{1}{2} - \dfrac{\sqrt{3}}{6}i$ [8.2.2]

20. 3   [7.4.1]   **21.** -3 [8.7.1]   **22.** $\{1, 2, 4, 5\}$ [3.2.1]   **23.** Yes   [3.2.1]   **24.** 2   [7.4.1]

25. $g[h(2)] = 10$ [9.2.2]   **26.** $f^{-1}(x) = -\dfrac{1}{3}x + 3$ [9.3.2]   **27.** The cost per pound of the mixture is

$3.96.   [2.3.1]   **28.** 25 lb of the 80% copper alloy must be used.   [2.4.2]   **29.** An additional 4.5 oz of
insecticide is required.   [6.5.1]   **30.** It would take the larger pipe 4 min to fill the tank.   [6.4.2]
31. A force of 40 lb will stretch the spring 24 in.   [6.5.2]   **32.** The average rate of change in the production of
gigawatts of energy is 6.50 gigawatts per year.   [3.1.4]   **33.** The frequency is 80 vibrations per minute.   [6.5.2]

Answers to Chapter 10 Selected Exercises

PREP TEST

1. $\dfrac{1}{9}$ [5.1.2]   **2.** 16   [5.1.2]   **3.** -3 [5.1.2]   **4.** 0; 108   [3.2.1]   **5.** -6 [2.1.1]

6. $-2, 8$ [8.1.1]   **7.** 6326.60   [1.3.2]   **8.**   [3.2.2]

CONCEPT REVIEW 10.1

1. Never true   **3.** Never true   **5.** Never true

SECTION 10.1

3. c   **5.** 1; 0; 1   **7. a.** 9   **b.** 1   **c.** $\dfrac{1}{9}$ **9. a.** 16   **b.** 4   **c.** $\dfrac{1}{4}$ **11. a.** 1

b. $\dfrac{1}{8}$ **c.** 16   **13. a.** 7.3891   **b.** 0.3679   **c.** 1.2840   **15. a.** 54.5982   **b.** 1

c. 0.1353   **17. a.** 16   **b.** 16   **c.** 1.4768   **19. a.** 0.1353   **b.** 0.1353   **c.** 0.0111

21. $\left(\dfrac{1}{2}\right)^{-3}$ **23.** Less than   **25.** $-3; 3^3; \dfrac{1}{27}; -3; \dfrac{1}{27}$ **27.**   **29.**

31.   **33.**   **35.**   **37.**   **39.** b and d

41. (0, 1)   **43.** There is no x-intercept. The y-intercept is (0, 1).   **45.** Greater than   **47.** $g(x) = b^x - a$

49.   1.6   **51.**   1.1   **53.**   The investment will be worth $1000 in 9 years.

55.   50% of the light will reach to a depth of 0.5 m.   **57. a.**   **b.** The point (4, 55.3) means that after 4 s, the object is moving at a speed of 55.3 ft/s.

CONCEPT REVIEW 10.2

1. Always true   **3.** Never true   **5.** Always true   **7.** Always true

SECTION 10.2

3. base b; x **5.** $\log_5 25 = 2$ **7.** $\log_4 \dfrac{1}{16} = -2$ **9.** $\log_{10} x = y$ **11.** $\log_a w = x$ **13.** $3^2 = 9$

15. $10^{-2} = 0.01$ **17.** $e^y = x$ **19.** $b^v = u$ **21.** $u = v$ **23.** 4   **25.** 7   **27.** 2

29. 3   **31.** 0   **33.** 4   **35.** 9   **37.** 64   **39.** $\dfrac{1}{7}$ **41.** 1   **43.** 316.23

45. 0.02   **47.** 7.39   **49.** 0.61   **51.** Greater than   **55.** $r\log_b x$ **57.** $\log_8 x + \log_8 z$

59. $5 \log_3 x$ **61.** $\ln r - \ln s$ **63.** $2 \log_3 x + 6 \log_3 y$ **65.** $3 \log_7 u - 4 \log_7 v$

67. $2 \log_2 r + 2 \log_2 s$ **69.** $2 \log_9 x + \log_9 y + \log_9 z$ **71.** $\ln x + 2 \ln y - 4 \ln z$

73. $2 \log_8 x - \log_8 y - 2 \log_8 z$ **75.** $\dfrac{1}{2} \log_7 x + \dfrac{1}{2} \log_7 y$ **77.** $\dfrac{1}{2} \log_2 x - \dfrac{1}{2} \log_2 y$ **79.** $\dfrac{3}{2} \ln x + \dfrac{1}{2} \ln y$

81. $\dfrac{3}{2}\log_7 x - \dfrac{1}{2}\log_7 y$ **83.** $\log_3 \dfrac{x^3}{y}$ **85.** $\log_8 x^4 y^2$ **87.** $\ln x^3$ **89.** $\log_5 x^3 y^4$ **91.** $\log_4 \dfrac{1}{x^2}$

93. $\log_3 \dfrac{x^2 z^2}{y}$ **95.** $\log_b \dfrac{x}{y^2 z}$ **97.** $\ln x^2 y^2$ **99.** $\log_6 \sqrt{\dfrac{x}{y}}$ **101.** $\log_4 \dfrac{s^2 r^2}{t^4}$ **103.** $\log_5 \dfrac{x}{y^2 z^2}$

105. $\ln \dfrac{t^3 v^2}{r^2}$ **107.** $\log_4 \sqrt{\dfrac{x^3 z}{y^2}}$ **109.** False **111.** True **113.** 1.3863 **115.** 1.0415

117. 0.8617 **119.** 2.1133 **121.** -0.6309 **123.** 0.2727 **125.** 1.6826 **127.** 1.9266

129. $\dfrac{\log(3x - 2)}{\log 3}$ **131.** $\dfrac{\log(4 - 9x)}{\log 8}$ **133.** $\dfrac{5}{\log 9}\log(6x + 7)$ **135.** $\dfrac{\ln(x + 5)}{\ln 2}$ **137.** $\dfrac{\ln(x^2 + 9)}{\ln 3}$

139. $\dfrac{7}{\ln 8}\ln(10x - 7)$ **141.** 8 **143.** 6 **145.** 2 **147.** 3 **149.** b **151.** 13.12

153. -6.59 **155.** 15.1543

CONCEPT REVIEW 10.3

1. Never true **3.** Always true

SECTION 10.3

5. y; exponential; $3^y + 1$; y; x **7.**   **9.**   **11.**

13.   **15.**   **17.**   **19.**   **21.**

23.   **25.**   **27.**   **29.** **b** and **d**

31. a.
b. The point (4, 49) means that after 4 months, the typist's proficiency has dropped to 49 words per minute.

33. a.
b. According to the model, energy production will first exceed 6 quadrillion BTU in 2006.
c. According to the model, energy production in 2010 will be 6.7 quadrillion BTU.

35. A quadratic function **37.** A linear function **39.** An exponential function **41.** A logarithmic function

CONCEPT REVIEW 10.4

1. Always true **3.** Never true **5.** Always true

SECTION 10.4

3. $3; 2; 4x; 3x - 1; 4x; -1$ **5.** 1 **7.** -3 **9.** 1.1133 **11.** 0.7211 **13.** -1.5850
15. 1.7095 **17.** 1.3222 **19.** -2.8074 **21.** 3.5850 **23.** 1.1309 **25.** 1 **27.** 6
29. 1.3754 and -1.3754 **31.** 1.5805 **33.** -0.6309 **35.** 1.6610 **37.** -1.5129 **39.** 1.5
41. **a, b,** and **c** **43.** 0.63 **45.** -1.86 and 3.44 **47.** -1.16 **51.** exponential form

53. a. Exercise 52 **b.** Exercise 51 **c.** Exercise 51 **d.** Exercise 52 **55.** 8 **57.** $\dfrac{11}{2}$

59. 2 and -4 **61.** $\dfrac{5}{3}$ **63.** $\dfrac{1}{2}$ **65.** 1,000,000,000 **67.** 4 **69.** 3 **71.** 3 **73.** 2

75. No solution **77.** 4 **79.** $\dfrac{5 \pm \sqrt{33}}{2}$ **81.** 1.76 **83.** 2.42 **85.** -1.51 and 2.10

87. 1.7233 **89.** 0.8060 **91.** 5.6910 **93.** 2774

95. a. **b.** It will take the object approximately 2.64 s to fall 100 ft.

CONCEPT REVIEW 10.5

1. Always true **3.** Always true

SECTION 10.5

3. 4000; 3000; 0.0025; unknown **5.** The value of the investment after 2 years is $1172. **7.** The investment will be worth $15,000 in 18 years. **9. a.** The amount of technetium will be 21.2 mg after 3 h. **b.** It takes 3.5 h for the amount of technetium to reach 20 mg. **11.** The half-life of promethium-147 is 2.5 years. **13.** 2 years **15. a.** The approximate pressure at 40 km above Earth is 0.098 newtons per square centimeter. **b.** The approximate pressure on Earth's surface is 10.13 newtons per square centimeter. **c.** The atmospheric pressure decreases as you rise above Earth's surface. **17.** The pH of milk is 6.4. **19.** At a depth of 2.5 m, the percent of light will be 75% of the light at the surface of the pool. **21.** Normal conversation is 65 decibels. **23.** The mass of the colony would be equal to the mass of Earth in 46 h. This is more time than predicted in the novel. **25.** A thickness of 0.4 cm is needed. **27.** The Richter scale magnitude of the earthquake was 9.5. **29.** The intensity of the earthquake was $316,228,000I_0$. **31.** The magnitude of the earthquake is 5.3. **33.** The magnitude of the earthquake is 5.6. **35.** Prices will double in 14 years. **37.** The value of the investment after 5 years is $3210.06. **39. a.** 104 months are required to reduce the loan amount to $90,000. **b.** 269 months are required to reduce the loan amount to one-half the original amount. **c.** The total interest paid exceeds $100,000 in month 163.

CHAPTER 10 REVIEW EXERCISES

1. 2 [10.2.1] **2.** $\log_3 \sqrt{\dfrac{x}{y}}$ [10.2.2] **3.** 1 [10.1.1] **4.** -3 [10.4.1] **5.** 1 [10.1.1]

6. $\dfrac{1}{9}$ [10.2.1] **7.** $\log_2 32 = 5$ [10.2.1] **8.** 6 [10.4.2] **9.** $\dfrac{1}{2}\log_6 x + \dfrac{3}{2}\log_6 y$ [10.2.2]

10. 2 [10.4.1] **11.** -2 [10.4.1] **12.** $\dfrac{1}{3}$ [10.1.1] **13.** 4 [10.2.1] **14.** 2 [10.4.2]

15. 2.3219 [10.2.2] **16.** 1.7251 [10.2.2] **17.** 3 [10.4.1] **18.** 4 [10.1.1]

19. $\dfrac{1}{2}\log_5 x - \dfrac{1}{2}\log_5 y$ [10.2.2] **20.** $\dfrac{1}{4}$ [10.4.2] **21.** 125 [10.2.1] **22.** $\dfrac{1}{2}$ [10.4.2]

23. $\log_b \dfrac{x^3}{y^5}$ [10.2.2]   **24.** 4 [10.1.1]   **25.** 2.6801 [10.2.2]   **26.** −0.5350 [10.4.1]

27. [10.1.2]   **28.** [10.1.2]   **29.** [10.3.1]

30. [10.3.1]   **31.** 1.0 [10.3.1]   **32.** The half-life is 33 h. [10.5.1]

33. The material must be 0.602 cm thick. [10.5.1]

CHAPTER 10 TEST

1. 1 [10.1.1]   **2.** $\dfrac{1}{64}$ [10.1.1]   **3.** 3 [10.2.1]   **4.** $\dfrac{1}{16}$ [10.2.1]

5. $\dfrac{2}{3} \log_6 x + \dfrac{5}{3} \log_6 y$ [10.2.2]   **6.** $\log_5 \sqrt{\dfrac{x}{y}}$ [10.2.2]   **7.** 3 [10.4.2]   **8.** $\dfrac{1}{3}$ [10.1.1]

9. 2.5789 [10.4.1]   **10.** 10 [10.4.2]   **11.** 3 [10.4.1]   **12.** −4 [10.4.1]   **13.** $\dfrac{3}{2}$ [10.4.2]

14. [10.1.2]   **15.** [10.1.2]   **16.** [10.3.1]

17. [10.3.1]   **18.** 1.6 [10.1.2]   **19.** The value of the investment after 6 years is $15,661. [10.5.1]

20. The half-life is 24 h. [10.5.1]

CUMULATIVE REVIEW EXERCISES

1. $\dfrac{8}{7}$ [2.1.2]   **2.** $L = \dfrac{S - 2WH}{2W + 2H}$ [6.6.1]   **3.** $\{x \mid 1 \le x \le 4\}$ [2.6.2]   **4.** $(4x^n + 3)(x^n + 1)$ [5.6.3]

5. $\{x \mid -5 \le x \le 1\}$ [8.5.1]   **6.** $\dfrac{x - 3}{x + 3}$ [6.3.1]   **7.** $\dfrac{x\sqrt{y} + y\sqrt{x}}{x - y}$ [7.2.4]   **8.** $-4x^2y^3\sqrt{2x}$ [7.2.2]

9. $-\dfrac{1}{5} + \dfrac{2}{5}i$ [7.5.4]   **10.** $y = 2x - 6$ [3.6.1]   **11.** $3x^2 + 8x - 3 = 0$ [8.1.2]   **12.** $2 + \sqrt{10}$ and $2 - \sqrt{10}$ [8.2.1, 8.2.2]   **13.** $\{-6, -4, 0\}$ [3.2.1]   **14.** 4 [9.2.2]   **15.** $(0, -1, 2)$ [4.2.2]

16. $\left(-\dfrac{1}{2}, -2\right)$ [4.1.2]   **17.** 243 [10.1.1]   **18.** 64 [10.2.1]   **19.** 8 [10.4.1]   **20.** 1 [10.4.2]

21. [1.1.2]   **22.** [8.5.1]   **23.** [8.6.1]

24. [3.2.2] **25.** [10.1.2] **26.** [10.3.1]

27. 800 lb of the alloy containing 25% tin and 1200 lb of the alloy containing 50% tin were used. [2.4.2]

28. To earn $3000 or more a month, the sales executive must make sales amounting to $31,250 or more. [2.5.3]

29. [3.1.3] **30.** With both printers operating, it would take 7.5 min to print the checks. [6.4.2]

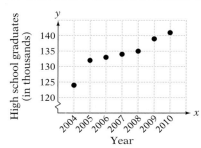

31. When the volume is 25 ft³, the pressure is 500 lb/in². [6.5.2] **32.** The cost per yard of the wool carpet is $24. [4.4.2] **33.** The value of the investment after 5 years is $15,657. [10.5.1]

Answers to Chapter 11 Selected Exercises

PREP TEST

1. 12 [1.2.4] **2.** $\frac{3}{4}$ [3.2.1] **3.** 18 [1.3.2] **4.** 96 [1.3.2] **5.** −410 [1.3.2]

6. $\frac{4}{9}$ [1.2.4] **7.** $x^2 + 2xy + y^2$ [5.3.3] **8.** $x^3 + 3x^2y + 3xy^2 + y^3$ [5.3.2, 5.3.3]

CONCEPT REVIEW 11.1

1. Always true **3.** Always true

SECTION 11.1

3. 8 **5.** first; second; nth **7.** 2, 3, 4, 5 **9.** 3, 5, 7, 9 **11.** 0, −2, −4, −6 **13.** 2, 4, 8, 16

15. 2, 5, 10, 17 **17.** $\frac{1}{2}, \frac{2}{5}, \frac{3}{10}, \frac{4}{17}$ **19.** $0, \frac{3}{2}, \frac{8}{3}, \frac{15}{4}$ **21.** 1, −2, 3, −4 **23.** $\frac{1}{2}, -\frac{1}{5}, \frac{1}{10}, -\frac{1}{17}$

25. −2, 4, −8, 16 **27.** $\frac{2}{9}, \frac{2}{27}, \frac{2}{81}, \frac{2}{243}$ **29.** 15 **31.** $\frac{12}{13}$ **33.** 24 **35.** $\frac{32}{243}$ **37.** 88

39. $\frac{1}{20}$ **41.** 38 **43.** False **47.** 1; 2; 3; 4; 4; 7; 10; 13; 34 **49.** 42 **51.** 28 **53.** 60

55. $\frac{25}{24}$ **57.** 28 **59.** $\frac{99}{20}$ **61.** $\frac{137}{120}$ **63.** −2 **65.** $-\frac{7}{12}$ **67.** $\frac{2}{x} + \frac{4}{x} + \frac{6}{x} + \frac{8}{x}$

69. $\frac{x}{2} + \frac{x^2}{3} + \frac{x^3}{4} + \frac{x^4}{5}$ **71.** $\frac{x^2}{3} + \frac{x^3}{5} + \frac{x^4}{7}$ **73.** $x + x^3 + x^5 + x^7$ **75.** c **77.** $a_n = 2n − 1$

79. $a_n = -2n + 1$ **81.** $a_n = 4n$ **83.** $\log 384$ **85.** 3 **87.** 1, 2, 3, 5 **89.** $\sum_{i=1}^{n} \frac{1}{i}$

CONCEPT REVIEW 11.2

1. Sometimes true **3.** Sometimes true

SECTION 11.2

3. a. 4; common   **b.** nth; 50; 3; 4; 199   **5.** 141   **7.** 50   **9.** 71   **11.** $\dfrac{27}{4}$ **13.** 17

15. 3.75   **17.** $a_n = n$ **19.** $a_n = -4n + 10$ **21.** $a_n = \dfrac{3n + 1}{2}$ **23.** $a_n = -5n - 3$

25. $a_n = -10n + 36$ **27.** 42   **29.** 16   **31.** 20   **33.** 20   **35.** 13   **37.** 20
39. True   **41.** True   **43.** 10; $n - 3$; 1; -2; 10; 7; Arithmetic Series; 10; 10; -2; 7; 5; 5; 25   **45.** 650
47. -605 **49.** $\dfrac{215}{4}$ **51.** 420   **53.** -210 **55.** -5 **57.** Negative   **59.** 8; 8; 3; 17; 80
61. In 9 weeks the person will walk 60 min per day.   **63.** There are 2180 seats in the theater.   **65.** The salary for the tenth month is $3550. The total salary for the 10-month period is $28,750.   **67.** Exercise 60
69. 8   **71.** -3 **73.** $1800°$; $180(n - 2)$ **75.** $a_n = 7.66n + 392.19$

CONCEPT REVIEW 11.3

1. Always true   **3.** Sometimes true   **5.** Never true

SECTION 11.3

3. a. 3; common ratio   **b.** nth; 7; 2; 3; 6; 729; 1458   **5.** 131,072   **7.** $\dfrac{128}{243}$ **9.** 16

11. 6, 4   **13.** $-2, \dfrac{4}{3}$ **15.** 12, -48 **17.** False   **19.** sum; number; first; common ratio

21. 2186   **23.** $\dfrac{2343}{64}$ **25.** 62   **27.** $\dfrac{121}{243}$ **29.** 1364   **31.** 2800   **33.** $\dfrac{2343}{1024}$

35. $\dfrac{1360}{81}$ **37. a.** No   **b.** Yes   **39.** -1; 1; 1   **41.** 9   **43.** $\dfrac{18}{5}$ **45.** $\dfrac{7}{9}$

47. a. Yes   **b.** No   **49.** $\dfrac{8}{9}$ **51.** $\dfrac{2}{9}$ **53.** $\dfrac{5}{11}$ **55.** $\dfrac{1}{6}$ **57.** 700; 1400; geometric;

350; 2   **59.** The nth term is $a_n = 3^{n-1}$.   **61.** There will be 7.8125 mg of radioactive material in the sample at the beginning of the seventh day.   **63.** The ball bounces to a height of 2.6 ft on the fifth bounce.   **65.** The value of the land in 15 years will be $82,103.49.   **67.** The value of the house in 30 years will be $432,194.24.
69. G; $-\dfrac{1}{2}$ **71.** A; 9.5   **73.** N; 25   **75.** G; x^2 **77.** A; 4 log x **79.** 27   **81.** The common difference is log 2.   **83.** The common ratio is 8.   **85. a.** $80.50 of the loan is repaid in the 27th payment.   **b.** The total amount repaid after 20 payments is $1424.65.   **c.** The unpaid balance on the loan after 20 payments is $3575.35.

CONCEPT REVIEW 11.4

1. Never true   **3.** Never true   **5.** Never true

SECTION 11.4

3. factorial   **5.** $n!$; $(n - r)!$ **7.** 6   **9.** 40,320   **11.** 1   **13.** 10   **15.** 1   **17.** 84
19. 21   **21.** 45   **23.** 1   **25.** 20   **27.** 11   **29.** 6   **31.** False   **33.** x^5; 32
35. $x^4 + 4x^3y + 6x^2y^2 + 4xy^3 + y^4$ **37.** $x^5 - 5x^4y + 10x^3y^2 - 10x^2y^3 + 5xy^4 - y^5$
39. $16m^4 + 32m^3 + 24m^2 + 8m + 1$ **41.** $32r^5 - 240r^4 + 720r^3 - 1080r^2 + 810r - 243$
43. $a^{10} + 10a^9b + 45a^8b^2$ **45.** $a^{11} - 11a^{10}b + 55a^9b^2$ **47.** $256x^8 + 1024x^7y + 1792x^6y^2$
49. $65,536x^8 - 393,216x^7y + 1,032,192x^6y^2$ **51.** $x^7 + 7x^5 + 21x^3$ **53.** $x^{10} + 15x^8 + 90x^6$

55. $-560x^4$ **57.** $-6x^{10}y^2$ **59.** $126y^5$ **61.** $5n^3$ **63.** $\dfrac{x^5}{32}$ **65.** Negative

67. 1 7 21 35 35 21 7 1   **69.** n **71.** $x^2 + 8x^{\frac{3}{2}} + 24x + 32x^{\frac{1}{2}} + 16$ **73.** $-8i$ **75.** 1
77. 1260

CHAPTER 11 REVIEW EXERCISES

1. $3x + 3x^2 + 3x^3 + 3x^4$ [11.1.2]   **2.** 16 [11.2.1]   **3.** 32 [11.3.1]   **4.** 16 [11.3.3]

5. 84 [11.4.1]   **6.** $\dfrac{1}{2}$ [11.1.1]   **7.** 44 [11.2.1]   **8.** 468 [11.2.2]   **9.** -66 [11.3.2]

10. 70 [11.4.1]   **11.** $2268x^3y^6$ [11.4.1]   **12.** 34 [11.2.2]   **13.** $\dfrac{7}{6}$ [11.1.1]

14. $a_n = -3n + 15$ [11.2.1]   **15.** $\dfrac{2}{27}$ [11.3.1]   **16.** $\dfrac{7}{30}$ [11.3.3]   **17.** -115 [11.2.1]

18. $\dfrac{665}{32}$ [11.3.2]   **19.** 1575 [11.2.2]   **20.** $-280x^4y^3$ [11.4.1]   **21.** 21 [11.2.1]

22. 48 [11.3.1]   **23.** 30 [11.2.2]   **24.** 341 [11.3.2]   **25.** 120 [11.4.1]   **26.** $240x^4$ [11.4.1]

27. 143 [11.2.1]   **28.** -575 [11.2.2]   **29.** $-\dfrac{5}{27}$ [11.1.1]   **30.** $2 + 2x + 2x^2 + 2x^3$ [11.1.2]

31. $\dfrac{23}{99}$ [11.3.3]   **32.** $\dfrac{16}{5}$ [11.3.3]   **33.** 726 [11.3.2]   **34.** $-42{,}240x^4y^7$ [11.4.1]

35. 0.996 [11.3.2]   **36.** 6 [11.3.3]   **37.** $\dfrac{19}{30}$ [11.3.3]

38. $x^5 - 15x^4y^2 + 90x^3y^4 - 270x^2y^6 + 405xy^8 - 243y^{10}$ [11.4.1]   **39.** 22 [11.2.1]   **40.** 99 [11.4.1]

41. $2x + 2x^2 + \dfrac{8x^3}{3} + 4x^4 + \dfrac{32x^5}{5}$ [11.1.2]   **42.** $-\dfrac{13}{60}$ [11.1.2]   **43.** The total salary for the 9-month
period is \$24,480. [11.2.3]   **44.** The temperature is 67.7°F. [11.3.4]

CHAPTER 11 TEST

1. $\dfrac{1}{3}$ [11.1.1]   **2.** $\dfrac{8}{9}, \dfrac{9}{10}$ [11.1.1]   **3.** 32 [11.1.2]   **4.** $2x^2 + 2x^4 + 2x^6 + 2x^8$ [11.1.2]

5. -120 [11.2.1]   **6.** $a_n = 2n - 5$ [11.2.1]   **7.** 22 [11.2.1]   **8.** 315 [11.2.2]

9. 1560 [11.2.2]   **10.** 252 [11.4.1]   **11.** $-64\sqrt{2}$ [11.3.1]   **12.** $\dfrac{81}{125}$ [11.3.1]

13. $\dfrac{781}{256}$ [11.3.2]   **14.** -55 [11.3.2]   **15.** 4 [11.3.3]   **16.** $\dfrac{7}{30}$ [11.3.3]   **17.** 330 [11.4.1]

18. $5670x^4y^4$ [11.4.1]   **19.** The inventory after the October 1 shipment was 2550 yd. [11.2.3]
20. There will be 20 mg of radioactive material in the sample at the beginning of the fifth day. [11.3.4]

CUMULATIVE REVIEW EXERCISES

1. $\dfrac{x^2 + 5x - 2}{(x + 2)(x - 1)}$ [6.2.2]   **2.** $2(x^2 + 2)(x^4 - 2x^2 + 4)$ [5.6.4]   **3.** $4y\sqrt{x} - y\sqrt{2}$ [7.2.3]

4. $\dfrac{1}{x^{26}}$ [7.1.1]   **5.** 4 [7.4.1]   **6.** $\dfrac{1}{4} - \dfrac{\sqrt{55}}{4}i$ and $\dfrac{1}{4} + \dfrac{\sqrt{55}}{4}i$ [8.2.2]   **7.** $\left(\dfrac{7}{6}, \dfrac{1}{2}\right)$ [4.2.1]

8. $\{x \mid x < -2 \text{ or } x > 2\}$ [2.5.2]   **9.** -10 [4.3.1]   **10.** $\dfrac{1}{2}\log_5 x - \dfrac{1}{2}\log_5 y$ [10.2.2]   **11.** 3 [10.4.1]

12. $a_5 = 20; a_6 = 30$ [11.1.1]   **13.** 6 [11.1.2]   **14.** $(2, 0, 1)$ [4.2.2]   **15.** 216 [10.4.2]

16. $2x^2 - x - 1 + \dfrac{6}{2x + 1}$ [5.4.1]   **17.** $-3h + 1$ [3.2.1]   **18.** $\left\{-1, 0, \dfrac{7}{5}\right\}$ [3.2.1]

19. [3.3.2]   **20.** [3.7.1]   **21.** The new computer would take 24 min to complete the payroll. The older computer would take 40 min to complete the payroll.   [6.4.2]

22. The rate of the boat in calm water is 6.25 mph. The rate of the current is 1.25 mph.   [4.4.1]   **23.** The half-life is 55 days.   [10.5.1]   **24.** The total number of seats in the theater is 1536.   [11.2.3]   **25.** The height the ball reaches on the fifth bounce is 3.3 ft.   [11.3.4]

Answers to Chapter 12 Selected Exercises

PREP TEST

1. 7.21   [3.1.2]   **2.** $x^2 - 8x + 16; (x - 4)^2$ [8.2.1]   **3.** $0; \pm 4$ [8.1.3]   **4.** $(1, -1)$ [4.1.2]
5. $(1, -5)$ [4.2.1]   **6.** $x = 2; (2, -2)$ [8.6.1]   **7.**   [8.6.1]   **8.**   [3.7.1]

9.   [4.5.1]

CONCEPT REVIEW 12.1

1. Sometimes true   **3.** Sometimes true   **5.** Sometimes true

SECTION 12.1

1. a. The axis of symmetry is a vertical line.   **b.** The parabola opens up.   **3. a.** The axis of symmetry is a horizontal line.   **b.** The parabola opens right.   **5. a.** The axis of symmetry is a horizontal line.
b. The parabola opens left.   **7.** y; positive; negative   **9.** Vertex: $(1, -5)$ **11.** Vertex: $(1, -2)$
Axis of symmetry: $x = 1$ Axis of symmetry: $x = 1$

13. Vertex: $(-4, -3)$ **15.** Vertex: $(1, -1)$ **17.** Vertex: $\left(\frac{5}{2}, -\frac{9}{4}\right)$
Axis of symmetry: $y = -3$ Axis of symmetry: $x = 1$ Axis of symmetry: $x = \frac{5}{2}$

19. Vertex: $(-6, 1)$
Axis of symmetry: $y = 1$

21. Vertex: $\left(-\frac{3}{2}, \frac{27}{4}\right)$
Axis of symmetry: $x = -\frac{3}{2}$

23. Vertex: $(4, 0)$
Axis of symmetry: $y = 0$

25. Vertex: $\left(\frac{1}{2}, 1\right)$
Axis of symmetry: $y = 1$

27. Vertex: $(-2, -8)$
Axis of symmetry: $x = -2$

29. $x = ay^2 + by + c$; a is positive; c is negative

31. $y = ax^2 + bx + c$; a is positive; c is positive

33. Domain: $\{x \mid x \in \text{real numbers}\}$
Range: $\{y \mid y \geq -6\}$

35. Domain: $\{x \mid x \geq -14\}$
Range: $\{y \mid y \in \text{real numbers}\}$

37. $\left(0, \frac{1}{8}\right)$

39. **a.** The equation of the mirror is $x = \frac{1}{2639}y^2$.

b. The equation is valid over the interval $\{0 \leq x \leq 3.79\}$.

CONCEPT REVIEW 12.2

1. Sometimes true   **3.** Always true   **5.** Never true

SECTION 12.2

3. $1; -4; 6; 1; -4; 6$

5.

7.

9.

11.

13. IV   **15.** $(x - 2)^2 + (y + 1)^2 = 4$ **17.** $(x + 1)^2 + (y - 1)^2 = 5$ **19.** $(x + 3)^2 + (y - 6)^2 = 8$

21. $(x + 2)^2 + (y - 1)^2 = 5$ **23.** **a.** $8x; 4y; 5$ **b.** $16; 4; 16; 4; 16; 4$ **c.** $x + 4; y - 2; 25$

25. $(x - 1)^2 + (y + 2)^2 = 25$ **27.** $(x + 3)^2 + (y + 4)^2 = 16$ **29.** $\left(x - \frac{1}{2}\right)^2 + (y + 2)^2 = 1$

31. $(x - 3)^2 + (y + 2)^2 = 9$ **33.** Circle B   **35.** Circle D   **37.** $(x - 3)^2 + y^2 = 9$

39. $(x + 1)^2 + (y - 1)^2 = 1$

CONCEPT REVIEW 12.3

1. Never true   **3.** Always true   **5.** Sometimes true

SECTION 12.3

1. ellipse; the origin; $(a, 0)$; $(-a, 0)$; $(0, b)$; $(0, -b)$ **3.**   **5.**   **7.**

9.   **11.**   **13.**   **15.** Less than   **19.** 25; 49

21. y; $(0, 7)$; $(0, -7)$ **23.**   **25.**   **27.**   **29.**

31.   **33.**   **35.**   **37.**   **39.**

41.   **43.**   **45.** **a.** $\dfrac{x^2}{324} + \dfrac{y^2}{20.25} = 1$ **b.** The aphelion is 3,293,400,000 mi from the sun.   **c.** The perihelion is 53,100,000 mi from the sun.

47. **a.** $\dfrac{x^2}{2.310} + \dfrac{x^2}{2.235} = 1$ **b.** The aphelion is 166,800,000 mi from the sun.

c. The perihelion is 115,800,000 mi from the sun.

CONCEPT REVIEW 12.4

1. Never true   **3.** Sometimes true   **5.** Always true

SECTION 12.4

3. $(-2, 5)$ and $(5, 19)$ **5.** $(-1, -2)$ and $(2, 1)$ **7.** $(2, -2)$ **9.** $(2, 2)$ and $\left(-\dfrac{2}{9}, -\dfrac{22}{9}\right)$ **11.** $(3, 2)$

and $(2, 3)$ **13.** $\left(\dfrac{\sqrt{3}}{2}, 3\right)$ and $\left(-\dfrac{\sqrt{3}}{2}, 3\right)$ **15.** No solution   **17.** $(1, 2)$, $(1, -2)$, $(-1, 2)$, and $(-1, -2)$

19. $(3, 2)$, $(3, -2)$, $(-3, 2)$, and $(-3, -2)$ **21.** $(2, 7)$ and $(-2, 11)$ **23.** $\left(3, \sqrt{2}\right)$, $\left(3, -\sqrt{2}\right)$, $\left(-3, \sqrt{2}\right)$, and

$\left(-3, -\sqrt{2}\right)$ **25.** No solution   **27.** $\left(\sqrt{2}, 3\right), \left(\sqrt{2}, -3\right), \left(-\sqrt{2}, 3\right)$, and $\left(-\sqrt{2}, -3\right)$ **29.** $(2, -1)$ and $(8, 11)$
31. $(1, 0)$ **33.** An ellipse and a circle that intersect in two points   **35.** A parabola and a straight line that
intersect in one point   **37.** $(1.000, 2.000)$ **39.** $(1.755, 0.811), (0.505, -0.986)$ **41.** $(5.562, -1.562)$,
$(0.013, 3.987)$

CONCEPT REVIEW 12.5

1. Always true   **3.** Never true   **5.** Sometimes true

SECTION 12.5

1. a. parabola   **b.** dashed   **c.** is   **3.**   **5.**   **7.**

9.   **11.**   **13.**   **15.**   **17.**

19.   **21.**   **23.**   **25.**   **27.** True

29. intersection   **31.**   **33.**   **35.**   **37.**

39.   **41.**   **43.** The solution set is the region inside the circle $x^2 + y^2 = a$.

45. The solution set is the region between the circles $x^2 + y^2 = a$ and $x^2 + y^2 = b$.   **47.**

49.   **51.**   **53.**   **55.**   **57.**

CHAPTER 12 REVIEW EXERCISES

1. Vertex: $(2, 4)$; axis of symmetry: $x = 2$ [12.1.1]   **2.** Vertex: $\left(\frac{7}{2}, \frac{17}{4}\right)$; axis of symmetry: $x = \frac{7}{2}$ [12.1.1]

3. [12.1.1]   **4.** [12.1.1]   **5.** $(x + 1)^2 + (y - 2)^2 = 18$ [12.2.1]

6. $(x + 1)^2 + (y - 5)^2 = 36$ [12.2.1]   **7.** [12.2.1]   **8.** [12.2.1]

9. $x^2 + (y + 3)^2 = 97$ [12.2.1]   **10.** $(x + 2)^2 + (y - 1)^2 = 9$ [12.2.2]   **11.** [12.3.1]

12. [12.3.1]   **13.** [12.3.2]   **14.** [12.3.2]

15. $(-2, -12)$ [12.4.1]   **16.** $(\sqrt{5}, 3), (-\sqrt{5}, 3), (\sqrt{5}, -3),$ and $(-\sqrt{5}, -3)$ [12.4.1]   **17.** $\left(\dfrac{2}{9}, \dfrac{1}{3}\right)$ and

$\left(1, \dfrac{3}{2}\right)$ [12.4.1]   **18.** $(1, \sqrt{5})$ and $(1, -\sqrt{5})$ [12.4.1]   **19.** [12.5.1]

20. [12.5.1]   **21.** [12.5.1]   **22.** [12.5.1]

23. [12.5.2]   **24.** [12.5.2]   **25.** [12.5.2]

26. [12.5.2]

CHAPTER 12 TEST

1. $x = 3$ [12.1.1]   **2.** $\left(\dfrac{3}{2}, \dfrac{1}{4}\right)$ [12.1.1]   **3.** [12.1.1]   **4.** [12.1.1]

5. $(x + 3)^2 + (y + 3)^2 = 16$ [12.2.1]   **6.** $(2, 0)$ and $\left(\dfrac{2}{3}, \dfrac{4}{3}\right)$ [12.4.1]   **7.** $(36, -4)$ and $\left(-\dfrac{9}{4}, \dfrac{1}{2}\right)$ [12.4.1]

8. $(5, 1), (-5, 1), (5, -1),$ and $(-5, -1)$ [12.4.1]   **9.** $(x + 1)^2 + (y + 3)^2 = 58$ [12.2.1]

10. [12.2.1]   **11.** $(x + 2)^2 + (y - 4)^2 = 9$ [12.2.1]   **12.** $(x + 2)^2 + (y - 1)^2 = 32$ [12.2.1]

13. $(x - 2)^2 + (y + 1)^2 = 4$ [12.2.2]   **14.** [12.3.2]   **15.** [12.3.2]

16. [12.3.1]   **17.** [12.5.1]   **18.** [12.5.2]

19. [12.5.1]   **20.** No real solution [12.5.2]

FINAL EXAM

1. -31 [1.2.4]   **2.** -1 [1.3.2]   **3.** $33 - 10x$ [1.3.3]   **4.** 8 [2.1.1]   **5.** $\dfrac{2}{3}$ [2.1.2]

6. 4 and $-\dfrac{2}{3}$ [2.6.1]   **7.** $\{x \mid -4 < x < -1\}$ [2.6.2]   **8.** $\left\{x \mid x > \dfrac{3}{2}\right\}$ [2.5.2]

9. $y = -\dfrac{2}{3}x - \dfrac{1}{3}$ [3.6.1]   **10.** $6a^3 - 5a^2 + 10a$ [5.3.1]   **11.** $\dfrac{6}{5} - \dfrac{3}{5}i$ [7.5.4]

12. $2x^2 - 3x - 2 = 0$ [8.1.2]   **13.** $(2 - xy)(4 + 2xy + x^2y^2)$ [5.6.2]   **14.** $(x - y)(1 + x)(1 - x)$ [5.6.4]

15. $x^2 - 2x - 3 - \dfrac{5}{2x - 3}$ [5.4.1]   **16.** $\dfrac{x(x - 1)}{2x - 5}$ [6.2.1]   **17.** $-\dfrac{10x}{(x + 2)(x - 3)}$ [6.2.2]

18. $\dfrac{x + 3}{x + 1}$ [6.3.1]   **19.** $-\dfrac{7}{4}$ [6.4.1]   **20.** $d = \dfrac{a_n - a_1}{n - 1}$ [6.6.1]   **21.** $\dfrac{y^4}{162x^3}$ [5.1.2]

22. $\dfrac{1}{64x^8y^5}$ [7.1.1]   **23.** $-2x^2y\sqrt{2y}$ [7.2.2]   **24.** $\dfrac{x^2\sqrt{2y}}{2y^2}$ [7.2.4]   **25.** $\dfrac{3 + \sqrt{17}}{4}$ and

$\dfrac{3 - \sqrt{17}}{4}$ [8.2.2]   **26.** 27 and -8 [8.3.1]   **27.** $y = -3x + 7$ [3.5.2]   **28.** $\dfrac{3}{2}$ and -2 [8.3.3]

29. $(3, 4)$ [4.2.1]   **30.** 10 [4.3.1]   **31.** 6 [10.4.2]   **32.** $2y + 2y^2 + 2y^3 + 2y^4 + 2y^5$ [11.1.2]

33. $\dfrac{23}{45}$ [11.3.3]   **34.** $144x^7y^2$ [11.4.1]   **35.** $\left(\dfrac{5}{2}, -\dfrac{3}{2}\right)$ [12.4.1]   **36.** $f^{-1}(x) = \dfrac{3}{2}x + 6$ [9.3.2]

37. $\log_2 \dfrac{a^2}{b^2}$ [10.2.2]   **38.** x-intercept: $\left(\dfrac{9}{2}, 0\right)$

y-intercept: $(0, -3)$

 [3.3.2]   **39.** [3.7.1]

40. [8.6.1/12.1.1]   **41.** [12.3.1]   **42.** [10.3.1]

43. $-2, 1.7$ [10.1.2]   **44.** [10.3.1]   **45.** The range of scores is 69 or better. [2.5.3]

46. The cyclist traveled 40 mi. [2.3.2]   **47.** The amount invested at 8.5% is $8000. The amount invested at 6.4% is $4000. [2.4.1]   **48.** The width is 7 ft and the length is 20 ft. [8.4.1]   **49.** The number of additional shares is 200. [6.5.1]   **50.** The rate of the plane was 420 mph. [6.4.3]   **51.** The distance the object has fallen is 88 ft. [7.4.2]   **52.** The rate of the plane for the first 360 mi was 120 mph. [8.4.1]   **53.** The intensity is 200 lumens. [6.5.2]   **54.** The rate of the boat in calm water is 12.5 mph. The rate of the current is 2.5 mph. [4.4.1]   **55.** The value of the investment is $4785.65. [10.5.1]   **56.** The value of the house would be $577,284. [11.3.4]

Glossary

abscissa The first number in an ordered pair; it measures a horizontal distance and is also called the first coordinate of an ordered pair. (Section 3.1)

absolute value equation An equation that contains the absolute value symbol. (Section 2.6)

absolute value of a number The distance of the number from zero on the number line. (Sections 1.1/2.6)

addition method An algebraic method of finding an exact solution of a system of linear equations. (Section 4.2)

additive inverse of a polynomial The polynomial with the sign of every term changed. (Section 5.2)

additive inverses Numbers that are the same distance from zero on the number line but lie on different sides of zero; also called opposites. (Sections 1.1/1.3)

analytic geometry Geometry in which a coordinate system is used to study relationships between variables. (Section 3.1)

antilogarithm If $\log_b M = N$, then the antilogarithm, base b, of N is M. (Section 10.2)

arithmetic progression A sequence in which the difference between any two consecutive terms is constant; also called an arithmetic sequence. (Section 11.2)

arithmetic sequence A sequence in which the difference between any two consecutive terms is constant; also called an arithmetic progression. (Section 11.2)

arithmetic series The indicated sum of the terms of an arithmetic sequence. (Section 11.2)

asymptotes The two straight lines that a hyperbola "approaches." (Section 12.3)

average rate of change The average rate of change of y with respect to x is the change in y divided by the change in x. (Section 3.1)

axes The two number lines that form a rectangular coordinate system; also called coordinate axes. (Section 3.1)

axis of symmetry of a hyperbola A line of symmetry that passes through the vertices of a hyperbola. (Section 12.3)

axis of symmetry of a parabola A line of symmetry that passes through the vertex of a parabola. (Sections 8.6/12.1)

base In an exponential expression, the number that is taken as a factor as many times as indicated by the exponent. (Section 1.2)

binomial A polynomial of two terms. (Section 5.2)

binomial factor A factor that has two terms. (Section 5.5)

center of a circle The central point that is equidistant from all the points that make up a circle. (Section 12.2)

center of an ellipse The intersection of the two axes of symmetry of the ellipse. (Section 12.3)

center of a hyperbola The point halfway between the two vertices of a hyperbola. (Section 12.3)

circle The set of all points (x, y) in the plane that are a fixed distance from a given point (h, k) called the center. (Section 12.2)

clear denominators Remove denominators from an equation that contains fractions by multiplying each side of the equation by the least common multiple (LCM) of the denominators. (Sections 2.1/6.4)

closed interval In interval notation, an interval that contains its endpoints. (Section 1.1)

cofactor of an element of a matrix $(-1)^{i+j}$ times the minor of that element of the matrix, where i is the row number of the element and j is its column number. (Section 4.3)

combined variation A variation in which two or more types of variation occur at the same time. (Section 6.5)

combine like terms Use the Distributive Property to add the coefficients of like variable terms; add like terms of a variable expression. (Section 1.3)

common difference of a sequence The difference between any two consecutive terms in an arithmetic sequence. (Section 11.2)

common logarithms Logarithms to the base 10. (Section 10.2)

common monomial factor A monomial factor that is a factor of the terms in a polynomial. (Section 5.5)

common ratio of a sequence In a geometric sequence, the nonzero constant that is used to find each successive term of the sequence. (Section 11.3)

complete the square Add to a binomial the constant term that makes it a perfect-square trinomial. (Section 8.2)

complex fraction A fraction whose numerator or denominator contains one or more fractions. (Sections 1.2/6.3)

complex number   A number of the form $a + bi$, where a and b are real numbers and $i = \sqrt{-1}$. (Section 7.5)

composite number   A natural number that is not a prime number. (Section 1.1)

composition of functions   The operation on two functions f and g denoted by $f \circ g$. The value of the composition of f and g is given by $(f \circ g)(x) = f[g(x)]$. (Section 9.2)

compound inequality   Two inequalities joined with a connective word such as "and" or "or." (Section 2.5)

compound interest   Interest that is computed not only on the original principal but also on the interest already earned. (Section 10.5)

conditional equation   An equation that is true if the variable it contains is replaced by the proper value. $x + 2 = 5$ is a conditional equation. (Section 2.1)

conic section   A curve that can be constructed from the intersection of a plane and a right circular cone. The four conic sections are the parabola, hyperbola, ellipse, and circle. (Section 12.1)

conjugates   Binomial expressions that differ only in the sign of a term. The expressions $a + b$ and $a - b$ are conjugates. (Section 7.2)

consecutive even integers   Even integers that follow one another in order. (Section 2.2)

consecutive integers   Integers that follow one another in order. (Section 2.2)

consecutive odd integers   Odd integers that follow one another in order. (Section 2.2)

constant function   A function given by $f(x) = b$, where b is a constant. (Section 3.3)

constant of proportionality k in a variation equation; also called the constant of variation. (Section 6.5)

constant of variation k in a variation equation; also called the constant of proportionality. (Section 6.5)

constant term   A term that contains no variable part. (Section 1.3)

coordinate axes   The two number lines that form a rectangular coordinate system; also called simply axes. (Section 3.1)

coordinates of a point   The numbers in the ordered pair that is associated with the point. (Section 3.1)

cube root of a perfect cube   One of the three equal factors of the perfect cube. (Section 5.6)

cubic function   A third-degree polynomial function. (Section 5.2)

degree of a monomial   The sum of the exponents of the variables in a monomial. (Section 5.1)

degree of a polynomial   The greatest of the degrees of any of the terms of a polynomial. (Section 5.2)

dependent system of equations   A system of equations whose graphs coincide. (Section 4.1)

dependent variable   A variable whose value depends on that of another variable, which is known as the independent variable. (Section 3.2)

descending order   The terms of a polynomial in one variable arranged so that the exponents of the variable decrease from left to right. (Section 5.2)

determinant   The number associated with a square matrix. (Section 4.3)

difference of two perfect cubes   A polynomial of the form $a^3 - b^3$. (Section 5.6)

difference of two perfect squares   A polynomial of the form $a^2 - b^2$. (Section 5.6)

direct variation   A special function that can be expressed as the equation $y = kx$, where k is a constant called the constant of variation or the constant of proportionality. (Section 6.5)

discriminant   For an equation of the form $ax^2 + bx + c = 0$, the quantity $b^2 - 4ac$. (Section 8.2)

domain   The set of the first coordinates of all the ordered pairs of a function. (Sections 1.1/3.2)

double root   The two equal roots of a quadratic equation. (Section 8.1)

element of a matrix   A number in a matrix. (Section 4.3)

elements of a set   The objects in the set. (Section 1.1)

ellipse   An oval shape that is one of the conic sections. (Section 12.3)

empty set   The set that contains no elements. (Section 1.1)

equation   A statement of the equality of two mathematical expressions. (Section 2.1)

evaluate a function   Determine $f(x)$ for a given value of x. (Section 3.2)

evaluate a variable expression   Replace the variable in a variable expression by a numerical value and then simplify the resulting expression. (Section 1.3)

even integer   An integer that is divisible by 2. (Section 2.2)

expand by cofactors   A technique for finding the value of a 3×3 or larger determinant. (Section 4.3)

exponent   In an exponential expression, the raised number that indicates how many times the factor, or base, occurs in the multiplication. (Section 1.2)

exponential equation   An equation in which the variable occurs in the exponent. (Section 10.4)

exponential form The expression 2^6 is in exponential form. Compare factored form. (Section 1.2)

exponential function The function with base b defined by $f(x) = b^x$, where b is a positive real number not equal to 1. (Section 10.1)

extraneous solution When each side of an equation is raised to an even power, the resulting equation may have a solution that is not a solution of the original equation. Such a solution is called an extraneous solution. (Section 7.4)

factor a polynomial Write the polynomial as a product of other polynomials. (Section 5.5)

factor by grouping Process of grouping and factoring terms in a polynomial in such a way that a common binomial factor is found. (Section 5.5)

factored form The multiplication $2 \cdot 2 \cdot 2 \cdot 2 \cdot 2$ is in factored form. Compare exponential form. (Section 1.2)

finite sequence A sequence that contains a finite number of terms. (Section 11.1)

finite set A set in which all the elements can be listed. (Section 1.1)

first coordinate of an ordered pair The first number of the ordered pair; it measures a horizontal distance and is also called the abscissa. (Section 3.1)

first-degree equation in one variable An equation that contains only one variable and that variable has an exponent of 1. (Section 2.1)

FOIL method A method of finding the product of two binomials in which the sum of the products of the first terms, the outer terms, the inner terms, and the last terms is found. (Section 5.3)

formula A literal equation that states a rule about measurement. (Section 6.6)

function A relation in which no two ordered pairs that have the same first coordinate have different second coordinates. (Section 3.2)

function notation Notation used for those equations that define functions. The letter f is commonly used to name a function. (Section 3.2)

general term of a sequence In the sequence $a_1, a_2, a_3, \ldots, a_n, \ldots$, the term a_n. (Section 11.1)

geometric progression A sequence in which each successive term of the sequence is the same nonzero constant multiple of the preceding term; also called a geometric sequence. (Section 11.3)

geometric sequence A sequence in which each successive term of the sequence is the same nonzero constant multiple of the preceding term; also called a geometric progression. (Section 11.3)

geometric series The indicated sum of the terms of a geometric sequence. (Section 11.3)

graph of a function A graph of the ordered pairs that belong to the function. (Section 3.2)

graph of an ordered pair The dot drawn at the coordinates of the point in the plane. (Section 3.1)

graph of a real number A heavy dot placed directly above the number on the number line. (Section 1.1)

graph of $x = a$ A vertical line passing through the point whose coordinates are $(a, 0)$. (Section 3.3)

graph of $y = b$ A horizontal line passing through the point whose coordinates are $(0, b)$. (Section 3.3)

greatest common factor of two numbers The greatest number that is a factor of the two numbers. (Section 1.2)

grouping symbols Parentheses ( ), brackets [ ], braces { }, the absolute value symbol, and the fraction bar. (Section 1.2)

half-plane The solution set of a linear inequality in two variables. (Section 3.7)

horizontal shift The displacement of a graph to the right or left on the coordinate axes; also known as a horizontal translation. (Section 9.1)

horizontal translation The displacement of a graph to the right or left on the coordinate axes; also known as a horizontal shift. (Section 9.1)

hyperbola A conic section formed by the intersection of a right circular cone and a plane perpendicular to the base of the cone. (Section 12.3)

hypotenuse In a right triangle, the side opposite the $90°$ angle. (Sections 3.1/7.4)

identity An equation in which any replacement for the variable will result in a true equation. $x + 2 = x + 2$ is an identity. (Section 2.1)

imaginary number A number of the form ai, where a is a real number and $i = \sqrt{-1}$. (Section 7.5)

imaginary part of a complex number For the complex number $a + bi$, b is the imaginary part. (Section 7.5)

inconsistent system of equations A system of equations that has no solution. (Section 4.1)

independent system of equations A system of equations that has exactly one solution. (Section 4.1)

independent variable A variable whose value determines that of another variable, which is known as the dependent variable. (Section 3.2)

index In the expression $\sqrt[n]{a}$, n is the index of the radical. (Section 7.1)

index of summation The variable used in summation notation. (Section 11.1)

infinite geometric series The indicated sum of the terms of an infinite geometric sequence. (Section 11.3)

infinite sequence A sequence that contains an infinite number of terms. (Section 11.1)

infinite set A set in which all the elements cannot be listed. (Section 1.1)

integers The numbers $\ldots, -3, -2, -1, 0, 1, 2, 3, \ldots$. (Section 1.1)

intersection of two sets The set that contains all elements that are common to both of the sets. (Section 1.1)

interval notation A type of set-builder notation in which the property that distinguishes the elements of the set is their location within a specified interval. (Section 1.1)

inverse of a function The set of ordered pairs formed by reversing the coordinates of each ordered pair of the function. (Section 9.3)

inverse variation A function that can be expressed as the equation $y = k/x$, where k is a constant. (Section 6.5)

irrational number A number that cannot be written in the form a/b, where a and b are integers and b is not equal to zero. (Sections 1.1/7.2)

joint variation A variation in which a variable varies directly as the product of two or more variables. A joint variation can be expressed as the equation $z = kxy$, where k is a constant. (Section 6.5)

leading coefficient In a polynomial, the coefficient of the variable with the largest exponent. (Section 5.2)

least common multiple (LCM) of two numbers The smallest number that is a multiple of each of the numbers. (Section 1.2)

least common multiple (LCM) of two polynomials The polynomial of least degree that contains the factors of each polynomial. (Section 6.2)

leg of a right triangle In a right triangle, one of the two sides that are not opposite the 90° angle. (Sections 3.1/7.4)

like terms Terms of a variable expression that have the same variable part. Having no variable part, constant terms are like terms. (Section 1.3)

linear equation in three variables An equation of the form $Ax + By + Cz = D$, where A, B, and C are coefficients of the variables and D is a constant. (Section 4.2)

linear equation in two variables An equation of the form $y = mx + b$, where m is the coefficient of x and b is a constant, or of the form $Ax + By = C$. Also called a linear function. (Section 3.3)

linear function An equation of the form $y = mx + b$, where m is the coefficient of x and b is a constant; also called a linear equation in two variables. Its graph is a straight line. (Section 3.3)

linear inequality in two variables An inequality of the form $y > mx + b$ or $Ax + By > C$. The symbol $>$ could be replaced by $\geq$, $<$, or $\leq$. (Section 3.7)

literal equation An equation that contains more than one variable. (Section 3.3)

logarithm The mathematical operation that is the inverse of exponentiation. The logarithm of a number x in base b is the number y such that $b^y = x$, written $\log_b x = y$. (Section 10.2)

lower limit In a tolerance, the lowest acceptable value. (Section 2.6)

lowest common denominator The smallest number that is a multiple of each denominator in question. (Section 1.2)

main diagonal The elements $a_{11}, a_{22}, a_{33}, \ldots, a_{nm}$ of a matrix. (Section 4.3)

main fraction bar The fraction bar that is placed between the numerator and denominator of a complex fraction. (Section 1.2)

matrix A rectangular array of numbers. (Section 4.3)

maximum value of a function The greatest value that the function can have. (Section 8.7)

midpoint of a line segment The point on a line segment that is equidistant from its end points. (Section 3.1)

minimum value of a function The least value that the function can have. (Section 8.7)

minor of an element The minor of an element in a 3×3 determinant is the 2×2 determinant obtained by eliminating the row and column that contain the element. (Section 4.3)

monomial A number, a variable, or a product of a number and variables; a polynomial of one term. (Section 5.1)

multiplicative inverse The multiplicative inverse of a nonzero real number a is $1/a$; also called the reciprocal of a. (Sections 1.2/1.3)

n factorial The product of the first n natural numbers, written $n!$. (Section 11.4)

natural exponential function The function defined by $f(x) = e^x$, where $e \approx 2.71828$. (Section 10.1)

natural logarithm Logarithm to the base e (the base of the natural exponential function), abbreviated $\ln x$. (Section 10.2)

natural numbers The numbers $1, 2, 3, \ldots$; also called the positive integers. (Section 1.1)

negative integers The numbers ..., −3, −2, −1. (Section 1.1)

negative slope The slope of a line that slants downward to the right. (Section 3.4)

nonfactorable over the integers A description of a polynomial that does not factor using only integers. (Section 5.5)

nonlinear system of equations A system of equations in which one or more of the equations are not linear equations. (Section 12.4)

null set A set that contains no elements; also called an empty set. (Section 1.1)

numerical coefficient The number part of a variable term. (Section 1.3)

odd integer An integer that is not divisible by 2. (Section 2.2)

one-to-one function A function in which, given any y, there is only one x that can be paired with the given y. (Section 9.3)

open interval In interval notation, an interval that does not contain its endpoints. (Section 1.1)

opposites Numbers that are the same distance from zero on the number line but lie on different sides of zero; also called additive inverses. (Section 1.1)

order $m \times n$ A matrix of m rows and n columns. (Section 4.3)

Order of Operations Agreement Rules that specify the order in which operations are performed in simplifying numerical expressions. (Section 1.2)

ordered pair A pair of numbers expressed in the form (a, b) and used to locate a point in a rectangular coordinate system. (Section 3.1)

ordered triple Three numbers expressed in the form (x, y, z) and used to locate a point in an xyz-coordinate system. (Section 4.2)

ordinate The second number of an ordered pair; it measures a vertical distance and is also called the second coordinate of an ordered pair. (Section 3.1)

origin The point of intersection of the two number lines that form a rectangular coordinate system. (Section 3.1)

parabola The name given to the graph of a quadratic function. (Sections 8.6/12.1)

parallel lines Lines that have the same slope and thus do not intersect. (Section 3.6)

Pascal's Triangle A triangular array of the numbers for the coefficients of the terms of the expansion of the binomial $(a + b)^n$. (Section 11.4)

percent mixture problem A problem that involves combining two solutions or alloys that have different concentrations of the same substance. (Section 2.4)

perfect cube The product of the same three factors. (Section 5.6)

perfect square The product of a term and itself. (Section 5.6)

perfect-square trinomial The square of a binomial. (Section 5.6)

perpendicular lines Lines that intersect at right angles. (Section 3.6)

plane The infinitely extending, two-dimensional space in which a rectangular coordinate system lies; may be pictured as a large, flat piece of paper. (Section 3.1)

polynomial A variable expression in which the terms are monomials. (Section 5.2)

positive integers The numbers 1, 2, 3,...; also called the natural numbers. (Section 1.1)

positive slope The slope of a line that slants upward to the right. (Section 3.4)

power In an exponential expression, the number of times (indicated by the exponent) that the factor, or base, occurs in the multiplication. (Section 1.2)

prime number A number whose only whole-number factors are 1 and itself. For example, 17 is a prime number. (Section 1.1)

prime polynomial A polynomial that is nonfactorable over the integers. (Section 5.5)

principal square root The positive square root of a number. (Section 7.1)

proportion An equation that states the equality of two ratios or rates. (Section 6.5)

quadrant One of the four regions into which a rectangular coordinate system divides the plane. (Section 3.1)

quadratic equation An equation that can be written in the form $ax^2 + bx + c = 0$, where a and b are coefficients, c is a constant and $a \neq 0$; also called a second-degree equation. (Sections 5.7/8.1)

quadratic function A function that can be expressed by the equation $f(x) = ax^2 + bx + c$, where a is not equal to zero. (Sections 5.2/8.6)

quadratic inequality in one variable An inequality that can be written in the form $ax^2 + bx + c < 0$ or $ax^2 + bx + c > 0$, where a is not equal to zero. The symbols $\leq$ and $\geq$ can also be used. (Section 8.5)

quadratic trinomial A trinomial of the form $ax^2 + bx + c$, where a and b are nonzero coefficients and c is a nonzero constant. (Section 5.5)

radical In a radical expression, the symbol $\sqrt{}$. (Section 7.1)

radical equation An equation that contains a variable expression in a radical. (Section 7.4)

radical function A function that contains a variable expression in a radical. (Section 6.1)

radicand In a radical expression, the expression within the radical. (Section 7.1)

radius of a circle The fixed distance, from the center of a circle, of all points that make up the circle. (Section 12.2)

range The set of the second coordinates of all the ordered pairs of a function. (Section 3.2)

rate The quotient of two quantities that have different units. (Section 6.5)

rate of work The part of a task that is completed in one unit of time. (Section 6.4)

ratio The quotient of two quantities that have the same unit. (Section 6.5)

rational expression A fraction in which the numerator and denominator are polynomials. (Section 6.1)

rational function A function that is written in terms of a rational expression. (Section 6.1)

rationalize the denominator The procedure used to remove a radical from the denominator of a fraction. (Section 7.2)

rational number A number of the form a/b, where a and b are integers and b is not equal to zero. (Section 1.1)

real numbers The rational numbers and the irrational numbers taken together. (Section 1.1)

real part of a complex number For the complex number $a + bi$, a is the real part. (Section 7.5)

reciprocal of a fraction The fraction that results when the numerator and denominator of a fraction are interchanged. (Section 1.2)

reciprocal of a rational expression A rational expression in which the numerator and denominator have been interchanged. (Section 6.2)

rectangular coordinate system A coordinate system formed by two number lines, one horizontal and one vertical, that intersect at the zero point of each line. (Section 3.1)

relation A set of ordered pairs. (Section 3.2)

repeating decimal A decimal formed when dividing the numerator of a fraction by its denominator, in which a digit or a sequence of digits in the decimal repeats infinitely. (Section 1.1)

right triangle A triangle that contains a 90° angle. (Section 3.1)

root(s) of an equation The replacement value(s) of the variable that will make the equation true; also called the solution(s) of the equation. (Section 2.1)

roster method A method of designating a set by enclosing a list of its elements in braces. (Section 1.1)

scatter diagram A graph of ordered-pair data. (Section 3.1)

scientific notation Notation in which each number is expressed as the product of a number between 1 and 10 and a power of 10. (Section 5.1)

second coordinate of an ordered pair The second number of the ordered pair; it measures a vertical distance and is also called the ordinate. (Section 3.1)

second-degree equation An equation of the form $ax^2 + bx + c = 0$, where a and b are coefficients, c is a constant, and $a \neq 0$; also called a quadratic equation. (Section 8.1)

sequence An ordered list of numbers. (Section 11.1)

series The indicated sum of the terms of a sequence. (Section 11.1)

set A collection of objects. (Section 1.1)

set-builder notation A method of designating a set that makes use of a variable and a certain property that only elements of that set possess. (Section 1.1)

sigma notation Notation used to represent a series in a compact form; also called summation notation. (Section 11.1)

slope A measure of the slant, or tilt, of a line. (Section 3.4)

slope-intercept form of a straight line The equation $y = mx + b$, where m is the slope of the line and $(0, b)$ is the y-intercept. (Section 3.4)

solution(s) of an equation The replacement value(s) of the variable that will make the equation true; also called the root(s) of the equation. (Section 2.1)

solution of an equation in two variables An ordered pair whose coordinates make the equation a true statement. (Section 3.1)

solution of a system of equations in three variables An ordered triple that is a solution of each equation of the system. (Section 4.2)

solution of a system of equations in two variables An ordered pair that is a solution of each equation of the system. (Section 4.1)

solution set of an inequality A set of numbers, each element of which, when substituted for the variable, results in a true inequality. (Section 2.5)

solution set of a system of inequalities The intersection of the solution sets of the individual inequalities. (Section 4.5)

solve an equation Find a root, or solution, of the equation. (Section 2.1)

square matrix A matrix that has the same number of rows as columns. (Section 4.3)

square of a binomial A polynomial that can be expressed in the form $(a + b)^2$. (Section 5.3)

square root of a perfect square One of the two equal factors of the perfect square. (Section 5.6)

standard form of a quadratic equation A quadratic equation written with the polynomial in descending order and equal to zero. $ax^2 + bx + c = 0$ is in standard form. (Sections 5.7/8.1)

substitution method An algebraic method of finding a solution of a system of linear equations. (Section 4.1)

summation notation Notation used to represent a series in a compact form; also called sigma notation. (Section 11.1)

synthetic division A shorter method of dividing a polynomial by a binomial of the form $x - a$. This method uses only the coefficients of the variable terms. (Section 5.4)

system of equations Two or more equations considered together. (Section 4.1)

system of inequalities Two or more inequalities considered together. (Section 4.5)

term of a sequence A number in a sequence. (Section 11.1)

terminating decimal A decimal formed when dividing the numerator of a fraction by its denominator and the remainder is zero. (Section 1.1)

terms of a variable expression The addends of the variable expression. (Section 1.3)

tolerance of a component The acceptable amount by which the component may vary from a given measurement. (Section 2.6)

trinomial A polynomial of three terms. (Section 5.2)

undefined slope The slope of a vertical line is undefined. (Section 3.4)

uniform motion The motion of an object whose speed and direction do not change. (Section 2.3)

union of two sets The set that contains all elements that belong to either of the sets. (Section 1.1)

upper limit In a tolerance, the greatest acceptable value. (Section 2.6)

value mixture problem A problem that involves combining two ingredients that have different prices into a single blend. (Section 2.3)

value of a function The value of the dependent variable for a given value of the independent variable. (Section 3.2)

variable A letter of the alphabet used to stand for a number that is unknown or that can change. (Section 1.1)

variable expression An expression that contains one or more variables. (Section 1.3)

variable part In a variable term, the variable or variables and their exponents. (Section 1.3)

variable term A term composed of a numerical coefficient and a variable part. When the numerical coefficient is 1 or -1, the 1 is not usually written. (Section 1.3)

vertex of a parabola The point on the parabola with the smallest y-coordinate or the largest y-coordinate. (Sections 8.6/12.1)

vertical shift The displacement of a graph up or down on the coordinate axes; also known as a vertical translation. (Section 9.1)

vertical translation The displacement of a graph up or down on the coordinate axes; also known as a vertical shift. (Section 9.1)

whole numbers The numbers 0, 1, 2, 3,…. The whole numbers include the natural numbers and zero. (Section 1.1)

x-coordinate The abscissa in an ordered pair. (Section 3.1)

x-intercept The point at which a graph crosses the x-axis. (Section 3.3)

xy-coordinate system A rectangular coordinate system in which the horizontal axis is labeled x and the vertical axis is labeled y. (Section 3.1)

xyz-coordinate system A three-dimensional coordinate system formed when a third coordinate axis (the z-axis) is located perpendicular to the xy-plane. (Section 4.2)

y-coordinate The ordinate in an ordered pair. (Section 3.1)

y-intercept The point at which a graph crosses the y-axis. (Section 3.3)

zero of a function A value of x for which $f(x) = 0$. (Section 3.3)

zero slope The slope of a horizontal line. (Section 3.4)

Keystroke Guide for the TI-83 and TI-83 Plus

This appendix contains some keystroke suggestions for many graphing calculator operations that are featured in this text. The keystrokes are for the TI-83 and TI-83 Plus calculators. The descriptions in the margin are the same as those used in the text and are arranged alphabetically. Please see your manual for additional information about your calculator.

Basic Operations

Numerical calculations are performed on the **home screen.** You can always return to the home screen by pressing [2nd] QUIT. Pressing [CLEAR] erases the home screen.

To evaluate the expression $-2(3 + 5) - 8 \div 4$, use the following keystrokes.

[(−)] 2 [(] 3 [+] 5 [)] [−] 8 [÷] 4 [ENTER]

Note: There is a difference between the key to enter a negative number, [(−)], and the key for subtraction, [−]. You cannot use these keys interchangeably.

The [2nd] key is used to access the commands in gold writing above a key. For instance, to evaluate the $\sqrt{49}$, press [2nd] $\sqrt{}$ 49 [)] [ENTER].

The [ALPHA] key is used to place a letter on the screen. One reason to do this is to store a value of a variable. The following keystrokes give A the value of 5.

5 [STO▸] [ALPHA] A [ENTER]

This value is now available in calculations. For instance, we can find the value of $3a^2$ by using the following keystrokes: 3 [ALPHA] A [x^2]. To display the value of the variable on the screen, press [2nd] RCL [ALPHA] A.

Note: When you use the [ALPHA] key, only capital letters are available on the TI-83 calculator.

Complex Numbers

To perform operations on complex numbers, first press [MODE] and then use the arrow keys to select a+bi. Then press [ENTER] [2nd] QUIT.

Addition of complex numbers   To add $(3 + 4i) + (2 - 7i)$, use the keystrokes

[(] 3 [+] 4 [2nd] i [)] [+]
[(] 2 [−] 7 [2nd] i [)] [ENTER].

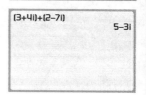

Division of complex numbers. To divide $\frac{26 + 2i}{2 + 4i}$, use the keystrokes (26 + 2 2nd i) ÷ (2 + 4 2nd i) ENTER .

Note: Operations for subtraction and multiplication are similar.

Additional operations on complex numbers can be found by selecting CPX under the MATH key.

To find the absolute value of $2 - 5i$, press MATH (scroll to CPX) (scroll to abs) ENTER (2 — 5 2nd i) ENTER .

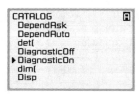

Correlation Coefficient

The value of the correlation coefficient for a regression equation calculation is not shown unless the DiagnosticOn feature is enabled. To enable this feature, press 2nd CATALOG D (scroll to DiagnosticOn) ENTER ENTER .

CATALOG   [A]   DiagnosticOn
    DependAsk   Done
    DependAuto
    det(
    DiagnosticOff
  ▶ DiagnosticOn
    dim(
    Disp

To calculate the correlation coefficient, proceed as if calculating a regression equation.

Evaluating Functions

There are various methods of evaluating a function but all methods require that the expression be entered as one of the ten functions Y₁ to Y₀. To evaluate $f(x) = \frac{x^2}{x - 1}$ when $x = -3$, enter the expression into, for instance, Y₁, and then press VARS ▶ 11 ((−) 3) ENTER .

TAKE NOTE

Use the down arrow key to scroll past Y₇ to see Y₈, Y₉, and Y₀.

Note: If you try to evaluate a function at a number that is not in the domain of the function, you will get an error message. For instance, 1 is not in the domain of $f(x) = \frac{x^2}{x - 1}$. If we try to evaluate the function at 1, the error screen at the right appears.

Evaluating Variable Expressions

To evaluate a variable expression, first store the values of each variable. Then enter the variable expression. For instance, to evaluate $s^2 + 2sl$ when $s = 4$ and $l = 5$, use the following keystrokes.

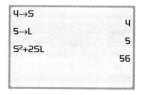

4 STO▶ ALPHA S ENTER 5 STO▶ ALPHA L ENTER ALPHA S x² + 2 ALPHA S ALPHA L ENTER

Graph

To graph a function, use the ⬛Y=⬛ key to enter the expression for the function, select a suitable viewing window, and then press ⬛GRAPH⬛. For instance, to graph $f(x) = 0.1x^3 - 2x - 1$ in the standard viewing window, use the following keystrokes.

⬛Y=⬛ 0.1 ⬛X,T,θ,n⬛ ⬛^⬛ 3 ⬛—⬛ 2 ⬛X,T,θ,n⬛ ⬛—⬛ 1 ⬛ZOOM⬛ (scroll to 6) ⬛ENTER⬛

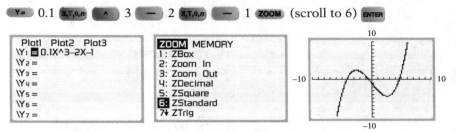

Note: For the keystrokes above, you do not have to scroll to 6. Alternatively, use ⬛ZOOM⬛ 6. This will select the standard viewing window and automatically start the graph. Use the ⬛WINDOW⬛ key to create a custom window for a graph.

Graphing Inequalities

To illustrate this feature, we will graph $y \leq 2x - 1$. Enter $2x - 1$ into Y_1. Because $y \leq 2x - 1$, we want to shade below the graph. Move the cursor to the left of Y_1 and press ⬛ENTER⬛ three times. Press ⬛GRAPH⬛.

Note: To shade above the graph, move the cursor to the left of Y_1 and press ⬛ENTER⬛ two times. An inequality with the symbol $\leq$ or $\geq$ should be graphed with a solid line, and an inequality with the symbol $<$ or $>$ should be graphed with a dashed line. However, the graph of a linear inequality on a graphing calculator does not distinguish between a solid line and a dashed line.

To graph the solution set of a system of inequalities, solve each inequality for y and graph each inequality. The solution set is the intersection of the two inequalities. The solution set of $\begin{array}{c} 3x + 2y > 10 \\ 4x - 3y \leq 5 \end{array}$ is shown at the right.

Intersect

The INTERSECT feature is used to solve a system of equations. To illustrate this feature, we will use the system of equations $\begin{array}{c} 2x - 3y = 13 \\ 3x + 4y = -6 \end{array}$.

Note: Some equations can be solved by this method. See the section "Solve an equation" below. Also, this method is used to find a number in the domain of a function for a given number in the range. See the section "Find a domain element."

Solve each of the equations in the system of equations for y. In this case, we have $y = \frac{2}{3}x - \frac{13}{3}$ and $y = -\frac{3}{4}x - \frac{3}{2}$.

Use the Y-editor to enter $\frac{2}{3}x - \frac{13}{3}$ into Y₁ and $-\frac{3}{4}x - \frac{3}{2}$ into Y₂. Graph the two functions in the standard viewing window. (If the window does not show the point of intersection of the two graphs, adjust the window until you can see the point of intersection.)

Press **2nd** CALC (scroll to 5, intersect) **ENTER**.

Alternatively, you can just press **2nd** CALC 5.

First curve? is shown at the bottom of the screen and identifies one of the two graphs on the screen. Press **ENTER**.

Second curve? is shown at the bottom of the screen and identifies the second of the two graphs on the screen. Press **ENTER**.

Guess? shown at the bottom of the screen asks you to use the left or right arrow key to move the cursor to the *approximate* location of the point of intersection. (If there are two or more points of intersection, it does not matter which one you choose first.) Press **ENTER**.

The solution of the system of equations is $(2, -3)$.

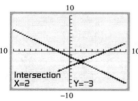

Solve an equation To illustrate the steps involved, we will solve the equation $2x + 4 = -3x - 1$. The idea is to write the equation as the system of equations $\begin{array}{l} y = 2x + 4 \\ y = -3x - 1 \end{array}$ and then use the steps for solving a system of equations.

Use the Y-editor to enter the left and right sides of the equation into Y₁ and Y₂. Graph the two functions and then follow the steps for Intersect.

The solution is -1, the x-coordinate of the point of intersection.

Find a domain element For this example, we will find a number in the domain of $f(x) = -\frac{2}{3}x + 2$ that corresponds to 4 in the range of the function. This is like solving the system of equations $y = -\frac{2}{3}x + 2$ and $y = 4$.

Use the Y= editor to enter the expression for the function in Y_1 and the desired output, 4, in Y_2. Graph the two functions and then follow the steps for Intersect.

The point of intersection is $(-3, 4)$. The number -3 in the domain of f produces an output of 4 in the range of f.

Math   Pressing **MATH** gives you access to many built-in functions. The following keystrokes will convert 0.125 to a fraction: .125 **MATH** 1 **ENTER** .

Additional built-in functions under **MATH** can be found by pressing **MATH** ▷ . For instance, to evaluate $-|-25|$, press (−) **MATH** ▷ 1 (−) 25) **ENTER** .

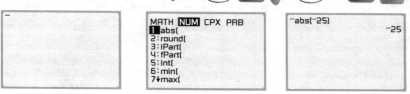

See your owner's manual for assistance with other functions under the **MATH** key.

Matrix   On a TI-83, **matrix operations** are accessed by pressing **MATRX**. On a TI-83 Plus, press **2nd** MATRX to access the matrix menu.

To enter the elements of a matrix, select the matrix key. Then use the right arrow to select EDIT. Now use the down arrow key to select the name of the matrix. There are 10 matrices with names A through J. By pressing the down arrow key, you can see the additional names. Once you have selected the name of the matrix, press **ENTER** .

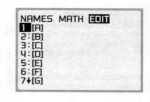

For instance, to enter the matrix $\begin{bmatrix} 2 & -3 & 4 \\ 1 & 5 & 3 \end{bmatrix}$ with 2 rows and 3 columns, access the matrix menu, arrow right to EDIT, and press **ENTER** . Now enter the dimension and the elements of the matrix, pressing **ENTER** after each number. You can change an element by using the arrow keys to select that element. After you have entered all the elements, press **2nd** QUIT to return to the home screen.

Elementary row operations Elementary row operations are performed by selecting MATH from the matrix menu. Use the down arrow key to scroll to those operations. Your screen should look something like this:

The operation row+(shown by D: is to add two rows. This is really the same as F: where the constant is 1.

Here are keystrokes for each elementary row operation. We will use the matrix $\begin{bmatrix} 1 & 3 & -4 & 6 \\ 3 & 2 & 0 & -1 \\ -2 & -5 & 3 & 4 \end{bmatrix}$ for this demonstration and assume it is stored in matrix [B].

Interchange rows: Access the matrix menu and highlight MATH. Scroll down to C:rowSwap(. Press ENTER. Access the matrix menu. Scroll to [B]; then press ENTER. Press (1 , 3) ENTER. (This interchanges row 1 and row 3. Change these numbers to interchange other rows.)

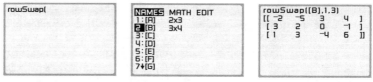

Multiply a row by a constant: Access the matrix menu and highlight MATH. Scroll down to E:*row(. Press ENTER (−) 2. (This is the constant that will multiply a row.) Press , . Access the matrix menu. Scroll to [B] and then press ENTER. Press , 3) ENTER. (Row 3 is being multiplied.)

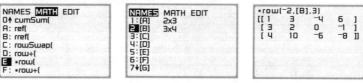

Multiply a row by a constant and then add it to another row: Access the matrix menu and highlight MATH. Scroll down to F:*row+(. Press ENTER 2. (This is the constant that will multiply a row.) Press , . Access the matrix menu. Scroll to [B]; then press ENTER. Press , 1 , 3) ENTER. (Row 1 is being multiplied by 2 and then added to row 3.)

Row echelon form The ref(function performs all of the elementary row operations on a matrix and directly produces a row echelon form of a matrix. The abbreviation ref stands for **r**ow **e**chelon **f**orm.

To write $\begin{bmatrix} 2 & 1 & 3 & -1 \\ 1 & 3 & 5 & -1 \\ -3 & -1 & 1 & 2 \end{bmatrix}$ in row echelon form, enter the matrix in, for instance, [A].

Press [2nd] QUIT. Then access the matrix menu and highlight MATH, scroll to ref(and press [ENTER], access the matrix menu, select [A], and press [ENTER] [)] [ENTER]. This will produce a matrix in row echelon form. Pressing [MATH] 1 [ENTER] will rewrite the matrix with fractions rather than decimals. (See MATH for assistance with the fraction command.)

Min and Max

The local minimum and the local maximum values of a function are calculated by accessing the CALC menu. For this demonstration, we will find the minimum value and the maximum value of $f(x) = 0.2x^3 + 0.3x^2 - 3.6x + 2$.

Enter the function into Y₁. Press [2nd] CALC (scroll to 3 for minimum of the function) [ENTER].

Alternatively, you can just press [2nd] CALC 3.

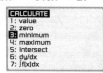

Left Bound? shown at the bottom of the screen asks you to use the left or right arrow key to move the cursor to the *left* of the minimum. Press [ENTER].

Right Bound? shown at the bottom of the screen asks you to use the left or right arrow key to move the cursor to the *right* of the minimum. Press [ENTER].

Guess? shown at the bottom of the screen asks you to use the left or right arrow key to move the cursor to the *approximate* location of the minimum. Press [ENTER].

The minimum value of the function is the *y*-coordinate. For this example, the minimum value of the function is −2.4.

The *x*-coordinate for the minimum is 2. However, because of rounding errors in the calculation, it is shown as a number close to 2.

To find the maximum value of the function, follow the same steps as above except select maximum under the CALC menu. The screens for this calculation are shown below.

The maximum value of the function is 10.1.

Radical Expressions

To evaluate a square-root expression, press **2nd** $\sqrt{}$.

For instance, to evaluate $0.15\sqrt{p^2 + 4p + 10}$ when $p = 100{,}000$, first store 100,000 in P. Then press 0.15 **2nd** $\sqrt{}$ **ALPHA** P x^2 **+** 4 **ALPHA** P **+** 10 **)** **ENTER** .

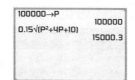

To evaluate a radical expression other than a square root, access $\sqrt[x]{}$ by pressing **MATH** . For instance, to evaluate $\sqrt[4]{67}$, press 4 (the index of the radical) **MATH** (scroll to 5) **ENTER** 67 **ENTER** .

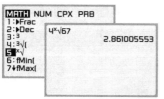

Regression

For the discussion of linear regression, we will use the data in this table.

Temperature, x (in °C)	20	35	50	60	75	90	100
Grams of sugar, y	50	80	120	145	175	205	230

All calculations and graphs involving statistical data begin by entering the data using the Edit option, which is accessed by pressing **STAT** .

For the data above, press **STAT** to access the statistics menu. Press 1 to Edit or enter data. To delete data already in a list, press the up arrow until the cursor is highlighting the list name. For instance, to delete data in L_1, highlight L_1. Then press **CLEAR** and **ENTER** . Now enter each value of the independent variable in L_1, pressing **ENTER** after each entry. Use the up and down arrow keys to change a value. When all values of the independent variable are entered, press **▷**. This will put you in the next column to enter the values of the dependent variable in L_2.

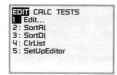

Create a scatter diagram Press **2nd** STATPLOT (use the down arrow key to select Plot1, Plot2, or Plot3) **ENTER** . Use arrow keys to move the cursor to ON and then press **ENTER** . The first graph type is for a scatter diagram. Move the cursor over that symbol and press **ENTER** . Be sure that Xlist and Ylist are the names of the lists into which you stored data. You can change these by pressing 2nd and then selecting the appropriate list, L₁ through L₆. Prepare to graph the data by adjusting the viewing window by pressing WINDOW and entering appropriate values. Now press GRAPH .

Note: You can tell that STAT PLOTS is active by pressing Y= . For one screen at the right, observe that PLOT1 is highlighted, indicating it is active. To turn STAT PLOTS off, use the up arrow key to highlight it, and then press ENTER . Now use the arrow key to move the cursor to the right of the equals sign for Y₁.

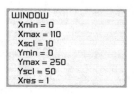

Find a linear regression equation   Press STAT ▷ (scroll to 4) ENTER 2nd L₁ , 2nd L₂ , VARS ▷ 1 1 ENTER . The values of the slope and y-intercept of the linear regression equation will be displayed on the screen. If DiagnosticOn is enabled (see Correlation coefficient), then the coefficient of determination r^2 and the correlation coefficient r are also shown.

  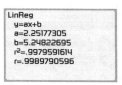

Note: If data are stored in L₁ and L₂, the keystrokes 2nd L₁ , 2nd L₂ are not necessary. The keystrokes VARS ▷ 11 ENTER place the regression equation in Y₁. These keystrokes are not necessary but are helpful if you need to graph the regression equation or evaluate the equation at a given value of the independent variable. See below for more details.

Graph a linear regression equation   Press STAT ▷ (scroll to 4) ENTER 2nd L₁ , 2nd L₂ , VARS ▷ 11 ENTER . This will store the regression equation in Y₁. Now press GRAPH . It may be necessary to adjust the viewing window.

Evaluate a regression equation   Complete the steps to graph a regression equation, but do not graph the equation. To evaluate the equation when $x = 50$, press VARS ▷ 11 (50) ENTER .

Other regression equations can be calculated. For instance, to find a regression equation of the form $y = ax^b$, called a power regression equation, enter the data and then select PwrReg from the CALC menu under the STAT menu.

Note: Because the data were entered into L1 and L2, it was not necessary to include them in PwrReg. We did include the optional Y1. This is good practice because it makes evaluating and graphing a regression equation much easier.

Scientific Notation

To enter a number in scientific notation, use **2nd** EE. For instance, to find $\frac{3.45 \times 10^{-12}}{1.5 \times 10^{25}}$, press 3.45 **2nd** EE **(−)** 12 **÷** 1.5 **2nd** EE 25 **ENTER**. The answer is 2.3×10^{-37}.

Sequences and Series

The terms of a sequence and the sum of a series can be calculated by using the **2nd** LIST feature.

Store a sequence A sequence is stored in one of the lists L1 through L6. For instance, to store the sequence 1, 3, 5, 7, 9 in L1, use the following keystrokes.

2nd { 1 **,** 3 **,** 5 **,** 7 **,** 9 **2nd** } **STO▸** **2nd** L1 **ENTER**

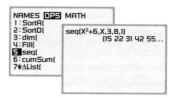

Display the terms of a sequence The terms of a sequence are displayed by using the function seq(expression, variable, begin, end, increment). For instance, to display the 3rd through 8th terms of the sequence given by $a_n = n^2 + 6$, enter the following keystrokes.

2nd LIST ▷ (scroll to 5)

ENTER **X,T,θ,n** **x²** **+** 6

, **X,T,θ,n** **,** 3 **,** 8

, 1 **ENTER** **STO▸** **2nd** L1 **ENTER**

The keystrokes **STO▸** **2nd** L1 **ENTER** store the terms of the sequence in L1. This is not necessary but is sometimes helpful if additional work will be done with that sequence.

Find a sequence of partial sums To find a sequence of partial sums, use the cumSum(function. For instance, to find the sequence of partial sums for 2, 4, 6, 8, 10, use the following keystrokes.

2nd LIST ▷ (scroll to 6)

ENTER **2nd** { 2 **,** 4 **,** 6

, 8 **,** 10 **2nd** } **)** **ENTER**

If a sequence is stored as a list in L_1, then the sequence of partial sums can be calculated by pressing [2nd] LIST [◊] (scroll to 6 [or press 6]) [ENTER] [2nd] L1 [)] [ENTER].

Find the sum of a series   The sum of a series is calculated using sum<list, start, end>. For instance, to find $\sum_{n=3}^{6} (n^2 + 2)$, enter the following keystrokes.

[2nd] LIST [◊] [◊] (scroll to 5)

[ENTER] [2nd] LIST [◊] (scroll to 5 [or press 5])

[ENTER] [X,T,θ,n] [x²] [+] 2 [,] [X,T,θ,n] [,] 3

[,] 6 [,] 1 [)] [ENTER]

Table   There are three steps in creating an input/output table for a function. First use the [Y=] editor to input the function. The second step is setting up the table, and the third step is displaying the table.

To set up the table, press [2nd] TBLSET. TblStart is the first value of the independent variable in the input/output table. △Tbl is the difference between successive values. Setting this to 1 means that, for this table, the input values are −2, −1, 0, 1, 2. . . . If △Tbl = 0.5, then the input values are −2, −1.5, −1, −0.5, 0, 0.5, . . .

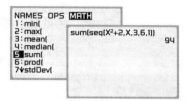

Indpnt is the independent variable. When this is set to Auto, values of the independent variable are automatically entered into the table. Depend is the dependent variable. When this is set to Auto, values of the dependent variable are automatically entered into the table.

To display the table, press [2nd] TABLE. An input/output table for $f(x) = x^2 - 1$ is shown at the right.

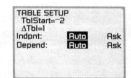

Once the table is on the screen, the up and down arrow keys can be used to display more values in the table. For the table at the right, we used the up arrow key to move to $x = -7$.

An input/output table for any given input can be created by selecting Ask for the independent variable. The table at the right shows an input/output table for $f(x) = \dfrac{4x}{x - 2}$ for selected values of x. Note the word ERROR when 2 was entered. This occurred because f is not defined when $x = 2$.

Note: Using the table feature in Ask mode is the same as evaluating a function for given values of the independent variable. For instance, from the table at the right, we have $f(4) = 8$.

Test   The TEST feature has many uses, one of which is to graph the solution set of a linear inequality in one variable. To illustrate this feature, we will graph the solution set of $x - 1 < 4$. Press **Y=** **X,T,θ,n** **—** 1 **2nd** TEST (scroll to 5) **ENTER** 4 **GRAPH** .

Trace   Once a graph is drawn, pressing **TRACE** will place a cursor on the screen, and the coordinates of the point below the cursor are shown at the bottom of the screen. Use the left and right arrow keys to move the cursor along the graph. For the graph at the right, we have $f(4.8) = 3.4592$, where $f(x) = 0.1x^3 - 2x + 2$ is shown at the top left of the screen.

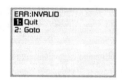

In TRACE mode, you can evaluate a function at any value of the independent variable that is within Xmin and Xmax. To do this, first graph the function. Now press **TRACE** (the value of x) **ENTER** . For the graph at the left below, we used $x = -3.5$. If a value of x is chosen outside the window, an error message is displayed.

   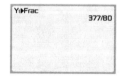

In the example above where we entered -3.5 for x, the value of the function was calculated as 4.7125. This means that $f(-3.5) = 4.7125$. The keystrokes **2nd** QUIT **VARS** ◃ 11 **MATH** 1 **ENTER** will convert the decimal value to a fraction.

When the TRACE feature is used with two or more graphs, the up and down arrow keys are used to move between the graphs. The graphs below are for the functions $f(x) = 0.1x^3 - 2x + 2$ and $g(x) = 2x - 3$. By using the up and down arrows, we can place the cursor on either graph. The right and left arrows are used to move along the graph.

Window   The viewing window for a graph is controlled by pressing **WINDOW** . Xmin and Xmax are the minimum value and maximum value, respectively, of the independent variable shown on the graph. Xscl is the distance between tic marks on the x-axis. Ymin and Ymax are the minimum value and maximum value, respectively, of the dependent variable shown on the graph. Yscl is the distance between tic marks on the y-axis. Leave Xres as 1.

Note: In the standard viewing window, the distance between tic marks on the x-axis is different from the distance between tic marks on the y-axis. This will distort a graph. A more accurate picture of a graph can be created by using a square viewing window. See ZOOM.

The [Y=] editor is used to enter the expression for a function. There are ten possible functions, labeled Y_1 to Y_0, that can be active at any one time. For instance, to enter $f(x) = x^2 + 3x - 2$ as Y_1, use the following keystrokes.

Note: If an expression is already entered for Y_1, place the cursor anywhere on that expression and press [CLEAR].

To enter $s = \dfrac{2v - 1}{v^3 - 3}$ into Y_2, place the cursor to the right of the equals sign for Y_2. Then press [( ] 2 [X,T,θ,n] [−] 1 [ )] [÷] [( ] [X,T,θ,n] [^] 3 [−] 3 [ )].

Note: When we enter an equation, the independent variable, v in the expression above, is entered using [X,T,θ,n]. The dependent variable, s in the expression above, is one of Y_1 to Y_0. Also note the use of parentheses to ensure the correct order of operations.

Observe the black rectangle that covers the equals sign for the two examples we have shown. This rectangle means that the function is "active." If we were to press [GRAPH], then the graph of both functions would appear. You can make a function inactive by using the arrow keys to move the cursor over the equals sign of that function and then pressing [ENTER]. This will remove the black rectangle. We have done that for Y_2, as shown at the right. Now if [GRAPH] is pressed, only Y_1 will be graphed.

It is also possible to control the appearance of the graph by moving the cursor on the [Y=] screen to the left of any Y. With the cursor in this position, pressing [ENTER] will change the appearance of the graph. The options are shown at the right.

Zero   The ZERO feature of a graphing calculator is used for various calculations: to find the x-intercepts of a function, to solve some equations, and to find the zero of a function.

x*-intercepts To illustrate the procedure for finding *x*-intercepts, we will use $f(x) = x^2 + x - 2$.

First, use the Y-editor to enter the expression for the function and then graph the function in the standard viewing window. (It may be necessary to adjust this window so that the intercepts are visible). Once the graph is displayed, use the keystrokes below to find the *x*-intercepts of the graph of the function.

Press **2nd** CALC (scroll to 2 for **zero** of the function) **ENTER**.

Alternatively, you can just press **2nd** CALC 2.

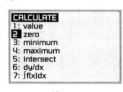

Left Bound? shown at the bottom of the screen asks you to use the left or right arrow key to move the cursor to the *left* of the desired *x*-intercept. Press **ENTER**.

Right Bound? shown at the bottom of the screen asks you to use the left or right arrow key to move the cursor to the *right* of the desired *x*-intercept. Press **ENTER**.

Guess? shown at the bottom of the screen asks you to use the left or right arrow key to move the cursor to the *approximate* location of the desired *x*-intercept. Press **ENTER**.

The *x*-coordinate of an *x*-intercept is -2. Therefore, an *x*-intercept is $(-2, 0)$.

To find the other *x*-intercept, follow the same steps as above. The screens for this calculation are shown below.

A second *x*-intercept is $(1, 0)$.

Solve an equation To use the ZERO feature to solve an equation, first rewrite the equation with all terms on one side. For instance, one way to solve $x^3 - x + 1 = -2x + 3$ is first to rewrite the equation as $x^3 + x - 2 = 0$. Enter $x^3 + x - 2$ into Y$_1$ and then follow the steps for finding *x*-intercepts.

Find the real zeros of a function   To find the real zeros of a function, follow the steps for finding *x*-intercepts.

Zoom   Pressing **zoom** allows you to select some preset viewing windows. This key also gives you access to ZBox, Zoom In, and Zoom Out. These functions enable you to redraw a selected portion of a graph in a new window. Some windows used frequently in this text are shown below.

Table of Equations and Formulas

Slope of a Straight Line

$$\text{Slope} = m = \frac{y_2 - y_1}{x_2 - x_1}, \; x_1 \neq x_2$$

Slope-intercept Form of a Straight Line

$$y = mx + b$$

Point-slope Formula for a Line

$$y - y_1 = m(x - x_1)$$

Quadratic Formula

$$x = \frac{-b \pm \sqrt{b^2 - 4ac}}{2a}$$

Perimeter and Area of a Triangle, and Sum of the Measures of the Angles

$$P = a + b + c$$
$$A = \frac{1}{2}bh$$
$$\angle A + \angle B + \angle C = 180°$$

Pythagorean Theorem

$$a^2 + b^2 = c^2$$

Perimeter and Area of a Rectangle

$$P = 2L + 2W$$
$$A = LW$$

Perimeter and Area of a Square

$$P = 4s$$
$$A = s^2$$

Circumference and Area of a Circle

$$C = 2\pi r \quad \text{or} \quad C = \pi d$$
$$A = \pi r^2$$

Area of a Trapezoid

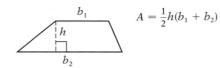

$$A = \frac{1}{2}h(b_1 + b_2)$$

Volume and Surface Area of a Rectangular Solid

$$V = LWH$$
$$SA = 2LW + 2LH + 2WH$$

Volume and Surface Area of a Cube

$$V = s^3$$
$$SA = 6s^2$$

Volume and Surface Area of a Right Circular Cylinder

$$V = \pi r^2 h$$
$$SA = 2\pi r^2 + 2\pi rh$$

Volume and Surface Area of a Right Circular Cone

$$V = \frac{1}{3}\pi r^2 h$$
$$SA = \pi r^2 + \pi rl$$

Volume and Surface Area of a Sphere

$$V = \frac{4}{3}\pi r^3$$
$$SA = 4\pi r^2$$

Table of Measurement Abbreviations

U.S. Customary System

Length		Capacity		Weight		Area	
in.	inches	oz	fluid ounces	oz	ounces	in²	square inches
ft	feet	c	cups	lb	pounds	ft²	square feet
yd	yards	qt	quarts				
mi	miles	gal	gallons				

Metric System

Length		Capacity		Weight/Mass		Area	
mm	millimeters (0.001 m)	ml	milliliters (0.001 L)	mg	milligrams (0.001 g)	cm²	square
cm	centimeters (0.01 m)	cl	centiliters (0.01 L)	cg	centigrams (0.01 g)		centimeters
dm	decimeters (0.1 m)	dl	deciliters (0.1 L)	dg	decigrams (0.1 g)	m²	square meters
m	meters	L	liters	g	grams		
dam	decameters (10 m)	dal	decaliters (10 L)	dag	decagrams (10 g)		
hm	hectometers (100 m)	hl	hectoliters (100 L)	hg	hectograms (100 g)		
km	kilometers (1000 m)	kl	kiloliters (1000 L)	kg	kilograms (1000 g)		

Time

h	hours	min	minutes	s	seconds

Table of Symbols

$+$	add		°	degree (for angles and temperature)
$-$	subtract		$\sqrt{a}$	the principal square root of a
$\cdot$, $(a)(b)$	multiply		$|a|$	the absolute value of a
$\frac{a}{b}$, $\div$	divide			
( )	parentheses, a grouping symbol			
[ ]	brackets, a grouping symbol			
π	pi, a number approximately equal to $\frac{22}{7}$ or 3.14			
$-a$	the opposite, or additive inverse, of a			
$\frac{1}{a}$	the reciprocal, or multiplicative inverse, of a			
$=$	is equal to			
$\approx$	is approximately equal to			
$\neq$	is not equal to			
$<$	is less than			
$\leq$	is less than or equal to			
$>$	is greater than			
$\geq$	is greater than or equal to			
(a, b)	an ordered pair whose first component is a and whose second component is b			

TI-30X IIS

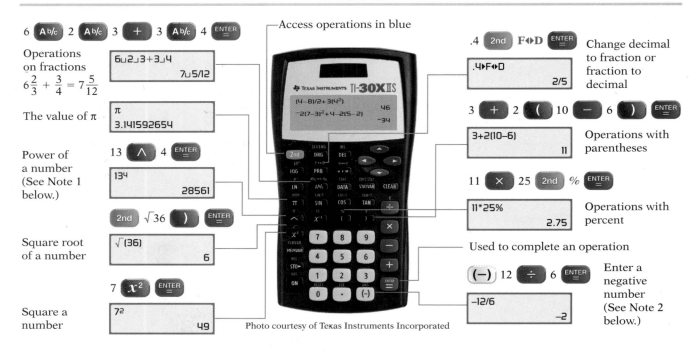

Photo courtesy of Texas Instruments Incorporated

fx-300MS

Photo courtesy of Casio, Inc.

NOTE 1: Some calculators use the y^x key to calculate a power.
For those calculators, enter 13 y^x 4 = to evaluate 13^4.

NOTE 2: Some calculators use the +/- key to enter a negative number.
For those calculators, enter 12 +/- ÷ 6 = to calculate $-12 \div 6$.